PEARSON ALWAYS LEARNING

# Mathematical Applications for the Health Sciences

Second Custom Edition for Sacred Heart University

Taken from:
*Mathematical Ideas*, Eleventh Edition
by Charles D. Miller, Vern E. Heeren, John Hornsby,
Margaret L. Morrow, and Jill Van Newenhizen

*The Mathematics of Drugs and Solutions*, Sixth Edition
by Lloyd I. Richardson, Jr., and Judith K. Richardson

Taken from:

*Mathematical Ideas*, Eleventh Edition
by Charles D. Miller, Vern E. Heeren, John Hornsby,
Margaret L. Morrow, and Jill Van Newenhizen

Published by Allyn and Bacon
Boston, Massachusetts 02116

*The Mathematics of Drugs and Solutions*, Sixth Edition
by Lloyd I. Richardson, Jr., and Judith K. Richardson


This special edition published in cooperation with Pearson Learning Solutions.



Pearson Learning Solutions, 501 Boylston Street, Suite 900, Boston, MA 02116
A Pearson Education Company
www.pearsoned.com

Printed in the United States of America

2 3 4 5 6 7 8 9 10 0BRV 18 17 16 15 14

000200010271839444

RM

ISBN 10: 1-269-57857-X
ISBN 13: 978-1-269-57857-8

From *Mathematical Ideas*, Eleventh Edition, by Charles D. Miller, Vern E. Heeren, John Hornsby, Margaret L. Morrow, and Jill Van Newenhizen

# CONTENTS

From *The Mathematics of Drugs and Solutions with Clinical Applications,* Sixth Edition, by Lloyd I. Richardson, Jr., and Judith K. Richardson

# PREFACE

After ten editions and nearly forty years, *Mathematical Ideas* continues to be one of the premier textbooks in liberal arts mathematics education. We are proud to present the eleventh edition of a text that offers non-physical science students a practical coverage that connects mathematics to the world around them. It is a flexible book that has evolved alongside changing trends but remains steadfast to its original objectives.

For the first time, this book features a theme that spans its entire contents. Movies and television have become entrenched in our society and appeal to a broad range of interests. With this in mind, we have rewritten every chapter opener with reference to a popular movie or television show, including discussion of a scene that deals with the mathematics covered in the chapter. The margin notes, long a popular hallmark of the book, have been updated to include similar references as well. These references are indicated with a movie camera icon. We hope that users of this edition will enjoy visiting Hollywood while learning mathematics.

*Mathematical Ideas* is written with a variety of students in mind. It is well suited for several courses, including those geared toward the aforementioned liberal arts audience and survey courses in mathematics, finite mathematics, and mathematics for prospective and in-service elementary and middle-school teachers. Numerous topics are included for a two-term course, yet the variety of topics and flexibility of sequence makes the text suitable for shorter courses as well. Our main objectives continue to be comprehensive coverage, appropriate organization, clear exposition, an abundance of examples, and well-planned exercise sets with numerous applications.

## Overview of Chapters

- **Chapter 1 (The Art of Problem Solving)** introduces the student to inductive reasoning, pattern recognition, and problem-solving techniques. Many of the new problems are taken from the popular monthly calendars found in the NCTM publication *Mathematics Teacher.*
- **Chapter 2 (The Basic Concepts of Set Theory) and Chapter 3 (Introduction to Logic)** give brief overviews of set theory and elementary logic. Instructors wishing to do so may cover Chapter 3 before Chapter 2.
- **Chapter 4 (Numeration and Mathematical Systems)** covers various types of numeration systems and group theory, as well as clock arithmetic and modular number systems.
- **Chapter 5 (Number Theory)** presents an introduction to topics such as prime and composite numbers, the Fibonacci sequence and magic squares. There is updated information on new developments in the field of prime numbers. New to this edition is an extension on modern crypotography.
- **Chapter 6 (The Real Numbers and Their Representations)** introduces some of the basic concepts of real numbers, their various forms of representation, and operations of arithmetic with them.

- **Chapter 7 (The Basic Concepts of Algebra) and Chapter 8 (Graphs, Functions, and Systems of Equations and Inequalities)** offer numerous new applications that help form the core of the text's algebra component.
- **Chapter 9 (Geometry)** covers the standard topics of elementary plane geometry, a section on transformational geometry, an extension on constructions, non-Euclidean geometry, and material on chaos and fractals.
- **Chapter 10 (Trigonometry)** includes angles in standard position, right angle trigonometry, and the laws of sines and cosines.
- **Chapter 11 (Counting Methods)** focuses on elementary counting techniques, in preparation for the chapter to follow.
- **Chapter 12 (Probability)** covers the basics of probability, odds, and expected value.
- **Chapter 13 (Statistics)** has been revised to include new data in examples and exercises.
- **Chapter 14 (Personal Financial Management)** provides the student with the basics of the mathematics of finance as applied to inflation, consumer debt, and house buying. The chapter includes a section on investing, with emphasis on stocks, bonds, and mutual funds. Examples and exercises have been updated to reflect current interest rates and investment returns.

The following chapters are available in the Expanded Edition of this text:

- **Chapter 15 (Graph Theory)** covers the basic concepts of graph theory and its applications. Material on graph coloring is new to this edition.
- **Chapter 16 (Voting and Apportionment)** deals with issues in voting methods and apportionment of votes, topics which have become increasingly popular in liberal arts mathematics courses.

## Course Outline Considerations

For the most part, the chapters in the text are independent and may be covered in the order chosen by the instructor. The few exceptions are as follows: Chapter 6 contains some material dependent on the ideas found in Chapter 5; Chapter 6 should be covered before Chapter 7 if student background so dictates; Chapters 7 and 8 form an algebraic "package" and should be covered in sequential order; a thorough coverage of Chapter 12 depends on knowledge of Chapter 11 material, although probability can be covered without teaching extensive counting methods by avoiding the more difficult exercises; and the latter part of Chapter 13, on inferential statistics, depends on an understanding of probability (Chapter 12).

## Features of the Eleventh Edition

**New: Chapter Openers** In keeping with the Hollywood theme of this edition, all chapter openers have been rewritten to address a scene or situation from a popular movie or a television series. Some openers illustrate the correct use of mathematics, while others address how mathematics is misused. In the latter case, we subscribe to the premise that we can all learn from the mistakes of others. Some openers (e.g., Chapters 1 and 9) include a problem statement that the reader is asked to solve. We hope that you enjoy reading these chapter openers as much as we have enjoyed preparing them.

**Enhanced: Varied Exercise Sets** We continue to present a variety of exercises that integrate drill, conceptual, and applied problems. The text contains a wealth of exercises to provide students with opportunities to practice, apply, connect, and extend the mathematical skills they are learning. We have updated the exercises that focus on real-life data and have retained their titles for easy identification. Several chapters are enriched with new applications, particularly Chapters 7, 8, 10, and 14. We continue to use graphs, tables, and charts when appropriate. Many of the graphs use a style similar to that seen by students in today's print and electronic media.

**Enhanced: Margin Notes** This popular feature is a hallmark of this text and has been retained and updated where appropriate. These notes are interspersed throughout the text and deal with various subjects such as lives of mathematicians, historical vignettes, philatelic and numismatic reproductions, anecdotes on mathematics textbooks of the past, newspaper and magazine articles, and current research in mathematics. Completely new Hollywood-related margin notes have been included as well.

**Collaborative Investigations** The importance of cooperative learning is addressed in this end-of-chapter feature.

**Problem-Solving Hints** Special paragraphs labeled "Problem-Solving Hint" relate the discussion of problem-solving strategies to techniques that have been presented earlier.

**Optional Graphing Technology** We continue to provide sample graphing calculator screens (generated by a TI-83/84 Plus calculator) to show how technology can be used to support results found analytically. It is not essential, however, that a student have a graphing calculator to study from this text; *the technology component is optional.*

**Flexibility** Some topics in the first six chapters require a basic knowledge of equation solving. Depending on the background of the students, the instructor may omit topics that require this skill. On the other hand, the two algebra chapters (Chapters 7 and 8) provide an excellent overview of algebra, and because of the flexibility of the text, they may be covered at almost any time.

**Art Program** The text continues to feature a full-color design. Color is used for instructional emphasis in text discussions, examples, graphs, and figures. New and striking photos have been incorporated to enhance applications and provide visual appeal.

**For Further Thought** These entries encourage students to share amongst themselves their reasoning processes in order to gain a deeper understanding of key mathematical concepts.

**New: Example Titles** The numerous, carefully selected examples that illustrate concepts and skills are now titled so that students can see at a glance the topic under consideration. They prepare students for the exercises that follow.

**Updated: Emphasis on Real Data in the Form of Graphs, Charts, and Tables** We continue to use up-to-date information from magazines, newspapers, and the Internet to create real applications that are relevant and meaningful.

**Chapter Tests** Each chapter concludes with a chapter test so that students can check their mastery of the material.

# MEDIA GUIDE

### MathXL®

MathXL is a powerful online homework, tutorial, and assessment system that accompanies this Addison-Wesley textbook. With MathXL, instructors can create, edit, and assign online homework and tests using algorithmically generated exercises correlated at the objective level to the text. Instructors can also create and assign their own online exercises and import TestGen tests for added flexibility. All student work is tracked in MathXL's online gradebook. Students can take chapter tests in MathXL and receive personalized study plans based on their test results. The study plan diagnoses weaknesses and links students directly to tutorial exercises for the objectives they need to study and on which they need to be retested. Students can also access supplemental animations and video clips directly from selected exercises. MathXL is available to qualified adopters. For more information, visit our Web site at www.mathxl.com or contact your local sales representative.

### MathXL® Tutorials on CD ISBN: 0-321-36972-6

This interactive tutorial CD-ROM provides algorithmically generated practice exercises that are correlated at the objective level to the exercises in the textbook. Every practice exercise is accompanied by an example and a guided solution designed to involve students in the solution process. Selected exercises may also include a video clip to help students visualize concepts. The software provides helpful feedback for incorrect answers and can generate printed summaries of students' progress.

### MyMathLab

MyMathLab is a series of text-specific, easily customizable online courses for Addison-Wesley textbooks in mathematics and statistics. MyMathLab is powered by CourseCompass™—Pearson Education's online teaching and learning environment—and by MathXL—our online homework, tutorial, and assessment system. MyMathLab gives instructors the tools needed to deliver all or a portion of their course online, whether students are in a lab setting or working from home. MyMathLab provides a rich and flexible set of course materials, featuring free-response exercises that are algorithmically generated for unlimited practice and mastery. Students can also use online tools, such as video lectures, animations, and a multimedia textbook, to independently improve their understanding and performance. Instructors can use MyMathLab's homework and test managers to select and assign online exercises correlated directly to the textbook, and they can also create and assign their own online exercises and import TestGen tests for added flexibility. MyMathLab's online gradebook—designed specifically for mathematics and statistics—automatically tracks students' homework and test results and gives the instructor control over how to calculate final grades. Instructors can also add off-line (paper-and-pencil) grades to the gradebook. MyMathLab is available to qualified adopters. For more information, visit our Web site at www.mymathlab.com or contact your local sales representative.

### InterAct Math Tutorial Web site www.interactmath.com

Get practice and tutorial help online! This interactive tutorial Web site provides algorithmically generated practice exercises that correlate directly to the exercises in the textbook. Students can retry an exercise as many times as they like, with new values each time, for unlimited practice and mastery. Every exercise is accompanied by an interactive guided solution that provides helpful feedback for incorrect answers, and students can also view a worked-out sample problem that steps them through an exercise similar to the one they are working on.

### Video Lectures on CD with Optional Captioning

In this comprehensive video series, an engaging team of instructors provide chapter- and section-based instruction on every topic in the textbook. These lessons present key concepts and show students how to work exercises, providing extra instruction for students who have missed a class or who are in need of a little extra help. The lectures are available on CD-ROM, for purchase with the text at minimal cost. Affordable and portable for students, this series makes it easy and convenient for students to watch the videos from a computer at home or on campus.

# SUPPLEMENTS to accompany MATHEMATICAL IDEAS

## Eleventh Edition • Expanded Eleventh Edition

### STUDENT SUPPLEMENTS

#### Student's Study Guide and Solutions Manual

- By Emmett Larson, *Brevard Community College*
- This manual provides solutions to the odd-numbered exercises in the exercise sets, the Extensions, and the Appendix exercises, as well as providing solutions for all the Chapter Test exercises. Chapter summaries review key points in the text, provide extra examples, and enumerate major topic objectives.

ISBN 0-321-36971-8

#### Video Lectures on CD with Optional Captions

- This is a complete set of digitized videos for student use at home or on campus, making it ideal for distance learning or supplemental instruction.

ISBN 0-321-36954-8

#### Addison-Wesley Math Tutor Center

- The Tutor Center provides tutoring through a registration number that can be packaged with a new textbook or purchased separately. The Tutor Center is staffed by qualified college mathematics instructors who provide students with tutoring on examples and odd-numbered exercises from the textbook. It is accessible via toll-free telephone, toll-free fax, e-mail, and the Internet (www.aw-bc.com/tutorcenter).

### INSTRUCTOR SUPPLEMENTS

#### NEW! Annotated Instructor's Edition

- This special edition of the text provides answers next to almost all of the text exercises for quick reference, where possible.

ISBN 0-321-36147-4

#### Instructor's Solutions Manual

- By Emmett Larson, *Brevard Community College*
- This manual contains solutions to all end-of-section exercises, Extension, Chapter Test, and Appendix exercises.

ISBN 0-321-36970-X

#### Instructor's Testing Manual

- This manual contains four tests for each chapter of the text. Answer keys are included.

ISBN 0-321-36969-6

#### TestGen®

- TestGen enables instructors to build, edit, print, and administer tests using a computerized bank of questions developed to cover all text objectives. The software is available on a dual-platform Windows/ Macintosh CD-ROM.

ISBN 0-321-36966-1

#### NEW! Insider's Guide to Teaching with Mathematical Ideas, 11e

- The Insider's Guide includes resources to help faculty with course preparation and classroom management. It provides helpful teaching tips correlated to each section of the text, as well as general teaching advice.

ISBN 0-321-49090-8

#### PowerPoint Lecture Presentation

- The PowerPoint classroom presentation slides are geared specifically to sequence this textbook. They are available within MyMathLab or at www.aw-bc. com/irc.

#### NEW! Adjunct Support Center

- The Center offers consultation on suggested syllabi, helpful tips on using the textbook support package, assistance with content, and advice on classroom strategies. It is available Sunday through Thursday evenings from 5 P.M. to midnight EST; telephone: 1-800-435-4084; e-mail: adjunctsupport @aw.com; fax: 1-877-262-9774.

# ACKNOWLEDGMENTS

We wish to thank the following reviewers for their helpful comments and suggestions for this and previous editions of the text. (Reviewers of the eleventh edition are noted with an asterisk.)

H. Achepohl, *College of DuPage*
Shahrokh Ahmadi, *Northern Virginia Community College*
Richard Andrews, *Florida A&M University*
Cindy Anfinson, *Palomar College*
Elaine Barber, *Germanna Community College*
Anna Baumgartner, *Carthage College*
James E. Beamer, *Northeastern State University*
Elliot Benjamin, *Unity College*
Jaime Bestard, *Barry University*
Joyce Blair, *Belmont University*
Gus Brar, *Delaware County Community College*
Roger L. Brown, *Davenport College*
Douglas Burke, *Malcolm X College*
John Busovicki, *Indiana University of Pennsylvania*
Ann Cascarelle, *St. Petersburg Junior College*
Kenneth Chapman, *St. Petersburg Junior College*
Gordon M. Clarke, *University of the Incarnate Word*
M. Marsha Cupitt, *Durham Technical Community College*
James Curry, *American River College*
*Rosemary Danaher, *Sacred Heart University*
Ken Davis, *Mesa State College*
Nancy Davis, *Brunswick Community College*
George DeRise, *Thomas Nelson Community College*
Catherine Dermott, *Hudson Valley Community College*
*Greg Dietrich, *Florida Community College at Jacksonville*
Diana C. Dwan, *Yavapai College*
Laura Dyer, *Belleville Area College*
Jan Eardley, *Barat College*
Joe Eitel, *Folsom College*
Azin Enshai, *American River College*
Gayle Farmer, *Northeastern State University*
Michael Farndale, *Waldorf College*
Gordon Feathers, *Passaic County Community College*
Thomas Flohr, *New River Community College*
Bill Fulton, *Black Hawk College—East*
Anne Gardner, *Wenatchee Valley College*
Donald Goral, *Northern Virginia Community College*
Glen Granzow, *Idaho State University*
Larry Green, *Lake Tahoe Community College*
Arthur D. Grissinger, *Lock Haven University*
Don Hancock, *Pepperdine University*
Denis Hanson, *University of Regina*
Marilyn Hasty, *Southern Illinois University*
Shelby L. Hawthorne, *Thomas Nelson Community College*
Jeff Heiking, *St. Petersburg Junior College*
*Laura Hillerbrand, *Broward Community College*
*Jacqueline Jensen, *Sam Houston State University*
Emanuel Jinich, *Endicott College*
*Frank Juric, *Brevard Community College-Palm Bay*
Karla Karstens, *University of Vermont*
Hilary Kight, *Wesleyan College*
Barbara J. Kniepkamp, *Southern Illinois University at Edwardsville*
Suda Kunyosying, *Shepherd College*
*Yu-Ju Kuo, *Indiana University of Pennsylvania*
Pam Lamb, *J. Sargeant Reynolds Community College*
*John Lattanzio, *Indiana University of Pennsylvania*
John W. Legge, *Pikeville College*
Leo Lusk, *Gulf Coast Community College*
Sherrie Lutsch, *Northwest Indian College*
Rhonda Macleod, *Florida State University*
Andrew Markoe, *Rider University*
Darlene Marnich, *Point Park College*
Victoria Martinez, *Okaloosa Walton Community College*
Chris Mason, *Community College of Vermont*

Mark Maxwell, *Maryville University*
Carol McCarron, *Harrisburg Area Community College*
Delois McCormick, *Germanna Community College*
Daisy McCoy, *Lyndon State College*
Cynthia McGinnis, *Okaloosa Walton Community College*
Vena McGrath, *Davenport College*
Robert Moyer, *Fort Valley State University*
Shai Neumann, *Brevard Community College*
*Vladimir Nikiforov, *University of Memphis*
Barbara Nienstedt, *Gloucester County College*
Chaitanya Nigam, *Gateway Community-Technical College*
Jean Okumura, *Windward Community College*
Bob Phillips, *Mesabi Range Community College*
Kathy Pinchback, *University of Memphis*
Priscilla Putman, *New Jersey City University*
Scott C. Radtke, *Davenport College*
John Reily, *Montclair State University*
Beth Reynolds, *Mater Dei College*
Shirley I. Robertson, *High Point University*
Andrew M. Rockett, *CW Post Campus of Long Island University*
Kathleen Rodak, *St. Mary's College of Ave Maria University*
*Abby Roscum, *Marshalltown Community College*
D. Schraeder, *McLennan Community College*
Wilfred Schulte, *Cosumnes River College*
Melinda Schulteis, *Concordia University*
Gary D. Shaffer, *Allegany College of Maryland*
*Doug Shaw, *University of North Iowa*
Jane Sinibaldi, *York College of Pennsylvania*
Larry Smith, *Peninsula College*
Marguerite Smith, *Merced College*
Charlene D. Snow, *Lower Columbia College*
H. Jeannette Stephens, *Whatcom Community College*
Suzanne J. Stock, *Oakton Community College*
Dian Thom, *McKendree College*
Claude C. Thompson, *Hollins University*
Mark Tom, *College of the Sequoias*
Ida Umphers, *University of Arkansas at Little Rock*
Karen Villarreal, *University of New Orleans*
Wayne Wanamaker, *Central Florida Community College*
David Wasilewski, *Luzerne County Community College*
William Watkins, *California State University, Northridge*
Susan Williford, *Columbia State Community College*
Tom Witten, *Southwest Virginia Community College*
Fred Worth, *Henderson State University*
Rob Wylie, *Carl Albert State College*
Henry Wyzinski, *Indiana University Northwest*

A project of this magnitude cannot be accomplished without the help of many other dedicated individuals. Anne Kelly served as sponsoring editor for this edition. Jeff Houck of Progressive Publishing Alternatives provided excellent production supervision. Ashley O'Shaughnessy, Greg Tobin, Barbara Atkinson, Becky Anderson, Peggy McMahon, Beth Anderson, and Joanne Ha of Addison-Wesley gave us their unwavering support. Terry McGinnis provided her usual excellent behind-the-scenes guidance. Thanks go to Dr. Margaret L. Morrow of Plattsburgh State University and Dr. Jill Van Newenhizen of Lake Forest College, who wrote the material on graph theory and voting/apportionment, respectively, for the Expanded Edition. Perian Herring, Cheryl Davids, Patricia Nelson, and Alicia Gordon did an outstanding job of accuracy- and answer-checking, and Becky Troutman provided the *Index of Applications*. And finally, we thank our loyal users over the past four decades for making this book one of the most successful in its market.

Vern E. Heeren
John Hornsby

# NUMBER THEORY

The first episode of the animated series *The Simpsons* aired on December 17, 1989 and has since become a pop culture icon, providing humor, social commentary, and even lessons in mathematics. An annual treat for fans is the *Treehouse of Horror* episode, which airs near Halloween. In the sixth installment, this episode featured a segment titled *Homer 3D* in which a two-dimensional Homer Simpson became trapped in the third dimension. Computer graphics portrayed a three-dimensional coordinate system, the Parthenon (an example of the *Golden Ratio*), a cone, a black hole, and several mathematical equations. One such equation was

$$1782^{12} + 1841^{12} = 1922^{12}.$$

In Section 5.2 you will learn that ***this equation cannot be true.*** It is of the form of an equation of Fermat's Last Theorem, one of the most famous theorems in *number theory*, the topic of this chapter. The theorem was stated by the French mathematician Pierre de Fermat over 400 years ago, but was not proved until 1994. A graphing calculator such as the TI-83/84 Plus will indicate that the equation is true, but only because the calculator is unable to compute powers of this size. Can you explain why it can't be true? (*Hint:* Show that one side is an odd number and the other is an even number.) See page 237 for the complete answer.

# 5.1 Prime and Composite Numbers

**Primes, Composites, and Divisibility • The Fundamental Theorem of Arithmetic • The Infinitude of Primes • The Search for Large Primes**

**Primes, Composites, and Divisibility** The famous German mathematician Carl Friedrich Gauss once remarked, "Mathematics is the Queen of Science, and number theory is the Queen of Mathematics." This chapter is centered around the study of number theory. **Number theory** is the branch of mathematics devoted to the study of the properties of the natural numbers. In earlier chapters we discussed the set of **natural numbers**, also called the **counting numbers** or the **positive integers:**

$$\{1, 2, 3, \ldots\}.$$

Number theory deals with the study of the properties of this set of numbers, and a key concept of number theory is the idea of *divisibility*. Informally, we say that one counting number is *divisible* by another if the operation of dividing the first by the second leaves a remainder 0. A formal definition follows.

Do not confuse $b \mid a$ with $b/a$. The expression $b \mid a$ denotes the *statement* "$b$ divides $a$." For example, $3 \mid 12$ is a true statement, while $5 \mid 14$ is a false statement. On the other hand, $b/a$ denotes the *operation* "$b$ divided by $a$." For example, 28/4 yields the result 7.

**Divisibility**

The natural number $a$ is **divisible** by the natural number $b$ if there exists a natural number $k$ such that $a = bk$. If $b$ divides $a$, then we write $b \mid a$.

Notice that if $b$ divides $a$, then the quotient $a/b$ or $\frac{a}{b}$ is a natural number. For example, 4 divides 20 because there exists a natural number $k$ such that $20 = 4k$. The value of $k$ here is 5, because $20 = 4 \cdot 5$. The natural number 20 is not divisible by 7, for example, since there is no natural number $k$ satisfying $20 = 7k$. Alternatively, we think "20 divided by 7 gives quotient 2 with remainder 6" and since there is a nonzero remainder, divisibility does not hold. We write $7 \nmid 20$ to indicate that 7 does not divide 20.

The ideas of **even** and **odd natural numbers** are based on the concept of divisibility. A natural number is even if it is divisible by 2 and odd if it is not. Every even number can be written in the form $2k$ (for some natural number $k$), while every odd number can be written in the form $2k + 1$. Another way to say the same thing: 2 divides every even number but fails to divide every odd number. (If $a$ is even, then $2 \mid a$, whereas if $a$ is odd, then $2 \nmid a$.)

If the natural number $a$ is divisible by the natural number $b$, then $b$ is a **factor** (or **divisor**) of $a$, and $a$ is a **multiple** of $b$. For example, 5 is a factor of 30, and 30 is a multiple of 5. Also, 6 is a factor of 30, and 30 is a multiple of 6. The number 30 equals $6 \cdot 5$; this product $6 \cdot 5$ is called a **factorization** of 30. Other factorizations of 30 include $3 \cdot 10$, $2 \cdot 15$, $1 \cdot 30$, and $2 \cdot 3 \cdot 5$.

### EXAMPLE 1 Checking Divisibility

Decide whether the first number is divisible by the second.

**(a)** 45; 9 **(b)** 60; 7 **(c)** 19; 19 **(d)** 26; 1

**SOLUTION**

**(a)** Is there a natural number $k$ that satisfies $45 = 9k$? The answer is yes, because $45 = 9 \cdot 5$, and 5 is a natural number. Therefore, 9 divides 45, written $9 \mid 45$.

(b) Because the quotient 60 ÷ 7 is not a natural number, 60 is not divisible by 7, written $7 \nmid 60$.

(c) The quotient 19 ÷ 19 is the natural number 1, so 19 is divisible by 19. (In fact, any natural number is divisible by itself.)

(d) The quotient 26 ÷ 1 is the natural number 26, so 26 is divisible by 1. (In fact, any natural number is divisible by 1.)

For any natural number $a$, it is true that $a \mid a$, and also that $1 \mid a$.

### EXAMPLE 2 Finding Factors

Find all the natural number factors of each number.

(a) 36  (b) 50  (c) 11

**SOLUTION**

(a) To find the factors of 36, try to divide 36 by 1, 2, 3, 4, 5, 6, and so on. Doing this gives the following list of natural number factors of 36:

1, 2, 3, 4, 6, 9, 12, 18, and 36.

(b) The factors of 50 are 1, 2, 5, 10, 25, and 50.

(c) The only natural number factors of 11 are 11 and 1.

Like the number 19 in Example 1(c), the number 11 has only two natural number factors, itself and 1. Such a natural number is called a *prime number*.

The 1997 movie *Contact,* based on the Carl Sagan novel of the same name, portrays Jodie Foster as scientist Ellie Arroway. After years of searching, Ellie makes contact with intelligent life in outer space. Her contact is verified after receiving radio signals that indicate **prime numbers:** 2, 3, 5, 7, 11, and so on. Her superiors are not convinced, asking why the aliens don't just speak English. Ellie's response:

*Well, maybe because 70% of the planet speaks other languages. Mathematics is the only true universal language, Senator. It's no coincidence that they're using primes . . . Prime numbers—that would be integers that are divisible only by themselves and 1.*

#### Prime and Composite Numbers

A natural number greater than 1 that has only itself and 1 as factors is called a **prime number.** A natural number greater than 1 that is not prime is called **composite.**

Mathematicians agree that the natural number 1 is neither prime nor composite. The following alternative definition of a prime number clarifies that 1 is not a prime.

#### Alternative Definition of a Prime Number

A **prime number** is a natural number that has *exactly* two different natural number factors.

There is a systematic method for identifying prime numbers in a list of numbers: 2, 3, . . . , $n$. The method, known as the **Sieve of Eratosthenes,** is named after the Greek geographer, poet, astronomer, and mathematician, who lived from about 276 to 192 B.C. To construct such a sieve, list all the natural numbers from 2 through some given natural number $n$, such as 100. The number 2 is prime, but all other multiples of 2 (4, 6, 8, 10, and so on) are composite. Circle the prime 2, and cross out all other multiples of 2. The next number not crossed out and not circled is 3, the next prime. Circle the 3, and cross out all other multiples of 3 (6, 9, 12, 15, and so on) that are not already crossed out. Circle the next prime, 5, and cross out all other multiples of 5 not already crossed out. Continue this process for all primes less than or equal to the square root of the last number in the list. For this list, we may stop with 7, because the next prime, 11, is greater than the square root of 100, which is 10. At this stage, simply circle all remaining numbers that are not crossed out.

Table 1 shows the Sieve of Eratosthenes for 2, 3, 4, . . . , 100, identifying the 25 primes in that range. Theoretically, such a sieve can be constructed for any value of $n$.

**TABLE 1** Sieve of Eratosthenes

| | | | | | | | | | | | | | |
|---|---|---|---|---|---|---|---|---|---|---|---|---|---|
| | (2) | (3) | ~~4~~ | (5) | ~~6~~ | (7) | ~~8~~ | ~~9~~ | ~~10~~ | (11) | ~~12~~ | (13) | ~~14~~ |
| ~~15~~ | ~~16~~ | (17) | ~~18~~ | (19) | ~~20~~ | ~~21~~ | ~~22~~ | (23) | ~~24~~ | ~~25~~ | ~~26~~ | ~~27~~ | ~~28~~ |
| (29) | ~~30~~ | (31) | ~~32~~ | ~~33~~ | ~~34~~ | ~~35~~ | ~~36~~ | (37) | ~~38~~ | ~~39~~ | ~~40~~ | (41) | ~~42~~ |
| (43) | ~~44~~ | ~~45~~ | ~~46~~ | (47) | ~~48~~ | ~~49~~ | ~~50~~ | ~~51~~ | ~~52~~ | (53) | ~~54~~ | ~~55~~ | ~~56~~ |
| ~~57~~ | ~~58~~ | (59) | ~~60~~ | (61) | ~~62~~ | ~~63~~ | ~~64~~ | ~~65~~ | ~~66~~ | (67) | ~~68~~ | ~~69~~ | ~~70~~ |
| (71) | ~~72~~ | (73) | ~~74~~ | ~~75~~ | ~~76~~ | ~~77~~ | ~~78~~ | (79) | ~~80~~ | ~~81~~ | ~~82~~ | (83) | ~~84~~ |
| ~~85~~ | ~~86~~ | ~~87~~ | ~~88~~ | (89) | ~~90~~ | ~~91~~ | ~~92~~ | ~~93~~ | ~~94~~ | ~~95~~ | ~~96~~ | (97) | ~~98~~ |
| ~~99~~ | ~~100~~ | | | | | | | | | | | | |

### EXAMPLE 3 Identifying Prime and Composite Numbers

Decide whether each number is prime or composite.

**(a)** 97 **(b)** 59,872 **(c)** 697

**SOLUTION**

**(a)** Because 97 is circled in Table 1, it is prime. If 97 had a smaller prime factor, 97 would have been crossed out as a multiple of that factor.

**(b)** The number 59,872 is even, so it is divisible by 2. It is composite. (There is only one even prime, the number 2 itself.)

**(c)** For 697 to be composite, there must be a number other than 697 and 1 that divides into it with remainder 0. Start by trying 2, and then 3. Neither works. There is no need to try 4. (If 4 divides with remainder 0 into a number, then 2 will also.) Try 5. There is no need to try 6 or any succeeding even number. (Why?) Try 7. Try 11. (Why not try 9?) Try 13. Keep trying numbers until one works, or until a number is tried whose square exceeds the given number, 697. Try 17:

$$697 \div 17 = 41.$$

The number 697 is composite: $697 = 17 \cdot 41.$ ■

**How to Use Up Lots of Chalk**
In 1903, the mathematician F. N. Cole presented before a meeting of the American Mathematical Society his discovery of a factorization of the number

$$2^{67} - 1.$$

He walked up to the chalkboard, raised 2 to the 67th power, and then subtracted 1. Then he moved over to another part of the board and multiplied out

$$193{,}707{,}721 \times 761{,}838{,}257{,}287.$$

The two calculations agreed, and Cole received a standing ovation for a presentation that did not include a single word.

An aid in determining whether a natural number is divisible by another natural number is called a **divisibility test.** Some simple divisibility tests exist for small natural numbers, and they are given in Table 2 on the next page. Divisibility tests for 7 and 11 are a bit involved, and they are discussed in the exercises for this section. Each test in the table is both a necessary and a sufficient condition. If the test statement is true, then divisibility occurs. If the test statement is not true, then divisibility does not occur.

Writing in the October 1, 1994 issue of *Science News*, Ivars Peterson gives a fascinating account of the recent discovery of a 75-year-old **factoring machine** ("Cranking Out Primes: Tracking Down a Long-lost Factoring Machine"). In 1989, Jeffrey Shallit of the University of Waterloo in Ontario came across an article in an obscure 1920 French journal, in which the author, Eugene Olivier Carissan, reported his invention of the factoring apparatus. Shallit and two colleagues embarked on a search for the machine. They contacted all telephone subscribers in France named Carissan and received a reply from Eugene Carissan's daughter. The machine was still in existence and in working condition, stored in a drawer at an astronomical observatory in Floirac, near Bordeaux.

Peterson explains in the article how the apparatus works. Using the machine, Carissan took just ten minutes to prove that 708,158,977 is a prime number, and he was able to factor a 13-digit number. While this cannot compare to what technology can accomplish today, it was a significant achievement for Carissan's day.

**TABLE 2** Divisibility Tests

| Divisible By | Test | Example |
|---|---|---|
| 2 | Number ends in 0, 2, 4, 6, or 8. (The last digit is even.) | 9,489,994 ends in 4; it is divisible by 2. |
| 3 | Sum of the digits is divisible by 3. | 897,432 is divisible by 3, since $8 + 9 + 7 + 4 + 3 + 2 =$ 33 is divisible by 3. |
| 4 | Last two digits form a number divisible by 4. | 7,693,432 is divisible by 4, since 32 is divisible by 4. |
| 5 | Number ends in 0 or 5. | 890 and 7635 are divisible by 5. |
| 6 | Number is divisible by both 2 and 3. | 27,342 is divisible by 6 since it is divisible by both 2 and 3. |
| 8 | Last three digits form a number divisible by 8. | 1,437,816 is divisible by 8, since 816 is divisible by 8. |
| 9 | Sum of the digits is divisible by 9. | 428,376,105 is divisible by 9 since sum of digits is 36, which is divisible by 9. |
| 10 | The last digit is 0. | 897,463,940 is divisible by 10. |
| 12 | Number is divisible by both 4 and 3. | 376,984,032 is divisible by 12. |

### EXAMPLE 4 Applying Divisibility Tests

In each case, decide whether the first number is divisible by the second.

**(a)** 2,984,094; 4 **(b)** 4,119,806,514; 9

**SOLUTION**

**(a)** The last two digits form the number 94. Since 94 is not divisible by 4, the given number is not divisible by 4.

**(b)** The sum of the digits is $4 + 1 + 1 + 9 + 8 + 0 + 6 + 5 + 1 + 4 = 39$, which is not divisible by 9. The given number is therefore not divisible by 9.

## The Fundamental Theorem of Arithmetic

A *composite* number can be thought of as "composed" of smaller factors. For example, 42 is composite: $42 = 6 \cdot 7$. If the smaller factors are all primes, then we have a *prime factorization*. For example, $42 = 2 \cdot 3 \cdot 7$. An important theorem in mathematics states that there is only one possible way to write the prime factorization of a given composite natural number. A form of this theorem was known to the ancient Greeks.*

*A theorem is a statement that can be proved true from other statements. For a proof of this theorem, see *What Is Mathematics?* by Richard Courant and Herbert Robbins (Oxford University Press, 1941), p. 23.

The following program, written by Charles W. Gantner and provided courtesy of Texas Instruments, can be used on the TI-83/84 Plus calculator to list all primes less than or equal to a given natural number $N$.

```
PROGRAM: PRIMES
: Disp "INPUT N ≥ 2"
: Disp "TO GET"
: Disp "PRIMES ≤ N"
: Input N
: 2 → T
: Disp T
: 1 → A
: Lbl 1
: A + 2 → A
: 3 → B
: If A > N
: Stop
: Lbl 2
: If B ≤ √(A)
: Goto 3
: Disp A
: Pause
: Goto 1
: Lbl 3
: If A/B ≤ int (A/B)
: Goto 1
: B + 2 → B
: Goto 2
```

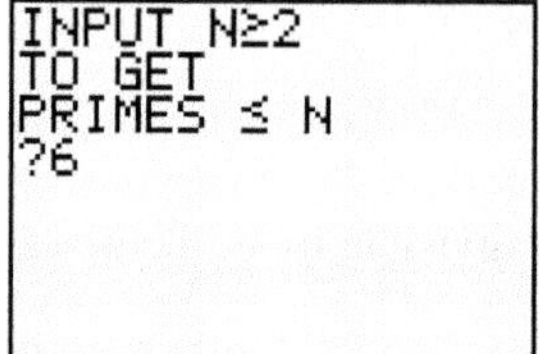


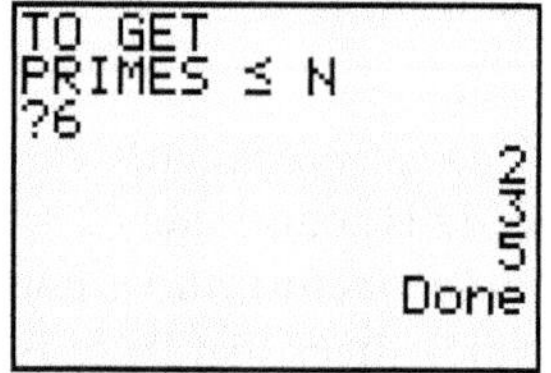


The display indicates that the primes less than or equal to 6 are 2, 3, and 5.

## The Fundamental Theorem of Arithmetic

Every natural number can be expressed in one and only one way as a product of primes (if the order of the factors is disregarded). This unique product of primes is called the **prime factorization** of the natural number.

Because a prime natural number is not composed of smaller factors, its prime factorization is simply itself. For example, $17 = 17$ (or $17 = 1 \cdot 17$).

The following example shows two ways to factor a composite number into primes: (1) using a "factor tree" and (2) using repeated division.

### EXAMPLE 5 Finding the Unique Prime Factorization of a Composite Number

Find the prime factorization of the number 504.

**SOLUTION**

The factor tree can start with $504 = 2 \cdot 252$, as shown below on the left. Then $252 = 2 \cdot 126$, and so on, until every branch of the tree ends with a prime. All the resulting prime factors are shown circled in the diagram.

Alternatively, the same factorization is obtained by repeated division by primes, as shown on the right. (In general, you would divide by the primes 2, 3, 5, 7, 11, and so on, each as many times as possible, until the answer is no longer composite.)

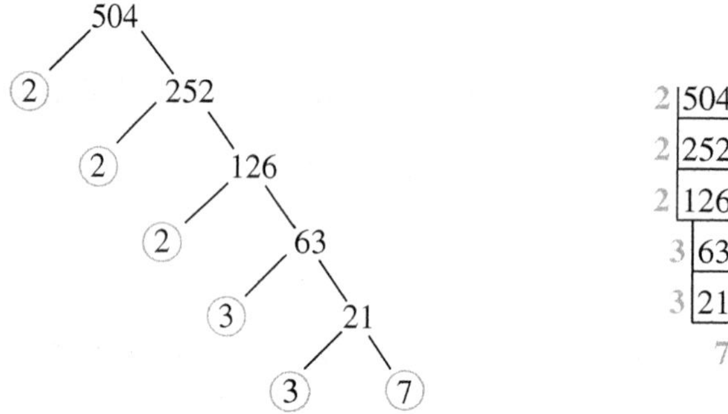


By either method, the prime factorization, in exponential form, is

$$504 = 2^3 \cdot 3^2 \cdot 7. \quad 2 \cdot 2 \cdot 2 = 2^3; 3 \cdot 3 = 3^2$$

## The Infinitude of Primes

Mathematicians (amateur as well as professional) have sought for thousands of years to learn as much as possible about prime numbers. One important basic result was proved by Euclid around 300 B.C., namely that there are infinitely many primes. This means that no matter how large a prime we identify, there are always others even larger. Euclid's proof remains today as one of the most elegant proofs in all of mathematics. (An *elegant* mathematical proof is one that demonstrates the desired result in a most direct, concise manner. Mathematicians strive for elegance in their proofs.) It is called a **proof by contradiction.**

**The Riemann Hypothesis** is an insightful conjecture stated in the mid-1800s by Georg Friedrich Bernhard Riemann (profiled on page 601). It concerns how the prime numbers are distributed on the number line and is undoubtedly the most important unproven claim in all of mathematics. Thousands of other "theorems" are built upon the assumption of its truth. If it were ever disproved, those results would fall apart. A proof, on the other hand, may provide sufficient understanding of the primes to demolish public key cryptography, upon which rests the security of all Internet commerce (among other things).

Two excellent books on the Riemann Hypothesis, and the mathematicians at the forefront of its study over the years, both published in 2003, are *Prime Obsession*, by John Derbyshire, and *The Music of the Primes*, by Marcus du Sautoy.

A statement can be proved by contradiction as follows: We assume that the negation of the statement is true. The assumption that the negation is true is used to produce some sort of contradiction, or absurdity. The fact that the negation of the original statement leads to a contradiction means that the original statement must be true.

In order to better understand a particular part of the proof that there are infinitely many primes, it is helpful to examine the following argument.

Suppose that $M = 2 \cdot 3 \cdot 5 \cdot 7 + 1 = 211$. Now $M$ is the product of the first four prime numbers, plus 1. If we divide 211 by each of the primes 2, 3, 5, and 7, the remainder is always 1.

$$\begin{array}{r} 105 \\ 2\overline{)211} \\ \underline{105} \\ 1 \end{array} \quad \begin{array}{r} 70 \\ 3\overline{)211} \\ \underline{210} \\ 1 \end{array} \quad \begin{array}{r} 42 \\ 5\overline{)211} \\ \underline{210} \\ 1 \end{array} \quad \begin{array}{r} 30 \\ 7\overline{)211} \\ \underline{210} \\ 1 \end{array}$$

All remainders are 1.

So 211 is not divisible by any of the primes 2, 3, 5, and 7.

Now we are ready to prove that there are infinitely many primes. If it can be shown that *there is no largest prime number*, then there must be infinitely many primes.

**THEOREM**

*Statement:* There is no largest prime number.

*Proof:* Suppose that there is a largest prime number and call it $P$. Now form the number $M$ such that

$$M = p_1 \cdot p_2 \cdot p_3 \cdots P + 1,$$

where $p_1, p_2, p_3, \ldots, P$ represent all the primes less than or equal to $P$. Now the number $M$ must be either prime or composite.

1. Suppose that $M$ is prime.
   $M$ is obviously larger than $P$, so if $M$ is prime, it is larger than the assumed largest prime $P$. We have reached a *contradiction*.
2. Suppose that $M$ is composite.
   If $M$ is composite, it must have a prime factor. But none of $p_1, p_2, p_3, \ldots, P$ are factors of $M$, because division by each will leave a remainder of 1. (Recall the above argument.) So if $M$ has a prime factor, it must be greater than $P$. But this is a *contradiction*, because $P$ is the assumed largest prime.

In either case 1 or 2, we reach a contradiction. The whole argument was based upon the assumption that a largest prime exists, but as this leads to contradictions, there must be no largest prime, or equivalently, there are infinitely many primes.

During the first season of the CBS television series *NUMB3RS*, the episode *Prime Suspect* was based on the premise that a mathematician was very close to proving the Riemann Hypothesis (which later proved to be erroneous). His daughter was kidnapped by people who were hoping to exchange her for the results in order to unlock financial security codes.

**The Search for Large Primes** Identifying larger and larger prime numbers and factoring large composite numbers into their prime components is of great practical importance today, because it is the basis of modern **cryptography systems,** or secret codes. Various codes have been used for centuries in military applications. Today the security of vast amounts of industrial, business, and personal data also depend upon the theory of prime numbers. See the Extension following Section 5.3.

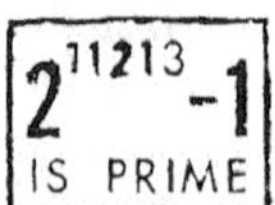

At one time, $2^{11,213} - 1$ was the largest known **Mersenne prime.** To honor its discovery, the Urbana, Illinois, post office used the cancellation picture above.

As mathematicians continue to search for larger and larger primes, a formula for generating all the primes would be nice (something similar, for example, to the formula $2n$, which generates all even counting numbers for $n = 1, 2, 3, \ldots$, or the formula $n^2$, which generates all the perfect squares). Numbers generated by the formula $M_n = 2^n - 1$ are called **Mersenne numbers** to honor the French monk Marin Mersenne (1588–1648). It was long known that a *composite* value of $n$ would always generate a composite Mersenne number. (See Exercises 83–88.) And some early mathematicians believed (incorrectly) that a *prime* value of $n$ would always generate a prime Mersenne number. That is, they believed that, starting with any known prime number $n$, one could always produce another, larger prime number $2^n - 1$. (Although "always generate a prime" is not the same as "generate all primes," at least it would have been an unending source of guaranteed primes.)

## EXAMPLE 6 Finding Mersenne Numbers

Find each Mersenne number $M_n$ for $n = 2, 3$, and 5.

**SOLUTION**

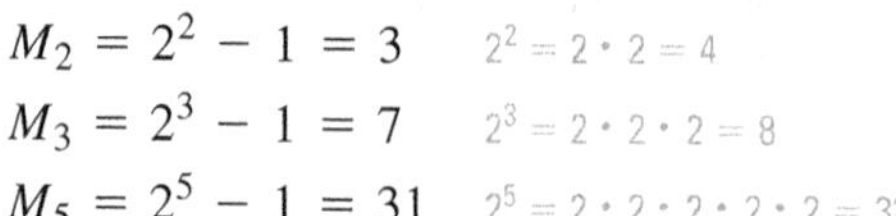

$$M_2 = 2^2 - 1 = 3 \qquad 2^2 = 2 \cdot 2 = 4$$
$$M_3 = 2^3 - 1 = 7 \qquad 2^3 = 2 \cdot 2 \cdot 2 = 8$$
$$M_5 = 2^5 - 1 = 31 \qquad 2^5 = 2 \cdot 2 \cdot 2 \cdot 2 \cdot 2 = 32$$

Note that all three values, 3, 7, and 31, are indeed primes.

**Marin Mersenne** (1588–1648), in his *Cogitata Physico-Mathematica* (1644), claimed that $M_n$ was prime for $n = 2, 3, 5, 7, 13, 17, 19, 31, 67, 127$, and 257, and composite for all other prime numbers $n$ less than 257. Other mathematicians at the time knew that Mersenne could not have actually tested all these values, but no one else could prove or disprove them either. It was more then 300 years later before all primes up to 257 were legitimately checked out, and Mersenne was finally revealed to have made five errors:

$M_{61}$ is prime.
$M_{67}$ is composite.
$M_{89}$ is prime.
$M_{107}$ is prime.
$M_{257}$ is composite.

It turns out that $M_7$ is also a prime (see Exercise 26), but it was discovered in 1536 that $M_{11} = 2^{11} - 1 = 2047$ is not prime (since it is $23 \cdot 89$). So prime values of $n$ do *not* always produce prime $M_n$. The question then became which prime values of $n$ do produce prime Mersenne numbers (the so-called **Mersenne primes**). Since no way was ever found to identify, in general, which prime values of $n$ result in Mersenne primes, it became a matter of checking out each prime $n$ value individually—not an easy task given that the Mersenne numbers rapidly become very large.

We can summarize the discussion of Mersenne numbers, up to this point, as follows.

### Mersenne Numbers and Mersenne Primes

For $n = 1, 2, 3, \ldots$, the **Mersenne numbers** are those generated by the formula

$$M_n = 2^n - 1.$$

**(1)** If $n$ is composite, then $M_n$ is also composite.
**(2)** If $n$ is prime, then $M_n$ may be either prime or composite.

The prime values of $M_n$ are called the **Mersenne primes.** Large primes being verified currently (though at a rather gradual pace) are commonly Mersenne primes.

The Mersenne prime search yielded results slowly. By about 1600, $M_n$ had been verified as prime for all prime $n$ up to 19 (except for 11, as mentioned above). The next one was $M_{31}$, verified by Euler in 1732. In 1876, French mathematician Edouard Lucas used a clever test he had developed to show that $M_{127}$ (a 39-digit number) is prime. In the 1930s Lucas's method was further simplified by D. H. Lehmer, and the

**Prime Does Pay** On December 15, 2005, the 43rd known Mersenne prime was identified by Curtis Cooper and Steven Boone of Central Missouri State University, using a 2 gigahertz (upgraded to 3 gigahertz) Pentium 4 computer, as part of the GIMPS program. The Electronic Frontier Foundation has paid $50,000 for record primes exceeding a million digits and offers $100,000 for the first ten-million-digit prime. Because the 2005 record has 9,152,052 digits, it left the big prize still "up for grabs."

If you would like to join the **Great Internet Mersenne Prime Search** (or just find out more about it), check out www.mersenne.org.

testing of Mersenne numbers for primality has been done ever since with the Lucas–Lehmer test. In 1952 an early computer verified that $M_{521}$, $M_{607}$, $M_{1279}$, $M_{2203}$, and $M_{2281}$ are primes.

Over the last half century, most new record-breaking primes have been identified by computer algorithms devised and implemented by mathematicians and programmers. In 1996, the **Great Internet Mersenne Prime Search (GIMPS)** was launched. Since then, many thousands of individuals have signed on, receiving free software and source code to run during slack time on personal computers throughout the world. The nine largest record Mersenne primes have been found by GIMPS.

As of early 2006, the record largest prime (discovered on December 15, 2005) was

$$M_{30,402,457} = 2^{30,402,457} - 1,$$

a number with 9,152,052 digits. It was the 43rd known Mersenne prime.

During the same general period that Mersenne was thinking about prime numbers, Pierre de Fermat (about 1601–1665) conjectured that the formula

$$2^{2^n} + 1$$

would always produce a prime, for any whole number value of $n$. Table 3 shows how this formula generates the first four **Fermat numbers,** which are all primes. The fifth Fermat number (from $n = 4$) is likewise prime. Fermat had verified these first five by around 1630. But the sixth Fermat number (from $n = 5$) turns out to be 4,294,967,297, which is *not* prime. (See Exercises 75 and 76.) To date, no more primes have been found among the Fermat numbers.

**TABLE 3** The Generation of Fermat Numbers

| $n$ | $2^n$ | $2^{2^n}$ | $2^{2^n} + 1$ |
|---|---|---|---|
| 0 | 1 | 2 | 3 |
| 1 | 2 | 4 | 5 |
| 2 | 4 | 16 | 17 |
| 3 | 8 | 256 | 257 |

Of historical note are a couple of polynomial formulas that produce primes. (A *polynomial* in a given variable involves adding or subtracting integer multiples of whole number powers of the variable. Polynomials are among the most basic mathematical functions. They are discussed in Section 7.6.) In 1732, Leonhard Euler offered the formula $n^2 - n + 41$, which generates primes for $n$ up to 40 and fails at $n = 41$. In 1879, E. B. Escott produced more primes with the formula $n^2 - 79n + 1601$, which first fails at $n = 80$.

## EXAMPLE 7 Finding Numbers Using Euler's and Escott's Formulas

Find the first five numbers produced by each of the polynomial formulas of Euler and Escott.

**SOLUTION**

Table 4 on the next page shows the required numbers.

**TABLE 4** A Few Polynomial-Generated Prime Numbers

| $n$ | Euler formula $n^2 - n + 41$ | Escott formula $n^2 - 79n + 1601$ |
|---|---|---|
| 1 | 41 | 1523 |
| 2 | 43 | 1447 |
| 3 | 47 | 1373 |
| 4 | 53 | 1301 |
| 5 | 61 | 1231 |

All values found here are primes. (Use Table 1 to verify the Euler values.)

Actually, it is not hard to prove that there can be no polynomial that will consistently generate primes. More complicated mathematical formulas exist for generating primes, but none produced so far can be practically applied in a reasonable amount of time, even using the fastest computers.

## 5.1 EXERCISES

*Decide whether each statement is* true *or* false.

**1.** Every natural number is divisible by 1.

**2.** No natural number is both prime and composite.

**3.** There are no even prime numbers.

**4.** If $n$ is a natural number and $9|n$, then $3|n$.

**5.** If $n$ is a natural number and $5|n$, then $10|n$.

**6.** 1 is the least prime number.

**7.** Every natural number is both a factor and a multiple of itself.

**8.** If 16 divides a natural number, then 2, 4, and 8 must also divide that natural number.

**9.** The composite number 50 has exactly two prime factorizations.

**10.** The prime number 53 has exactly two natural number factors.

**11.** The number $2^{11} - 1$ is an example of a Mersenne prime.

**12.** As of early 2006, only five Fermat primes had ever been found.

*Find all natural number factors of each number.*

**13.** 12 **14.** 18

**15.** 20 **16.** 28

**17.** 120 **18.** 172

*Use divisibility tests to decide whether the given number is divisible by each number.*

**(a)** 2 **(b)** 3 **(c)** 4 **(d)** 5 **(e)** 6 **(f)** 8
**(g)** 9 **(h)** 10 **(i)** 12

**19.** 315 **20.** 630

**21.** 25,025 **22.** 45,815

**23.** 123,456,789 **24.** 987,654,321

**25. (a)** In constructing the Sieve of Eratosthenes for 2 through 100, we said that any composite in that range had to be a multiple of some prime less than or equal to 7 (since the next prime, 11, is greater than the square root of 100). Explain.

**(b)** To extend the Sieve of Eratosthenes to 200, what is the largest prime whose multiples would have to be considered?

**(c)** Complete this statement: In seeking prime factors of a given number, we need only consider all primes up to and including the _____ ___ of that number, since a prime factor greater than the _____ ___ can only occur if there is at least one other prime factor less than the _____ ___.

(d) Complete this statement: If no prime less than or equal to $\sqrt{n}$ divides $n$, then $n$ is a _____ number.

**26.** (a) Continue the Sieve of Eratosthenes in Table 1 from 101 to 200 and list the primes between 100 and 200. How many are there?

(b) From your list in part (a), verify that the Mersenne number $M_7$ is indeed prime.

**27.** List two primes that are consecutive natural numbers. Can there be any others?

**28.** Can there be three primes that are consecutive natural numbers? Explain.

**29.** For a natural number to be divisible by both 2 and 5, what must be true about its last digit?

**30.** Consider the divisibility tests for 2, 4, and 8 (all powers of 2). Use inductive reasoning to predict the divisibility test for 16. Then, use the test to show that 456,882,320 is divisible by 16.

**31.** Redraw the factor tree of Example 5, assuming that you first observe that $504 = 12 \cdot 42$, then that $12 = 3 \cdot 4$ and $42 = 6 \cdot 7$. Complete the process and give the resulting prime factorization.

**32.** Explain how your result in Exercise 31 verifies the fundamental theorem of arithmetic.

*Find the prime factorization of each composite number.*

**33.** 240 **34.** 300

**35.** 360 **36.** 425

**37.** 663 **38.** 885

*Here is a divisibility test for 7.*

**(a)** *Double the last digit of the given number, and subtract this value from the given number with the last digit omitted.*

**(b)** *Repeat the process of part* **(a)** *as many times as necessary until the number obtained can easily be divided by 7.*

**(c)** *If the final number obtained is divisible by 7, then the given number also is divisible by 7. If the final number is not divisible by 7, then neither is the given number.*

*Use this divisibility test to determine whether each number is divisible by 7.*

**39.** 142,891 **40.** 409,311

**41.** 458,485 **42.** 287,824

*Here is a divisibility test for 11.*

**(a)** *Starting at the left of the given number, add together every other digit.*

**(b)** *Add together the remaining digits.*

**(c)** *Subtract the smaller of the two sums from the larger. (If they are the same, the difference is 0.)*

**(d)** *If the final number obtained is divisible by 11, then the given number also is divisible by 11. If the final number is not divisible by 11, then neither is the given number.*

*Use this divisibility test to determine whether each number is divisible by 11.*

**43.** 8,493,969 **44.** 847,667,942

**45.** 453,896,248 **46.** 552,749,913

**47.** Consider the divisibility test for the composite number 6, and make a conjecture for the divisibility test for the composite number 15.

**48.** Explain what is meant by a "proof by contradiction."

**49.** Give two factorizations of the number 75 that are not prime factorizations.

**50.** Explain, in general, when a factorization is a prime factorization.

*Determine all possible digit replacements for x so that the first number is divisible by the second. For example, 37,58x is divisible by 2 if*

$$x = 0, 2, 4, 6, \text{ or } 8.$$

**51.** 398,87$x$; 2 **52.** 2,45$x$,765; 3

**53.** 64,537,84$x$; 4 **54.** 2,143,89$x$; 5

**55.** 985,23$x$; 6 **56.** 7,643,24$x$; 8

**57.** 4,329,7$x$5; 9 **58.** 23,$x$54,470; 10

*There is a method to determine the* **number of divisors** *of a composite number. To do this, write the composite number in its prime factored form, using exponents. Add 1 to each exponent and multiply these numbers. Their product gives the number of divisors of the composite number. For example,*

$$24 = 2^3 \cdot 3 = 2^3 \cdot 3^1.$$

*Now add 1 to each exponent:*

$$3 + 1 = 4, 1 + 1 = 2.$$

*Multiply $4 \cdot 2$ to get 8. There are 8 divisors of 24. (Because 24 is rather small, this can be verified easily. The divisors are 1, 2, 3, 4, 6, 8, 12, and 24, a total of eight as predicted.)*

*(continued)*

*Find the number of divisors of each composite number.*

**59.** 48

**60.** 144

**61.** $2^8 \cdot 3^2$

**62.** $2^4 \cdot 3^4 \cdot 5^2$

*Leap years occur when the year number is divisible by 4. An exception to this occurs when the year number is divisible by 100 (that is, it ends in two zeros). In such a case, the number must be divisible by 400 in order for the year to be a leap year. Determine which years are leap years.*

**63.** 1776

**64.** 1894

**65.** 2400

**66.** 1800

**67.** Why is the following *not* a valid divisibility test for 8? "A number is divisible by 8 if it is divisible by both 4 and 2." Support your answer with an example.

**68.** Choose any three consecutive natural numbers, multiply them together, and divide the product by 6. Repeat this several times, using different choices of three consecutive numbers. Make a conjecture concerning the result.

**69.** Explain why the product of three consecutive natural numbers must be divisible by 6.

**70.** Choose any 6-digit number consisting of three digits followed by the same three digits in the same order (for example, 467,467). Divide by 13. Divide by 11. Divide by 7. What do you notice? Why do you think this happens?

**71.** Verify that Euler's polynomial prime-generating formula

$$n^2 - n + 41$$

fails to produce a prime for $n = 41$.

**72.** Evaluate Euler's polynomial formula for **(a)** $n = 42$, and **(b)** $n = 43$.

**73.** Choose the correct completion: For $n > 41$, Euler's formula produces a prime
**A.** never. **B.** sometimes. **C.** always.
(*Hint:* If no prime less than or equal to $\sqrt{n}$ divides $n$, then $n$ is prime.)

**74.** Recall that Escott's formula, $n^2 - 79n + 1601$, fails to produce a prime for $n = 80$. Evaluate this formula for $n = 81$ and $n = 82$ and then complete the following statement: For $n > 80$, Escott's formula produces a prime
**A.** never. **B.** sometimes. **C.** always.

**75.** **(a)** Evaluate the Fermat number $2^{2^n} + 1$ for $n = 4$.
**(b)** In seeking possible prime factors of the Fermat number of part (a), what is the largest potential prime factor that one would have to try? (As stated in the text, this "fifth" Fermat number is in fact prime.)

**76.** **(a)** Verify the value given in the text for the "sixth" Fermat number (i.e., $2^{2^5} + 1$).
**(b)** Divide this Fermat number by 641. (Euler discovered this factorization in 1732, proving that the sixth Fermat number is not prime.)

**77.** Write a short report on the Great Internet Mersenne Prime Search (GIMPS).

**78.** Write a short report identifying the 40th, 41st, and 42nd known Mersenne primes and how, when, and by whom they were found.

**79.** The Mersenne margin note on page 228 cites a 1644 claim that was not totally resolved for some 300 years. Find out when, and by whom, Mersenne's five errors were demonstrated. (*Hint:* One was mentioned in the margin note on page 224.)

**80.** In Euclid's proof that there is no largest prime, we formed a number $M$ by taking the product of primes and adding 1. Observe the pattern below.

| | |
|---|---|
| $M = 2 + 1 = 3$ | (3 is prime) |
| $M = 2 \cdot 3 + 1 = 7$ | (7 is prime) |
| $M = 2 \cdot 3 \cdot 5 + 1 = 31$ | (31 is prime) |
| $M = 2 \cdot 3 \cdot 5 \cdot 7 + 1 = 211$ | (211 is prime) |
| $M = 2 \cdot 3 \cdot 5 \cdot 7 \cdot 11 + 1 = 2311$ | (2311 is prime) |

It seems as though this pattern will always yield a prime number. Now evaluate

$$M = 2 \cdot 3 \cdot 5 \cdot 7 \cdot 11 \cdot 13 + 1.$$

**81.** Is $M$ prime or composite? If composite, give its prime factorization.

**82.** Explain in your own words the proof by Euclid that there is no largest prime.

*The text stated that the Mersenne number $M_n$ is composite whenever $n$ is composite. Exercises 83–86 on the next page develop one way you can always find a factor of such a Mersenne number.*

**83.** For the composite number $n = 6$, find

$$M_n = 2^n - 1.$$

**84.** Notice that $p = 3$ is a prime factor of $n = 6$. Find $2^p - 1$ for $p = 3$. Is $2^p - 1$ a factor of $2^n - 1$?

**85.** Complete this statement: If $p$ is a prime factor of $n$, then _____ is a factor of the Mersenne number $2^n - 1$.

**86.** Find $M_n = 2^n - 1$ for $n = 10$.

**87.** Use the statement of Exercise 85 to find two distinct factors of $M_{10}$.

**88.** Do you think this procedure will always produce *prime* factors of $M_n$ for composite $n$? (*Hint:* Consider $n = 22$ and its prime factor $p = 11$, and recall the statement following Example 6.) Explain.

# 5.2 Selected Topics from Number Theory

**Perfect Numbers • Deficient and Abundant Numbers • Amicable (Friendly) Numbers • Goldbach's Conjecture • Twin Primes • Fermat's Last Theorem**

The mathematician **Albert Wilansky,** when phoning his brother-in-law, Mr. Smith, noticed an interesting property concerning Smith's phone number (493–7775). The number 4,937,775 is composite, and its prime factorization is $3 \cdot 5 \cdot 5 \cdot 65{,}837$. When the digits of the phone number are added, the result, 42, is equal to the sum of the digits in the prime factors: $3 + 5 + 5 + 6 + 5 + 8 + 3 + 7 = 42$. Wilansky termed such a number a **Smith number.** In 1985 it was proved that there are infinitely many Smith numbers, but there still are many unanswered questions about them.

## Perfect Numbers

In an earlier chapter we introduced figurate numbers, a topic investigated by the Pythagoreans. This group of Greek mathematicians and musicians held their meetings in secret, and were led by Pythagoras. In this section we examine some of the other special numbers that fascinated the Pythagoreans and are still studied by mathematicians today.

Divisors of a natural number were covered in Section 5.1. The **proper divisors** of a natural number include all divisors of the number except the number itself. For example, the proper divisors of 8 are 1, 2, and 4. (8 is *not* a proper divisor of 8.)

### Perfect Numbers

A natural number is said to be **perfect** if it is equal to the sum of its proper divisors.

Is 8 perfect? No, because $1 + 2 + 4 = 7$, and $7 \neq 8$. The least perfect number is 6, because the proper divisors of 6 are 1, 2, and 3, and

$$1 + 2 + 3 = 6. \quad \text{6 is perfect.}$$

### EXAMPLE 1 Verifying a Perfect Number

Show that 28 is a perfect number.

**SOLUTION**

The proper divisors of 28 are 1, 2, 4, 7, and 14. The sum of these is 28:

$$1 + 2 + 4 + 7 + 14 = 28.$$

By the definition, 28 is perfect.

The numbers 6 and 28 are the two least perfect numbers. The next two are 496 and 8128. The pattern of these first four perfect numbers led early writers to conjecture that

1. The $n$th perfect number contains exactly $n$ digits.
2. The even perfect numbers end in the digits 6 and 8, alternately.

} Conjectures

(Exercises 41–43 will help you evaluate these conjectures.)

There still are many unanswered questions about perfect numbers. Euclid showed that if $2^n - 1$ is prime, then $2^{n-1}(2^n - 1)$ is perfect, and conversely. Because the prime values of $2^n - 1$ are the Mersenne primes (discussed in the previous section), this means that for every new Mersenne prime discovered, another perfect number is automatically revealed. (Hence, as of early 2006, there were also 43 known perfect numbers.) It is also known that all even perfect numbers must take the form $2^{n-1}(2^n - 1)$ and it is strongly suspected that no odd perfect numbers exist. (Any odd one would have at least eight different prime factors and would have at least 300 decimal digits.) Therefore, Euclid and the early Greeks most likely identified the form of all perfect numbers.

**Deficient and Abundant Numbers** Earlier we saw that 8 is not perfect because it is not equal to the sum of its proper divisors ($8 \neq 7$). Next we define two alternative categories for natural numbers that are *not* perfect.

A number is said to be a **weird number** if it is abundant without being equal to the sum of any set of its own proper divisors. For example, 70 is weird because it is abundant ($1 + 2 + 5 + 7 + 10 + 14 + 35 = 74 > 70$), but no set of the factors 1, 2, 5, 7, 10, 14, 35 adds up to 70.

### Deficient and Abundant Numbers

A natural number is **deficient** if it is greater than the sum of its proper divisors. It is **abundant** if it is less than the sum of its proper divisors.

Based on this definition, a *deficient number* is one with proper divisors that add up to less than the number itself, while an *abundant number* is one with proper divisors that add up to more than the number itself. For example, because the proper divisors of 8 (1, 2, and 4) add up to 7, which is less than 8, the number 8 is deficient.

### EXAMPLE 2 Identifying Deficient and Abundant Numbers

Decide whether each number is deficient or abundant.

**(a)** 12 **(b)** 10

**SOLUTION**

**(a)** The proper divisors of 12 are 1, 2, 3, 4, and 6. The sum of these divisors is 16. Because $16 > 12$, the number 12 is abundant.

**(b)** The proper divisors of 10 are 1, 2, and 5. Since $1 + 2 + 5 = 8$, and $8 < 10$, the number 10 is deficient.

**Amicable (Friendly) Numbers** Suppose that we add the proper divisors of 284:

$$1 + 2 + 4 + 71 + 142 = 220.$$

Their sum is 220. Now, add the proper divisors of 220:

$$1 + 2 + 4 + 5 + 10 + 11 + 20 + 22 + 44 + 55 + 110 = 284.$$

An extension of the idea of amicable numbers results in **sociable numbers.** In a chain of sociable numbers, the sum of the proper divisors of each number is the next number in the chain, and the sum of the proper divisors of the last number in the chain is the first number. Here is a 5-link chain of sociable numbers:

12,496
14,288
15,472
14,536
14,264.

The number 14,316 starts a 28-link chain of sociable numbers.

Notice that the sum of the proper divisors of 220 is 284, while the sum of the proper divisors of 284 is 220. Number pairs such as these are said to be *amicable,* or *friendly.*

### Amicable or Friendly Numbers

The natural numbers $a$ and $b$ are **amicable,** or **friendly,** if the sum of the proper divisors of $a$ is $b$, and the sum of the proper divisors of $b$ is $a$.

The smallest pair of amicable numbers, 220 and 284, was known to the Pythagoreans, but it was not until more than 1000 years later that the next pair, 17,296 and 18,416, was discovered. Many more pairs were found over the next few decades, but it took a 16-year-old Italian boy named Nicolo Paganini to discover in the year 1866 that the pair of amicable numbers 1184 and 1210 had been overlooked for centuries!

Today, powerful computers continually extend the lists of known amicable pairs. The last time we checked, over ten million pairs were known. It still is unknown, however, if there are infinitely many such pairs. Finally, no one has found an amicable pair without prime factors in common, but the possibility of such a pair has not been eliminated.

**A Dull Number?** The Indian mathematician **Srinivasa Ramanujan** (1887–1920) developed many ideas in number theory. His friend and collaborator on occasion was G. H. Hardy, also a number theorist and professor at Cambridge University in England.

A story has been told about Ramanujan that illustrates his genius. Hardy once mentioned to Ramanujan that he had just taken a taxicab with a rather dull number: 1729. Ramanujan countered by saying that this number isn't dull at all; it is the smallest natural number that can be expressed as the sum of two cubes in two different ways:

$$1^3 + 12^3 = 1729$$
and
$$9^3 + 10^3 = 1729.$$

Show that 85 can be written as the sum of two squares in two ways.

## Goldbach's Conjecture

One of the most famous unsolved problems in mathematics is Goldbach's conjecture. The mathematician Christian Goldbach (1690–1764) stated the following conjecture (guess).

### Goldbach's Conjecture (Not Proved)

Every even number greater than 2 can be written as the sum of two prime numbers.

*Examples:* $8 = 5 + 3$
$10 = 5 + 5$ (or $10 = 7 + 3$)

Mathematicians have tried to prove the conjecture but have not been successful. However, the conjecture has been verified (as of early 2006) for numbers up to $2 \times 10^{17}$.

### EXAMPLE 3 Expressing Numbers as Sums of Primes

Write each even number as the sum of two primes.

**(a)** 18 **(b)** 60

**SOLUTION**

**(a)** $18 = 5 + 13$. Another way of writing it is $7 + 11$. Notice that $1 + 17$ is *not* valid because by definition 1 is not a prime number.

**(b)** $60 = 7 + 53$. Can you find other ways? Why is $3 + 57$ not valid?

Mathematics professor Gregory Larkin, played by Jeff Bridges, woos colleague Rose Morgan (Barbra Streisand) in the 1996 film *The Mirror Has Two Faces*. Larkin's research and book focus on the **twin prime conjecture,** which he correctly states in a dinner scene. He is amazed that his nonmathematician friend actually understands what he is talking about.

**Twin Primes** Prime numbers that differ by 2 are called **twin primes.** Some twin primes are 3 and 5, 5 and 7, 11 and 13, and so on. Like Goldbach's conjecture, the following conjecture about twin primes has never been proved, although significant progress toward a proof was announced in 2005.

**Twin Prime Conjecture (Not Proved)**

There are infinitely many pairs of twin primes.

You may wish to verify that there are eight such pairs less than 100, using the Sieve of Eratosthenes in Table 1. As of early 2006, the largest known twin primes were

$$16{,}869{,}987{,}339{,}975 \cdot 2^{171{,}960} \pm 1.$$

Each contains 51,779 digits.

Recall from Section 5.1 that Euclid's proof of the infinitude of primes used numbers of the form $p_1 \cdot p_2 \cdot p_3 \ldots p_n + 1$, where all the $p$s are prime. It may seem that any such number must be prime, but that is not so. (See Exercise 80 of Section 5.1.) However, this form often does produce primes (as does the same form with the plus replaced by a minus). When *all* the primes up to $p_n$ are included, the resulting numbers, if prime, are called **primorial primes.** They are denoted

$$p\# \pm 1.$$

For example, $5\# + 1 = 2 \cdot 3 \cdot 5 + 1 = 31$ is a primorial prime. (In late 2005, the largest known primorial prime was $392{,}113\# + 1$, a number with 169,966 digits.) The primorial primes are a popular place to look for twin primes.

**Sophie Germain** (1776–1831) studied at the École Polytechnique in Paris in a day when female students were not admitted. A **Sophie Germain prime** is an odd prime $p$ for which $2p + 1$ also is prime. Lately, large Sophie Germain primes have been discovered at the rate of several per year. As of early 2006, the largest one known was $137{,}211{,}941{,}292{,}195 \cdot 2^{171{,}960} - 1$, which has 51,780 digits.

*Source:* www.utm.edu/research/primes

### EXAMPLE 4 Verifying Twin Primes

Verify that the primorial formula $p\# \pm 1$ produces twin prime pairs for both **(a)** $p = 3$ and **(b)** $p = 5$.

**SOLUTION**

**(a)** $3\# \pm 1 = 2 \cdot 3 \pm 1 = 6 \pm 1 = 5$ and $7$ Twin primes

Multiply, then add and subtract.

**(b)** $5\# \pm 1 = 2 \cdot 3 \cdot 5 \pm 1 = 30 \pm 1 = 29$ and $31$ Twin primes

**Fermat's Last Theorem** In any right triangle with shorter sides $a$ and $b$, and longest side (hypotenuse) $c$, the equation $a^2 + b^2 = c^2$ will hold true. This is the famous Pythagorean theorem. For example,

$$3^2 + 4^2 = 5^2 \quad a = 3,\ b = 4,\ c = 5$$
$$9 + 16 = 25$$
$$25 = 25.$$

It is known that there are infinitely many such triples $(a, b, c)$ that satisfy the equation

$$a^2 + b^2 = c^2.$$

Is something similar true of the equation

$$a^n + b^n = c^n$$

for natural numbers $n \geq 3$? Pierre de Fermat, profiled in a margin note on page 241, thought that not only were there not infinitely many such triples, but that there were, in fact, none. He made the following claim in the 1600s.

**Fermat's Last Theorem (Proved in the 1990s)**

For *any* natural number $n \geq 3$, there are *no* triples $(a, b, c)$ that satisfy the equation

$$a^n + b^n = c^n.$$

Fermat wrote in the margin of a book that he had "a truly wonderful proof" for this, but that the margin was "too small to contain it." Did he indeed have a proof, or did he have an incorrect proof?

Whatever the case, Fermat's assertion was the object of some 350 years of attempts by mathematicians to provide a suitable proof. While it was verified for many specific cases (Fermat himself proved it for $n = 3$), a proof of the general case could not be found until the Princeton mathematician Andrew Wiles announced a proof in the spring of 1993. Although some flaws were discovered in his argument, Wiles was able, by the fall of 1994, to repair and even improve the proof.

There were probably about 100 mathematicians around the world qualified to understand the Wiles proof. Many of these examined and approved it. Today Fermat's Last Theorem finally is regarded by the mathematics community as officially proved.

The solution to the Chapter Opener problem is as follows.

The first term on the left side, $1782^{12}$, must be an even number, because raising an even number to any power yields an even number. The second term on the left side, $1841^{12}$, must be odd, because raising an odd number to any power yields an odd number (in this case, we know that it must have 1 as units digit as well). The sum on the left side must be odd, because even + odd = odd.

The right side must be an even number using the earlier reasoning. So the equation indicates that an odd number is equal to an even number, which is impossible.

### EXAMPLE 5 Using a Theorem Proved by Fermat

One of the theorems legitimately proved by Fermat is as follows:

*Every odd prime can be expressed as the difference of two squares in one and only one way.*

Express each odd prime as the difference of two squares.

**(a)** 3 **(b)** 7

**SOLUTION**

**(a)** $3 = 4 - 1 = 2^2 - 1^2$

**(b)** $7 = 16 - 9 = 4^2 - 3^2$

**For Further Thought**

### Curious and Interesting

One of the most remarkable books on number theory is *The Penguin Dictionary of Curious and Interesting Numbers* (1986) by David Wells. This book contains fascinating numbers and their properties, including the following.

- There are only three sets of three digits that form prime numbers in all possible arrangements: {1, 1, 3}, {1, 9, 9}, {3, 3, 7}.
- Find the sum of the cubes of the digits of 136: $1^3 + 3^3 + 6^3 = 244$. Repeat the process with the digits of 244: $2^3 + 4^3 + 4^3 = 136$. We're back to where we started.
- 635,318,657 is the least number that can be expressed as the sum of two fourth powers in two ways:

$$635{,}318{,}657 = 59^4 + 158^4 = 133^4 + 134^4.$$

- The number 24,678,050 has an interesting property:

$$24{,}678{,}050 = 2^8 + 4^8 + 6^8 + 7^8 + 8^8 + 0^8 + 5^8 + 0^8.$$

- The number 54,748 has a similar interesting property:

$$54{,}748 = 5^5 + 4^5 + 7^5 + 4^5 + 8^5.$$

- The number 3435 has this property:

$$3435 = 3^3 + 4^4 + 3^3 + 5^5.$$

For anyone whose curiosity is piqued by such facts, this book is for you!

### For Group Discussion or Individual Investigation

Have each student in the class choose a three-digit number that is a multiple of 3. Add the cubes of the digits. Repeat the process until the same number is obtained over and over. Then, have the students compare their results. What is curious and interesting about this process?

## 5.2 Exercises

*Decide whether each statement in Exercises 1–10 is* true *or* false.

**1.** There are infinitely many prime numbers.

**2.** The prime numbers 2 and 3 are twin primes.

**3.** There is no perfect number between 496 and 8128.

**4.** $2^n - 1$ is prime if and only if $2^{n-1}(2^n - 1)$ is perfect.

**5.** Any prime number must be deficient.

**6.** The equation $17 + 51 = 68$ verifies Goldbach's conjecture for the number 68.

**7.** There are more Mersenne primes known than there are perfect numbers.

**8.** The number 31 cannot be represented as the difference of two squares.

**9.** The number $2^6(2^7 - 1)$ is perfect.

**10.** A natural number greater than 1 will be one and only one of the following: perfect, deficient, or abundant.

**11.** The proper divisors of 496 are 1, 2, 4, 8, 16, 31, 62, 124, and 248. Use this information to verify that 496 is perfect.

**12.** The proper divisors of 8128 are 1, 2, 4, 8, 16, 32, 64, 127, 254, 508, 1016, 2032, and 4064. Use this information to verify that 8128 is perfect.

**13.** As mentioned in the text, when $2^n - 1$ is prime, $2^{n-1}(2^n - 1)$ is perfect. By letting $n = 2, 3, 5,$ and 7, we obtain the first four perfect numbers. Show that $2^n - 1$ is prime for $n = 13$, and then find the decimal digit representation for the fifth perfect number.

**14.** At the end of 2005, the largest known prime number was $2^{30{,}402{,}457} - 1$. Use the formula in Exercise 13 to write an expression for the perfect number generated by this prime number.

**15.** It has been proved that the reciprocals of *all* the positive divisors of a perfect number have a sum of 2. Verify this for the perfect number 6.

**16.** Consider the following equations.

$$6 = 1 + 2 + 3$$
$$28 = 1 + 2 + 3 + 4 + 5 + 6 + 7$$

Show that a similar equation is valid for the third perfect number, 496.

*Determine whether each number is* abundant *or* deficient.

**17.** 36 **18.** 30

**19.** 75 **20.** 95

**21.** There are four abundant numbers between 1 and 25. Find them. (*Hint:* They are all even, and no prime number is abundant.)

**22.** Explain why a prime number must be deficient.

**23.** The first odd abundant number is 945. Its proper divisors are 1, 3, 5, 7, 9, 15, 21, 27, 35, 45, 63, 105, 135, 189, and 315. Use this information to verify that 945 is abundant.

**24.** Explain in your own words the terms *perfect number, abundant number,* and *deficient number.*

**25.** Nicolo Paganini's numbers 1184 and 1210 are amicable. The proper divisors of 1184 are 1, 2, 4, 8, 16, 32, 37, 74, 148, 296, and 592. The proper divisors of 1210 are 1, 2, 5, 10, 11, 22, 55, 110, 121, 242, and 605. Use the definition of amicable (friendly) numbers to show that they are indeed amicable.

**26.** An Arabian mathematician of the ninth century stated the following.

If the three numbers

$$x = 3 \cdot 2^{n-1} - 1,$$
$$y = 3 \cdot 2^{n} - 1,$$
and
$$z = 9 \cdot 2^{2n-1} - 1$$

are all prime and $n \geq 2$, then $2^n xy$ and $2^n z$ are amicable numbers.

(a) Use $n = 2$, and show that the result is the least pair of amicable numbers, namely 220 and 284.

(b) Use $n = 4$ to obtain another pair of amicable numbers.

*Write each even number as the sum of two primes. (There may be more than one way to do this.)*

**27.** 14 **28.** 22

**29.** 26 **30.** 32

**31.** Joseph Louis Lagrange (1736–1813) conjectured that every odd natural number greater than 5 can be written as a sum $a + 2b$, where $a$ and $b$ are both primes. Verify this for the odd natural number 11.

**32.** Another unproved conjecture in number theory states that every natural number multiple of 6 can be written as the difference of two primes. Verify this for 6, 12, and 18.

*Find one pair of twin primes between the two numbers given.*

**33.** 65, 80

**34.** 85, 105

**35.** 125, 140

*While Pierre de Fermat probably is best known for his now famous "last theorem," he did provide proofs of many other theorems in number theory. Exercises 36–40 investigate some of these theorems.*

**36.** If $p$ is prime and the natural numbers $a$ and $p$ have no common factor except 1, then $a^{p-1} - 1$ is divisible by $p$.

(a) Verify this for $p = 5$ and $a = 3$.

(b) Verify this for $p = 7$ and $a = 2$.

**37.** Every odd prime can be expressed as the difference of two squares in one and only one way.

(a) Find this one way for the prime number 5.

(b) Find this one way for the prime number 11.

**38.** A prime number of the form $4k + 1$ can be represented as the sum of two squares.

(a) The prime number 5 satisfies the conditions of the theorem, with $k = 1$. Verify this theorem for 5.

(b) Verify this theorem for 13 (here, $k = 3$).

**39.** There is only one solution in natural numbers for $a^2 + 2 = b^3$, and it is $a = 5$, $b = 3$. Verify this solution.

**40.** There are only two solutions in integers for $a^2 + 4 = b^3$. One solution is $a = 2$, $b = 2$. Find the other solution.

*The first four perfect numbers were identified in the text:* 6, 28, 496, *and* 8128. *The next two are* 33,550,336 *and* 8,589,869,056. *Use this information about perfect numbers to work Exercises 41–43.*

**41.** Verify that each of these six perfect numbers ends in either 6 or 28. (In fact, this is true of all even perfect numbers.)

**42.** Is conjecture (1) in the text (that the $n$th perfect number contains exactly $n$ digits) true or false? Explain.

**43.** Is conjecture (2) in the text (that the even perfect numbers end in the digits 6 and 8, alternately) true or false? Explain.

*According to the Web site* www.shyamsundergupta.com/amicable.htm, *a natural number is* happy *if the process of repeatedly summing the squares of its decimal digits finally ends in* 1. *For example, the least natural number (greater than* 1*) that is happy is* 7, *as shown here.*

$$7^2 = 49, \quad 4^2 + 9^2 = 97, \quad 9^2 + 7^2 = 130,$$
$$1^2 + 3^2 + 0^2 = 10, \quad 1^2 + 0^2 = 1.$$

*An amicable pair is a* **happy amicable pair** *if and only if both members of the pair are happy numbers. (The first* 5000 *amicable pairs include only* 111 *that are happy amicable pairs.) For each amicable pair, determine whether neither, one, or both of the members are happy, and whether the pair is a happy amicable pair.*

**44.** 220 and 284

**45.** 1184 and 1210

**46.** 10,572,550 and 10,854,650

**47.** 35,361,326 and 40,117,714

**48.** If the early Greeks knew the form of all even perfect numbers, namely $2^{n-1}(2^n - 1)$, then why did they not discover all the ones that are known today?

**49.** Explain why the primorial formula $p\# \pm 1$ does not result in a pair of twin primes for the prime value $p = 2$.

**50.** **(a)** What two numbers does the primorial formula produce for $p = 7$?
**(b)** Which, if either, of these numbers is prime?

**51.** Choose the correct completion: The primorial formula produces twin primes
**A.** never. **B.** sometimes. **C.** always.

*See the margin note (on page 236) defining a Sophie Germain prime, and complete this table.*

| | $p$ | $2p + 1$ | Is $p$ a Sophie Germain prime? |
|---|---|---|---|
| **52.** | 2 | ____ | ____ |
| **53.** | 3 | ____ | ____ |
| **54.** | 5 | ____ | ____ |
| **55.** | 7 | ____ | ____ |
| **56.** | 11 | ____ | ____ |
| **57.** | 13 | ____ | ____ |

**Factorial primes** *are of the form* $n! \pm 1$ *for natural numbers n. (n! denotes "n factorial," the product of* all *natural numbers up to n, not just the primes as in the primorial primes. For example,* $4! = 1 \cdot 2 \cdot 3 \cdot 4 = 24$.*) As of early 2006, the largest verified factorial prime was* $34{,}790! - 1$, *which has* 142,891 *digits. Find the missing entries in this table.*

| | $n$ | $n!$ | $n! - 1$ | $n! + 1$ | Is $n! - 1$ prime? | Is $n! + 1$ prime? |
|---|---|---|---|---|---|---|
| | 2 | 2 | 1 | 3 | no | yes |
| **58.** | 3 | ____ | ____ | ____ | ____ | ____ |
| **59.** | 4 | ____ | ____ | ____ | ____ | ____ |
| **60.** | 5 | ____ | ____ | ____ | ____ | ____ |

**61.** Explain why the factorial prime formula does not give twin primes for $n = 2$.

*Based on the preceding table, complete each statement with one of the following:* **A.** *never,* **B.** *sometimes, or* **C.** *always. When applied to particular values of n, the factorial formula* $n! \pm 1$ *produces*

**62.** no primes ____ **63.** exactly one prime ____ **64.** twin primes ____

# 5.3 Greatest Common Factor and Least Common Multiple

**Greatest Common Factor • Least Common Multiple**

**Pierre de Fermat** (about 1601–1665), a government official who did not interest himself in mathematics until he was past 30, devoted leisure time to its study. He was a worthy scholar, best known for his work in number theory. His other major contributions involved certain applications in geometry and his original work in probability.

Much of Fermat's best work survived only on loose sheets or jotted, without proof, in the margins of works that he read. Mathematicians of subsequent generations have not always had an easy time verifying some of those results, though their truth has generally not been doubted.

## Greatest Common Factor

The **greatest common factor** is defined as follows.

### Greatest Common Factor

The **greatest common factor (GCF)** of a group of natural numbers is the largest natural number that is a factor of all the numbers in the group.

*Examples:* 18 is the GCF of 36 and 54, because 18 is the largest natural number that divides both 36 and 54.

1 is the GCF of 7 and 16.

Greatest common factors can be found by using prime factorizations. To verify the GCF of 36 and 54, first write the prime factorization of each number (perhaps by using factor trees or repeated division):

$$36 = 2^2 \cdot 3^2 \quad \text{and} \quad 54 = 2^1 \cdot 3^3.$$

The GCF is the product of the primes common to the factorizations, with each prime raised to the power indicated by the *least* exponent that it has in any factorization. Here, the prime 2 has 1 as the smallest exponent (in $54 = 2^1 \cdot 3^3$), while the prime 3 has 2 as the least exponent (in $36 = 2^2 \cdot 3^2$). The GCF of 36 and 54 is

$$2^1 \cdot 3^2 = 2 \cdot 9 = 18,$$

as stated earlier. We summarize as follows.

### Finding the Greatest Common Factor (Prime Factors Method)

***Step 1*** Write the prime factorization of each number.

***Step 2*** Choose all primes common to *all* factorizations, with each prime raised to the *least* exponent that it has in any factorization.

***Step 3*** Form the product of all the numbers in Step 2; this product is the greatest common factor.

### EXAMPLE 1 Finding the Greatest Common Factor by the Prime Factors Method

Find the greatest common factor of 360 and 2700.

**SOLUTION**

Write the prime factorization of each number:

$$360 = 2^3 \cdot 3^2 \cdot 5 \quad \text{and} \quad 2700 = 2^2 \cdot 3^3 \cdot 5^2.$$

Now find the primes common to both factorizations, with each prime having as its exponent the *least* exponent from either product: $2^2$, $3^2$, 5. Then form the product of these numbers.

The calculator shows that the greatest common divisor (factor) of 360 and 2700 is 180. Compare with Example 1.

$$\text{GCF} = 2^2 \cdot 3^2 \cdot 5 = 180$$ Use the smallest exponents.

The greatest common factor of 360 and 2700 is 180.

### EXAMPLE 2 Finding the Greatest Common Factor by the Prime Factors Method

Find the greatest common factor of 720, 1000, and 1800.

**SOLUTION**

Write the prime factorization for each number:

$$720 = 2^4 \cdot 3^2 \cdot 5, \quad 1000 = 2^3 \cdot 5^3, \quad \text{and} \quad 1800 = 2^3 \cdot 3^2 \cdot 5^2.$$

Use the smallest exponent on each prime common to the factorizations:

$$\text{GCF} = 2^3 \cdot 5 = 40.$$

(The prime 3 is not used in the greatest common factor because it does not appear in the prime factorization of 1000.)

### EXAMPLE 3 Finding the Greatest Common Factor by the Prime Factors Method

Find the greatest common factor of 80 and 63.

**SOLUTION**

Start with

$$80 = 2^4 \cdot 5 \quad \text{and} \quad 63 = 3^2 \cdot 7.$$

There are no primes in common here, so the GCF is 1. The number 1 is the largest number that will divide into both 80 and 63.

Two numbers, such as 80 and 63, with a greatest common factor of 1 are called **relatively prime numbers**—that is, they are prime *relative* to one another. (They have no common factors other than 1.)

Another method of finding the greatest common factor involves dividing the numbers by common prime factors.

**Finding the Greatest Common Factor (Dividing by Prime Factors Method)**

*Step 1* Write the numbers in a row.

*Step 2* Divide each of the numbers by a common prime factor. Try 2, then try 3, and so on.

*Step 3* Divide the quotients by a common prime factor. Continue until no prime will divide into all the quotients.

*Step 4* The product of the primes in Steps 2 and 3 is the greatest common factor.

### EXAMPLE 4 Finding the Greatest Common Factor by Dividing by Prime Factors

Find the greatest common factor of 12, 18, and 60.

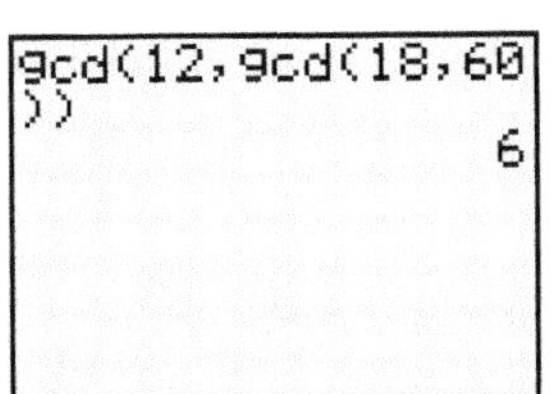


This screen uses the fact that gcd $(a, b, c) = \text{gcd}(a, \text{gcd}(b, c))$. Compare with Example 4.

**SOLUTION**

Write the numbers in a row and divide by 2.

$$\begin{array}{r|rrr} 2 & 12 & 18 & 60 \\ \hline & 6 & 9 & 30 \end{array}$$

The numbers 6, 9, and 30 are not all divisible by 2, but they are divisible by 3.

$$\begin{array}{r|rrr} 2 & 12 & 18 & 60 \\ \hline 3 & 6 & 9 & 30 \\ \hline & 2 & 3 & 10 \end{array}$$

No prime divides into 2, 3, and 10, so the greatest common factor of the numbers 12, 18, and 60 is given by the product of the primes on the left, 2 and 3.

$$\begin{array}{r|rrr} 2 & 12 & 18 & 60 \\ \hline 3 & 6 & 9 & 30 \\ \hline & 2 & 3 & 10 \end{array}$$

$2 \cdot 3 = 6$

The GCF of 12, 18, and 60 is 6.

There is yet another method of finding the greatest common factor of two numbers (but not more than two) that does not require factoring into primes or successively dividing by primes. It is called the **Euclidean algorithm,*** and it is illustrated in the next example.

### EXAMPLE 5 Finding the Greatest Common Factor Using the Euclidean Algorithm

Use the Euclidean algorithm to find the greatest common factor of 90 and 168.

**SOLUTION**

***Step 1*** Begin by dividing the larger, 168, by the smaller, 90. Disregard the quotient, but note the remainder.

$$\begin{array}{r} 1 \\ 90\overline{)168} \\ \underline{90} \\ 78 \end{array}$$

***Step 2*** Divide the smaller of the two numbers by the remainder obtained in Step 1. Once again, note the remainder.

$$\begin{array}{r} 1 \\ 78\overline{)90} \\ \underline{78} \\ 12 \end{array}$$

***Step 3*** Continue dividing the successive remainders, as many times as necessary to obtain a remainder of 0.

$$\begin{array}{r} 6 \\ 12\overline{)78} \\ \underline{72} \\ 6 \end{array}$$

Greatest common factor

***Step 4*** The *last positive remainder* in this process is the greatest common factor of 90 and 168. It can be seen that their GCF is 6.

$$\begin{array}{r} 2 \\ 6\overline{)12} \\ \underline{12} \\ 0 \end{array}$$

*For a proof that this process does indeed give the greatest common factor, see *Elementary Introduction to Number Theory, Second Edition*, by Calvin T. Long, pp. 34–35.

The Euclidean algorithm is particularly useful if the two numbers are difficult to factor into primes. We summarize the algorithm here.

### Finding the Greatest Common Factor (Euclidean Algorithm)

To find the greatest common factor of two unequal numbers, divide the larger by the smaller. Note the remainder, and divide the previous divisor by this remainder. Continue the process until a remainder of 0 is obtained. The greatest common factor is the last positive remainder obtained in this process.

**Least Common Multiple** Closely related to the idea of the greatest common factor is the concept of the *least common multiple*, which we define as follows.

### Least Common Multiple

The **least common multiple (LCM)** of a group of natural numbers is the smallest natural number that is a multiple of all the numbers in the group.

*Example:* 30 is the LCM of 15 and 10 because 30 is the smallest number that appears in both sets of multiples.

Multiples of 15: {15, **30,** 45, 60, 75, 90, 105, . . . }
Multiples of 10: {10, 20, **30,** 40, 50, 60, 70, . . . }

```
lcm(15,10)
                30
```

The least common multiple of 15 and 10 is 30.

The set of natural numbers that are multiples of *both* 15 and 10 form the set of *common multiples:*

$$\{30, 60, 90, 120, \ldots\}.$$

While there are infinitely many common multiples, the *least* common multiple is observed to be 30.

A method similar to the first one given for the greatest common factor may be used to find the least common multiple of a group of numbers.

### Finding the Least Common Multiple (Prime Factors Method)

***Step 1*** Write the prime factorization of each number.

***Step 2*** Choose all primes belonging to *any* factorization, with each prime raised to the power indicated by the *largest* exponent that it has in any factorization.

***Step 3*** Form the product of all the numbers in Step 2; this product is the least common multiple.

### EXAMPLE 6 Finding the Least Common Multiple by the Prime Factors Method

Find the least common multiple of 135, 280, and 300.

```
lcm(135,lcm(280,
300))
                37800
```

The least common multiple of 135, 280, and 300 is 37,800. Compare with Example 6.

**SOLUTION**

Write the prime factorizations:

$$135 = 3^3 \cdot 5, \quad 280 = 2^3 \cdot 5 \cdot 7, \quad \text{and} \quad 300 = 2^2 \cdot 3 \cdot 5^2.$$

Form the product of all the primes that appear in *any* of the factorizations. Use the *largest* exponent from any factorization.

$$\text{LCM} = 2^3 \cdot 3^3 \cdot 5^2 \cdot 7 = 37{,}800$$

Use the largest exponents.

The smallest natural number divisible by 135, 280, and 300 is 37,800.

The least common multiple of a group of numbers can also be found by dividing by prime factors. The process is slightly different than that for finding the GCF.

#### Finding the Least Common Multiple (Dividing by Prime Factors Method)

***Step 1*** Write the numbers in a row.

***Step 2*** Divide each of the numbers by a common prime factor. Try 2, then try 3, and so on.

***Step 3*** Divide the quotients by a common prime factor. When no prime will divide all quotients, but a prime will divide some of them, divide where possible and bring any nondivisible quotients down. Continue until no prime will divide any two quotients.

***Step 4*** The product of all prime divisors from Steps 2 and 3 as well as all remaining quotients is the least common multiple.

### EXAMPLE 7 Finding the Least Common Multiple by Dividing by Prime Factors

Find the least common multiple of 12, 18, and 60.

**SOLUTION**

Proceed just as in Example 4 to obtain the following.

```
2|12  18  60
3| 6   9  30
   2   3  10
```

Now, even though no prime will divide 2, 3, and 10, the prime 2 will divide 2 and 10. Divide the 2 and the 10 and bring down the 3.

```
2|12  18  60
3| 6   9  30
2| 2   3  10
   1   3   5    2 · 3 · 2 · 1 · 3 · 5 = 180
```

The LCM of 12, 18, and 60 is 180.

It is shown in more advanced courses that the least common multiple of two numbers $m$ and $n$ can be obtained by dividing their product by their greatest common factor.

**Finding the Least Common Multiple (Formula)**

The least common multiple of $m$ and $n$ is given by

$$\text{LCM} = \frac{m \cdot n}{\textbf{greatest common factor of } m \textbf{ and } n}.$$

(This method works only for two numbers, not for more than two.)

```
(90*168)/gcd(90,
168)
                2520
```

This supports the result in Example 8.

**EXAMPLE 8 Finding the Least Common Multiple by Formula**

Use the formula to find the least common multiple of 90 and 168.

**SOLUTION**

In Example 5 we used the Euclidean algorithm to find that the greatest common factor of 90 and 168 is 6. Therefore, the formula gives us

$$\text{Least common multiple of 90 and 168} = \frac{90 \cdot 168}{6} = 2520.$$

**PROBLEM-SOLVING HINT** Problems that deal with questions such as "How many objects will there be in each group if each group contains the same number of objects?" and "When will two events occur at the same time?" can sometimes be solved using the ideas of greatest common factor and least common multiple.

**EXAMPLE 9 Finding Common Starting Times of Movie Cycles**

The King Theatre and the Star Theatre run movies continuously, and each starts its first feature at 1:00 P.M. If the movie shown at the King lasts 80 minutes and the movie shown at the Star lasts 2 hours, when will the two movies start again at the same time?

**SOLUTION**

First, convert 2 hours to 120 minutes. The question can be restated as follows: "What is the smallest number of minutes it will take for the two movies to start at the same time again?" This is equivalent to asking, "What is the least common multiple of 80 and 120?" Using any of the methods described in this section, it can be shown that the least common multiple of 80 and 120 is 240. Therefore, it will take 240 minutes, or $\frac{240}{60} = 4$ hours for the movies to start again at the same time. By adding 4 hours to 1:00 P.M., we find that they will start together again at 5:00 P.M.

## EXAMPLE 10 Finding the Largest Common Size of Stacks of Cards

Joshua Hornsby has 450 football cards and 840 baseball cards. He wants to place them in stacks on a table so that each stack has the same number of cards, and no stack has different types of cards within it. What is the largest number of cards that he can have in each stack?

**SOLUTION**

Here, we are looking for the largest number that will divide evenly into 450 and 840. This is, of course, the greatest common factor of 450 and 840. Using any of the methods described in this section, we find that

$$\text{greatest common factor of 450 and 840} = 30.$$

Therefore, the largest number of cards he can have in each stack is 30.

## 5.3 EXERCISES

*Decide whether each statement is* true *or* false.

**1.** Two even natural numbers cannot be relatively prime.

**2.** Two different prime numbers must be relatively prime.

**3.** If $p$ is a prime number, then the greatest common factor of $p$ and $p^2$ is $p$.

**4.** If $p$ is a prime number, then the least common multiple of $p$ and $p^2$ is $p^3$.

**5.** There is no prime number $p$ such that the greatest common factor of $p$ and 2 is 2.

**6.** The set of all common multiples of two given natural numbers is finite.

**7.** Two natural numbers must have at least one common factor.

**8.** The least common multiple of two different primes is their product.

**9.** Two composite numbers may be relatively prime.

**10.** The set of all common factors of two given natural numbers is finite.

*Use the prime factors method to find the greatest common factor of each group of numbers.*

**11.** 70 and 120

**12.** 180 and 300

**13.** 480 and 1800

**14.** 168 and 504

**15.** 28, 35, and 56

**16.** 252, 308, and 504

*Use the method of dividing by prime factors to find the greatest common factor of each group of numbers.*

**17.** 60 and 84

**18.** 130 and 455

**19.** 310 and 460

**20.** 234 and 470

**21.** 12, 18, and 30

**22.** 450, 1500, and 432

*Use the Euclidean algorithm to find the greatest common factor of each group of numbers.*

**23.** 36 and 60

**24.** 25 and 70

**25.** 84 and 180

**26.** 72 and 120

**27.** 210 and 560

**28.** 150 and 480

**29.** Explain in your own words how to find the greatest common factor of a group of numbers.

**30.** Explain in your own words how to find the least common multiple of a group of numbers.

*Use the prime factors method to find the least common multiple of each group of numbers.*

**31.** 24 and 30

**32.** 12 and 32

**33.** 56 and 96

**34.** 28 and 70

**35.** 30, 40, and 70

**36.** 24, 36, and 48

*Use the method of dividing by prime factors to find the least common multiple of each group of numbers.*

**37.** 24 and 32

**38.** 35 and 56

**39.** 45 and 75

**40.** 48, 54, and 60

**41.** 16, 120, and 216

**42.** 210, 385, and 2310

*Use the formula given in the text and the results of Exercises 23–28 to find the least common multiple of each group of numbers.*

**43.** 36 and 60

**44.** 25 and 70

**45.** 84 and 180

**46.** 72 and 120

**47.** 210 and 560

**48.** 150 and 480

**49.** If $p$, $q$, and $r$ are different primes, and $a$, $b$, and $c$ are natural numbers such that $a > b > c$,
**(a)** what is the greatest common factor of $p^a q^c r^b$ and $p^b q^a r^c$?
**(b)** what is the least common multiple of $p^b q^a$, $q^b r^c$, and $p^a r^b$?

**50.** Find **(a)** the greatest common factor and **(b)** the least common multiple of

$$2^{31} \cdot 5^{17} \cdot 7^{21} \quad \text{and} \quad 2^{34} \cdot 5^{22} \cdot 7^{13}.$$

Leave your answers in prime factored form.

*It is possible to extend the Euclidean algorithm in order to find the greatest common factor of more than two numbers. For example, if we wish to find the greatest common factor of* 150, 210, *and* 240, *we can first use the algorithm to find the greatest common factor of two of these (say, for example,* 150 *and* 210*). Then we find the greatest common factor of that result and the third number,* 240. *The final result is the greatest common factor of the original group of numbers. Use the Euclidean algorithm as described above to find the greatest common factor of each group of numbers.*

**51.** 150, 210, and 240

**52.** 12, 75, and 120

**53.** 90, 105, and 315

**54.** 48, 315, and 450

**55.** 144, 180, and 192

**56.** 180, 210, and 630

*If we allow repetitions of prime factors, we can use Venn diagrams (Chapter 2) to find the greatest common factor and the least common multiple of two numbers. For example, consider* $36 = 2^2 \cdot 3^2$ *and* $45 = 3^2 \cdot 5$. *Their greatest common factor is* $3^2 = 9$, *and their least common multiple is* $2^2 \cdot 3^2 \cdot 5 = 180$.

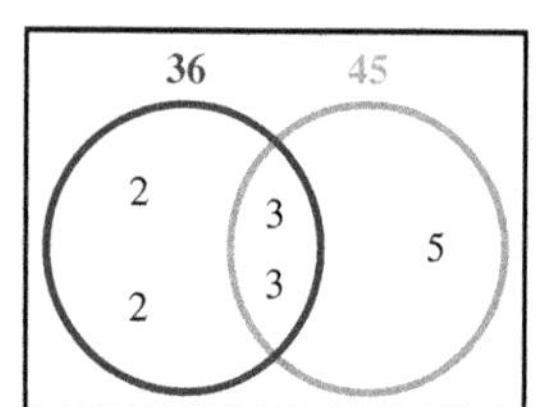

Intersection gives 3, 3.
Union gives 2, 2, 3, 3, 5.

*Use this method to find* **(a)** *the greatest common factor and* **(b)** *the least common multiple of the two numbers given.*

**57.** 12 and 18

**58.** 27 and 36

**59.** 54 and 72

**60.** Suppose that the least common multiple of $p$ and $q$ is $q$. What can we say about $p$ and $q$?

**61.** Suppose that the least common multiple of $p$ and $q$ is $pq$. What can we say about $p$ and $q$?

**62.** Suppose that the greatest common factor of $p$ and $q$ is $p$. What can we say about $p$ and $q$?

**63.** Recall some of your early experiences in mathematics (for example, in the elementary grade classroom). What topic involving fractions required the use of the least common multiple? Give an example.

**64.** Recall some of your experiences in elementary algebra. What topics required the use of the greatest common factor? Give an example.

*Refer to Examples 9 and 10 to solve each problem.*

65. ***Inspecting Calculators*** Colleen Jones and Nancy Barre work on an assembly line, inspecting electronic calculators. Colleen inspects the electronics of every sixteenth calculator, while Nancy inspects the workmanship of every thirty-sixth calculator. If they both start working at the same time, which calculator will be the first that they both inspect?

66. ***Night Off for Security Guards*** Paul Crockett and Cindy Herring work as security guards at a publishing company. Paul has every sixth night off, and Cindy has every tenth night off. If both are off on July 1, what is the next night that they will both be off together?

67. ***Stacking Coins*** Sheila Abbruzzo has 240 pennies and 288 nickels. She wants to place the pennies and nickels in stacks so that each stack has the same number of coins, and each stack contains only one denomination of coin. What is the largest number of coins that she can place in each stack?

68. ***Bicycle Racing*** Kathryn Campbell and Tami Dreyfus are in a bicycle race, following a circular track. If they start at the same place and travel in the same direction, and Kathryn completes a revolution every 40 seconds and Tami completes a revolution every 45 seconds, how long will it take them before they reach the starting point again simultaneously?

69. ***Selling Books*** John Cross sold some books at $24 each, and used the money to buy some concert tickets at $50 each. He had no money left over after buying the tickets. What is the least amount of money he could have earned from selling the books? What is the least number of books he could have sold?

70. ***Sawing Lumber*** Jill Bos has some pieces of two-by-four lumber. Some are 60 inches long, and some are 72 inches long. She wishes to saw them so as to obtain equal-length pieces. What is the longest such piece she can saw so that no lumber is left over?

# EXTENSION
## Modern Cryptography

**Cryptography** involves secret codes, ways of disguising information in order that a "sender" can transmit it to an intended "receiver" so that an "adversary" who somehow intercepts the transmission will be unable to discern its meaning. It has become customary in discussions of cryptography to refer to the sender and receiver (in either order) as Alice and Bob (*A* and *B*) and to the adversary as Eve (*E*). We follow that practice here. Converting a message to disguised form is called **encryption,** and converting it back to original form is called **decryption.**

Cryptography has been employed for thousands of years. It became more crucial as the extent of military, diplomatic, then industrial, and now even personal applications expanded. As the "code makers" became more adept at designing their systems, the "code breakers" became more adept at compromising those systems. If intercepting secret information is very important to an adversary, then vast resources will likely be expended in that effort.

The basis of a cryptography system is normally some mathematical function, the "encryption algorithm," that encrypts (disguises) the message. (*Functions* are used extensively in mathematics. They are discussed in Chapter 8 of this book.). An example of a simple (and very insecure) encryption algorithm is the following:

> Replace every letter of the alphabet with the letter that *follows* it.
> (Replace z with a.)

*(continued)*

Then the message "zebra" would be encrypted as "afcsb." Analyzing one or more intercepted messages encrypted using this function, and trying various possibilities, would enable an adversary to quickly determine the function, and its inverse, which would be the following:

> Replace every letter of the alphabet with the letter that *precedes* it. (Replace a with z.)

More advanced systems also use a **key,** which is some additional information needed to perform the algorithm correctly.

By the middle of the twentieth century, state-of-the-art requirements for an effective cryptography system were the following.

**Basic Requirements of a Cryptography System**

1. A *secret* algorithm (or function) for encrypting and decrypting data
2. A *secret* key that provides additional information necessary for a receiver to carry out the decrypting process

The difficulty with requirement number 1 was that all known encryption functions at the time were two-way functions. Once an adversary obtained the encryption algorithm, the inverse (that is, the decryption algorithm) could be deduced mathematically. The difficulty with requirement number 2 was that the security of the key frequently dropped off after a period of use. This meant that Bob and Alice must exchange a new key fairly often so that their communications would continue to be safe. But this measure may be self-defeating, because every key exchange may be vulnerable to interception. This dilemma became known as the **key exchange problem** (or the **key distribution problem** in the case of multiple intended receivers).

The world of cryptography was revolutionized in the 1970s when researchers discovered how to construct a *one-way* function that overcame both difficulties. That *exponential function* is given by

$$C = M^k \pmod{n},$$

with the calculation carried out modulo $n$. The practical success of this formula, the achievement of an essentially one-way, rather than two-way, function, is made possible by the theory of large prime numbers (studied earlier in this chapter), the nature of modular arithmetic (introduced in Section 4.4), and the present state of computer hardware and algorithms.

**The Diffie-Hellman-Merkle Key Exchange Scheme** First the key exchange problem was solved by the **Diffie-Hellman-Merkle key exchange scheme** (announced in 1976 and named for the Stanford University team of Whitfield Diffie, Martin Hellman, and Ralph Merkle). Basically, it works as follows.

## The Diffie-Hellman-Merkle Key Exchange Scheme

Alice and Bob can establish a key (a number) that they both will know, but that Eve cannot find out, even if she observes the communications between Bob and Alice as they set up their key. Alice and Bob can agree to use the function $C = M^k \pmod{n}$ with specific values for $M$ and $n$. (They can agree to all this by mail, telephone, e-mail, or even casual conversation. It won't matter if Eve finds out.) Then they carry out the following sequence of individual steps.

| *Alice's Actions* | | *Bob's Actions* | |
|---|---|---|---|
| ***Step 1*** | Choose a value of $a$. (Keep this value secret.) | ***Step 1*** | Choose a value of $b$. (Keep this value secret.) |
| ***Step 2*** | Compute $\alpha = M^a \pmod{n}$. | ***Step 2*** | Compute $\beta = M^b \pmod{n}$. |
| ***Step 3*** | Send the value of $\alpha$ to Bob. | ***Step 3*** | Send the value of $\beta$ to Alice. |
| ***Step 4*** | Receive the value of $\beta$ from Bob. | ***Step 4*** | Receive the value of $\alpha$ from Alice. |
| ***Step 5*** | Compute the key: $\mathbf{K = \beta^a \pmod{n}}$. | ***Step 5*** | Compute the key: $\mathbf{K = \alpha^b \pmod{n}}$. |

By this procedure, Alice and Bob will arrive at the same key value $K$ because

$$\begin{aligned}
\beta^a &= (M^b)^a && \beta = M^b \\
&= M^{ba} && \text{Rule of exponents: } (a^m)^n = a^{mn} \\
&= M^{ab} && \text{Commutative property: } ab = ba \\
&= (M^a)^b && \text{Rule of exponents: } (a^m)^n = a^{mn} \\
&= \alpha^b. && \alpha = M^a
\end{aligned}$$

We illustrate the basic procedures using much smaller numbers than would be used in practice so that our computations can be done on a handheld calculator. (It is not recommended that you try working any of the following examples *without* a calculator.)

One of the essential aspects of the schemes we use here is the nature of modular arithmetic. Given a modulus $n$, every natural number $a$ is "equivalent" (actually congruent) to the remainder obtained when $a$ is divided by $n$. This remainder is called the **residue** of $a$, modulo $n$. To find the residue can be thought of as to "mod." In Example 1 to follow, for instance, one of the calculations will be to find the residue of 16,807, modulo 13. A quick procedure to accomplish this on a calculator is as follows.

```
16807/13
       1292.846154
Ans-1292
      .8461538462
Ans*13
                11
```

The display shows that the residue of 16,807, modulo 13, is 11.

***Step 1*** Divide 16,807 by 13, obtaining 1292.846154.

***Step 2*** Subtract the integer part of the quotient, obtaining .846154.

***Step 3*** Multiply by 13, obtaining 11.

So, we see that $16{,}807 \equiv 11 \pmod{13}$. We have shown that $16{,}807 = 1292 \cdot 13 + 11$.

*(continued)*

(*Note:* In the work that follows, we carry out some lengthy sequences of modular arithmetic. We sometimes use equals signs, =, rather than congruence symbols, ≡, and when the modulus is understood, we sometimes omit the designation (mod $n$).)

This calculator routine can be summarized.

### Calculator Routine for Finding the Residue of $a$, Modulo $n$

In a modular system, the residue modulo $n$ for a number $a$ can be found by completing these three steps, in turn.

*Step 1* Divide $a$ by the modulus $n$.

*Step 2* Subtract the integer part of the quotient to obtain only the fractional part.

*Step 3* Multiply the fractional part of the quotient by $n$.

The final result is the residue modulo $n$.

### EXAMPLE 1 Using the Diffie-Hellman-Merkle Key Exchange Scheme

Establish a common key for Alice and Bob by using specific values for $M$, $n$, $a$, and $b$, and completing the steps outlined earlier for the Diffie-Hellman-Merkle key exchange scheme.

**SOLUTION**

Suppose Alice and Bob agree to use the values $M = 7$ and $n = 13$.

*Alice's Actions*

*Step 1* Choose a value of $a$, say 5. (Alice keeps this value secret.)

*Step 2* $\alpha = M^a \pmod{n}$
$= 7^5 \pmod{13}$
$= 16{,}807 \pmod{13}$
$= 11$

*Step 3* Send $\alpha = 11$ to Bob.

*Step 4* Receive $\beta = 3$.

*Step 5* Compute the key:
$K = \beta^a \pmod{n}$
$= 3^5 \pmod{13}$
$= 243 \pmod{13}$
$= 9.$

*Bob's Actions*

*Step 1* Choose a value of $b$, say 8. (Bob keeps this value secret.)

*Step 2* $\beta = M^b \pmod{n}$
$= 7^8 \pmod{13}$
$= 5{,}764{,}801 \pmod{13}$
$= 3$

*Step 3* Send $\beta = 3$ to Alice.

*Step 4* Receive $\alpha = 11$.

*Step 5* Compute the key:
$K = \alpha^b \pmod{n}$
$= 11^8 \pmod{13}$
$= 214{,}358{,}881 \pmod{13}$
$= 9.$

```
11^8
            214358881
Ans/13
          16489144.69
Ans-16489144
              .692308
```

```
Ans*13
             9.000004
```

The display shows the calculation of $K$ in the right column. (Ignore the tiny roundoff error.)

Both Alice and Bob arrived at the same key value, $K = 9$, which they can use for encrypting future communications to one another.

Suppose, at Step 3 in Example 1, Eve intercepts Bob's transmission of the value $\beta = 3$ to Alice. This will not help her, because she cannot deduce Bob's value of $b$ that generated $\beta$. In fact it could have been any of the values

$$8, 20, 32, 44, 56, \ldots,$$

an infinite list of possibilities. Also, Eve does not know what exponent Alice will apply to 3 to obtain the key. The value $a = 5$ is Alice's secret, never communicated to anyone else, not even Bob, so Eve cannot know what key Alice will obtain. The same argument applies if Eve intercepts Alice's transmission to Bob of the value $\alpha = 11$. (She is stymied even if she intercepts both transmissions.)

**RSA Public Key Cryptography** At practically the same time that Diffie, Hellman, and Merkle solved the key exchange problem, another team of researchers, Ron Rivest, Adi Shamir, and Leonard Adleman, at MIT, used the same type of mathematical function to provide an even better solution that eliminated the need for key exchange. Their scheme, known as RSA (from their surnames), is called **public key cryptography.** Anyone who wants the capability of receiving encrypted data simply makes known their public key, which anyone else can then use to encrypt messages to them. The beauty of the system is that the receiver possesses another private key, necessary for decrypting but never released to anyone else.

What makes RSA successful is that we have the mathematical understanding to identify very large prime numbers, and to multiply them to obtain a product. But if the prime factors are large enough, it is impossible, given the present state of knowledge, for anyone to determine the two original factors. This is true even using very powerful computers. Large prime factors can be used so that it would take one hundred million personal computers, working together, over a thousand years to break the code. This sort of security is due to the fact that factoring large primes is mathematically much more difficult than multiplying large primes (again, even for computers).

Using RSA, Alice can receive encrypted messages from Bob in such a way that Eve cannot discern their meaning even if she intercepts them (the usual goal of cryptography). Again, we use rather small values in our examples (relative to values used in practice). Although we give examples of specific portions of the process later, we show here a complete outline of all the basic procedures, from setting up the scheme to encrypting and then decrypting a message.

When the **RSA code** was first introduced in 1977, Martin Gardner's "Mathematical Games" column in *Scientific American* challenged researchers to decode a message using an $n$ with 129 digits. Some estimated it would take approximately 20,000 years to decipher without any knowledge of $p$ or $q$. However, with the aid of number theory, it took 600 mathematicians in 25 different countries only 17 years to factor $n$ into 64- and 65-digit prime factors, as shown here

114,381,625,757,888,867,669,235, 779,976,146,612,010,218,296,721, 242,362,562,561,842,935,706,935, 245,733,897,830,597,123,563,958, 705,058,989,075,147,599,290,026, 879,543,541 = 3,490,529,510,847, 650,949,147,849,619,903,898,133, 417,764,638,493,387,843,990,820, 577 × 32,769,132,993,266,709, 549,961,988,190,834,461,413,177, 642,967,992,942,539,798,288,533.

The decoded message said, "The magic words are squeamish ossifrage."

Today, RSA users select much larger values of $p$ and $q$, resulting in an $n$ of well over 300 digits. It is thought that breaking such an encryption would take all the computers in the world, working together, more time than the age of the universe. So until someone discovers new factoring techniques, or new computer designs, RSA would seem to be safe from attack.

### RSA Basics: A Public Key Cryptography Scheme

Alice (the receiver) completes the following steps.

***Step 1*** Choose two prime numbers, $p$ and $q$, which she keeps secret.

***Step 2*** Compute the *modulus* $n$ (which is the product $p \cdot q$).

***Step 3*** Compute $\ell = (p - 1)(q - 1)$.

***Step 4*** Choose the *encryption exponent* $e$, which can be any integer between 1 and $\ell$ that is relatively prime to $\ell$, that is, has no common factors with $\ell$.

***Step 5*** Find her *decryption exponent* $d$, a number satisfying

$$e \cdot d = 1 \pmod{\ell}.$$

She keeps $d$ secret.

***Step 6*** Provide Bob with her *public key*, which consists of the modulus $n$ and the encryption exponent $e$.

(Bob's steps are on the next page.)

*(continued)*

Now Bob (the sender) completes the following steps. (Recall that the purpose of all this is for Bob to be able to send Alice secure messages.)

*Step 7* Convert the message to be sent to Alice into a number $M$ (sometimes called the *plaintext*).

*Step 8* Encrypt $M$, that is, use Alice's public key ($n$ and $e$) to generate the encrypted message $C$ (sometimes called the *ciphertext*) according to the formula $C = M^e \pmod{n}$.

*Step 9* Transmit $C$ to Alice.

When Alice receives $C$, she completes the final step:

*Step 10* Decrypt $C$, that is, use her private key, consisting of $n$ (also part of her public key) and $d$, to reproduce the original plaintext message $M$ according to the formula $M = C^d \pmod{n}$.

**James Ellis, Clifford Cocks, and Malcolm Williamson** all worked for Britain's Government Communications Headquarters in the 1970s. In a strange twist of fate, they actually discovered the mathematics of public key cryptography several years before the work at Stanford and MIT was announced (and subsequently patented). The British work was classified top secret and never came to light until some twenty years later, at approximately the same time that RSA Data Security, the company that had been built on U.S. RSA patents, was sold for $200 million.

### EXAMPLE 2 Devising a Public Encryption Key

Use the values $p = 7$ and $q = 13$ (arbitrarily chosen primes) to devise Alice's public key by completing Steps 2–4 of the above outline of RSA basics.

**SOLUTION**

*Step 2* $n = p \cdot q = 7 \cdot 13 = 91$

*Step 3* $\ell = (p - 1)(q - 1) = 6 \cdot 12 = 72$

*Step 4* There are many choices here, but a prime less than 72 will certainly meet the requirements. We arbitrarily choose $e = 11$.

Alice's public key is $n = 91$, $e = 11$. (Prime factors $p$ and $q$ must be kept secret.) ■

### EXAMPLE 3 Finding a Private Decryption Key

Complete Step 5 of the RSA basics outline to find Alice's private decryption key.

**SOLUTION**

*Step 5* The decryption exponent $d$ must satisfy

$$e \cdot d = 1 \pmod{\ell} \quad \text{or} \quad 11d = 1 \pmod{72}.$$

One way to satisfy this equation is to check the powers of 11 until we find one equal (actually congruent) to 1, modulo 72:

Mod 72 congruences

$$11^1 = 11, \quad 11^2 = 121 = 49, \quad 11^3 = 1331 = 35,$$

$$11^4 = 14{,}641 = 25, \quad 11^5 = 161{,}051 = 59, \quad 11^6 = 1{,}771{,}561 = 1.$$

(The residues were found using the calculator routine explained before Example 1.) Because we found that $11^6 = 1$, we take $d = 11^5 = 59$. This way,

$$e \cdot d = 11 \cdot 11^5 = 11^6 = 1, \qquad \text{as required.}$$

Alice's private key is $n = 91$, $d = 59$. ■

## EXAMPLE 4 Encrypting a Message for Transmission

Complete Steps 7 and 8 of the RSA basics outline to encrypt the message "HI" for Bob to send Alice. Use Alice's public key found in Example 2: $n = 91$, $e = 11$.

**SOLUTION**

***Step 7*** A simple way to convert "HI" to a number is to note that H and I are the $8^{th}$ and $9^{th}$ letters of the English alphabet. Simply let the plaintext message be $M = 89$.

***Step 8*** Now compute the ciphertext $C$.

$$C = M^e \pmod{n} = 89^{11} \pmod{91}$$

This presents a new difficulty, because $89^{11}$ is too large to be handled as we did the powers of 11 in Example 3. But we can use a trick here, expressing 11 as $1 + 2 + 8$. (1, 2, and 8 are the unique powers of 2 that sum to 11. So we are doing something like what we did when discussing the binary system in Section 4.3.) Now we can rewrite $89^{11}$ in terms of smaller powers and then make use of rules of exponents (which are covered in Section 7.5).

$$\begin{aligned} 89^{11} &= 89^{1+2+8} && 1+2+8=11 \\ &= 89^1 \cdot 89^2 \cdot 89^8 && \text{Rule of exponents: } a^{n+m} = a^n \cdot a^m \end{aligned}$$

Now it will help to follow the maxim "mod before you multiply," in other words, compute the residue of individual factors first, then multiply those results. This keeps the numbers we must deal with smaller.

$$\begin{aligned} 89^1 &= 89 && \text{Definition of first power} \\ 89^2 &= 7921 = 4 && \text{Mod} \\ 89^8 &= 3.936588806\text{E}15 && \text{Calculator result} \end{aligned}$$

This last factor is far too large to handle like the others. But because of the way we "split up" the exponent, each subsequent power of 89 can be written as a power of an earlier one, again using rules of exponents. Specifically,

$$\begin{aligned} 89^8 &= (89^2)^4 && \text{Rule of exponents: } a^{m \cdot n} = (a^m)^n \\ &= 4^4 && 89^2 = 4 \text{ from above} \\ &= 256 && \text{Evaluate } 4^4. \\ &= 74. && \text{Mod} \end{aligned}$$

Finally we obtain

$$\begin{aligned} 89^{11} &= 89 \cdot 4 \cdot 74 && \text{Substitute.} \\ &= 26{,}344 && \text{Multiply.} \\ &= 45. && \text{Mod} \end{aligned}$$

The plaintext $M = 89$ (for the message "HI") has been converted to the ciphertext $C = 45$.

Now let's see if Alice can successfully decrypt the message 45 when she receives it.

*(continued)*

### EXAMPLE 5 Decrypting a Received Message

Complete Step 10 of the RSA basics outline to decrypt the message $C = 45$ from Example 4. Use Alice's private key, found in Example 3: $d = 59$ (also, $n = 91$).

**SOLUTION**

***Step 10*** The decryption formula gives

$$\begin{aligned} M &= C^d \pmod{n} \\ &= 45^{59} \pmod{91} \\ &= 45^{1+2+8+16+32} \pmod{91} \\ &= 45 \cdot 45^2 \cdot 45^8 \cdot 45^{16} \cdot 45^{32} \pmod{91}. \end{aligned}$$

Start with the smaller powers and "mod" each factor individually.

$$\begin{aligned} 45^2 &= 2025 = 23 \\ 45^8 &= (45^2)^4 = 23^4 = 279{,}841 = 16 \\ 45^{16} &= (45^8)^2 = 16^2 = 256 = 74 \\ 45^{32} &= (45^{16})^2 = 74^2 = 5476 = 16 \end{aligned}$$

Inserting these values in the product above for $M$, we get

$$\begin{aligned} M &= 45 \cdot 23 \cdot 16 \cdot 74 \cdot 16 \\ &= 19{,}607{,}040 \\ &= 89. \end{aligned}$$

We have correctly decrypted $C = 45$ to obtain

$$M = 89 = \text{HI}.$$

## EXTENSION EXERCISES

*Find the residue in each case.*

**1.** 45 (mod 6)

**2.** 67 (mod 10)

**3.** 225 (mod 13)

**4.** 418 (mod 15)

**5.** $5^9$ (mod 12)

**6.** $4^{11}$ (mod 9)

**7.** $8^7$ (mod 11)

**8.** $14^5$ (mod 13)

**9.** $8^{27}$ (mod 17)

**10.** $45^7$ (mod 23)

**11.** $11^{14}$ (mod 18)

**12.** $14^9$ (mod 19)

***Finding a Common Key*** *Find Alice and Bob's common key K by using the Diffie-Hellman-Merkle key exchange scheme with the given values of M, n, a, and b.*

| | $M$ | $n$ | $a$ | $b$ |
|---|---|---|---|---|
| **13.** | 5 | 13 | 7 | 6 |
| **14.** | 11 | 9 | 5 | 4 |
| **15.** | 5 | 11 | 6 | 7 |
| **16.** | 17 | 5 | 6 | 3 |

*Apply the RSA scheme to find each missing value.*

| | $p$ | $q$ | $n$ | $\ell$ |
|---|---|---|---|---|
| **17.** | 5 | 11 | ____ | ____ |
| **18.** | 11 | 3 | ____ | ____ |
| **19.** | 5 | 13 | ____ | ____ |
| **20.** | 17 | 7 | ____ | ____ |

***Encrypting Plaintext*** *Given the modulus n, the encryption exponent e, and the plaintext M, use RSA encryption to find the ciphertext C in each case.*

| | $n$ | $e$ | $M$ |
|---|---|---|---|
| **21.** | 55 | 7 | 15 |
| **22.** | 33 | 7 | 8 |
| **23.** | 65 | 5 | 16 |
| **24.** | 119 | 11 | 12 |

***Decrypting Ciphertext*** *Given the prime factors p and q, the encryption exponent e, and the ciphertext C, apply the RSA algorithm to find* **(a)** *the decryption exponent d and* **(b)** *the plaintext message M.*

| | $p$ | $q$ | $e$ | $C$ |
|---|---|---|---|---|
| **25.** | 5 | 11 | 3 | 30 |
| **26.** | 11 | 3 | 13 | 24 |
| **27.** | 5 | 13 | 35 | 17 |
| **28.** | 17 | 7 | 5 | 40 |

**29.** Describe the breakthrough represented by Diffie-Hellman-Merkle and RSA as opposed to all earlier forms of cryptography.

**30.** Explain why RSA would fail if mathematicians could (using computers) factor arbitrarily large numbers.

# 5.4 The Fibonacci Sequence and the Golden Ratio

**The Fibonacci Sequence • The Golden Ratio**

The solution of Fibonacci's rabbit problem is examined in Chapter 1, pages 21–22.

## The Fibonacci Sequence

One of the most famous problems in elementary mathematics comes from the book *Liber Abaci*, written in 1202 by Leonardo of Pisa, a.k.a. Fibonacci. The problem is as follows:

> A man put a pair of rabbits in a cage. During the first month the rabbits produced no offspring, but each month thereafter produced one new pair of rabbits. If each new pair thus produced reproduces in the same manner, how many pairs of rabbits will there be at the end of one year?

The solution of this problem leads to a sequence of numbers known as the **Fibonacci sequence.** Here are the first fifteen terms of the Fibonacci sequence:

$$1, 1, 2, 3, 5, 8, 13, 21, 34, 55, 89, 144, 233, 377, 610.$$

Notice the pattern established in the sequence. After the first two terms (both 1), each term is obtained by adding the two previous terms. For example, the third term is obtained by adding $1 + 1$ to get 2, the fourth term is obtained by adding $1 + 2$ to get 3, and so on. This can be described by a mathematical formula known as a *recursion formula*.

If $F_n$ represents the Fibonacci number in the $n$th position in the sequence, then

$$F_1 = 1$$
$$F_2 = 1$$
$$F_n = F_{n-2} + F_{n-1}, \quad \text{for } n \geq 3.$$

Using the recursion formula $F_n = F_{n-2} + F_{n-1}$, we obtain

$$F_3 = F_1 + F_2 = 1 + 1 = 2, \quad F_4 = F_2 + F_3 = 1 + 2 = 3, \quad \text{and so on.}$$

The Fibonacci sequence exhibits many interesting patterns, and by inductive reasoning we can make many conjectures about these patterns. However, as we have indicated many times earlier, simply observing a finite number of examples does not provide a proof of a statement. Proofs of the properties of the Fibonacci sequence often involve mathematical induction (covered in college algebra texts). Here we simply observe the patterns and do not attempt to provide such proofs.

The **Fibonacci Association** is a research organization dedicated to investigation into the **Fibonacci sequence** and related topics. Check your library to see if it has the journal *Fibonacci Quarterly*. The first two journals of 1963 contain a basic introduction to the Fibonacci sequence.

As an example of the many interesting properties of the Fibonacci sequence, choose any term of the sequence after the first and square it. Then multiply the terms on either side of it, and subtract the smaller result from the larger. The difference is always 1. For example, choose the sixth term in the sequence, 8. The square of 8 is 64. Now multiply the terms on either side of 8: $5 \cdot 13 = 65$. Subtract 64 from 65 to get $65 - 64 = 1$. This pattern continues throughout the sequence.

The following program for the TI-83/84 Plus utilizes the *Binet form* of the *n*th Fibonacci number (see Exercises 33–38) to determine its value.

```
PROGRAM: FIB
: Clr Home
: Disp "WHICH TERM"
: Disp "OF THE"
: Disp "SEQUENCE DO"
: Disp "YOU WANT?"
: Input N
: (1 + √(5))/2 → A
: (1 − √(5))/2 → B
: (A^N − B^N)/√(5) → F
: Disp F
```

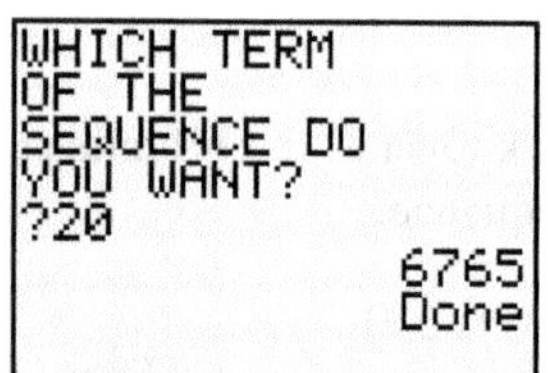


This screen indicates that the twentieth Fibonacci number is 6765.

## EXAMPLE 1 Observing a Pattern of the Fibonacci Numbers

Find the sum of the squares of the first $n$ Fibonacci numbers for $n = 1, 2, 3, 4, 5$, and examine the pattern. Generalize this relationship.

**SOLUTION**

$$1^2 = 1 = 1 \cdot 1 = F_1 \cdot F_2$$
$$1^2 + 1^2 = 2 = 1 \cdot 2 = F_2 \cdot F_3$$
$$1^2 + 1^2 + 2^2 = 6 = 2 \cdot 3 = F_3 \cdot F_4$$
$$1^2 + 1^2 + 2^2 + 3^2 = 15 = 3 \cdot 5 = F_4 \cdot F_5$$
$$1^2 + 1^2 + 2^2 + 3^2 + 5^2 = 40 = 5 \cdot 8 = F_5 \cdot F_6$$

The sum of the squares of the first $n$ Fibonacci numbers seems to always be the product of $F_n$ and $F_{n+1}$. This has been proven to be true, in general, using mathematical induction.

There are many other patterns similar to the one examined in Example 1, and some of them are discussed in the exercises of this section. An interesting property of the decimal value of the reciprocal of 89, the eleventh Fibonacci number, is examined in the next example.

## EXAMPLE 2 Observing the Fibonacci Sequence in a Long Division Problem

Observe the steps of the long division process used to find the first few decimal places for $\frac{1}{89}$.

**SOLUTION**

```
       .011235. . .
   89)1.000000
        89
        110
         89
         210
         178
          320
          267
           530
           445
            850. . .
```

Notice that after the 0 in the tenths place, the next five digits are the first five terms of the Fibonacci sequence. In addition, as indicated in color in the process, the digits 1, 1, 2, 3, 5, 8 appear in the division steps. Now, look at the digits next to the ones in color, beginning with the second "1"; they, too, are 1, 1, 2, 3, 5, . . . .

If the division process is continued past the final step shown above, the pattern seems to stop, since to ten decimal places, $\frac{1}{89} \approx .0112359551$. (The decimal representation actually begins to repeat later in the process, since $\frac{1}{89}$ is a rational number.) However, the sum below indicates how the Fibonacci numbers are actually "hidden" in this decimal.

$$
\begin{array}{r@{}l}
 & .01 \\
 & .001 \\
 & .0002 \\
 & .00003 \\
 & .000005 \\
 & .0000008 \\
 & .00000013 \\
 & .000000021 \\
 & .0000000034 \\
 & .00000000055 \\
 & \underline{.000000000089} \\
\frac{1}{89} = & .0112359550. . . .
\end{array}
$$

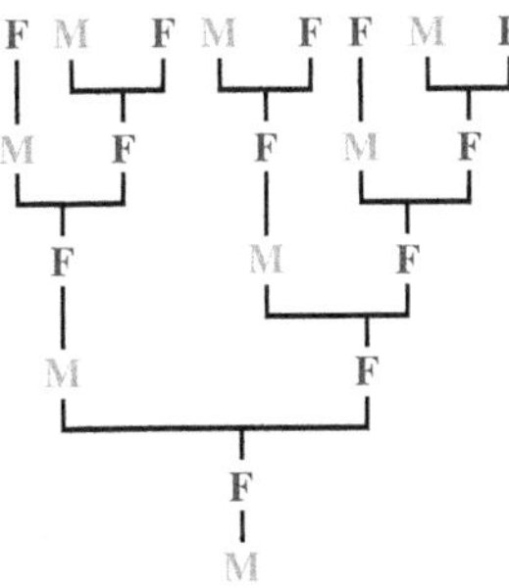


**FIGURE 1**

Fibonacci patterns have been found in numerous places in nature. For example, male honeybees (drones) hatch from eggs which have not been fertilized, so a male bee has only one parent, a female. On the other hand, female honeybees hatch from fertilized eggs, so a female has two parents, one male and one female. Figure 1 shows several generations of ancestors for a male honeybee.

Notice that in the first generation, starting at the bottom, there is 1 bee, in the second there is 1 bee, in the third there are 2 bees, and so on. These are the terms of the Fibonacci sequence. Furthermore, beginning with the second generation, the numbers of female bees form the sequence, and beginning with the third generation, the numbers of male bees also form the sequence.

Successive terms in the Fibonacci sequence also appear in some plants. For example, the photo (at the left on the next page) shows the double spiraling of a daisy head, with 21 clockwise spirals and 34 counterclockwise spirals. These numbers are successive terms in the sequence. Most pineapples (see the photo on the right) exhibit the Fibonacci sequence in the following way: Count the spirals formed by the "scales" of the cone, first counting from lower left to upper right. Then count the spirals from lower right to upper left. You should find that in one direction you get 8 spirals, and in the other you get 13 spirals, once again successive terms of the Fibonacci sequence. Many pinecones exhibit 5 and 8 spirals, and the cone of the giant sequoia has 3 and 5 spirals.

A fraction such as

$$1+\cfrac{1}{1+\cfrac{1}{1+\cfrac{1}{1+\ddots}}}$$

is called a **continued fraction.** This continued fraction can be evaluated as follows.

Let $x = 1+\cfrac{1}{1+\cfrac{1}{1+\ddots}}$

Then $x = 1 + \frac{1}{x}$

$$x^2 = x + 1$$

$$x^2 - x - 1 = 0.$$

By the quadratic formula from algebra,

$$x = \frac{1 \pm \sqrt{1-4(1)(-1)}}{2(1)}$$

$$x = \frac{1 \pm \sqrt{5}}{2}.$$

Notice that the positive solution

$$\frac{1+\sqrt{5}}{2}$$

is the **golden ratio.**

**The Golden Ratio** If we consider the quotients of successive Fibonacci numbers, a pattern emerges.

$$\frac{1}{1} = 1 \qquad \frac{13}{8} = 1.625$$

$$\frac{2}{1} = 2 \qquad \frac{21}{13} \approx 1.615384615$$

$$\frac{3}{2} = 1.5 \qquad \frac{34}{21} \approx 1.619047619$$

$$\frac{5}{3} = 1.666\ldots \qquad \frac{55}{34} \approx 1.617647059$$

$$\frac{8}{5} = 1.6 \qquad \frac{89}{55} = 1.618181818\ldots$$

These quotients seem to be approaching some "limiting value" close to 1.618. In fact, as we go farther into the sequence, these quotients approach the number

$$\frac{1+\sqrt{5}}{2},$$

known as the **golden ratio,** and often symbolized by $\phi$, the Greek letter phi.

The golden ratio appears over and over in art, architecture, music, and nature. Its origins go back to the days of the ancient Greeks, who thought that a golden rectangle exhibited the most aesthetically pleasing proportion. A **golden rectangle** is one that can be divided into a square and another (smaller) rectangle the same shape as the original rectangle. (See Figure 2 on the next page.) If we let the smaller rectangle have

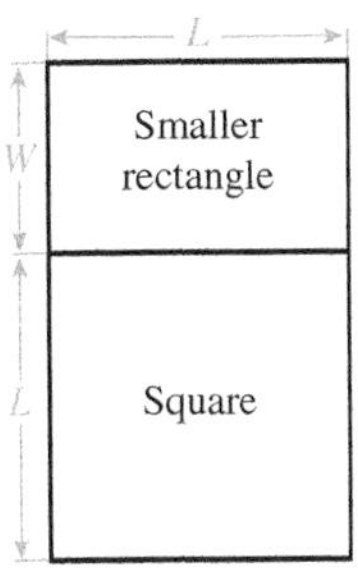


FIGURE 2

length $L$ and width $W$, as shown in the figure, then we see that the original rectangle has length $L + W$ and width $L$. Both rectangles (being "golden") have their lengths and widths in the golden ratio, $\phi$, given above, so we have

$$\frac{L}{W} = \frac{L+W}{L}$$

$$\frac{L}{W} = \frac{L}{L} + \frac{W}{L} \quad \text{Write the right side as two fractions.}$$

$$\phi = 1 + \frac{1}{\phi} \quad \text{Substitute } \tfrac{L}{W} = \phi,\ \tfrac{L}{L} = 1, \text{ and } \tfrac{W}{L} = \tfrac{1}{\phi}.$$

$$\phi^2 = \phi + 1 \quad \text{Multiply both sides by } \phi.$$

$$\phi^2 - \phi - 1 = 0. \quad \text{Write in standard quadratic form.}$$

Using the quadratic formula from algebra, the positive solution of this equation is found to be $\frac{1+\sqrt{5}}{2} \approx 1.618033989$, the golden ratio.

The Parthenon (see the photo), built on the Acropolis in ancient Athens during the fifth century B.C., is an example of architecture exhibiting many distinct golden rectangles.

**A Golden Rectangle in Art** The rectangle outlining the figure in *St. Jerome* by Leonardo da Vinci is an example of a golden rectangle.

To see an interesting connection between the terms of the Fibonacci sequence, the golden ratio, and a phenomenon of nature, we can start with a rectangle measuring 89 by 55 units. (See Figure 3.)

This is a very close approximation to a golden rectangle. Within this rectangle a square is then constructed, 55 units on a side. The remaining rectangle is also approximately a golden rectangle, measuring 55 units by 34 units. Each time this process is repeated, a square and an approximate golden rectangle are formed. As indicated in the figure, vertices of the square may be joined by a smooth curve known as a *spiral*. This spiral resembles the outline of a cross section of the shell of the chambered nautilus, as shown in the photograph next to Figure 3.

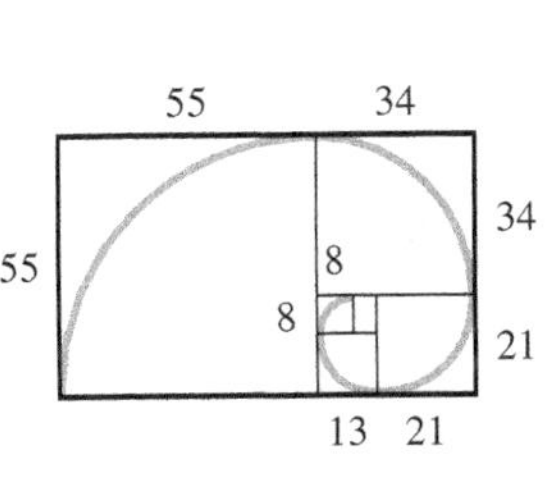


FIGURE 3

## For Further Thought

### Mathematical Animation

The 1959 animated film *Donald in Mathmagic Land* has endured for nearly 50 years as a classic. It provides a 25-minute trip with Donald Duck, led by the Spirit of Mathematics, through the world of mathematics. Several minutes of the film are devoted to the golden ratio (or, as it is termed there, the golden section). (*Donald in Mathmagic Land* is also discussed in the opener to Chapter 3 on page 97.)

© The Walt Disney Company

Disney provides animation to explain the golden ratio in a way that the printed word simply cannot do. The golden ratio is seen in architecture, nature, and the human body.

### For Group Discussion or Individual Investigation

1. Verify the following Fibonacci pattern in the conifer family. Obtain a pineapple, and count spirals formed by the "scales" of the cone, first counting from lower left to upper right. Then count the spirals from lower right to upper left. What do you find?
2. Two popular sizes of index cards are 3″ by 5″ and 5″ by 8″. Why do you think that these are industry-standard sizes?
3. Divide your height by the height to your navel. Find a class average. What value does this come close to?

## 5.4 Exercises

*Answer each question concerning the Fibonacci sequence or the golden ratio.*

1. The sixteenth Fibonacci number is 987 and the seventeenth Fibonacci number is 1597. What is the eighteenth Fibonacci number?

2. Recall that $F_n$ represents the Fibonacci number in the $n$th position in the sequence. What are the only two values of $n$ such that $F_n = n$?

3. $F_{23} = 28{,}657$ and $F_{25} = 75{,}025$. What is the value of $F_{24}$?

4. If two successive terms of the Fibonacci sequence are both odd, is the next term even or odd?

5. What is the exact value of the golden ratio?

6. What is the approximate value of the golden ratio to the nearest thousandth?

*In each of Exercises 7–14, a pattern is established involving terms of the Fibonacci sequence. Use inductive reasoning to make a conjecture concerning the next equation in the pattern, and verify it. You may wish to refer to the first few terms of the sequence given in the text.*

7. $1 = 2 - 1$
   $1 + 1 = 3 - 1$
   $1 + 1 + 2 = 5 - 1$
   $1 + 1 + 2 + 3 = 8 - 1$
   $1 + 1 + 2 + 3 + 5 = 13 - 1$

8. $1 = 2 - 1$
   $1 + 3 = 5 - 1$
   $1 + 3 + 8 = 13 - 1$
   $1 + 3 + 8 + 21 = 34 - 1$
   $1 + 3 + 8 + 21 + 55 = 89 - 1$

**9.** $1 = 1$
$1 + 2 = 3$
$1 + 2 + 5 = 8$
$1 + 2 + 5 + 13 = 21$
$1 + 2 + 5 + 13 + 34 = 55$

**10.** $1^2 + 1^2 = 2$
$1^2 + 2^2 = 5$
$2^2 + 3^2 = 13$
$3^2 + 5^2 = 34$
$5^2 + 8^2 = 89$

**11.** $2^2 - 1^2 = 3$
$3^2 - 1^2 = 8$
$5^2 - 2^2 = 21$
$8^2 - 3^2 = 55$

**12.** $2^3 + 1^3 - 1^3 = 8$
$3^3 + 2^3 - 1^3 = 34$
$5^3 + 3^3 - 2^3 = 144$
$8^3 + 5^3 - 3^3 = 610$

**13.** $1 = 1^2$
$1 - 2 = -1^2$
$1 - 2 + 5 = 2^2$
$1 - 2 + 5 - 13 = -3^2$
$1 - 2 + 5 - 13 + 34 = 5^2$

**14.** $1 - 1 = -1 + 1$
$1 - 1 + 2 = 1 + 1$
$1 - 1 + 2 - 3 = -2 + 1$
$1 - 1 + 2 - 3 + 5 = 3 + 1$
$1 - 1 + 2 - 3 + 5 - 8 = -5 + 1$

**15.** Every natural number can be expressed as a sum of Fibonacci numbers, where no number is used more than once. For example, $25 = 21 + 3 + 1$. Express each of the following in this way.
**(a)** 37 **(b)** 40 **(c)** 52

**16.** It has been shown that if $m$ divides $n$, then $F_m$ is a factor of $F_n$. Show that this is true for the following values of $m$ and $n$.
**(a)** $m = 2, n = 6$ **(b)** $m = 3, n = 9$
**(c)** $m = 4, n = 8$

**17.** It has been shown that if the greatest common factor of $m$ and $n$ is $r$, then the greatest common factor of $F_m$ and $F_n$ is $F_r$. Show that this is true for the following values of $m$ and $n$.
**(a)** $m = 10, n = 4$ **(b)** $m = 12, n = 6$
**(c)** $m = 14, n = 6$

**18.** For any prime number $p$ except 2 or 5, either $F_{p+1}$ or $F_{p-1}$ is divisible by $p$. Show that this is true for the following values of $p$.
**(a)** $p = 3$ **(b)** $p = 7$ **(c)** $p = 11$

**19.** Earlier we saw that if a term of the Fibonacci sequence is squared and then the product of the terms on each side of the term is found, there will always be a difference of 1. Follow the steps below, choosing the seventh Fibonacci number, 13.
**(a)** Square 13. Multiply the terms of the sequence two positions away from 13 (i.e., 5 and 34). Subtract the smaller result from the larger, and record your answer.
**(b)** Square 13. Multiply the terms of the sequence three positions away from 13. Once again, subtract the smaller result from the larger, and record your answer.
**(c)** Repeat the process, moving four terms away from 13.
**(d)** Make a conjecture about what will happen when you repeat the process, moving five terms away. Verify your answer.

**20.** ***A Number Trick*** Here is a number trick that you can perform. Ask someone to pick any two numbers at random and to write them down. Ask the person to determine a third number by adding the first and second, a fourth number by adding the second and third, and so on, until ten numbers are determined. Then ask the person to add these ten numbers. You will be able to give the sum before the person even completes the list, because the sum will always be 11 times the seventh number in the list. Verify that this is true, by using $x$ and $y$ as the first two numbers arbitrarily chosen. (*Hint:* Remember the distributive property from algebra.)

*Another Fibonacci-type sequence that has been studied by mathematicians is the* **Lucas sequence,** *named after a French mathematician of the nineteenth century. The first ten terms of the Lucas sequence are*

$$1, 3, 4, 7, 11, 18, 29, 47, 76, 123.$$

**21.** What is the eleventh term of the Lucas sequence?

**22.** Choose any term of the Lucas sequence and square it. Then multiply the terms on either side of the one you chose. Subtract the smaller result from the larger. Repeat this for a different term of the sequence. Do you get the same result? Make a conjecture about this pattern.

**23.** The first term of the Lucas sequence is 1. Add the first and third terms. Record your answer. Now add the first, third, and fifth terms and record your answer. Continue this pattern, each time adding another term that is in an *odd* position in the sequence. What do you notice about all of your sums?

**24.** The second term of the Lucas sequence is 3. Add the second and fourth terms. Record your answer. Now add the second, fourth, and sixth terms and record your answer. Continue this pattern, each time adding another term that is in an *even* position of the sequence. What do you notice about all of your sums?

**25.** Many interesting patterns exist between the terms of the Fibonacci sequence and the Lucas sequence. Make a conjecture about the next equation that would appear in each of the lists and then verify it.

**(a)**
$1 \cdot 1 = 1$
$1 \cdot 3 = 3$
$2 \cdot 4 = 8$
$3 \cdot 7 = 21$
$5 \cdot 11 = 55$

**(b)**
$1 + 2 = 3$
$1 + 3 = 4$
$2 + 5 = 7$
$3 + 8 = 11$
$5 + 13 = 18$

**(c)**
$1 + 1 = 2 \cdot 1$
$1 + 3 = 2 \cdot 2$
$2 + 4 = 2 \cdot 3$
$3 + 7 = 2 \cdot 5$
$5 + 11 = 2 \cdot 8$

**26.** In the text we illustrate that the quotients of successive terms of the Fibonacci sequence approach the golden ratio. Make a similar observation for the terms of the Lucas sequence; that is, find the decimal approximations for the quotients

$$\frac{3}{1}, \frac{4}{3}, \frac{7}{4}, \frac{11}{7}, \frac{18}{11}, \frac{29}{18},$$

and so on, using a calculator. Then make a conjecture about what seems to be happening.

*Recall the* **Pythagorean theorem** *from geometry: If a right triangle has legs of lengths a and b and hypotenuse of length c, then*

$$a^2 + b^2 = c^2.$$

*Suppose that we choose any four successive terms of the Fibonacci sequence. Multiply the first and fourth. Double the product of the second and third. Add the squares of the second and third. The three results obtained form a* **Pythagorean triple** *(three numbers that satisfy the equation $a^2 + b^2 = a^2$). Find the Pythagorean triple obtained this way using the four given successive terms of the Fibonacci sequence.*

**27.** 1, 1, 2, 3

**28.** 1, 2, 3, 5

**29.** 2, 3, 5, 8

**30.** Look at the values of the hypotenuse ($c$) in the answers to Exercises 27–29. What do you notice about each of them?

**31.** The following array of numbers is called **Pascal's triangle.**

1
1 1
1 2 1
1 3 3 1
1 4 6 4 1
1 5 10 10 5 1
1 6 15 20 15 6 1

This array is important in the study of counting techniques and probability (see later chapters) and appears in algebra in the binomial theorem. If the triangular array is written in a different form, as follows, and the sums along the diagonals as indicated by the dashed lines are found, there is an interesting occurrence. What do you find when the numbers are added?

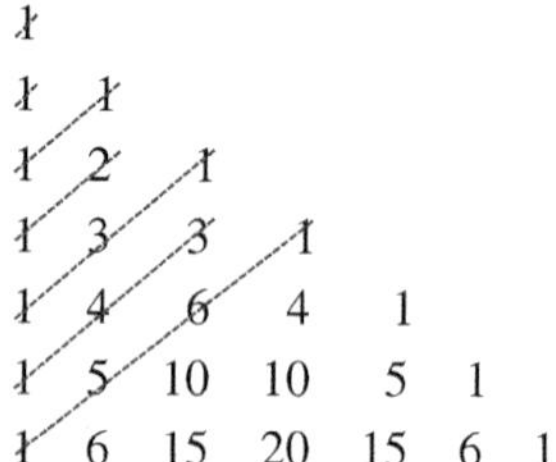

**32.** Write a paragraph explaining some of the occurrences of the Fibonacci sequence and the golden ratio in your everyday surroundings.

*Exercises 33–38 require a scientific calculator.*

**33.** The positive solution of the equation $x^2 - x - 1 = 0$ is $\frac{1 + \sqrt{5}}{2}$, as indicated in the text. The negative solution is $\frac{1 - \sqrt{5}}{2}$. Find the decimal approximations for both. What similarity do you notice between the two decimals?

**34.** In some cases, writers define the golden ratio to be the *reciprocal* of $\frac{1 + \sqrt{5}}{2}$. Find a decimal approximation for the reciprocal of $\frac{1 + \sqrt{5}}{2}$. What similarity do you notice between the decimals for $\frac{1 + \sqrt{5}}{2}$ and its reciprocal?

*A remarkable relationship exists between the two solutions of $x^2 - x - 1 = 0$,*

$$\phi = \frac{1 + \sqrt{5}}{2} \quad \textit{and} \quad \bar{\phi} = \frac{1 - \sqrt{5}}{2},$$

*and the Fibonacci numbers. To find the nth Fibonacci number without using the recursion formula, evaluate*

$$\frac{\phi^n - \bar{\phi}^n}{\sqrt{5}}$$

*using a calculator. For example, to find the thirteenth Fibonacci number, evaluate*

$$\frac{\left(\frac{1 + \sqrt{5}}{2}\right)^{13} - \left(\frac{1 - \sqrt{5}}{2}\right)^{13}}{\sqrt{5}}$$

*This form is known as the* **Binet form** *of the nth Fibonacci number. Use the Binet form and a calculator to find the nth Fibonacci number for each of the following values of n.*

**35.** $n = 14$

**36.** $n = 20$

**37.** $n = 22$

**38.** $n = 25$

# EXTENSION

## Magic Squares

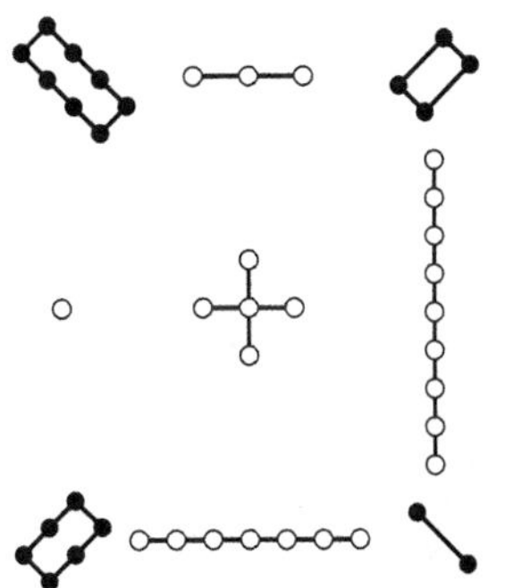

**FIGURE 4**

Legend has it that in about 2200 B.C. the Chinese Emperor Yu discovered on the bank of the Yellow River a tortoise whose shell bore the diagram in Figure 4. This so-called *lo-shu* is an early example of a **magic square.** If the numbers of dots are counted and arranged in a square fashion, the array in Figure 5 is obtained. A magic square is a square array of numbers with the property that the sum along each row, column, and diagonal is the same. This common value is called the "magic sum." The **order** of a magic square is simply the number of rows (and columns) in the square. The magic square of Figure 5 is an order 3 magic square.

By using the formula for the sum of the first $n$ terms of an arithmetic sequence, it can be shown that if a magic square of order $n$ has entries $1, 2, 3, \ldots, n^2$, then the sum of *all entries* in the square is

$$\frac{n^2(n^2 + 1)}{2}.$$

| 8 | 3 | 4 |
|---|---|---|
| 1 | 5 | 9 |
| 6 | 7 | 2 |

**FIGURE 5**

Because there are $n$ rows (and columns), the magic sum of the square may be found by dividing the above expression by $n$. This results in the following formula for finding the magic sum.

### Magic Sum Formula

If a magic square of order $n$ has entries $1, 2, 3, \ldots, n^2$, then the magic sum MS is given by the formula

$$\mathbf{MS} = \frac{n(n^2 + 1)}{2}.$$

*(continued)*

With $n = 3$ in this formula we find that the magic sum of the square in Figure 5, which may be verified by direct addition, is

$$MS = \frac{3(3^2 + 1)}{2} = 15.$$

There is a method of constructing an odd-order magic square which is attributed to an early French envoy, *de la Loubere,* that is sometimes referred to as the "staircase method." The method is described below for an order 5 square, with entries 1, 2, 3, . . . , 25.

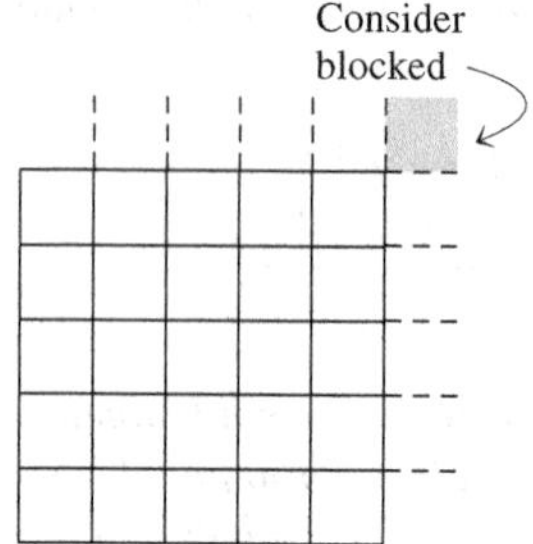


**FIGURE 6**

Begin by sketching a square divided into 25 cells into which the numbers 1–25 are to be entered. Proceed as described below, referring to Figures 6 and 7 for clarification.

| | 18 | 25 | 2 | 9 | 16 |
|---|---|---|---|---|---|
| 17 | 24 | 1 | 8 | 15 | 17 |
| 23 | 5 | 7 | 14 | 16 | 23 |
| 4 | 6 | 13 | 20 | 22 | 4 |
| 10 | 12 | 19 | 21 | 3 | 10 |
| 11 | 18 | 25 | 2 | 9 | |

**FIGURE 7**

***Step 1*** Write 1 in the middle cell of the top row.

***Step 2*** Always try to enter numbers in sequence in the cells by moving diagonally from lower left to upper right. There are two exceptions to this:

**(a)** If you go outside of the magic square, move all the way across the row or down the column to enter the number. Then proceed to move diagonally.

**(b)** If you run into a cell which is already occupied (that is, you are "blocked"), drop down one cell from the last entry written and enter the next number there. Then proceed to move diagonally.

***Step 3*** Your last entry, 25, will be in the middle cell of the bottom row.

Figure 7 shows the completed magic square. Its magic sum is 65.

---

**Benjamin Franklin** admitted that he would amuse himself while in the Pennysylvania Assembly with magic squares or circles "or any thing to avoid Weariness." He wrote about the usefulness of mathematics in the *Gazette* in 1735, saying that no employment can be managed without arithmetic, no mechanical invention without geometry. He also thought that mathematical demonstrations are better than academic logic for training the mind to reason with exactness and distinguish truth from falsity even outside of mathematics.

The square shown here is one developed by Franklin. It has a sum of 2056 in each row and diagonal, and, in Franklin's words, has the additional property "that a four-square hole being cut in a piece of paper of such size as to take in and show through it just 16 of the little squares, when laid on the greater square, the sum of the 16 numbers so appearing through the hole, wherever it was placed on the greater square should likewise make 2056." He claimed that it was "the most magically magic square ever made by any magician."

| | | | | | | | | | | | | | | | |
|---|---|---|---|---|---|---|---|---|---|---|---|---|---|---|---|
| 200 | 217 | 232 | 249 | 8 | 25 | 40 | 57 | 72 | 89 | 104 | 121 | 136 | 153 | 168 | 185 |
| 58 | 39 | 26 | 7 | 250 | 231 | 218 | 199 | 186 | 167 | 154 | 135 | 122 | 103 | 90 | 71 |
| 198 | 219 | 230 | 251 | 6 | 27 | 38 | 59 | 70 | 91 | 102 | 123 | 134 | 155 | 166 | 187 |
| 60 | 37 | 28 | 5 | 252 | 229 | 220 | 197 | 188 | 165 | 156 | 133 | 124 | 101 | 92 | 69 |
| 201 | 216 | 233 | 248 | 9 | 24 | 41 | 56 | 73 | 88 | 105 | 120 | 137 | 152 | 169 | 184 |
| 55 | 42 | 23 | 10 | 247 | 234 | 215 | 202 | 183 | 170 | 151 | 138 | 119 | 106 | 87 | 74 |
| 203 | 214 | 235 | 246 | 11 | 22 | 43 | 54 | 75 | 86 | 107 | 118 | 139 | 150 | 171 | 182 |
| 53 | 44 | 21 | 12 | 245 | 236 | 213 | 204 | 181 | 172 | 149 | 140 | 117 | 108 | 85 | 76 |
| 205 | 212 | 237 | 244 | 13 | 20 | 45 | 52 | 77 | 84 | 109 | 116 | 141 | 148 | 173 | 180 |
| 51 | 46 | 19 | 14 | 243 | 238 | 211 | 206 | 179 | 174 | 147 | 142 | 115 | 110 | 83 | 78 |
| 207 | 210 | 239 | 242 | 15 | 18 | 47 | 50 | 79 | 82 | 111 | 114 | 143 | 146 | 175 | 178 |
| 49 | 48 | 17 | 16 | 241 | 240 | 209 | 208 | 177 | 176 | 145 | 144 | 113 | 112 | 81 | 80 |
| 196 | 221 | 228 | 253 | 4 | 29 | 36 | 61 | 68 | 93 | 100 | 125 | 132 | 157 | 164 | 189 |
| 62 | 35 | 30 | 3 | 254 | 227 | 222 | 195 | 190 | 163 | 158 | 131 | 126 | 99 | 94 | 67 |
| 194 | 223 | 226 | 255 | 2 | 31 | 34 | 63 | 66 | 95 | 98 | 127 | 130 | 159 | 162 | 191 |
| 64 | 33 | 32 | 1 | 256 | 225 | 224 | 193 | 192 | 161 | 160 | 129 | 128 | 97 | 96 | 65 |

B. Franklin inv., J. Ferguson delin. J. Mynde sc.

You might wish to verify the following property of this magic square: The sum of any four numbers that are opposite each other and at equal distances from the center is 514 (which is one-fourth of the magic sum).

## EXTENSION EXERCISES

*Given a magic square, other magic squares may be obtained by rotating the given one. For example, starting with the magic square in Figure 5, a 90° rotation in a clockwise direction gives the magic square shown here.*

| | | |
|---|---|---|
| 6 | 1 | 8 |
| 7 | 5 | 3 |
| 2 | 9 | 4 |

*Start with Figure 5 and give the magic square obtained by each rotation described.*

1. 180° in a clockwise direction
2. 90° in a counterclockwise direction

*Start with Figure 7 and give the magic square obtained by each rotation described.*

3. 90° in a clockwise direction
4. 180° in a clockwise direction
5. 90° in a counterclockwise direction
6. Try to construct an order 2 magic square containing the entries 1, 2, 3, 4. What happens?

*Given a magic square, other magic squares may be obtained by adding or subtracting a constant value to or from each entry, multiplying each entry by a constant value, or dividing each entry by a nonzero constant value. In Exercises 7–10, start with the magic square whose figure number is indicated, and perform the operation described to find a new magic square. Give the new magic sum.*

7. Figure 5, multiply by 3
8. Figure 5, add 7
9. Figure 7, divide by 2
10. Figure 7, subtract 10

*According to a fanciful story by Charles Trigg in* Mathematics Magazine *(September 1976, page 212), the Emperor Charlemagne (742–814) ordered a five-sided fort to be built at an important point in his kingdom. As good-luck charms, he had magic squares placed on all five sides of the fort. He had one restriction for these magic squares: all the numbers in them must be prime.*

*Charlemagne's magic squares are given in Exercises 11–15, with one missing entry. Find the missing entry in each square.*

**11.**

| | | |
|---|---|---|
| | 71 | 257 |
| 47 | 269 | 491 |
| 281 | 467 | 59 |

**12.**

| | | |
|---|---|---|
| 389 | | 227 |
| 107 | 269 | 431 |
| 311 | 347 | 149 |

**13.**

| | | |
|---|---|---|
| 389 | 227 | 191 |
| 71 | 269 | |
| 347 | 311 | 149 |

**14.**

| | | |
|---|---|---|
| 401 | 227 | 179 |
| 47 | 269 | 491 |
| 359 | | 137 |

**15.**

| | | |
|---|---|---|
| 401 | 257 | 149 |
| 17 | | 521 |
| 389 | 281 | 137 |

16. Compare the magic sums in Exercises 11–15. Charlemagne had stipulated that each magic sum should be the year in which the fort was built. What was that year?

*Find the missing entries in each magic square.*

**17.**

| | | |
|---|---|---|
| 75 | 68 | (a) |
| (b) | 72 | (c) |
| 71 | 76 | (d) |

**18.**

| | | | |
|---|---|---|---|
| 1 | 8 | 13 | (a) |
| (b) | 14 | 7 | 2 |
| 16 | 9 | 4 | (c) |
| (d) | (e) | (f) | 15 |

**19.**

| | | | | |
|---|---|---|---|---|
| 3 | 20 | (a) | 24 | 11 |
| (b) | 14 | 1 | 18 | 10 |
| 9 | 21 | 13 | (c) | 17 |
| 16 | 8 | 25 | 12 | (d) |
| (e) | 2 | (f) | (g) | (h) |

*(continued)*

**20.**

| 3 | 36 | 2 | 35 | 31 | 4 |
|---|---|---|---|---|---|
| 10 | 12 | **(a)** | 26 | 7 | 27 |
| 21 | 13 | 17 | 14 | **(b)** | 22 |
| 16 | **(c)** | 23 | **(d)** | 18 | 15 |
| 28 | 30 | 8 | **(e)** | 25 | 9 |
| **(f)** | 1 | 32 | 5 | 6 | 34 |

**21.** Use the "staircase method" to construct a magic square of order 7, containing the entries 1, 2, 3, . . . , 49.

*The magic square shown in the photograph is from a woodcut by Albrecht Dürer entitled* Melancholia.

*The two bottom center numbers give* 1514, *the date of the woodcut. Refer to this magic square for Exercises 22–30.*

| 16 | 3 | 2 | 13 |
|---|---|---|---|
| 5 | 10 | 11 | 8 |
| 9 | 6 | 7 | 12 |
| 4 | 15 | 14 | 1 |

**Dürer's Magic Square**

**22.** What is the magic sum?

**23.** Verify: The sum of the entries in the four corners is equal to the magic sum.

**24.** Verify: The sum of the entries in any 2 by 2 square at a corner of the given magic square is equal to the magic sum.

**25.** Verify: The sum of the entries in the diagonals is equal to the sum of the entries not in the diagonals.

**26.** Verify: The sum of the squares of the entries in the diagonals is equal to the sum of the squares of the entries not in the diagonals.

**27.** Verify: The sum of the cubes of the entries in the diagonals is equal to the sum of the cubes of the entries not in the diagonals.

**28.** Verify: The sum of the squares of the entries in the top two rows is equal to the sum of the squares of the entries in the bottom two rows.

**29.** Verify: The sum of the squares of the entries in the first and third rows is equal to the sum of the squares of the entries in the second and fourth rows.

**30.** Find another interesting property of Dürer's magic square and state it.

**31.** A magic square of order 4 may be constructed as follows. Lightly sketch in the diagonals of the blank magic square. Beginning at the upper left, move across each row from left to right, counting the cells as you go along. If the cell is on a diagonal, count it but do not enter its number. If it is not on a diagonal, enter its number. When this is completed, reverse the procedure, beginning at the bottom right and moving across from right to left. As you count the cells, enter the number if the cell is not occupied. If it is already occupied, count it but do not enter its number. You should obtain a magic square similar to the one given for Exercises 22–30. How do they differ?

*With chosen values for a, b, and c, an order 3 magic square can be constructed by substituting these values in the generalized form shown here.*

| $a+b$ | $a-b-c$ | $a+c$ |
|---|---|---|
| $a-b+c$ | $a$ | $a+b-c$ |
| $a-c$ | $a+b+c$ | $a-b$ |

*Use the given values of a, b, and c to construct an order 3 magic square, using this generalized form.*

**32.** $a = 5, \quad b = 1, \quad c = -3$

**33.** $a = 16, \quad b = 2, \quad c = -6$

**34.** $a = 5, \quad b = 4, \quad c = -8$

**35.** It can be shown that if an order $n$ magic square has least entry $k$, and its entries are consecutive counting numbers, then its magic sum is given by the formula

$$\text{MS} = \frac{n(2k + n^2 - 1)}{2}.$$

Construct an order 7 magic square with least entry 10 using the staircase method. Find its magic sum.

**36.** Use the formula of Exercise 35 to find the missing entries in the following order 4 magic square whose least entry is 24.

| (a) | 38 | 37 | 27 |
|---|---|---|---|
| 35 | (b) | 30 | 32 |
| 31 | 33 | (c) | 28 |
| (d) | 26 | 25 | (e) |

*In a 1769 letter from Benjamin Franklin to a Mr. Peter Collinson, Franklin exhibited the following semimagic square of order 8. (Note: A square is semimagic if it is magic except that one or both diagonals fail to give the magic sum.)*

| 52 | 61 | 4 | 13 | 20 | 29 | 36 | 45 |
|---|---|---|---|---|---|---|---|
| 14 | 3 | 62 | 51 | 46 | 35 | 30 | 19 |
| 53 | 60 | 5 | 12 | 21 | 28 | 37 | 44 |
| 11 | 6 | 59 | 54 | 43 | 38 | 27 | 22 |
| 55 | 58 | 7 | 10 | 23 | 26 | 39 | 42 |
| 9 | 8 | 57 | 56 | 41 | 40 | 25 | 24 |
| 50 | 63 | 2 | 15 | 18 | 31 | 34 | 47 |
| 16 | 1 | 64 | 49 | 48 | 33 | 32 | 17 |

**37.** What is the magic sum?

*Verify the following properties of this semimagic square.*

**38.** The sums in the first half of each row and the second half of each row are both equal to half the magic sum.

**39.** The four corner entries added to the four center entries is equal to the magic sum.

**40.** The "bent diagonals" consisting of eight entries, going up four entries from left to right and down four entries from left to right, give the magic sum. (For example, starting with 16, one bent diagonal sum is $16 + 63 + 57 + 10 + 23 + 40 + 34 + 17$.)

*If we use a "knight's move" (up two, right one) from chess, a variation of the staircase method gives rise to the magic square shown here. (When blocked, we move to the cell just below the previous entry.)*

| 10 | 18 | 1 | 14 | 22 |
|---|---|---|---|---|
| 11 | 24 | 7 | 20 | 3 |
| 17 | 5 | 13 | 21 | 9 |
| 23 | 6 | 19 | 2 | 15 |
| 4 | 12 | 25 | 8 | 16 |

*Use a similar process to construct an order 5 magic square, starting with 1 in the cell described.*

**41.** fourth row, second column (up two, right one; when blocked, move to the cell just below the previous entry)

**42.** third row, third column (up one, right two; when blocked, move to the cell just to the left of the previous entry)

# COLLABORATIVE INVESTIGATION

## Investigating an Interesting Property of Number Squares

In the Extension at the end of this chapter, we looked at magic squares. Now in this group activity we will investigate another property of squares of numbers. Begin by dividing up the class into groups of three or four students. Each student in the group should prepare a square of numbers like the one that follows:

| 1 | 2 | 3 | 4 | 5 |
|---|---|---|---|---|
| 6 | 7 | 8 | 9 | 10 |
| 11 | 12 | 13 | 14 | 15 |
| 16 | 17 | 18 | 19 | 20 |
| 21 | 22 | 23 | 24 | 25 |

## Topics for Discussion

1. Each student should do the following individually:

   Choose any number in the first row. Circle it, and cross out all entries in the column below it. (For example, if you circle 4, cross out 9, 14, 19, and 24.) Now circle any remaining number in the second row, and cross out all entries in the column below it.

   Repeat this procedure for the third and fourth rows, and then circle the final remaining number in the fifth row.

   Now each student in the group should add the circled numbers and compare his or her sum with all others in the group. What do you notice?

2. How does the sum obtained in Exercise 1 compare with the magic sum for an order 5 magic square?

3. Suppose Exercise 1 was done as shown here:

| 1 | (2) | 3 | 4 | 5 |
|---|---|---|---|---|
| 6 | ~~7~~ | (8) | 9 | 10 |
| 11 | ~~12~~ | ~~13~~ | 14 | (15) |
| (16) | ~~17~~ | ~~18~~ | 19 | ~~20~~ |
| ~~21~~ | ~~22~~ | ~~23~~ | (24) | ~~25~~ |

Notice that summing the circled entries is just like summing $1 + 2 + 3 + 4 + 5$, except that

3 is replaced by $3 + 5$,
5 is replaced by $5 + 10$,
1 is replaced by $1 + 15$,
4 is replaced by $4 + 20$.

We can express this as

$$\begin{aligned} \text{sum} &= (1 + 2 + 3 + 4 + 5) \\ &\quad + (5 + 10 + 15 + 20) \\ &= 15 + 50 = 65. \end{aligned}$$

4. Explain why, whatever entries you choose to circle in the various rows, the sum is always the same.

5. Prepare a similar square of the natural numbers 1 through 36. Then repeat Exercise 1. Discuss your results. How does the sum compare with the magic sum for an order 6 magic square?

6. As a group, fill in the entries in this equation for the 6 by 6 square.

   sum = (____ + ____ + ____ + ____ + ____ + ____) + (____ + ____ + ____ + ____ + ____)

7. As a group, predict the sum of the circled numbers in a 7 by 7 square by expressing it as follows. (Do not actually construct the square.)

   sum = (____ + ____ + ____ + ____ + ____ + ____ + ____) + (____ + ____ + ____ + ____ + ____ + ____)

   How does the sum compare with the magic sum for an order 7 magic square?

8. Each individual should now prepare another 5 by 5 square and repeat Exercise 1, except this time start with a number in the first *column* and cross out remaining numbers in *rows*. In your group, discuss and explain what you observe.

## CHAPTER 5 TEST

*In Exercises 1–5, decide whether each statement is* true *or* false.

1. No two prime numbers differ by 1.

2. There are infinitely many prime numbers.

3. If a natural number is divisible by 9, then it must also be divisible by 3.

4. If $p$ and $q$ are different primes, 1 is their greatest common factor and $pq$ is their least common multiple.

5. For all natural numbers $n$, 1 is a factor of $n$ and $n$ is a multiple of $n$.

**6.** Use divisibility tests to determine whether the number

331,153,470

is divisible by each of the following.

| | | |
|---|---|---|
| **(a)** 2 | **(b)** 3 | **(c)** 4 |
| **(d)** 5 | **(e)** 6 | **(f)** 8 |
| **(g)** 9 | **(h)** 10 | **(i)** 12 |

**7.** Decide whether each number is prime, composite, or neither.

**(a)** 93 **(b)** 1 **(c)** 59

**8.** Give the prime factorization of 1440.

**9.** In your own words state the Fundamental Theorem of Arithmetic.

**10.** Decide whether each number is perfect, deficient, or abundant.

**(a)** 17 **(b)** 6 **(c)** 24

**11.** Which of the following statements is false?

**A.** There are no known odd perfect numbers.
**B.** Every even perfect number must end in 6 or 28.
**C.** Goldbach's Conjecture for the number 8 is verified by the equation $8 = 7 + 1$.

**12.** Give a pair of twin primes between 40 and 50.

**13.** Find the greatest common factor of 270 and 450.

**14.** Find the least common multiple of 24, 36, and 60.

**15.** ***Day Off for Fast-food Workers*** Both Sherrie Firavich and Della Daniel work at a fast-food outlet. Sherrie has every sixth day off and Della has every fourth day off. If they are both off on Wednesday of this week, what will be the day of the week that they are next off together?

**16.** The twenty-second Fibonacci number is 17,711 and the twenty-third Fibonacci number is 28,657. What is the twenty-fourth Fibonacci number?

**17.** Make a conjecture about the next equation in the following list, and verify it.

$$8 - (1 + 1 + 2 + 3) = 1$$
$$13 - (1 + 2 + 3 + 5) = 2$$
$$21 - (2 + 3 + 5 + 8) = 3$$
$$34 - (3 + 5 + 8 + 13) = 5$$
$$55 - (5 + 8 + 13 + 21) = 8$$

**18.** Choose the correct completion of this statement: If $p$ is a prime number, then $2^p - 1$ is prime

**A.** never **B.** sometimes **C.** always.

**19. (a)** Give the first eight terms of a Fibonacci-type sequence with first term 1 and second term 5.

**(b)** Choose any term after the first in the sequence just formed. Square it. Multiply the two terms on either side of it. Subtract the smaller result from the larger. Now repeat the process with a different term. Make a conjecture about what this process will yield for any term of the sequence.

**20.** Which one of the following is the *exact* value of the golden ratio?

**A.** $\frac{1 + \sqrt{5}}{2}$ **B.** $\frac{1 - \sqrt{5}}{2}$ **C.** 1.6 **D.** 1.618

**21.** Briefly state what Fermat's Last Theorem says, and describe the circumstances of its proof.

**22.** Write a brief explanation of the acronym GIMPS. Include a definition and several examples of the term represented by the letters MP.

# 6 THE REAL NUMBERS AND THEIR REPRESENTATIONS

The original *Star Trek* series first aired on NBC on September 8, 1966, and spawned an entire generation of science fiction fans. In its second season, the episode "Wolf in the Fold" told the story of an alien entity that had taken over the computer of the starship *Enterprise.* In an effort to drive the entity out of the computer, Captain Kirk suggested the following to Mr. Spock:

KIRK: Spock, don't you have a compulsory scan unit built into the computer banks?

SPOCK: Yes we do, Captain, but with the entity in control. . . .

KIRK: Well aren't there certain mathematical problems which simply cannot be solved?

SPOCK: Indeed. If we can focus the attention of the computer on one of them. . .

KIRK: That ought to do it.

Later, they are able to do just that:

SPOCK: Ready?

KIRK: Implement.

SPOCK: Computer, this is a class "A" compulsory directive. Compute to the last digit the value of pi.

COMPUTER: No, no, no, no, no, . . .

SPOCK (TO KIRK): As we know, the value of pi is a transcendental figure without resolution. The computer banks will work on this problem to the exclusion of all else until we order it to stop.

KIRK: Yes, that should keep that thing busy for a while.

The alien could not comply with the compulsory directive, because pi ($\pi$) is an irrational number, and its decimal representation has no last digit. As a result, ingenuity and mathematics saved the *Enterprise.* In this chapter, we study the rational numbers and irrational numbers, which together form the real number system.

# 6.1 Real Numbers, Order, and Absolute Value

**Sets of Real Numbers • Order in the Real Numbers • Additive Inverses and Absolute Value • Applications**

**The Origins of Zero** The Mayan Indians of Mexico and Central America had one of the earliest numeration systems that included a symbol for zero. The very early Babylonians had a positional system, but they placed only a space between "digits" to indicate a missing power. When the Greeks absorbed Babylonian astronomy, they used the letter omicron, ο, of their alphabet or ō to represent "no power," or "zero." The Greek numeration system was gradually replaced by the Roman numeration system.

The Roman system was the one most commonly used in Europe from the time of Christ until perhaps 1400 A.D., when the Hindu-Arabic system began to take over. The original Hindu word for zero was *sunya*, meaning "void." The Arabs adopted this word as *sifr*, or "vacant." The word *sifr* passed into Latin as *zephirum*, which over the years became *zevero*, *zepiro*, and finally, *zero*.

## Sets of Real Numbers

As mathematics developed, it was discovered that the *counting,* or *natural, numbers* did not satisfy all requirements of mathematicians. Consequently, new, expanded number systems were created. The mathematician Leopold Kronecker (1823–1891) once made the statement, "God made the integers, all the rest is the work of man." The *natural numbers* are those numbers with which we count discrete objects. By including 0 in the set, we obtain the set of *whole numbers.*

**Natural Numbers**

$\{1, 2, 3, 4, \ldots\}$ is the set of **natural numbers.**

**Whole Numbers**

$\{0, 1, 2, 3, \ldots\}$ is the set of **whole numbers.**

These numbers, along with many others, can be represented on **number lines** like the one pictured in Figure 1. We draw a number line by locating any point on the line and calling it 0. Choose any point to the right of 0 and call it 1. The distance between 0 and 1 gives a unit of measure used to locate other points, as shown in Figure 1. The points labeled in Figure 1 and those continuing in the same way to the right correspond to the set of whole numbers.

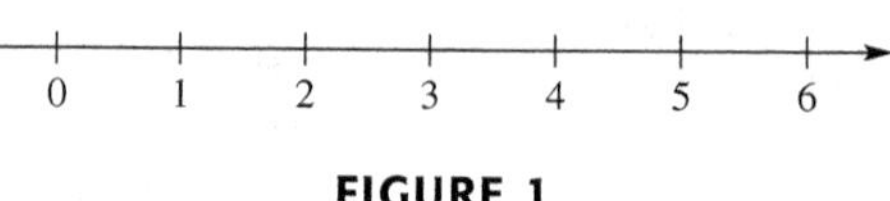


**FIGURE 1**

All the whole numbers starting with 1 are located to the right of 0 on the number line. But numbers may also be placed to the left of 0. These numbers, written $-1$, $-2$, $-3$, and so on, are shown in Figure 2. (The negative sign is used to show that the numbers are located to the *left* of 0.)

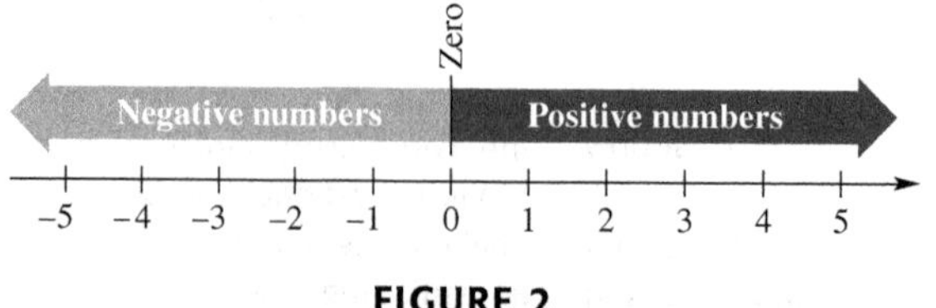


**FIGURE 2**

The numbers to the *left* of 0 are **negative numbers.** The numbers to the *right* of 0 are **positive numbers.** The number 0 itself is neither positive nor negative. Positive numbers and negative numbers are called **signed numbers.**

**The Origins of Negative Numbers** Negative numbers can be traced back to the Chinese between 200 B.C. and 220 A.D. Mathematicians at first found negative numbers ugly and unpleasant, even though they kept cropping up in the solutions of problems. For example, an Indian text of about 1150 A.D. gives the solution of an equation as $-5$ and then makes fun of anything so useless.

**Leonardo of Pisa (Fibonacci),** while working on a financial problem, was forced to conclude that the solution must be a negative number (that is, a financial loss). In 1545 A.D., the rules governing operations with negative numbers were published by **Girolamo Cardano** in his *Ars Magna* (Great Art).

There are many practical applications of negative numbers. For example, temperatures sometimes fall below zero. The lowest temperature ever recorded in meteorological records was $-128.6°F$ at Vostok, Antarctica, on July 22, 1983. Altitudes below sea level can be represented by negative numbers. The shore surrounding the Dead Sea is 1312 feet below sea level; this can be represented as $-1312$ feet.

The set of numbers marked on the number line in Figure 2, including positive and negative numbers and zero, is part of the set of *integers*.

## Integers

$\{\ldots, -3, -2, -1, 0, 1, 2, 3, \ldots\}$ is the set of **integers.**

Not all numbers are integers. For example, $\frac{1}{2}$ is not; it is a number halfway between the integers 0 and 1. Also, $3\frac{1}{4}$ is not an integer. Several numbers that are not integers are *graphed* in Figure 3. The **graph** of a number is a point on the number line. Think of the graph of a set of numbers as a picture of the set. All the numbers in Figure 3 can be written as quotients of integers. These numbers are examples of *rational numbers*.

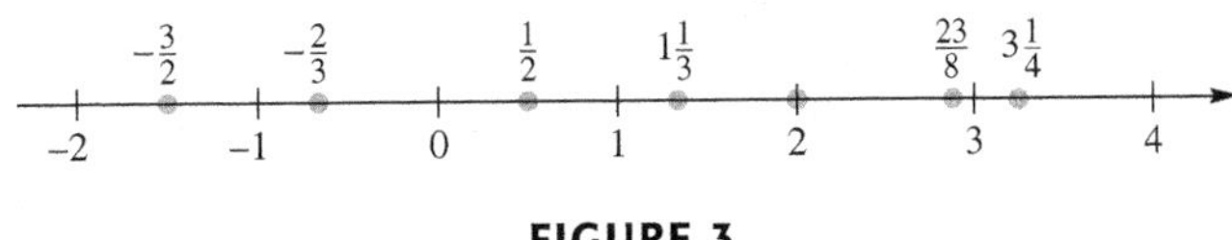


**FIGURE 3**

Notice that an integer, such as 2, is also a rational number; for example, $2 = \frac{2}{1}$.

## Rational Numbers

$\{x \mid x$ is a quotient of two integers, with denominator not equal to $0\}$ is the set of **rational numbers.**

(Read the part in the braces as "the set of all numbers $x$ such that $x$ is a quotient of two integers, with denominator not equal to 0.")

The set symbolism used in the definition of rational numbers,

$$\{x \mid x \textbf{ has a certain property}\},$$

is called **set-builder notation.** This notation is convenient to use when it is not possible, or practical, to list all the elements of the set.

Although a great many numbers are rational, not all are. For example, a square that measures one unit on a side has a diagonal whose length is the square root of 2, written $\sqrt{2}$. See Figure 4. It will be shown later that $\sqrt{2}$ cannot be written as a quotient of integers. Because of this, $\sqrt{2}$ is not rational; it is *irrational.*

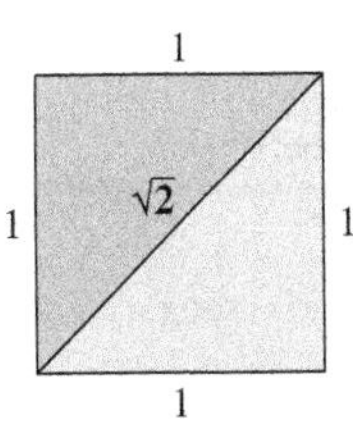


**FIGURE 4**

### Irrational Numbers

$\{x|x$ is a number on the number line that is not rational$\}$ is the set of **irrational numbers.**

Examples of irrational numbers include $\sqrt{3}$, $\sqrt{7}$, $-\sqrt{10}$, and $\pi$, which is the ratio of the distance around a circle (its *circumference*) to the distance across it (its *diameter*).

All numbers that can be represented by points on the number line are called *real numbers*.

### Real Numbers

$\{x|x$ is a number that can be represented by a point on the number line$\}$ is the set of **real numbers.**

Real numbers can be written as decimal numbers. Any rational number can be written as a decimal that will come to an end (terminate), or repeat in a fixed "block" of digits. For example, $\frac{2}{5} = .4$ and $\frac{27}{100} = .27$ are rational numbers with terminating decimals; $\frac{1}{3} = .3333\ldots$ and $\frac{3}{11} = .27272727\ldots$ are repeating decimals. The decimal representation of an irrational number will neither terminate nor repeat. Decimal representations of rational and irrational numbers will be discussed further later in this chapter.

Figure 5 illustrates two ways to represent the relationships among the various sets of real numbers.

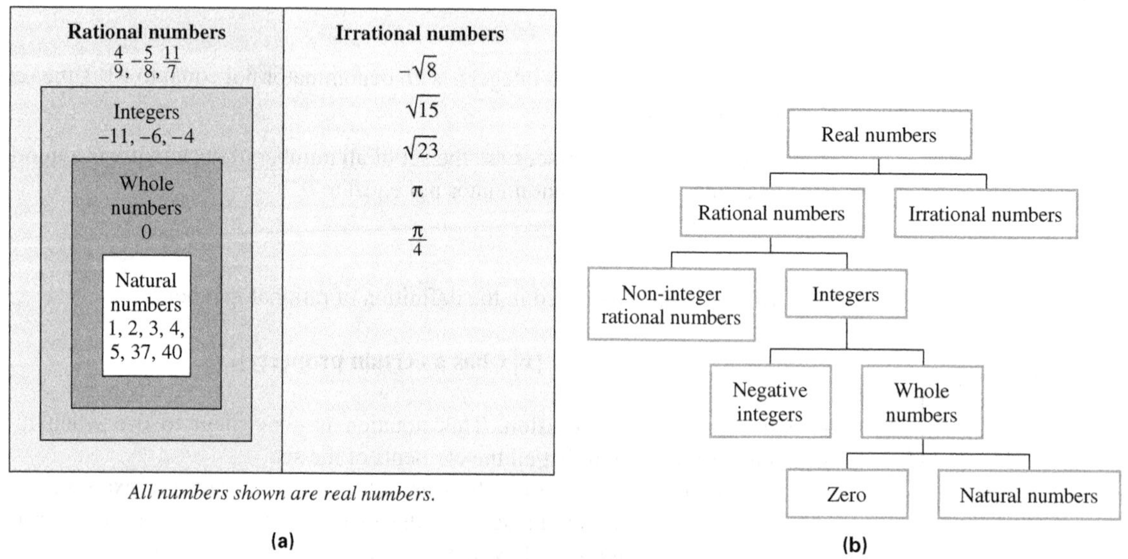


**FIGURE 5**

## EXAMPLE 1 Identifying Elements of a Set of Numbers

List the numbers in the set

$$\left\{-5, -\frac{2}{3}, 0, \sqrt{2}, \frac{13}{4}, 5, 5.8\right\}$$

that belong to each set of numbers.

**(a)** natural numbers **(b)** whole numbers **(c)** integers
**(d)** rational numbers **(e)** irrational numbers **(f)** real numbers

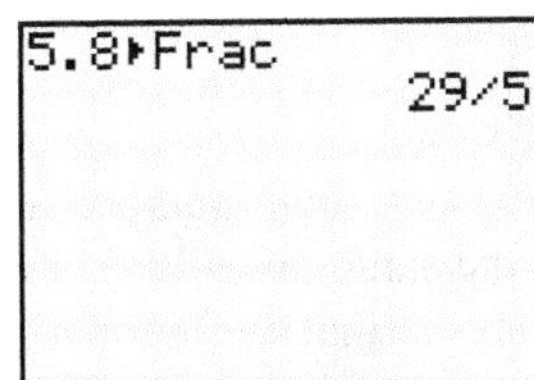


The TI-83/84 Plus calculator will convert a decimal to a fraction. See Example 1(d).

**SOLUTION**

**(a)** The only natural number in the set is 5.

**(b)** The whole numbers consist of the natural numbers and 0. So, the elements of the set that are whole numbers are 0 and 5.

**(c)** The integers in the set are $-5$, 0, and 5.

**(d)** The rational numbers are $-5$, $-\frac{2}{3}$, 0, $\frac{13}{4}$, 5, and 5.8, because each of these numbers *can* be written as the quotient of two integers. For example, $5.8 = \frac{58}{10} = \frac{29}{5}$.

**(e)** The only irrational number in the set is $\sqrt{2}$.

**(f)** All the numbers in the set are real numbers.

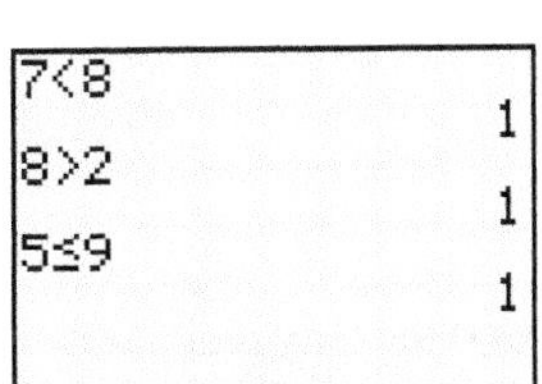


The calculator returns a 1 for these statements of inequality, signifying that each is true.

**Order in the Real Numbers** Two real numbers may be compared, or ordered, using the ideas of equality and inequality. Suppose that $a$ and $b$ represent two real numbers. If their graphs on the number line are the same point, they are **equal.** If the graph of $a$ lies to the left of $b$, $a$ **is less than** $b$, and if the graph of $a$ lies to the right of $b$, $a$ **is greater than** $b$. The **law of trichotomy** says that for two numbers $a$ and $b$, one and only one of the following is true:

$$a = b, \quad a < b, \quad \text{or} \quad a > b.$$

When read from left to right, the symbol $<$ means "is less than," so

$$7 < 8. \quad \text{7 is less than 8.}$$

The symbol $>$ means "is greater than." For example,

$$8 > 2. \quad \text{8 is greater than 2.}$$

***Notice that the symbol always points to the lesser number.*** For example,

$$\text{Lesser number} \longrightarrow 8 < 15.$$

The symbol $\leq$ means "is less than or equal to," so

$$5 \leq 9. \quad \text{5 is less than or equal to 9.}$$

This statement is true, since $5 < 9$ is true. ***If either the $<$ part or the $=$ part is true, then the inequality $\leq$ is true.*** Also, $8 \leq 8$ is true since $8 = 8$ is true. But it is not true that $13 \leq 9$ because neither $13 < 9$ nor $13 = 9$ is true.

The symbol $\geq$ means "is greater than or equal to." Again,

$$9 \geq 5 \quad \text{9 is greater than or equal to 5.}$$

is true because $9 > 5$ is true.

**The symbol for equality, =,** was first introduced by the Englishman Robert Recorde in his 1557 algebra text *The Whetstone of Witte.* He used two parallel line segments, because, he claimed, no two things can be more equal.

The symbols for order relationships, < and >, were first used by Thomas Harriot (1560–1621), another Englishman. These symbols were not immediately adopted by other mathematicians.

6≠6
0
25≥30
0
12≥12
1

The inequalities in Example 2(a) and (d) are false, as signified by the 0. The statement in Example 2(e) is true.

### EXAMPLE 2 Comparing Real Numbers

Determine whether each statement is *true* or *false*.

**(a)** $6 \neq 6$ **(b)** $5 < 19$ **(c)** $15 \leq 20$ **(d)** $25 \geq 30$ **(e)** $12 \geq 12$

**SOLUTION**

**(a)** The statement $6 \neq 6$ is false, because 6 *is equal to* 6.
**(b)** Since 5 is indeed less than 19, this statement is true.
**(c)** The statement $15 \leq 20$ is true, since $15 < 20$.
**(d)** Both $25 > 30$ and $25 = 30$ are false, so $25 \geq 30$ is false.
**(e)** Since $12 = 12$, the statement $12 \geq 12$ is true.

**Additive Inverses and Absolute Value** For any real number $x$ (except 0), there is exactly one number on the number line the same distance from 0 as $x$ but on the opposite side of 0. For example, Figure 6 shows that the numbers 3 and $-3$ are both the same distance from 0 but are on opposite sides of 0. The numbers 3 and $-3$ are called **additive inverses, negatives,** or **opposites,** of each other.

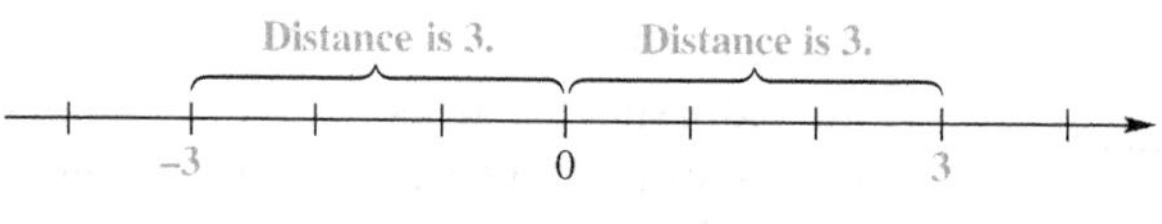


**FIGURE 6**

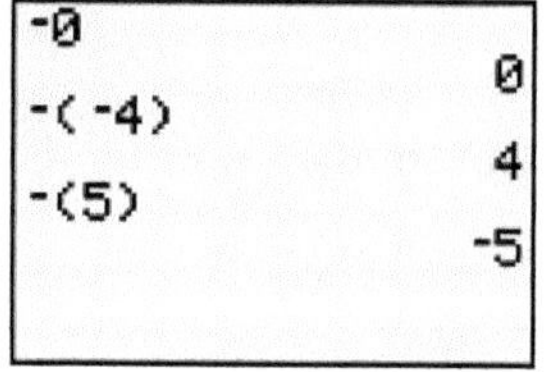


The TI-83/84 Plus distinguishes between the negative symbol (−) and the operation of subtraction.

The additive inverse of the number 0 is 0 itself. This makes 0 the only real number that is its own additive inverse. Other additive inverses occur in pairs. For example, 4 and $-4$, and 5 and $-5$, are additive inverses of each other. Several pairs of additive inverses are shown in Figure 7.

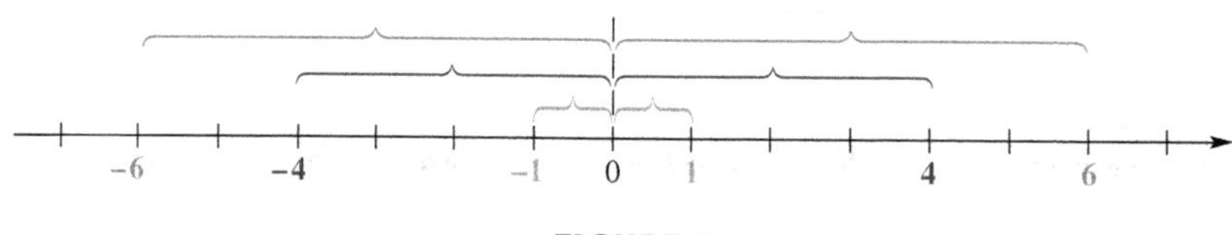


**FIGURE 7**

The additive inverse of a number can be indicated by writing the symbol − in front of the number. With this symbol, the additive inverse of 7 is written $-7$. The additive inverse of $-4$ is written $-(-4)$, and can also be read "the opposite of $-4$" or "the negative of $-4$." Figure 7 suggests that 4 is an additive inverse of $-4$. Since a number can have only one additive inverse, the symbols 4 and $-(-4)$ must represent the same number, which means that

$$-(-4) = 4.$$

This idea can be generalized as follows.

### Double Negative Rule

For any real number $x$,

$$-(-x) = x.$$

**TABLE 1**

| Number | Additive Inverse |
|---|---|
| $-4$ | $-(-4)$ or 4 |
| 0 | 0 |
| 19 | $-19$ |
| $-\frac{2}{3}$ | $\frac{2}{3}$ |

Table 1 shows several numbers and their additive inverses. An important property of additive inverses will be studied later in this chapter: $a + (-a) = (-a) + a = 0$ for all real numbers $a$.

As mentioned above, additive inverses are numbers that are the same distance from 0 on the number line. See Figure 7. This idea can also be expressed by saying that a number and its additive inverse have the same absolute value. The **absolute value** of a real number can be defined as the distance between 0 and the number on the number line. The symbol for the absolute value of the number $x$ is $|x|$, read **"the absolute value of $x$."** For example, the distance between 2 and 0 on the number line is 2 units, so

$$|2| = 2.$$

Because the distance between $-2$ and 0 on the number line is also 2 units,

$$|-2| = 2.$$

Since distance is a physical measurement, which is never negative, ***the absolute value of a number is never negative.*** For example, $|12| = 12$ and $|-12| = 12$, since both 12 and $-12$ lie at a distance of 12 units from 0 on the number line. Also, since 0 is a distance of 0 units from 0, $|0| = 0$.

In symbols, the absolute value of $x$ is defined as follows.

### Formal Definition of Absolute Value

For any real number $x$,

$$|x| = \begin{cases} x & \text{if } x \geq 0 \\ -x & \text{if } x < 0. \end{cases}$$

By this definition, if $x$ is a positive number or 0, then its absolute value is $x$ itself. For example, since 8 is a positive number, $|8| = 8$. However, if $x$ is a negative number, then its absolute value is the additive inverse of $x$. This means that if $x = -9$, then $|-9| = -(-9) = 9$, since the additive inverse of $-9$ is 9.

The formal definition of absolute value can be confusing if it is not read carefully. The "$-x$" in the second part of the definition *does not* represent a negative number. Since $x$ is negative in the second part, $-x$ represents the opposite of a negative number, that is, a positive number.

### EXAMPLE 3 Using Absolute Value

Simplify by finding the absolute value.

**(a)** $|5|$ **(b)** $|-5|$ **(c)** $-|5|$

**(d)** $-|-14|$ **(e)** $|8 - 2|$ **(f)** $-|8 - 2|$

```
abs(-5)
                5
-abs(-14)
              -14
-abs(8-2)
               -6
```

This screen supports the results of Example 3(b), (d), and (f).

**SOLUTION**

(a) $|5| = 5$  (b) $|-5| = -(-5) = 5$

(c) $-|5| = -(5) = -5$  (d) $-|-14| = -(14) = -14$

(e) $|8 - 2| = |6| = 6$  (f) $-|8 - 2| = -|6| = -6$

Part (e) of Example 3 shows that absolute value bars also serve as grouping symbols. You must perform any operations that appear inside absolute value symbols before finding the absolute value.

## Applications

A table of data provides a concise way of relating information.

**EXAMPLE 4 Interpreting Change Using a Table**

The projected annual rates of employment change (in percent) in some of the fastest growing and most rapidly declining industries from 1994 through 2005 are shown in Table 2. What industry in the list is expected to see the greatest change? the least change?

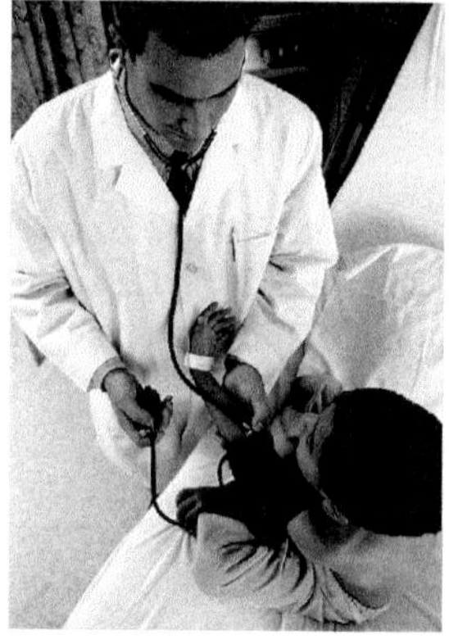

**TABLE 2**

| Industry (1994–2005) | Percent Rate of Change |
|---|---|
| Health services | 5.7 |
| Computer and data processing services | 4.9 |
| Child day care services | 4.3 |
| Footware, except rubber and plastic | −6.7 |
| Household audio and video equipment | −4.2 |
| Luggage, handbags, and leather products | −3.3 |

*Source:* U.S. Bureau of Labor Statistics.

**SOLUTION**

We want the greatest *change,* without regard to whether the change is an increase or a decrease. Look for the number in the list with the greatest absolute value. That number is found in footware, since $|-6.7| = 6.7$. Similarly, the least change is in the luggage, handbags, and leather products industry: $|-3.3| = 3.3$.

## 6.1 Exercises

*In Exercises 1– 6, give a number that satisfies the given condition.*

**1.** An integer between 3.5 and 4.5

**2.** A rational number between 3.8 and 3.9

**3.** A whole number that is not positive and is less than 1

**4.** A whole number greater than 4.5

**5.** An irrational number that is between $\sqrt{11}$ and $\sqrt{13}$

**6.** A real number that is neither negative nor positive

*In Exercises 7–10, decide whether each statement is true or false.*

**7.** Every natural number is positive.

**8.** Every whole number is positive.

**9.** Every integer is a rational number.

**10.** Every rational number is a real number.

*In Exercises 11 and 12, list all numbers from each set that are* **(a)** *natural numbers;* **(b)** *whole numbers;* **(c)** *integers;* **(d)** *rational numbers;* **(e)** *irrational numbers;* **(f)** *real numbers.*

**11.** $\left\{-9, -\sqrt{7}, -1\frac{1}{4}, -\frac{3}{5}, 0, \sqrt{5}, 3, 5.9, 7\right\}$

**12.** $\left\{-5.3, -5, -\sqrt{3}, -1, -\frac{1}{9}, 0, 1.2, 1.8, 3, \sqrt{11}\right\}$

**13.** Explain in your own words the different sets of numbers introduced in this section, and give an example of each kind.

**14.** What two possible situations exist for the decimal representation of a rational number?

*Use an integer to express each number representing a change or measurement in the following applications.*

**15.** ***Height of the Sears Tower*** The Sears Tower in Chicago is 1450 feet high. (*Source:* Council on Tall Buildings and Urban Habitat.)

**16.** ***Population of Laredo*** Between 2000 and 2004, the population of Laredo, TX increased by 26,636. (*Source:* Estimate of the U.S. Census Bureau.

**17.** ***Height of Mt. Arenal*** The height of Mt. Arenal, an active volcano in Costa Rica, is 5436 feet above sea level. (*Source: The New York Times Almanac 2006.*)

**18.** ***Boiling Point of Chlorine*** The boiling point of chlorine is approximately 30° below 0° Fahrenheit.

**19.** ***Melting Point of Fluorine*** The melting point of fluorine gas is 220° below 0° Celsius.

**20.** ***Population of Detroit*** Between 2000 and 2004, the population of Detroit, MI decreased by 51,072. (*Source:* Estimate of the U.S. Census Bureau.)

**21.** ***Windchill*** When the wind speed is 20 miles per hour and the actual temperature is 10° Fahrenheit, the windchill factor is 9° below 0° Fahrenheit. (Give three responses.)

**22.** ***Elevation of New Orleans*** The city of New Orleans lies 8 feet below sea level. (*Source:* U.S. Geological Survey, *Elevations and Distances in the United States.*)

**23.** ***Depths and Heights of Seas and Mountains*** The chart gives selected depths and heights of bodies of water and mountains.

| Bodies of Water | Average Depth in Feet (as a negative number) | Mountains | Altitude in Feet (as a positive number) |
|---|---|---|---|
| Pacific Ocean | −12,925 | McKinley | 20,320 |
| South China Sea | −4802 | Point Success | 14,150 |
| Gulf of California | −2375 | Matlalcueyetl | 14,636 |
| Caribbean Sea | −8448 | Ranier | 14,410 |
| Indian Ocean | −12,598 | Steele | 16,644 |

*Source: The World Almanac and Book of Facts.*

**(a)** List the bodies of water in order, starting with the deepest and ending with the shallowest.

**(b)** List the mountains in order, starting with the lowest and ending with the highest.

**(c)** *True or false:* The absolute value of the depth of the Pacific Ocean is greater than the absolute value of the depth of the Indian Ocean.

**(d)** *True or false:* The absolute value of the depth of the Gulf of California is greater than the absolute value of the depth of the Caribbean Sea.

**24.** ***Personal Savings*** The bar graph in the figure illustrates the amount of personal savings, in billions of dollars, accumulated during the years 1997 through 2001.

(a) Which year had the greatest amount of savings? Which had the least?

(b) Which years had amounts greater than \$200 billion?

(c) Estimate the amounts for 1997 and 1998.

(d) Estimate the difference of the amounts for the years 1997 and 1998.

(e) How did personal savings in 1998 compare to personal savings in 1999?

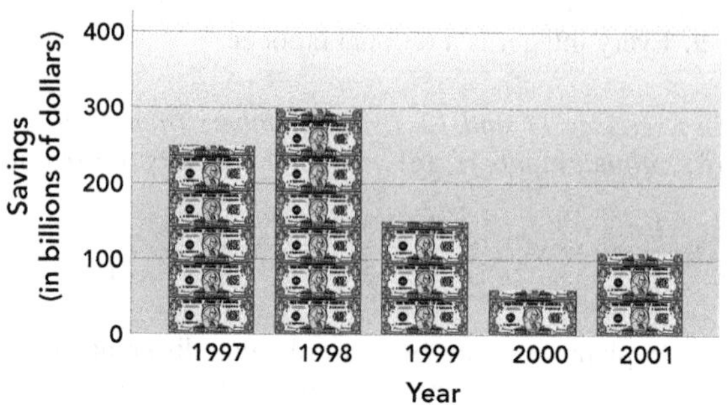


*Source:* U.S. Bureau of Economic Analysis.

*Graph each group of numbers on a number line.*

**25.** $-2, -6, -4, 3, 4$

**26.** $-5, -3, -2, 0, 4$

**27.** $\frac{1}{4}, 2\frac{1}{2}, -3\frac{4}{5}, -4, -1\frac{5}{8}$

**28.** $5\frac{1}{4}, 4\frac{5}{9}, -2\frac{1}{3}, 0, -3\frac{2}{5}$

**29.** Match each expression in Column I with its value in Column II. Some choices in Column II may not be used.

| I | II |
|---|---|
| (a) $\lvert -7 \rvert$ | A. 7 |
| (b) $-(-7)$ | B. $-7$ |
| (c) $-\lvert -7 \rvert$ | C. neither A nor B |
| (d) $-\lvert -(-7) \rvert$ | D. both A and B |

**30.** Fill in the blanks with the correct values: The opposite of $-2$ is _____ , while the absolute value of $-2$ is _____ . The additive inverse of $-2$ is _____, while the additive inverse of the absolute value of $-2$ is _____ .

*Find* **(a)** *the additive inverse (or opposite) of each number and* **(b)** *the absolute value of each number.*

**31.** $-2$

**32.** $-8$

**33.** 6

**34.** 11

**35.** $7 - 4$

**36.** $8 - 3$

**37.** $7 - 7$

**38.** $3 - 3$

**39.** Use the results of Exercises 35 and 36 to complete the following: If $a - b > 0$, then the absolute value of $a - b$ in terms of $a$ and $b$ is _____ .

**40.** Look at Exercises 37 and 38 and use the results to complete the following: If $a - b = 0$, then the absolute value of $a - b$ is _____ .

*Select the lesser of the two given numbers.*

**41.** $-12, -4$

**42.** $-9, -14$

**43.** $-8, -1$

**44.** $-15, -16$

**45.** $3, \lvert -4 \rvert$

**46.** $5, \lvert -2 \rvert$

**47.** $\lvert -3 \rvert, \lvert -4 \rvert$

**48.** $\lvert -8 \rvert, \lvert -9 \rvert$

**49.** $-\lvert -6 \rvert, -\lvert -4 \rvert$

**50.** $-\lvert -2 \rvert, -\lvert -3 \rvert$

**51.** $\lvert 5 - 3 \rvert, \lvert 6 - 2 \rvert$

**52.** $\lvert 7 - 2 \rvert, \lvert 8 - 1 \rvert$

*Decide whether each statement is true or false.*

**53.** $6 > -(-2)$

**54.** $-8 > -(-2)$

**55.** $-4 \leq -(-5)$

**56.** $-6 \leq -(-3)$

**57.** $\lvert -6 \rvert < \lvert -9 \rvert$

**58.** $\lvert -12 \rvert < \lvert -20 \rvert$

59. $-|8| > |-9|$

60. $-|12| > |-15|$

61. $-|-5| \geq -|-9|$

62. $-|-12| \leq -|-15|$

63. $|6 - 5| \geq |6 - 2|$

64. $|13 - 8| \leq |7 - 4|$

***Producer Price Index*** *The table shows the percent change in the Producer Price Index (PPI) for selected industries from 2002 to 2003 and from 2003 to 2004. Use the table to answer Exercises 65–68.*

65. Which industry in which year represents the greatest percentage increase?

66. Which industry in which year represents the greatest percentage decrease?

67. Which industry in which year represents the least change?

68. Which industries represent a decrease for both years?

| Industry | Change from 2002 to 2003 | Change from 2003 to 2004 |
|---|---|---|
| Book publishers | 3.7 | 3.8 |
| Telephone apparatus manufacturing | −3.5 | −5.1 |
| Construction machinery manufacturing | 1.4 | 3.1 |
| Petroleum refineries | 25.9 | 25.0 |
| Electronic computer manufacturing | −19.6 | −12.3 |

*Source:* U.S. Bureau of Labor Statistics.

69. ***Comparing Employment Data*** Refer to the table in Example 4. Of the household audio/video equipment industry and computer/data processing services, which shows the greater change (without regard to sign)?

70. Students often say "Absolute value is always positive." Is this true? If not, explain why.

*Give three numbers between −6 and 6 that satisfy each given condition.*

71. Positive real numbers but not integers

72. Real numbers but not positive numbers

73. Real numbers but not whole numbers

74. Rational numbers but not integers

75. Real numbers but not rational numbers

76. Rational numbers but not negative numbers

# 6.2 Operations, Properties, and Applications of Real Numbers

**Operations • Order of Operations • Properties of Addition and Multiplication of Real Numbers • Applications of Real Numbers**

## Operations

The result of adding two numbers is called their **sum.** The numbers being added are called **addends** (or **terms**).

### Adding Real Numbers

***Like Signs*** Add two numbers with the *same* sign by adding their absolute values. The sign of the sum (either + or −) is the same as the sign of the two numbers.

***Unlike Signs*** Add two numbers with *different* signs by subtracting the smaller absolute value from the larger to find the absolute value of the sum. The sum is positive if the positive number has the larger absolute value. The sum is negative if the negative number has the larger absolute value.

**Practical Arithmetic** From the time of Egyptian and Babylonian merchants, practical aspects of arithmetic complemented mystical (or "Pythagorean") tendencies. This was certainly true in the time of **Adam Riese** (1489–1559), a "reckon master" influential when commerce was growing in Northern Europe. Riese's likeness on the stamp above comes from the title page of one of his popular books on *Rechnung* (or "reckoning"). He championed new methods of reckoning using Hindu-Arabic numerals and quill pens. (The Roman methods then in common use moved counters on a ruled board.) Riese thus fulfilled Fibonacci's efforts 300 years earlier to supplant Roman numerals and methods.

For example, to add $-12$ and $-8$, first find their absolute values:

$$|-12| = 12 \quad \text{and} \quad |-8| = 8.$$

Since $-12$ and $-8$ have the *same* sign, add their absolute values: $12 + 8 = 20$. Give the sum the sign of the two numbers. Since both numbers are negative, the sum is negative and

$$-12 + (-8) = -20.$$

Find $-17 + 11$ by subtracting the absolute values, because these numbers have different signs.

$$|-17| = 17 \quad \text{and} \quad |11| = 11$$
$$17 - 11 = 6$$

Give the result the sign of the number with the larger absolute value.

$$-17 + 11 = -6 \quad \text{Negative since } |-17| > |11|$$

## EXAMPLE 1 Adding Signed Numbers

Find each sum.

**(a)** $-6 + (-3)$ **(b)** $-12 + (-4)$ **(c)** $4 + (-1)$
**(d)** $-9 + 16$ **(e)** $-16 + 12$

**SOLUTION**

**(a)** $-6 + (-3) = -(6 + 3) = -9$
**(b)** $-12 + (-4) = -(12 + 4) = -16$
**(c)** $4 + (-1) = 3$ **(d)** $-9 + 16 = 7$ **(e)** $-16 + 12 = -4$

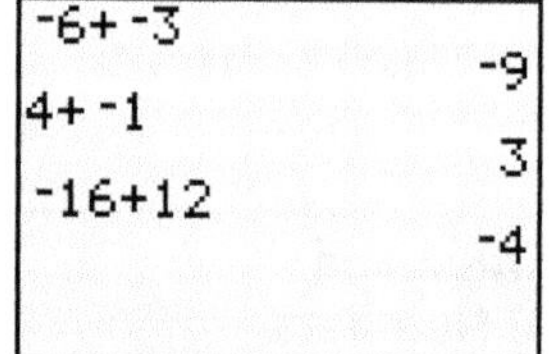


The calculator supports the results of Example 1(a), (c), and (e).

The result of subtracting two numbers is called their **difference.** In $a - b$, $a$ is called the **minuend,** and $b$ is called the **subtrahend.** Compare the two statements below.

$$7 - 5 = 2$$
$$7 + (-5) = 2$$

In a similar way, $9 - 3 = 9 + (-3)$. That is, to subtract 3 from 9, add the additive inverse of 3 to 9.

These examples suggest the following rule for subtraction.

**Definition of Subtraction**

For all real numbers $a$ and $b$,

$$a - b = a + (-b).$$

(Change the sign of the subtrahend and add.)

## EXAMPLE 2 Subtracting Signed Numbers

Find each difference.

**(a)** $6 - 8$ **(b)** $-12 - 4$

**(c)** $-10 - (-7)$ **(d)** $15 - (-3)$

**SOLUTION**

```
6-8
            -2
-12-4
           -16
-10-(-7)
            -3
```

The calculator supports the results of Example 2(a), (b), and (c).

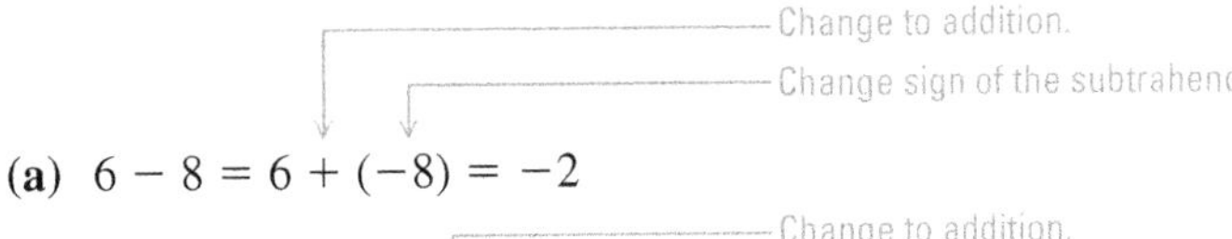


**(a)** $6 - 8 = 6 + (-8) = -2$

Change to addition.
Sign changed.

**(b)** $-12 - 4 = -12 + (-4) = -16$

**(c)** $-10 - (-7) = -10 + [-(-7)]$ This step can be omitted.

$= -10 + 7$

$= -3$

**(d)** $15 - (-3) = 15 + 3 = 18$

The result of multiplying two numbers is called their **product.** The two numbers being multiplied are called **factors.** Any rules for multiplication with negative real numbers should be consistent with the usual rules for multiplication of positive real numbers and zero. To inductively obtain a rule for multiplying a positive real number and a negative real number, observe the pattern of products below.

$$4 \cdot 5 = 20$$
$$4 \cdot 4 = 16$$
$$4 \cdot 3 = 12$$
$$4 \cdot 2 = 8$$
$$4 \cdot 1 = 4$$
$$4 \cdot 0 = 0$$
$$4 \cdot (-1) = ?$$

What number must be assigned as the product $4 \cdot (-1)$ so that the pattern is maintained? The numbers just to the left of the equality signs decrease by 1 each time, and the products to the right decrease by 4 each time. To maintain the pattern, the number to the right in the bottom equation must be 4 less than 0, which is $-4$, so

$$4 \cdot (-1) = -4.$$

The pattern continues with

$$4 \cdot (-2) = -8$$
$$4 \cdot (-3) = -12$$
$$4 \cdot (-4) = -16,$$

and so on. In the same way,

$$-4 \cdot 2 = -8$$
$$-4 \cdot 3 = -12$$
$$-4 \cdot 4 = -16,$$

**Early ways of writing the basic operation symbols** were quite different from those used today. The **addition symbol** shown below was derived from the Italian word *piú* (plus) in the sixteenth century. The + sign used today is shorthand for the Latin *et* (and).

The **subtraction symbol** shown below was used by Diophantus in Greece sometime during the second or third century A.D. Our subtraction bar may be derived from a bar used by medieval traders to mark differences in weights of products.

**Early ways of writing the multiplication and division symbols** were also quite different. In the seventeenth century, Leibniz used the **multiplication symbol** below to avoid × as too similar to the "unknown" *x*. The multiplication symbol × is based on St. Andrew's Cross.

The **division symbol** shown below was used by Gallimard in the eighteenth century. The familiar ÷ symbol may come from the fraction bar, embellished with the dots above and below.

and so on. A similar observation can be made about the product of two negative real numbers. Look at the pattern that follows.

$$\begin{aligned} -5 \cdot 4 &= -20 \\ -5 \cdot 3 &= -15 \\ -5 \cdot 2 &= -10 \\ -5 \cdot 1 &= -5 \\ -5 \cdot 0 &= 0 \\ -5 \cdot (-1) &= ? \end{aligned}$$

The numbers just to the left of the equality signs decrease by 1 each time. The products on the right increase by 5 each time. To maintain the pattern, the product $-5 \cdot (-1)$ must be 5 more than 0, so

$$-5 \cdot (-1) = 5.$$

Continuing this pattern gives

$$\begin{aligned} -5 \cdot (-2) &= 10 \\ -5 \cdot (-3) &= 15 \\ -5 \cdot (-4) &= 20, \end{aligned}$$

and so on. These observations lead to the following rules for multiplication.

$(+) \cdot (+) = +$
$(-) \cdot (-) = +$
$(+) \cdot (-) = -$
$(-) \cdot (+) = -$

## Multiplying Real Numbers

***Like Signs*** Multiply two numbers with the *same* sign by multiplying their absolute values to find the absolute value of the product. The product is positive.

***Unlike Signs*** Multiply two numbers with *different* signs by multiplying their absolute values to find the absolute value of the product. The product is negative.

## EXAMPLE 3 Multiplying Signed Numbers

Find each product.

**(a)** $-9 \cdot 7$ **(b)** $14 \cdot (-5)$ **(c)** $-8 \cdot (-4)$

**SOLUTION**

**(a)** $-9 \cdot 7 = -63$ **(b)** $14 \cdot (-5) = -70$ **(c)** $-8 \cdot (-4) = 32$ ■

The result of dividing two numbers is called their **quotient.** In the quotient $a \div b$ (or $\frac{a}{b}$), where $b \neq 0$, $a$ is called the **dividend** (or numerator), and $b$ is called the **divisor** (or denominator). For real numbers $a$, $b$, and $c$, if

$$\frac{a}{b} = c, \qquad \text{then} \qquad a = b \cdot c.$$

```
-9*7
                -63
14*-5
                -70
-8*-4
                 32
```

An asterisk (*) represents multiplication on this screen. The display supports the results of Example 3.

To illustrate this, consider the quotient $\frac{10}{-2}$. The value of this quotient is obtained by asking, "What number multiplied by $-2$ gives 10?" From our discussion of multiplication, the answer to this question must be "$-5$." Therefore,

$$\frac{10}{-2} = -5,$$

because $-2 \cdot (-5) = 10$. Similar reasoning leads to the following results.

$$\frac{-10}{2} = -5 \quad \text{and} \quad \frac{-10}{-2} = 5$$

These facts, along with the fact that the quotient of two positive numbers is positive, lead to the following rule for division.

$(+)/(+) = +$
$(-)/(-) = +$
$(+)/(-) = -$
$(-)/(+) = -$

### Dividing Real Numbers

***Like Signs*** Divide two numbers with the *same* sign by dividing their absolute values to find the absolute value of the quotient. The quotient is positive.

***Unlike Signs*** Divide two numbers with *different* signs by dividing their absolute values to find the absolute value of the quotient. The quotient is negative.

### EXAMPLE 4 Dividing Signed Numbers

Find each quotient.

**(a)** $\frac{15}{-5}$ **(b)** $\frac{-100}{-25}$ **(c)** $\frac{-60}{3}$

```
15/-5
                 -3
-100/-25
                  4
-60/3
                -20
```

The division operation is represented by a slash (/). This screen supports the results of Example 4.

**SOLUTION**

**(a)** $\frac{15}{-5} = -3$ This is true because $-5 \cdot (-3) = 15$.

**(b)** $\frac{-100}{-25} = 4$ **(c)** $\frac{-60}{3} = -20$

If 0 is divided by a nonzero number, the quotient is 0. That is,

$$\mathbf{\frac{0}{a} = 0, \quad \text{for } a \neq 0.}$$

This is true because $a \cdot 0 = 0$. However, we cannot divide by 0. There is a good reason for this. Whenever a division is performed, we want to obtain one and only one quotient. Now consider the division problem

$$\frac{7}{0}.$$

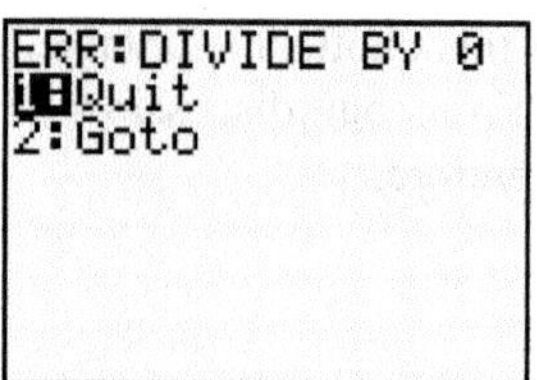


Dividing by zero leads to this message on the TI-83/84 Plus.

We must ask ourselves "What number multiplied by 0 gives 7?" There is no such number, since the product of 0 and any number is zero. On the other hand, if we consider the quotient

$$\frac{0}{0},$$

there are infinitely many answers to the question, "What number multiplied by 0 gives 0?" Since division by 0 does not yield a *unique* quotient, it is not permitted. To summarize these two situations, we make the following statement.

**Division by Zero**

***Division by 0 is undefined.***

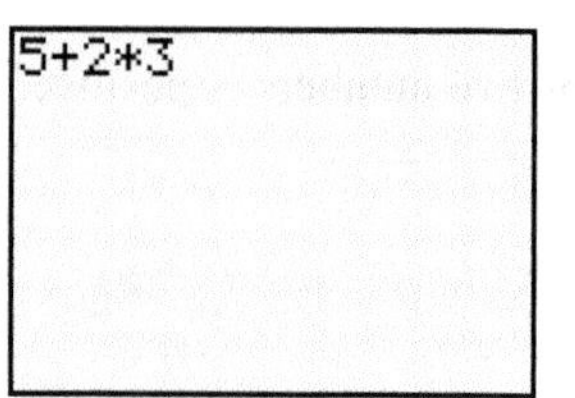


What result does the calculator give? The order of operations determines the answer. (See Example 5(a).)

**Order of Operations** Given a problem such as $5 + 2 \cdot 3$, should 5 and 2 be added first or should 2 and 3 be multiplied first? When a problem involves more than one operation, we use the following **order of operations.**

The sentence **"Please excuse my dear Aunt Sally"** is often used to help us remember the rule for order of operations. The letters **P, E, M, D, A, S** are the first letters of the words of the sentence, and they stand for ***parentheses, exponents, multiply, divide, add, subtract.*** (*Remember also that M and D have equal priority, as do A and S. Operations with equal priority are performed in order from left to right.*)

**Order of Operations**

*If parentheses or square brackets are present:*

***Step 1*** Work separately above and below any **fraction bar.**

***Step 2*** Use the rules below within each set of **parentheses or square brackets.** Start with the innermost set and work outward.

*If no parentheses or brackets are present:*

***Step 1*** Apply any **exponents.**

***Step 2*** Do any **multiplications or divisions** in the order in which they occur, working from left to right.

***Step 3*** Do any **additions or subtractions** in the order in which they occur, working from left to right.

When evaluating an exponential expression that involves a negative sign, be aware that $(-a)^n$ and $-a^n$ do not necessarily represent the same quantity. For example, if $a = 2$ and $n = 6$,

$$(-2)^6 = (-2)(-2)(-2)(-2)(-2)(-2) = 64 \quad \text{The base is } -2.$$

while $$-2^6 = -(2 \cdot 2 \cdot 2 \cdot 2 \cdot 2 \cdot 2) = -64. \quad \text{The base is 2.}$$

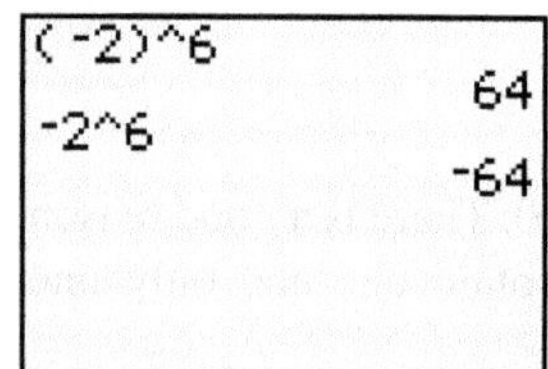


Notice the difference in the two expressions. This supports $(-2)^6 \neq -2^6$.

**EXAMPLE 5 Using the Order of Operations**

Use the order of operations to simplify each expression.

**(a)** $5 + 2 \cdot 3$

**(b)** $4 \cdot 3^2 + 7 - (2 + 8)$

**(c)** $\dfrac{2(8 - 12) - 11(4)}{5(-2) - 3}$

**(d)** $-4^4$

**(e)** $(-4)^4$

**(f)** $(-8)(-3) - [4 - (3 - 6)]$

**SOLUTION**

**(a)** $5 + 2 \cdot 3 = 5 + 6$ Multiply.

$= 11$ Add.

Be careful! Multiply first.

**(b)** $4 \cdot 3^2 + 7 - (2 + 8) = 4 \cdot 3^2 + 7 - 10$ Work within parentheses first.

$= 4 \cdot 9 + 7 - 10$ Apply the exponent.

$3^2 = 3 \cdot 3$, not $3 \cdot 2$.

$= 36 + 7 - 10$ Multiply.

$= 43 - 10$ Add.

$= 33$ Subtract.

**(c)** $\dfrac{2(8 - 12) - 11(4)}{5(-2) - 3} = \dfrac{2(-4) - 11(4)}{5(-2) - 3}$ Work separately above and below fraction bar.

$= \dfrac{-8 - 44}{-10 - 3}$ Multiply.

$= \dfrac{-52}{-13}$ Subtract.

$= 4$ Divide.

**(d)** $-4^4 = -(4 \cdot 4 \cdot 4 \cdot 4) = -256$

The base is 4, not −4.

**(e)** $(-4)^4 = (-4)(-4)(-4)(-4) = 256$

The base is −4 here.

**(f)** $-8(-3) - [4 - (3 - 6)] = -8(-3) - [4 - (-3)]$ Work within parentheses.

Start here.

$= -8(-3) - [4 + 3]$ Definition of subtraction

$= -8(-3) - 7$ Work within brackets.

$= 24 - 7$ Multiply.

$= 17$ Subtract.

```
5+2*3
                11
-4^4
              -256
-8*-3-(4-(3-6))
                17
```

The calculator supports the results in Example 5(a), (d), and (f).

## Properties of Addition and Multiplication of Real Numbers

### Properties of Addition and Multiplication

For real numbers *a*, *b*, and *c*, the following properties hold.

**Closure Properties** $a + b$ **and** $ab$ **are real numbers.**

**Commutative Properties** $a + b = b + a \qquad ab = ba$

**Associative Properties** $(a + b) + c = a + (b + c)$

$(ab)c = a(bc)$

**Identity Properties** There is a real number 0 such that

$$a + 0 = a \quad \text{and} \quad 0 + a = a.$$

There is a real number 1 such that

$$a \cdot 1 = a \quad \text{and} \quad 1 \cdot a = a.$$

*(continued)*

**Properties of Addition and Multiplication, Continued**

| | |
|---|---|
| **Inverse Properties** | For each real number $a$, there is a single real number $-a$ such that $$\mathbf{a + (-a) = 0 \quad \text{and} \quad (-a) + a = 0.}$$ For each nonzero real number $a$, there is a single real number $\frac{1}{a}$ such that $$\mathbf{a \cdot \frac{1}{a} = 1 \quad \text{and} \quad \frac{1}{a} \cdot a = 1.}$$ |
| **Distributive Property of Multiplication with Respect to Addition** | $$\mathbf{a(b + c) = ab + ac}$$ $$\mathbf{(b + c)a = ba + ca}$$ |

The set of real numbers is said to be closed with respect to the operations of addition and multiplication. This means that the sum of two real numbers and the product of two real numbers are themselves real numbers. The commutative properties state that two real numbers may be added or multiplied in either order without affecting the result. The associative properties allow us to group terms or factors in any manner we wish without affecting the result.

The number 0 is called the **identity element for addition,** and it may be added to any real number to obtain that real number as a sum. Similarly, 1 is called the **identity element for multiplication,** and multiplying a real number by 1 will always yield that real number. Each real number $a$ has an **additive inverse,** $-a$, such that the sum of $a$ and its additive inverse is the additive identity element 0. Each nonzero real number $a$ has a **multiplicative inverse,** or **reciprocal,** $\frac{1}{a}$, such that the product of $a$ and its multiplicative inverse is the multiplicative identity element 1. The distributive property allows us to change certain products to sums and certain sums to products.

```
X+Y=Y+X
                 1
X+(Y+Z)=(X+Y)+Z
                 1
5(X+Y)=5X+5Y
                 1
```

No matter what values are stored in X, Y, and Z, the commutative, associative, and distributive properties assure us that these statements are true.

### EXAMPLE 6 Identifying Properties of Addition and Multiplication

Identify the property of addition or multiplication illustrated in each statement.

**(a)** $5 + 7$ is a real number.

**(b)** $5 + (6 + 8) = (5 + 6) + 8$

**(c)** $8 + 0 = 8$

**(d)** $-4\left(-\frac{1}{4}\right) = 1$

**(e)** $4 + (3 + 9) = 4 + (9 + 3)$

**(f)** $5(x + y) = 5x + 5y$

**SOLUTION**

**(a)** The statement that the sum of two real numbers is also a real number is an example of the closure property of addition.

**(b)** Because the grouping of the terms is different on the two sides of the equation, this illustrates the associative property of addition.

**(c)** Adding 0 to a number yields the number itself. This is an example of the identity property of addition.

(d) Multiplying a number by its reciprocal yields 1, and this illustrates the inverse property of multiplication.
(e) The order of the addends (terms) 3 and 9 is different, so this is justified by the commutative property of addition.
(f) The factor 5 is distributed to the terms $x$ and $y$. This is an example of the distributive property of multiplication with respect to addition.

**Applications of Real Numbers** The usefulness of negative numbers can be seen by considering situations that arise in everyday life. For example, we need negative numbers to express the temperatures on January days in Anchorage, Alaska, where they often drop below zero. The phrases "in the red" and "in the black" mean losing money and making money, respectively. (These descriptions go back to the days when bookkeepers used red ink to represent losses and black ink to represent gains.)

**PROBLEM-SOLVING HINT** When problems deal with gains and losses, the gains may be interpreted as positive numbers and the losses as negative numbers. Temperatures below 0° are negative, and those above 0° are positive. Altitudes above sea level are considered positive, and those below sea level are considered negative.

### EXAMPLE 7 Analyzing the Producer Price Index

The Producer Price Index is the oldest continuous statistical series published by the Bureau of Labor Statistics. It measures the average changes in prices received by producers of all commodities produced in the United States. The bar graph in Figure 8 gives the Producer Price Index (PPI) for construction materials between 1996 and 2003.

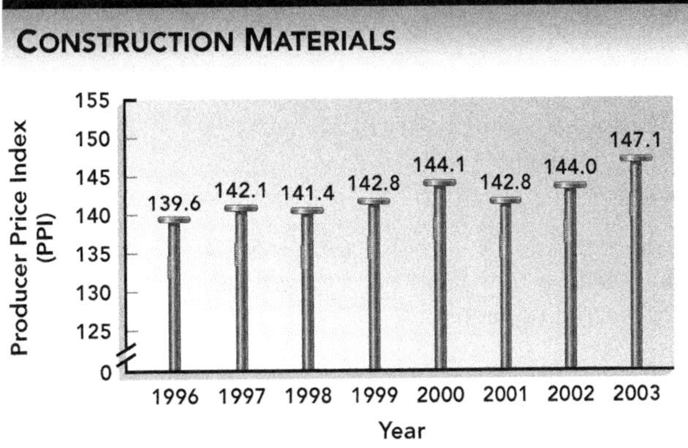


*Source:* U.S. Bureau of Labor Statistics, Producer Price Indexes, monthly and annual.

**FIGURE 8**

Use a signed number to represent the change in the PPI from

(a) 1999 to 2000. (b) 2000 to 2001.

**SOLUTION**

**(a)** To find this change, we start with the index number from 2000 and subtract from it the index number from 1999.

$$\underbrace{144.1}_{\text{The 2000 index}} - \underbrace{142.8}_{\text{The 1999 index}} = \underbrace{\mathbf{1.3}}_{\text{A positive number indicates an increase.}}$$

**(b)** Use the same procedure as in part (a).

$$\underbrace{142.8}_{\text{The 2001 index}} - \underbrace{144.1}_{\text{The 2000 index}} = 142.8 + (-144.1) = \underbrace{\mathbf{-1.3}}_{\text{A negative number indicates a decrease.}}$$

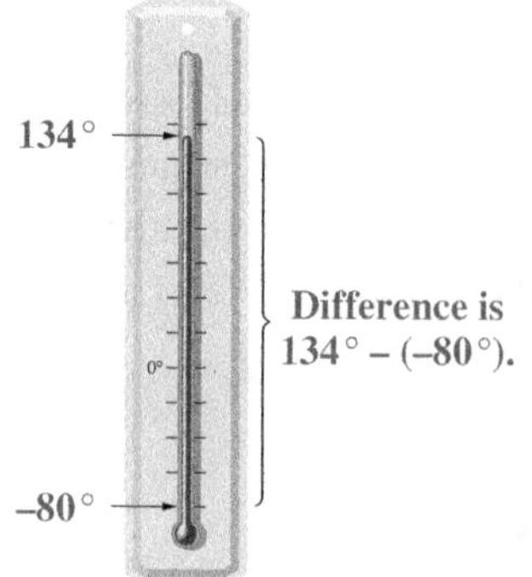


FIGURE 9

### EXAMPLE 8 Determining Difference of Temperatures

The record high temperature in the United States was 134° Fahrenheit, recorded at Death Valley, California, in 1913. The record low was $-80°$F, at Prospect Creek, Alaska, in 1971. See Figure 9. How much greater was the highest temperature than the lowest temperature? (*Source: The World Almanac and Book of Facts 2006.*)

**SOLUTION**

We must subtract the lower temperature from the higher temperature.

$$\begin{aligned} 134 - (-80) &= 134 + 80 && \text{Use the definition of subtraction.} \\ &= 214 && \text{Add.} \end{aligned}$$

The difference of the two temperatures is 214°F.

## 6.2 EXERCISES

*Fill in each blank with the correct response.*

**1.** The sum of two negative numbers will always be a ______________ number. (positive/negative)

**2.** The sum of a number and its opposite will always be _____.

**3.** To simplify the expression $8 + [-2 + (-3 + 5)]$, I should begin by adding _____ and _____, according to the rule for order of operations.

**4.** If I am adding a positive number and a negative number, and the negative number has the larger absolute value, the sum will be a ______________ number. (positive/negative)

**5.** Explain in words how to add signed numbers. Consider the various cases and give examples.

**6.** Explain in words how to multiply signed numbers.

*Perform the indicated operations, using the order of operations as necessary.*

**7.** $-12 + (-8)$

**8.** $-5 + (-2)$

**9.** $12 + (-16)$

**10.** $-6 + 17$

**11.** $-12 - (-1)$

**12.** $-3 - (-8)$

**13.** $-5 + 11 + 3$

**14.** $-9 + 16 + 5$

**15.** $12 - (-3) - (-5)$

**16.** $15 - (-6) - (-8)$

**17.** $-9 - (-11) - (4 - 6)$

**18.** $-4 - (-13) + (-5 + 10)$

**19.** $(-12)(-2)$

**20.** $(-3)(-5)$

**21.** $9(-12)(-4)(-1)3$

**22.** $-5(-17)(2)(-2)4$

**23.** $\dfrac{-18}{-3}$

**24.** $\dfrac{-100}{-50}$

**25.** $\dfrac{36}{-6}$

**26.** $\dfrac{52}{-13}$

**27.** $\dfrac{0}{12}$

**28.** $\dfrac{0}{-7}$

**29.** $-6 + [5 - (3 + 2)]$

**30.** $-8[4 + (7 - 8)]$

**31.** $-8(-2) - [(4^2) + (7 - 3)]$

**32.** $-7(-3) - [2^3 - (3 - 4)]$

**33.** $-4 - 3(-2) + 5^2$

**34.** $-6 - 5(-8) + 3^2$

**35.** $(-8 - 5)(-2 - 1)$

**36.** $\dfrac{(-10 + 4) \cdot (-3)}{-7 - 2}$

**37.** $\dfrac{(-6 + 3) \cdot (-4)}{-5 - 1}$

**38.** $\dfrac{2(-5 + 3)}{-2^2} - \dfrac{(-3^2 + 2)3}{3 - (-4)}$

**39.** $\dfrac{2(-5) + (-3)(-2^2)}{-3^2 + 9}$

**40.** $\dfrac{3(-4) + (-5)(-2)}{2^3 - 2 + (-6)}$

**41.** $-\dfrac{1}{4}[3(-5) + 7(-5) + 1(-2)]$

**42.** $\dfrac{5 - 3\left(\dfrac{-5 - 9}{-7}\right) - 6}{-9 - 11 + 3 \cdot 7}$

**43.** Which of the following expressions are undefined?

A. $\dfrac{8}{0}$ B. $\dfrac{9}{6 - 6}$ C. $\dfrac{4 - 4}{5 - 5}$ D. $\dfrac{0}{-1}$

**44.** If you have no money in your pocket and you divide it equally among your three siblings, how much does each get? Use this situation to explain division of zero by a positive integer.

*Identify the property illustrated by each statement.*

**45.** $6 + 9 = 9 + 6$

**46.** $8 \cdot 4 = 4 \cdot 8$

**47.** $7 + (2 + 5) = (7 + 2) + 5$

**48.** $(3 \cdot 5) \cdot 4 = 4 \cdot (3 \cdot 5)$

**49.** $9 + (-9) = 0$

**50.** $12 + 0 = 12$

**51.** $9 \cdot 1 = 9$

**52.** $\left(\frac{1}{-3}\right) \cdot (-3) = 1$

**53.** $0 + 283 = 283$

**54.** $6 \cdot (4 \cdot 2) = (6 \cdot 4) \cdot 2$

**55.** $2 \cdot (4 + 3) = 2 \cdot 4 + 2 \cdot 3$

**56.** $9 \cdot 6 + 9 \cdot 8 = 9 \cdot (6 + 8)$

**57.** $0 = -8 + 8$

**58.** $19 + 12$ is a real number.

**59.** $19 \cdot 12$ is a real number.

**60.** Work the following problem in two ways, first using the order of operations, and then using the distributive property: Evaluate $9(11 + 15)$.

*Exercises 61–68 are designed to explore the properties of real numbers in further detail.*

**61.** **(a)** Evaluate $6 - 8$ and $8 - 6$.
**(b)** By the results of part (a), we may conclude that subtraction is not a(n) ____________ operation.
**(c)** Are there *any* real numbers $a$ and $b$ for which $a - b = b - a$? If so, give an example.

**62.** **(a)** Evaluate $4 \div 8$ and $8 \div 4$.
**(b)** By the results of part (a), we may conclude that division is not a(n) ____________ operation.
**(c)** Are there *any* real numbers $a$ and $b$ for which $a \div b = b \div a$? If so, give an example.

**63.** Many everyday occurrences can be thought of as operations that have opposites or inverses. For example, the inverse operation for "going to sleep" is "waking up." For each of the given activities, specify its inverse activity.
**(a)** cleaning up your room
**(b)** earning money
**(c)** increasing the volume on your MP3 player

**64.** Many everyday activities are commutative; that is, the order in which they occur does not affect the outcome. For example, "putting on your shirt" and "putting on your pants" are commutative operations. Decide whether the given activities are commutative.
**(a)** putting on your shoes; putting on your socks
**(b)** getting dressed; taking a shower
**(c)** combing your hair; brushing your teeth

**65.** The following conversation actually took place between one of the authors of this text and his son, Jack, when Jack was four years old.

DADDY: "Jack, what is $3 + 0$?"
JACK: "3"
DADDY: "Jack, what is $4 + 0$?"
JACK: "4. . . and Daddy, *string* plus zero equals *string!*" What property of addition of real numbers did Jack recognize?

**66.** The phrase *defective merchandise counter* is an example of a phrase that can have different meanings depending upon how the words are grouped (think of the associative properties). For example, (*defective merchandise*) *counter* is a location at which we would return an item that does not work, while *defective* (*merchandise counter*) is a broken place where items are bought and sold. For each of the following phrases, determine why the associative property does not hold.
**(a)** difficult test question
**(b)** woman fearing husband
**(c)** man biting dog

**67.** The distributive property holds for multiplication with respect to addition. Does the distributive property hold for addition with respect to multiplication? That is, is $a + (b \cdot c) = (a + b) \cdot (a + c)$ true for all values of $a$, $b$, and $c$? (*Hint:* Let $a = 2$, $b = 3$, and $c = 4$.)

**68.** Suppose that a student shows you the following work.

$$-3(4 - 6) = -3(4) - 3(6) = -12 - 18 = -30$$

The student has made a very common error in applying the distributive property. Explain the student's mistake, and work the problem correctly.

*Each expression in Exercises 69–76 is equal to either* 81 *or* $-81$. *Decide which of these is the correct value.*

**69.** $-3^4$

**70.** $-(3^4)$

**71.** $(-3)^4$

**72.** $-(-3^4)$

**73.** $-(-3)^4$

**74.** $[-(-3)]^4$

**75.** $-[-(-3)]^4$

**76.** $-[-(-3^4)]$

**77.** ***Federal Budget Outlays*** The bar graph shows federal budget outlays for the U.S. Treasury Department for the years 2002 through 2005. Use a signed number to represent the change in outlay for each time period.
**(a)** 2002 to 2003
**(b)** 2003 to 2004
**(c)** 2004 to 2005
**(d)** 2002 to 2005

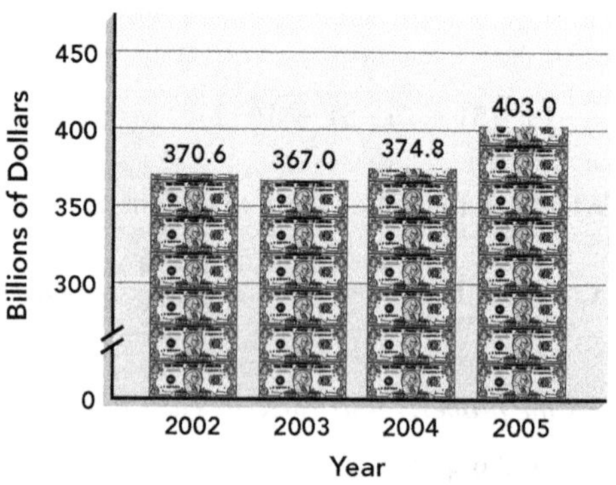


*Source:* U.S. Office of Management and Budget.

**78.** ***Heights of Mountains and Depths of Trenches*** The chart shows the heights in feet of some selected mountains and the depths in feet (as negative numbers) of some selected ocean trenches.

| Mountain | Height | Trench | Depth |
|---|---|---|---|
| Foraker | 17,400 | Philippine | −32,995 |
| Wilson | 14,246 | Cayman | −24,721 |
| Pikes Peak | 14,110 | Java | −23,376 |

*Source: The World Almanac and Book of Facts 2006.*

**(a)** What is the difference between the height of Mt. Foraker and the depth of the Philippine Trench?

**(b)** What is the difference between the height of Pikes Peak and the depth of the Java Trench?

(c) How much deeper is the Cayman Trench than the Java Trench?
(d) How much deeper is the Philippine Trench than the Cayman Trench?

79. ***Social Security Finances*** The table shows Social Security tax revenue and cost of benefits (in billions of dollars).

| Year | Tax Revenue | Cost of Benefits |
|---|---|---|
| 2000 | 538 | 409 |
| 2010* | 916 | 710 |
| 2020* | 1479 | 1405 |
| 2030* | 2041 | 2542 |

*Projected
*Source:* Social Security Board of Trustees.

(a) Find the difference between Social Security tax revenue and cost of benefits for each year shown in the table.
(b) Interpret your answer for 2030.

80. ***House of Representatives*** Based on census population projections for 2020, New York will lose 5 seats in the U.S. House of Representatives, Pennsylvania will lose 4 seats, and Ohio will lose 3. Write a signed number that represents the total projected change in the number of seats for these three states. (*Source:* Population Reference Bureau.)

81. ***House of Representatives*** Michigan is projected to lose 3 seats in the U.S. House of Representatives and Illinois 2 in 2020. The states projected to gain the most seats are California with 9, Texas with 5, Florida with 3, Georgia with 2, and Arizona with 2. Write a signed number that represents the algebraic sum of these changes. (*Source:* Population Reference Bureau.)

82. ***Checking Account Balance*** Shalita's checking account balance is \$54.00. She then takes a gamble by writing a check for \$89.00. What is her new balance? (Write the balance as a signed number.)

83. ***Checking Account Balance*** In August, Marilyn Cazayoux began with a checking account balance of \$904.89. Her checks and deposits for August are given below:

| Checks | Deposits |
|---|---|
| \$35.84 | \$85.00 |
| \$26.14 | \$120.76 |
| \$3.12 | |

Assuming no other transactions, what was her account balance at the end of August?

84. ***Checking Account Balances*** In September, Carter Fenton began with a checking account balance of \$904.89. His checks and deposits for September are given below:

| Checks | Deposits |
|---|---|
| \$41.29 | \$80.59 |
| \$13.66 | \$276.13 |
| \$84.40 | |

Assuming no other transactions, what was his account balance at the end of September?

85. ***Difference in Elevations*** The top of Mt. Whitney, visible from Death Valley, has an altitude of 14,494 feet above sea level. The bottom of Death Valley is 282 feet below sea level. Using 0 as sea level, find the difference of these two elevations. (*Source: World Almanac and Book of Facts 2006.*)

86. ***Altitude of Hikers*** The surface, or rim, of a canyon is at altitude 0. On a hike down into the canyon, a party of hikers stops for a rest at 130 meters below the surface. They then descend another 54 meters. What is their new altitude? (Write the altitude as a signed number.)

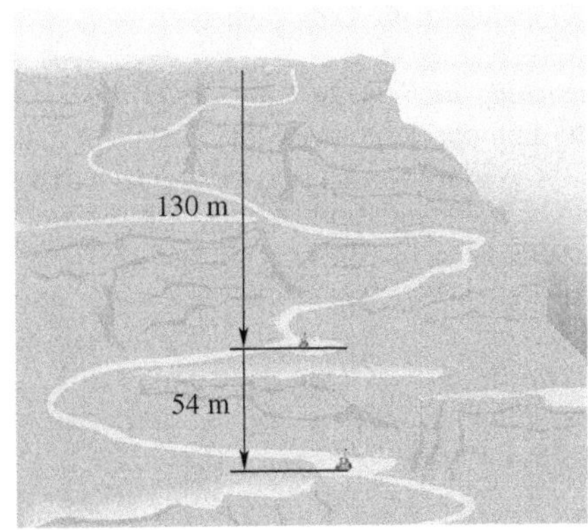


87. ***Drastic Temperature Change*** On January 23, 1943, the temperature rose 49°F in two minutes in Spearfish, South Dakota. If the starting temperature was −4°F, what was the temperature two minutes later? (*Source: Guinness World Records 2006.*)

88. ***Drastic Temperature Change*** The largest change in temperature ever recorded within a 24-hour period occurred in Browning, Montana, on January 23–24, 1916. The temperature fell 100°F from a starting temperature of 44°F. What was the low temperature during this period? (*Source: Guinness World Records, 2006.*)

89. ***Extreme Temperatures in Little Rock*** The lowest temperature ever recorded in Little Rock, Arkansas, was $-5°$F. The highest temperature ever recorded there was 117°F more than the lowest. What was this highest temperature? (*Source: The World Almanac and Book of Facts 2006.*)

90. ***Extreme Temperatures in Tennessee*** The lowest temperature ever recorded in Tennessee was $-32°$F. The highest temperature ever recorded there was 145°F more than the lowest. What was this highest temperature? (*Source:* National Climatic Data Center.)

91. ***Low Temperatures in Chicago and Huron*** The lowest temperature recorded in Chicago, Illinois, was $-27°$F in 1985. The record low in Huron, South Dakota, was set in 1994 and was 14°F lower than $-27°$F. What was the record low in Huron? (*Source: The World Almanac and Book of Facts 2006.*)

92. ***Low Temperatures in Illinois and Utah*** The lowest temperature ever recorded in Illinois was $-36°$F on January 5, 1999. The lowest temperature ever recorded in Utah was observed on February 1, 1985 and was 33°F lower than Illinois's record low. What is the record low temperature for Utah? (*Source:* National Climatic Data Center.)

93. ***Breaching of Humpback Whales*** No one knows just why humpback whales heave their 45-ton bodies out of the water, but leap they do. (This activity is called *breaching.*) Mark and Debbie, two researchers based on the island of Maui, noticed that one of their favorite whales, "Pineapple," leaped 15 feet above the surface of the ocean while her mate cruised 12 feet below the surface. (See the diagram at the top of the next column.) What is the difference between these two levels?

94. ***Highest Point in Louisiana*** The highest point in Louisiana is Driskill Mountain, at an altitude of 535 feet. The lowest point is at Spanish Fort, 8 feet below sea level. Using zero as sea level, find the difference of these two elevations. (*Source: The World Almanac and Book of Facts 2002.*)

95. ***Birth Date of a Greek Mathematician*** A certain Greek mathematician was born in 426 B.C. Her father was born 43 years earlier. In what year was her father born?

96. ***Federal Budget*** In 2000, the federal budget had a surplus of \$236 billion. In 2004, the federal budget had a deficit of \$413 billion. Find the difference of these amounts. (*Source:* Treasury Department.)

97. ***Credit Card Balance*** In 1998, undergraduate college students had an average credit card balance of \$1879. The average balance increased \$869 by 2000 and then dropped \$579 by 2004. What was the average credit card balance of undergraduate college students in 2004? (*Source:* Nellie Mae.)

98. ***Airline Ticket Price*** In 1999, companies paid an average of \$243 for an airline ticket. This average price had increased \$16 by 2001 and then had decreased \$40 by 2005. What was the average price companies paid for an airline ticket in 2005? (*Source:* American Express.)

## 6.3 Rational Numbers and Decimal Representation

**Definition and the Fundamental Property • Operations with Rational Numbers • Density and the Arithmetic Mean • Decimal Form of Rational Numbers**

**Definition and the Fundamental Property** The set of real numbers is composed of two important mutually exclusive subsets: the rational numbers and the irrational numbers. (Two sets are *mutually exclusive* if they contain no elements in common.)

**Benjamin Banneker** (1731–1806) spent the first half of his life tending a farm in Maryland. He gained a reputation locally for his mechanical skills and abilities in mathematical problem solving. In 1772 he acquired astronomy books from a neighbor and devoted himself to learning astronomy, observing the skies, and making calculations. In 1789 Banneker joined the team that surveyed what is now the District of Columbia.

Banneker published almanacs yearly from 1792 to 1802. He sent a copy of his first almanac to Thomas Jefferson along with an impassioned letter against slavery. Jefferson subsequently championed the cause of this early African-American mathematician.

Recall from Section 6.1 that quotients of integers are called **rational numbers.** Think of the rational numbers as being made up of all the fractions (quotients of integers with denominator not equal to zero) and all the integers. Any integer can be written as the quotient of two integers. For example, the integer 9 can be written as the quotient $\frac{9}{1}$, or $\frac{18}{2}$, or $\frac{27}{3}$, and so on. Also, $-5$ can be expressed as a quotient of integers as $\frac{-5}{1}$ or $\frac{-10}{2}$, and so on. (How can the integer 0 be written as a quotient of integers?)

### Rational Numbers

**Rational numbers** $= \{x \mid x$ is a quotient of two integers, with denominator not $0\}$

A rational number is said to be in **lowest terms** if the greatest common factor of the numerator (top number) and the denominator (bottom number) is 1. (The greatest common factor and least common multiple were discussed in Section 5.3.) Rational numbers are written in lowest terms by using the *fundamental property of rational numbers.*

### Fundamental Property of Rational Numbers

If $a$, $b$, and $k$ are integers with $b \neq 0$ and $k \neq 0$, then

$$\frac{a \cdot k}{b \cdot k} = \frac{a}{b}.$$

### EXAMPLE 1 Writing a Fraction in Lowest Terms

Write $\frac{36}{54}$ in lowest terms.

**SOLUTION**

Since the greatest common factor of 36 and 54 is 18,

$$\frac{36}{54} = \frac{2 \cdot 18}{3 \cdot 18} = \frac{2}{3}.$$

```
36/54▸Frac
           2/3
```

The calculator gives 36/54 in lowest terms, as illustrated in Example 1.

In Example 1, $\frac{36}{54} = \frac{2}{3}$. If we multiply the numerator of the fraction on the left by the denominator of the fraction on the right, we obtain $36 \cdot 3 = 108$. If we multiply the denominator of the fraction on the left by the numerator of the fraction on the right, we obtain $54 \cdot 2 = 108$. The result is the same in both cases.

One way of determining whether two fractions are equal is to perform this test. If the product of the **"extremes"** (36 and 3 in this case) equals the product of the **"means"** (54 and 2), the fractions are equal. This test for equality of rational numbers is called the **cross-product test.**

### Cross-Product Test for Equality of Rational Numbers

For rational numbers $\frac{a}{b}$ and $\frac{c}{d}$, $b \neq 0$, $d \neq 0$,

$$\frac{a}{b} = \frac{c}{d} \quad \textbf{if and only if} \quad a \cdot d = b \cdot c.$$

**Operations with Rational Numbers** The operation of addition of rational numbers can be illustrated by the sketches in Figure 10. The rectangle at the top left is divided into three equal portions, with one of the portions in color. The rectangle at the top right is divided into five equal parts, with two of them in color.

The total of the areas in color is represented by the sum

$$\frac{1}{3} + \frac{2}{5}.$$

To evaluate this sum, the areas in color must be redrawn in terms of a common unit. Since the least common multiple of 3 and 5 is 15, redraw both rectangles with 15 parts. See Figure 11. In the figure, 11 of the small rectangles are in color, so

$$\frac{1}{3} + \frac{2}{5} = \frac{5}{15} + \frac{6}{15} = \frac{11}{15}.$$

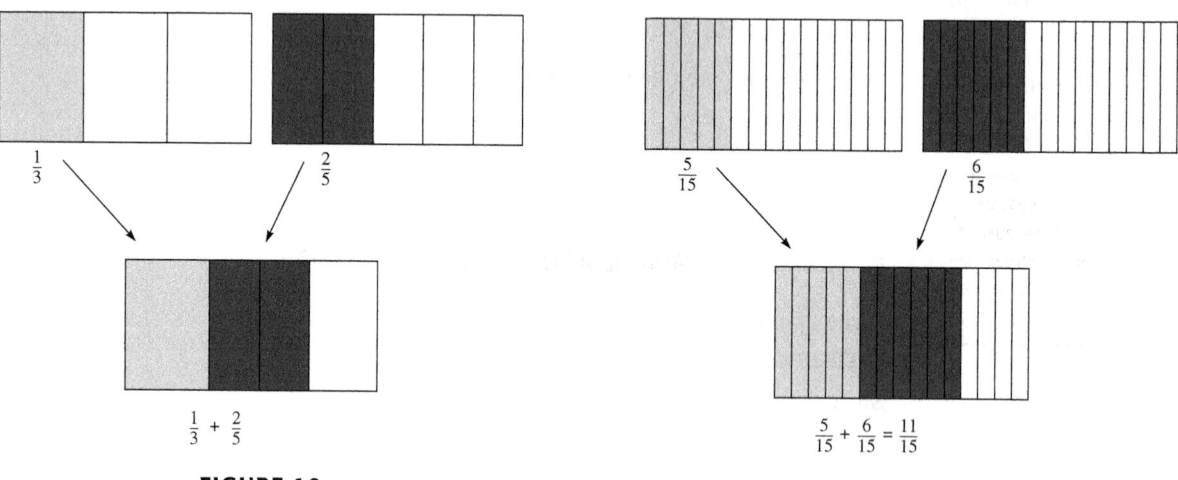


**FIGURE 10**

**FIGURE 11**

A similar example could be given for the difference of rational numbers. A formal definition of addition and subtraction of rational numbers follows.

**Adding and Subtracting Rational Numbers**

If $\frac{a}{b}$ and $\frac{c}{d}$ are rational numbers, then

$$\frac{a}{b} + \frac{c}{d} = \frac{ad + bc}{bd} \quad \text{and} \quad \frac{a}{b} - \frac{c}{d} = \frac{ad - bc}{bd}.$$

This formal definition is seldom used in practice. In practical problems involving addition and subtraction of rational numbers, we usually rewrite the fractions with the least common multiple of their denominators, called the **least common denominator.**

```
2/15+1/10▸Frac
            7/30
173/180-69/1200▸
Frac
       3253/3600
```

The results of Example 2 are illustrated in this screen.

**EXAMPLE 2 Adding and Subtracting Rational Numbers**

Perform each operation.

**(a)** $\frac{2}{15} + \frac{1}{10}$ **(b)** $\frac{173}{180} - \frac{69}{1200}$

**SOLUTION**

**(a)** The least common multiple of 15 and 10 is 30. Now write $\frac{2}{15}$ and $\frac{1}{10}$ with denominators of 30, and then add the numerators. Proceed as follows:

Since $30 \div 15 = 2$, $$\frac{2}{15} = \frac{2 \cdot 2}{15 \cdot 2} = \frac{4}{30},$$

and since $30 \div 10 = 3$, $$\frac{1}{10} = \frac{1 \cdot 3}{10 \cdot 3} = \frac{3}{30}.$$

Thus, $$\frac{2}{15} + \frac{1}{10} = \frac{4}{30} + \frac{3}{30} = \frac{7}{30}.$$

**(b)** The least common multiple of 180 and 1200 is 3600.

$$\frac{173}{180} - \frac{69}{1200} = \frac{3460}{3600} - \frac{207}{3600} = \frac{3460 - 207}{3600} = \frac{3253}{3600}$$

The product of two rational numbers is defined as follows.

**Multiplying Rational Numbers**

If $\frac{a}{b}$ and $\frac{c}{d}$ are rational numbers, then

$$\frac{a}{b} \cdot \frac{c}{d} = \frac{ac}{bd}.$$

```
(3/4)*(7/10)▸Fra
c
           21/40
(5/18)*(3/10)▸Fr
ac
            1/12
```

To illustrate the results of Example 3, we use parentheses around the fraction factors.

**EXAMPLE 3 Multiplying Rational Numbers**

Find each product.

**(a)** $\frac{3}{4} \cdot \frac{7}{10}$ **(b)** $\frac{5}{18} \cdot \frac{3}{10}$

**SOLUTION**

**(a)** $\frac{3}{4} \cdot \frac{7}{10} = \frac{3 \cdot 7}{4 \cdot 10} = \frac{21}{40}$

**(b)** $\frac{5}{18} \cdot \frac{3}{10} = \frac{5 \cdot 3}{18 \cdot 10} = \frac{15}{180} = \frac{1 \cdot 15}{12 \cdot 15} = \frac{1}{12}$

In practice, a multiplication problem such as this is often solved by using slash marks to indicate that common factors have been divided out of the numerator and denominator.

$$\frac{\overset{1}{\cancel{5}}}{\underset{6}{\cancel{18}}} \cdot \frac{\overset{1}{\cancel{3}}}{\underset{2}{\cancel{10}}} = \frac{1}{6} \cdot \frac{1}{2} \qquad \text{3 is divided out of the terms 3 and 18; 5 is divided out of 5 and 10.}$$

$$= \frac{1}{12}$$

In a fraction, the fraction bar indicates the operation of division. Recall that, in the previous section, we defined the multiplicative inverse, or reciprocal, of the nonzero number $b$. The multiplicative inverse of $b$ is $\frac{1}{b}$. We can now define division using multiplicative inverses.

## For Further Thought

### The Influence of Spanish Coinage on Stock Prices

Until August 28, 2000, when decimalization of the U.S. stock market began, market prices were reported with fractions having denominators with powers of 2, such as $17\frac{3}{4}$ and $112\frac{5}{8}$. Did you ever wonder why this was done?

During the early years of the United States, prior to the minting of its own coinage, the Spanish eight-reales coin, also known as the Spanish milled dollar, circulated freely in the states. Its fractional parts, the four reales, two reales, and one real, were known as **pieces of eight,** and were described as such in pirate and treasure lore. When the New York Stock Exchange was founded in 1792, it chose to use the Spanish milled dollar as its price basis, rather than the decimal base as proposed by Thomas Jefferson that same year.

In the September 1997 issue of *COINage*, Tom Delorey's article "The End of 'Pieces of Eight'" gives the following account:

> *As the Spanish dollar and its fractions continued to be legal tender in America alongside the decimal coins until 1857, there was no urgency to change the system—and by the time the Spanish-American money was withdrawn in 1857, pricing stocks in eighths of a dollar—and no less—was a tradition carved in stone. Being somewhat a conservative organization, the NYSE saw no need to fix what was not broken.*

All prices on the U.S. stock markets are now reported in decimals. (*Source:* "Stock price tables go to decimal listings," *The Times Picayune,* June 27, 2000.)

### For Group Discussion or Individual Investigation

Consider this: Have you ever heard this old cheer? "Two bits, four bits, six bits, a dollar. All for the (home team), stand up and holler." The term **two bits** refers to 25 cents. Discuss how this cheer is based on the Spanish eight-reales coin.

**Early U.S. cents** and **half cents** used fractions to denote their denominations. The half cent used $\frac{1}{200}$ and the cent used $\frac{1}{100}$. (See Exercise 18 for a photo of an interesting error coin.)

The coins shown here were part of the collection of Louis E. Eliasberg, Sr. **Louis Eliasberg** was the only person ever to assemble a complete collection of United States coins. The Eliasberg gold coins were auctioned in 1982, while the copper, nickel, and silver coins were auctioned in two sales in 1996 and 1997. The half cent pictured sold for $506,000 and the cent sold for $27,500. The cent shown in Exercise 18 went for a mere $2970.

### Definition of Division

If $a$ and $b$ are real numbers, $b \neq 0$, then

$$\frac{a}{b} = a \cdot \frac{1}{b}.$$

You have probably heard the rule, "To divide fractions, invert the divisor and multiply." But have you ever wondered why this rule works? To illustrate it, suppose that you have $\frac{7}{8}$ of a gallon of milk and you wish to find how many quarts you have. Since a quart is $\frac{1}{4}$ of a gallon, you must ask yourself, "How many $\frac{1}{4}$s are there in $\frac{7}{8}$?" This would be interpreted as

$$\frac{7}{8} \div \frac{1}{4} \quad \text{or} \quad \frac{\frac{7}{8}}{\frac{1}{4}}.$$

The fundamental property of rational numbers discussed earlier can be extended to rational number values of $a$, $b$, and $k$. With $a = \frac{7}{8}$, $b = \frac{1}{4}$, and $k = 4$ (the reciprocal of $b = \frac{1}{4}$),

$$\frac{a}{b} = \frac{a \cdot k}{b \cdot k} = \frac{\frac{7}{8} \cdot 4}{\frac{1}{4} \cdot 4} = \frac{\frac{7}{8} \cdot 4}{1} = \frac{7}{8} \cdot \frac{4}{1}.$$

Now notice that we began with the division problem $\frac{7}{8} \div \frac{1}{4}$ which, through a series of equivalent expressions, led to the multiplication problem $\left(\frac{7}{8} \cdot \frac{4}{1}\right)$. So dividing by $\frac{1}{4}$ is equivalent to multiplying by its reciprocal, $\frac{4}{1}$. By the definition of multiplication of fractions,

$$\frac{7}{8} \cdot \frac{4}{1} = \frac{28}{8} = \frac{7}{2},$$

and thus there are $\frac{7}{2}$ or $3\frac{1}{2}$ quarts in $\frac{7}{8}$ gallon.*

We now state the rule for dividing $\frac{a}{b}$ by $\frac{c}{d}$.

### Dividing Rational Numbers

If $\frac{a}{b}$ and $\frac{c}{d}$ are rational numbers, where $\frac{c}{d} \neq 0$, then

$$\frac{a}{b} \div \frac{c}{d} = \frac{a}{b} \cdot \frac{d}{c} = \frac{ad}{bc}.$$

---

*$3\frac{1}{2}$ is a **mixed number.** Mixed numbers are covered in the exercises for this section.

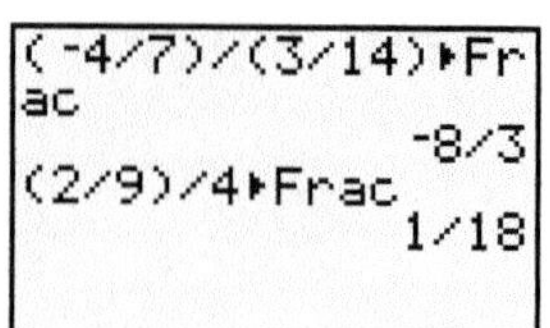

This screen supports the results in Example 4(b) and (c).

## EXAMPLE 4 Dividing Rational Numbers

Find each quotient.

**(a)** $\frac{3}{5} \div \frac{7}{15}$ **(b)** $\frac{-4}{7} \div \frac{3}{14}$ **(c)** $\frac{2}{9} \div 4$

**SOLUTION**

**(a)** $\frac{3}{5} \div \frac{7}{15} = \frac{3}{5} \cdot \frac{15}{7} = \frac{45}{35} = \frac{9 \cdot 5}{7 \cdot 5} = \frac{9}{7}$

**(b)** $\frac{-4}{7} \div \frac{3}{14} = \frac{-4}{7} \cdot \frac{14}{3} = \frac{-56}{21} = \frac{-8 \cdot 7}{3 \cdot 7} = \frac{-8}{3} = -\frac{8}{3}$

**(c)** $\frac{2}{9} \div 4 = \frac{2}{9} \div \frac{4}{1} = \frac{2}{9} \cdot \frac{1}{4} = \frac{\overset{1}{\cancel{2}}}{9} \cdot \frac{1}{\underset{2}{\cancel{4}}} = \frac{1}{18}$

$\frac{-a}{b}$, $\frac{a}{-b}$, and $-\frac{a}{b}$ are all equal.

## Density and the Arithmetic Mean

There is no integer between two consecutive integers, such as 3 and 4. However, a rational number can always be found between any two distinct rational numbers. For this reason, the set of rational numbers is said to be *dense.*

### Density Property of the Rational Numbers

If $r$ and $t$ are distinct rational numbers, with $r < t$, then there exists a rational number $s$ such that

$$r < s < t.$$

Repeated applications of the density property lead to the conclusion that there are *infinitely many* rational numbers between two distinct rational numbers.

To find the **arithmetic mean,** or **average,** of $n$ numbers, we add the numbers and then divide the sum by $n$. For two numbers, the number that lies halfway between them is their average.

## EXAMPLE 5 Finding the Arithmetic Mean (Average)

Find the rational number halfway between $\frac{2}{3}$ and $\frac{5}{6}$ (that is, their arithmetic mean, or average).

**SOLUTION**

First, find their sum.

$$\frac{2}{3} + \frac{5}{6} = \frac{4}{6} + \frac{5}{6} = \frac{9}{6} = \frac{3}{2}$$ Find a common denominator.

Now divide by 2.

$$\frac{3}{2} \div 2 = \frac{3}{2} \cdot \frac{1}{2} = \frac{3}{4}$$ To divide, multiply by the reciprocal.

The number $\frac{3}{4}$ is halfway between $\frac{2}{3}$ and $\frac{5}{6}$.

**TABLE 3**

| Year | Number (in thousands) |
|---|---|
| 1998 | 16,211 |
| 1999 | 16,477 |
| 2000 | 16,258 |
| 2001 | 16,289 |
| 2002 | 15,979 |
| 2003 | 15,776 |

*Source:* U.S. Bureau of Labor Statistics.

### EXAMPLE 6 Finding the Arithmetic Mean (Average)

Table 3 shows the number of labor union or employee association members, in thousands, for the years 1998–2003. What is the average number, in thousands, for this six-year period?

**SOLUTION**

To find this average, divide the sum by 6.

$$\frac{16{,}211 + 16{,}477 + 16{,}258 + 16{,}289 + 15{,}979 + 15{,}776}{6} = \frac{96{,}990}{6} = 16{,}165$$

The average number of workers for the six-year period is 16,165 thousand (or 16,165,000).

The computation in Example 6 is shown here.

It is also true that between any two *real* numbers there is another *real* number. Thus, we say that the set of real numbers is dense.

## Decimal Form of Rational Numbers

We have discussed rational numbers in the form of quotients of integers. Rational numbers can also be expressed as decimals. Decimal numerals have place values that are powers of 10. For example, the decimal numeral 483.039475 is read "four hundred eighty-three and thirty-nine thousand, four hundred seventy-five millionths." The place values are as shown here.

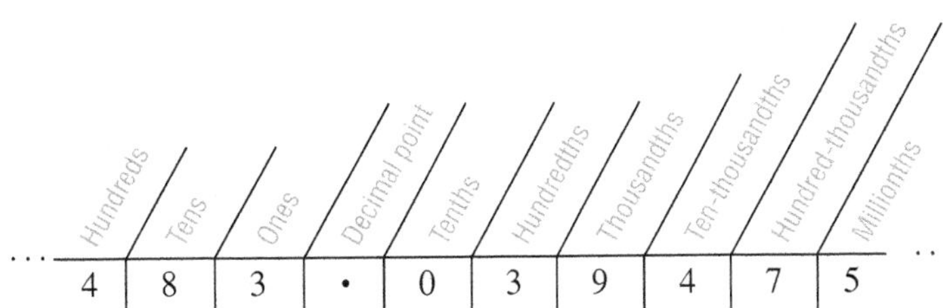


$$\begin{array}{r} .375 \\ 8\overline{)3.000} \\ \underline{24} \\ 60 \\ \underline{56} \\ 40 \\ \underline{40} \\ 0 \end{array} \qquad \begin{array}{r} .3636\ldots \\ 11\overline{)4.00000\ldots} \\ \underline{33} \\ 70 \\ \underline{66} \\ 40 \\ \underline{33} \\ 70 \\ \underline{66} \\ 40 \\ \vdots \end{array}$$

Given a rational number in the form $\frac{a}{b}$, it can be expressed as a decimal most easily by entering it into a calculator. For example, to write $\frac{3}{8}$ as a decimal, enter 3, then enter the operation of division, then enter 8. Press the equals key to find the following equivalence.

$$\frac{3}{8} = .375$$

This same result may be obtained by long division, as shown in the margin. By this result, the rational number $\frac{3}{8}$ is the same as the decimal .375. A decimal such as .375, which stops, is called a **terminating decimal.** Other examples of terminating decimals are

$$\frac{1}{4} = .25, \quad \frac{7}{10} = .7, \quad \text{and} \quad \frac{89}{1000} = .089. \quad \text{Terminating decimals}$$

Not all rational numbers can be represented by terminating decimals. For example, convert $\frac{4}{11}$ into a decimal by dividing 11 into 4 using a calculator. The display shows

$$.3636363636, \quad \text{or perhaps} \quad .363636364.$$

However, we see that the long division process, shown in the margin, indicates that we will actually get .3636 . . . , with the digits 36 repeating over and over indefinitely.

```
2/3
      .6666666667
```

While 2/3 has a repeating decimal representation ($2/3 = .\overline{6}$), the calculator rounds off in the final decimal place displayed.

To indicate this, we write a bar (called a *vinculum*) over the "block" of digits that repeats. Therefore, we can write

$$\frac{4}{11} = .\overline{36}.$$

A decimal such as $.\overline{36}$, which continues indefinitely, is called a **repeating decimal.** Other examples of repeating decimals are

$$\frac{5}{11} = .\overline{45}, \quad \frac{1}{3} = .\overline{3}, \quad \text{and} \quad \frac{5}{6} = .8\overline{3}.$$ Repeating decimals

Because of the limitations of the display of a calculator, and because some rational numbers have repeating decimals, it is important to be able to interpret calculator results accordingly when obtaining repeating decimals.

```
5/11
      .4545454545
1/3
      .3333333333
5/6
      .8333333333
```

Although only ten decimal digits are shown, all three fractions have decimals that repeat endlessly.

While we shall distinguish between *terminating* and *repeating* decimals in this book, some mathematicians prefer to consider all rational numbers as repeating decimals. This can be justified by thinking this way: if the division process leads to a remainder of 0, then zeros repeat without end in the decimal form. For example, we can consider the decimal form of $\frac{3}{4}$ as follows.

$$\frac{3}{4} = .75\overline{0}$$

By considering the possible remainders that may be obtained when converting a quotient of integers to a decimal, we can draw an important conclusion about the decimal form of rational numbers. If the remainder is never zero, the division will produce a repeating decimal. This happens because each step of the division process must produce a remainder that is less than the divisor. Since the number of different possible remainders is less than the divisor, the remainders must eventually begin to repeat. This makes the digits of the quotient repeat, producing a repeating decimal.

### Decimal Representation of Rational Numbers

Any rational number can be expressed as either a terminating decimal or a repeating decimal.

**Simon Stevin** (1548–1620) worked as a bookkeeper in Belgium and became an engineer in the Netherlands army. He is usually given credit for the development of **decimals.**

To determine whether the decimal form of a quotient of integers will terminate or repeat, we use the following rule.

### Criteria for Terminating and Repeating Decimals

A rational number $\frac{a}{b}$ in lowest terms results in a **terminating decimal** if the only prime factor of the denominator is 2 or 5 (or both).

A rational number $\frac{a}{b}$ in lowest terms results in a **repeating decimal** if a prime other than 2 or 5 appears in the prime factorization of the denominator.

**To find a baseball player's batting average,** we divide the number of hits by the number of al-bats. A surprising paradox exists concerning averages; it is possible for Player *A* to have a higher batting average than Player *B* in each of two successive years, yet for the two-year period, Player *B* can have a higher total batting average. Look at the chart.

| Year | Player *A* | Player *B* |
|---|---|---|
| 1998 | $\frac{20}{40} = .500$ | $\frac{90}{200} = .450$ |
| 1999 | $\frac{60}{200} = .300$ | $\frac{10}{40} = .250$ |
| Two-year total | $\frac{80}{240} = .333$ | $\frac{100}{240} = .417$ |

In both individual years, Player *A* had a higher average, but for the two-year period, Player *B* had the higher average. This is an example of **Simpson's paradox** from statistics.

```
.437▸Frac
         437/1000
8.2▸Frac
             41/5
```

The results of Example 8 are supported in this screen.

Justification of this rule is based on the fact that the prime factors of 10 are 2 and 5, and the decimal system uses ten as its base.

## EXAMPLE 7 Determining Whether a Decimal Terminates or Repeats

Without actually dividing, determine whether the decimal form of the given rational number terminates or repeats.

**(a)** $\frac{7}{8}$ **(b)** $\frac{13}{150}$ **(c)** $\frac{6}{75}$

**SOLUTION**

**(a)** The rational number $\frac{7}{8}$ is in lowest terms. Its denominator is 8, and since 8 factors as $2^3$, the decimal form will terminate. No primes other than 2 or 5 divide the denominator.

**(b)** The rational number $\frac{13}{150}$ is in lowest terms with denominator $150 = 2 \cdot 3 \cdot 5^2$. Since 3 appears as a prime factor of the denominator, the decimal form will repeat.

**(c)** First write the rational number $\frac{6}{75}$ in lowest terms.

$$\frac{6}{75} = \frac{2}{25} \quad \text{Denominator is 25.}$$

Since $25 = 5^2$, the decimal form will terminate.

We have seen that a rational number will be represented by either a terminating or a repeating decimal. Must a terminating decimal or a repeating decimal represent a rational number? The answer is *yes*. For example, the terminating decimal .6 represents a rational number.

$$.6 = \frac{6}{10} = \frac{3}{5}$$

## EXAMPLE 8 Writing Terminating Decimals as Quotients of Integers

Write each terminating decimal as a quotient of integers.

**(a)** .437 **(b)** 8.2

**SOLUTION**

**(a)** $.437 = \frac{437}{1000}$ Read as "four hundred thirty-seven thousandths" and then write as a fraction.

**(b)** $8.2 = 8 + \frac{2}{10} = \frac{82}{10} = \frac{41}{5}$ Read as a decimal, write as a sum, and then add.

Repeating decimals cannot be converted into quotients of integers quite so quickly.

## EXAMPLE 9 Writing a Repeating Decimal as a Quotient of Integers

Find a quotient of two integers equal to $.\overline{85}$.

**SOLUTION**

***Step 1*** Let $x = .\overline{85}$, so $x = .858585\ldots$.

$1 = .999999999999...$

**Terminating or Repeating?**

One of the most baffling truths of elementary mathematics is the following:

$$1 = .9999....$$

Most people believe that $.\overline{9}$ has to be less than 1, but this is not the case. The following argument shows why. Let $x = .9999....$ Then

$$\begin{aligned} 10x &= 9.9999... \\ x &= \phantom{9}.9999... \\ \hline 9x &= 9 && \text{Subtract.} \\ x &= 1. && \text{Divide.} \end{aligned}$$

Therefore, $1 = .9999....$ Similarly, it can be shown that any terminating decimal can be represented as a repeating decimal with an endless string of 9s. For example, $.5 = .49999...$ and $2.6 = 2.59999....$ This is a way of justifying that any rational number may be represented as a repeating decimal.

***Step 2*** Multiply both sides of the equation $x = .858585...$ by 100. (Use 100 since there are two digits in the part that repeats, and $100 = 10^2$.)

$$\begin{aligned} x &= .858585... \\ 100x &= 100(.858585...) \\ 100x &= 85.858585... \end{aligned}$$

***Step 3*** Subtract the expressions in Step 1 from the final expressions in Step 2.

$$\begin{aligned} 100x &= 85.858585... && \text{(Recall that } x = 1x \text{ and} \\ x &= \phantom{85}.858585... && 100x - x = 99x.) \\ \hline 99x &= 85 && \text{Subtract.} \end{aligned}$$

***Step 4*** Solve the equation $99x = 85$ by dividing both sides by 99.

$$\begin{aligned} 99x &= 85 \\ \frac{99x}{99} &= \frac{85}{99} && \text{Divide by 99.} \\ x &= \frac{85}{99} && \frac{99x}{99} = x \\ .\overline{85} &= \frac{85}{99} && x = .\overline{85} \end{aligned}$$

When checking with a calculator, remember that the calculator will only show a finite number of decimal places and may round off in the final decimal place shown. ■

## 6.3 EXERCISES

*Choose the expression(s) that is (are) equivalent to the given rational number.*

**1.** $\frac{4}{8}$

**A.** $\frac{1}{2}$ **B.** $\frac{8}{4}$ **C.** $.5$
**D.** $.5\overline{0}$ **E.** $.\overline{55}$

**2.** $\frac{2}{3}$

**A.** $.67$ **B.** $.\overline{6}$ **C.** $\frac{20}{30}$
**D.** $.666...$ **E.** $.6$

**3.** $\frac{5}{9}$

**A.** $.56$ **B.** $.55$ **C.** $.\overline{5}$
**D.** $\frac{9}{5}$ **E.** $1\frac{4}{5}$

**4.** $\frac{1}{4}$

**A.** $.25$ **B.** $.24\overline{9}$ **C.** $\frac{25}{100}$
**D.** $4$ **E.** $\frac{10}{400}$

*Use the fundamental property of rational numbers to write each fraction in lowest terms.*

**5.** $\frac{16}{48}$ **6.** $\frac{21}{28}$

**7.** $-\frac{15}{35}$ **8.** $-\frac{8}{48}$

*Use the fundamental property to write each fraction in three other ways.*

**9.** $\frac{3}{8}$ **10.** $\frac{9}{10}$

**11.** $-\frac{5}{7}$ **12.** $-\frac{7}{12}$

**13.** Write a fraction in lowest terms that represents the portion of each figure that is in color.

(a)

(b)

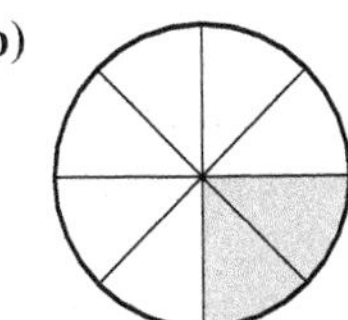

(c)

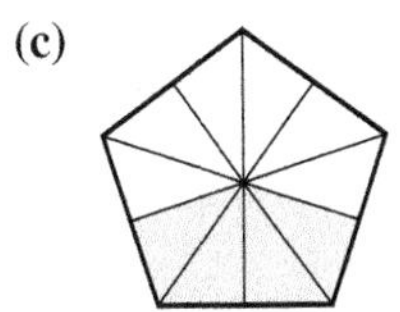

(d)

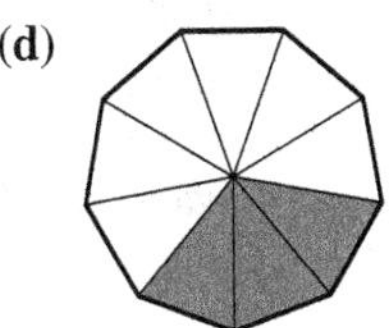

**14.** Write a fraction in lowest terms that represents the region described.

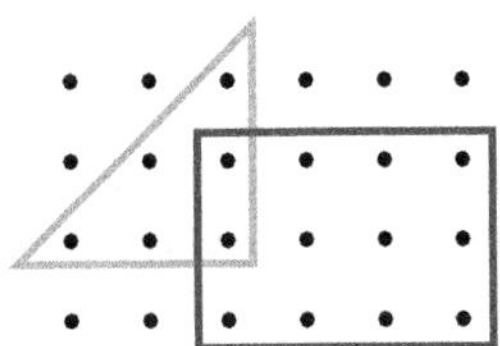

(a) the dots in the rectangle as a part of the dots in the entire figure

(b) the dots in the triangle as a part of the dots in the entire figure

(c) the dots in the rectangle as a part of the dots in the union of the triangle and the rectangle

(d) the dots in the intersection of the triangle and the rectangle as a part of the dots in the union of the triangle and the rectangle

**15.** Refer to the figure for Exercise 14 and write a description of the region that is represented by the fraction $\frac{1}{12}$.

**16.** ***Batting Averages*** In a softball league, the first six games produced the following results: Greg Tobin got 8 hits in 20 at-bats, and Jason Jordan got 12 hits in 30 at-bats. Which player (if either) had the higher batting average?

**17.** ***Batting Averages*** After ten games, the statistics at the top of the next column were obtained.

| Player | At-bats | Hits | Home Runs |
|---|---|---|---|
| Anne Kelly | 40 | 9 | 2 |
| Christine O'Brien | 36 | 12 | 3 |
| Joanne Ha | 11 | 5 | 1 |
| Otis Taylor | 16 | 8 | 0 |
| Carol Britz | 20 | 10 | 2 |

Answer each of the following, using estimation skills as necessary.

(a) Which player got a hit in exactly $\frac{1}{3}$ of his or her at-bats?

(b) Which player got a hit in just less than $\frac{1}{2}$ of his or her at-bats?

(c) Which player got a home run in just less than $\frac{1}{10}$ of his or her at-bats?

(d) Which player got a hit in just less than $\frac{1}{4}$ of his or her at-bats?

(e) Which two players got hits in exactly the same fractional parts of their at-bats? What was the fractional part, reduced to lowest terms?

**18.** Refer to the margin note discussing the use of common fractions on early U.S. copper coinage. The photo here shows an error near the bottom that occurred on an 1802 large cent. Discuss the error and how it represents a mathematical impossibility.

*Perform the indicated operations and express answers in lowest terms. Use the order of operations as necessary.*

**19.** $\frac{3}{8} + \frac{1}{8}$ **20.** $\frac{7}{9} + \frac{1}{9}$

**21.** $\frac{5}{16} + \frac{7}{12}$ **22.** $\frac{1}{15} + \frac{7}{18}$

**23.** $\frac{2}{3} - \frac{7}{8}$ **24.** $\frac{13}{20} - \frac{5}{12}$

**25.** $\frac{5}{8} - \frac{3}{14}$ **26.** $\frac{19}{15} - \frac{7}{12}$

**27.** $\frac{3}{4} \cdot \frac{9}{5}$ **28.** $\frac{3}{8} \cdot \frac{2}{7}$

29. $-\frac{2}{3} \cdot -\frac{5}{8}$

30. $-\frac{2}{4} \cdot \frac{3}{9}$

31. $\frac{5}{12} \div \frac{15}{4}$

32. $\frac{15}{16} \div \frac{30}{8}$

33. $-\frac{9}{16} \div -\frac{3}{8}$

34. $-\frac{3}{8} \div \frac{5}{4}$

35. $\left(\frac{1}{3} \div \frac{1}{2}\right) + \frac{5}{6}$

36. $\frac{2}{5} \div \left(-\frac{4}{5} \div \frac{3}{10}\right)$

37. ***Recipe for Grits*** The following chart appears on a package of Quaker® Quick Grits.

| | Microwave | Stove Top | | |
|---|---|---|---|---|
| **Servings** | **1** | **1** | **4** | **6** |
| Water | $\frac{3}{4}$ cup | 1 cup | 3 cups | 4 cups |
| Grits | 3 Tbsp | 3 Tbsp | $\frac{3}{4}$ cup | 1 cup |
| Salt (optional) | dash | dash | $\frac{1}{4}$ tsp | $\frac{1}{2}$ tsp |

(a) How many cups of water would be needed for 6 microwave servings?
(b) How many cups of grits would be needed for 5 stove-top servings? (*Hint:* 5 is halfway between 4 and 6.)

38. ***U.S. Immigrants*** More than 8 million immigrants were admitted to the United States during the first eight years of the 1990s. The circle graph gives the fractional number from each region of birth for these immigrants.

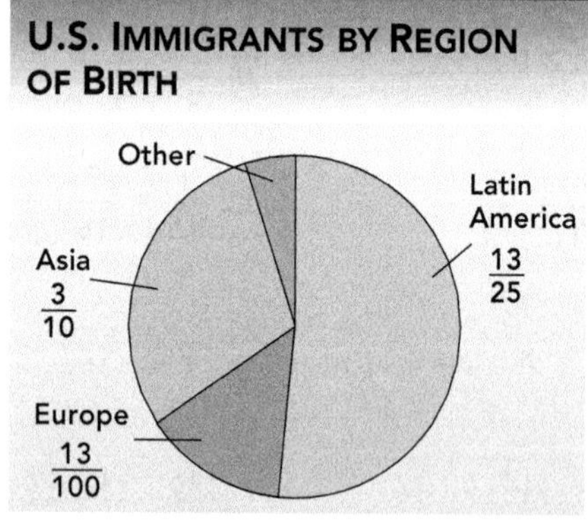


*Source:* U.S. Census Bureau

(a) What fractional part of the immigrants were from other regions?
(b) What fractional part of the immigrants were from Latin America or Asia?
(c) How many (in millions) were from Europe?

*The* **mixed number** $2\frac{5}{8}$ *represents the sum* $2 + \frac{5}{8}$. *We can convert* $2\frac{5}{8}$ *to a fraction as follows:*

$$2\frac{5}{8} = 2 + \frac{5}{8} = \frac{2}{1} + \frac{5}{8} = \frac{16}{8} + \frac{5}{8} = \frac{21}{8}.$$

*The fraction* $\frac{21}{8}$ *can be converted back to a mixed number by dividing 8 into 21. The quotient is 2, the remainder is 5, and the divisor is 8.*

*Convert each mixed number to a fraction, and convert each fraction to a mixed number.*

39. $4\frac{1}{3}$

40. $3\frac{7}{8}$

41. $2\frac{9}{10}$

42. $\frac{18}{5}$

43. $\frac{27}{4}$

44. $\frac{19}{3}$

*It is possible to add mixed numbers by first converting them to fractions, adding, and then converting the sum back to a mixed number. For example,*

$$2\frac{1}{3} + 3\frac{1}{2} = \frac{7}{3} + \frac{7}{2} = \frac{14}{6} + \frac{21}{6} = \frac{35}{6} = 5\frac{5}{6}.$$

*The other operations with mixed numbers may be performed in a similar manner.*

*Perform each operation and express your answer as a mixed number.*

45. $3\frac{1}{4} + 2\frac{7}{8}$

46. $6\frac{1}{5} - 2\frac{7}{15}$

47. $-4\frac{7}{8} \cdot 3\frac{2}{3}$

48. $-4\frac{1}{6} \div 1\frac{2}{3}$

*Solve each problem.*

49. ***Socket Wrench Measurements*** A hardware store sells a 40-piece socket wrench set. The measure of the largest socket is $\frac{3}{4}$ in., while the measure of the smallest socket is $\frac{3}{16}$ in. What is the difference between these measures?

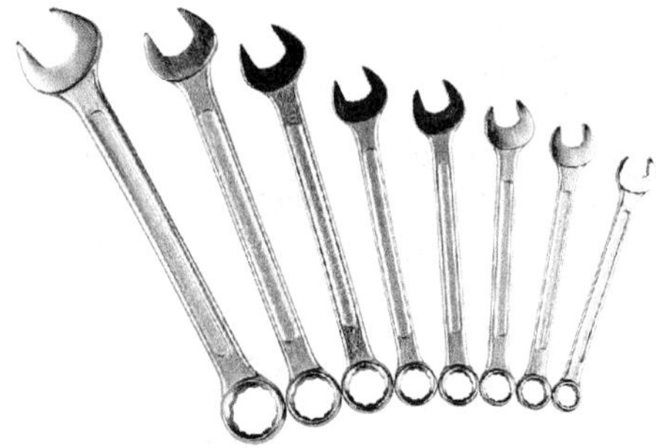

50. ***Swiss Cheese Hole Sizes*** Under existing standards, most of the holes in Swiss cheese must have diameters between $\frac{11}{16}$ and $\frac{13}{16}$ in. To accommodate new high-speed slicing machines, the USDA wants to reduce the minimum size to $\frac{3}{8}$ in. How much smaller is $\frac{3}{8}$ in. than $\frac{11}{16}$ in.? (*Source:* U.S. Department of Agriculture.)

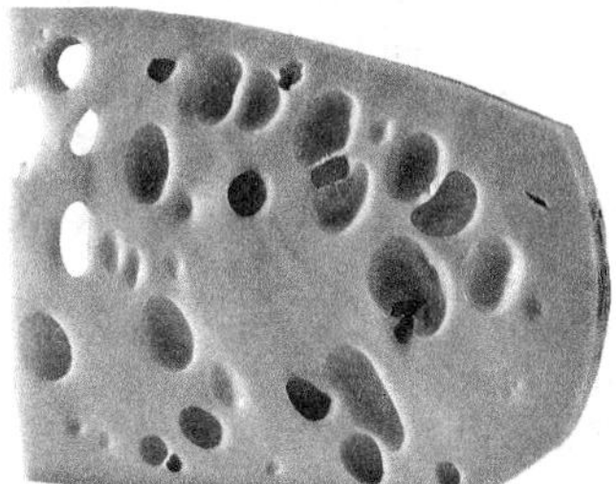

*A quotient of quantities containing fractions (with denominator not zero) is called a* **complex fraction.** *There are two methods that are used to simplify a complex fraction.*

***Method 1*** *Simplify the numerator and denominator separately. Then rewrite as a division problem, and proceed as you would when dividing fractions.*

***Method 2*** *Multiply both the numerator and denominator by the least common denominator of all the fractions found within the complex fraction. (This is, in effect, multiplying the fraction by 1, which does not change its value.) Apply the distributive property, if necessary, and simplify.*

*Use one of the methods above to simplify each complex fraction.*

51. $\dfrac{\frac{1}{2}+\frac{1}{4}}{\frac{1}{2}-\frac{1}{4}}$ 52. $\dfrac{\frac{2}{3}+\frac{1}{6}}{\frac{2}{3}-\frac{1}{6}}$ 53. $\dfrac{\frac{5}{8}-\frac{1}{4}}{\frac{1}{8}+\frac{3}{4}}$

54. $\dfrac{\frac{3}{16}-\frac{1}{2}}{\frac{5}{16}+\frac{1}{8}}$ 55. $\dfrac{\frac{7}{11}+\frac{3}{10}}{\frac{1}{11}-\frac{9}{10}}$ 56. $\dfrac{\frac{11}{15}+\frac{1}{9}}{\frac{13}{15}-\frac{2}{3}}$

*The expressions in Exercises 57 and 58 are called* ***continued fractions.*** *Write each in the form $\frac{p}{q}$ reduced to lowest terms. (Hint: Start at the bottom and work up.)*

57. $2+\dfrac{1}{1+\dfrac{1}{3+\dfrac{1}{2}}}$ 58. $4+\dfrac{1}{2+\dfrac{1}{1+\dfrac{1}{3}}}$

*Find the rational number halfway between the two given rational numbers.*

59. $\frac{1}{2}, \frac{3}{4}$ 60. $\frac{1}{3}, \frac{5}{12}$ 61. $\frac{3}{5}, \frac{2}{3}$

62. $\frac{7}{12}, \frac{5}{8}$ 63. $-\frac{2}{3}, -\frac{5}{6}$ 64. $-3, -\frac{5}{2}$

*Solve each problem.*

65. ***Average Annual Salary*** The table shows the average annual salary in the eight highest-paying metropolitan areas in the United States. Find the average of these amounts to the nearest dollar.

| Metropolitan Area | Average Annual Salary |
|---|---|
| San Jose, CA | \$63,056 |
| New York, NY | \$57,708 |
| San Francisco, CA | \$56,602 |
| New Haven, CT, area | \$51,170 |
| Middlesex, NJ, area | \$50,457 |
| Jersey City, NJ | \$49,562 |
| Newark, NJ | \$48,781 |
| Washington, DC, area | \$48,430 |

*Source:* Bureau of Labor Statistics.

66. ***Adoption of Chinese Babies*** Since 2000, the country of China has been the most popular foreign country for U.S. adoptions. Find the average annual number of adoptions during the period 2000–2004, based on the figures in the table.

| Year | Number of Adoptions |
|---|---|
| 2000 | 4943 |
| 2001 | 4629 |
| 2002 | 6062 |
| 2003 | 6638 |
| 2004 | 7033 |

*Source:* Department of Homeland Security, Office of Immigration Statistics.

*In the March 1973 issue of* The Mathematics Teacher *there appeared an article by Laurence Sherzer, an eighth-grade mathematics teacher, that immortalized one of his students, Robert McKay. The class was studying the density property and Sherzer was explaining how to find a rational number between two given positive rational numbers by finding the average. McKay pointed out that there was no need to go to all that trouble. To find a number (not necessarily their average) between two positive rational numbers $\frac{a}{b}$ and $\frac{c}{d}$, he claimed, simply add the numerators and add the denominators. Much to Sherzer's surprise, this method really does work.*

*For example, to find a rational number between $\frac{1}{3}$ and $\frac{1}{4}$, add $1 + 1 = 2$ to get the numerator and $3 + 4 = 7$ to get the denominator. Therefore, by* **McKay's theorem,** *$\frac{2}{7}$ is between $\frac{1}{3}$ and $\frac{1}{4}$. Sherzer provided a proof of this method in the article.*

*Use* McKay's theorem *to find a rational number between the two given rational numbers.*

**67.** $\frac{5}{6}$ and $\frac{9}{13}$ **68.** $\frac{10}{11}$ and $\frac{13}{19}$

**69.** $\frac{4}{13}$ and $\frac{9}{16}$ **70.** $\frac{6}{11}$ and $\frac{13}{14}$

**71.** 2 and 3 **72.** 3 and 4

**73.** Apply McKay's theorem to any pair of consecutive integers, and make a conjecture about what always happens in this case.

**74.** Explain in your own words how to find the rational number that is one-fourth of the way between two different rational numbers.

*Convert each rational number into either a repeating or a terminating decimal. Use a calculator if your instructor so allows.*

**75.** $\frac{3}{4}$ **76.** $\frac{7}{8}$ **77.** $\frac{3}{16}$ **78.** $\frac{9}{32}$

**79.** $\frac{3}{11}$ **80.** $\frac{9}{11}$ **81.** $\frac{2}{7}$ **82.** $\frac{11}{15}$

*Convert each terminating decimal into a quotient of integers. Write each in lowest terms.*

**83.** .4 **84.** .9 **85.** .85

**86.** .105 **87.** .934 **88.** .7984

*Use the method of Example 7 to decide whether each rational number would yield a repeating or a terminating decimal. (Hint: Write in lowest terms before trying to decide.)*

**89.** $\frac{8}{15}$ **90.** $\frac{8}{35}$ **91.** $\frac{13}{125}$

**92.** $\frac{3}{24}$ **93.** $\frac{22}{55}$ **94.** $\frac{24}{75}$

**95.** Follow through on all parts of this exercise in order.
  **(a)** Find the decimal for $\frac{1}{3}$.
  **(b)** Find the decimal for $\frac{2}{3}$.
  **(c)** By adding the decimal expressions obtained in parts (a) and (b), obtain a decimal expression for $\frac{1}{3} + \frac{2}{3} = \frac{3}{3} = 1$.
  **(d)** Does your result seem bothersome? Read the margin note on terminating and repeating decimals in this section, which refers to this idea.

**96.** It is a fact that $\frac{1}{3} = .333\ldots$. Multiply both sides of this equation by 3. Does your answer bother you? See the margin note on terminating and repeating decimals in this section.

*Use the method of Example 9 to write each rational number as a quotient of integers in lowest terms.*

**97.** **(a)** .8 **(b)** $.7\overline{9}$

**98.** **(a)** .75 **(b)** $.74\overline{9}$

**99.** **(a)** .66 **(b)** $.65\overline{9}$

**100.** Based on your results in Exercises 97–99, predict the lowest terms form of the rational number $.4\overline{9}$.

## 6.4 Irrational Numbers and Decimal Representation

**Definition and Basic Concepts • Irrationality of $\sqrt{2}$ and Proof by Contradiction • Operations with Square Roots • The Irrational Numbers $\pi$, $\phi$, and $e$**

**Definition and Basic Concepts** In the previous section, we saw that every rational number has a decimal form that terminates or repeats. Also, every repeating or terminating decimal represents a rational number. Some decimals, however, neither repeat nor terminate. For example, the decimal

**Tsu Ch'ung-chih** (about 500 A.D.), the Chinese mathematician honored on the above stamp, investigated the digits of $\pi$. **Aryabhata,** his Indian contemporary, gave 3.1416 as the value.

$$.102001000200001000002\ldots$$

does not terminate and does not repeat. (It is true that there is a pattern in this decimal, but no single block of digits repeats indefinitely.)*

### Irrational Numbers

**Irrational numbers** $= \{x \mid x$ is a number represented by a nonrepeating, nonterminating decimal$\}$.

As the name implies, an irrational number cannot be represented as a quotient of integers.

The decimal number mentioned above is an irrational number. Other irrational numbers include $\sqrt{2}$, $\frac{1+\sqrt{5}}{2}$ ($\phi$, from Section 5.5), $\pi$ (the ratio of the circumference of a circle to its diameter), and $e$ (a constant *approximately equal to* 2.71828). There are infinitely many irrational numbers.

**The irrational number $\sqrt{2}$** was discovered by the Pythagoreans in about 500 B.C. This discovery was a great setback to their philosophy that everything is based upon the whole numbers. The Pythagoreans kept their findings secret, and legend has it that members of the group who divulged this discovery were sent out to sea, and, according to Proclus (410–485), "perished in a shipwreck, to a man."

**Irrationality of $\sqrt{2}$ and Proof by Contradiction** Figure 12 illustrates how a point with coordinate $\sqrt{2}$ can be located on a number line.

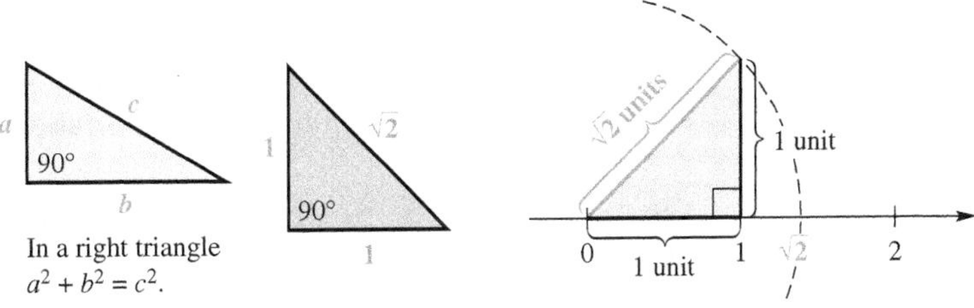


**FIGURE 12**

The proof that $\sqrt{2}$ is irrational is a classic example of a **proof by contradiction.** We begin by assuming that $\sqrt{2}$ is rational, which leads to a contradiction, or absurdity. The method is also called **reductio ad absurdum** (Latin for "reduce to the absurd"). In order to understand the proof, we consider three preliminary facts:

1. When a rational number is written in lowest terms, the greatest common factor of the numerator and denominator is 1.
2. If an integer is even, then it has 2 as a factor and may be written in the form $2k$, where $k$ is an integer.
3. If a perfect square is even, then its square root is even.

*In this section, we will assume that the digits of a number such as this continue indefinitely in the pattern established. The next few digits would be 000000100000002, and so on.

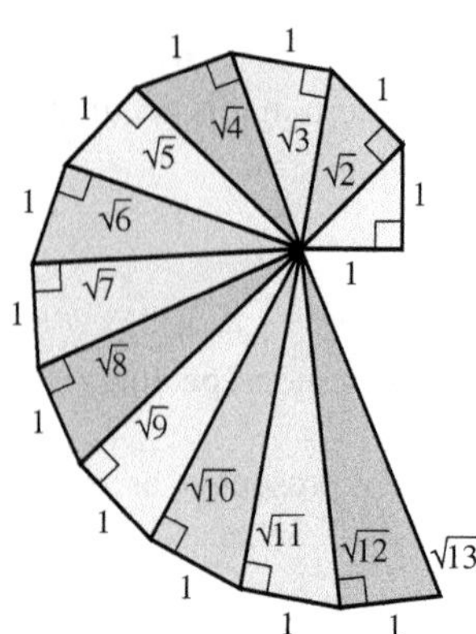


**An interesting way** to represent the lengths corresponding to $\sqrt{2}$, $\sqrt{3}$, $\sqrt{4}$, $\sqrt{5}$, and so on, is shown in the figure. Use the **Pythagorean theorem** to verify the lengths in the figure.

### THEOREM

*Statement:* $\sqrt{2}$ is an irrational number.
*Proof:* Assume that $\sqrt{2}$ is a rational number. Then by definition,

$$\sqrt{2} = \frac{p}{q}, \quad \text{for some integers } p \text{ and } q.$$

Furthermore, assume that $\frac{p}{q}$ is the form of $\sqrt{2}$ that is written in lowest terms, so the greatest common factor of $p$ and $q$ is 1.

$$2 = \frac{p^2}{q^2} \quad \text{Square both sides of the equation.}$$

$$2q^2 = p^2 \quad \text{Multiply by } q^2.$$

This last equation indicates that 2 is a factor of $p^2$. So $p^2$ is even, and thus $p$ is even. Since $p$ is even, it may be written in the form $2k$, where $k$ is an integer.

Now, substitute $2k$ for $p$ in the last equation and simplify:

$$2q^2 = (2k)^2 \quad \text{Let } p = 2k.$$

$$2q^2 = 4k^2 \quad (2k)^2 = 2k \cdot 2k = 4k^2$$

$$q^2 = 2k^2. \quad \text{Divide by 2.}$$

Since 2 is a factor of $q^2$, $q^2$ must be even, and thus $q$ must be even. This leads to a contradiction: $p$ and $q$ cannot both be even because they would then have a common factor of 2, although it was assumed that their greatest common factor is 1.

Therefore, since the original assumption that $\sqrt{2}$ is rational has led to a contradiction, it must follow that $\sqrt{2}$ is irrational. ∎

**Operations with Square Roots** In everyday mathematical work, nearly all of our calculations deal with rational numbers, usually in decimal form. In our study of mathematics, however, we must sometimes perform operations with irrational numbers, and in many instances, the irrational numbers are square roots. Some examples are

$$\sqrt{2}, \quad \sqrt{3}, \quad \text{and} \quad \sqrt{13}. \quad \text{Square roots that are irrational.}$$

However, not all square roots are irrational. For example,

$$\sqrt{4} = 2, \quad \sqrt{36} = 6, \quad \text{and} \quad \sqrt{100} = 10 \quad \text{Square roots that are rational.}$$

are all rational numbers. If $n$ is a positive integer that is not the square of an integer, then $\sqrt{n}$ is an irrational number.

```
√(2)
      1.414213562
√(6)
      2.449489743
√(1949)
      44.14748011
```

These are calculator approximations of irrational numbers.

A calculator with a square root key can give approximations of square roots of numbers that are not perfect squares. To show that they are approximations, we use the ≈ symbol to indicate "is approximately equal to." Some such calculator approximations are as follows:

$$\sqrt{2} \approx 1.414213562, \quad \sqrt{6} \approx 2.449489743, \quad \text{and} \quad \sqrt{1949} \approx 44.14748011.$$

Recall that $\sqrt{a}$, for $a \geq 0$, is the nonnegative number whose square is $a$; that is, $\left(\sqrt{a}\right)^2 = a$. We will now look at some simple operations with square roots.

Notice that

$$\sqrt{4} \cdot \sqrt{9} = 2 \cdot 3 = 6$$

and

$$\sqrt{4 \cdot 9} = \sqrt{36} = 6.$$

Thus, $\sqrt{4} \cdot \sqrt{9} = \sqrt{4 \cdot 9}$. This is a particular case of the following product rule.

**Product Rule for Square Roots**

For nonnegative real numbers $a$ and $b$,

$$\sqrt{a} \cdot \sqrt{b} = \sqrt{a \cdot b}.$$

Just as every rational number $\frac{a}{b}$ can be written in simplest (lowest) terms (by using the fundamental property of rational numbers), every square root radical has a simplified form.

**Conditions Necessary for the Simplified Form of a Square Root Radical**

A square root radical is in **simplified form** if the following three conditions are met.

1. The number under the radical (**radicand**) has no factor (except 1) that is a perfect square.
2. The radicand has no fractions.
3. No denominator contains a radical.

```
√(27)=3√(3)
                1
√(27)
      5.196152423
3√(3)
      5.196152423
```

The 1 after the first line indicates that the equality is true. The calculator also shows the same approximations for $\sqrt{27}$ and $3\sqrt{3}$ in the second and third answers. (See Example 1.)

### EXAMPLE 1 Simplifying a Square Root Radical (Product Rule)

Simplify $\sqrt{27}$.

**SOLUTION**

Since 9 is a factor of 27 and 9 is a perfect square, $\sqrt{27}$ is not in simplified form. The first condition of simplified form is not met. We simplify as follows.

$$\begin{aligned} \sqrt{27} &= \sqrt{9 \cdot 3} \\ &= \sqrt{9} \cdot \sqrt{3} && \text{Use the product rule.} \\ &= 3\sqrt{3} && \sqrt{9} = 3, \text{ since } 3^2 = 9. \end{aligned}$$

Expressions such as $\sqrt{27}$ and $3\sqrt{3}$ are *exact values* of the square root of 27. If we use the square root key of a calculator, we find

$$\sqrt{27} \approx 5.196152423.$$

If we find $\sqrt{3}$ and then multiply the result by 3, we get

$$3\sqrt{3} \approx 3(1.732050808) \approx 5.196152423.$$

Notice that these approximations are the same, as we would expect. (Due to various methods of calculating, there may be a discrepancy in the final digit of the calculation.) Understand, however, that the calculator approximations do not actually

**The radical symbol** above comes from the Latin word for root, *radix.* It was first used by **Leonardo of Pisa** (Fibonacci) in 1220. The sixteenth-century German symbol we use today probably is also derived from the letter r.

*prove* that the two numbers are equal, but only strongly suggest equality. The work done in Example 1 actually provides the mathematical justification that they are indeed equal.

A rule similar to the product rule exists for quotients.

### Quotient Rule for Square Roots

For nonnegative real numbers $a$ and positive real numbers $b$,

$$\frac{\sqrt{a}}{\sqrt{b}} = \sqrt{\frac{a}{b}}.$$

### EXAMPLE 2 Simplifying Square Root Radicals (Quotient Rule)

Simplify each radical.

(a) $\sqrt{\frac{25}{9}}$ (b) $\sqrt{\frac{3}{4}}$ (c) $\sqrt{\frac{1}{2}}$

**SOLUTION**

**(a)** Because the radicand contains a fraction, the radical expression is not simplified. (See condition 2 of simplified form preceding Example 1.) Use the quotient rule as follows.

$$\sqrt{\frac{25}{9}} = \frac{\sqrt{25}}{\sqrt{9}} = \frac{5}{3}$$

**(b)** $\sqrt{\frac{3}{4}} = \frac{\sqrt{3}}{\sqrt{4}} = \frac{\sqrt{3}}{2}$

**(c)** $\sqrt{\frac{1}{2}} = \frac{\sqrt{1}}{\sqrt{2}} = \frac{1}{\sqrt{2}}$

This expression is not yet in simplified form, since condition 3 of simplified form is not met. To give an equivalent expression with no radical in the denominator, we use a procedure called **rationalizing the denominator.** Multiply $\frac{1}{\sqrt{2}}$ by $\frac{\sqrt{2}}{\sqrt{2}}$, which is a form of 1, the identity element for multiplication.

$$\frac{1}{\sqrt{2}} = \frac{1}{\sqrt{2}} \cdot \frac{\sqrt{2}}{\sqrt{2}} = \frac{\sqrt{2}}{2} \qquad \sqrt{2} \cdot \sqrt{2} = 2$$

The simplified form of $\sqrt{\frac{1}{2}}$ is $\frac{\sqrt{2}}{2}$.

Is $\sqrt{4} + \sqrt{9} = \sqrt{4 + 9}$ a true statement? Computation shows that the answer is *no,* since $\sqrt{4} + \sqrt{9} = 2 + 3 = 5$, while $\sqrt{4 + 9} = \sqrt{13}$, and $5 \neq \sqrt{13}$. ***Square root radicals may be combined, however, if they have the same radicand.*** Such radicals are **like radicals.** We add (and subtract) like radicals using the distributive property.

**EXAMPLE 3 Adding and Subtracting Square Root Radicals**

Add or subtract as indicated.

**(a)** $3\sqrt{6} + 4\sqrt{6}$ **(b)** $\sqrt{18} - \sqrt{32}$

**SOLUTION**

**(a)** Since both terms contain $\sqrt{6}$, they are like radicals, and may be combined.

$$\begin{aligned} 3\sqrt{6} + 4\sqrt{6} &= (3 + 4)\sqrt{6} && \text{Distributive property} \\ &= 7\sqrt{6} && \text{Add.} \end{aligned}$$

**(b)** If we simplify $\sqrt{18}$ and $\sqrt{32}$, then this operation can be performed.

$$\begin{aligned} \sqrt{18} - \sqrt{32} &= \sqrt{9 \cdot 2} - \sqrt{16 \cdot 2} && \text{Factor so that perfect squares are in the radicands.} \\ &= \sqrt{9} \cdot \sqrt{2} - \sqrt{16} \cdot \sqrt{2} && \text{Product rule} \\ &= 3\sqrt{2} - 4\sqrt{2} && \text{Take square roots.} \\ &= (3 - 4)\sqrt{2} && \text{Distributive property} \\ &= -1\sqrt{2} && \text{Subtract.} \\ &= -\sqrt{2} && -1 \cdot a = -a \end{aligned}$$

```
π
       3.141592654
(1+√(5))/2
       1.618033989
e
       2.718281828
```

**FIGURE 13**

From Example 3, we see that like radicals may be added or subtracted by adding or subtracting their coefficients (the numbers by which they are multiplied) and keeping the same radical. For example,

$$9\sqrt{7} + 8\sqrt{7} = 17\sqrt{7} \quad (\text{since } 9 + 8 = 17)$$
$$4\sqrt{3} - 12\sqrt{3} = -8\sqrt{3}, \quad (\text{since } 4 - 12 = -8)$$

and so on.

In the statements of the product and quotient rules for square roots, the radicands could not be negative. While $-\sqrt{2}$ is a real number, for example, $\sqrt{-2}$ is not: there is no real number whose square is $-2$. The same may be said for any negative radicand. In order to handle this situation, mathematicians have extended our number system to include *complex numbers,* discussed in the Extension at the end of this chapter.

**This poem,** dedicated to **Archimedes** ("the immortal Syracusan"), allows us to learn the first 31 digits of the decimal representation of $\pi$. By replacing each word with the number of letters it contains, with a decimal point following the initial 3, the decimal is found. The poem was written by A. C. Orr, and appeared in the *Literary Digest* in 1906.

*Now I, even I, would celebrate*
*In rhymes unapt, the great*
*Immortal Syracusan, rivaled*
*nevermore,*
*Who in his wondrous lore*
*Passed on before,*
*Left men his guidance*
*How to circles mensurate.*

## The Irrational Numbers $\pi$, $\phi$, and e

Figure 13 shows approximations for three of the most interesting and important irrational numbers in mathematics. The first of these, $\pi$, represents the ratio of the circumference of a circle to its diameter. The second, $\phi$, is the Golden Ratio, covered in detail in Section 5.5. Its exact value is $\frac{1+\sqrt{5}}{2}$. The third is $e$, a fundamental number in our universe. It is the base of the *natural exponential* and *natural logarithmic* functions, as seen in Section 8.6. The letter $e$ was chosen to honor Leonhard Euler, who published extensive research on the number in 1746.

**Pi ($\pi$)**

$$\pi \approx 3.141592653589793238462643383279$$

The computation of the digits of $\pi$ has fascinated mathematicians since ancient times. Archimedes was the first to explore it extensively, and mathematicians have

today computed its value to over 1 trillion digits. Yasumasa Kanada of the University of Tokyo and the brothers Gregory and David Chudnovsky are among the foremost of today's pi researchers. The book *A History of π* by Petr Beckmann is a classic, now in its third edition. Numerous Web sites are devoted to the history and methods of computation of pi. Some of them are as follows:

www.joyofpi.com/

www.math.utah.edu/~alfeld/Archimedes/Archimedes.html

www.super-computing.org/

www.pbs.org/wgbh/nova/sciencenow/3210/04.html

One of the methods of computing pi involves the topic of *infinite series,* as seen in Example 4.

## EXAMPLE 4 Computing the Digits of Pi Using an Infinite Series

It is shown in higher mathematics that the *infinite series*

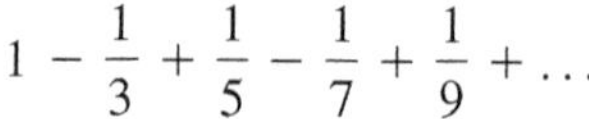

$$1 - \frac{1}{3} + \frac{1}{5} - \frac{1}{7} + \frac{1}{9} + \ldots$$

"converges" to $\frac{\pi}{4}$. That is, as more and more terms are considered, its value becomes closer and closer to $\frac{\pi}{4}$. With a calculator, approximate the value of pi using twenty-one terms of this series.

**SOLUTION**

Figure 14 shows the necessary calculation on the TI-83/84 Plus calculator. The sum of the first twenty-one terms is multiplied by 4, to obtain the approximation

$$3.189184782.$$

(While this is only correct to the first decimal place, better approximations are obtained using more terms of the series.)

Northern Exposure, which ran between 1990 and 1995 on the CBS network, starred Rob Morrow as Dr. Joel Fleischman, a doctor practicing in Alaska. In the episode "Nothing's Perfect" (10/12/92), he meets and falls in love with a mathematician (played by Wendel Meldrum) after accidentally running over her dog. Her area of research is **computation of the decimal digits of pi.** She mentions that a string of eight 8s appears in the decimal relatively early in the expansion. A search at The Pi Searcher (www.angio.net/pi/bigpi/cgi) confirms that this string starts at position 46,663,520 counting from the first digit after the decimal point.

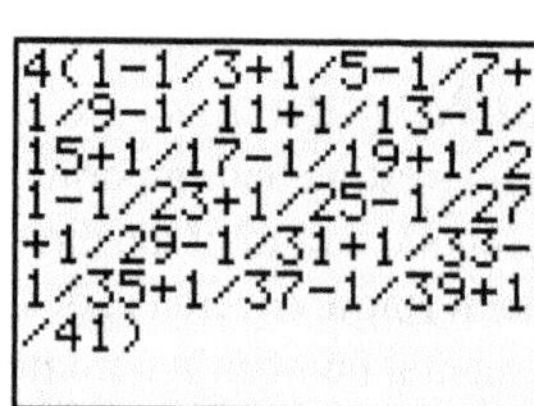


1/9-1/11+1/13-1/
15+1/17-1/19+1/2
1-1/23+1/25-1/27
+1/29-1/31+1/33-
1/35+1/37-1/39+1
/41)
3.189184782

This is a continuation of the previous screen.

**FIGURE 14**

A rectangle that satisfies the condition that the ratio of its length to its width is equal to the ratio of the sum of its length and width to its length is called a **Golden Rectangle.** This ratio is called the **Golden Ratio.** (See Section 5.5.) The exact value of the Golden Ratio is the irrational number $\frac{1+\sqrt{5}}{2}$, and it is represented by the Greek letter $\phi$ (phi).

**Phi ($\phi$)**

$$\phi = \frac{1 + \sqrt{5}}{2} \approx 1.6180339887498948482045868343 65$$

Two readily accessible books on phi are *The Divine Proportion, A Study in Mathematical Beauty* by H. E. Huntley, and the more recent *The Golden Ratio* by Mario Livio. Some popular Web sites devoted to this irrational number are as follows:

www.mcs.surrey.ac.uk/Personal/R.Knott/Fibonacci/

www.goldennumber.net/

www.mathforum.org/dr.math/faq/faq.golden.ratio.html

www.geom.uiuc.edu/~demo5337/s97b/art.htm

In 1767 **J. H. Lambert** proved that $\pi$ is irrational (and thus its decimal will never terminate and never repeat). Nevertheless, the 1897 Indiana state legislature considered a bill that would have *legislated* the value of $\pi$. In one part of the bill, the value was stated to be 4, and in another part, 3.2. Amazingly, the bill passed the House, but the Senate postponed action on the bill indefinitely.

## EXAMPLE 5 Computing the Digits of Phi Using the Fibonacci Sequence

The first twelve terms of the Fibonacci sequence are

$$1, 1, 2, 3, 5, 8, 13, 21, 34, 55, 89, 144.$$

Each term after the first two terms is obtained by adding the two previous terms. Thus, the thirteenth term is $89 + 144 = 233$. As one goes farther and farther out in the sequence, the ratio of a term to its predecessor gets closer and closer to $\phi$. How far out must one go in order to approximate $\phi$ so that the first five decimal places agree?

**SOLUTION**

After 144, the next three Fibonacci numbers are 233, 377, and 610. Figure 15 shows that $\frac{610}{377} \approx 1.618037135$, which agrees with $\phi$ to the fifth decimal place.

```
233/144
       1.618055556
377/233
       1.618025751
610/377
       1.618037135
```

**FIGURE 15**

Most applications of the irrational number $e$ are beyond the scope of this text. However, $e$ is a fundamental constant in mathematics, and if there are intelligent beings elsewhere in the universe, they will no doubt know about this number. If you study Section 8.6, you will encounter it as a base of the important exponential and logarithmic functions.

**e**

$$e \approx 2.7182818284590452353602874713 53$$

The nature of $e$ has made it less understood by the layman than $\pi$ (or even $\phi$, for that matter). The 1994 book *e: The Story of a Number* by Eli Maor has attempted to rectify this situation. These Web sites also give information on $e$:

www.mathforum.org/dr.math/faq/faq.e.html

www-groups.dcs.st-and.ac.uk/~history/HistTopics/e.html

http://antwrp.gsfc.nasa.gov/htmltest/gifcity/e.1mil

www.math.toronto.edu/mathnet/answers/ereal.html

Example 6 illustrates another infinite series, but this one converges to $e$.

### EXAMPLE 6 Computing the Digits of e Using an Infinite Series

The infinite series

$$2 + \frac{1}{1 \cdot 2} + \frac{1}{1 \cdot 2 \cdot 3} + \frac{1}{1 \cdot 2 \cdot 3 \cdot 4} + \cdots$$

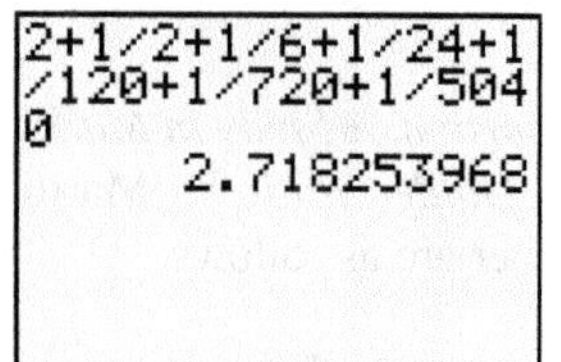


**FIGURE 16**

converges to $e$. Use a calculator to approximate $e$ using the first seven terms of this series.

**SOLUTION**

Figure 16 shows the sum of the first seven terms. (The denominators have all been multiplied out.) The sum is 2.718253968, which agrees with $e$ to four decimal places. This series converges more rapidly than the one for $\pi$ in Example 4.

## 6.4 Exercises

*Identify each number as* rational *or* irrational.

**1.** $\frac{4}{9}$ **2.** $\frac{7}{8}$ **3.** $\sqrt{10}$ **4.** $\sqrt{14}$ **5.** 1.618

**6.** 2.718 **7.** $.\overline{41}$ **8.** $.\overline{32}$ **9.** $\pi$ **10.** $\frac{1 + \sqrt{5}}{2}$

**11.** .878778777877778. . . **12.** $e$ **13.** 3.14159 **14.** $\frac{22}{7}$

**15.** **(a)** Find the sum.

$$\begin{array}{r} .272772777277772\ldots \\ +.616116111611116\ldots \\ \hline \end{array}$$

**(b)** Based on the result of part (a), we can conclude that the sum of two ________ numbers may be a(n) ______ number.

**16.** **(a)** Find the sum.

$$\begin{array}{r} .010110111011110\ldots \\ +.252552555255552\ldots \\ \hline \end{array}$$

**(b)** Based on the result of part (a), we can conclude that the sum of two ________ numbers may be a(n) ________ number.

*Use a calculator to find a rational decimal approximation for each irrational number. Give as many places as your calculator shows.*

**17.** $\sqrt{39}$ **18.** $\sqrt{44}$ **19.** $\sqrt{15.1}$ **20.** $\sqrt{33.6}$

**21.** $\sqrt{884}$ **22.** $\sqrt{643}$ **23.** $\sqrt{\frac{9}{8}}$ **24.** $\sqrt{\frac{6}{5}}$

*Use the methods of Examples 1 and 2 to simplify each expression. Then, use a calculator to approximate both the given expression and the simplified expression. (Both should be the same.)*

**25.** $\sqrt{50}$ **26.** $\sqrt{32}$ **27.** $\sqrt{75}$

**28.** $\sqrt{150}$ **29.** $\sqrt{288}$ **30.** $\sqrt{200}$

**31.** $\frac{5}{\sqrt{6}}$ **32.** $\frac{3}{\sqrt{2}}$ **33.** $\sqrt{\frac{7}{4}}$

**34.** $\sqrt{\frac{8}{9}}$ **35.** $\sqrt{\frac{7}{3}}$ **36.** $\sqrt{\frac{14}{5}}$

*Use the method of Example 3 to perform the indicated operations.*

**37.** $\sqrt{17} + 2\sqrt{17}$ **38.** $3\sqrt{19} + \sqrt{19}$ **39.** $5\sqrt{7} - \sqrt{7}$ **40.** $3\sqrt{27} - \sqrt{27}$

**41.** $3\sqrt{18} + \sqrt{2}$ **42.** $2\sqrt{48} - \sqrt{3}$ **43.** $-\sqrt{12} + \sqrt{75}$ **44.** $2\sqrt{27} - \sqrt{300}$

*Exercises 45–58 deal with $\pi$, $\phi$, or e. Use a calculator or computer as necessary.*

**45.** Move one matchstick to make the equation approximately true. (*Source:* www.joyofpi.com)

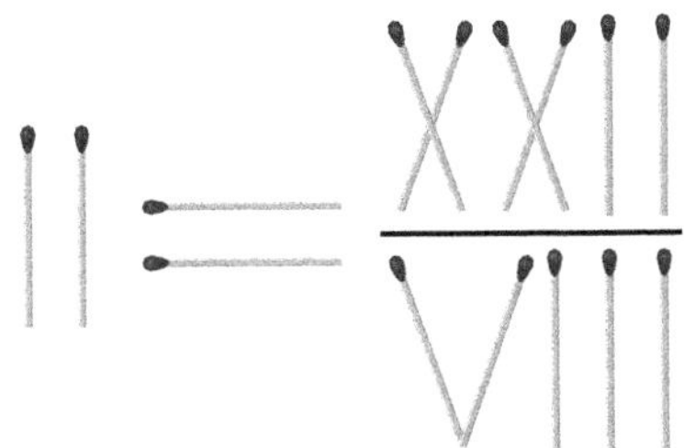

**46.** Find the square root of $\frac{2143}{22}$ using a calculator. Then find the square root of that result. Compare your result to the decimal given for $\pi$ in the margin note. What do you notice?

**47.** Find the first eight digits in the decimal for $\frac{355}{113}$. Compare the result to the decimal for $\pi$ given in the text. What do you notice?

**48.** You may have seen the statements "use $\frac{22}{7}$ for $\pi$" and "use 3.14 for $\pi$." Since $\frac{22}{7}$ is the quotient of two integers, and 3.14 is a terminating decimal, do these statements suggest that $\pi$ is rational?

**49.** In the Bible (I Kings 7:23), a verse describes a circular pool at King Solomon's temple, about 1000 B.C. The pool is said to be ten cubits across, "and a line of 30 cubits did compass it round about." What value of $\pi$ does this imply?

**50.** The ancient Egyptians used a method for finding the area of a circle that is equivalent to a value of 3.1605 for $\pi$. Write this decimal as a mixed number.

**51.** The computation of $\pi$ has fascinated mathematicians and laymen for centuries. In the nineteenth century, the British mathematician William Shanks spent many years of his life calculating $\pi$ to 707 decimal places. It turned out that only the first 527 were correct. Use an Internet search to find the 528th decimal digit of $\pi$ (following the whole number part 3.).

**52.** One of the reasons for computing so many digits of $\pi$ is to determine how often each digit appears and to identify any interesting patterns among the digits. Gregory and David Chudnovsky have spent a great deal of time and effort looking for patterns in the digits. For example, six 9s in a row appear relatively early in the decimal, within the first 800 decimal places. Use an Internet search to find the positions of these six 9s in a row.

**53.** The expression $\frac{2 \cdot 2 \cdot 4 \cdot 4 \cdot 6 \cdot 6 \cdot 8 \cdots}{1 \cdot 3 \cdot 3 \cdot 5 \cdot 5 \cdot 7 \cdot 7 \cdots}$ converges to $\frac{\pi}{2}$. Use a calculator to evaluate only the digits of the expression as shown here, and then multiply by 2. What value for an approximation for $\pi$ does this give (to one decimal place)?

**54.** A *mnemonic device* is a scheme whereby one is able to recall facts by memorizing something completely unrelated to the facts. One way of learning the first few digits of the decimal for $\pi$ is to memorize a sentence (or several sentences) and count the letters in each word of the sentence. For example, "See, I know a digit," will give the first 5 digits of $\pi$: "See" has 3 letters, "I" has 1 letter, "know" has 4 letters, "a" has 1 letter, and "digit" has 5 letters. So the first five digits are 3.1415.

Verify that the following mnemonic devices work.

**(a)** "May I have a large container of coffee?"

**(b)** "See, I have a rhyme assisting my feeble brain, its tasks ofttimes resisting."

**(c)** "How I want a drink, alcoholic of course, after the heavy lectures involving quantum mechanics."

**55.** Use a calculator to find the decimal approximations for $\phi = \frac{1+\sqrt{5}}{2}$ and its *conjugate*, $\frac{1-\sqrt{5}}{2}$. Comment on the similarities and differences in the two decimals.

**56.** In some literature, the Golden Ratio is defined to be the reciprocal of $\frac{1+\sqrt{5}}{2}$— that is, $\frac{2}{1+\sqrt{5}}$. Use a calculator to find a decimal approximation for $\frac{2}{1+\sqrt{5}}$ and compare it to $\phi$ as defined in this text. What do you observe?

**57.** An approximation for $e$ is 2.718281828. A student noticed that there seems to be a repetition of four digits in this number (1, 8, 2, 8) and concluded that it is rational, because repeating decimals represent rational numbers. Was the student correct? Why or why not?

**58.** Use a calculator with an exponential key to find values for the following: $(1.1)^{10}$, $(1.01)^{100}$, $(1.001)^{1000}$, $(1.0001)^{10,000}$, and $(1.00001)^{100,000}$. Compare your results to the approximation given for $e$ in this section. What do you find?

*Solve each problem. Use a calculator as necessary, and give approximations to the nearest tenth unless specified otherwise.*

**59. *Period of a Pendulum*** The period of a pendulum in seconds depends on its length, $L$, in feet, and is given by the formula

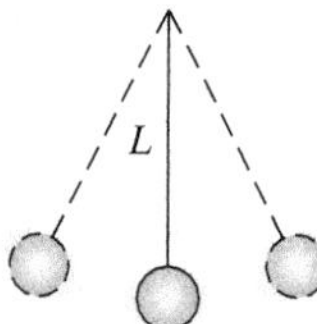


$$P = 2\pi\sqrt{\frac{L}{32}}.$$

If a pendulum is 5.1 feet long, what is its period? Use 3.14 for $\pi$.

**60. *Radius of an Aluminum Can*** The radius of the circular top or bottom of an aluminum can with surface area $S$ and height $h$ is given by

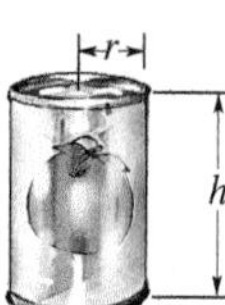


$$r = \frac{-h + \sqrt{h^2 + .64S}}{2}.$$

What radius should be used to make a can with height 12 inches and surface area 400 square inches?

**61. *Distance to the Horizon*** Jack Adrian, a friend of one of the authors of this text, has a beautiful 14th floor condo, with a stunning view, in downtown Chicago. The floor is 150 feet above the ground. Knowing that this author is a mathematics teacher, Jack emailed the author and told him that he called once having studied a formula for calculating the distance to the horizon, but could not remember it. He wanted to know how far he can see from his condo. The author responded:

> *To find the distance to the horizon in miles, take the square root of the height of your view and multiply that result by 1.224. That will give you the number of miles to the horizon.*

Assuming Jack's eyes are 6 feet above his floor, the total height from the ground is $150 + 6 = 156$ feet.

To the nearest tenth of a mile, how far can he see to the horizon?

**62. *Electronics Formula*** The formula

$$I = \sqrt{\frac{2P}{L}}$$

relates the coefficient of self-induction $L$ (in henrys), the energy $P$ stored in an electronic circuit (in joules), and the current $I$ (in amps). Find $I$ if $P = 120$ joules and $L = 80$ henrys.

**63. *Area of the Bermuda Triangle*** *Heron's formula* gives a method of finding the area of a triangle if the lengths of its sides are known. Suppose that $a$, $b$, and $c$ are the lengths of the sides. Let $s$ denote one-half of the perimeter of the triangle (called the *semiperimeter*); that is,

$$s = \frac{1}{2}(a + b + c).$$

Then the area $A$ of the triangle is given by

$$A = \sqrt{s(s - a)(s - b)(s - c)}.$$

Find the area of the Bermuda Triangle, if the "sides" of this triangle measure approximately 850 miles, 925 miles, and 1300 miles. Give your answer to the nearest thousand square miles.

**64. *Area Enclosed by the Vietnam Veterans' Memorial*** The Vietnam Veterans' Memorial in Washington, D.C., is in the shape of an unenclosed isosceles triangle with equal sides of length 246.75 feet. If the triangle were enclosed, the third side would have length 438.14 feet. Use Heron's formula from the previous exercise to find the area of this enclosure to the nearest hundred square feet. (*Source:* Information pamphlet obtained at the Vietnam Veterans' Memorial.)

**65.** ***Perfect Triangles*** A *perfect triangle* is a triangle whose sides have whole number lengths and whose area is numerically equal to its perimeter. Use Heron's formula to show that the triangle with sides of length 9, 10, and 17 is perfect.

**66.** ***Heron Triangles*** A *Heron triangle* is a triangle having integer sides and area. Use Heron's formula to show that each of the following is a Heron triangle.
**(a)** $a = 11, b = 13, c = 20$
**(b)** $a = 13, b = 14, c = 15$
**(c)** $a = 7, b = 15, c = 20$

**67.** ***Diagonal of a Box*** The length of the diagonal of a box is given by

$$D = \sqrt{L^2 + W^2 + H^2},$$

where $L$, $W$, and $H$ are the length, the width, and the height of the box. Find the length of the diagonal, $D$, of a box that is 4 feet long, 3 feet wide, and 2 feet high.

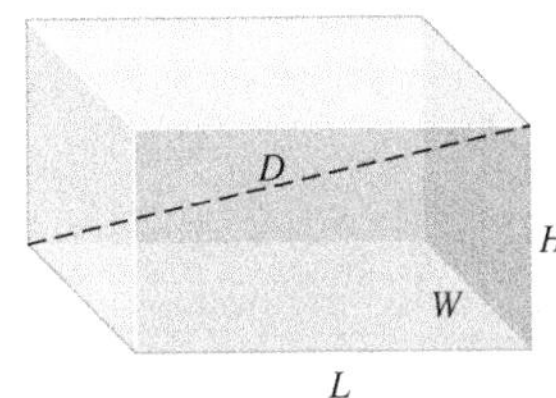


**68.** ***Rate of Return of an Investment*** If an investment of $P$ dollars grows to $A$ dollars in two years, the annual rate of return on the investment is given by

$$r = \frac{\sqrt{A} - \sqrt{P}}{\sqrt{P}}.$$

First rationalize the denominator and then find the annual rate of return (as a decimal) if $50,000 increases to $58,320.

**69.** ***Accident Reconstruction*** Police sometimes use the following procedure to estimate the speed at which a car was traveling at the time of an accident. A police officer drives the car involved in the accident under conditions similar to those during which the accident took place and then skids to a stop. If the car is driven at 30 miles per hour, then the speed at the time of the accident is given by

$$s = 30\sqrt{\frac{a}{p}},$$

where $a$ is the length of the skid marks left at the time of the accident and $p$ is the length of the skid marks in the police test. Find $s$ for the following values of $a$ and $p$.
**(a)** $a = 862$ feet; $p = 156$ feet
**(b)** $a = 382$ feet; $p = 96$ feet
**(c)** $a = 84$ feet; $p = 26$ feet

**70.** ***Law of Tensions*** In the study of sound, one version of the law of tensions is

$$f_1 = f_2\sqrt{\frac{F_1}{F_2}}.$$

Find $f_1$ to the nearest unit if $F_1 = 300$, $F_2 = 60$, and $f_2 = 260$.

*The concept of square (second) root can be extended to* **cube (third) root, fourth root,** *and so on. If $n \geq 2$ and $a$ is a nonnegative number, $\sqrt[n]{a}$ represents the nonnegative number whose nth power is a. For example,*

$$\sqrt[3]{8} = 2 \text{ because } 2^3 = 8,$$
$$\sqrt[3]{1000} = 10 \text{ because } 10^3 = 1000,$$
$$\sqrt[4]{81} = 3 \text{ because } 3^4 = 81,$$

*and so on. Find each root.*

**71.** $\sqrt[3]{64}$
**72.** $\sqrt[3]{125}$
**73.** $\sqrt[3]{343}$
**74.** $\sqrt[3]{729}$
**75.** $\sqrt[3]{216}$
**76.** $\sqrt[3]{512}$
**77.** $\sqrt[4]{1}$
**78.** $\sqrt[4]{16}$
**79.** $\sqrt[4]{256}$
**80.** $\sqrt[4]{625}$
**81.** $\sqrt[4]{4096}$
**82.** $\sqrt[4]{2401}$

*Use a calculator to approximate each root. Give as many places as your calculator shows. (Hint: To find the fourth root, find the square root of the square root.)*

**83.** $\sqrt[3]{43}$
**84.** $\sqrt[3]{87}$
**85.** $\sqrt[3]{198}$
**86.** $\sqrt[4]{2107}$
**87.** $\sqrt[4]{10,265.2}$
**88.** $\sqrt[4]{863.5}$

# 6.5 Applications of Decimals and Percents

**Operations with Decimals • Rounding Decimals • Percent • Applications**

## Operations with Decimals

Because calculators have, for the most part, replaced paper-and-pencil methods for operations with decimals and percent, we will only briefly mention these latter methods. *We strongly suggest that the work in this section be done with a calculator at hand.*

```
.46+3.9+12.58
            16.94
12.1-8.723
            3.377
```

This screen supports the results in Example 1.

### Addition and Subtraction of Decimals

To add or subtract decimal numbers, line up the decimal points in a column and perform the operation.

### EXAMPLE 1 Adding and Subtracting Decimal Numbers

Find each of the following.

**(a)** .46 + 3.9 + 12.58 **(b)** 12.1 − 8.723

**SOLUTION**

**(a)** To compute the sum .46 + 3.9 + 12.58, use the following method.

$$\begin{array}{r} .46 \\ 3.90 \\ +12.58 \\ \hline 16.94 \end{array}$$

.46 — Line up decimal points.
3.90 — Attach a zero as a placeholder.
16.94 ← Sum

**(b)** To compute the difference 12.1 − 8.723, use this method.

$$\begin{array}{r} 12.100 \\ -\ 8.723 \\ \hline 3.377 \end{array}$$

12.100 — Attach zeros.
3.377 ← Difference

Recall that when two numbers are multiplied, the numbers are called *factors* and the answer is called the *product.* When two numbers are divided, the number being divided is called the *dividend,* the number doing the dividing is called the *divisor,* and the answer is called the *quotient.*

**Technology** pervades the world outside school. There is no question that students will be expected to use calculators in other settings; this technology is now part of our culture. . . students no longer have the same need to perform these (paper-and-pencil) procedures with large numbers of lengthy expressions that they might have had in the past without ready access to technology.

From *Computation, Calculators, and Common Sense (A Position of the National Council of Teachers of Mathematics).*

### Multiplication and Division of Decimals

***Multiplication*** To multiply decimals, multiply in the same manner as integers are multiplied. The number of decimal places to the right of the decimal point in the product is the *sum* of the numbers of places to the right of the decimal points in the factors.

***Division*** To divide decimals, move the decimal point to the right the same number of places in the divisor and the dividend so as to obtain a whole number in the divisor. Divide in the same manner as integers are divided. The number of decimal places to the right of the decimal point in the quotient is the same as the number of places to the right in the dividend.

## EXAMPLE 2 Multiplying and Dividing Decimal Numbers

Find each of the following.

**(a)** $4.613 \times 2.52$ **(b)** $65.175 \div 8.25$

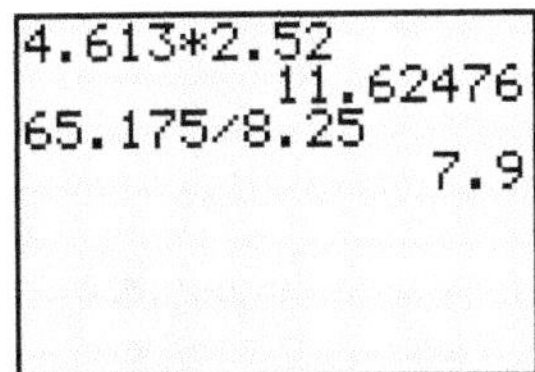


This screen supports the results in Example 2.

**SOLUTION**

**(a)** To find the product $4.613 \times 2.52$, use the following method.

$$\begin{array}{r l} 4.613 & \leftarrow \text{3 decimal places} \\ \times \quad 2.52 & \leftarrow \text{2 decimal places} \\ \hline 9226 & \\ 23065\phantom{0} & \\ 9226\phantom{00} & \\ \hline 11.62476 & \leftarrow 3 + 2 = \text{5 decimal places} \end{array}$$

**(b)** To find the quotient $65.175 \div 8.25$, follow these steps.

$$\begin{array}{r} 7.9 \\ 825\overline{)6517.5} \\ 5775\phantom{.5} \\ \hline 742\,5 \\ 742\,5 \\ \hline 0 \end{array}$$

Bring the decimal point straight up in the answer.

TI-83 Plus

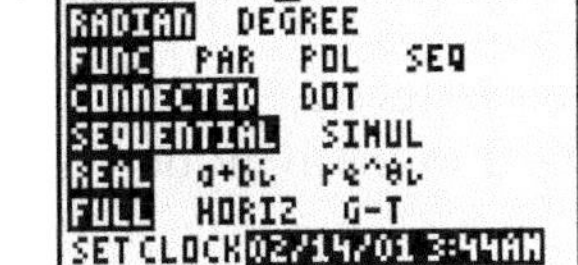


TI-84 Plus

Here the TI-83/84 Plus is set to round the answer to two decimal places.

**Rounding Decimals** Operations with decimals often result in long strings of digits in the decimal places. Since all these digits may not be needed in a practical problem, it is common to *round* a decimal to the necessary number of decimal places. For example, in preparing federal income tax, money amounts are rounded to the nearest dollar. Round as shown in the next example.

## EXAMPLE 3 Rounding a Decimal Number

Round 3.917 to the nearest hundredth.

**SOLUTION**

The hundredths place in 3.917 contains the digit 1.

3.917
↑ Hundredths place

To round this decimal, locate 3.91 and 3.92 on a number line as in Figure 17.

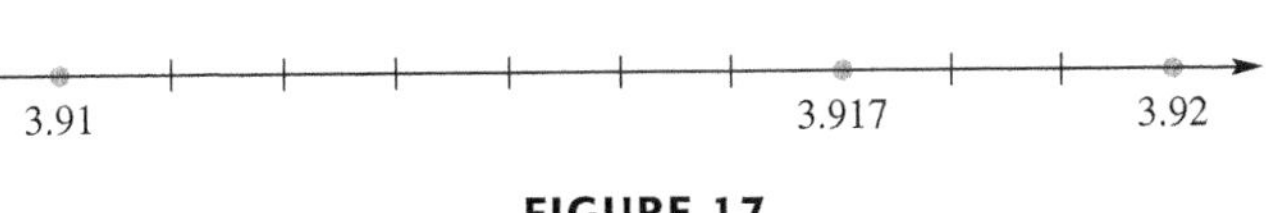


**FIGURE 17**

The distance from 3.91 to 3.92 is divided into ten equal parts. The seventh of these ten parts locates the number 3.917. As the number line shows, 3.917 is closer to 3.92 than it is to 3.91, so 3.917 rounded to the nearest hundredth is 3.92.

3.917
3.92

The calculator rounds 3.917 to the nearest hundredth.

If the number line method of Example 3 were used to round 3.915 to the nearest hundredth, a problem would develop—the number 3.915 is exactly halfway between 3.91 and 3.92. An arbitrary decision is then made to round *up:* 3.915 rounded to the nearest hundredth is 3.92.

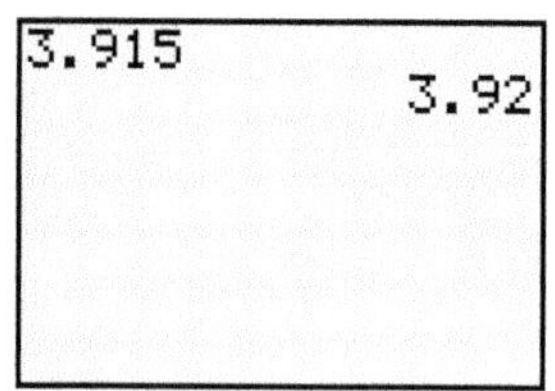


The calculator rounds 3.915 *up* to 3.92.

### Rules for Rounding Decimals

*Step 1* Locate the **place** to which the number is being rounded.

*Step 2* Look at the next **digit to the right** of the place to which the number is being rounded.

*Step 3A* If this digit is **less than 5,** drop all digits to the right of the place to which the number is being rounded. Do *not change* the digit in the place to which the number is being rounded.

*Step 3B* If this digit is **5 or greater,** drop all digits to the right of the place to which the number is being rounded. *Add one* to the digit in the place to which the number is being rounded.

### EXAMPLE 4 Rounding a Decimal Number

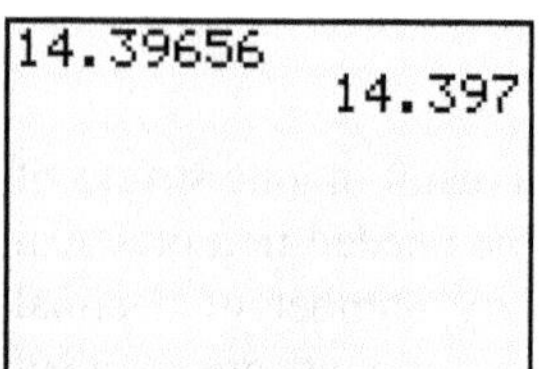


With the calculator set to round to three decimal places, the result of Example 4 is supported.

Round 14.39656 to the nearest thousandth.

**SOLUTION**

*Step 1* Use an arrow to locate the place to which the number is being rounded.

*Step 2* Check to see if the first digit to the right of the arrow is 5 or greater.

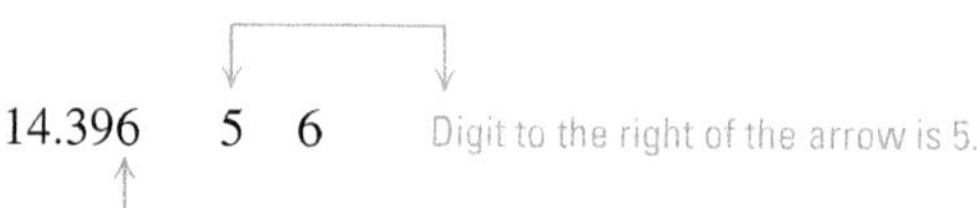


*Step 3* Since the digit to the right of the arrow is 5 or greater, increase by 1 the digit to which the arrow is pointing. Drop all digits to the right of the arrow.

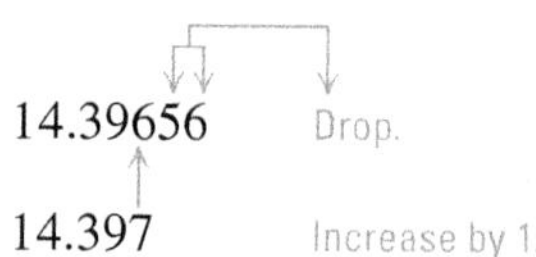


Finally, 14.39656 rounded to the nearest thousandth is 14.397.

**The percent sign, %,** probably evolved from a symbol introduced in an Italian manuscript of 1425. Instead of "per 100," "P 100," or "P cento," which were common at that time, the author used "P$\overset{\circ}{\text{P}}$." By about 1650 the $\overset{\circ}{\text{P}}$ had become $\frac{0}{0}$, so "per $\frac{0}{0}$," was often used. Finally the "per" was dropped, leaving $\frac{0}{0}$ or %.

From *Historical Topics for the Mathematics Classroom,* the Thirty-first Yearbook of the National Council of Teachers of Mathematics, 1969.

**Percent** One of the main applications of decimals comes from problems involving **percents.** In consumer mathematics, interest rates and discounts are often given as percents. The word *percent* means "per hundred." The symbol % represents "percent."

Gene Wilder has appeared in nearly 40 movies in his career. Among his most notable characters are accountant Leo Bloom in the 1969 version of *The Producers* and Willy Wonka in *Willy Wonka and the Chocolate Factory*, both of whom deliver interesting lines involving **percent**.

In *The Producers*, he and Max Bialystock (Zero Mostel) scheme to make a fortune by overfinancing what they think will be a Broadway flop. After enumerating the percent of profits all of Max's little old ladies have been offered in the production, reality sets in.

MAX: Leo, how much percentage of a play can there be altogether?
LEO: Max, you can only sell 100% of anything.
MAX: And how much for *Springtime for Hitler* have we sold?
LEO: 25,000%
MAX (reaching for Leo's blue security blanket): 25,000%. . . Give me that blue thing.

As Willy Wonka, upon preparing a mixture in his laboratory, Wilder delivers the following as he drinks his latest concoction.

WILLY WONKA: Invention, my dear friends, is 93% perspiration, 6% electricity, 4% evaporation, and 2% butterscotch ripple.
FEMALE VOICE: That's 105%.
MALE VOICE: Any good?
WILLY WONKA: Yes!

### Percent

$$1\% = \frac{1}{100} = .01$$

### EXAMPLE 5 Converting Percents to Decimals

Convert each percent to a decimal.

**(a)** 98% **(b)** 3.4% **(c)** .2%

**SOLUTION**

**(a)** $98\% = 98(1\%) = 98(.01) = .98$
**(b)** $3.4\% = 3.4(1\%) = 3.4(.01) = .034$
**(c)** $.2\% = .2(1\%) = .2(.01) = .002$

### EXAMPLE 6 Converting Decimals to Percents

Convert each decimal to a percent.

**(a)** .13 **(b)** .532 **(c)** 2.3

**SOLUTION**

**(a)** $.13 = 13(.01) = 13(1\%) = 13\%$
**(b)** $.532 = 53.2(.01) = 53.2(1\%) = 53.2\%$
**(c)** $2.3 = 230(.01) = 230(1\%) = 230\%$

From Examples 5 and 6, we see that the following procedures can be used when converting between percents and decimals.

### Converting Between Decimals and Percents

***To convert a percent to a decimal,*** drop the % sign and move the decimal point two places to the left, inserting zeros as placeholders if necessary.

***To convert a decimal to a percent,*** move the decimal point two places to the right, inserting zeros as placeholders if necessary, and attach a % sign.

### EXAMPLE 7 Converting Fractions to Percents

Convert each fraction to a percent.

**(a)** $\frac{3}{5}$ **(b)** $\frac{14}{25}$

**SOLUTION**

**(a)** First write $\frac{3}{5}$ as a decimal. Dividing 5 into 3 gives $\frac{3}{5} = .6 = 60\%$.

The 2004 movie *Mean Girls* stars Lindsay Lohan as Cady Heron, who has been home-schooled until her senior year in high school. A scene in the school cafeteria features her sitting with The Plastics (the "mean girls" of the title). Regina George, played by Rachel McAdams, is reading a candy bar wrapper.

REGINA: 120 calories and 48 calories from fat. What **percent** is that? I'm only eating food with less than 30% calories from fat.
CADY: It's 40%. (Responding to a quizzical look from Regina.) Well, 48 over 120 equals $x$ over 100, and then you cross-multiply and get the value of $x$.
REGINA: Whatever. I'm getting cheese fries.

**(b)** $\frac{14}{25} = .56 = 56\%$

The procedure of Example 7 is summarized as follows.

**Converting a Fraction to a Percent**

***To convert a fraction to a percent,*** convert the fraction to a decimal, and then convert the decimal to a percent.

In the following examples involving percents, three methods are shown. The second method in each case involves using cross-products. The third method involves the percent key of a basic calculator.

## EXAMPLE 8 Finding a Percent of a Number

Find 18% of 250.

**SOLUTION**

***Method 1*** The key word here is "of." The word "of" translates as "times," with 18% of 250 given by

$$(18\%)(250) = (.18)(250) = 45.$$

***Method 2*** Think "18 is to 100 as what ($x$) is to 250?" This translates into the equation

$$\frac{18}{100} = \frac{x}{250}$$

$$100x = 18 \cdot 250 \quad \frac{a}{b} = \frac{c}{d} \text{ if and only if } ad = bc$$

$$x = \frac{18 \cdot 250}{100} \quad \text{Divide by 100.}$$

$$x = 45. \quad \text{Simplify.}$$

***Method 3*** Use the percent key on a calculator with the following keystrokes:

45 .

With any of these methods, we find that 18% of 250 is 45.

## EXAMPLE 9 Finding What Percent One Number Is of Another

What percent of 500 is 75?

**SOLUTION**

***Method 1*** Let the phrase "what percent" be represented by $x \cdot 1\%$ or $.01x$. Again the word "of" translates as "times," while "is" translates as "equals." Thus,

$$.01x \cdot 500 = 75$$
$$5x = 75 \quad \text{Multiply on the left side.}$$
$$x = 15. \quad \text{Divide by 5.}$$

*Method 2* Think "What ($x$) is to 100 as 75 is to 500?" This translates as

$$\frac{x}{100} = \frac{75}{500}$$
$$500x = 7500 \quad \text{Cross-products}$$
$$x = 15. \quad \text{Divide by 500.}$$

*Method 3* [7] [5] [÷] [5] [0] [0] [%] **15**

In each case, 15 is the percent, so we conclude that 75 is 15% of 500.

### EXAMPLE 10 Finding a Number of Which a Given Number Is a Given Percent

38 is 5% of what number?

**SOLUTION**

*Method 1*

$$38 = .05x$$
$$x = \frac{38}{.05} \quad \text{Divide by .05.}$$
$$x = 760 \quad \text{Simplify.}$$

*Method 2* Think "38 is to what number ($x$) as 5 is to 100?"

$$\frac{38}{x} = \frac{5}{100}$$
$$5x = 3800 \quad \text{Cross-products}$$
$$x = 760 \quad \text{Divide by 5.}$$

*Method 3* [3] [8] [÷] [5] [%] **760**

Each method shows us that 38 is 5% of 760.

There are various shortcuts that can be used to work with percents. Suppose that you need to compute 20% of 50. Here are two such shortcuts.

1. You think "20% means $\frac{1}{5}$, and to find $\frac{1}{5}$ of something I divide by 5, so 50 divided by 5 is 10. The answer is 10."
2. You think "20% is twice 10%, and to find 10% of something I move the decimal point one place to the left. So, 10% of 50 is 5, and 20% is twice 5, or 10. The answer is 10."

## Applications

**PROBLEM-SOLVING HINT** When applying percent it is often a good idea to restate the problem as a question similar to those found in Examples 8–10, and then answer that question. One strategy of problem solving deals with solving a simpler, similar problem.

### EXAMPLE 11 Interpreting Percents from a Graph

In 2003, people in the United States spent an estimated \$29.7 billion on their pets. Use the graph in Figure 18 to determine how much of this amount was spent on pet food.

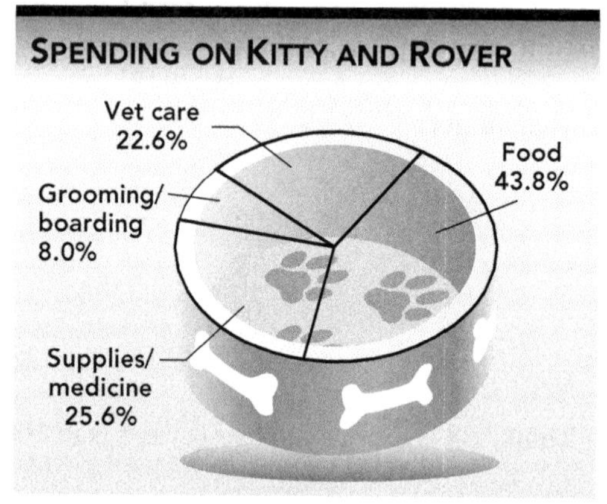


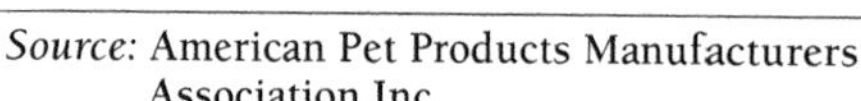

*Source:* American Pet Products Manufacturers Association Inc.

Dotty

**FIGURE 18**

**SOLUTION**

According to the graph, 43.8% was spent on food. We use Method 1 of Example 8 to find 43.8% of \$29.7 billion.

$$\underbrace{.438}_{43.8\%} \underbrace{\times}_{\text{of}} \underbrace{\$29.7 \text{ billion}}_{\text{Total amount}} = \underbrace{\$13.0 \text{ billion}}_{\substack{\text{Amount spent} \\ \text{on pet food}}}$$

In many applications we are asked to find the percent increase or percent decrease from one quantity to another. The following guidelines summarize how to do this.

## Finding Percent Increase or Decrease

1. To find the **percent increase from $a$ to $b$,** where $b > a$, subtract $a$ from $b$, and divide this result by $a$. Convert to a percent.

*Example:* The percent increase from 4 to 7 is $\frac{7-4}{4} = \frac{3}{4} = 75\%$.

2. To find the **percent decrease from $a$ to $b$,** where $b < a$, subtract $b$ from $a$, and divide this result by $a$. Convert to a percent.

*Example:* The percent decrease from 8 to 6 is $\frac{8-6}{8} = \frac{2}{8} = \frac{1}{4} = 25\%$.

## EXAMPLE 12 Finding Percent Increase of Las Vegas Population

Las Vegas, Nevada, is the fastest-growing city in the United States. In 1990, the population of Las Vegas was 258,295. By 2000, it had grown to 478,434. (*Source:* U.S. Census Bureau.)

**(a)** Estimate the percent increase over this period.
**(b)** Find the actual percent increase, to the nearest tenth of a percent, over this period.

**SOLUTION**

**(a)** For easy computation, think of the 2000 population as 470,000 and the 1990 population as 270,000. The difference is

$$470{,}000 - 270{,}000 = 200{,}000.$$

Now, think of the 1990 population as 250,000 and answer the question "What percent of 250,000 (the *original* population) is 200,000?" The fraction $\frac{200{,}000}{250{,}000}$ simplifies to $\frac{20}{25} = \frac{4}{5}$, which is 80%. Therefore, the population increased by about 80% over the ten-year period.

**(b)** We must find the difference between the two populations, and then determine what percent of 258,295 this difference comprises.

$$\underbrace{478{,}434}_{\text{Population in 2000}} - \underbrace{258{,}295}_{\text{Population in 1990}} = \underbrace{220{,}139}_{\text{Increase in population}}$$

Now solve the problem "What percent of 258,295 is 220,139?" This is similar to the problem in Example 9. Any of the methods explained there will indicate that the answer is approximately 85.2%.

## For Further Thought

### It's Time to End Decimal Point Abuse

Using a decimal point erroneously with a ¢ symbol is seen almost on a daily basis. Think about it... \$.99 represents $\frac{99}{100}$ of a dollar, or 99 cents, while 99¢ also represents 99 cents (since ¢ is the symbol for *cent*). So what does .99¢ represent? That's right, $\frac{99}{100}$ of one cent!

Look at the photos provided by one of the authors. A 20-oz single of FlavorSplash is advertised for .99¢. What do you think would happen if you gave the clerk a dime and asked for ten bottles and change? You would most likely get a dumbfounded look. A similar response would probably be forthcoming if you asked for Sierra Mist, which costs even less: .79¢. To vacuum your car, it costs .50¢, a mere half cent. At The Floor Place, fabulous floors really do cost less... a lot less: less than half a cent per square foot for Berber flooring. Now here's a deal: a 2 liter bottle of Coca Cola for .09¢! (No doubt, the 1 preceding the decimal point fell off. Even then, one such bottle would cost only a tiny bit more than one penny.) On the Cherokee Turnpike, you are expected to provide exact change of .25¢. Could you possibly do it?

### For Group Discussion or Individual Investigation

Assume that the products shown in the photos are actually being sold for the indicated prices. Answer each of the following.

1. How many 20-oz singles of FlavorSplash should you get for \$1.00? How much change would the store owe you?
2. How much does one ounce of Sierra Mist cost?
3. If you deposit two quarters to have your car vacuumed, how many times should you be able to vacuum?
4. You want to cover your room area with 400 square feet of Berber flooring. How much will this cost?
5. How many 2 liter bottles of Coca Cola would nine cents get you?
6. How many trips on the Cherokee Turnpike should you get for a quarter?

## 6.5 EXERCISES

*Decide whether each statement is true or false.*

1. 300% of 12 is 36.
2. 25% of a quantity is the same as $\frac{1}{4}$ of that quantity.
3. When 759.367 is rounded to the nearest hundredth, the result is 759.40.
4. When 759.367 is rounded to the nearest hundred, the result is 759.37.
5. To find 50% of a quantity, we may simply divide the quantity by 2.
6. A soccer team that has won 12 games and lost 8 games has a winning percentage of 60%.
7. If 70% is the lowest passing grade on a quiz that has 50 items of equal value, then answering at least 35 items correctly will assure you of a passing grade.
8. 30 is more than 40% of 120.
9. .99¢ = 99 cents
10. If an item usually costs \$70.00 and it is discounted 10%, then the discount price is \$7.00.

*Calculate each of the following using either a calculator or paper-and-pencil methods, as directed by your instructor.*

11. $8.53 + 2.785$
12. $9.358 + 7.2137$
13. $8.74 - 12.955$
14. $2.41 - 3.997$
15. $25.7 \times .032$
16. $45.1 \times 8.344$
17. $1019.825 \div 21.47$
18. $-262.563 \div 125.03$
19. $\dfrac{118.5}{1.45 + 2.3}$
20. $2.45(1.2 + 3.4 - 5.6)$

***Change in Population*** The table shows the percent change in population from 1990 through 2000 for some large cities in the United States.

| City | Percent Change |
|---|---|
| New York | 8.8 |
| Los Angeles | 9.7 |
| Cleveland | 2.2 |
| Pittsburgh | −1.5 |
| Baltimore | 7.2 |
| Buffalo | −1.6 |

*Source:* U.S. Census Bureau.

21. Which city had the greatest percent change? What was this change? Was it an increase or a decrease?
22. Which city had the least percent change? What was this change? Was it an increase or a decrease?

***Postage Stamp Pricing*** *Refer to* For Further Thought *on decimal point abuse. At one time, the United States Postal Service sold rolls of 33-cent stamps that featured fruit berries. One such stamp is shown on the left. On the right is a photo of the pricing information found on the cellophane wrapper of such a roll.*

100 STAMPS PSA
.33¢ ea. TOTAL \$33.00
FRUIT BERRIES
ITEM 7757
BCA

23. Look at the second line of the pricing information. According to the price listed *per stamp,* how many stamps should you be able to purchase for one cent?
24. The total price listed is the amount the Postal Service actually charges. If you were to multiply the listed price *per stamp* by the number of stamps, what should the total price be?

***Pricing of Pie and Coffee*** *The photos here were taken at a flea market near Natchez, MS. The handwritten signs indicate that a piece of pie costs .10¢ and a cup of coffee ("ffee") costs .5¢. Assuming these are the actual prices, answer the questions in Exercises 25–28.*

25. How much will 10 pieces of pie and 10 cups of coffee cost?

**26.** How much will 20 pieces of pie and 10 cups of coffee cost?

**27.** How many pieces of pie can you get for $1.00?

**28.** How many cups of coffee can you get for $1.00?

*Exercises 29–32 are based on formulas found in* Auto Math Handbook: Mathematical Calculations, Theory, and Formulas for Automotive Enthusiasts, *by John Lawlor (1991, HP Books).*

**29.** ***Blood Alcohol Concentration*** The Blood Alcohol Concentration (BAC) of a person who has been drinking is given by the formula

$$\text{BAC} = \frac{(\text{ounces} \times \text{percent alcohol} \times .075)}{\text{body weight in lb}} - (\text{hours of drinking} \times .015).$$

*Suppose a policeman stops a 190-pound man who, in two hours, has ingested four 12-ounce beers, each having a 3.2 percent alcohol content. The formula would then read*

$$\text{BAC} = \frac{[(4 \times 12) \times 3.2 \times .075]}{190} - (2 \times .015).$$

(a) Find this BAC.

(b) Find the BAC for a 135-pound woman who, in three hours, has drunk three 12-ounce beers, each having a 4.0 percent alcohol content.

**30.** ***Approximate Automobile Speed*** The approximate speed of an automobile in miles per hour (MPH) can be found in terms of the engine's revolutions per minute (rpm), the tire diameter in inches, and the overall gear ratio by the formula

$$\text{MPH} = \frac{\text{rpm} \times \text{tire diameter}}{\text{gear ratio} \times 336}.$$

If a certain automobile has an rpm of 5600, a tire diameter of 26 inches, and a gear ratio of 3.12, what is its approximate speed (MPH)?

**31.** ***Engine Horsepower*** Horsepower can be found from indicated mean effective pressure (mep) in pounds per square inch, engine displacement in cubic inches, and revolutions per minute (rpm) using the formula

$$\text{Horsepower} = \frac{\text{mep} \times \text{displacement} \times \text{rpm}}{792{,}000}.$$

Suppose that an engine has displacement of 302 cubic inches, and indicated mep of 195 pounds per square inch at 4000 rpm. What is its approximate horsepower?

**32.** ***Torque Approximation*** To determine the torque at a given value of rpm, the formula below applies:

$$\text{Torque} = \frac{5252 \times \text{horsepower}}{\text{rpm}}.$$

If the horsepower of a certain vehicle is 400 at 4500 rpm, what is the approximate torque?

*Round each number to the nearest* **(a)** *tenth;* **(b)** *hundredth. Always round from the original number.*

**33.** 78.414

**34.** 3689.537

**35.** .0837

**36.** .0658

**37.** 12.68925

**38.** 43.99613

*Convert each decimal to a percent.*

**39.** .42

**40.** .87

**41.** .365

**42.** .792

**43.** .008

**44.** .0093

**45.** 2.1

**46.** 8.9

*Convert each fraction to a percent.*

**47.** $\frac{1}{5}$

**48.** $\frac{2}{5}$

**49.** $\frac{1}{100}$

**50.** $\frac{1}{50}$

**51.** $\frac{3}{8}$

**52.** $\frac{5}{6}$

**53.** $\frac{3}{2}$

**54.** $\frac{7}{4}$

**55.** Explain the difference between $\frac{1}{2}$ of a quantity and $\frac{1}{2}\%$ of the quantity.

**56.** On the next page Group I shows some common percents, found in many everyday situations. In Group II are fractional equivalents of these percents. Match the fractions in Group II with their equivalent percents in Group I.

| I | | II | |
|---|---|---|---|
| (a) 25% | (b) 10% | A. $\frac{1}{3}$ | B. $\frac{1}{50}$ |
| (c) 2% | (d) 20% | C. $\frac{3}{4}$ | D. $\frac{1}{10}$ |
| (e) 75% | (f) $33\frac{1}{3}\%$ | E. $\frac{1}{4}$ | F. $\frac{1}{5}$ |

**57.** Fill in each blank with the appropriate numerical response.
(a) 5% means _____ in every 100.
(b) 25% means 6 in every _____.
(c) 200% means _____ for every 4.
(d) .5% means _____ in every 100.
(e) _____% means 12 for every 2.

**58.** The Venn diagram shows the number of elements in the four regions formed.

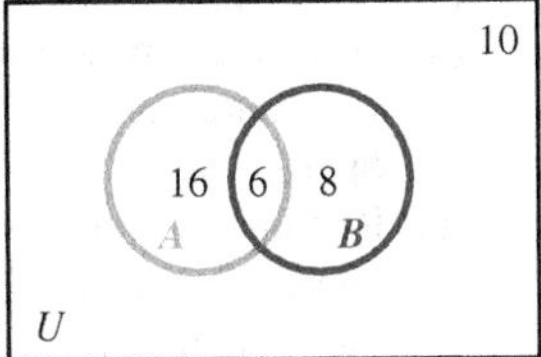


(a) What percent of the elements in the universe are in $A \cap B$?
(b) What percent of the elements in the universe are in $A$ but not in $B$?
(c) What percent of the elements in $A \cup B$ are in $A \cap B$?
(d) What percent of the elements in the universe are in neither $A$ nor $B$?

**59.** ***Discount and Markup*** Suppose that an item regularly costs \$60.00 and it is discounted 20%. If it is then marked up 20%, is the resulting price \$60.00? If not, what is it?

**60.** The figures in Exercise 13 of Section 6.3 are reproduced here. Express the fractional parts represented by the shaded areas as percents.

(a)

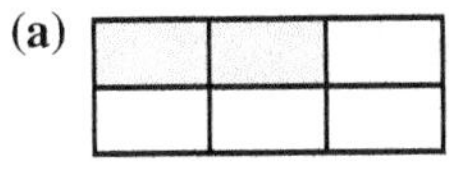

(b)

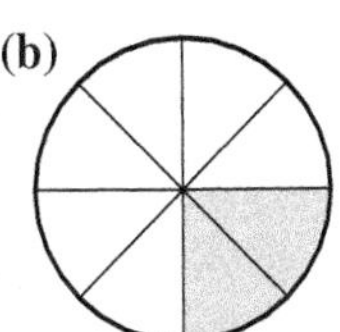

(c)

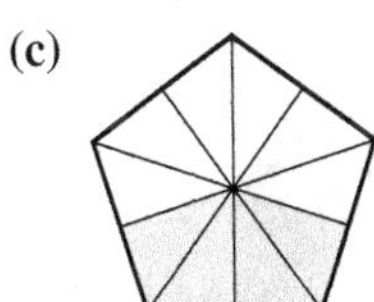

(d)

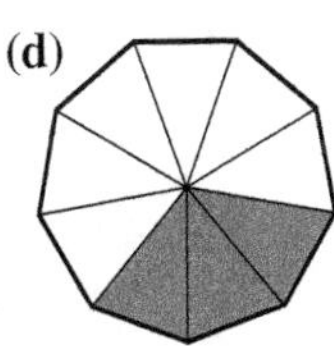

***Win-Loss Record*** *Exercises 61 and 62 deal with winning percentage in the standings of sports teams.*

**61.** At the end of the regular 2005 Major League Baseball season, the standings of the Central Division of the American League were as shown. Winning percentage is commonly expressed as a decimal rounded to the nearest thousandth. To find the winning percentage of a team, divide the number of wins (W) by the total number of games played (W + L). Find the winning percentage of each team.
(a) Chicago (b) Cleveland (c) Detroit

| Team | W | L |
|---|---|---|
| Chicago | 99 | 63 |
| Cleveland | 93 | 69 |
| Minnesota | 83 | 79 |
| Detroit | 71 | 91 |
| Kansas City | 56 | 106 |

**62.** Repeat Exercise 61 for the following standings for the East Division of the National League.
(a) Atlanta (b) Philadelphia
(c) Florida and New York

| Team | W | L |
|---|---|---|
| Atlanta | 90 | 72 |
| Philadelphia | 88 | 74 |
| Florida | 83 | 79 |
| New York | 83 | 79 |
| Washington | 81 | 81 |

*Work each problem involving percent.*

**63.** What is 26% of 480?

**64.** Find 38% of 12.

**65.** Find 10.5% of 28.

**66.** What is 48.6% of 19?

**67.** What percent of 30 is 45?

**68.** What percent of 48 is 20?

**69.** 25% of what number is 150?

**70.** 12% of what number is 3600?

**71.** .392 is what percent of 28?

**72.** 78.84 is what percent of 292?

*Use mental techniques to answer the questions in Exercises 73–76. Try to avoid using paper and pencil or a calculator.*

**73.** ***Allowance Increase*** Dierdre Lynch's allowance was raised from $4.00 per week to $5.00 per week. What was the percent of the increase?
**A.** 25% **B.** 20% **C.** 50% **D.** 30%

**74.** ***Boat Purchase and Sale*** Jane Gunton bought a boat five years ago for $5000 and sold it this year for $2000. What percent of her original purchase did she lose on the sale?
**A.** 40% **B.** 50% **C.** 20% **D.** 60%

**75.** ***Population of Alabama*** The 2000 U.S. census showed that the population of Alabama was 4,447,000, with 26.0% represented by African Americans. What is the best estimate of the African American population in Alabama? (*Source:* U.S. Census Bureau.)
**A.** 500,000 **B.** 1,500,000
**C.** 1,100,000 **D.** 750,000

**76.** ***Population of Hawaii*** The 2000 U.S. census showed that the population of Hawaii was 1,212,000, with 21.4% of the population being of two or more races. What is the best estimate of this population of Hawaii? (*Source:* U.S. Census Bureau.)
**A.** 240,000 **B.** 300,000
**C.** 21,400 **D.** 24,000

***Gasoline Prices*** *The line graph shows the average price, adjusted for inflation, that Americans have paid for a gallon of gasoline for selected years between 1970 and 2000. Use this information in Exercises 77 and 78.*

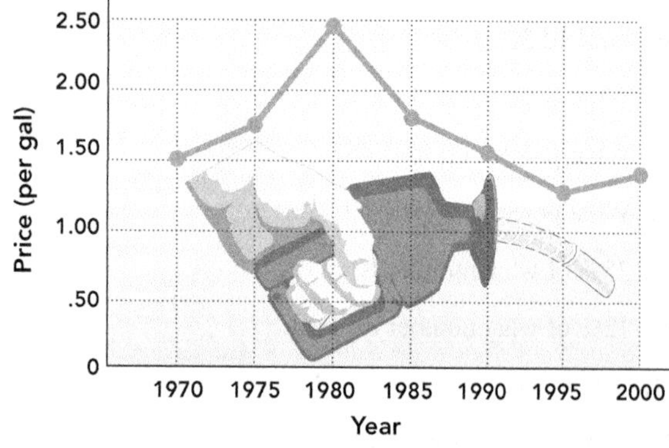


*Source:* American Petroleum Institute; AP research.

**77.** By what percent did prices increase from 1970 to 1980?

**78.** By what percent did prices decrease from 1980 to 1990?

***Metabolic Units*** *One way to measure a person's cardio fitness is to calculate how many METs, or metabolic units, he or she can reach at peak exertion. One MET is the amount of energy used when sitting quietly. To calculate ideal METs, we can use one of the following expressions.*

$$14.7 - \text{age} \cdot .13 \quad \text{For women}$$
$$14.7 - \text{age} \cdot .11 \quad \text{For men}$$

(*Source: New England Journal of Medicine,* August, 2005.)

**79.** A 40-year-old woman wishes to calculate her ideal MET.
**(a)** Write the expression using her age.
**(b)** Calculate her ideal MET. (*Hint:* Use the order of operations.)
**(c)** Researchers recommend that a person reach approximately 85% of their MET when exercising. Calculate 85% of the ideal MET from part (b). Then refer to the following table. What activity can the woman do that is approximately this value?

| Activity | METs | Activity | METs |
|---|---|---|---|
| Golf (with cart) | 2.5 | Skiing (water or downhill) | 6.8 |
| Walking (3 mph) | 3.3 | Swimming | 7.0 |
| Mowing lawn (power mower) | 4.5 | Walking (5 mph) | 8.0 |
| Ballroom or square dancing | 5.5 | Jogging | 10.2 |
| Cycling | 5.7 | Rope skipping | 12.0 |

*Source:* Harvard School of Public Health.

**80.** Repeat parts **(a)**–**(c)** of Exercise 79 for a 55-year-old man.

**81.** ***Value of 1916-D Mercury Dime*** The 1916 Mercury dime minted in Denver is quite rare. In 1979 its value in Extremely Fine condition was \$625. The 2005 value had increased to \$6000. What was the percent increase in the value of this coin from 1979 to 2005? (*Sources: A Guide Book of United States Coins; Coin World Coin Values.*)

**82.** ***Value of 1903-O Morgan Dollar*** In 1963, the value of a 1903 Morgan dollar minted in New Orleans in typical Uncirculated condition was \$1500. Due to a discovery of a large hoard of these dollars late that year, the value plummeted. Its value in 2005 was \$550. What was the percent decrease in its value from 1963 to 2005? (*Sources: A Guide Book of United States Coins; Coin World Coin Values.*)

***Tipping Procedure*** *It is customary in our society to "tip" waiters and waitresses when dining in restaurants. One common rate for tipping is 15%. A quick way of figuring a tip that will give a close approximation of 15% is as follows:*

1 *Round off the bill to the nearest dollar.*
2 *Find 10% of this amount by moving the decimal point one place to the left.*
3 *Take half of the amount obtained in Step 2 and add it to the result of Step 2.*

*This will give you approximately 15% of the bill. The amount obtained in Step 3 is 5%, and*

$$10\% + 5\% = 15\%.$$

*Use the method above to find an approximation of 15% for each restaurant bill.*

**83.** \$29.57 **84.** \$38.32

**85.** \$5.15 **86.** \$7.89

*Suppose that you get extremely good service and decide to tip 20%. You can use the first two steps listed, and then in Step 3, double the amount you obtained in Step 2. Use this method to find an approximation of 20% for each restaurant bill.*

**87.** \$59.96 **88.** \$40.24

**89.** \$180.43 **90.** \$199.86

**91.** A television reporter once asked a professional wrist-wrestler what percent of his sport was physical and what percent was mental. The athlete responded "I would say it's 50% physical and 90% mental." Comment on this response.

**92.** According to *The Yogi Book,* consisting of quotes by baseball Hall-of-Famer Yogi Berra, he claims that "90% of the game is half mental." Comment on this statement.

# EXTENSION
## Complex Numbers

Numbers such as $\sqrt{-5}$ and $\sqrt{-16}$ were called *imaginary* by the early mathematicians who would not permit these numbers to be used as solutions to problems. Gradually, however, applications were found that required the use of these numbers, making it necessary to expand the set of real numbers to form the set of **complex numbers.**

Consider the equation $x^2 + 1 = 0$. It has no real number solution, since any solution must be a number whose square is $-1$. In the set of real numbers all squares are nonnegative numbers, because the product of either two positive numbers or two negative numbers is positive. To provide a solution for the equation $x^2 + 1 = 0$, a new number $i$ is defined so that

$$i^2 = -1.$$

*(continued)*

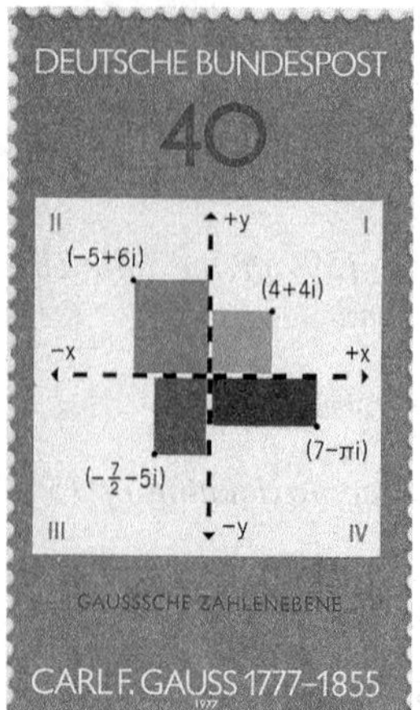


**Gauss and the Complex Numbers** The stamp shown above honors the many contributions made by Gauss to our understanding of complex numbers. In about 1831 he was able to show that numbers of the form $a + bi$ can be represented as points on the plane (as the stamp shows) just as real numbers are. He shared this contribution with **Robert Argand,** a bookkeeper in Paris, who wrote an essay on the geometry of the complex numbers in 1806. This went unnoticed at the time.

That is, $i$ is a number whose square is $-1$. This definition of $i$ makes it possible to define the square root of any negative number as follows.

**$\sqrt{-b}$**

For any positive real number $b$, $\quad \sqrt{-b} = i\sqrt{b}$.

## EXAMPLE 1 Writing Square Roots Using $i$

Write each number as a product of a real number and $i$.

**(a)** $\sqrt{-100}$ **(b)** $\sqrt{-2}$

**SOLUTION**

**(a)** $\sqrt{-100} = i\sqrt{100} = 10i$

**(b)** $\sqrt{-2} = \sqrt{2}i = i\sqrt{2}$

It is easy to mistake $\sqrt{2}i$ for $\sqrt{2i}$, with the $i$ under the radical. For this reason, it is common to write $\sqrt{2}i$ as $i\sqrt{2}$.

When finding a product such as $\sqrt{-4} \cdot \sqrt{-9}$, the product rule for radicals cannot be used, since that rule applies only when both radicals represent real numbers. For this reason, always change $\sqrt{-b}$ $(b > 0)$ to the form $i\sqrt{b}$ before performing any multiplications or divisions. For example,

$$\sqrt{-4} \cdot \sqrt{-9} = i\sqrt{4} \cdot i\sqrt{9} = i \cdot 2 \cdot i \cdot 3 = 6i^2.$$

Since $i^2 = -1$,

$$6i^2 = 6(-1) = -6.$$

An ***incorrect*** use of the product rule for radicals would give a wrong answer.

$$\sqrt{-4} \cdot \sqrt{-9} = \sqrt{(-4)(-9)} = \sqrt{36} = 6 \quad \text{Incorrect}$$

## EXAMPLE 2 Multiplying Expressions Involving $i$

Multiply.

**(a)** $\sqrt{-3} \cdot \sqrt{-7}$ **(b)** $\sqrt{-2} \cdot \sqrt{-8}$ **(c)** $\sqrt{-5} \cdot \sqrt{6}$

**SOLUTION**

**(a)** $\sqrt{-3} \cdot \sqrt{-7} = i\sqrt{3} \cdot i\sqrt{7} = i^2\sqrt{3 \cdot 7} = (-1)\sqrt{21} = -\sqrt{21}$

**(b)** $\sqrt{-2} \cdot \sqrt{-8} = i\sqrt{2} \cdot i\sqrt{8} = i^2\sqrt{2 \cdot 8} = (-1)\sqrt{16} = (-1)4 = -4$

**(c)** $\sqrt{-5} \cdot \sqrt{6} = i\sqrt{5} \cdot \sqrt{6} = i\sqrt{30}$

When the TI-83/84 Plus calculator is in complex mode, denoted by $a + bi$, it will perform complex number arithmetic.

## EXAMPLE 3 Dividing Expressions Involving $i$

Divide.

**(a)** $\dfrac{\sqrt{-75}}{\sqrt{-3}}$ **(b)** $\dfrac{\sqrt{-32}}{\sqrt{8}}$

```
√(-2)*√(-8)
                -4
√(-75)/√(-3)
                 5
√(-32)/√(8)
                2i
```

This screen supports the results of Examples 2(b), 3(a), and 3(b).

**SOLUTION**

(a) $\dfrac{\sqrt{-75}}{\sqrt{-3}} = \dfrac{i\sqrt{75}}{i\sqrt{3}} = \sqrt{\dfrac{75}{3}} = \sqrt{25} = 5$

(b) $\dfrac{\sqrt{-32}}{\sqrt{8}} = \dfrac{i\sqrt{32}}{\sqrt{8}} = i\sqrt{\dfrac{32}{8}} = i\sqrt{4} = 2i$

*Complex numbers* are defined as follows.

### Complex Numbers

If $a$ and $b$ are real numbers, then any number of the form $\boldsymbol{a + bi}$ is called a **complex number.**

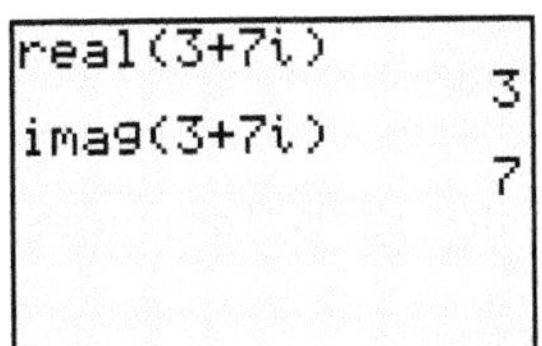


The TI-83/84 Plus calculator identifies the real and imaginary parts of $3 + 7i$.

In the complex number $a + bi$, the number $a$ is called the **real part** and $b$ is called the **imaginary part.*** When $b = 0$, $a + bi$ is a real number, so the real numbers are a subset of the complex numbers. Complex numbers of the form $bi$, where $b \neq 0$, are called **pure imaginary numbers.** In spite of their name, such numbers are very useful in applications, particularly in work with electricity.

An interesting pattern emerges when we consider various powers of $i$. By definition, $i^0 = 1$, and $i^1 = i$. We have seen that $i^2 = -1$, and greater powers of $i$ can be found as shown in the following list.

$$i^3 = i \cdot i^2 = i(-1) = -i \qquad i^6 = i^2 \cdot i^4 = (-1) \cdot 1 = -1$$
$$i^4 = i^2 \cdot i^2 = (-1)(-1) = 1 \qquad i^7 = i^3 \cdot i^4 = (-i) \cdot 1 = -i$$
$$i^5 = i \cdot i^4 = i \cdot 1 = i \qquad i^8 = i^4 \cdot i^4 = 1 \cdot 1 = 1$$

A few powers of $i$ are listed here.

```
i²
                -1
i³
                -i
i^4
                 1
```

The calculator computes powers of $i$. Compare to the powers in the chart.

### Powers of *i*

| | | | |
|---|---|---|---|
| $i^1 = i$ | $i^5 = i$ | $i^9 = i$ | $i^{13} = i$ |
| $i^2 = -1$ | $i^6 = -1$ | $i^{10} = -1$ | $i^{14} = -1$ |
| $i^3 = -i$ | $i^7 = -i$ | $i^{11} = -i$ | $i^{15} = -i$ |
| $i^4 = 1$ | $i^8 = 1$ | $i^{12} = 1$ | $i^{16} = 1$ |

As these examples suggest, the powers of $i$ rotate through the four numbers $i$, $-1$, $-i$, and 1. Larger powers of $i$ can be simplified by using the fact that $i^4 = 1$. For example,

$$i^{75} = (i^4)^{18} \cdot i^3 = 1^{18} \cdot i^3 = 1 \cdot i^3 = -i.$$

*In some texts, $bi$ is called the imaginary part.

*(continued)*

### Simplifying Large Powers of $i$

*Step 1* Divide the exponent by 4.

*Step 2* Observe the remainder obtained in Step 1. The large power of $i$ is the same as $i$ raised to the power determined by this remainder. Refer to the previous chart to complete the simplification. (If the remainder is 0, the power simplifies to $i^0 = 1$.)

### EXAMPLE 4 Simplifying Powers of $i$

Simplify each power of $i$.

**(a)** $i^{12}$ **(b)** $i^{39}$

**SOLUTION**

**(a)** $i^{12} = (i^4)^3 = 1^3 = 1$

**(b)** To find $i^{39}$, start by dividing 39 by 4 (Step 1), as shown in the margin. The remainder is 3. So $i^{39} = i^3 = -i$ (Step 2).

Another way to simplify $i^{39}$ is as follows.

$$i^{39} = i^{36} \cdot i^3 = (i^4)^9 \cdot i^3 = 1^9 \cdot (-i) = -i$$

## EXTENSION EXERCISES

*Use the method of Examples 1–3 to write each expression as a real number or a product of a real number and i.*

**1.** $\sqrt{-144}$ **2.** $\sqrt{-196}$ **3.** $-\sqrt{-225}$ **4.** $-\sqrt{-400}$

**5.** $\sqrt{-3}$ **6.** $\sqrt{-19}$ **7.** $\sqrt{-75}$ **8.** $\sqrt{-125}$

**9.** $\sqrt{-5} \cdot \sqrt{-5}$ **10.** $\sqrt{-3} \cdot \sqrt{-3}$ **11.** $\sqrt{-9} \cdot \sqrt{-36}$

**12.** $\sqrt{-4} \cdot \sqrt{-81}$ **13.** $\sqrt{-16} \cdot \sqrt{-100}$ **14.** $\sqrt{-81} \cdot \sqrt{-121}$

**15.** $\dfrac{\sqrt{-200}}{\sqrt{-100}}$ **16.** $\dfrac{\sqrt{-50}}{\sqrt{-2}}$ **17.** $\dfrac{\sqrt{-54}}{\sqrt{6}}$

**18.** $\dfrac{\sqrt{-90}}{\sqrt{10}}$ **19.** $\dfrac{\sqrt{-288}}{\sqrt{-8}}$ **20.** $\dfrac{\sqrt{-48} \cdot \sqrt{-3}}{\sqrt{-2}}$

**21.** Why is it incorrect to use the product rule for radicals to multiply $\sqrt{-3} \cdot \sqrt{-12}$?

**22.** In your own words describe the relationship between complex numbers and real numbers.

*Use the method of Example 4 to simplify each power of i.*

**23.** $i^8$ **24.** $i^{16}$ **25.** $i^{42}$ **26.** $i^{86}$

**27.** $i^{47}$ **28.** $i^{63}$ **29.** $i^{101}$ **30.** $i^{141}$

# COLLABORATIVE INVESTIGATION

## Budgeting to Buy a Car

You are shopping for a sports car and have put aside a certain amount of money each month for a car payment. Your instructor will assign this amount to you. After looking through a variety of resources, you have narrowed your choices to the cars listed in the table.

| Year/Make/Model | Retail Price | Fuel Tank Size (in gallons) | Miles per Gallon (city) | Miles per Gallon (highway) |
|---|---|---|---|---|
| 2006 Ford Mustang | $26,320 | 16.0 | 18 | 23 |
| 2006 Ford Five Hundred | $22,230 | 20.0 | 20 | 27 |
| 2006 Toyota Camry | $25,805 | 18.5 | 20 | 28 |
| 2006 Mazda MX-5 Miata | $26,700 | 12.7 | 23 | 30 |
| 2006 Honda CR-V XLE | $25,450 | 15.3 | 22 | 27 |
| 2006 Chevrolet Tracker | $23,900 | 17.0 | 19 | 25 |

*Source:* www.edmunds.com

As a group, work through the following steps to determine which car you can afford to buy.

**A.** Decide which cars you think are within your budget.

**B.** Select one of the cars you identified in part A. Have each member of the group calculate the monthly payment for this car using a different financing option. Use the formula given below, where $P$ is principal, $r$ is interest rate, and $m$ is the number of monthly payments, along with the financing options table.

**Financing Options**

| Time (in years) | Interest Rate |
|---|---|
| 4 | 7.0% |
| 5 | 8.5% |
| 6 | 10.0% |

$$\text{Monthly Payment} = \frac{\frac{Pr}{12}}{1 - \left(\frac{12}{12 + r}\right)^{m}}$$

**C.** Have each group member determine the amount of money paid in interest over the duration of the loan for his or her financing option.

**D.** Consider fuel expenses.

1. Assume you will travel an average of 75 miles in the city and 400 miles on the highway each week. How many gallons of gas will you need to buy each month?
2. Using typical prices for gas in your area at this time, how much money will you need to have available for buying gas?

**E.** Repeat parts B–D as necessary until your group can reach a consensus on the car you will buy and the financing option you will use. Write a paragraph to explain your choices.

# CHAPTER 6 TEST

1. Consider $\{-4, -\sqrt{5}, -\frac{3}{2}, -.5, 0, \sqrt{3}, 4.1, 12\}$. List the elements of the set that belong to each of the following.
   (a) natural numbers
   (b) whole numbers
   (c) integers
   (d) rational numbers
   (e) irrational numbers
   (f) real numbers

2. Match each set in (a)–(d) with the correct set-builder notation description in A–D.
   (a) $\{\ldots, -4, -3, -2, -1\}$
   (b) $\{3, 4, 5, 6, \ldots\}$
   (c) $\{1, 2, 3, 4, \ldots\}$
   (d) $\{-12, \ldots, -2, -1, 0, 1, 2, \ldots, 12\}$

   **A.** $\{x | x$ is an integer with absolute value less than or equal to $12\}$
   **B.** $\{x | x$ is an integer greater than $2.5\}$
   **C.** $\{x | x$ is a negative integer$\}$
   **D.** $\{x | x$ is a positive integer$\}$

3. Decide whether each statement is true or false.
   (a) The absolute value of a number is always positive.
   (b) $|-7| = -(-7)$
   (c) $\frac{2}{5}$ is an example of a real number that is not an integer.
   (d) Every real number is either positive or negative.

*Perform the indicated operations. Use the order of operations as necessary.*

4. $6^2 - 4(9 - 1)$

5. $(-3)(-2) - [5 + (8 - 10)]$

6. $\dfrac{(-8 + 3) - (5 + 10)}{7 - 9}$

7. ***Changes in Car Sales*** The graph shows the percent change in car sales from January 2000 to January 2001 for various automakers. Use this graph to answer the following. (Consider absolute value.)
   (a) Which automaker had the greatest change in sales? What was that change?
   (b) Which automaker had the least change in sales? What was that change?

**CAR SALES**

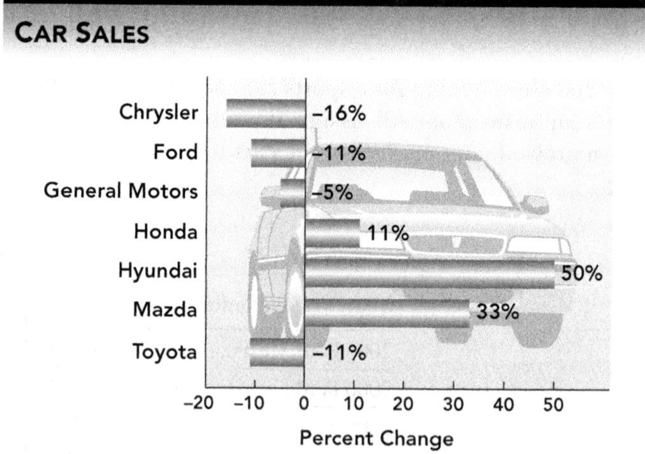


*Source:* Automakers.

   (c) *True* or *false:* The absolute value of the percent change for Honda was greater than the absolute value of the percent change for Toyota.
   (d) *True* or *false:* The percent change for Hyundai was more than four times greater than the percent change for Honda.

8. ***Altitude of a Plane*** The surface of the Dead Sea has altitude 1299 ft below sea level. Vangie is flying 80 ft above that surface. How much altitude must she gain to clear a 3852 ft pass by 225 ft? (*Source: The World Almanac and Book of Facts.*)

9. ***Median Home Prices*** Median pricings for existing homes in the United States for the years 1997 through 2002 are shown in the table. Complete the table, determining the change from one year to the next by subtraction.

| Year | Median-Priced Existing Homes | Change from Previous Year |
|---|---|---|
| 1997 | \$121,800 | |
| 1998 | \$128,400 | \$6600 |
| (a) 1999 | \$133,300 | |
| (b) 2000 | \$139,000 | |
| (c) 2001 | \$147,800 | |
| (d) 2002 | \$158,100 | |

*Source:* National Association of Realtors.

**10.** Match each statement in (a)–(f) with the property that justifies it in A–F.

**(a)** $7 \cdot (8 \cdot 5) = (7 \cdot 8) \cdot 5$
**(b)** $3x + 3y = 3(x + y)$
**(c)** $8 \cdot 1 = 1 \cdot 8 = 8$
**(d)** $7 + (6 + 9) = (6 + 9) + 7$
**(e)** $9 + (-9) = -9 + 9 = 0$
**(f)** $5 \cdot 8$ is a real number.

**A.** Distributive property
**B.** Identity property
**C.** Closure property
**D.** Commutative property
**E.** Associative property
**F.** Inverse property

**11.** ***Basketball Shot Statistics*** Six players on the local high school basketball team had the following shooting statistics.

| Player | Field Goal Attempts | Field Goals Made |
|---|---|---|
| Ed Moura | 40 | 13 |
| Jack Pritchard | 10 | 4 |
| Chuck Miller | 20 | 8 |
| Ben Whitney | 6 | 4 |
| Charlie Dawkins | 7 | 2 |
| Jason McElwain ("J-Mac") | 7 | 6 |

Answer each question, using estimation skills as necessary.

**(a)** Which player made more than half of his attempts?
**(b)** Which players made just less than $\frac{1}{3}$ of the attempts?
**(c)** Which player made exactly $\frac{2}{3}$ of his attempts?
**(d)** Which two players made the same fractional parts of their attempts? What was the fractional part, reduced to lowest terms?
**(e)** Which player had the greatest fractional part of shots made?

*Perform each operation. Write your answer in lowest terms.*

**12.** $\frac{3}{16} + \frac{1}{2}$

**13.** $\frac{9}{20} - \frac{3}{32}$

**14.** $\frac{3}{8} \cdot \left(-\frac{16}{15}\right)$

**15.** $\frac{7}{9} \div \frac{14}{27}$

**16.** Convert each rational number into a repeating or terminating decimal. Use a calculator if your instructor so allows.

**(a)** $\frac{9}{20}$ **(b)** $\frac{5}{12}$

**17.** Convert each decimal into a quotient of integers, reduced to lowest terms.

**(a)** $.72$ **(b)** $.\overline{58}$

**18.** Identify each number as rational or irrational.

**(a)** $\sqrt{10}$ **(b)** $\sqrt{16}$
**(c)** $.01$ **(d)** $.\overline{01}$
**(e)** $.0101101110\ldots$ **(f)** $\pi$

*For each of the following,* **(a)** *use a calculator to find a decimal approximation and* **(b)** *simplify the radical according to the guidelines in this chapter.*

**19.** $\sqrt{150}$

**20.** $\frac{13}{\sqrt{7}}$

**21.** $2\sqrt{32} - 5\sqrt{128}$

**22.** A student using her powerful new calculator states that the *exact* value of $\sqrt{65}$ is 8.062257748. Is she correct? If not, explain.

**23.** Work each of the following using either a calculator or paper-and-pencil methods, as directed by your instructor.

**(a)** $4.6 + 9.21$ **(b)** $12 - 3.725 - 8.59$
**(c)** $86(.45)$ **(d)** $236.439 \div (-9.73)$

**24.** Round 9.0449 to the following place values:

**(a)** hundredths **(b)** thousandths.

**25. (a)** Find 18.5% of 90.
**(b)** What number is 145% of 70?

**26.** Consider the figure.

**(a)** What percent of the total number of shapes are circles?
**(b)** What percent of the total number of shapes are not stars?

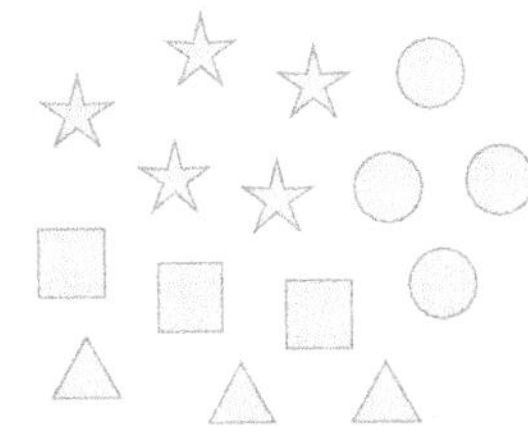

27. ***Sales of Books*** Use estimation techniques to answer the following: In 2005, Bill Schoof sold \$300,000 worth of books. In 2006, he sold \$900,000. His 2006 sales were _____ of his 2005 sales.

 A. 30% B. $33\frac{1}{3}\%$

 C. 200% D. 300%

28. ***Creature Comforts*** From a list of "everyday items" often taken for granted, adults were recently surveyed as to those items they wouldn't want to live without. Complete the results shown in the table if 1200 adults were surveyed.

| Item | Percent That Wouldn't Want to Live Without | Number That Wouldn't Want to Live Without |
|---|---|---|
| Toilet paper | 69% | |
| Zipper | 42% | |
| Frozen Food | | 190 |
| Self-stick note pads | | 75 |

(Other items included tape, hairspray, pantyhose, paper clips, and Velcro.)
*Source:* Market Facts for Kleenex Cottonelle.

29. ***Composition of U.S. Workforce*** The U.S. Bureau of Labor Statistics projected the composition of the U.S. workforce for the year 2006. The projected total number of people in the workforce for that year is 148,847,000. To the nearest thousand, how many of these will be in the Hispanic category?

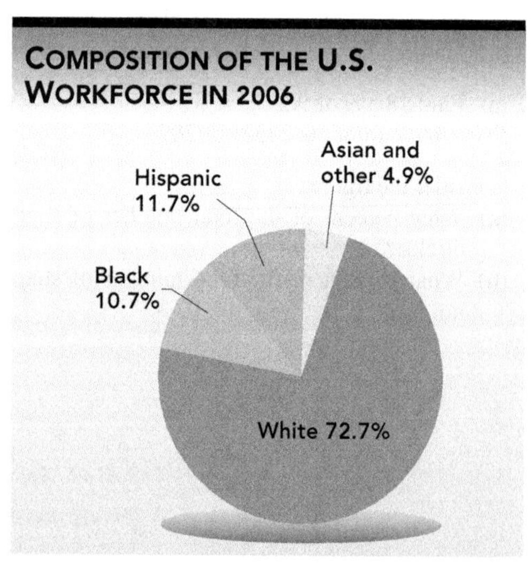


*Source:* U.S. Bureau of Labor Statistics.

30. ***Medicare Funding*** Current projections indicate that funding for Medicare will not cover its costs unless the program changes. The line graph shows projections for the years 2004 through 2013. What signed number represents how much the funding will have changed from 2004 to 2013?

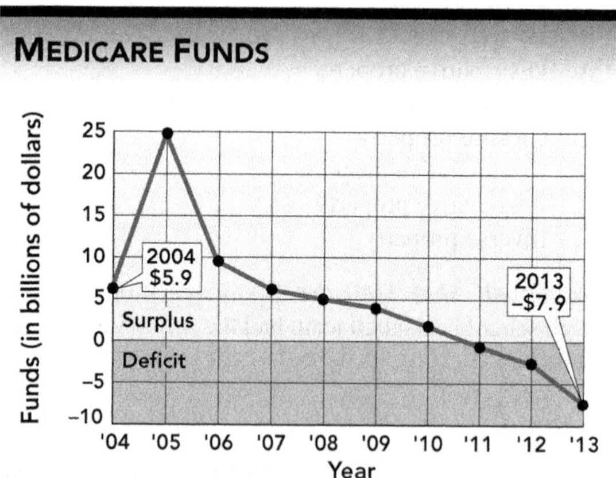


*Source:* Centers for Medicare and Medicaid Services.

7

# THE BASIC CONCEPTS OF ALGEBRA

In the 1994 movie *Little Big League*, young Billy Heywood (Luke Edwards) inherits the Minnesota Twins baseball team and becomes manager. He leads the team to the Division Championship and then to the playoffs. But before the final playoff game, the biggest game of the year, he can't keep his mind on his job, because a homework problem is giving him trouble.

*If Joe can paint a house in 3 hours, and Sam can paint the same house in 5 hours, how long does it take for them to do it together?*

One of his players provides a method to solve the problem, where $a$ and $b$ are the individual times. He claims that the expression $\frac{a \times b}{a + b}$ gives the correct answer. With $a = 5$ and $b = 3$, the answer he gives is

$$\frac{5 \times 3}{5 + 3} = \frac{15}{8} = 1\frac{7}{8} \text{ hours.}$$

However, the scriptwriters never say whether this is truly mathematically correct. Can you determine whether this answer is indeed the correct one? See the solution on page 414.

# 7.1 Linear Equations

**Solving Linear Equations • Special Kinds of Linear Equations • Literal Equations and Formulas • Models**

**al-jabr, algebrista, algebra** The word **algebra** comes from the title of the work *Hisâb al-jabr w'al muquâbalah*, a ninth-century treatise by the Arab Mohammed ibn Mûsâ al-Khowârizmî. The title translates as "the science of reunion and reduction," or more generally, "the science of transposition and cancellation."

In the title of Khowârizmî's book, *jabr* ("restoration") refers to transposing negative quantities across the equals symbol in solving equations. From Latin versions of Khowârizmî's text, **"al-jabr"** became the broad term covering the art of equation solving. (The prefix *al* means "the.")

## Solving Linear Equations

An **algebraic expression** involves only the basic operations of addition, subtraction, multiplication, or division (except by 0), or raising to powers or taking roots on any collection of variables and numbers.

$$8x + 9, \quad \sqrt{y} + 4, \quad \text{and} \quad \frac{x^3y^8}{z} \qquad \text{Algebraic expressions}$$

An **equation** is a statement that two algebraic expressions are equal. A *linear equation in one variable* involves only real numbers and one variable.

$$x + 1 = -2, \quad y - 3 = 5, \quad \text{and} \quad 2k + 5 = 10 \qquad \text{Linear equations}$$

### Linear Equation in One Variable

An equation in the variable $x$ is **linear** if it can be written in the form

$$Ax + B = C,$$

where $A$, $B$, and $C$ are real numbers, with $A \neq 0$.

A linear equation in one variable is also called a **first-degree equation,** because the greatest power on the variable is one.

If the variable in an equation is replaced by a real number that makes the statement true, then that number is a **solution** of the equation. For example, 8 is a solution of the equation $x - 3 = 5$, because replacing $x$ with 8 gives a true statement. An equation is **solved** by finding its **solution set,** the set of all solutions. The solution set of the equation $x - 3 = 5$ is $\{8\}$.

**Equivalent equations** are equations with the same solution set. Equations generally are solved by starting with a given equation and producing a series of simpler equivalent equations. For example,

$$8x + 1 = 17, \quad 8x = 16, \quad \text{and} \quad x = 2 \qquad \text{Equivalent equations}$$

are equivalent equations because each has the same solution set, $\{2\}$. We use the addition and multiplication properties of equality to produce equivalent equations.

### Addition Property of Equality

For all real numbers $A$, $B$, and $C$, the equations

$$A = B \quad \text{and} \quad A + C = B + C$$

are equivalent. (The same number may be added to both sides of an equation without changing the solution set.)

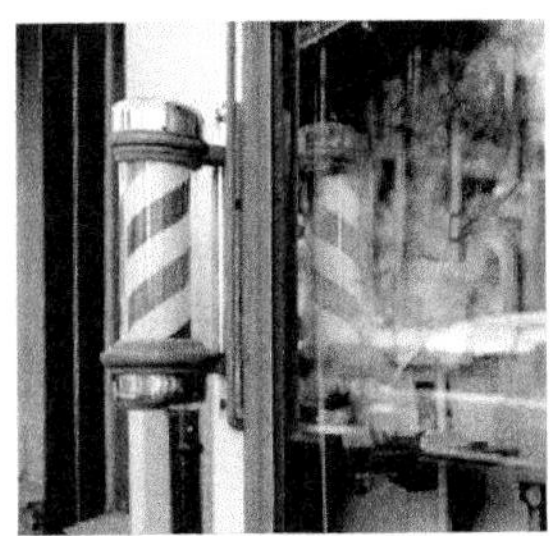

**algebrista, algebra** In Spain under Moslem rule, the word **algebrista** referred to the person who restored (reset) broken bones. Signs outside barber shops read *Algebrista y Sangrador* (bonesetter and bloodletter). Such services were part of the barber's trade. The traditional red-and-white striped barber pole symbolizes blood and bandages.

### Multiplication Property of Equality

For all real numbers $A$, $B$, and $C$, where $C \neq 0$, the equations

$$A = B \qquad \text{and} \qquad AC = BC$$

are equivalent. (Both sides of an equation may be multiplied by the same nonzero number without changing the solution set.)

Because subtraction and division are defined in terms of addition and multiplication, respectively, the same number may be subtracted from both sides of an equation, and both sides may be divided by the same nonzero number, without affecting the solution set.

The distributive property allows us to combine *like terms*, such as $4y$ and $2y$. For example,

$$4y - 2y = (4 - 2)y = 2y.$$

### EXAMPLE 1 Using the Addition and Multiplication Properties to Solve a Linear Equation

Solve $4x - 2x - 5 = 4 + 6x + 3$.

**SOLUTION**

The goal is to get $x$ alone on one side of the equation.

$$\begin{aligned} 4x - 2x - 5 &= 4 + 6x + 3 \\ 2x - 5 &= 7 + 6x && \text{Combine like terms.} \end{aligned}$$

Use the addition property to get the terms with $x$ on the same side of the equation and the remaining terms (the numbers) on the other side.

$$\begin{aligned} 2x - 5 + 5 &= 7 + 6x + 5 && \text{Add 5.} \\ 2x &= 12 + 6x && \text{Combine like terms.} \\ 2x - 6x &= 12 + 6x - 6x && \text{Subtract } 6x. \\ -4x &= 12 && \text{Combine like terms.} \\ \frac{-4x}{-4} &= \frac{12}{-4} && \text{Divide by } -4. \\ x &= -3 \end{aligned}$$

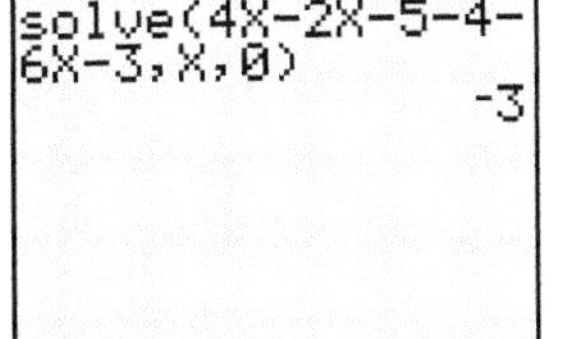


Graphing calculators can solve equations of the form

expression in X = 0.

The TI-83/84 Plus requires that you input the expression, the variable for which you are solving, and a "guess," separated by commas. The screen here shows how to solve the equation in Example 1.

Check that $-3$ is the solution by substituting it for $x$ in the *original* equation.

*Check:*

$$\begin{aligned} 4x - 2x - 5 &= 4 + 6x + 3 && \text{Original equation} \\ 4(-3) - 2(-3) - 5 &\stackrel{?}{=} 4 + 6(-3) + 3 && \text{Let } x = -3. \\ -12 + 6 - 5 &\stackrel{?}{=} 4 - 18 + 3 && \text{Multiply.} \\ -11 &= -11 && \text{True} \end{aligned}$$

This is not the solution. → $-11 = -11$

The true statement indicates that $\{-3\}$ is the solution set.

### Solving a Linear Equation in One Variable

*Step 1* **Clear fractions.** Eliminate any fractions by multiplying both sides of the equation by a common denominator.

*Step 2* **Simplify each side separately.** Use the distributive property to clear parentheses, and combine like terms as needed.

*Step 3* **Isolate the variable terms on one side.** Use the addition property of equality to get all terms with variables on one side of the equation and all numbers on the other.

*Step 4* **Transform so that the coefficient of the variable is 1.** Use the multiplication property of equality to get an equation with just the variable (with coefficient 1) on one side.

*Step 5* **Check.** Substitute the solution into the original equation.

### EXAMPLE 2 Using the Distributive Property to Solve a Linear Equation

Solve $2(k - 5) + 3k = k + 6$.

**SOLUTION**

*Step 1* Because there are no fractions in this equation, Step 1 does not apply.

*Step 2* Use the distributive property to simplify and combine terms on the left side.

$$2(k - 5) + 3k = k + 6$$
$$2k - 10 + 3k = k + 6 \quad \text{Distributive property}$$
$$5k - 10 = k + 6 \quad \text{Combine like terms.}$$

*Step 3* Next, use the addition property of equality.

$$5k - 10 + 10 = k + 6 + 10 \quad \text{Add 10.}$$
$$5k = k + 16 \quad \text{Combine like terms.}$$
$$5k - k = k + 16 - k \quad \text{Subtract } k.$$
$$4k = 16 \quad \text{Combine like terms.}$$

*Step 4* Use the multiplication property of equality to get just $k$ on the left.

$$\frac{4k}{4} = \frac{16}{4} \quad \text{Divide by 4.}$$
$$k = 4$$

*Step 5* Check that the solution set is $\{4\}$ by substituting 4 for $k$ in the original equation.

Because of space limitations, we will not always show the check when solving an equation. ***You should always check your work.***

When fractions or decimals appear as numerical factors of terms in equations, our work can be made easier if we multiply each side of the equation by the least common denominator (LCD) of all the fractions. This is an application of the multiplication property of equality.

The problem-solving strategy of guessing and checking, discussed in Chapter 1, was actually used by the early Egyptians in equation solving. This method, called the **Rule of False Position,** involved making an initial guess at the solution of an equation, and then following up with an adjustment in the likely event that the guess was incorrect. For example (using our modern notation), if the equation

$$6x + 2x = 32$$

was to be solved, an initial guess might have been $x = 3$. Substituting 3 for $x$ gives

$$6(3) + 2(3) = 32 \quad ?$$
$$18 + 6 = 32 \quad ?$$
$$24 = 32. \quad \textbf{False}$$

The guess, 3, gives a value (24) which is smaller than the desired value (32). Since 24 is $\frac{3}{4}$ of 32, the guess, 3, is $\frac{3}{4}$ of the actual solution. The actual solution, therefore, must be 4, since 3 is $\frac{3}{4}$ of 4.

Use the methods explained in this section to verify this result.

**François Viète** (1540–1603) was a lawyer at the court of Henry IV of France and studied equations. Viète simplified the notation of algebra and was among the first to use letters to represent numbers. For centuries, algebra and arithmetic were expressed in a cumbersome way with words and occasional symbols. Since the time of Viète, algebra has gone beyond equation solving; the abstract nature of higher algebra depends on its symbolic language.

**Algebra** dates back to the Babylonians of 2000 B.C. The Egyptians also worked problems in algebra, but the problems were not as complex as those of the Babylonians. In about the sixth century, the Hindus developed methods for solving problems involving interest, discounts, and partnerships.

Many Hindu and Greek works on mathematics were preserved only because Moslem scholars from about 750 to 1250 made translations of them. The Arabs took the work of the Greeks and Hindus and greatly expanded it. For example, Mohammed ibn Mûsâ al-Khowârizmî wrote books on algebra and on the Hindu numeration system (the one we use) that had tremendous influence in Western Europe; his name is remembered today in the word *algorithm*.

## EXAMPLE 3 Solving a Linear Equation with Fractions

Solve $\frac{x+7}{6} + \frac{2x-8}{2} = -4$.

**SOLUTION**

*Step 1* $6\left(\frac{x+7}{6} + \frac{2x-8}{2}\right) = 6(-4)$ Multiply both sides by the LCD, 6, to eliminate the fractions.

*Step 2* $6\left(\frac{x+7}{6}\right) + 6\left(\frac{2x-8}{2}\right) = 6(-4)$ Distributive property

Multiply each term by 6.

$x + 7 + 3(2x - 8) = -24$ Multiply.

$x + 7 + 6x - 24 = -24$ Distributive property

$7x - 17 = -24$ Combine like terms.

*Step 3* $7x - 17 + 17 = -24 + 17$ Add 17.

$7x = -7$ Combine like terms.

*Step 4* $\frac{7x}{7} = \frac{-7}{7}$ Divide by 7.

$x = -1$

*Step 5* *Check*: $\frac{x+7}{6} + \frac{2x-8}{2} = -4$ Original equation

$\frac{-1+7}{6} + \frac{2(-1)-8}{2} = -4$ ? Let $x = -1$.

$\frac{6}{6} + \frac{-10}{2} = -4$ ?

$1 - 5 = -4$ ?

$-4 = -4$ True

The solution $-1$ checks, so the solution set is $\{-1\}$.

## EXAMPLE 4 Solving a Linear Equation with Decimals

Solve $.06x + .09(15 - x) = .07(15)$.

**SOLUTION**

Because each decimal number is in hundredths, multiply both sides of the equation by 100. (This is done by moving the decimal points two places to the right.) To multiply the second term, $.09(15 - x)$, by 100, multiply $100(.09)$ first to get 9, so the product $100(.09)(15 - x)$ becomes $9(15 - x)$.

$.06x + .09(15 - x) = .07(15)$ Original equation

$.06x + .09(15 - x) = .07(15)$ Multiply each term by 100.

$6x + 9(15 - x) = 7(15)$

$6x + 9(15) - 9x = 105$ Distributive property; multiply.

$-3x + 135 = 105$ Combine like terms; multiply.

$$-3x + 135 - 135 = 105 - 135 \quad \text{Subtract 135.}$$
$$-3x = -30$$
$$\frac{-3x}{-3} = \frac{-30}{-3} \quad \text{Divide by } -3.$$
$$x = 10$$

Check to verify that the solution set is $\{10\}$.

**Special Kinds of Linear Equations** The preceding equations had solution sets containing one element; for example,

$$2(k - 5) + 3k = k + 6 \quad \text{has solution set } \{4\}.$$

Some equations that appear to be linear have no solutions, while others have an infinite number of solutions. Table 1 gives the names of these types of equations.

**TABLE 1**

| Type of Equation | Number of Solutions | Indication When Solving |
|---|---|---|
| **Conditional** | One | Final line is $x =$ a number. (See Example 5(a).) |
| **Identity** | Infinite; solution set {all real numbers} | Final line is true, such as $0 = 0$. (See Example 5(b).) |
| **Contradiction** | None; solution set $\emptyset$ | Final line is false, such as $0 = 1$. (See Example 5(c).) |

**Sofia Kovalevskaya** (1850–1891) was the most widely known Russian mathematician in the late nineteenth century. She did most of her work in the theory of **differential equations**—equations invaluable for expressing rates of change. For example, in biology, the rate of growth of a population, say of microbes, can be precisely stated by differential equations.

Kovalevskaya studied privately because public lectures were not open to women. She eventually received a degree (1874) from the University of Göttingen, Germany. In 1884 she became a lecturer at the University of Stockholm and later was appointed professor of higher mathematics.

## EXAMPLE 5 Recognizing Conditional Equations, Identities, and Contradictions

Solve each equation. Decide whether it is a *conditional equation*, an *identity*, or a *contradiction*.

**(a)** $5x - 9 = 4(x - 3)$ **(b)** $5x - 15 = 5(x - 3)$ **(c)** $5x - 15 = 5(x - 4)$

**SOLUTION**

**(a)**
$$5x - 9 = 4(x - 3)$$
$$5x - 9 = 4x - 12 \quad \text{Distributive property}$$
$$5x - 9 - 4x = 4x - 12 - 4x \quad \text{Subtract } 4x.$$
$$x - 9 = -12 \quad \text{Combine like terms.}$$
$$x - 9 + 9 = -12 + 9 \quad \text{Add 9.}$$
$$x = -3$$

The solution set, $\{-3\}$, has only one element, so $5x - 9 = 4(x - 3)$ is a conditional equation.

**(b)** $5x - 15 = 5(x - 3)$
$$5x - 15 = 5x - 15 \quad \text{Distributive property}$$
$$0 = 0 \quad \text{Subtract } 5x \text{ and add 15.}$$

The final line, $0 = 0$, indicates that the solution set is {all real numbers}, and the equation $5x - 15 = 5(x - 3)$ is an identity. (*Note:* The first step yielded $5x - 15 = 5x - 15$, which is true for all values of $x$. We could have identified the equation as an identity at that point.)

**(c)**

| | |
|---|---|
| $5x - 15 = 5(x - 4)$ | |
| $5x - 15 = 5x - 20$ | Distributive property |
| $5x - 15 - 5x = 5x - 20 - 5x$ | Subtract $5x$. |
| $\mathbf{-15 = -20}$ | False |

Because the result, $-15 = -20$, is *false*, the equation has no solution. The solution set is $\emptyset$, so the equation $5x - 15 = 5(x - 4)$ is a contradiction.

## For Further Thought

### The Axioms of Equality

When we solve an equation, we must make sure that it remains "balanced"—that is, any operation that is performed on one side of an equation must also be performed on the other side in order to assure that the set of solutions remains the same.

Underlying the rules for solving equations are four axioms of equality, listed below. For all real numbers $a$, $b$, and $c$,

1. **Reflexive axiom** $a = a$
2. **Symmetric axiom** If $a = b$, then $b = a$.
3. **Transitive axiom** If $a = b$ and $b = c$, then $a = c$.
4. **Substitution axiom** If $a = b$, then $a$ may replace $b$ in any statement without affecting the truth or falsity of the statement.

A relation, such as equality, which satisfies the first three of these axioms (reflexive, symmetric, and transitive), is called an equivalence relation.

**For Group Discussion or Individual Investigation**

1. Give an example of an everyday relation that does not satisfy the symmetric axiom.
2. Does the transitive axiom hold in sports competition, with the relation "defeats"?
3. Give an example of a relation that does not satisfy the transitive axiom.

**Literal Equations and Formulas** An equation involving *variables* (or letters), such as $cx + d = e$, is called a **literal equation.** The most useful examples of literal equations are *formulas*. The solution of a problem in algebra often depends on the use of a mathematical statement or **formula** in which more than one letter is used to express a relationship. Examples of formulas are

$$d = rt, \quad I = prt, \quad \text{and} \quad P = 2L + 2W. \qquad \text{Formulas}$$

In some applications, the necessary formula must be solved for one of its variables. This process is called **solving for a specified variable.** The steps used are similar to those used in solving linear equations. ***When you are solving for a specified variable, the key is to treat that variable as if it were the only one; treat all other variables like numbers (constants).***

**Solving for a Specified Variable**

*Step 1* Transform the equation so that all terms containing the specified variable are on one side of the equation and all terms without that variable are on the other side.

*Step 2* If necessary, use the distributive property to combine the terms with the specified variable. The result should be the product of a sum or difference and the variable.

*Step 3* Divide both sides by the factor that is multiplied by the specified variable.

### EXAMPLE 6 Solving for a Specified Variable

Solve the formula $P = 2L + 2W$ for $W$.

**SOLUTION**

Solve the formula for the perimeter (distance around) of a rectangle (Figure 1) for $W$ by isolating $W$ on one side of the equals sign.



Perimeter, $P$, the sum of the lengths of the sides of the rectangle, is given by

$P = 2L + 2W.$

**FIGURE 1**

*Step 1*

$$P = 2L + 2W$$

$$P - 2L = 2L + 2W - 2L \quad \text{Subtract } 2L.$$

$$P - 2L = 2W$$

*Step 2* Step 2 is not needed here.

*Step 3*

$$\frac{P - 2L}{2} = \frac{2W}{2} \quad \text{Divide both sides by 2.}$$

$$\frac{P - 2L}{2} = W \quad \text{or} \quad W = \frac{P}{2} - L$$

## Models

A **mathematical model** is an equation (or inequality) that describes the relationship between two quantities. A *linear model* is a linear equation.

### EXAMPLE 7 Modeling the Prevention of Indoor Pollutants

One of the most effective ways of removing contaminants such as carbon monoxide and nitrogen dioxide from the air while cooking is to use a vented range hood. If a range hood removes contaminants at a flow rate of $F$ liters of air per second, then the percent $P$ of contaminants that are also removed from the surrounding air can be modeled by the linear equation

$$P = 1.06F + 7.18,$$

where $10 \leq F \leq 75$. What flow rate $F$ must a range hood have to remove 50% of the contaminants from the air? (*Source:* Rezvan, R. L., "Effectiveness of Local Ventilation in Removing Simulated Pollutants from Point Sources," 65–75. In *Proceedings of the Third International Conference on Indoor Air Quality and Climate*, 1984.)

**SOLUTION**

Because $P = 50$, the equation becomes

$$\begin{aligned} 50 &= 1.06F + 7.18 \\ 5000 &= 106F + 718 && \text{Multiply by 100.} \\ 4282 &= 106F && \text{Subtract 718.} \\ F &\approx 40.40. && \text{Divide by 106.} \end{aligned}$$

Therefore, to remove 50% of the contaminants, the flow rate must be approximately 40.40 L of air per second.

## 7.1 EXERCISES

1. Which equations are linear equations in $x$?
   A. $3x + x - 1 = 0$ B. $8 = x^2$
   C. $6x + 2 = 9$ D. $\frac{1}{2}x - \frac{1}{x} = 0$

2. Which of the equations in Exercise 1 are not linear equations in $x$? Explain why.

3. Decide whether 6 is a solution of $3(x + 4) = 5x$ by substituting 6 for $x$. If it is not a solution, explain why.

4. Use substitution to decide whether $-2$ is a solution of $5(x + 4) - 3(x + 6) = 9(x + 1)$. If it is not a solution, explain why.

5. If two equations are equivalent, they have the same ______ ______.

6. The equation $4[x + (2 - 3x)] = 2(4 - 4x)$ is an identity. Let $x$ represent the number of letters in your last name. Is this number a solution of this equation? Check your answer.

7. Which expression is equivalent to $.06(10 - x)(100)$?
   A. $.06 - .06x$ B. $60 - 6x$
   C. $6 - 6x$ D. $6 - .06x$

8. Describe in your own words the steps used to solve a linear equation.

*Solve each equation.*

9. $7k + 8 = 1$
10. $5m - 4 = 21$
11. $8 - 8x = -16$
12. $9 - 2r = 15$
13. $7x - 5x + 15 = x + 8$
14. $2x + 4 - x = 4x - 5$
15. $12w + 15w - 9 + 5 = -3w + 5 - 9$
16. $-4t + 5t - 8 + 4 = 6t - 4$
17. $2(x + 3) = -4(x + 1)$
18. $4(x - 9) = 8(x + 3)$
19. $3(2w + 1) - 2(w - 2) = 5$
20. $4(x - 2) + 2(x + 3) = 6$
21. $2x + 3(x - 4) = 2(x - 3)$
22. $6x - 3(5x + 2) = 4(1 - x)$
23. $6p - 4(3 - 2p) = 5(p - 4) - 10$
24. $-2k - 3(4 - 2k) = 2(k - 3) + 2$
25. $-[2z - (5z + 2)] = 2 + (2z + 7)$
26. $-[6x - (4x + 8)] = 9 + (6x + 3)$
27. $-3m + 6 - 5(m - 1) = -(2m - 4) - 5m + 5$
28. $4(k + 2) - 8k - 5 = -3k + 9 - 2(k + 6)$
29. $-[3x - (2x + 5)] = -4 - [3(2x - 4) - 3x]$
30. $2[-(x - 1) + 4] = 5 + [-(6x - 7) + 9x]$

**31.** $-(9 - 3a) - (4 + 2a) - 4 = -(2 - 5a) - a$

**32.** $(2 - 4x) - (3 - 4x) + 4 = -(-3 + 6x) + x$

**33.** $(2m - 6) - (3m - 4) = -(-4 + m) - 4m + 6$

**34.** $(3x - 4) - (5x - 8) = -(x + 12) - 6x + 1$

**35.** To solve the linear equation

$$.05x + .12(x + 5000) = 940,$$

we can multiply both sides by a power of 10 so that all coefficients are integers. What is the smallest power of 10 that will accomplish this goal?

**36.** Suppose that in solving the equation

$$\frac{1}{3}x + \frac{1}{2}x = \frac{1}{6}x,$$

you begin by multiplying both sides by 12, rather than the *least* common denominator, 6. Should you get the correct solution anyway? Explain.

*Solve each equation.*

**37.** $\frac{3x}{4} + \frac{5x}{2} = 13$

**38.** $\frac{8x}{3} - \frac{2x}{4} = -13$

**39.** $\frac{x - 8}{5} + \frac{8}{5} = -\frac{x}{3}$

**40.** $\frac{2r - 3}{7} + \frac{3}{7} = -\frac{r}{3}$

**41.** $\frac{4t + 1}{3} = \frac{t + 5}{6} + \frac{t - 3}{6}$

**42.** $\frac{2x + 5}{5} = \frac{3x + 1}{2} + \frac{-x + 7}{2}$

**43.** $.05x + .12(x + 5000) = 940$

**44.** $.09k + .13(k + 300) = 61$

**45.** $.02(50) + .08r = .04(50 + r)$

**46.** $.20(14{,}000) + .14t = .18(14{,}000 + t)$

**47.** $.05x + .10(200 - x) = .45x$

**48.** $.08x + .12(260 - x) = .48x$

**49.** The equation $x + 2 = x + 2$ is called a(n)________, because its solution set is {all real numbers}. The equation $x + 1 = x + 2$ is called a(n)____________, because its solution set is $\emptyset$.

**50.** Which equation is a conditional equation?
**A.** $2x + 1 = 3$
**B.** $x = 3x - 2x$
**C.** $3x + 1 = 3x$
**D.** $\frac{1}{2}x = \frac{1}{2}x$

*Decide whether each equation is conditional, an identity, or a contradiction. Give the solution set.*

**51.** $-2p + 5p - 9 = 3(p - 4) - 5$

**52.** $-6k + 2k - 11 = -2(2k - 3) + 4$

**53.** $6x + 2(x - 2) = 9x + 4$

**54.** $-4(x + 2) = -3(x + 5) - x$

**55.** $-11m + 4(m - 3) + 6m = 4m - 12$

**56.** $3p - 5(p + 4) + 9 = -11 + 15p$

**57.** $7[2 - (3 + 4r)] - 2r = -9 + 2(1 - 15r)$

**58.** $4[6 - (1 + 2m)] + 10m = 2(10 - 3m) + 8m$

**59.** When a formula is solved for a particular variable, several different equivalent forms may be possible. If we solve $A = \frac{1}{2}bh$ for $h$, one possible correct answer is

$$h = \frac{2A}{b}.$$

Which of the formulas is *not* equivalent to this?

**A.** $h = 2\left(\frac{A}{b}\right)$
**B.** $h = 2A\left(\frac{1}{b}\right)$
**C.** $h = \frac{A}{\frac{1}{2}b}$
**D.** $h = \frac{\frac{1}{2}A}{b}$

**60.** One source for geometric formulas gives the formula for the perimeter of a rectangle as

$$P = 2L + 2W,$$

while another gives it as

$$P = 2(L + W).$$

Are these equivalent? If so, what property justifies their equivalence?

***Mathematical Formulas*** *Solve each formula for the specified variable.*

61. $d = rt$; for $t$ (distance)

62. $I = prt$; for $r$ (simple interest)

63. $A = bh$; for $b$ (area of a parallelogram)

64. $P = 2L + 2W$; for $L$ (perimeter of a rectangle)

65. $P = a + b + c$; for $a$ (perimeter of a triangle)

66. $V = LWH$; for $W$ (volume of a rectangular solid)

67. $A = \frac{1}{2}bh$; for $b$ (area of a triangle)

68. $C = 2\pi r$; for $r$ (circumference of a circle)

69. $S = 2\pi rh + 2\pi r^2$; for $h$ (surface area of a right circular cylinder)

70. $A = \frac{1}{2}(B + b)h$; for $B$ (area of a trapezoid)

71. $\mathrm{C} = \frac{5}{9}(\mathrm{F} - 32)$; for F (Fahrenheit to Celsius)

72. $\mathrm{F} = \frac{9}{5}\mathrm{C} + 32$; for C (Celsius to Fahrenheit)

73. $A = 2HW + 2LW + 2LH$; for $H$ (surface area of a rectangular solid)

74. $V = \frac{1}{3}Bh$; for $h$ (volume of a right pyramid)

*Work each problem involving a linear model.*

75. ***College Enrollment*** The linear model

$$y = .2145x + 15.69$$

provides the projected approximate enrollment, in millions, for degree-granting institutions between the years 2003 and 2012, where $x = 0$ corresponds to 2003, $x = 1$ to 2004, and so on, and $y$ is in millions of students.

**(a)** Use the model to determine projected enrollment for Fall 2008.

**(b)** Use the model to determine the year in which enrollment is projected to reach 17 million.

76. ***Mobility of Americans*** The linear model

$$y = -.9x + 21.2,$$

where $y$ represents the percent moving each year in decade $x$, approximates the percent of Americans moving each year since the 1950s fairly well. Here $x = 1$ represents the 1950s, $x = 2$ represents the 1960s, and so on. Use this model to answer each question.

**(a)** What was the approximate percent of Americans moving in the 1960s?

**(b)** What was the approximate percent of Americans moving in the 1980s?

77. ***Indoor Air Quality and Control*** The excess lifetime cancer risk $R$ is a measure of the likelihood that an individual will develop cancer from a particular pollutant. For example, if $R = .01$ then a person has a 1% increased chance of developing cancer during a lifetime. (This would translate into 1 case of

cancer for every 100 people during an average lifetime.) The value of $R$ for formaldehyde, a highly toxic indoor air pollutant, can be calculated using the linear model $R = kd$, where $k$ is a constant, and $d$ is the daily dose in parts per million. The constant $k$ for formaldehyde can be calculated using the formula

$$k = \frac{.132B}{W},$$

where $B$ is the total number of cubic meters of air a person breathes in one day, and $W$ is a person's weight in kilograms. (*Source*: Hines, A., T. Ghosh, S. Loyalka, and R. Warder, *Indoor Air: Quality & Control*, Prentice-Hall, 1993; Ritchie, I., and R. Lehnen, "An Analysis of Formaldehyde Concentration in Mobile and Conventional Homes," *J. Env. Health* 47: 300–305.)

**(a)** Find $k$ for a person who breathes in 20 cubic meters of air per day and weighs 75 kilograms.

**(b)** Mobile homes in Minnesota were found to have a mean daily dose $d$ of .42 part per million. Calculate $R$ using the value of $k$ found in part (a).

**(c)** For every 5000 people, how many cases of cancer could be expected each year from these levels of formaldehyde? Assume an average life expectancy of 72 years.

**78.** ***Indoor Air Quality and Control*** (See Exercise 77.) For nonsmokers exposed to environmental tobacco smoke (passive smokers), $R = .0015$. (*Source*: Hines, A., T. Ghosh, S. Loyalka, and R. Warder, *Indoor Air: Quality & Control*, Prentice-Hall, 1993.)

**(a)** If the average life expectancy is 72 years, what is the excess lifetime cancer risk from secondhand tobacco smoke per year?

**(b)** Write a linear equation that will model the expected number of cancer cases $C$ per year if there are $x$ passive smokers.

**(c)** Estimate the number of cancer cases each year per 100,000 passive smokers.

**(d)** The excess lifetime risk of death from smoking is $R = .44$. Currently 26% of the U.S. population smoke. If the U.S. population is 260 million, approximate the excess number of deaths caused by smoking each year.

**79.** ***Eye Irritation from Formaldehyde*** When concentrations of formaldehyde in the air exceed 33 $\mu$g per cubic foot (1 $\mu$g = 1 microgram = .000001 gram), a strong odor and irritation to the eyes often occurs. One square foot of hardwood plywood paneling can emit 3365 $\mu$g of formaldehyde per day. (*Source*: Hines, A., T. Ghosh, S. Loyalka, and R. Warder, *Indoor Air: Quality & Control*, Prentice-Hall, 1993.)

A 4-foot by 8-foot sheet of this paneling is attached to an 8-foot wall in a room having floor dimensions of 10 feet by 10 feet.

**(a)** Determine how many cubic feet of air are in the room.

**(b)** Find the total number of micrograms of formaldehyde that are released into the air by the paneling each day.

**(c)** If there is no ventilation in the room, write a linear equation that models the amount of formaldehyde $F$ that there would be in the room after $x$ days.

**(d)** How long will it take before a person's eyes become irritated in the room?

**80.** ***Classroom Ventilation*** According to the American Society of Heating, Refrigerating and Air-Conditioning Engineers, Inc. (ASHRAE), a nonsmoking classroom should have a ventilation rate of 15 cubic feet per minute for each person in the classroom. (*Source: ASHRAE*, 1989.)

**(a)** Write an equation that models the total ventilation $V$ (in cubic feet per hour) necessary for a classroom with $x$ students.

**(b)** A common unit of ventilation is an air change per hour (ach). 1 ach is equivalent to exchanging all of the air in a room every hour. If $x$ students are in a classroom having volume 15,000 cubic feet, determine how many air exchanges per hour ($A$) are necessary to keep the room properly ventilated.

**(c)** Find the necessary number of ach $A$ if the classroom has 40 students in it.

**(d)** In areas like bars and lounges that allow smoking, the ventilation rate should be increased to 50 cubic feet per minute per person. Compared to classrooms, ventilation should be increased by what factor in heavy smoking areas?

# 7.2 Applications of Linear Equations

**Translating Words into Symbols • Guidelines for Applications • Finding Unknown Quantities • Mixture and Interest Problems • Monetary Denomination Problems • Motion Problems**

## Translating Words into Symbols

When algebra is used to solve practical applications, we must translate the verbal statements of the problems into mathematical statements.

**PROBLEM-SOLVING HINT** Usually there are key words and phrases in a verbal problem that translate into mathematical expressions involving addition, subtraction, multiplication, and division.

### Translation from Words to Mathematical Expressions

| Verbal Expression | Mathematical Expression (where $x$ and $y$ are numbers) |
|---|---|
| **Addition** | |
| The **sum** of a number and 7 | $x + 7$ |
| 6 **more than** a number | $x + 6$ |
| 3 **plus** 8 | $3 + 8$ |
| 24 **added to** a number | $x + 24$ |
| A number **increased by** 5 | $x + 5$ |
| The **sum** of two numbers | $x + y$ |
| **Subtraction** | |
| 2 **less than** a number | $x - 2$ |
| 12 **minus** a number | $12 - x$ |
| A number **decreased by** 12 | $x - 12$ |
| The **difference between** two numbers | $x - y$ |
| A number **subtracted from** 10 | $10 - x$ |
| **Multiplication** | |
| 16 **times** a number | $16x$ |
| A number **multiplied by** 6 | $6x$ |
| $\frac{2}{3}$ **of** a number (as applied to fractions and percent) | $\frac{2}{3}x$ |
| **Twice** (2 times) a number | $2x$ |
| The **product** of two numbers | $xy$ |
| **Division** | |
| The **quotient** of 8 and a number | $\frac{8}{x} \quad (x \neq 0)$ |
| A number **divided by** 13 | $\frac{x}{13}$ |
| The **ratio** of two numbers or the **quotient** of two numbers | $\frac{x}{y} \quad (y \neq 0)$ |

The symbol of equality, **=**, is often indicated by the word ***is***. In fact, since equal mathematical expressions represent different names for the same number, words that indicate the idea of "sameness" translate as =. For example,

**If the product of a number and 12 is decreased by 7, the result is 105**

translates to the mathematical equation

$$12x - 7 = 105,$$

where $x$ represents the unknown number. (Why would $7 - 12x = 105$ be incorrect?)

## Guidelines for Applications

While there is no one method that allows us to solve all types of applied problems, the following six steps are helpful.

**George Polya's problem-solving procedure** can be adapted to applications of algebra as seen in the steps in the box. Steps 1 and 2 make up the first stage of Polya's procedure (*Understand the Problem*), Step 3 forms the second stage (*Devise a Plan*), Step 4 comprises the third stage (*Carry Out the Plan*), and Steps 5 and 6 form the last stage (*Look Back*).

### Solving an Applied Problem

*Step 1* **Read** the problem carefully until you understand what is given and what is to be found.

*Step 2* **Assign a variable** to represent the unknown value, using diagrams or tables as needed. Write down what the variable represents. If necessary, express any other unknown values in terms of the variable.

*Step 3* **Write an equation** using the variable expression(s).

*Step 4* **Solve** the equation.

*Step 5* **State the answer.** Does it seem reasonable?

*Step 6* **Check** the answer in the words of the *original* problem.

The third step is often the hardest. To translate the problem into an equation, write the given phrases as mathematical expressions. Since equal mathematical expressions are names for the same number, translate any words that mean *equal* or *same* as the = symbol. The = symbol leads to an equation to be solved.

## Finding Unknown Quantities

**PROBLEM-SOLVING HINT** A common type of problem involves finding two quantities when the sum of the quantities is known. Choose a variable to represent one of the unknowns and then represent the other quantity in terms of the same variable, using information from the problem. Then write an equation based on the words of the problem.

### EXAMPLE 1 Finding Numbers of Strikeouts

Two outstanding major league pitchers in recent years are Randy Johnson and Pedro Martinez. In 2002, they combined for a total of 573 strikeouts. Johnson had 95 more strikeouts than Martinez. How many strikeouts did each pitcher have? (*Source: World Almanac and Book of Facts 2004.*)

**SOLUTION**

*Step 1* **Read** the problem. We are asked to find the number of strikeouts each pitcher had.

*Step 2* **Assign a variable** to represent the number of strikeouts for one of the men.

Let $s$ = the number of strikeouts for Pedro Martinez.

We must also find the number of strikeouts for Randy Johnson. Because he had 95 more strikeouts than Martinez,

$s + 95$ = the number of strikeouts for Johnson.

*Step 3* **Write an equation.** The sum of the numbers of strikeouts is 573, so

$$\underbrace{s}_{\text{Martinez's strikeouts}} + \underbrace{(s + 95)}_{\text{Johnson's strikeouts}} = \underbrace{573.}_{\text{Total}}$$

*Step 4* **Solve** the equation.

$$\begin{aligned} s + (s + 95) &= 573 \\ 2s + 95 &= 573 && \text{Combine like terms.} \\ 2s + 95 - 95 &= 573 - 95 && \text{Subtract 95.} \\ 2s &= 478 && \text{Combine like terms.} \\ \frac{2s}{2} &= \frac{478}{2} && \text{Divide by 2.} \\ s &= 239 \end{aligned}$$

*Step 5* **State the answer.** We let $s$ represent the number of strikeouts for Martinez, so Martinez had 239. Then the number of strikeouts for Johnson is

$s + 95 = 239 + 95 = 334.$ ⟵ Be sure to find the second answer.

*Step 6* **Check.** 334 is 95 more than 239, and the sum of 239 and 334 is 573. The conditions of the problem are satisfied, and our answer checks. ■

Here is an application of linear equations, taken from the **Greek Anthology** (about 500 A.D.), a group of 46 number problems.

*Demochares has lived a fourth of his life as a boy, a fifth as a youth, a third as a man, and has spent 13 years in his dotage. How old is he?*

(Answer: 60 years old)

## EXAMPLE 2 Finding Lengths of Pieces of Wood

The instructions for a woodworking project call for three pieces of wood. The longest piece must be twice the length of the middle-sized piece, and the shortest piece must be 10 inches shorter than the middle-sized piece. Jean Loeb has a board 70 inches long that she wishes to use. How long can each piece be?

**SOLUTION**

*Step 1* **Read** the problem. There will be three answers.

*Step 2* **Assign a variable.** Because the middle-sized piece appears in both pairs of comparisons, let $x$ represent the length, in inches, of the middle-sized piece. We have

$$\begin{aligned} x &= \text{the length of the middle-sized piece,} \\ 2x &= \text{the length of the longest piece, and} \\ x - 10 &= \text{the length of the shortest piece.} \end{aligned}$$

A sketch is helpful here. See Figure 2.

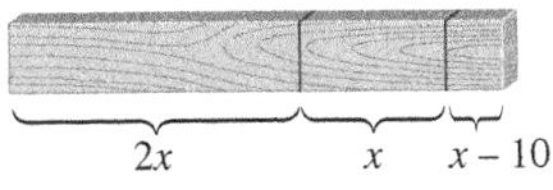


**FIGURE 2**

Problems involving age have been around since antiquity. The *Greek Anthology* gives the only information known about the life of the mathematician **Diophantus:**

> *Diophantus passed $\frac{1}{6}$ of his life in childhood, $\frac{1}{12}$ in youth, and $\frac{1}{7}$ more as a bachelor. Five years after his marriage was born a son who died 4 years before his father, at $\frac{1}{2}$ his father's final age.*

Try to write an equation and solve it to show that Diophantus was 84 years old when he died.

In the 1941 movie *Buck Privates*, Bud Abbott and Lou Costello perform a routine that pokes fun at such problems. Slicker Smith (Abbott) tells Herbie Brown (Costello) that he is really dumb, and to prove it, he challenges Herbie to answer this question:

> *Suppose you're 40 years old and you're in love with a little girl that's 10 years old. You're 4 times as old as that little girl. Now, you couldn't marry that little girl, could you? So you wait 5 years. Now you're 45 and she's 15. You're three times as old as the little girl. You still can't marry her, so you wait another 15 years. Now you're twice as old as that little girl. How long will you have to wait before she catches up to you?*

Watch the movie to hear Herbie's clever answer.

*Step 3* **Write an equation.**

| Longest | | Middle-sized | | Shortest | is | Total length |
|---|---|---|---|---|---|---|
| ↓ | | ↓ | | ↓ | ↓ | ↓ |
| $2x$ | $+$ | $x$ | $+$ | $(x - 10)$ | $=$ | $70$ |

*Step 4* **Solve.**

$$4x - 10 = 70 \qquad \text{Combine like terms.}$$
$$4x - 10 + 10 = 70 + 10 \qquad \text{Add 10.}$$
$$4x = 80 \qquad \text{Combine like terms.}$$
$$x = 20 \qquad \text{Divide by 4.}$$

*Step 5* **State the answer.** The middle-sized piece is 20 inches long, the longest piece is $2(20) = 40$ inches long, and the shortest piece is $20 - 10 = 10$ inches long.

*Step 6* **Check.** The sum of the lengths is 70 inches. All conditions of the problem are satisfied.

## Mixture and Interest Problems

**PROBLEM-SOLVING HINT** Percents often are used in problems involving mixing different concentrations of a substance or different interest rates. In each case, to get the amount of pure substance or the interest, we multiply.

| Mixture Problems | Interest Problems (annual) |
|---|---|
| **base × rate (%) = percentage** | **principal × rate (%) = interest** |
| $b \times r = p$ | $P \times r = I$ |

In an equation, the percent should be written as a decimal. For example, 35% is written .35, not 35, and 7% is written .07, not 7.

### EXAMPLE 3 Using Percents in Applications

**(a)** If a chemist has 40 liters of a 35% acid solution, how much pure acid is there?
**(b)** If \$1300 is invested for one year at 2% simple interest, how much interest is earned in one year?

**SOLUTION**

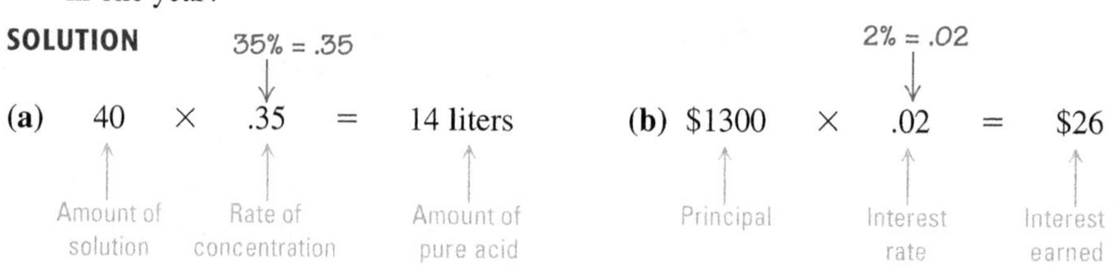

**PROBLEM-SOLVING HINT** Sometimes we use tables to organize the information in a problem. A table enables us to more easily set up an equation for the problem, which is usually the most difficult step.

## EXAMPLE 4 Solving a Mixture Problem

A chemist must mix 8 liters of a 40% acid solution with some 70% solution to obtain a 50% solution. How much of the 70% solution should be used?

**SOLUTION**

*Step 1* **Read** the problem. The problem asks for the amount of 70% solution to be used.

*Step 2* **Assign a variable.** Let $x$ = the number of liters of 70% solution to be used. The information in the problem is illustrated in Figure 3.

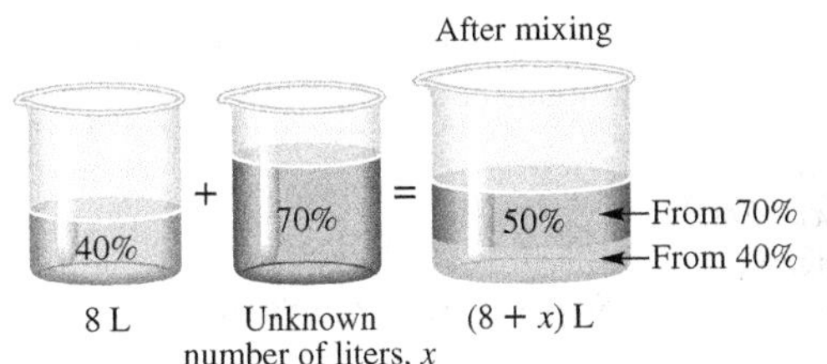


**FIGURE 3**

Use the given information to complete the table.

| Percent (as a decimal) | Number of Liters | Liters of Pure Acid |
|---|---|---|
| $40\% = .40$ | 8 | $.40(8) = 3.2$ |
| $70\% = .70$ | $x$ | $.70x$ |
| $50\% = .50$ | $8 + x$ | $.50(8 + x)$ |

Sum must equal

The numbers in the right column were found by multiplying the strengths and the numbers of liters. The number of liters of pure acid in the 40% solution plus the number of liters of pure acid in the 70% solution must equal the number of liters of pure acid in the 50% solution.

*Step 3* **Write an equation.**

$$3.2 + .70x = .50(8 + x)$$

*Step 4* **Solve.** We will do so here without clearing the decimals.

$$3.2 + .70x = 4 + .50x \quad \text{Distributive property}$$
$$.20x = .8 \quad \text{Subtract 3.2 and } .50x.$$
$$x = 4 \quad \text{Divide by .20.}$$

*Step 5* **State the answer.** The chemist should use 4 liters of the 70% solution.

The 1995 action thriller *Die Hard: With a Vengeance* features John McClane (Bruce Willis) and Zeus Carver (Samuel L. Jackson) matching wits with villain Simon Gruber (Jeremy Irons) who is planting bombs around New York. In one scene, Simon communicates with McClane and Carver on a pay telephone and tells them that in order to keep a bomb from detonating, they must dial a number that requires their solving the following riddle.

*As I was going to St. Ives,*
*I met a man with seven wives,*
*Every wife had seven sacks,*
*Every sack had seven cats,*
*Every cat had seven kits.*
*Kits, cats, sacks, and wives,*
*How many were going to*
*St. Ives?*

The rhyme is a derivation of an old application found in the **Rhind papyrus,** an Egyptian manuscript that dates back to about 1650 B.C. **Leonardo of Pisa (Fibonacci)** also included a similar problem in *Liber Abaci* in 1202.

The answer to the question is 1. Only "I" was *going* to St. Ives.

*Step 6* **Check.** 8 liters of 40% solution plus 4 liters of 70% solution is

$$8(.40) + 4(.70) = 6 \text{ liters}$$

of acid. Similarly, 8 + 4 or 12 liters of 50% solution has

$$12(.50) = 6 \text{ liters}$$

of acid in the mixture. The total amount of pure acid is 6 liters both before and after mixing, so the answer checks.

The next example uses the formula for simple interest, $I = prt$. Remember that when $t = 1$, the formula becomes $I = pr$, as shown in the Problem-Solving Hint just before Example 3. Once again the idea of multiplying the total amount (principal) by the rate (rate of interest) gives the percentage (amount of interest).

### EXAMPLE 5 Solving an Investment Problem

After winning the state lottery, Mark LeBeau has $40,000 to invest. He will put part of the money in an account paying 4% interest and the remainder into stocks paying 6% interest. His accountant tells him that the total annual income from these investments should be $2040. How much should he invest at each rate?

**SOLUTION**

*Step 1* **Read** the problem again. We must find the two amounts.

*Step 2* **Assign a variable.**

Let $x$ = the amount to invest at 4%;
then $40{,}000 - x$ = the amount to invest at 6%.

The formula for interest is $I = prt$. Here the time, $t$, is 1 year. We organize the given information in a table.

| Rate (as a decimal) | Principal | Interest |
|---|---|---|
| 4% = .04 | $x$ | $.04x$ |
| 6% = .06 | $40{,}000 - x$ | $.06(40{,}000 - x)$ |
| | 40,000 | 2040 | ← Totals

*Step 3* **Write an equation.** The last column of the table gives the equation.

Interest at 4% + Interest at 6% = Total interest

$$.04x + .06(40{,}000 - x) = 2040$$

*Step 4* **Solve** the equation. We do so without clearing decimals.

$$.04x + .06(40{,}000) - .06x = 2040 \quad \text{Distributive property}$$
$$.04x + 2400 - .06x = 2040 \quad \text{Multiply.}$$
$$-.02x + 2400 = 2040 \quad \text{Combine like terms.}$$
$$-.02x = -360 \quad \text{Subtract 2400.}$$
$$x = 18{,}000 \quad \text{Divide by } -.02.$$

*Step 5* **State the answer.** Mark should invest \$18,000 at 4%. At 6%, he should invest \$40,000 − \$18,000 = \$22,000.

*Step 6* **Check** by finding the annual interest at each rate.

$$.04(\$18{,}000) = \$720 \quad \text{and} \quad .06(\$22{,}000) = \$1320$$

They total $\$720 + \$1320 = \$2040$, as required.

## Monetary Denomination Problems

**PROBLEM-SOLVING HINT** Problems that involve different denominations of money or items with different monetary values are similar to mixture and investment problems.

**Money Problems**

**Number × Value of one = Total value**

For example, if a jar contains 37 quarters, the monetary value of the coins is

$$37 \times \$.25 = \$9.25.$$

Number of coins (37) — Denomination (\$.25) — Monetary value (\$9.25)

### EXAMPLE 6 Solving a Monetary Denomination Problem

For a bill totaling \$5.65, a cashier received 25 coins consisting of nickels and quarters. How many of each type of coin did the cashier receive?

**SOLUTION**

*Step 1* **Read** the problem. The problem asks that we find the number of nickels and the number of quarters the cashier received.

*Step 2* **Assign a variable.**

Let $x$ = the number of nickels;
then $25 - x$ = the number of quarters.

We organize the information in a table.

| Denomination | Number of Coins | Value |
|---|---|---|
| \$.05 | $x$ | $.05x$ |
| \$.25 | $25 - x$ | $.25(25 - x)$ |
| | 25 | 5.65 ← Totals |

*Step 3* **Write an equation.** From the last column of the table,

$$.05x + .25(25 - x) = 5.65.$$

**Can we average averages?**
A car travels from $A$ to $B$ at 40 miles per hour and returns at 60 miles per hour. What is its rate for the entire trip?

The correct answer is not 50 miles per hour, as you might expect. Remembering the distance, rate, time relationship and letting $x$ = the distance between $A$ and $B$, we can simplify a complex fraction to find the correct answer.

$$\text{Average rate for entire trip} = \frac{\text{Total distance}}{\text{Total time}} = \frac{x + x}{\frac{x}{40} + \frac{x}{60}} = \frac{2x}{\frac{3x}{120} + \frac{2x}{120}} = \frac{2x}{\frac{5x}{120}} = 2x \cdot \frac{120}{5x} = 48$$

The average rate for the entire trip is 48 miles per hour.

*Step 4* **Solve.**

$$\begin{aligned} 5x + 25(25 - x) &= 565 && \text{Multiply by 100.} \\ 5x + 625 - 25x &= 565 && \text{Distributive property} \\ -20x &= -60 && \text{Subtract 625; combine terms.} \\ x &= 3 && \text{Divide by } -20. \end{aligned}$$

*Step 5* **State the answer.** The cashier has 3 nickels and $25 - 3 = 22$ quarters.

*Step 6* **Check.** The cashier has $3 + 22 = 25$ coins, and the value of the coins is $\$.05(3) + \$.25(22) = \$5.65$, as required. ■

## Motion Problems

If an automobile travels at an average rate of 50 miles per hour for two hours, then it travels $50 \times 2 = 100$ miles. This is an example of the basic relationship between distance, rate, and time:

$$\text{distance} = \text{rate} \times \text{time},$$

given by the formula $d = rt$. By solving, in turn, for $r$ and $t$ in the formula, we obtain two other equivalent forms of the formula. The three forms are given below.

**Distance, Rate, Time Relationship**

$$d = rt \qquad r = \frac{d}{t} \qquad t = \frac{d}{r}$$

### EXAMPLE 7 Using the Distance, Rate, Time Relationship

**(a)** The speed of sound is 1088 feet per second at sea level at 32°F. In 5 seconds under these conditions, how far does sound travel?

**(b)** The winner of the first Indianapolis 500 race (in 1911) was Ray Harroun, driving a Marmon Wasp at an average speed of 74.59 miles per hour. How long did it take for him to complete the 500-mile course? (*Source: The Universal Almanac 1997*, John W. Wright, General Editor.)

**(c)** At the 2004 Olympic Games in Athens, Greece, Chinese swimmer Luo Xuejuan set an Olympic record in the women's 100-m breastroke swimming event of 66.64 seconds. What was her rate? (*Source: World Almanac and Book of Facts 2006.*)

**SOLUTION**

**(a)**

$$\underset{\text{Rate}}{1088} \times \underset{\text{Time}}{5} = \underset{\text{Distance}}{5440 \text{ feet}}$$

Here we found distance given rate and time using $d = rt$.

**(b)** To complete the 500 miles, it took Harroun

$$\frac{500 \leftarrow \text{Distance}}{74.59 \leftarrow \text{Rate}} = 6.70 \text{ hours} \quad \text{(rounded).} \leftarrow \text{Time}$$

Here, we found time given rate and distance, using $t = \frac{d}{r}$. To convert .70 hour to minutes, multiply by 60 to get $.70(60) = 42$ minutes. The race took him 6 hours, 42 minutes to complete.

**(c)** Her rate was

$$\text{Rate} = \frac{\text{Distance}}{\text{Time}} \rightarrow \frac{100}{66.64} = 1.50 \text{ meters per second (rounded).}$$

**PROBLEM-SOLVING HINT** Motion problems use the distance formula, $d = rt$. In this formula, ***when rate (or speed) is given in miles per hour, time must be given in hours.*** To solve such problems, ***draw a sketch*** to illustrate what is happening in the problem, and ***make a table*** to summarize the given information.

## EXAMPLE 8 Solving a Motion Problem

Jeff can bike to work in $\frac{3}{4}$ hour. By bus, the trip takes $\frac{1}{4}$ hour. If the bus travels 20 mph faster than Jeff rides his bike, how far is it to his workplace?

**SOLUTION**

*Step 1* **Read** the problem. We must find the distance between Jeff's home and his workplace.

*Step 2* **Assign a variable.** Although the problem asks for a distance, it is easier here to let $x$ be Jeff's speed when he rides his bike to work. Then the speed of the bus is $x + 20$. Thus,

$$d = rt = x \cdot \frac{3}{4} = \frac{3}{4}x, \quad \text{Trip by bike}$$

and

$$d = rt = (x + 20) \cdot \frac{1}{4} = \frac{1}{4}(x + 20). \quad \text{Trip by bus}$$

We summarize this information in a table.

| | Rate | Time | Distance |
|---|---|---|---|
| **Bike** | $x$ | $\frac{3}{4}$ | $\frac{3}{4}x$ |
| **Bus** | $x + 20$ | $\frac{1}{4}$ | $\frac{1}{4}(x + 20)$ |

(Distances: Same)

*Step 3* **Write an equation.** The key to setting up the correct equation is to realize that the distance in each case is the same. See Figure 4.

**FIGURE 4**

$$\frac{3}{4}x = \frac{1}{4}(x + 20) \quad \text{The distance is the same.}$$

*Step 4* **Solve.** $4\left(\frac{3}{4}x\right) = 4\left(\frac{1}{4}\right)(x + 20)$ Multiply by 4.

$3x = x + 20$ Multiply.

$2x = 20$ Subtract $x$.

$x = 10$ Divide by 2.

*Step 5* **State the answer.** The required distance is given by

$$d = \frac{3}{4}x = \frac{3}{4}(10) = \frac{30}{4} = 7.5 \text{ mi.}$$

*Step 6* **Check** by finding the distance using

$$d = \frac{1}{4}(x + 20) = \frac{1}{4}(10 + 20) = \frac{30}{4} = 7.5 \text{ mi,}$$

which yields the same result.

**PROBLEM-SOLVING HINT** In motion problems such as the one in Example 8, once you have filled in two pieces of information in each row of the table, you should automatically fill in the third piece of information, using the appropriate form of the formula relating distance, rate, and time. Set up the equation based upon your sketch and the information in the table.

## 7.2 EXERCISES

*Decide whether each of the following translates into an expression or an equation.*

**1.** the product of a number and 5

**2.** 36% of a number

**3.** $\frac{2}{3}$ of a number is 18.

**4.** 9 is 4 more than a number.

**5.** the ratio of a number and 12

**6.** 48 divided by a number is 4.

**7.** Rework Example 6, letting the variable represent the number of quarters. Is the answer to the problem the same?

**8.** Explain why $19 - x$ is *not* a correct translation of "19 less than a number."

*Translate each verbal phrase into a mathematical expression. Use x to represent the unknown number.*

**9.** a number decreased by 14

**10.** 8 more than a number

**11.** the product of 7 less than a number and 5 more than the number

**12.** the quotient of a number and 8

**13.** the ratio of 15 and a nonzero number

**14.** $\frac{4}{7}$ of a number

**15.** Write a few sentences describing the six steps for problem solving.

**16.** Which is *not* a valid translation of "30% of a number"?

**A.** $.30x$ **B.** $.3x$ **C.** $\frac{3x}{10}$ **D.** $.30$

***Unknown Numbers*** *Let x represent the number, write an equation for the sentence, and then solve.*

17. If 2 is added to five times a number, the result is equal to 5 more than four times the number. Find the number.

18. If four times a number is added to 8, the result is three times the number added to 5. Find the number.

19. If 2 is subtracted from a number and this difference is tripled, the result is 6 more than the number. Find the number.

20. If 3 is added to a number and this sum is doubled, the result is 2 more than the number. Find the number.

21. The sum of three times a number and 7 more than the number is the same as the difference between $-11$ and twice the number. What is the number?

22. If 4 is added to twice a number and this sum is multiplied by 2, the result is the same as if the number is multiplied by 3 and 4 is added to the product. What is the number?

*Use the methods of Examples 1 and 2 or your own method to solve each problem.*

23. ***Concert Revenues*** Bruce Springsteen and the E Street Band generated top revenue on the concert circuit in 2003. Springsteen and second-place Céline Dion together took in \$196.4 million from ticket sales. If Céline Dion took in \$35.4 million less than Bruce Springsteen and the E Street Band, how much revenue did each generate? (*Source: Parade*, February 15, 2004.)

24. ***Automobile Sales*** The Toyota Camry was the top-selling passenger car in the United States in 2004, followed by the Honda Accord. Honda Accord sales were 40 thousand less than Toyota Camry sales, and 814 thousand of these two cars were sold. How many of each model of car were sold? (*Source:* Ward's Communications.)

25. ***NBA Record*** In the 2004–2005 NBA regular season, the Phoenix Suns won two more than three times as many games as they lost. The Suns played 82 games. How many wins and losses did the team have? (*Source: World Almanac and Book of Facts 2006.*)

26. ***MLB Record*** In the 2005 Major League Baseball season, the Chicago White Sox won 27 fewer than twice as many games as they lost. They played 162 regular season games. How many wins and losses did the team have? (*Source: World Almanac and Book of Facts 2006.*)

27. ***U.S. Senate*** During the 109th Congress (2005–2006), the U.S. Senate had a total of 99 Democrats and Republicans. There were 11 more Republicans than Democrats. How many Democrats and Republicans were there in the Senate? (*Source: World Almanac and Book of Facts 2006.*)

28. ***U.S. House of Representatives*** The total number of Democrats and Republicans in the U.S. House of Representatives during the 109th Congress was 434. There were 30 more Republicans than Democrats. How many members of each party were there? (*Source: World Almanac and Book of Facts 2006.*)

29. ***Submarine Sandwich*** Nagaraj Nanjappa has a party-length submarine sandwich 59 inches long. He wants to cut it into three pieces so that the middle piece is 5 inches longer than the shortest piece, and the shortest piece is 9 inches shorter than the longest piece. How long should the three pieces be?

30. ***Office Manager Duties*** Tyrone Moseley, an office manager, must book airline tickets for the business trips that employees of his company need to make. In one week, he booked 55 tickets, divided among three airlines. He booked 7 more tickets on American Airlines than United Airlines. On Southwest Airlines, he booked 4 more than twice as many tickets as on United. How many tickets did he book on each airline?

31. ***U.S. Olympic Medals*** The United States earned a total of 103 medals at the 2004 Athens Olympics. The number of gold medals earned was 6 more than the number of bronze medals. The number of silver medals earned was 10 more than the number of bronze medals. How many of each kind of medal did the United States earn? (*Source:* U.S. Olympic Committee.)

32. ***Textbook Editor Duties*** In her job as a mathematics textbook editor, Joanne Ha works $7\frac{1}{2}$ hours a day. She spent a recent day making telephone calls, writing e-mails, and attending meetings. On that day, she spent twice as much time attending meetings as making telephone calls, and spent $\frac{1}{2}$ hour longer writing e-mails than making telephone calls. How many hours did she spend on each task?

*Use basic formulas, as in Example 3, to solve each problem.*

33. ***Acid Mixture*** How much pure acid is in 250 milliliters of a 14% acid solution?

34. ***Alcohol Mixture*** How much pure alcohol is in 150 liters of a 30% alcohol solution?

35. ***Interest Earned*** If $10,000 is invested for one year at 3.5% simple interest, how much interest is earned?

36. ***Interest Earned*** If $25,000 is invested at 3% simple interest for 2 years, how much interest is earned?

37. ***Monetary Value of Coins*** What is the monetary amount of 283 nickels?

38. ***Monetary Value of Coins*** What is the monetary amount of 35 half-dollars?

*Use the method of Example 4 or your own method to solve each problem.*

39. ***Alcohol Mixture*** In a chemistry class, 12 liters of a 12% alcohol solution must be mixed with a 20% solution to get a 14% solution. How many liters of the 20% solution are needed?

| Strength | Liters of Solution | Liters of Alcohol |
|---|---|---|
| 12% | 12 | |
| 20% | | |
| 14% | | |

40. ***Alcohol Mixture*** How many liters of a 10% alcohol solution must be mixed with 40 liters of a 50% solution to get a 40% solution?

| Strength | Liters of Solution | Liters of Alcohol |
|---|---|---|
| | $x$ | |
| | 40 | |
| 40% | | |

41. ***Alcohol Mixture in First Aid Spray*** A medicated first aid spray on the market is 78% alcohol by volume. If the manufacturer has 50 liters of the spray containing 70% alcohol, how much pure alcohol should be added so that the final mixture is the required 78% alcohol? (*Hint:* Pure alcohol is 100% alcohol.)

42. ***Insecticide Mixture*** How much water must be added to 3 gallons of a 4% insecticide solution to reduce the concentration to 3%? (*Hint:* Water is 0% insecticide.)

43. ***Antifreeze Mixture*** It is necessary to have a 40% antifreeze solution in the radiator of a certain car. The radiator now holds 20 liters of 20% solution. How many liters of this should be drained and replaced with 100% antifreeze to get the desired strength? (*Hint:* The number of liters drained is equal to the number of liters replaced.)

44. ***Chemical Mixture*** A tank holds 80 liters of a chemical solution. Currently, the solution has a strength of 30%. How much of this should be drained and replaced with a 70% solution to get a final strength of 40%?

*Use the method of Example 5 or your own method to solve each problem. Assume all rates and amounts are annual.*

45. ***Investments at Different Rates*** John Allen earned $12,000 last year by giving tennis lessons. He invested part at 3% simple interest and the rest at 4%.

He earned a total of \$440 in interest. How much did he invest at each rate?

| Rate (as a Decimal) | Principal | Interest in One Year |
|---|---|---|
| .03 | | |
| .04 | | |
| | 12,000 | 440 |

46. ***Investments at Different Rates*** Kackie Smith won \$60,000 in a slot machine in Las Vegas. She invested part at 2% simple interest and the rest at 3%. She earned a total of \$1600 in interest. How much was invested at each rate?

| Rate (as a Decimal) | Principal | Interest in One Year |
|---|---|---|
| .02 | $x$ | $.02x$ |
| | $60{,}000 - x$ | |
| | | 1600 |

47. ***Investments at Different Rates*** Jerome Dugas invested some money at 4.5% simple interest and \$1000 less than twice this amount at 3%. His total income from the interest was \$1020. How much was invested at each rate?

48. ***Investments at Different Rates*** Margaret Maggio invested some money at 3.5% simple interest, and \$5000 more than 3 times this amount at 4%. She earned \$1440 in interest. How much did she invest at each rate?

49. ***Investments at Different Rates*** Ed Moura has \$29,000 invested in stocks paying 5%. How much additional money should he invest in certificates of deposit paying 2% so that the average return on the two investments is 3%?

50. ***Investments at Different Rates*** Terry McGinnis placed \$15,000 in an account paying 6%. How much additional money should she deposit at 4% so that the average return on the two investments is 5.5%?

*Use the method of Example 6 or your own method to solve each problem.*

51. ***Coin Mixture*** Mike Easley has a box of coins that he uses when playing poker with his friends. The box currently contains 44 coins, consisting of pennies, dimes, and quarters. The number of pennies is equal to the number of dimes, and the total value is \$4.37. How many of each denomination of coin does he have in the box?

| Denomination | Number of Coins | Value | |
|---|---|---|---|
| .01 | $x$ | $.01x$ | |
| | $x$ | | |
| .25 | | | |
| | 44 | 4.37 | Totals |

52. ***Coin Mixture*** Melena Fenn found some coins while looking under her sofa pillows. There were equal numbers of nickels and quarters, and twice as many half-dollars as quarters. If she found \$2.60 in all, how many of each denomination of coin did she find?

| Denomination | Number of Coins | Value | |
|---|---|---|---|
| .05 | $x$ | $.05x$ | |
| | $x$ | | |
| .50 | $2x$ | | |
| | | 2.60 | Total |

53. ***Attendance at a School Play*** The school production of *Hamlet* was a big success. For opening night, 410 tickets were sold. Students paid \$3 each, while nonstudents paid \$7 each. If a total of \$1650 was collected, how many students and how many nonstudents attended?

54. ***Attendance at a Concert*** A total of 550 people attended a Maynard Ferguson concert. Floor tickets cost \$40 each, while balcony tickets cost \$28 each. If a total of \$20,800 was collected, how many of each type of ticket were sold?

55. ***Attendance at a Sporting Event*** At the Sacramento Monarchs home games, Row 1 seats cost \$35 each and Row 2 seats cost \$30 each. The 105 seats in these rows were sold out for the season. The total receipts for them were \$3420. How many of each type of seat were sold? (*Source:* Sacramento Monarchs.)

56. ***Coin Mixture*** In the nineteenth century, the United States minted two-cent and three-cent pieces. Frances Steib has three times as many three-cent pieces as two-cent pieces, and the face value of these coins is \$1.21. How many of each denomination does she have?

57. ***Stamp Denominations*** In January 2006, U.S. first-class mail rates increased to 39 cents for the first ounce, plus 24 cents for each additional ounce. If Sabrina spent $15.00 for a total of 45 stamps of these two denominations, how many stamps of each denomination did she buy? (*Source:* U.S. Postal Service.)

58. ***Movie Ticket Prices*** A movie theater has two ticket prices: $8 for adults and $5 for children. If the box office took in $4116 from the sale of 600 tickets, how many tickets of each kind were sold?

From **Harry Potter and the Chamber of Secrets**

***Automobile Racing*** *In Exercises 59–62, find the time based on the information provided. Use a calculator and round your answers to the nearest thousandth. (Source: The World Almanac and Book of Facts 2006.)*

| | Event and Year | Participant | Distance | Rate |
|---|---|---|---|---|
| **59.** | Indianapolis 500, 2005 | Dan Weldon (Honda) | 500 miles | 157.579 mph |
| **60.** | Daytona 500, 2001 | Michael Waltrip (Chevrolet) | 500 miles | 161.794 mph |
| **61.** | Indianapolis 500, 1980 | Johnny Rutherford (Hy-Gain McLaren/Goodyear) | 255 miles* | 148.725 mph |
| **62.** | Indianapolis 500, 1975 | Bobby Unser (Jorgensen Eagle) | 435 miles* | 149.213 mph |

*rain-shortened

***Olympic Results*** *In Exercises 63–66, find the rate based on the information provided. Use a calculator and round your answers to the nearest hundredth. All events were at the 2004 Olympics. (Source: World Almanac and Book of Facts 2006.)*

| | Event | Participant | Distance | Time |
|---|---|---|---|---|
| **63.** | 100-m hurdles, Women | Joanna Hayes, USA | 100 meters | 12.37 seconds |
| **64.** | 400-m hurdles, Women | Fani Halkia, Greece | 400 meters | 52.82 seconds |
| **65.** | 400-m hurdles, Men | Felix Sanchez, Dominican Republic | 400 meters | 47.63 seconds |
| **66.** | 400-m run, Men | Jeremy Wariner, USA | 400 meters | 44.00 seconds |

*Use the formula $d = rt$ in Exercises 67–70.*

67. ***Distance Between Cities*** A driver averaged 53 miles per hour and took 10 hours to travel from Memphis to Chicago. What is the distance between Memphis and Chicago?

68. ***Distance Between Cities*** A small plane traveled from Warsaw to Rome, averaging 164 miles per hour. The trip took two hours. What is the distance from Warsaw to Rome?

69. Suppose that an automobile averages 45 miles per hour, and travels for 30 minutes. Is the distance traveled $45 \cdot 30 = 1350$ miles? If not, explain why not, and give the correct distance.

70. Which of the following choices is the best *estimate* for the average speed of a trip of 405 miles that lasted 8.2 hours?
**A.** 50 miles per hour **B.** 30 miles per hour
**C.** 60 miles per hour **D.** 40 miles per hour

*Use the method of Example 8 or your own method to solve each problem.*

71. ***Travel Times of Trains*** A train leaves Little Rock, Arkansas, and travels north at 85 kilometers per hour. Another train leaves at the same time and travels south at 95 kilometers per hour. How long will it take before they are 315 kilometers apart?

| | Rate | Time | Distance |
|---|---|---|---|
| First train | 85 | $t$ | |
| Second train | | | |

72. ***Travel Times of Steamers*** Two steamers leave a port on a river at the same time, traveling in opposite directions. Each is traveling 22 miles per hour. How long will it take for them to be 110 miles apart?

| | Rate | Time | Distance |
|---|---|---|---|
| First steamer | | $t$ | |
| Second steamer | 22 | | |

73. ***Travel Times of Commuters*** Nancy and Mark commute to work, traveling in opposite directions. Nancy leaves the house at 8:00 A.M. and averages 35 miles per hour. Mark leaves at 8:15 A.M. and averages 40 miles per hour. At what time will they be 140 miles apart?

74. ***Travel Times of Bicyclers*** Jeff leaves his house on his bicycle at 8:30 A.M. and averages 5 miles per hour. His wife, Joan, leaves at 9:00 A.M., following the same path and averaging 8 miles per hour. At what time will Joan catch up with Jeff?

75. ***Distance Traveled to Work*** When Wayne Pourciau drives his car to work, the trip takes 30 minutes. When he rides the bus, it takes 45 minutes. The average speed of the bus is 12 miles per hour less than his speed when driving. Find the distance he travels to work.

76. ***Distance Traveled to School*** Latoya can get to school in 15 minutes if she rides her bike. It takes her 45 minutes if she walks. Her speed when walking is 10 miles per hour slower than her speed when riding. How far does she travel to school?

77. ***Time Traveled by a Pleasure Boat*** A pleasure boat on the Mississippi River traveled from New Roads, LA, to New Orleans with a stop at White Castle. On the first part of the trip, the boat traveled at an average speed of 10 miles per hour. From White Castle to New Orleans the average speed was 15 miles per hour. The entire trip covered 100 miles. How long did the entire trip take if the two parts each took the same number of hours?

78. ***Time Traveled on a Visit*** Steve leaves Nashville to visit his cousin David in Napa, 80 miles away. He travels at an average speed of 50 miles per hour. One-half hour later David leaves to visit Steve, traveling at an average speed of 60 miles per hour. How long after David leaves will they meet?

## 7.3 Ratio, Proportion, and Variation

**Writing Ratios • Unit Pricing • Solving Proportions • Direct Variation • Inverse Variation • Joint and Combined Variation**

**Writing Ratios** One of the most frequently used mathematical concepts in everyday life is *ratio*. A baseball player's batting average is actually a ratio. The slope, or pitch, of a roof on a building may be expressed as a ratio. Ratios provide a way of comparing two numbers or quantities.

During the first season (1960) of ***The Andy Griffith Show,*** the episode "Opie's Charity" featured a conversation between Opie and Andy during which Andy explained to Opie that his donation of three cents to the underprivileged children's drive at school was "a piddlin' amount."

ANDY: I was reading here just the other day where there's somewhere like 400 needy boys in this county alone, or one and a half boys per square mile.
OPIE: There is?
ANDY: Sho' is.
OPIE: I've never seen one, Pa.
ANDY: Never seen one what?
OPIE: A half a boy.
ANDY: Well it's not really a half a boy. It's **a ratio.**
OPIE: Horatio who?
ANDY: Not *Ho*ratio, *a* ratio. It's mathematics. Arithmetic. Look now Opie, just forget that part of it. Forget the part about the half a boy.
OPIE: It's pretty hard to forget a thing like that, Pa.
ANDY: Well try.
OPIE: Poor Horatio.

### Ratio

A **ratio** is a quotient of two quantities. The ratio of the number $a$ to the number $b$ is written

$$a \text{ to } b, \quad \frac{a}{b}, \quad \text{or} \quad a:b.$$

***When ratios are used in comparing units of measure, the units should be the same.***

### EXAMPLE 1 Writing Ratios

Write a ratio for each word phrase.

**(a)** 5 hours to 3 hours **(b)** 6 hours to 3 days

**SOLUTION**

**(a)** The ratio of 5 hr to 3 hr is $\frac{5 \text{ hr}}{3 \text{ hr}} = \frac{5}{3}$.

**(b)** To find the ratio of 6 hr to 3 days, first convert 3 days to hours:

$$3 \text{ days} = 3 \text{ days} \cdot \frac{24 \text{ hr}}{1 \text{ day}} = 72 \text{ hr}.$$

The ratio of 6 hr to 3 days is thus

$$\frac{6 \text{ hr}}{3 \text{ days}} = \frac{6 \text{ hr}}{72 \text{ hr}} = \frac{6}{72} = \frac{1}{12}.$$

**Unit Pricing** Ratios can be applied in unit pricing, to see which size of an item offered in different sizes produces the best price per unit. To do this, set up the ratio of the price of the item to the number of units on the label. Then divide to obtain the price per unit.

### EXAMPLE 2 Finding Price per Unit

The Cub Foods supermarket in Coon Rapids, Minnesota, charges the following prices for a jar of extra crunchy peanut butter

**Peanut Butter**

| Size | Price |
|---|---|
| 18-oz | $1.50 |
| 40-oz | $4.14 |
| 64-oz | $6.29 |

Which size is the best buy? That is, which size has the lowest unit price?

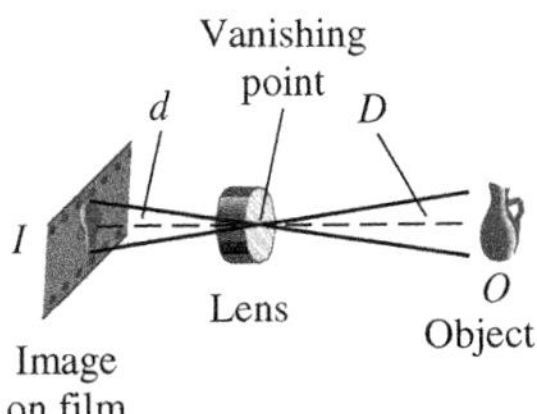


When you look a long way down a straight road or railroad track, it seems to narrow as it vanishes in the distance. The point where the sides seem to touch is called the **vanishing point.** The same thing occurs in the lens of a camera, as shown in the figure. Suppose $I$ represents the length of the image, $O$ the length of the object, $d$ the distance from the lens to the film, and $D$ the distance from the lens to the object. Then

$$\frac{\text{Image length}}{\text{Object length}} = \frac{\text{Image distance}}{\text{Object distance}}$$

or $$\frac{I}{O} = \frac{d}{D}.$$

Given the length of the image on the film and its distance from the lens, then the length of the object determines how far away the lens must be from the object to fit on the film.

**SOLUTION**

To find the best buy, write ratios comparing the price for each size jar to the number of units (ounces) per jar. The results in Table 2 are rounded to the nearest thousandth.

**TABLE 2**

| Size | Unit Cost (dollars per ounce) | |
|---|---|---|
| 18-oz | $\frac{\$1.50}{18} = \$.083$ | ← The best buy |
| 40-oz | $\frac{\$4.14}{40} = \$.104$ | |
| 64-oz | $\frac{\$6.29}{64} = \$.098$ | |

Because the 18-oz size produces the lowest unit cost, it is the best buy. Buying the largest size does not always provide the best buy, although this is often true. ■

## Solving Proportions

We now define a special type of equation called a *proportion*.

**Proportion**

A **proportion** is a statement that says that two ratios are equal.

For example, $$\frac{3}{4} = \frac{15}{20} \quad \text{Proportion}$$

is a proportion that says that the ratios $\frac{3}{4}$ and $\frac{15}{20}$ are equal. In the proportion

$$\frac{a}{b} = \frac{c}{d} \quad (b, d \neq 0),$$

$a$, $b$, $c$, and $d$ are the **terms** of the proportion. The $a$ and $d$ terms are called the **extremes,** and the $b$ and $c$ terms are called the **means.** We read the proportion $\frac{a}{b} = \frac{c}{d}$ as "$a$ is to $b$ as $c$ is to $d$." Multiplying each side of this proportion by the common denominator, $bd$, gives

$$bd \cdot \frac{a}{b} = bd \cdot \frac{c}{d}$$

$$\frac{b}{b}(d \cdot a) = \frac{d}{d}(b \cdot c) \quad \text{Associative and commutative properties}$$

$$ad = bc. \quad \text{Commutative and identity properties}$$

We can also find the products $ad$ and $bc$ by multiplying diagonally.

$$\frac{a}{b} = \frac{c}{d} \quad \begin{matrix} bc \\ \\ ad \end{matrix}$$

For this reason, *ad* and *bc* are called **cross products.**

### Cross Products

**If** $\frac{a}{b} = \frac{c}{d}$, **then the cross products** $ad$ **and** $bc$ **are equal.**

Also, if $ad = bc$, then $\frac{a}{b} = \frac{c}{d}$ (as long as $b \neq 0, d \neq 0$).

From this rule, if $\frac{a}{b} = \frac{c}{d}$ then $ad = bc$; that is, ***the product of the extremes equals the product of the means.***

If $\frac{a}{c} = \frac{b}{d}$, then $ad = cb$, or $ad = bc$. This means that the two corresponding proportions are equivalent, and

$$\text{the proportion } \frac{a}{b} = \frac{c}{d} \text{ can also be written as } \frac{a}{c} = \frac{b}{d} \quad (c \neq 0).$$

Sometimes one form is more convenient to work with than the other.

### EXAMPLE 3 Solving Proportions

Solve each proportion.

**(a)** $\frac{63}{x} = \frac{9}{5}$ **(b)** $\frac{8}{5} = \frac{12}{r}$

**SOLUTION**

**(a)**

$$\frac{63}{x} = \frac{9}{5}$$

$$63 \cdot 5 = 9x \quad \text{Set the cross products equal.}$$

$$315 = 9x \quad \text{Multiply.}$$

$$35 = x \quad \text{Divide by 9.}$$

The solution set is $\{35\}$.

**(b)**

$$\frac{8}{5} = \frac{12}{r}$$

$$8r = 5 \cdot 12 \quad \text{Set the cross products equal.}$$

$$8r = 60 \quad \text{Multiply.}$$

$$r = \frac{60}{8} = \frac{15}{2} \quad \text{Divide by 8; express in lowest terms.}$$

The solution set is $\left\{\frac{15}{2}\right\}$.

### EXAMPLE 4 Solving an Equation Using Cross Products

Solve the equation $\frac{m-2}{5} = \frac{m+1}{3}$.

**SOLUTION**

Find the cross products, and set them equal to each other.

Be sure to use parentheses.

$$\begin{aligned} 3(m-2) &= 5(m+1) && \text{Cross products} \\ 3m - 6 &= 5m + 5 && \text{Distributive property} \\ 3m &= 5m + 11 && \text{Add 6.} \\ -2m &= 11 && \text{Subtract } 5m. \\ m &= -\frac{11}{2} && \text{Divide by } -2. \end{aligned}$$

The solution set is $\left\{-\frac{11}{2}\right\}$.

### EXAMPLE 5 Using a Proportion to Predict Population

Biologists use algebra to estimate the number of fish in a lake. They first catch a sample of fish and mark each specimen with a harmless tag. Some weeks later, they catch a similar sample of fish from the same areas of the lake and determine the proportion of previously tagged fish in the new sample. The total fish population is estimated by assuming that the proportion of tagged fish in the new sample is the same as the proportion of tagged fish in the entire lake.

Suppose biologists tag 300 fish on May 1. When they return on June 1 and take a new sample of 400 fish, 5 of the 400 were previously tagged. Estimate the number of fish in the lake.

**SOLUTION**

Let $x$ represent the number of fish in the lake. Set up and solve a proportion.

Tagged fish on May 1 → 300; Total fish in the lake → $x$; Tagged fish in the June 1 sample ← 5; Total number in the June 1 sample ← 400

$$\begin{aligned} \frac{300}{x} &= \frac{5}{400} \\ 5x &= 120{,}000 && \text{Cross products} \\ x &= 24{,}000 && \text{Divide by 5.} \end{aligned}$$

There are approximately 24,000 fish in the lake.

**TABLE 3**

| Number of Rooms | Cost of the Job |
|---|---|
| 1 | \$ 49.99 |
| 2 | \$ 99.98 |
| 3 | \$149.97 |
| 4 | \$199.96 |
| 5 | \$249.95 |

**Direct Variation** Suppose that a carpet cleaning service charges 49.99 per room to shampoo a carpet. Table 3 shows the relationship between the number of rooms cleaned and the cost of the total job for 1 through 5 rooms.

If we divide the cost of the job by the number of rooms, in each case we obtain the quotient, or ratio, 49.99 (dollars per room). Suppose that we let $x$ represent the number of rooms and $y$ represent the cost for cleaning that number of rooms. Then the relationship between $x$ and $y$ is given by the equation

$$\frac{y}{x} = 49.99, \quad \text{or} \quad y = 49.99x.$$

This relationship between $x$ and $y$ is an example of *direct variation*.

### Direct Variation

***y* varies directly as *x*,** or ***y* is directly proportional to *x*,** if there exists a nonzero constant $k$ such that

$$y = kx, \quad \text{or, equivalently,} \quad \frac{y}{x} = k.$$

The constant $k$ is a numerical value called the **constant of variation.**

### EXAMPLE 6 Solving a Direct Variation Problem

Suppose $y$ varies directly as $x$, and $y = 50$ when $x = 20$. Find $y$ when $x = 14$.

**SOLUTION**

Since $y$ varies directly as $x$, there exists a constant $k$ such that $y = kx$. Find $k$ by replacing $y$ with 50 and $x$ with 20.

$$y = kx \quad \text{Variation equation}$$

$$50 = k \cdot 20 \quad \text{Substitute the given values.}$$

$$\frac{5}{2} = k \quad \text{Divide by 20; express in lowest terms.}$$

Since $y = kx$ and $k = \frac{5}{2}$,

$$y = \frac{5}{2}x.$$

Now find $y$ when $x = 14$.

$$y = \frac{5}{2} \cdot 14 = 35$$

The value of $y$ is 35 when $x = 14$.

### EXAMPLE 7 Solving a Direct Variation Problem

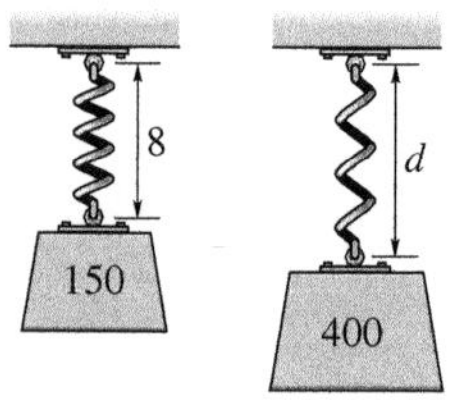

Hooke's law for an elastic spring states that the distance a spring stretches is directly proportional to the force applied. If a force of 150 pounds stretches a certain spring 8 centimeters, how much will a force of 400 pounds stretch the spring? See Figure 5.



**FIGURE 5**

**SOLUTION**

If $d$ is the distance the spring stretches and $f$ is the force applied, then $d = kf$ for some constant $k$.

$$d = kf \quad \text{Formula}$$

$$8 = k \cdot 150 \quad \text{Let } d = 8 \text{ and } f = 150.$$

$$k = \frac{8}{150} = \frac{4}{75} \quad \text{Find } k.$$

Thus $d = \frac{4}{75}f$.

For a force of 400 pounds,

$$d = \frac{4}{75}(400) = \frac{64}{3}. \quad \text{Let } f = 400.$$

The spring will stretch $\frac{64}{3}$ centimeters if a force of 400 pounds is applied.

In summary, follow these steps to solve a variation problem.

### Solving a Variation Problem

***Step 1*** Write the variation equation.

***Step 2*** Substitute the initial values and solve for $k$.

***Step 3*** Rewrite the variation equation with the value of $k$ from Step 2.

***Step 4*** Substitute the remaining values, solve for the unknown, and find the required answer.

In some cases one quantity will vary directly as a *power* of another.

### Direct Variation as a Power

**$y$ varies directly as the $n$th power of $x$** if there exists a nonzero real number $k$ such that

$$y = kx^n.$$

An example of direct variation as a power involves the area of a circle. See Figure 6. The formula for the area of a circle is $A = \pi r^2$. Here, $\pi$ is the constant of variation, and the area $A$ varies directly as the square of the radius $r$.

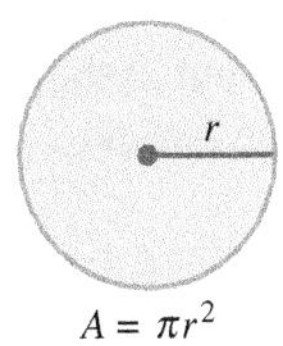


$A = \pi r^2$

**FIGURE 6**

## EXAMPLE 8 Solving a Direct Variation Problem

The distance a body falls from rest varies directly as the square of the time it falls (here we disregard air resistance). If a skydiver falls 64 feet in 2 seconds, how far will she fall in 8 seconds?

**SOLUTION**

***Step 1*** If $d$ represents the distance the skydiver falls and $t$ the time it takes to fall, then $d$ is a function of $t$, and, for some constant $k$, $d = kt^2$.

***Step 2*** To find the value of $k$, use the fact that the skydiver falls 64 feet in 2 seconds.

$$\begin{aligned} d &= kt^2 && \text{Formula} \\ 64 &= k(2)^2 && \text{Let } d = 64 \text{ and } t = 2. \\ k &= 16 && \text{Find } k. \end{aligned}$$

***Step 3*** With this result, the variation equation becomes

$$d = 16t^2.$$

*Step 4* Now let $t = 8$ to find the number of feet the skydiver will fall in 8 seconds.

$$d = 16t^2 = 16(8)^2 = 1024 \quad \text{Let } t = 8.$$

$8^2 = 8 \cdot 8 = 64$

The skydiver will fall 1024 feet in 8 seconds.

**Inverse Variation** ***In direct variation where $k > 0$, as $x$ increases, $y$ increases, and similarly as $x$ decreases, $y$ decreases.*** Another type of variation is *inverse variation.*

### Inverse Variation

***y* varies inversely as *x*** if there exists a nonzero real number $k$ such that

$$y = \frac{k}{x}, \quad \text{or, equivalently,} \quad xy = k.$$

Also, ***y* varies inversely as the *n*th power of *x*** if there exists a nonzero real number $k$ such that

$$y = \frac{k}{x^n}.$$

**Johann Kepler** (1571–1630) established the importance of the **ellipse** in 1609, when he discovered that the orbits of the planets around the sun were elliptical, not circular.

Halley's comet, which has been studied since 467 B.C., has an elliptical orbit which is long and narrow, with one axis much longer than the other. This comet was named for the British astronomer and mathematician **Edmund Halley** (1656–1742), who predicted its return after observing it in 1682. The comet appears regularly every 76 years.

### EXAMPLE 9 Solving an Inverse Variation Problem

The weight of an object above Earth varies inversely as the square of its distance from the center of Earth. A space vehicle in an elliptical orbit has a maximum distance from the center of Earth (apogee) of 6700 miles. Its minimum distance from the center of Earth (perigee) is 4090 miles. See Figure 7 (not to scale). If an astronaut in the vehicle weighs 57 pounds at its apogee, what does the astronaut weigh at the perigee?

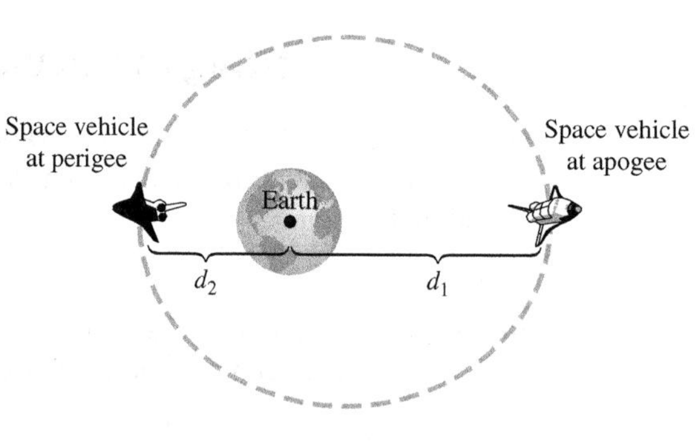


**FIGURE 7**

**SOLUTION**

If $w$ is the weight and $d$ is the distance from the center of Earth, then

$$w = \frac{k}{d^2}$$

for some constant $k$.

At the apogee the astronaut weighs 57 pounds and the distance from the center of Earth is 6700 miles. Use these values to find $k$.

$$
\begin{aligned}
57 &= \frac{k}{(6700)^2} && \text{Let } w = 57 \text{ and } d = 6700. \\
k &= 57(6700)^2 && \text{Multiply by } (6700)^2\text{; rewrite.}
\end{aligned}
$$

Then the weight at the perigee with $d = 4090$ miles is

$$w = \frac{57(6700)^2}{(4090)^2} \approx 153 \text{ pounds.} \quad \text{Use a calculator.}$$

**Joint and Combined Variation** If one variable varies as the product of several other variables (perhaps raised to powers), the first variable is said to **vary jointly** as the others.

## EXAMPLE 10 Solving a Joint Variation Problem

The strength of a rectangular beam varies jointly as its width and the square of its depth. If the strength of a beam 2 inches wide by 10 inches deep is 1000 pounds per square inch, what is the strength of a beam 4 inches wide and 8 inches deep?

**SOLUTION**

If $S$ represents the strength, $w$ the width, and $d$ the depth, then, for some constant $k$

$$
\begin{aligned}
S &= kwd^2 \\
1000 &= k(2)(10)^2 && \text{Let } S = 1000,\ w = 2, \text{ and } d = 10. \\
&\quad 10^2 = 10 \cdot 10 = 100 \\
1000 &= 200k && \text{Apply the exponent; multiply.} \\
k &= 5, && \text{Divide by 200; rewrite.} \\
\text{so} \quad S &= 5wd^2.
\end{aligned}
$$

Find $S$ when $w = 4$ and $d = 8$ by substitution in $S = 5wd^2$.

$$S = 5(4)(8)^2 = 1280 \quad \text{Let } w = 4 \text{ and } d = 8.$$

The strength of the beam is 1280 pounds per square inch.

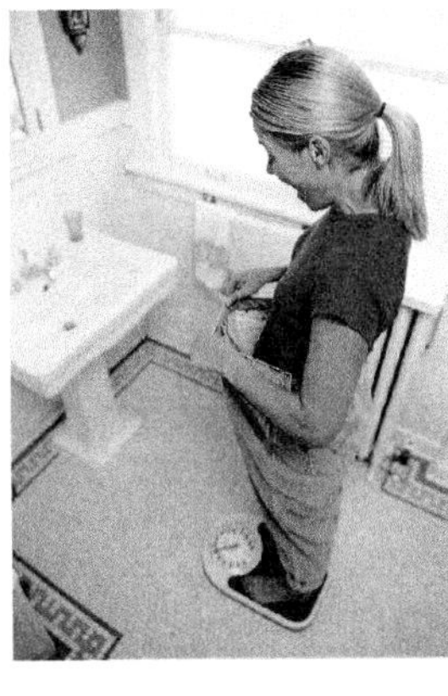

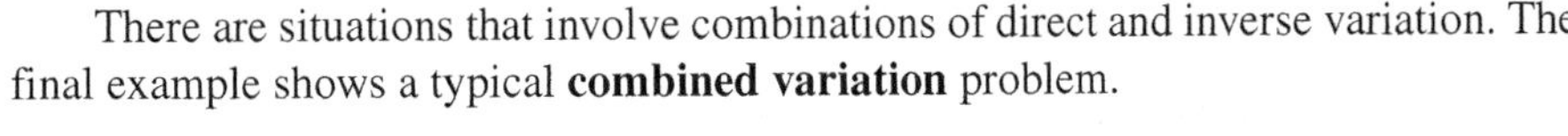

There are situations that involve combinations of direct and inverse variation. The final example shows a typical **combined variation** problem.

## EXAMPLE 11 Solving a Combined Variation Problem

Body mass index, or BMI, is used by physicians to assess a person's level of fatness. A BMI from 19 through 25 is considered desirable. BMI varies directly as an individual's weight in pounds and inversely as the square of the individual's height in inches. A person who weighs 118 lb and is 64 in. tall has a BMI of 20. (The BMI is rounded to the nearest whole number.) Find the BMI of a person who weighs 165 lb with a height of 70 in.

**SOLUTION**

Let $B$ represent the BMI, $w$ the weight, and $h$ the height. Then

$$B = \frac{kw}{h^2}$$ ← BMI varies directly as the weight. ← BMI varies inversely as the square of the height.

$$20 = \frac{k(118)}{64^2}$$ Let $B = 20$, $w = 118$, and $h = 64$.

$$k = \frac{20(64^2)}{118}$$ Multiply by $64^2$; divide by 118.

$$k \approx 694.$$ Use a calculator.

Now find $B$ when $k = 694$, $w = 165$, and $h = 70$.

$$B = \frac{694(165)}{70^2} \approx 23$$ Nearest whole number

The person's BMI is 23.

## 7.3 Exercises

*Determine the ratio and write it in lowest terms.*

1. 25 feet to 40 feet
2. 16 miles to 48 miles
3. 18 dollars to 72 dollars
4. 300 people to 250 people
5. 144 inches to 6 feet
6. 60 inches to 2 yards
7. 5 days to 40 hours
8. 75 minutes to 2 hours
9. Which ratio is not the same as the ratio 2 to 5?
   **A.** .4 **B.** 4 to 10 **C.** 20 to 50 **D.** 5 to 2
10. Give three ratios that are equivalent to the ratio 4 to 3.
11. Explain the distinction between *ratio* and *proportion*. Give examples.
12. Suppose that someone told you to use cross products in order to multiply fractions. How would you explain to the person what is wrong with his or her thinking?

*Decide whether each proportion is* true *or* false.

13. $\frac{5}{35} = \frac{8}{56}$
14. $\frac{4}{12} = \frac{7}{21}$
15. $\frac{120}{82} = \frac{7}{10}$
16. $\frac{27}{160} = \frac{18}{110}$
17. $\frac{\frac{1}{2}}{5} = \frac{1}{10}$
18. $\frac{\frac{1}{3}}{6} = \frac{1}{18}$

*Solve each equation.*

19. $\frac{k}{4} = \frac{175}{20}$
20. $\frac{49}{56} = \frac{z}{8}$
21. $\frac{3x - 2}{5} = \frac{6x - 5}{11}$
22. $\frac{5 + x}{3} = \frac{x + 7}{5}$
23. $\frac{3t + 1}{7} = \frac{2t - 3}{6}$
24. $\frac{2p + 7}{3} = \frac{p - 1}{4}$

*Solve each problem. In Exercises 25–31, assume all items are equally priced.*

25. ***Price of Candy Bars*** If 16 candy bars cost \$20.00, how much do 24 candy bars cost?

26. ***Price of Ringtones*** If 12 ringtones cost \$30.00, how much do 8 ringtones cost?

27. ***Price of Oil*** Eight quarts of oil cost \$14.00. How much do 5 quarts of oil cost?

28. ***Price of Tires*** Four tires cost \$398.00. How much do 7 tires cost?

29. ***Price of Jeans*** If 9 pairs of jeans cost \$121.50, find the cost of 5 pairs.

30. ***Price of Shirts*** If 7 shirts cost \$87.50, find the cost of 11 shirts.

31. ***Price of Gasoline*** If 6 gallons of premium unleaded gasoline cost \$15.54, how much would it cost to completely fill a 15-gallon tank?

32. ***Sales Tax*** If sales tax on a \$16.00 DVD is \$1.32, how much would the sales tax be on a \$120.00 DVD player?

33. ***Distance Between Cities*** The distance between Kansas City, Missouri, and Denver is 600 miles. On a certain wall map, this is represented by a length of 2.4 feet. On the map, how many feet would there be between Memphis and Philadelphia, two cities that are actually 1000 miles apart?

34. ***Distance Between Cities*** The distance between Singapore and Tokyo is 3300 miles. On a certain wall map, this distance is represented by 11 inches. The actual distance between Mexico City and Cairo is 7700 miles. How far apart are they on the same map?

35. ***Distance Between Cities*** A wall map of the United States has a distance of 8.5 inches between Memphis and Denver, two cities that are actually 1040 miles apart. The actual distance between St. Louis and Des Moines is 333 miles. How far apart are St. Louis and Des Moines on the map?

36. ***Distance Between Cities*** The same map of the United States mentioned in the previous exercise has a distance of 8.0 inches between New Orleans and Chicago, two cities that are actually 912 miles apart. The actual distance between Milwaukee and Seattle is 1940 miles. How far apart are Milwaukee and Seattle on the map?

37. ***Distance Between Cities*** On a world globe, the distance between Capetown and Bangkok, two cities that are actually 10,080 kilometers apart, is 12.4 inches. The actual distance between Moscow and Berlin is 1610 kilometers. How far apart are Moscow and Berlin on this globe?

38. ***Distance Between Cities*** On a world globe, the distance between Rio de Janeiro and Hong Kong, two cities that are actually 17,615 kilometers apart, is 21.5 inches. The actual distance between Paris and Stockholm is 1605 kilometers. How far apart are Paris and Stockholm on this globe?

39. ***Cleaning Mixture*** According to the directions on a bottle of Armstrong® Concentrated Floor Cleaner, for routine cleaning, $\frac{1}{4}$ cup of cleaner should be mixed with 1 gallon of warm water. How much cleaner should be mixed with $10\frac{1}{2}$ gallons of water?

40. ***Cleaning Mixture*** The directions on the bottle mentioned in Exercise 39 also specify that for extra-strength cleaning, $\frac{1}{2}$ cup of cleaner should be used for each gallon of water. For extra-strength cleaning, how much cleaner should be mixed with $15\frac{1}{2}$ gallons of water?

41. ***Exchange Rate (Dollars and Euros)*** The euro is the common currency used by most European countries, including Italy. On January 29, 2006, the exchange rate between euros and U.S. dollars was 1 euro to \$1.2128. Ashley went to Rome and exchanged her U.S. currency for euros, receiving 300 euros. How much in U.S. dollars did she exchange? (*Source:* www.xe.com/ucc)

42. ***Exchange Rate (U.S. and Mexico)*** If 8 U.S. dollars can be exchanged for 84.30 Mexican pesos, how many pesos can be obtained for \$65? (Round to the nearest hundredth.)

43. ***Tagging Fish for a Population Estimate*** Biologists tagged 250 fish in an oxbow lake known as False River on October 5. On a later date they found 7 tagged fish in a sample of 350. Estimate the total number of fish in False River to the nearest hundred.

44. ***Tagging Fish for a Population Estimate*** On May 13 researchers at Argyle Lake tagged 420 fish. When they returned a few weeks later, their sample of 500 fish contained 9 that were tagged. Give an approximation of the fish population in Argyle Lake to the nearest hundred.

***Merchandise Pricing*** *A supermarket was surveyed to find the prices charged for items in various sizes. Find the best buy (based on price per unit) for each particular item.*

45. **Granulated Sugar**

| Size | Price |
|---|---|
| 4-lb | $1.78 |
| 10-lb | $4.39 |

46. **Ground Coffee**

| Size | Price |
|---|---|
| 13-oz | $2.58 |
| 39-oz | $4.44 |

47. **Salad Dressing**

| Size | Price |
|---|---|
| 16-oz | $2.44 |
| 32-oz | $2.98 |
| 48-oz | $4.95 |

48. **Black Pepper**

| Size | Price |
|---|---|
| 2-oz | $1.79 |
| 4-oz | $2.59 |
| 8-oz | $5.59 |

49. **Vegetable Oil**

| Size | Price |
|---|---|
| 16-oz | $1.54 |
| 24-oz | $2.08 |
| 64-oz | $3.63 |
| 128-oz | $5.65 |

50. **Mouthwash**

| Size | Price |
|---|---|
| 8.5-oz | $.99 |
| 16.9-oz | $1.87 |
| 33.8-oz | $2.49 |
| 50.7-oz | $2.99 |

51. **Tomato Ketchup**

| Size | Price |
|---|---|
| 14-oz | $1.39 |
| 24-oz | $1.55 |
| 36-oz | $1.78 |
| 64-oz | $3.99 |

52. **Grape Jelly**

| Size | Price |
|---|---|
| 12-oz | $1.05 |
| 18-oz | $1.73 |
| 32-oz | $1.84 |
| 48-oz | $2.88 |

*Two triangles are* ***similar*** *if they have the same shape (but not necessarily the same size). Similar triangles have sides that are proportional. The figure shows two similar triangles.*

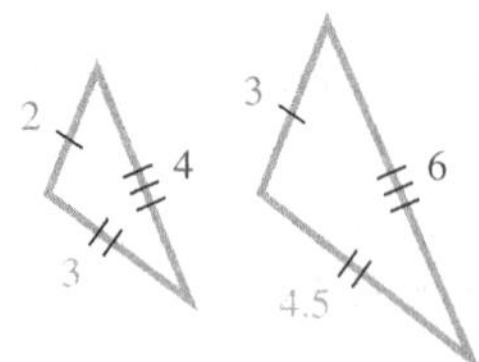


*Notice that the ratios of the corresponding sides are all equal to* $\frac{3}{2}$:

$$\frac{3}{2} = \frac{3}{2} \qquad \frac{4.5}{3} = \frac{3}{2} \qquad \frac{6}{4} = \frac{3}{2}.$$

*If we know that two triangles are similar, we can set up a proportion to solve for the length of an unknown side. Use a proportion to find the lengths x and y given that the pair of triangles are similar.*

53.

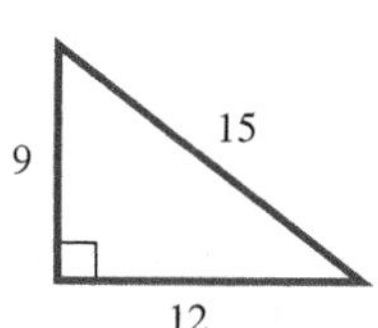


54.

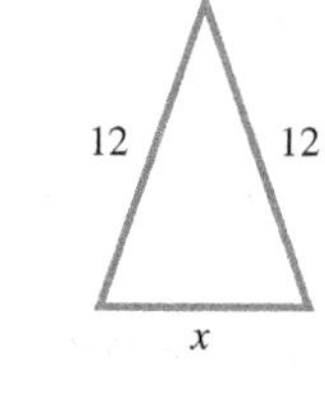


55.

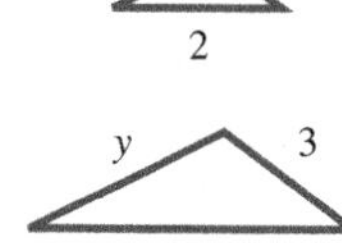


56.

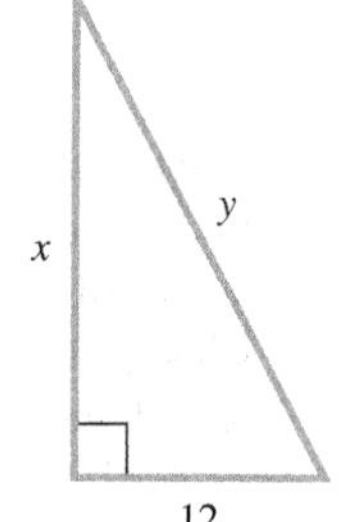

*For the problems in Exercises 57 and 58,* **(a)** *draw a sketch consisting of two right triangles, depicting the situation described, and* **(b)** *solve the problem. (Source: Guinness World Records.)*

**57.** ***George Washington's Chair*** An enlarged version of the chair used by George Washington at the Constitutional Convention casts a shadow 18 feet long at the same time a vertical pole 12 feet high casts a shadow 4 feet long. How tall is the chair?

**58.** ***Candle at an Exhibition*** One of the tallest candles ever constructed was exhibited at the 1897 Stockholm Exhibition. If it cast a shadow 5 feet long at the same time a vertical pole 32 feet high cast a shadow 2 feet long, how tall was the candle?

***Consumer Price Index*** *The Consumer Price Index, issued by the U.S. Bureau of Labor Statistics, provides a means of determining the purchasing power of the U.S. dollar from one year to the next. Using the period from 1982 to 1984 as a measure of* 100.0, *the Consumer Price Index for selected years from 1990 to 2004 is shown here.*

| Year | Consumer Price Index |
|---|---|
| 1990 | 130.7 |
| 1992 | 140.3 |
| 1994 | 148.2 |
| 1996 | 156.9 |
| 1998 | 163.0 |
| 2000 | 172.2 |
| 2002 | 179.9 |
| 2004 | 188.9 |

*Source*: Bureau of Labor Statistics.

*To use the Consumer Price Index to predict a price in a particular year, we can set up a proportion and compare it with a known price in another year, as follows:*

$$\frac{\text{Price in year } A}{\text{Index in year } A} = \frac{\text{Price in year } B}{\text{Index in year } B}.$$

*Use the Consumer Price Index figures in the table to find the amount that would be charged for the purchase of the same amount of groceries that cost \$120 in 1990. Give your answer to the nearest dollar.*

**59.** in 1996

**60.** in 2000

**61.** in 2002

**62.** in 2004

*Solve each problem involving variation.*

**63.** If $x$ varies directly as $y$, and $x = 27$ when $y = 6$, find $x$ when $y = 2$.

**64.** If $z$ varies directly as $x$, and $z = 30$ when $x = 8$, find $z$ when $x = 4$.

**65.** If $m$ varies directly as $p^2$, and $m = 20$ when $p = 2$, find $m$ when $p = 5$.

**66.** If $a$ varies directly as $b^2$, and $a = 48$ when $b = 4$, find $a$ when $b = 7$.

**67.** If $p$ varies inversely as $q^2$, and $p = 4$ when $q = \frac{1}{2}$, find $p$ when $q = \frac{3}{2}$.

**68.** If $z$ varies inversely as $x^2$, and $z = 9$ when $x = \frac{2}{3}$, find $z$ when $x = \frac{5}{4}$.

**69.** ***Interest on an Investment*** The interest on an investment varies directly as the rate of interest. If the interest is \$48 when the interest rate is 5%, find the interest when the rate is 4.2%.

**70.** ***Area of a Triangle*** For a given base, the area of a triangle varies directly as its height. Find the area of a triangle with a height of 6 inches, if the area is 10 square inches when the height is 4 inches.

**71.** ***Speed of a Car*** Over a specified distance, speed varies inversely with time. If a car goes a certain distance in one-half hour at 30 miles per hour, what speed is needed to go the same distance in three-fourths of an hour?

**72.** ***Length of a Rectangle*** For a constant area, the length of a rectangle varies inversely as the width. The length of a rectangle is 27 feet when the width is 10 feet. Find the length of a rectangle with the same area if the width is 18 feet.

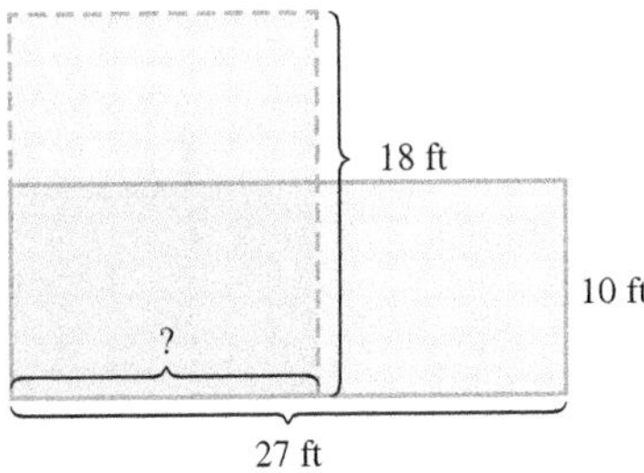


**73.** ***Weight of a Moose*** The weight of an object on the moon varies directly as the weight of the object on Earth. According to *Guinness World Records*, "Shad," a goat owned by a couple in California, is the largest known goat, weighing 352 pounds. Shad would weigh about 59 pounds on the moon. A bull moose weighing 1800 pounds was shot in Canada and is the largest confirmed moose. How much would the moose have weighed on the moon?

74. ***Voyage in a Paddleboat*** According to *Guinness World Records*, the longest recorded voyage in a paddle boat is 2226 miles in 103 days by the foot power of two boaters down the Mississippi River. Assuming a constant rate, how far would they have gone if they had traveled 120 days? (Distance varies directly as time.)

75. ***Pressure Exerted by a Liquid*** The pressure exerted by a certain liquid at a given point varies directly as the depth of the point beneath the surface of the liquid. The pressure at a depth of 10 feet is 50 pounds per square inch. What is the pressure at a depth of 20 feet?

76. ***Pressure of a Gas in a Container*** If the volume is constant, the pressure of a gas in a container varies directly as the temperature. If the pressure is 5 pounds per square inch at a temperature of 200 degrees Kelvin, what is the pressure at a temperature of 300 degrees Kelvin?

77. ***Pressure of a Gas in a Container*** If the temperature is constant, the pressure of a gas in a container varies inversely as the volume of the container. If the pressure is 10 pounds per square foot in a container with 3 cubic feet, what is the pressure in a container with 1.5 cubic feet?

78. ***Force Required to Compress a Spring*** The force required to compress a spring varies directly as the change in the length of the spring. If a force of 12 pounds is required to compress a certain spring 3 inches, how much force is required to compress the spring 5 inches?

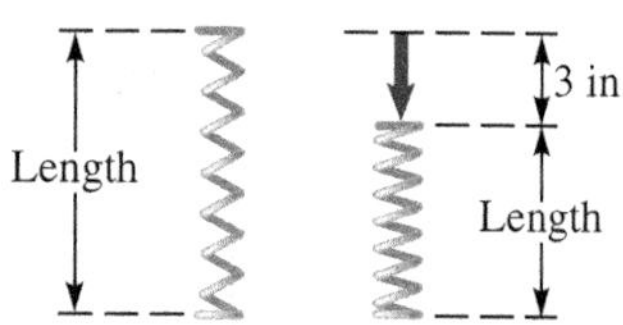


79. ***Falling Body*** For a body falling freely from rest (disregarding air resistance), the distance the body falls varies directly as the square of the time. If an object is dropped from the top of a tower 400 feet high and hits the ground in 5 seconds, how far did it fall in the first 3 seconds?

80. ***Illumination from a Light Source*** The illumination produced by a light source varies inversely as the square of the distance from the source. If the illumination produced 4 feet from a light source is 75 foot-candles, find the illumination produced 9 feet from the same source.

81. ***Volume of Gas*** Natural gas provides 35.8% of U.S. energy. (*Source*: U.S. Energy Department.) The volume of gas varies inversely as the pressure and directly as the temperature. [Temperature must be measured in *Kelvin* (K), a unit of measurement used in physics.] If a certain gas occupies a volume of 1.3 liters at 300 K and a pressure of 18 newtons, find the volume at 340 K and a pressure of 24 newtons.

82. ***Skidding Car*** The force needed to keep a car from skidding on a curve varies inversely as the radius of the curve and jointly as the weight of the car and the square of the speed. If 242 pounds of force keep a 2000-pound car from skidding on a curve of radius 500 feet at 30 miles per hour, what force would keep the same car from skidding on a curve of radius 750 feet at 50 miles per hour?

83. ***Load Supported by a Column*** The maximum load that a cylindrical column with a circular cross section can hold varies directly as the fourth power of the diameter of the cross section and inversely as the square of the height. A 9-meter column 1 meter in diameter will support 8 metric tons. How many metric tons can be supported by a column 12 meters high and $\frac{2}{3}$ meter in diameter?

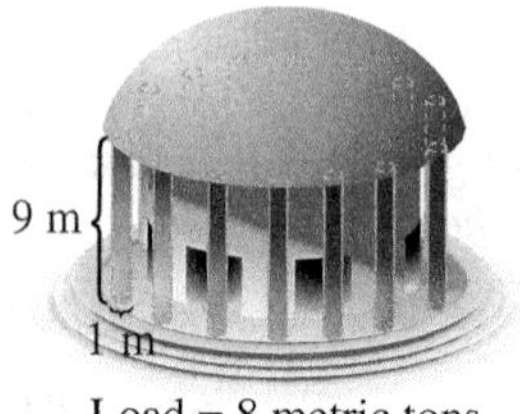


Load = 8 metric tons

***Fish Weight-Estimation*** *Exercises 84 and 85 describe weight-estimation formulas that fishermen have used over the years. Girth is the distance around the body of the fish. (Source: Sacramento Bee, November 9, 2000.)*

**84.** The weight of a bass varies jointly as its girth and the square of its length. A prize-winning bass weighed in at 22.7 pounds and measured 36 inches long with a 21-inch girth. How much would a bass 28 inches long with an 18-inch girth weigh?

**85.** The weight of a trout varies jointly as its length and the square of its girth. One angler caught a trout that weighed 10.5 pounds and measured 26 inches long with an 18-inch girth. Find the weight of a trout that is 22 inches long with a 15-inch girth.

**86.** Bill Veeck was the owner of several major league baseball teams in the 1950s and 1960s. He was known to often sit in the stands and enjoy games with his paying customers. Here is a quote attributed to him:

*"I have discovered in 20 years of moving around a ballpark, that the knowledge of the game is usually in inverse proportion to the price of the seats."*

Explain in your own words the meaning of this statement. (To prove his point, Veeck once allowed the fans (as shown in the photo) to vote on managerial decisions.)

## 7.4 Linear Inequalities

**Number Lines and Interval Notation • Addition Property of Inequality • Multiplication Property of Inequality • Solving Linear Inequalities • Applications • Three-Part Inequalities**

### Number Lines and Interval Notation

Inequalities are algebraic expressions related by

| | |
|---|---|
| $<$ "is less than," | $\leq$ "is less than or equal to," |
| $>$ is greater than," | $\geq$ "is greater than or equal to." |

We solve an inequality by finding all real number solutions for it. For example, the solution set of $x \leq 2$ includes *all real numbers* that are less than or equal to 2, not just the *integers* less than or equal to 2.

We show the solution set of an inequality by graphing. We graph all the real numbers satisfying $x \leq 2$ by placing a square bracket at 2 on a number line and drawing an arrow from the bracket to the left (to show that all numbers less than 2 are also part of the graph).* See Figure 8.

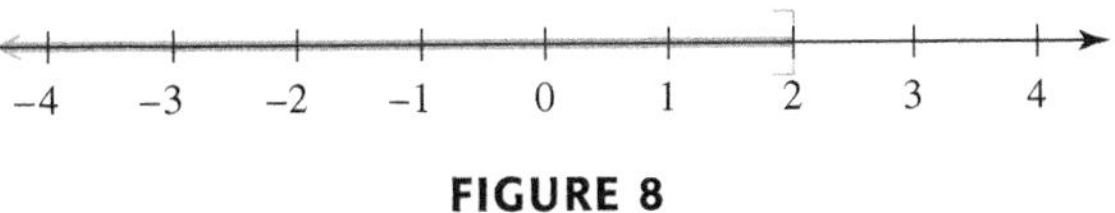


**FIGURE 8**

*Some texts use solid circles rather than square brackets to indicate that the end point is included on a number line graph. [Open circles are also used to indicate noninclusion rather than parentheses, as described in Example 1(a).]

**Archimedes,** one of the greatest mathematicians of antiquity, is shown on this Italian stamp. He was born in the Greek city of Syracuse about 287 B.C.

A colorful story about Archimedes relates his reaction to one of his discoveries. While taking a bath, he noticed that an immersed object, if heavier than a fluid, "will, if placed in it, descend to the bottom of the fluid, and the solid will, when weighed in the fluid, be lighter than its true weight by the weight of the fluid displaced." This discovery so excited him that he ran through the streets shouting "Eureka!" ("I have found it!") without bothering to clothe himself!

Archimedes met his death at age 75 during the pillage of Syracuse. He was using a sand tray to draw geometric figures when a Roman soldier came upon him. He ordered the soldier to move clear of his "circles," and the soldier obliged by killing him.

The set of numbers less than or equal to 2 is an example of an **interval** on the number line. To write intervals, we use **interval notation.** For example, using this notation, the interval of all numbers less than or equal to 2 is written as $(-\infty, 2]$. The **negative infinity** symbol $-\infty$ does not indicate a number. It is used to show that the interval includes all real numbers less than 2. As on the number line, the square bracket indicates that 2 is part of the solution. ***A parenthesis is always used next to the infinity symbol.*** The set of real numbers is written in interval notation as $(-\infty, \infty)$.

Examples of other sets written in interval notation are shown in Table 4. In these intervals, assume that $a < b$.

**TABLE 4**

| Type of Interval | Set | Interval Notation | Graph |
|---|---|---|---|
| | $\{x \mid x > a\}$ | $(a, \infty)$ | 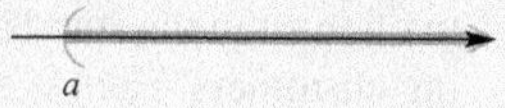 |
| Open interval | $\{x \mid a < x < b\}$ | $(a, b)$ | 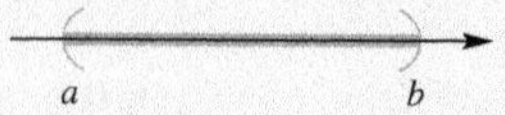 |
| | $\{x \mid x < b\}$ | $(-\infty, b)$ | 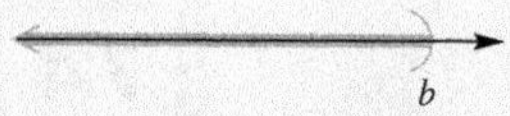 |
| | $\{x \mid x \geq a\}$ | $[a, \infty)$ |  |
| Half-open interval | $\{x \mid a < x \leq b\}$ | $(a, b]$ |  |
| | $\{x \mid a \leq x < b\}$ | $[a, b)$ |  |
| | $\{x \mid x \leq b\}$ | $(-\infty, b]$ |  |
| Closed interval | $\{x \mid a \leq x \leq b\}$ | $[a, b]$ | 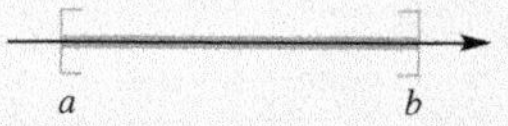 |

## EXAMPLE 1 Graphing Intervals Written in Interval Notation on a Number Line

Write each inequality in interval notation and graph the interval.

**(a)** $x > -5$ **(b)** $-1 \leq x < 3$

**SOLUTION**

**(a)** The statement $x > -5$ says that $x$ can be any number greater than $-5$ but cannot be $-5$. The interval is written $(-5, \infty)$. On a graph we place a parenthesis at $-5$ and draw an arrow to the right, as shown in Figure 9 on the next page. The parenthesis at $-5$ indicates that $-5$ is not part of the graph.

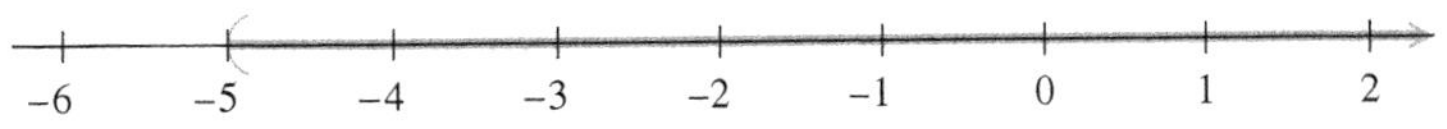

FIGURE 9

**(b)** The statement is read "$-1$ is less than or equal to $x$ *and* $x$ is less than 3." Thus, we want the set of numbers that are *between* $-1$ and 3, with $-1$ included and 3 excluded. In interval notation, we write $[-1, 3)$, using a square bracket at $-1$ because $-1$ is part of the graph, and a parenthesis at 3 because 3 is not part of the graph. The graph is shown in Figure 10.

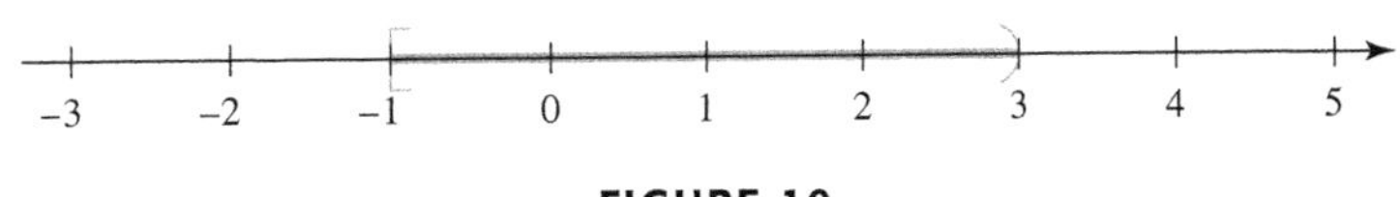


FIGURE 10

## Addition Property of Inequality

### Linear Inequality in One Variable

A **linear inequality in one variable** can be written in the form

$$Ax + B < C,$$

where $A$, $B$, and $C$ are real numbers, with $A \neq 0$. (The symbol $<$ may be replaced by $>$, $\leq$, or $\geq$.)

Examples of linear inequalities in one variable include

$x + 5 < 2,\quad y - 3 \geq 5,\quad$ and $\quad 2k + 5 \leq 10.$ Linear inequalities

Consider the inequality $2 < 5$. If 4 is added to each side, the result is

$$2 + 4 < 5 + 4$$

$$6 < 9. \quad \text{True}$$

Start over and subtract 8 from each side:

$$2 - 8 < 5 - 8$$

$$-6 < -3. \quad \text{True}$$

These examples suggest the **addition property of inequality.**

### Addition Property of Inequality

For any real numbers $A$, $B$, and $C$, the inequalities

$$A < B \quad \text{and} \quad A + C < B + C$$

have exactly the same solutions.

That is, the same number may be added to each side of an inequality without changing the solutions.

The same number may also be *subtracted* from each side of an inequality.

**EXAMPLE 2 Using the Addition Property of Inequality**

Solve $7 + 3x > 2x - 5$.

**SOLUTION**

Use the addition property of inequality twice, once to isolate the terms containing $x$ on one side of the inequality and a second time to get the integers together on the other side. (These steps can be done in either order.)

$$7 + 3x > 2x - 5$$

$$7 + 3x - 2x > 2x - 5 - 2x \quad \text{Subtract } 2x.$$

$$7 + x > -5 \quad \text{Combine like terms.}$$

$$7 + x - 7 > -5 - 7 \quad \text{Subtract 7.}$$

$$x > -12 \quad \text{Combine like terms.}$$

The solution set is $(-12, \infty)$. Its graph is shown in Figure 11.

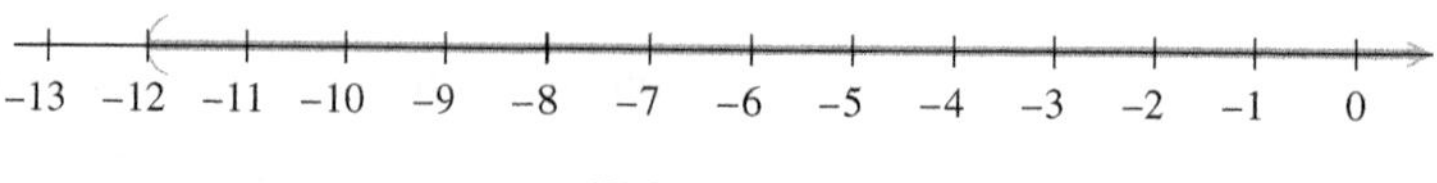


**FIGURE 11**

**Multiplication Property of Inequality** The addition property of inequality cannot be used to solve inequalities such as $4x \geq 28$. These inequalities require the *multiplication property of inequality*. To see how this property works, we look at some examples.

Multiply each side of the inequality $3 < 7$ by the positive number 2.

$$3 < 7 \quad \text{True}$$

$$2(3) < 2(7) \quad \text{Multiply each side by 2.}$$

$$6 < 14 \quad \text{True}$$

Now multiply each side of $3 < 7$ by the negative number $-5$.

$$3 < 7 \quad \text{True}$$

$$-5(3) < -5(7) \quad \text{Multiply each side by } -5.$$

$$-15 < -35 \quad \text{False}$$

To get a true statement when multiplying each side by $-5$, we must reverse the direction of the inequality symbol.

$$3 < 7 \quad \text{True}$$

$$-5(3) > -5(7) \quad \text{Multiply by } -5\text{; reverse the inequality symbol.}$$

$$-15 > -35 \quad \text{True}$$

Multiply each side of the inequality $-6 < 2$ by the positive number 4.

$$-6 < 2 \quad \text{True}$$

$$4(-6) < 4(2) \quad \text{Multiply by 4.}$$

$$-24 < 8 \quad \text{True}$$

Multiplying each side of $-6 < 2$ by $-5$ *and at the same time reversing the direction of the inequality symbol* gives

$$-6 < 2 \quad \text{True}$$
$$-5(-6) > -5(2) \quad \text{Multiply by } -5\text{; reverse the inequality symbol.}$$
$$30 > -10. \quad \text{True}$$

In summary, the **multiplication property of inequality** has two parts.

## Multiplication Property of Inequality

For any real numbers $A$, $B$, and $C$, with $C \neq 0$,

1. if $C$ is *positive,* then the inequalities

$$A < B \quad \text{and} \quad AC < BC$$

have the same solutions;

2. if $C$ is *negative,* then the inequalities

$$A < B \quad \text{and} \quad AC > BC$$

have the same solutions.

That is, each side of an inequality may be multiplied by the same positive number without changing the solutions. If the multiplier is negative, we must reverse the direction of the inequality symbol.

The multiplication property of inequality also permits *division* of each side of an inequality by the same nonzero number.

It is important to remember the differences in the multiplication property for positive and negative numbers.

1. When each side of an inequality is multiplied or divided by a positive number, the direction of the inequality symbol *does not change.* (Also, adding or subtracting terms on each side does not change the symbol.)
2. When each side of an inequality is multiplied or divided by a negative number, the direction of the symbol *does change.* ***Reverse the direction of the inequality symbol only when multiplying or dividing each side by a negative number.***

## EXAMPLE 3 Using the Multiplication Property of Inequality

Solve each inequality and graph the solution set.

**(a)** $3x < -18$ **(b)** $-4x \geq 8$

**SOLUTION**

**(a)**

$$3x < -18$$

$$\frac{3x}{3} < \frac{-18}{3} \quad \text{Divide by 3, a } \textit{positive} \text{ number.}$$

3 is a positive number, so the inequality symbol does not change.

$$x < -6$$

The solution set is $(-\infty, -6)$. The graph is shown in Figure 12 on the next page.

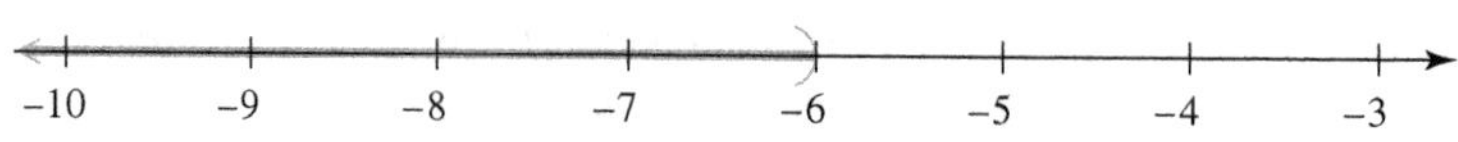


**FIGURE 12**

**(b)**

$$-4x \geq 8$$

$$\frac{-4x}{-4} \leq \frac{8}{-4} \quad \text{Divide by } -4 \text{, a } \textit{negative} \text{ number; reverse the inequality symbol.}$$

Reverse the inequality when multiplying or dividing by a negative number.

$$x \leq -2$$

The solution set $(-\infty, -2]$ is graphed in Figure 13.

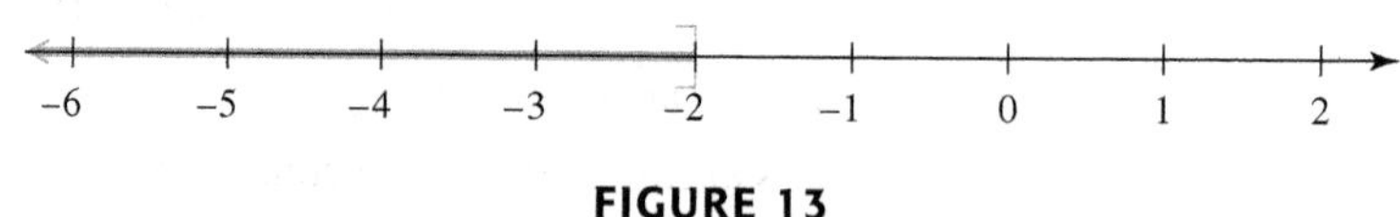


**FIGURE 13**

**Solving Linear Inequalities** To solve a linear inequality, follow these steps.

### Solving a Linear Inequality in One Variable

*Step 1* **Simplify each side separately.** Use the distributive property to clear parentheses and combine like terms on each side as needed.

*Step 2* **Isolate the variable terms on one side.** Use the addition property of inequality to get all terms with variables on one side of the inequality and all numbers on the other side.

*Step 3* **Isolate the variable.** Use the multiplication property of inequality to change the inequality to the form $x < k$ or $x > k$, where $k$ is a number.

***Remember: Reverse the direction of the inequality symbol only when multiplying or dividing each side of an inequality by a negative number.***

### EXAMPLE 4 Solving a Linear Inequality

Solve $5(x - 3) - 7x \geq 4(x - 3) + 9$. Give the solution set in interval form, and then graph.

**SOLUTION**

*Step 1* Simplify and combine like terms.

$$5(x - 3) - 7x \geq 4(x - 3) + 9$$

$$5x - 15 - 7x \geq 4x - 12 + 9 \quad \text{Distributive property}$$

$$-2x - 15 \geq 4x - 3 \quad \text{Combine like terms.}$$

*Step 2* Use the addition property of inequality.

$$-2x - 15 - 4x \geq 4x - 3 - 4x \quad \text{Subtract } 4x.$$
$$-6x - 15 \geq -3$$
$$-6x - 15 + 15 \geq -3 + 15 \quad \text{Add 15.}$$
$$-6x \geq 12$$

*Step 3* Use the multiplication property of inequality.

Remember to reverse the inequality symbol.

$$\frac{-6x}{-6} \leq \frac{12}{-6} \quad \text{Divide by } -6 \text{, a } \textit{negative} \text{ number; reverse the symbol.}$$
$$x \leq -2$$

The solution set is $(-\infty, -2]$. Its graph is shown in Figure 14.

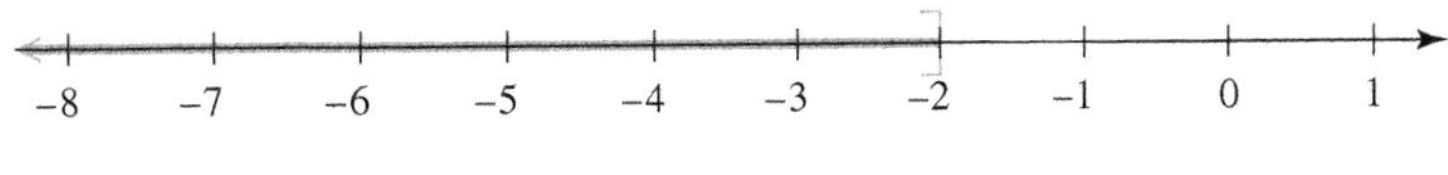


**FIGURE 14**

## Applications

**PROBLEM-SOLVING HINT** Inequalities can be used to solve applied problems involving phrases that suggest inequality. The table gives some of the more common such phrases along with examples and translations.

| Phrase | Example | Inequality |
|---|---|---|
| Is more than | A number *is more than* 4. | $x > 4$ |
| Is less than | A number *is less than* −12. | $x < -12$ |
| Is at least | A number *is at least* 6. | $x \geq 6$ |
| Is at most | A number *is at most* 8. | $x \leq 8$ |

We use the same six problem-solving steps from Section 7.2, changing Step 3 to "Write an inequality" instead of "Write an equation."

The next example shows an application of algebra that is important to anyone who has ever asked, "What score can I make on my next test and have a (particular grade) in this course?" It uses the idea of finding the average of a number of grades. In general, to find the average of $n$ numbers, add the numbers, then divide by $n$.

### EXAMPLE 5 Finding an Average Test Score

Brent has test grades of 86, 88, and 78 on his first three tests in geometry. If he wants an average of at least 80 after his fourth test, what are the possible scores he can make on his fourth test?

**SOLUTION**

*Step 1* **Read** the problem again.

*Step 2* **Assign a variable.** Let $x$ = Brent's score on his fourth test.

*Step 3* **Write an inequality.** To find his average after 4 tests, add the test scores and divide by 4.

$$\underbrace{\frac{86 + 88 + 78 + x}{4}}_{\text{Average}} \underbrace{\geq}_{\text{is at least}} \underbrace{80}_{80.}$$

*Step 4* **Solve.**

$$\frac{252 + x}{4} \geq 80 \quad \text{Add the known scores.}$$

$$4\left(\frac{252 + x}{4}\right) \geq 4(80) \quad \text{Multiply by 4 to clear the fraction.}$$

$$252 + x \geq 320$$

$$252 + x - 252 \geq 320 - 252 \quad \text{Subtract 252.}$$

$$x \geq 68 \quad \text{Combine like terms.}$$

*Step 5* **State the answer.** He must score 68 or more on the fourth test to have an average of *at least* 80.

*Step 6* **Check.** Determine whether a score of 68 gives an average of 80.

$$\frac{86 + 88 + 78 + 68}{4} = \frac{320}{4} = 80$$

### EXAMPLE 6 Using a Linear Inequality to Solve a Rental Problem

A rental company charges \$15.00 to rent a chain saw, plus \$2.00 per hour. Mamie Zwettler can spend no more than \$35.00 to clear some logs from her yard. What is the maximum amount of time she can use the rented saw?

**SOLUTION**

Let $h$ = the number of hours she can rent the saw. She must pay \$15.00, plus \$2.00$h$, to rent the saw for $h$ hours, and this amount must be *no more than* \$35.00.

$$\underbrace{15 + 2h}_{\text{Cost of renting}} \underbrace{\leq}_{\text{is no more than}} \underbrace{35}_{\text{35 dollars.}}$$

$$15 + 2h - 15 \leq 35 - 15 \quad \text{Subtract 15.}$$

$$2h \leq 20$$

$$h \leq 10 \quad \text{Divide by 2.}$$

Mamie can use the saw for a maximum of 10 hours. (Of course, she may use it for less time, as indicated by the inequality $h \leq 10$.)

**Three-Part Inequalities** Inequalities that say that one number is *between* two other numbers are **three-part inequalities.** For example,

$$-3 < 5 < 7 \quad \text{Three-part inequality}$$

says that 5 is between $-3$ and 7.

For some applications, it is necessary to work with an inequality such as

$$3 < x + 2 < 8,$$

where $x + 2$ is between 3 and 8. To solve this inequality, we subtract 2 from each of the three parts of the inequality, giving

$$3 - 2 < x + 2 - 2 < 8 - 2$$
$$1 < x < 6.$$

The idea is to get the inequality in the form

$$\text{a number} < x < \text{another number},$$

The symbols must point in the same direction and toward the lesser number.

using "is less than." The solution set (in this case the interval (1, 6)) can then easily be graphed.

## EXAMPLE 7 Solving Three-Part Inequalities

Solve $4 \leq 3x - 5 < 6$. Give the solution set in interval form, and then graph.

**SOLUTION**

$$4 \leq 3x - 5 < 6$$
$$4 + 5 \leq 3x - 5 + 5 < 6 + 5 \quad \text{Add 5 to each part.}$$
$$9 \leq 3x < 11$$

Remember to divide all three parts by 3.

$$\frac{9}{3} \leq \frac{3x}{3} < \frac{11}{3} \quad \text{Divide each part by 3.}$$
$$3 \leq x < \frac{11}{3}$$

The solution set is $\left[3, \frac{11}{3}\right)$. Its graph is shown in Figure 15.

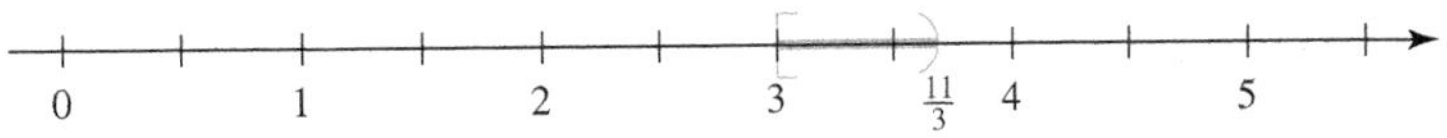


**FIGURE 15**

# 7.4 EXERCISES

*In Exercises 1–6, match each set in Column I with the correct graph or interval notation in A–F in Column II. See Example 1.*

**I**

1. $\{x \mid x \leq 3\}$
2. $\{x \mid x > 3\}$
3. $\{x \mid x < 3\}$
4. $\{x \mid x \geq 3\}$
5. $\{x \mid -3 \leq x \leq 3\}$
6. $\{x \mid -3 < x < 3\}$

**II**

**A.** 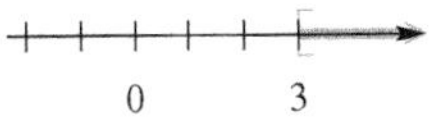


**B.** 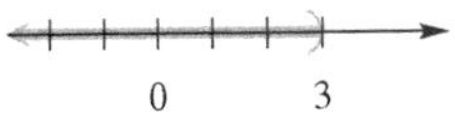


**C.** $(3, \infty)$

**D.** $(-\infty, 3]$

**E.** $(-3, 3)$

**F.** $[-3, 3]$

7. How does one determine whether to use parentheses or brackets when graphing the solution set of an inequality?

8. Describe the steps used to solve a linear inequality. Explain when it is necessary to reverse the inequality symbol.

*Solve each inequality. Give the solution set in both interval and graph forms.*

9. $4x + 1 \geq 21$

10. $5t + 2 \geq 52$

11. $\frac{3k - 1}{4} > 5$

12. $\frac{5z - 6}{8} < 8$

13. $-4x < 16$

14. $-2m > 10$

15. $-\frac{3}{4}r \geq 30$

16. $-1.5x \leq -\frac{9}{2}$

17. $-1.3m \geq -5.2$

18. $-2.5x \leq -1.25$

19. $\frac{2k - 5}{-4} > 5$

20. $\frac{3z - 2}{-5} < 6$

21. $x + 4(2x - 1) \geq x$

22. $m - 2(m - 4) \leq 3m$

23. $-(4 + r) + 2 - 3r < -14$

24. $-(9 + k) - 5 + 4k \geq 4$

25. $-3(z - 6) > 2z - 2$

26. $-2(x + 4) \leq 6x + 16$

27. $\frac{2}{3}(3k - 1) \geq \frac{3}{2}(2k - 3)$

28. $\frac{7}{5}(10m - 1) < \frac{2}{3}(6m + 5)$

29. $-\frac{1}{4}(p + 6) + \frac{3}{2}(2p - 5) < 10$

30. $\frac{3}{5}(k - 2) - \frac{1}{4}(2k - 7) \leq 3$

31. $3(2x - 4) - 4x < 2x + 3$

32. $7(4 - x) + 5x < 2(16 - x)$

33. $8\left(\frac{1}{2}x + 3\right) < 8\left(\frac{1}{2}x - 1\right)$

34. $10x + 2(x - 4) < 12x - 10$

35. A student solved the inequality $5x < -20$ by dividing both sides by 5 and reversing the direction of the inequality symbol. His reasoning was that since $-20$ is a negative number, reversing the direction of the symbol was required. Is this correct? Explain why or why not.

36. Match each set given in interval notation with its description.

| | |
|---|---|
| **(a)** $(0, \infty)$ | **A.** positive real numbers |
| **(b)** $[0, \infty)$ | **B.** negative real numbers |
| **(c)** $(-\infty, 0]$ | **C.** nonpositive real numbers |
| **(d)** $(-\infty, 0)$ | **D.** nonnegative real numbers |

*Solve each inequality. Give the solution set in both interval and graph forms.*

37. $-4 < x - 5 < 6$

38. $-1 < x + 1 < 8$

39. $-9 \leq k + 5 \leq 15$

40. $-4 \leq m + 3 \leq 10$

41. $-6 \leq 2z + 4 \leq 16$

42. $-15 < 3p + 6 < -12$

43. $-19 \leq 3x - 5 \leq 1$

44. $-16 < 3t + 2 < -10$

45. $-1 \leq \frac{2x - 5}{6} \leq 5$

46. $-3 \leq \frac{3m + 1}{4} \leq 3$

47. $4 \leq 5 - 9x < 8$

48. $4 \leq 3 - 2x < 8$

**Tornado Activity** *In Exercises 49–52, answer the questions based on the graph.*

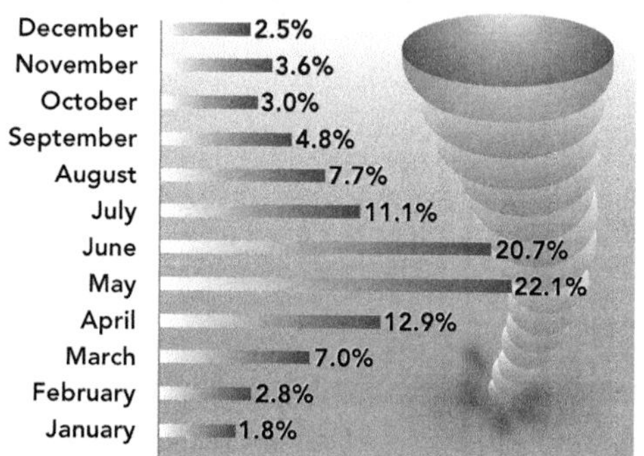


Source: *The USA Today Weather Book.*

49. In which months did the percent of tornadoes exceed 7.7%?

50. In which months was the percent of tornadoes at least 12.9%?

51. The data used to determine the graph were based on the number of tornadoes sighted in the United States during a twenty-year period. A total of 17,252 tornadoes were reported. In which months were fewer than 1500 reported?

52. How many more tornadoes occurred during March than October? (Use the total given in Exercise 51.)

***Olympic Temperature Preferences*** *The weather forecast by time of day for the U.S. Olympic Track and Field Trials, held in Sacramento, California, is shown in the figure. Use this graph to work Exercises 53–56.*

**TRACKING THE HEAT**

**The forecast for the U.S. Olympic Track and Field Trials by time of day. (Average temperature this time of year is a high of 93.5, low of 60.5.)**

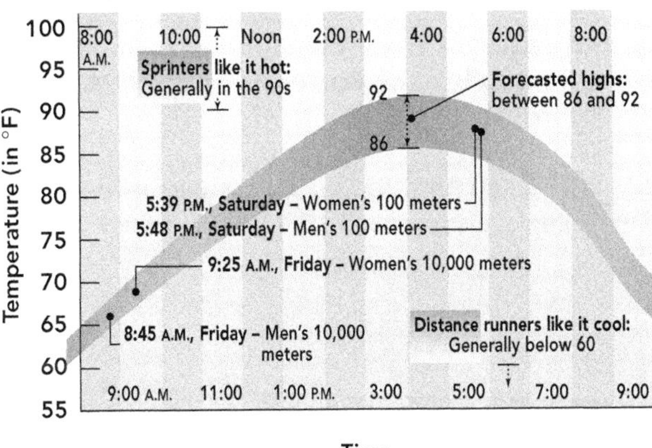


*Source:* Accuweather, *Sacramento Bee* research.

53. Sprinters prefer Fahrenheit temperatures in the 90s. Using the upper boundary of the forecast, in what time period is the temperature expected to be at least 90° F?

54. Distance runners prefer cool temperatures. During what time period are temperatures predicted to be no more than 70° F? Use the lower forecast boundary.

55. What range of temperatures is predicted for the Women's 100-meter event?

56. What range of temperatures is forecast for the Men's 10,000-meter event?

*Solve each problem.*

57. ***Taxicab Fare*** In a midwestern city, taxicabs charge \$3.00 for the first $\frac{1}{5}$ mile and \$.50 for each additional $\frac{1}{5}$ mile. Ed d'Hemecourt has only \$7.50 in his pocket. What is the maximum distance he can travel (not including a tip for the cabbie)?

58. ***Taxicab Fare*** Ten years ago taxicab fares in the city in Exercise 57 were \$.90 for the first $\frac{1}{7}$ mile and \$.10 for each additional $\frac{1}{7}$ mile. Based on the information given there and the answer you found, how much farther could Ed have traveled at that time?

59. ***Grade Average*** Allen Wells earned scores of 90 and 82 on his first two tests in English Literature. What score must he make on his third test to keep an average of 84 or greater?

60. ***Grade Average*** Beth Anderson scored 92 and 96 on her first two tests in Methods in Photography. What score must she make on her third test to keep an average of 90 or greater?

61. ***Car Rental*** A couple wishes to rent a car for one day while on vacation. Avis wants \$35.00 per day and 14¢ per mile, while Downtown Toyota wants \$34.00 per day and 16¢ per mile. After how many miles would the price to rent from Downtown Toyota exceed the price to rent from Avis?

62. ***Car Rental*** John and Sherry Gainey went to New Jersey for a week. They needed to rent a car, so they checked out two rental firms. Avis wanted \$28 per day, with no mileage fee. Downtown Toyota wanted \$108 per week and 14¢ per mile. How many miles would they have to drive before the Avis price is less than the Toyota price?

63. ***Body Mass Index*** A BMI (body mass index) between 19 and 25 is considered healthy. Use the formula

$$\text{BMI} = \frac{704 \times (\text{weight in pounds})}{(\text{height in inches})^2}$$

to find the weight range $w$, to the nearest pound, that gives a healthy BMI for each height. (*Source: Washington Post.*)

**(a)** 72 inches **(b)** Your height in inches

**64.** ***Target Heart Rate*** To achieve the maximum benefit from exercising, the heart rate in beats per minute should be in the target heart rate zone (THR). For a person aged $A$, the formula is

$$.7(220 - A) \leq \text{THR} \leq .85(220 - A).$$

Find the THR to the nearest whole number for each age. (*Source:* Hockey, Robert V., *Physical Fitness: The Pathway to Healthful Living,* Times Mirror/Mosby College Publishing, 1989.)

**(a)** 35 **(b)** Your age

***Profit/Cost Analysis*** *A product will produce a profit only when the revenue $R$ from selling the product exceeds the cost $C$ of producing it ($R$ and $C$ in dollars). Find the least whole number of units $x$ that must be sold for the business to show a profit for the item described.*

**65.** Peripheral Visions, Inc. finds that the cost to produce $x$ studio quality DVDs is $C = 20x + 100$, while the revenue produced from them is $R = 24x$.

**66.** Speedy Delivery finds that the cost to make $x$ deliveries is $C = 3x + 2300$, while the revenue produced from them is $R = 5.50x$.

# 7.5 Properties of Exponents and Scientific Notation

**Exponents and Exponential Expressions • The Product Rule • Zero and Negative Exponents • The Quotient Rule • The Power Rules • Summary of Rules for Exponents • Scientific Notation**

## Exponents and Exponential Expressions

*Exponents* are used to write products of repeated factors. For example, the product $3 \cdot 3 \cdot 3 \cdot 3$ is written

The number 4 shows that 3 appears as a factor four times. The number 4 is the **exponent** and 3 is the **base.** The quantity $3^4$ is called an **exponential expression.** Read $3^4$ as "3 to the fourth power," or "3 to the fourth." Multiplying out the four 3s gives

$$3^4 = 3 \cdot 3 \cdot 3 \cdot 3 = 81.$$

The term **googol,** meaning $10^{100}$, was coined by Professor Edward Kasner of Columbia University. A googol is made up of a 1 with one hundred zeros following it. This number exceeds the estimated number of electrons in the universe, which is $10^{79}$.

The Web search engine Google is named after a googol. Sergey Brin, president and cofounder of Google, Inc., was a mathematics major. He chose the name Google to describe the vast reach of this search engine. (*Source: The Gazette,* March 2, 2001.) The term "googling" is now part of the English language.

If a googol isn't big enough for you, try a **googolplex:**

$$\text{googolplex} = 10^{\text{googol}}.$$

### Exponential Expression

If $a$ is a real number and $n$ is a natural number, then the exponential expression $a^n$ is defined as

$$a^n = \underbrace{a \cdot a \cdot a \cdot \ldots \cdot a}_{n \text{ factors of } a}.$$

The number $a$ is the *base* and $n$ is the *exponent.*

### EXAMPLE 1 Evaluating Exponential Expressions

Evaluate each exponential expression.

**(a)** $7^2$ **(b)** $5^3$ **(c)** $(-2)^4$ **(d)** $(-2)^5$ **(e)** $5^1$

**SOLUTION**

**(a)** $7^2 = 7 \cdot 7 = 49$ Read $7^2$ as "7 squared."

$7^2 = 7 \cdot 7$, *not* $7 \cdot 2$.

**(b)** $5^3 = 5 \cdot 5 \cdot 5 = 125$ Read $5^3$ as "5 cubed."

**(c)** $(-2)^4 = (-2)(-2)(-2)(-2) = 16$

**(d)** $(-2)^5 = (-2)(-2)(-2)(-2)(-2) = -32$

**(e)** $5^1 = 5$

In the exponential expression $3z^7$, the base of the exponent 7 is $z$, *not* $3z$. That is,

$$3z^7 = 3 \cdot z \cdot z \cdot z \cdot z \cdot z \cdot z \cdot z \quad \text{Base is } z.$$

while

$$(3z)^7 = (3z)(3z)(3z)(3z)(3z)(3z)(3z). \quad \text{Base is } 3z.$$

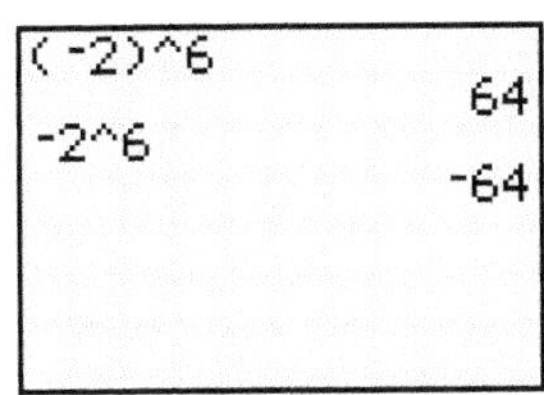


This screen supports the discussion preceding Example 2.

To evaluate $(-2)^6$, the parentheses around $-2$ indicate that the base is $-2$, so

$$(-2)^6 = (-2)(-2)(-2)(-2)(-2)(-2) = 64. \quad \text{Base is } -2.$$

In the expression $-2^6$, the base is 2, *not* $-2$. The $-$ sign tells us to find the negative, or additive inverse, of $2^6$. It acts as a symbol for the factor $-1$.

$$-2^6 = -(2 \cdot 2 \cdot 2 \cdot 2 \cdot 2 \cdot 2) = -64 \quad \text{Base is } 2.$$

Therefore, since $64 \neq -64$, $(-2)^6 \neq -2^6$.

## EXAMPLE 2 Evaluating Exponential Expressions

Evaluate each exponential expression.

**(a)** $-4^2$ **(b)** $-8^4$ **(c)** $-2^4$

**SOLUTION**

**(a)** $-4^2 = -(4 \cdot 4) = -16$ **(b)** $-8^4 = -(8 \cdot 8 \cdot 8 \cdot 8) = -4096$

**(c)** $-2^4 = -(2 \cdot 2 \cdot 2 \cdot 2) = -16$

## The Product Rule

There are several useful rules that simplify work with exponents. For example, the product $2^5 \cdot 2^3$ can be simplified as follows.

$$\overbrace{2^5 \cdot 2^3}^{5+3=8} = (2 \cdot 2 \cdot 2 \cdot 2 \cdot 2)(2 \cdot 2 \cdot 2) = 2^8$$

This result—products of exponential expressions with the same base are found by adding exponents—is generalized as the **product rule for exponents.**

### Product Rule for Exponents

If $m$ and $n$ are natural numbers and $a$ is any real number, then

$$a^m \cdot a^n = a^{m+n}.$$

**EXAMPLE 3 Applying the Product Rule**

Apply the product rule for exponents in each case.

**(a)** $3^4 \cdot 3^7$ **(b)** $5^3 \cdot 5$ **(c)** $y^3 \cdot y^8 \cdot y^2$
**(d)** $(5y^2)(-3y^4)$ **(e)** $(7p^3q)(2p^5q^2)$

**SOLUTION**

**(a)** $3^4 \cdot 3^7 = 3^{4+7} = 3^{11}$

Do not make the error of writing $3 \cdot 3 = 9$ as the base.

**(b)** $5^3 \cdot 5 = 5^3 \cdot 5^1 = 5^{3+1} = 5^4$

**(c)** $y^3 \cdot y^8 \cdot y^2 = y^{3+8+2} = y^{13}$

**(d)** $(5y^2)(-3y^4) = 5(-3)y^2y^4$ Associative and commutative properties

$= -15y^{2+4}$ Multiply; product rule

$= -15y^6$

**(e)** $(7p^3q)(2p^5q^2) = 7(2)p^3p^5qq^2$

$= 14p^8q^3$

**Zero and Negative Exponents** We now consider 0 as an exponent. How can we define an expression such as $4^0$ so that it is consistent with the product rule? By the product rule, we should have

$$4^2 \cdot 4^0 = 4^{2+0} = 4^2.$$

For the product rule to hold true, $4^0$ must equal 1. This leads to the definition of $a^0$ for any nonzero real number $a$.

**Zero Exponent**

If $a$ is any nonzero real number, then $\mathbf{a^0 = 1}$.

The expression $\mathbf{0^0}$ **is undefined.***

**EXAMPLE 4 Applying the Definition of Zero Exponent**

Evaluate each expression.

**(a)** $12^0$ **(b)** $(-6)^0$ **(c)** $-6^0$
**(d)** $5^0 + 12^0$ **(e)** $(8k)^0, \quad k \neq 0$

**SOLUTION**

**(a)** $12^0 = 1$

**(b)** $(-6)^0 = 1$ Base is $-6$.

**(c)** $-6^0 = -(6^0) = -1$ Base is 6.

**(d)** $5^0 + 12^0 = 1 + 1 = 2$

**(e)** $(8k)^0 = 1, \quad k \neq 0$

```
(-6)^0
                1
-6^0
               -1
5^0+12^0
                2
```

This screen supports the results in parts (b), (c), and (d) of Example 4.

*In advanced studies, $0^0$ is called an *indeterminate form*.

How should we define a negative exponent? Using the product rule again,

$$8^2 \cdot 8^{-2} = 8^{2+(-2)} = 8^0 = 1.$$

This indicates that $8^{-2}$ is the reciprocal of $8^2$. But $\frac{1}{8^2}$ is the reciprocal of $8^2$, and a number can have only one reciprocal. Therefore, it is reasonable to conclude that $8^{-2} = \frac{1}{8^2}$. We can generalize and make the following definition.

**Negative Exponent**

For any natural number $n$ and any nonzero real number $a$,

$$a^{-n} = \frac{1}{a^n}.$$

With this definition, and the ones given earlier for positive and zero exponents, the expression $a^n$ is meaningful for any integer exponent $n$ and any nonzero real number $a$.

### EXAMPLE 5 Applying the Definition of Negative Exponents

Write the following expressions with only positive exponents. Assume that all variables represent nonzero real numbers.

**(a)** $2^{-3}$ **(b)** $3^{-2}$ **(c)** $6^{-1}$ **(d)** $(5z)^{-3}$
**(e)** $5z^{-3}$ **(f)** $(5z^2)^{-3}$ **(g)** $-m^{-2}$ **(h)** $(-m)^{-4}$

**SOLUTION**

**(a)** $2^{-3} = \frac{1}{2^3} = \frac{1}{8}$

**(b)** $3^{-2} = \frac{1}{3^2} = \frac{1}{9}$

**(c)** $6^{-1} = \frac{1}{6^1} = \frac{1}{6}$

**(d)** $(5z)^{-3} = \frac{1}{(5z)^3}$ Base is $5z$.

**(e)** $5z^{-3} = 5\left(\frac{1}{z^3}\right) = \frac{5}{z^3}$ Base is $z$.

**(f)** $(5z^2)^{-3} = \frac{1}{(5z^2)^3}$

**(g)** $-m^{-2} = -\frac{1}{m^2}$

**(h)** $(-m)^{-4} = \frac{1}{(-m)^4}$

### EXAMPLE 6 Evaluating Exponential Expressions

Evaluate each expression.

**(a)** $3^{-1} + 4^{-1}$ **(b)** $5^{-1} - 2^{-1}$ **(c)** $\frac{1}{2^{-3}}$ **(d)** $\frac{2^{-3}}{3^{-2}}$

```
3⁻¹+4⁻¹▸Frac
            7/12
5⁻¹-2⁻¹▸Frac
           -3/10
(2^-3)/(3^-2)▸Fr
ac
             9/8
```

This screen supports the results in parts (a), (b), and (d) of Example 6.

**SOLUTION**

**(a)** $3^{-1} + 4^{-1} = \frac{1}{3} + \frac{1}{4} = \frac{4}{12} + \frac{3}{12} = \frac{7}{12}$ $3^{-1} = \frac{1}{3}; 4^{-1} = \frac{1}{4}$

**(b)** $5^{-1} - 2^{-1} = \frac{1}{5} - \frac{1}{2} = \frac{2}{10} - \frac{5}{10} = -\frac{3}{10}$

**(c)** $\dfrac{1}{2^{-3}} = \dfrac{1}{\frac{1}{2^3}} = 1 \div \dfrac{1}{2^3} = 1 \cdot \dfrac{2^3}{1} = 2^3 = 8$

To divide, multiply by the reciprocal.

**(d)** $\dfrac{2^{-3}}{3^{-2}} = \dfrac{\frac{1}{2^3}}{\frac{1}{3^2}} = \dfrac{1}{2^3} \div \dfrac{1}{3^2} = \dfrac{1}{2^3} \cdot \dfrac{3^2}{1} = \dfrac{3^2}{2^3} = \dfrac{9}{8}$ ■

Parts (c) and (d) of Example 6 suggest the following generalizations.

**Special Rules for Negative Exponents**

If $a \neq 0$ and $b \neq 0$, then $\dfrac{1}{a^{-n}} = a^n$ and $\dfrac{a^{-n}}{b^{-m}} = \dfrac{b^m}{a^n}$.

**The Quotient Rule** A quotient, such as $\frac{a^8}{a^3}$, can be simplified in much the same way as a product. (In all quotients of this type, assume that the denominator is not 0.) Using the definition of an exponent,

$$\frac{a^8}{a^3} = \frac{a \cdot a \cdot a \cdot a \cdot a \cdot a \cdot a \cdot a}{a \cdot a \cdot a} = a \cdot a \cdot a \cdot a \cdot a = a^5.$$

Notice that $8 - 3 = 5$. In the same way,

$$\frac{a^3}{a^8} = \frac{a \cdot a \cdot a}{a \cdot a \cdot a \cdot a \cdot a \cdot a \cdot a \cdot a} = \frac{1}{a^5} = a^{-5}.$$

Here, $3 - 8 = -5$. These examples suggest the **quotient rule for exponents.**

**Quotient Rule for Exponents**

If $a$ is any nonzero real number and $m$ and $n$ are integers, then

$$\frac{a^m}{a^n} = a^{m-n}.$$

**EXAMPLE 7 Applying the Quotient Rule**

Apply the quotient rule for exponents in each case. Assume that all variables represent nonzero real numbers.

**(a)** $\dfrac{3^7}{3^2}$ **(b)** $\dfrac{p^6}{p^2}$ **(c)** $\dfrac{12^{10}}{12^9}$ **(d)** $\dfrac{7^4}{7^6}$ **(e)** $\dfrac{k^7}{k^{12}}$

**SOLUTION**

Numerator exponent ↓, Denominator exponent ↓, Minus sign ↑

(a) $\dfrac{3^7}{3^2} = 3^{7-2} = 3^5$ (b) $\dfrac{p^6}{p^2} = p^{6-2} = p^4$

(c) $\dfrac{12^{10}}{12^9} = 12^{10-9} = 12^1 = 12$ (d) $\dfrac{7^4}{7^6} = 7^{4-6} = 7^{-2} = \dfrac{1}{7^2}$

(e) $\dfrac{k^7}{k^{12}} = k^{7-12} = k^{-5} = \dfrac{1}{k^5}$

## EXAMPLE 8 Applying the Quotient Rule

Write each quotient using only positive exponents. Assume that all variables represent nonzero real numbers.

(a) $\dfrac{2^7}{2^{-3}}$ (b) $\dfrac{8^{-2}}{8^5}$ (c) $\dfrac{6^{-5}}{6^{-2}}$ (d) $\dfrac{4}{4^{-1}}$ (e) $\dfrac{z^{-5}}{z^{-8}}$

```
(2^7)/(2^-3)=2^1
0
                1
4/4⁻¹=4²
                1
```

This screen supports the results in parts (a) and (d) of Example 8.

**SOLUTION**

Be careful when subtracting a negative number.

(a) $\dfrac{2^7}{2^{-3}} = 2^{7-(-3)} = 2^{10}$ (b) $\dfrac{8^{-2}}{8^5} = 8^{-2-5} = 8^{-7} = \dfrac{1}{8^7}$

(c) $\dfrac{6^{-5}}{6^{-2}} = 6^{-5-(-2)} = 6^{-3} = \dfrac{1}{6^3}$ (d) $\dfrac{4}{4^{-1}} = \dfrac{4^1}{4^{-1}} = 4^{1-(-1)} = 4^2$

(e) $\dfrac{z^{-5}}{z^{-8}} = z^{-5-(-8)} = z^3$

**The Power Rules** The expression $(3^4)^2$ can be simplified as $(3^4)^2 = 3^4 \cdot 3^4 = 3^{4+4} = 3^8$, where $4 \cdot 2 = 8$. This example suggests the first of the **power rules for exponents.** The other two parts can be demonstrated with similar examples.

### Power Rules for Exponents

If $a$ and $b$ are real numbers, and $m$ and $n$ are integers, then

$$(a^m)^n = a^{mn}, \quad (ab)^m = a^m b^m, \quad \text{and} \quad \left(\frac{a}{b}\right)^m = \frac{a^m}{b^m} \quad (b \neq 0).$$

In the statements of rules for exponents, we always assume that zero never appears to a negative power or to the power zero.

## EXAMPLE 9 Applying the Power Rules

Use a power rule in each case. Assume that all variables represent nonzero real numbers.

(a) $(p^8)^3$ (b) $\left(\dfrac{2}{3}\right)^4$ (c) $(3y)^4$ (d) $(6p^7)^2$ (e) $\left(\dfrac{-2m^5}{z}\right)^3$

**SOLUTION**

**(a)** $(p^8)^3 = p^{8 \cdot 3} = p^{24}$ **(b)** $\left(\frac{2}{3}\right)^4 = \frac{2^4}{3^4} = \frac{16}{81}$

**(c)** $(3y)^4 = 3^4y^4 = 81y^4$ **(d)** $(6p^7)^2 = 6^2p^{7 \cdot 2} = 6^2p^{14} = 36p^{14}$

**(e)** $\left(\frac{-2m^5}{z}\right)^3 = \frac{(-2)^3m^{5 \cdot 3}}{z^3} = \frac{(-2)^3m^{15}}{z^3} = \frac{-8m^{15}}{z^3}$ ■

Notice that

$$6^{-3} = \left(\frac{1}{6}\right)^3 = \frac{1}{216} \quad \text{and} \quad \left(\frac{2}{3}\right)^{-2} = \left(\frac{3}{2}\right)^2 = \frac{9}{4}.$$

These are examples of two special rules for negative exponents.

**Special Rules for Negative Exponents**

If $a \neq 0$ and $b \neq 0$ and $n$ is an integer, then

$$a^{-n} = \left(\frac{1}{a}\right)^n \quad \text{and} \quad \left(\frac{a}{b}\right)^{-n} = \left(\frac{b}{a}\right)^n.$$

```
(3/7)^-2►Frac
           49/9
(4/5)^-3►Frac
         125/64
```

This screen supports the results of Example 10.

**EXAMPLE 10 Applying Special Rules for Negative Exponents**

Write each expression with only positive exponents, and then evaluate.

**(a)** $\left(\frac{3}{7}\right)^{-2}$ **(b)** $\left(\frac{4}{5}\right)^{-3}$

**SOLUTION**

**(a)** $\left(\frac{3}{7}\right)^{-2} = \left(\frac{7}{3}\right)^2 = \frac{49}{9}$ **(b)** $\left(\frac{4}{5}\right)^{-3} = \left(\frac{5}{4}\right)^3 = \frac{125}{64}$ ■

**Summary of Rules for Exponents** The definitions and rules of this section are summarized here.

**Definitions and Rules for Exponents**

For all integers $m$ and $n$ and all real numbers $a$ and $b$,

**Product Rule** $a^m \cdot a^n = a^{m+n}$

**Quotient Rule** $\frac{a^m}{a^n} = a^{m-n} \quad (a \neq 0)$

**Zero Exponent** $a^0 = 1 \quad (a \neq 0)$

**Negative Exponent** $a^{-n} = \frac{1}{a^n} \quad (a \neq 0)$

*(continued)*

**Power Rules** $(a^m)^n = a^{mn}$ $(ab)^m = a^m b^m$

$$\left(\frac{a}{b}\right)^m = \frac{a^m}{b^m} \quad (b \neq 0)$$

**Special Rules for Negative Exponents**

$$\frac{1}{a^{-n}} = a^n \quad (a \neq 0) \qquad \frac{a^{-n}}{b^{-m}} = \frac{b^m}{a^n} \quad (a, b \neq 0)$$

$$a^{-n} = \left(\frac{1}{a}\right)^n \quad (a \neq 0)$$

$$\left(\frac{a}{b}\right)^{-n} = \left(\frac{b}{a}\right)^n \quad (a, b \neq 0).$$

## EXAMPLE 11 Writing Expressions with No Negative Exponents

Simplify each expression so that no negative exponents appear in the final result. Assume that all variables represent nonzero real numbers.

**(a)** $3^2 \cdot 3^{-5}$ **(b)** $x^{-3} \cdot x^{-4} \cdot x^2$ **(c)** $(4^{-2})^{-5}$

**(d)** $(x^{-4})^6$ **(e)** $\dfrac{x^{-4}y^2}{x^2y^{-5}}$ **(f)** $(2^3x^{-2})^{-2}$

**SOLUTION**

**(a)** $3^2 \cdot 3^{-5} = 3^{2+(-5)} = 3^{-3} = \dfrac{1}{3^3}$ or $\dfrac{1}{27}$

**(b)** $x^{-3} \cdot x^{-4} \cdot x^2 = x^{-3+(-4)+2} = x^{-5} = \dfrac{1}{x^5}$

**(c)** $(4^{-2})^{-5} = 4^{-2(-5)} = 4^{10}$

**(d)** $(x^{-4})^6 = x^{(-4)6} = x^{-24} = \dfrac{1}{x^{24}}$

**(e)**
$$\frac{x^{-4}y^2}{x^2y^{-5}} = \frac{x^{-4}}{x^2} \cdot \frac{y^2}{y^{-5}}$$
$$= x^{-4-2} \cdot y^{2-(-5)}$$
$$= x^{-6}y^7$$
$$= \frac{y^7}{x^6}$$

**(f)**
$$(2^3x^{-2})^{-2} = (2^3)^{-2} \cdot (x^{-2})^{-2}$$
$$= 2^{-6}x^4$$
$$= \frac{x^4}{2^6} \text{ or } \frac{x^4}{64}$$

**Scientific Notation** Many of the numbers that occur in science are very large, such as the number of one-celled organisms that will sustain a whale for a few hours: 400,000,000,000,000. Other numbers are very small, such as the shortest wavelength of visible light, about .0000004 meter. Writing these numbers is simplified by using *scientific notation*.

In the episode "Court-Martial" from the original *Star Trek* television series, Captain Kirk makes this statement during a scene on the bridge of the Enterprise:

*Gentlemen, this computer has an auditory sensor. It can, in effect, hear sounds. By installing a booster we can increase that capability on an order of one to the fourth power. The computer should be able to bring us every sound occurring on the ship.*

Can you identify the error in Kirk's statement? What do you think he might have really meant? (Think about scientific notation.)

### Scientific Notation

A number is written in **scientific notation** when it is expressed in the form

$$a \times 10^n,$$

where $1 \le |a| < 10$, and $n$ is an integer.

As stated in the definition, scientific notation requires that the number be written as a product of a number between 1 and 10 (or $-1$ and $-10$) and some integer power of 10. (1 and $-1$ are allowed as values of $a$, but 10 and $-10$ are not.) For example, since

$$8000 = 8 \cdot 1000 = 8 \cdot 10^3,$$

the number 8000 is written in scientific notation as

$$8000 = 8 \times 10^3. \longleftarrow \text{Scientific notation}$$

***When using scientific notation, it is customary to use × instead of a dot to show multiplication.***

The steps involved in writing a number in scientific notation follow. (If the number is negative, ignore the minus sign, go through these steps, and then attach a minus sign to the result.)

### Converting to Scientific Notation

*Step 1* **Position the decimal point.** Place a caret, $\wedge$, to the right of the first nonzero digit, where the decimal point will be placed.

*Step 2* **Determine the numeral for the exponent.** Count the number of digits from the decimal point to the caret. This number gives the absolute value of the exponent on 10.

*Step 3* **Determine the sign for the exponent.** Decide whether multiplying by $10^n$ should make the result of Step 1 larger or smaller. The exponent should be positive to make the result larger; it should be negative to make the result smaller.

It is helpful to remember that for $n \ge 1$, $10^{-n} < 1$ and $10^n \ge 10$.

### EXAMPLE 12 Converting to Scientific Notation

Convert each number from standard notation to scientific notation.

**(a)** 8,200,000 **(b)** .000072

**SOLUTION**

**(a)** Place a caret to the right of the 8 (the first nonzero digit) to mark the new location of the decimal point.

$$8_\wedge200{,}000$$

| 8200000 | |
|---|---|
| | 8.2E6 |
| .000072 | |
| | 7.2E-5 |

If a graphing calculator is set in scientific notation mode, it will give results as shown here. E6 means "times $10^6$" and $E^-5$ means "times $10^{-5}$". Compare to the results of Example 12.

Count from the decimal point, which is understood to be after the last 0, to the caret.

$$8_{\wedge}200{,}000. \leftarrow \text{Decimal point}$$

Count 6 places.

Because the number 8.2 is to be made larger, the exponent on 10 is positive.

$$8{,}200{,}000 = 8.2 \times 10^6$$

**(b)** $.00007_{\wedge}2$ Count from left to right.

5 places

Since the number 7.2 is to be made smaller, the exponent on 10 is negative.

$$.000072 = 7.2 \times 10^{-5}$$

To convert a number written in scientific notation to standard notation, just work in reverse.

## Converting from Scientific Notation to Standard Notation

Multiplying a number by a positive power of 10 makes the number larger, so move the decimal point to the right if $n$ is positive in $10^n$.

Multiplying by a negative power of 10 makes a number smaller, so move the decimal point to the left if $n$ is negative.

If $n$ is zero, leave the decimal point where it is.

## EXAMPLE 13 Converting from Scientific Notation

Convert each number from scientific notation to standard notation.

**(a)** $6.93 \times 10^5$ **(b)** $4.7 \times 10^{-6}$ **(c)** $-1.083 \times 10^0$

**SOLUTION**

**(a)** $6.93 \times 10^5 = 6.93000$ Attach 0s as necessary.

5 places

The decimal point was moved 5 places to the right.

$$6.93 \times 10^5 = 693{,}000$$

**(b)** $4.7 \times 10^{-6} = 000004.7$ Attach 0s as necessary.

6 places

The decimal point was moved 6 places to the left.

$$4.7 \times 10^{-6} = .0000047$$

**(c)** $-1.083 \times 10^0 = -1.083$

We can use scientific notation and the rules for exponents to simplify calculations.

### EXAMPLE 14 Using Scientific Notation in Computation

Evaluate $\dfrac{1{,}920{,}000 \times .0015}{.000032 \times 45{,}000}$ by using scientific notation.

**SOLUTION**

$$\frac{1{,}920{,}000 \times .0015}{.000032 \times 45{,}000} = \frac{1.92 \times 10^6 \times 1.5 \times 10^{-3}}{3.2 \times 10^{-5} \times 4.5 \times 10^4}$$ Express all numbers in scientific notation.

$$= \frac{1.92 \times 1.5 \times 10^6 \times 10^{-3}}{3.2 \times 4.5 \times 10^{-5} \times 10^4}$$ Commutative and associative properties

$$= \frac{1.92 \times 1.5}{3.2 \times 4.5} \times 10^4$$ Product and quotient rules

$$= .2 \times 10^4$$ Simplify.

$$= (2 \times 10^{-1}) \times 10^4$$ Write .2 using scientific notation.

$$= 2 \times 10^3, \quad \text{or} \quad 2000$$ Product rule; multiply.

### EXAMPLE 15 Using Scientific Notation to Solve Problems

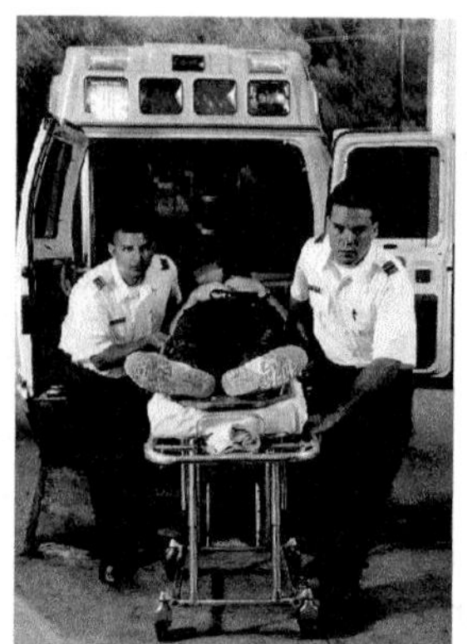

In 1990, the national health care expenditure was \$695.6 billion. By 2000, this figure had risen by a factor of 1.9; that is, it almost doubled in only 10 years. (*Source:* U.S. Centers for Medicare & Medicaid Services.)

**(a)** Write the 1990 health care expenditure using scientific notation.
**(b)** What was the expenditure in 2000?

**SOLUTION**

**(a)** $695.6 \text{ billion} = 695.6 \times 10^9$ 1 billion $= 10^9$

$$= (6.956 \times 10^2) \times 10^9$$

$$= 6.956 \times 10^{11}$$ Product rule

In 1990, the expenditure was $\$6.956 \times 10^{11}$.

**(b)** Multiply the result in part (a) by 1.9.

$$(6.956 \times 10^{11}) \times 1.9 = (1.9 \times 6.956) \times 10^{11}$$ Commutative and associative properties

$$= 13.216 \times 10^{11}$$ Round to three decimal places.

The 2000 expenditure was about \$1,321,600,000,000 (over \$1 trillion).

## 7.5 EXERCISES

*Match the exponential expressions in Exercises 1–6 with their equivalent expressions in Choices A–F. Choices may be used once, more than once, or not at all.*

**1.** $\left(\frac{5}{3}\right)^2$ **2.** $\left(\frac{3}{5}\right)^2$ **3.** $\left(-\frac{3}{5}\right)^{-2}$ **4.** $\left(-\frac{5}{3}\right)^{-2}$ **5.** $-\left(-\frac{3}{5}\right)^2$ **6.** $-\left(-\frac{5}{3}\right)^2$

**A.** $\frac{25}{9}$ **B.** $-\frac{25}{9}$ **C.** $\frac{9}{25}$ **D.** $-\frac{9}{25}$ **E.** none of these **F.** all of these

*Evaluate each exponential expression.*

**7.** $5^4$ **8.** $10^3$ **9.** $(-2)^5$ **10.** $(-5)^4$

**11.** $-2^3$ **12.** $-3^2$ **13.** $-(-3)^4$ **14.** $-(-5)^2$

**15.** $7^{-2}$ **16.** $4^{-1}$ **17.** $-7^{-2}$ **18.** $-4^{-1}$

**19.** $\dfrac{2}{(-4)^{-3}}$ **20.** $\dfrac{2^{-3}}{3^{-2}}$ **21.** $\dfrac{5^{-1}}{4^{-2}}$ **22.** $\left(\dfrac{1}{2}\right)^{-3}$

**23.** $\left(\dfrac{1}{5}\right)^{-3}$ **24.** $\left(\dfrac{2}{3}\right)^{-2}$ **25.** $\left(\dfrac{4}{5}\right)^{-2}$ **26.** $3^{-1} + 2^{-1}$

**27.** $4^{-1} + 5^{-1}$ **28.** $8^0$ **29.** $12^0$ **30.** $(-23)^0$

**31.** $(-4)^0$ **32.** $-2^0$ **33.** $3^0 - 4^0$ **34.** $-8^0 - 7^0$

**35.** In order to raise a fraction to a negative power, we may change the fraction to its ________ and change the exponent to the ______ ______ of the original exponent.

**36.** Explain in your own words how to raise a power to a power.

**37.** Which one of the following is correct?

**A.** $-\dfrac{3}{4} = \left(\dfrac{3}{4}\right)^{-1}$ **B.** $\dfrac{3^{-1}}{4^{-1}} = \left(\dfrac{4}{3}\right)^{-1}$

**C.** $\dfrac{3^{-1}}{4} = \dfrac{3}{4^{-1}}$ **D.** $\dfrac{3^{-1}}{4^{-1}} = \left(\dfrac{3}{4}\right)^{-1}$

**38.** Which one of the following is incorrect?

**A.** $(3r)^{-2} = 3^{-2}r^{-2}$ **B.** $3r^{-2} = (3r)^{-2}$

**C.** $(3r)^{-2} = \dfrac{1}{(3r)^2}$ **D.** $(3r)^{-2} = \dfrac{r^{-2}}{9}$

*Use the product, quotient, and power rules to simplify each expression. Write answers with only positive exponents. Assume that all variables represent nonzero real numbers.*

**39.** $x^{12} \cdot x^4$ **40.** $\dfrac{x^{12}}{x^4}$ **41.** $\dfrac{5^{17}}{5^{16}}$ **42.** $\dfrac{3^{12}}{3^{13}}$

**43.** $\dfrac{3^{-5}}{3^{-2}}$ **44.** $\dfrac{2^{-4}}{2^{-3}}$ **45.** $\dfrac{9^{-1}}{9}$ **46.** $\dfrac{12}{12^{-1}}$

**47.** $t^5t^{-12}$ **48.** $p^5p^{-6}$ **49.** $(3x)^2$ **50.** $(-2x^{-2})^2$

**51.** $a^{-3}a^2a^{-4}$ **52.** $k^{-5}k^{-3}k^4$ **53.** $\dfrac{x^7}{x^{-4}}$ **54.** $\dfrac{p^{-3}}{p^5}$

**55.** $\dfrac{r^3r^{-4}}{r^{-2}r^{-5}}$ **56.** $\dfrac{z^{-4}z^{-2}}{z^3z^{-1}}$ **57.** $7k^2(-2k)(4k^{-5})$ **58.** $3a^2(-5a^{-6})(-2a)$

**59.** $(z^3)^{-2}z^2$ **60.** $(p^{-1})^3p^{-4}$ **61.** $-3r^{-1}(r^{-3})^2$ **62.** $2(y^{-3})^4(y^6)$

**63.** $(3a^{-2})^3(a^3)^{-4}$ **64.** $(m^5)^{-2}(3m^{-2})^3$ **65.** $(x^{-5}y^2)^{-1}$ **66.** $(a^{-3}b^{-5})^2$

**67.** Which one of the following does *not* represent the reciprocal of $x$ ($x \neq 0$)?

**A.** $x^{-1}$ **B.** $\dfrac{1}{x}$ **C.** $\left(\dfrac{1}{x^{-1}}\right)^{-1}$ **D.** $-x$

**68.** Which one of the following is *not* in scientific notation?

**A.** $6.02 \times 10^{23}$ **B.** $14 \times 10^{-6}$

**C.** $1.4 \times 10^{-5}$ **D.** $3.8 \times 10^3$

*Convert each number from standard notation to scientific notation.*

**69.** 230 **70.** 46,500 **71.** .02 **72.** .0051

*Convert each number from scientific notation to standard notation.*

**73.** $6.5 \times 10^3$ **74.** $2.317 \times 10^5$ **75.** $1.52 \times 10^{-2}$ **76.** $1.63 \times 10^{-4}$

*Use scientific notation to perform each of the following computations. Leave the answers in scientific notation.*

**77.** $\frac{.002 \times 3900}{.000013}$ **78.** $\frac{.009 \times 600}{.02}$ **79.** $\frac{.0004 \times 56,000}{.000112}$

**80.** $\frac{.018 \times 20,000}{300 \times .0004}$ **81.** $\frac{840,000 \times .03}{.00021 \times 600}$ **82.** $\frac{28 \times .0045}{140 \times 1500}$

*Solve each problem.*

**83.** ***U.S. Budget*** The U.S. budget first passed **\$1,000,000,000** in 1917. Seventy years later in 1987 it exceeded **\$1,000,000,000,000** for the first time. President George W. Bush's budget request for fiscal 2003 was **\$2,128,000,000,000**. If stacked in dollar bills, this amount would stretch **144,419** mi, almost two-thirds of the distance to the moon. Write the four boldfaced numbers in scientific notation. (*Source: The Gazette*, February 5, 2002.)

**84.** ***Wal-Mart Employment*** In 1970, Wal-Mart had **1500** employees. In 1997, Wal-Mart became the largest private employer in the United States, with **680,000** employees. In 1999, Wal-Mart became the largest private employer in the world, with **1,100,000** employees. By 2007, the company is expected to have **2,200,000** employees. Write these four numbers in scientific notation. (*Source:* Wal-Mart.)

**85.** ***NASA Budget*** The budget for the Operating Plan in 2005 for the National Aeronautics and Space Administration was **\$16,196.4 million.** Write this amount in scientific notation. (*Source:* www.nasa.gov)

**86.** ***Motor Vehicle Registrations*** In 2002, there were **229,620,000** motor vehicle registrations in the United States. Write this number in scientific notation. (*Source:* U.S. Federal Highway Administration.)

***Astronomy Data*** *Each of the following statements (Exercises 87–90) comes from* Astronomy! A Brief Edition *by James B. Kaler (Addison-Wesley, 1997). If the number in the statement is in scientific notation, write it in standard notation without using exponents. If the number is in standard notation, write it in scientific notation.*

**87.** Multiplying this view over the whole sky yields a galaxy count of more than **10 billion.** (page 496)

**88.** The circumference of the solar orbit is . . . about **4.7 million** km . . . . (in reference to the orbit of Jupiter, page 395)

**89.** The solar luminosity requires that $\mathbf{2 \times 10^9}$ kg of mass be converted into energy every second. (page 327)

**90.** At maximum, a cosmic ray particle—a mere atomic nucleus of only $\mathbf{10^{-13}}$ cm across—can carry the energy of a professionally pitched baseball. (page 445)

*Solve each problem.*

**91.** ***Defense Budget*** The federal budget outlay for defense functions in the United States in 2003 was \$404.9 billion. The estimated population of the United States in 2003 was 290,810 thousand. To the nearest dollar, what was the amount devoted to defense per person? (*Source:* U.S. Office of Management and Budget, U.S. Census Bureau.)

**92.** ***Powerball Lottery*** In the early years of the Powerball Lottery, a player had to choose five numbers from 1 through 49 and one number from 1 through 42. It can be shown that there are about $8.009 \times 10^7$ different ways to do this. Suppose that a group of 2000 people decided to purchase tickets for all these numbers and each ticket cost \$1.00. How much should each person have expected to pay? (*Source:* www.powerball.com)

93. ***Distance of Uranus from the Sun*** A parsec, a unit of length used in astronomy, is $1.9 \times 10^{13}$ miles. The mean distance of Uranus from the sun is $1.8 \times 10^7$ miles. How many parsecs is Uranus from the sun?

94. ***Number of Inches in a Mile*** An inch is approximately $1.57828 \times 10^{-5}$ mile. Find the reciprocal of this number to determine the number of inches in a mile.

95. ***Speed of Light*** The speed of light is approximately $3 \times 10^{10}$ centimeters per second. How long will it take light to travel $9 \times 10^{12}$ centimeters?

96. ***Rocket from Earth to the Sun*** The average distance from Earth to the sun is $9.3 \times 10^7$ miles. How long would it take a rocket, traveling at $2.9 \times 10^3$ miles per hour, to reach the sun?

97. ***Miles in a Light-Year*** A *light-year* is the distance that light travels in one year. Find the number of miles in a light-year if light travels $1.86 \times 10^5$ miles per second.

98. ***Time for Light to Travel*** Use the information given in the previous two exercises to find the number of minutes necessary for light from the sun to reach Earth.

99. ***Rocket from Venus to Mercury*** The planet Mercury has an average distance from the sun of $3.6 \times 10^7$ miles, while the mean distance of Venus from the sun is $6.7 \times 10^7$ miles. How long would it take a spacecraft traveling at $1.55 \times 10^3$ miles per hour to travel from Venus to Mercury? Assume the trip could be timed so that its start and finish would occur when the respective planets are at their average distances from the sun and the same direction from the sun. (Give your answer in hours, without scientific notation.)

100. ***Distance from an Object to the Moon*** When the distance between the centers of the moon and Earth is $4.60 \times 10^8$ meters, an object on the line joining the centers of the moon and Earth exerts the same gravitational force on each when it is $4.14 \times 10^8$ meters from the center of Earth. How far is the object from the center of the moon at that point?

# 7.6 Polynomials and Factoring

**Basic Terminology • Addition and Subtraction • Multiplication • Special Products • Factoring • Factoring Out the Greatest Common Factor • Factoring by Grouping • Factoring Trinomials • Factoring Special Binomials**

## Basic Terminology

A **term,** or **monomial,** is defined to be a number, a variable, or a product of numbers and variables. A **polynomial** is a term or a finite sum or difference of terms, with only nonnegative integer exponents permitted on the variables. If the terms of a polynomial contain only the variable $x$, then the polynomial is called a **polynomial in** $\boldsymbol{x}$. (Polynomials in other variables are defined similarly.) Examples of polynomials include

$$5x^3 - 8x^2 + 7x - 4, \quad 9p^5 - 3, \quad 8r^2, \quad \text{and} \quad 6. \qquad \text{Polynomials}$$

The expression $9x^2 - 4x - \frac{6}{x}$ is not a polynomial because of the presence of $-\frac{6}{x}$. The terms of a polynomial cannot have variables in a denominator.

The greatest exponent in a polynomial in one variable is the **degree** of the polynomial. A nonzero constant is said to have degree 0. (The polynomial 0 has no degree.) For example, $3x^6 - 5x^2 + 2x + 3$ is a polynomial of degree 6.

A polynomial can have more than one variable. A term containing more than one variable has degree equal to the sum of all the exponents appearing on the variables in the term. For example, $-3x^4y^3z^5$ is of degree $4 + 3 + 5 = 12$. The degree of a polynomial in more than one variable is equal to the greatest degree of any term appearing in the polynomial. By this definition, the polynomial $2x^4y^3 - 3x^5y + x^6y^2$ is of degree 8 because the $x^6y^2$ term has degree 8.

A polynomial containing exactly three terms is called a **trinomial** and one containing exactly two terms is a **binomial.** Table 5 shows several polynomials and gives the degree and type of each.

**TABLE 5**

| Polynomial | Degree | Type |
|---|---|---|
| $9p^7 - 4p^3 + 8p^2$ | 7 | Trinomial |
| $29x^{11} + 8x^{15}$ | 15 | Binomial |
| $-10r^6s^8$ | 14 | Monomial |
| $5a^3b^7 - 3a^5b^5 + 4a^2b^9 - a^{10}$ | 11 | None of these |

## Addition and Subtraction

Since the variables used in polynomials represent real numbers, a polynomial represents a real number. This means that all the properties of the real numbers mentioned in this book hold for polynomials. In particular, the distributive property holds, so

$$3m^5 - 7m^5 = (3 - 7)m^5 = -4m^5.$$

**Like terms** are terms that have the exact same variable factors. Thus, polynomials are added by adding coefficients of like terms; polynomials are subtracted by subtracting coefficients of like terms.

### EXAMPLE 1 Adding and Subtracting Polynomials

Add or subtract, as indicated.

**(a)** $(2y^4 - 3y^2 + y) + (4y^4 + 7y^2 + 6y)$ **(b)** $(-3m^3 - 8m^2 + 4) - (m^3 + 7m^2 - 3)$

**(c)** $8m^4p^5 - 9m^3p^5 + (11m^4p^5 + 15m^3p^5)$

**(d)** $4(x^2 - 3x + 7) - 5(2x^2 - 8x - 4)$

**SOLUTION**

**(a)** $(2y^4 - 3y^2 + y) + (4y^4 + 7y^2 + 6y)$

$$= (2 + 4)y^4 + (-3 + 7)y^2 + (1 + 6)y$$

$$= 6y^4 + 4y^2 + 7y$$

**(b)** $(-3m^3 - 8m^2 + 4) - (m^3 + 7m^2 - 3)$

$= (-3 - 1)m^3 + (-8 - 7)m^2 + [4 - (-3)]$

$= -4m^3 - 15m^2 + 7$

This − symbol changes the sign of each coefficient in $m^3 + 7m^2 - 3$.

**(c)** $8m^4p^5 - 9m^3p^5 + (11m^4p^5 + 15m^3p^5) = 19m^4p^5 + 6m^3p^5$

**(d)** $4(x^2 - 3x + 7) - 5(2x^2 - 8x - 4)$

$= 4x^2 - 4(3x) + 4(7) - 5(2x^2) - 5(-8x) - 5(-4)$ Distributive property

$= 4x^2 - 12x + 28 - 10x^2 + 40x + 20$ Associative property

$= -6x^2 + 28x + 48$ Combine like terms. ■

As shown in parts (a), (b), and (d) of Example 1, polynomials in one variable are often written with their terms in **descending powers;** so the term of greatest degree is first, the one with the next greatest degree is second, and so on.

**Multiplication** The associative and distributive properties, together with the properties of exponents, can also be used to find the product of two polynomials. For example, to find the product of $3x - 4$ and $2x^2 - 3x + 5$, treat $3x - 4$ as a single expression and use the distributive property as follows.

$$(3x - 4)(2x^2 - 3x + 5) = (3x - 4)(2x^2) - (3x - 4)(3x) + (3x - 4)(5)$$

Now use the distributive property three separate times on the right to get

$$= (3x)(2x^2) - 4(2x^2) - (3x)(3x) - (-4)(3x) + (3x)5 - 4(5)$$

$$= 6x^3 - 8x^2 - 9x^2 + 12x + 15x - 20$$

$$= 6x^3 - 17x^2 + 27x - 20.$$

It is sometimes more convenient to write such a product vertically, as follows.

$$\begin{array}{rrrrl}
 & 2x^2 & - 3x & + 5 & \\
 & & 3x & - 4 & \\
\hline
 & -8x^2 & + 12x & - 20 & \leftarrow -4(2x^2 - 3x + 5) \\
6x^3 & - 9x^2 & + 15x & & \leftarrow 3x(2x^2 - 3x + 5) \\
\hline
6x^3 & - 17x^2 & + 27x & - 20 & \text{Add in columns.}
\end{array}$$

Be sure to place like terms in columns.

**EXAMPLE 2 Multiplying Polynomials Vertically**

Multiply $(3p^2 - 4p + 1)(p^3 + 2p - 8)$.

**SOLUTION**

Multiply each term of the second polynomial by each term of the first and add.

$$\begin{array}{rrrrrrl}
 & & & 3p^2 & - 4p & + 1 & \\
 & & & p^3 & + 2p & - 8 & \\
\hline
 & & & -24p^2 & + 32p & - 8 & \text{Multiply } 3p^2 - 4p + 1 \text{ by } -8. \\
 & & 6p^3 & - 8p^2 & + 2p & & \text{Multiply } 3p^2 - 4p + 1 \text{ by } 2p. \\
3p^5 & - 4p^4 & + p^3 & & & & \text{Multiply } 3p^2 - 4p + 1 \text{ by } p^3. \\
\hline
3p^5 & - 4p^4 & + 7p^3 & - 32p^2 & + 34p & - 8 & \text{Add in columns.}
\end{array}$$

■

The FOIL method is a convenient way to find the product of two binomials. The memory aid FOIL (for First, Outside, Inside, Last) gives the pairs of terms to be multiplied to get the product, as shown in the next examples.

### EXAMPLE 3 Using the FOIL Method

Find each product.

**(a)** $(6m + 1)(4m - 3)$ **(b)** $(2x + 7)(2x - 7)$

**SOLUTION**

**(a)** $(6m + 1)(4m - 3) = \overset{F}{(6m)(4m)} + \overset{O}{(6m)(-3)} + \overset{I}{1(4m)} + \overset{L}{1(-3)}$

$= 24m^2 - 18m + 4m - 3$

$= 24m^2 - 14m - 3$ Combine like terms.

**(b)** $(2x + 7)(2x - 7) = 4x^2 - 14x + 14x - 49$ FOIL

$= 4x^2 - 49$ Combine like terms.

The **special product**

$$(x + y)(x - y) = x^2 - y^2$$

can be used to solve some multiplication problems. For example,

$$\begin{aligned} 51 \times 49 &= (50 + 1)(50 - 1) \\ &= 50^2 - 1^2 \\ &= 2500 - 1 \\ &= 2499 \end{aligned}$$

$$\begin{aligned} 102 \times 98 &= (100 + 2)(100 - 2) \\ &= 100^2 - 2^2 \\ &= 10{,}000 - 4 \\ &= 9996. \end{aligned}$$

Once these patterns are recognized, multiplications of this type can be done mentally.

## Special Products

In part (a) of Example 3, the product of two binomials was a trinomial, while in part (b) the product of two binomials was a binomial. ***The product of two binomials of the forms $x + y$ and $x - y$ is always a binomial.*** Check by multiplying that the following is true.

**Product of the Sum and Difference of Two Terms**

$$(x + y)(x - y) = x^2 - y^2$$

The product $x^2 - y^2$ is called the **difference of two squares.**

### EXAMPLE 4 Finding Special Products

Find each product.

**(a)** $(3p + 11)(3p - 11)$ **(b)** $(5m^3 - 3)(5m^3 + 3)$

**(c)** $(9k - 11r^3)(9k + 11r^3)$

**SOLUTION**

**(a)** Using the pattern discussed above, replace $x$ with $3p$ and $y$ with 11.

$$\begin{aligned} (3p + 11)(3p - 11) &= (3p)^2 - 11^2 \\ &= 9p^2 - 121 \end{aligned}$$

**(b)** $(5m^3 - 3)(5m^3 + 3) = (5m^3)^2 - 3^2$

$= 25m^6 - 9$

**(c)** $(9k - 11r^3)(9k + 11r^3) = (9k)^2 - (11r^3)^2$

$= 81k^2 - 121r^6$

The **squares of binomials** are also special products.

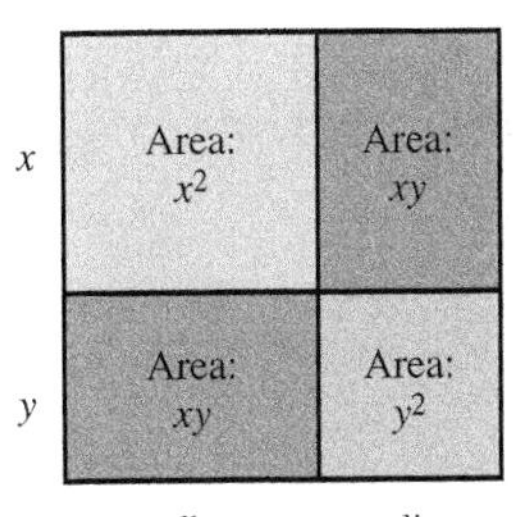


The **special product**

$$(x + y)^2 = x^2 + 2xy + y^2$$

can be illustrated geometrically using the diagram shown here. Each side of the large square has length $x + y$, so the area of the square is

$$(x + y)^2.$$

The large square is made up of two smaller squares and two congruent rectangles. The sum of the areas of these figures is

$$x^2 + 2xy + y^2.$$

Since these expressions represent the same quantity, they must be equal, thus giving us the pattern for squaring a binomial.

### Squares of Binomials

$$(x + y)^2 = x^2 + 2xy + y^2$$
$$(x - y)^2 = x^2 - 2xy + y^2$$

### EXAMPLE 5 Finding Special Products

Find each product.

**(a)** $(2m + 5)^2$ **(b)** $(3x - 7y^4)^2$

**SOLUTION**

**(a)** $(2m + 5)^2 = (2m)^2 + 2(2m)(5) + (5)^2$
$= 4m^2 + 20m + 25$

**(b)** $(3x - 7y^4)^2 = (3x)^2 - 2(3x)(7y^4) + (7y^4)^2$
$= 9x^2 - 42xy^4 + 49y^8$

The square of a binomial has three terms. $(x + y)^2 \neq x^2 + y^2$

**Factoring** The process of finding polynomials whose product equals a given polynomial is called **factoring.** For example, since

$$4x + 12 = 4(x + 3),$$

both 4 and $x + 3$ are called **factors** of $4x + 12$. Also, $4(x + 3)$ is called a **factored form** of $4x + 12$. A polynomial that cannot be written as a product of two polynomials with integer coefficients is a **prime polynomial.** A polynomial is **factored completely** when it is written as a product of prime polynomials with integer coefficients.

**Factoring Out the Greatest Common Factor** Some polynomials are factored by using the distributive property. We look for a monomial that is the greatest common factor (GCF) of all the terms of the polynomial. For example,

$$6x^2y^3 + 9xy^4 + 18y^5 = (3y^3)(2x^2) + (3y^3)(3xy) + (3y^3)(6y^2) \quad \text{GCF} = 3y^3$$
$$= 3y^3(2x^2 + 3xy + 6y^2).$$

### EXAMPLE 6 Factoring Out the Greatest Common Factor

Factor out the greatest common factor from each polynomial.

**(a)** $9y^5 + y^2$ **(b)** $6x^2t + 8xt + 12t$

**(c)** $14m^4(m + 1) - 28m^3(m + 1) - 7m^2(m + 1)$

**SOLUTION**

**(a)** $9y^5 + y^2 = y^2 \cdot 9y^3 + y^2 \cdot 1$ The greatest common factor is $y^2$.
$= y^2(9y^3 + 1)$

**(b)** $6x^2t + 8xt + 12t = 2t(3x^2 + 4x + 6)$

**(c)** $14m^4(m + 1) - 28m^3(m + 1) - 7m^2(m + 1)$
The greatest common factor is $7m^2(m + 1)$. Use the distributive property.

$$\begin{aligned} 14m^4(m + 1) - 28m^3(m + 1) - 7m^2(m + 1) &= [7m^2(m + 1)](2m^2 - 4m - 1) \\ &= 7m^2(m + 1)(2m^2 - 4m - 1) \end{aligned}$$

**Factoring by Grouping** When a polynomial has more than three terms, it can sometimes be factored by a method called **factoring by grouping.** For example,

$$\begin{aligned} ax + ay + 6x + 6y &= (ax + ay) + (6x + 6y) && \text{Group the terms.} \\ &= a(x + y) + 6(x + y) && \text{Factor each group.} \\ &= (x + y)(a + 6). && \text{Factor out } (x + y). \end{aligned}$$

Experience and repeated trials are the most reliable tools for factoring by grouping.

### EXAMPLE 7 Factoring by Grouping

Factor by grouping.

**(a)** $mp^2 + 7m + 3p^2 + 21$ **(b)** $2y^2 - 2z - ay^2 + az$

**SOLUTION**

**(a)**
$$\begin{aligned} mp^2 + 7m + 3p^2 + 21 &= (mp^2 + 7m) + (3p^2 + 21) && \text{Group the terms.} \\ &= m(p^2 + 7) + 3(p^2 + 7) && \text{Factor each group.} \\ &= (p^2 + 7)(m + 3) && p^2 + 7 \text{ is a common factor.} \end{aligned}$$

**(b)**
$$\begin{aligned} 2y^2 - 2z - ay^2 + az &= (2y^2 - 2z) + (-ay^2 + az) && \text{Group the terms.} \\ &= 2(y^2 - z) + a(-y^2 + z) && \text{Factor each group.} \end{aligned}$$

The expression $-y^2 + z$ is the negative of $y^2 - z$, so factor out $-a$ instead of $a$.

$$\begin{aligned} &= 2(y^2 - z) - a(y^2 - z) && \text{Factor out } -a. \\ &= (y^2 - z)(2 - a) && \text{Factor out } y^2 - z. \end{aligned}$$

**Factoring Trinomials** ***Factoring is the inverse of multiplying.*** Since the product of two binomials is usually a trinomial, we can expect factorable trinomials (that have terms with no common factor) to have two binomial factors. Thus, factoring trinomials requires using FOIL in an inverse manner.

### EXAMPLE 8 Factoring Trinomials

Factor each trinomial.

**(a)** $4y^2 - 11y + 6$ **(b)** $6p^2 - 7p - 5$

**SOLUTION**

**(a)** To factor this polynomial, we must find integers $a$, $b$, $c$, and $d$ such that

$$4y^2 - 11y + 6 = (ay + b)(cy + d).$$

By using FOIL, we see that $ac = 4$ and $bd = 6$. The positive factors of 4 are 4 and 1 or 2 and 2. Since the middle term is negative, we consider only negative factors of 6. The possibilities are $-2$ and $-3$ or $-1$ and $-6$. Now we try various arrangements of these factors until we find one that gives the correct coefficient of $y$.

$$(2y - 1)(2y - 6) = 4y^2 - \mathbf{14y} + 6 \quad \text{Incorrect}$$
$$(2y - 2)(2y - 3) = 4y^2 - \mathbf{10y} + 6 \quad \text{Incorrect}$$
$$(y - 2)(4y - 3) = 4y^2 - 11y + 6 \quad \text{Correct}$$

The last trial gives the correct factorization.

**(b)** Again, we try various possibilities. The positive factors of 6 could be 2 and 3 or 1 and 6. As factors of $-5$ we have only $-1$ and 5 or $-5$ and 1. Try different combinations of these factors until the correct one is found.

$$(2p - 5)(3p + 1) = 6p^2 - \mathbf{13p} - 5 \quad \text{Incorrect}$$
$$(3p - 5)(2p + 1) = 6p^2 - 7p - 5 \quad \text{Correct}$$

Thus, $6p^2 - 7p - 5$ factors as $(3p - 5)(2p + 1)$.

Each of the special patterns of multiplication given earlier can be used in reverse to get a pattern for factoring. Perfect square trinomials can be factored as follows.

**Perfect Square Trinomials**

$$x^2 + 2xy + y^2 = (x + y)^2$$
$$x^2 - 2xy + y^2 = (x - y)^2$$

## EXAMPLE 9 Factoring Perfect Square Trinomials

Factor each polynomial.

**(a)** $16p^2 - 40pq + 25q^2$ **(b)** $169x^2 + 104xy^2 + 16y^4$

**SOLUTION**

**(a)** Make sure that the middle term of the trinomial being factored, $-40pq$ here, is twice the product of the two terms in the binomial $4p - 5q$.

$$-40pq = 2(4p)(-5q)$$

Since $16p^2 = (4p)^2$ and $25q^2 = (5q)^2$, use the second pattern shown above with $4p$ replacing $x$ and $5q$ replacing $y$ to obtain

$$16p^2 - 40pq + 25q^2 = (4p)^2 - 2(4p)(5q) + (5q)^2$$
$$= (4p - 5q)^2.$$

**(b)** $169x^2 + 104xy^2 + 16y^4 = (13x + 4y^2)^2$, since $2(13x)(4y^2) = 104xy^2$.

**Factoring Special Binomials** The pattern for the product of the sum and difference of two terms gives the following factorization.

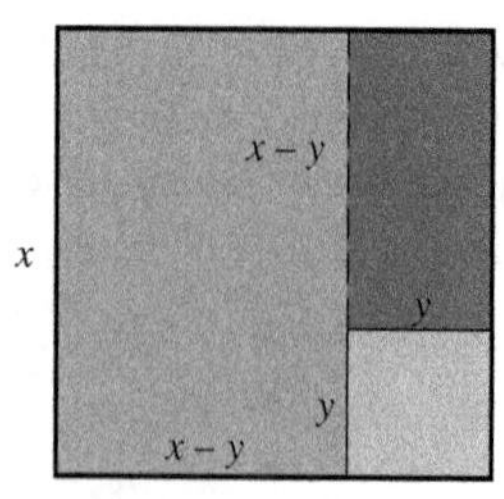


A **geometric proof** for the difference of squares property is shown above. (The proof is only valid for $x > y > 0$.)

$$x^2 - y^2 = x(x - y) + y(x - y)$$
$$= (x - y)(x + y)$$

Factor out $x - y$ in the second step.

**Difference of Squares**

$$x^2 - y^2 = (x + y)(x - y)$$

### EXAMPLE 10 Factoring Differences of Squares

Factor each polynomial.

(a) $4m^2 - 9$ (b) $256k^4 - 625m^4$ (c) $x^2 - 6x + 9 - y^4$

**SOLUTION**

(a) First, recognize that $4m^2 - 9$ is the difference of squares, since $4m^2 = (2m)^2$ and $9 = 3^2$. Use the pattern for the difference of squares with $2m$ replacing $x$ and 3 replacing $y$.

$$4m^2 - 9 = (2m)^2 - 3^2$$
$$= (2m + 3)(2m - 3)$$

(b) $256k^4 - 625m^4 = (16k^2)^2 - (25m^2)^2$ Difference of squares
$= (16k^2 + 25m^2)(16k^2 - 25m^2)$
$= (16k^2 + 25m^2)(4k + 5m)(4k - 5m)$ Difference of squares

(c) $x^2 - 6x + 9 - y^4 = (x^2 - 6x + 9) - y^4$ Group the first three terms.
$= (x - 3)^2 - (y^2)^2$ Perfect square trinomial
$= [(x - 3) + y^2][(x - 3) - y^2]$ Difference of squares
$= (x - 3 + y^2)(x - 3 - y^2)$ ■

Two other special results of factoring are listed below. Each can be verified by multiplying on the right side of the equation.

**Sum and Difference of Cubes**

| | |
|---|---|
| **Sum of Cubes** | $x^3 + y^3 = (x + y)(x^2 - xy + y^2)$ |
| **Difference of Cubes** | $x^3 - y^3 = (x - y)(x^2 + xy + y^2)$ |

### EXAMPLE 11 Factoring Sums and Differences of Cubes

Factor each polynomial.

(a) $x^3 + 27$ (b) $m^3 - 64n^3$ (c) $8q^6 + 125p^9$

**SOLUTION**

(a) $x^3 + 27 = x^3 + 3^3$ Sum of cubes
$= (x + 3)(x^2 - 3x + 9)$

(b) $m^3 - 64n^3 = m^3 - (4n)^3$ Difference of cubes
$= (m - 4n)[m^2 + m(4n) + (4n)^2]$
$= (m - 4n)(m^2 + 4mn + 16n^2)$

**Solution to the Chapter Opener** The player's expression and answer are correct. Suppose $a$ and $b$ are the individual times. Then the hourly rates for the players are $\frac{1}{a}$ and $\frac{1}{b}$ job per hour. Multiplying rate by time worked gives the fractional part of the job performed by each player. If $x$ represents the time they must work together to complete one whole job, then we have

$$\frac{1}{a}x + \frac{1}{b}x = 1$$
Linear equation

$$ab\left(\frac{1}{a}x + \frac{1}{b}x\right) = ab \cdot 1$$
Multiply by $ab$.

$$bx + ax = ab$$
Distributive property

$$x(a + b) = ab$$
Factor out $x$.

$$x = \frac{ab}{a + b}.$$
Divide by $a + b$.

The answer given in the movie is correct.

(c) $8q^6 + 125p^9 = (2q^2)^3 + (5p^3)^3$
$= (2q^2 + 5p^3)[(2q^2)^2 - (2q^2)(5p^3) + (5p^3)^2]$
$= (2q^2 + 5p^3)(4q^4 - 10q^2p^3 + 25p^6)$

## 7.6 EXERCISES

*Find each sum or difference.*

1. $(3x^2 - 4x + 5) + (-2x^2 + 3x - 2)$
2. $(4m^3 - 3m^2 + 5) + (-3m^3 - m^2 + 5)$
3. $(12y^2 - 8y + 6) - (3y^2 - 4y + 2)$
4. $(8p^2 - 5p) - (3p^2 - 2p + 4)$
5. $(6m^4 - 3m^2 + m) - (2m^3 + 5m^2 + 4m) + (m^2 - m)$
6. $-(8x^3 + x - 3) + (2x^3 + x^2) - (4x^2 + 3x - 1)$
7. $5(2x^2 - 3x + 7) - 2(6x^2 - x + 12)$
8. $8x^2y - 3xy^2 + 2x^2y - 9xy^2$

*Find each product.*

9. $(x + 3)(x - 8)$
10. $(y - 3)(y - 9)$
11. $(4r - 1)(7r + 2)$
12. $(5m - 6)(3m + 4)$
13. $4x^2(3x^3 + 2x^2 - 5x + 1)$
14. $2b^3(b^2 - 4b + 3)$
15. $(2m + 3)(2m - 3)$
16. $(8s - 3t)(8s + 3t)$
17. $(4m + 2n)^2$
18. $(a - 6b)^2$
19. $(5r + 3t^2)^2$
20. $(2z^4 - 3y)^2$
21. $(2z - 1)(-z^2 + 3z - 4)$
22. $(k + 2)(12k^3 - 3k^2 + k + 1)$
23. $(m - n + k)(m + 2n - 3k)$
24. $(r - 3s + t)(2r - s + t)$
25. $(a - b + 2c)^2$
26. $(k - y + 3m)^2$
27. Which one of the following is a trinomial in descending powers, having degree 6?
    A. $5x^6 - 4x^5 + 12$ B. $6x^5 - x^6 + 4$
    C. $2x + 4x^2 - x^6$ D. $4x^6 - 6x^4 + 9x + 1$
28. Give an example of a polynomial of four terms in the variable $x$, having degree 5, written in descending powers, lacking a fourth degree term.
29. The exponent in the expression $6^3$ is 3. Explain why the degree of $6^3$ is not 3. What is its degree?
30. Explain in your own words how to square a binomial.

*Factor the greatest common factor from each polynomial.*

31. $8m^4 + 6m^3 - 12m^2$
32. $2p^5 - 10p^4 + 16p^3$
33. $4k^2m^3 + 8k^4m^3 - 12k^2m^4$
34. $28r^4s^2 + 7r^3s - 35r^4s^3$
35. $2(a + b) + 4m(a + b)$
36. $4(y - 2)^2 + 3(y - 2)$
37. $2(m - 1) - 3(m - 1)^2 + 2(m - 1)^3$
38. $5(a + 3)^3 - 2(a + 3) + (a + 3)^2$

*Factor each polynomial by grouping.*

39. $6st + 9t - 10s - 15$
40. $10ab - 6b + 35a - 21$
41. $rt^3 + rs^2 - pt^3 - ps^2$
42. $2m^4 + 6 - am^4 - 3a$
43. $16a^2 + 10ab - 24ab - 15b^2$
44. $15 - 5m^2 - 3r^2 + m^2r^2$
45. $20z^2 - 8zx - 45zx + 18x^2$
46. $4 - 2y - 2x + xy$
47. $1 - a + ab - b$

**48.** Consider the polynomial $1 - a + ab - b$ from Exercise 47. The answer given in the answer section is $(1 - a)(1 - b)$. However, there are other acceptable factored forms. Which one of A–D is *not* a factored form of this polynomial?

**A.** $(a - 1)(b - 1)$
**B.** $(-a + 1)(-b + 1)$
**C.** $(-1 + a)(-1 + b)$
**D.** $(1 - a)(b + 1)$

*Factor each trinomial.*

**49.** $x^2 - 2x - 15$ **50.** $r^2 + 8r + 12$ **51.** $y^2 + 2y - 35$ **52.** $x^2 - 7x + 6$

**53.** $6a^2 - 48a - 120$ **54.** $8h^2 - 24h - 320$ **55.** $3m^3 + 12m^2 + 9m$

**56.** $9y^4 - 54y^3 + 45y^2$ **57.** $6k^2 + 5kp - 6p^2$ **58.** $14m^2 + 11mr - 15r^2$

**59.** $5a^2 - 7ab - 6b^2$ **60.** $12s^2 + 11st - 5t^2$ **61.** $21x^2 - xy - 2y^2$

**62.** $30a^2 + am - m^2$ **63.** $24a^4 + 10a^3b - 4a^2b^2$ **64.** $18x^5 + 15x^4z - 75x^3z^2$

**65.** When a student was given the polynomial

$$4x^2 + 2x - 20$$

to factor completely on a test, she lost some credit by giving the answer $(4x + 10)(x - 2)$. She then complained to her teacher that the product $(4x + 10) \cdot (x - 2)$ is indeed $4x^2 + 2x - 20$. Do you think that the teacher was justified in not giving her full credit? Explain.

**66.** Write an explanation as to why most people would find it more difficult to factor

$$36x^2 - 44x - 15$$

than

$$37x^2 - 183x - 10.$$

*Factor each polynomial, using the method for factoring a perfect square trinomial. It may be necessary to factor out a common factor first.*

**67.** $9m^2 - 12m + 4$ **68.** $16p^2 - 40p + 25$ **69.** $32a^2 - 48ab + 18b^2$

**70.** $20p^2 - 100pq + 125q^2$ **71.** $4x^2y^2 + 28xy + 49$ **72.** $9m^2n^2 - 12mn + 4$

*Factor each difference of squares.*

**73.** $x^2 - 36$ **74.** $t^2 - 64$ **75.** $y^2 - w^2$ **76.** $25 - w^2$ **77.** $9a^2 - 16$

**78.** $16q^2 - 25$ **79.** $25s^4 - 9t^2$ **80.** $36z^2 - 81y^4$ **81.** $p^4 - 625$ **82.** $m^4 - 81$

*Factor each sum or difference of cubes.*

**83.** $8 - a^3$ **84.** $r^3 + 27$ **85.** $125x^3 - 27$

**86.** $8m^3 - 27n^3$ **87.** $27y^9 + 125z^6$ **88.** $27z^3 + 729y^3$

*Each polynomial may be factored using one of the methods described in this section. Decide on the method, and then factor the polynomial completely.*

**89.** $x^2 + xy - 5x - 5y$ **90.** $8r^2 - 10rs - 3s^2$ **91.** $p^4(m - 2n) + q(m - 2n)$

**92.** $36a^2 + 60a + 25$ **93.** $4z^2 + 28z + 49$ **94.** $6p^4 + 7p^2 - 3$

**95.** $1000x^3 + 343y^3$ **96.** $b^2 + 8b + 16 - a^2$ **97.** $125m^6 - 216$

**98.** $q^2 + 6q + 9 - p^2$ **99.** $12m^2 + 16mn - 35n^2$ **100.** $216p^3 + 125q^3$

**101.** The sum of squares usually cannot be factored. For example, $x^2 + y^2$ is prime. Notice that $x^2 + y^2 \neq (x + y)(x + y)$. By choosing $x = 4$ and $y = 2$, show that this statement is true.

**102.** The binomial $9x^2 + 36$ is a sum of squares. Can it be factored? If so, factor it.

# 7.7 Quadratic Equations and Applications

**Quadratic Equations • Zero-Factor Property • Square Root Property • Quadratic Formula • Applications**

## Quadratic Equations

Recall that a linear equation is one that can be written in the form $ax + b = c$, where $a$, $b$, and $c$ are real numbers, $a \neq 0$.

> **Quadratic Equation**
>
> An equation that can be written in the form
>
> $$ax^2 + bx + c = 0$$
>
> where $a$, $b$, and $c$ are real numbers, with $a \neq 0$, is a **quadratic equation.**

A quadratic equation written in the form $ax^2 + bx + c = 0$ is in **standard form.**

## Zero-Factor Property

The simplest method of solving a quadratic equation, but one that is not always easily applied, is by factoring. This method depends on the following property.

> **Zero-Factor Property**
>
> If $ab = 0$, then $a = 0$ or $b = 0$ or both.

***When solving a quadratic equation by the zero-factor property, the equation must be in standard form before factoring.***

### EXAMPLE 1 Using the Zero-Factor Property

Solve $6x^2 + 7x = 3$.

**SOLUTION**

$$6x^2 + 7x = 3$$

$$6x^2 + 7x - 3 = 0 \quad \text{Standard form}$$

$$(3x - 1)(2x + 3) = 0 \quad \text{Factor.}$$

$$3x - 1 = 0 \quad \text{or} \quad 2x + 3 = 0 \quad \text{Zero-factor property}$$

$$3x = 1 \quad \text{or} \quad 2x = -3 \quad \text{Solve each equation.}$$

$$x = \frac{1}{3} \quad \text{or} \quad x = -\frac{3}{2}$$

Check by first substituting $\frac{1}{3}$ and then $-\frac{3}{2}$ in the original equation. The solution set is $\left\{\frac{1}{3}, -\frac{3}{2}\right\}$.

```
solve(6X²+7X-3,X
,0)▸Frac
                1/3
solve(6X²+7X-3,X
,-5)▸Frac
               -3/2
```

The *solve* feature gives the two solutions of the equation in Example 1. Notice that the guess 0 yields the solution 1/3, while the guess −5 yields the solution −3/2. Compare to Example 1.

**Square Root Property** A quadratic equation of the form $x^2 = k$, $k \geq 0$, can be solved by factoring.

$$x^2 = k$$
$$x^2 - k = 0$$
$$\left(x + \sqrt{k}\right)\left(x - \sqrt{k}\right) = 0$$
$$x + \sqrt{k} = 0 \quad \text{or} \quad x - \sqrt{k} = 0$$
$$x = -\sqrt{k} \quad \text{or} \quad x = \sqrt{k}$$

This proves the square root property for solving equations.

**Square Root Property**

If $k \geq 0$, then the solutions of $x^2 = k$ are $\mathbf{x = \pm\sqrt{k}}$.

***If $k > 0$, the equation $x^2 = k$ has two real solutions. If $k = 0$, there is only one solution, 0. If $k < 0$, there are no real solutions.*** (However, in this case, there *are* imaginary solutions. Imaginary numbers are discussed briefly in the Extension on complex numbers at the end of Chapter 6.)

**Completing the square,** used in deriving the quadratic formula, has important applications in algebra. To transform the expression $x^2 + kx$ into the square of a binomial, we add to it the square of half the coefficient of $x$, that is, $\left[\left(\frac{1}{2}\right)k\right]^2 = \frac{k^2}{4}$. We then get

$$x^2 + kx + \frac{k^2}{4} = \left(x + \frac{k}{2}\right)^2.$$

For example, to make $x^2 + 6x$ the square of a binomial, we add 9, since $9 = \left[\frac{1}{2}(6)\right]^2$. This results in the trinomial $x^2 + 6x + 9$, which is equal to $(x + 3)^2$.

The Greeks had a method of completing the square geometrically. For example, to complete the square for $x^2 + 6x$, begin with a square of side $x$. Add three rectangles of width 1 and length $x$ to the right side and the bottom. Each rectangle has area $1x$ or $x$, so the total area of the figure is now $x^2 + 6x$. To fill in the corner (that is, "complete the square"), we add 9 1-by-1 squares as shown. The new completed square has sides of length $x + 3$ and area

$$(x + 3)^2 = x^2 + 6x + 9.$$

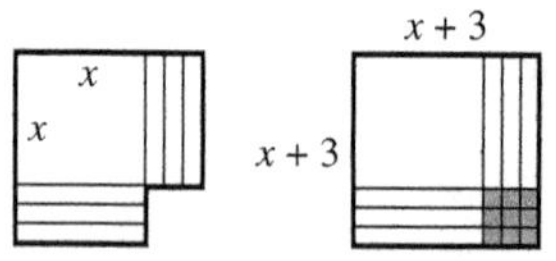


## EXAMPLE 2 Using the Square Root Property

Use the square root property to solve each quadratic equation for real solutions.

**(a)** $x^2 = 25$ **(b)** $r^2 = 18$ **(c)** $z^2 = -3$ **(d)** $(x - 4)^2 = 12$

**SOLUTION**

**(a)** Since $\sqrt{25} = 5$, the solution set of the equation $x^2 = 25$ is $\{5, -5\}$, which may be abbreviated $\{\pm 5\}$.

**(b)**

$$r^2 = 18$$
$$r = \pm\sqrt{18} \quad \text{Square root property}$$
$$r = \pm\sqrt{9 \cdot 2}$$
$$r = \pm\sqrt{9} \cdot \sqrt{2} \quad \text{Product rule for square roots}$$
$$r = \pm 3\sqrt{2} \quad \sqrt{9} = 3$$

The solution set is $\{\pm 3\sqrt{2}\}$.

**(c)** Since $-3 < 0$, there are no real roots, and the solution set is $\emptyset$.

**(d)** Use a generalization of the square root property, working as follows.

$$(x - 4)^2 = 12$$
$$x - 4 = \pm\sqrt{12} \quad \text{Square root property}$$
$$x = 4 \pm \sqrt{12} \quad \text{Add 4.}$$
$$x = 4 \pm \sqrt{4 \cdot 3} \quad \text{Simplify } \sqrt{12}.$$
$$x = 4 \pm 2\sqrt{3}$$

The solution set is $\left\{4 \pm 2\sqrt{3}\right\}$.

A first-season episode of *Blue Collar TV* (2004) featured Bill Engvall paying a sarcastic tribute to an underappreciated figure in his life.

*To my high school algebra teacher, for teaching me that x equals minus b plus or minus the square root of b squared minus 4ac all over 2a, because Lord knows I use that information EVERY DAY!*

Bill's teacher evidently did a good job, because he used the word "all" before 2*a*. A common student error is to forget to write the $-b$ in the numerator with the radical expression in the **quadratic formula.** See Exercise 44 in this section.

**Quadratic Formula** By using a procedure called *completing the square* (see the margin note) we can derive one of the most important formulas in algebra, the *quadratic formula*. We begin with the standard quadratic equation and assume $a > 0$.

$$ax^2 + bx + c = 0$$

$$x^2 + \frac{b}{a}x + \frac{c}{a} = 0 \qquad \text{Divide by } a.$$

$$x^2 + \frac{b}{a}x = -\frac{c}{a} \qquad \text{Add } -\frac{c}{a}.$$

$$x^2 + \frac{b}{a}x + \frac{b^2}{4a^2} = \frac{b^2}{4a^2} - \frac{c}{a} \qquad \text{Add } \frac{b^2}{4a^2}.$$

$$\left(x + \frac{b}{2a}\right)^2 = \frac{b^2 - 4ac}{4a^2} \qquad \text{Factor on the left; combine terms on the right.}$$

$$x + \frac{b}{2a} = \pm\sqrt{\frac{b^2 - 4ac}{4a^2}} \qquad \text{Square root property}$$

$$x + \frac{b}{2a} = \pm\frac{\sqrt{b^2 - 4ac}}{\sqrt{4a^2}} \qquad \text{Quotient rule for square roots}$$

$$x = -\frac{b}{2a} \pm \frac{\sqrt{b^2 - 4ac}}{2a} \qquad \text{Subtract } \frac{b}{2a}.$$

$$x = \frac{-b \pm \sqrt{b^2 - 4ac}}{2a} \qquad \text{Combine terms.}$$

Be careful; $-b \pm \sqrt{b^2 - 4ac}$ is all written over $2a$.

The formula is also valid for $a < 0$.

**Quadratic Formula**

The solutions of $ax^2 + bx + c = 0$, $a \neq 0$, are

$$x = \frac{-b \pm \sqrt{b^2 - 4ac}}{2a}.$$

### EXAMPLE 3 Using the Quadratic Formula

Solve $x^2 - 4x + 2 = 0$.

**SOLUTION**

Here $a = 1$, $b = -4$, and $c = 2$. Substitute these values into the quadratic formula.

$$x = \frac{-b \pm \sqrt{b^2 - 4ac}}{2a} \qquad \text{Quadratic formula}$$

$$x = \frac{-(-4) \pm \sqrt{(-4)^2 - 4(1)2}}{2(1)} \qquad a = 1, b = -4, c = 2$$

$$x = \frac{4 \pm \sqrt{16 - 8}}{2}$$

**A Radical Departure from the Other Methods of Evaluating the Golden Ratio** Recall from a previous chapter that the golden ratio is found in numerous places in mathematics, art, and nature. In a margin note there, we showed that

$$1+\cfrac{1}{1+\cfrac{1}{1+\cfrac{1}{1+\cdots}}}$$

is equal to the golden ratio, $\frac{1+\sqrt{5}}{2}$. Now consider this "nested" radical:

$$\sqrt{1+\sqrt{1+\sqrt{1+\cdots}}}$$

Let $x$ represent this radical. Because it appears "within itself," we can write

$$x=\sqrt{1+x}$$
$$x^2=1+x$$
$$x^2-x-1=0.$$

Using the quadratic formula, with $a=1$, $b=-1$, and $c=-1$, it can be shown that the positive solution of this equation, and thus the value of the nested radical is . . . (you guessed it!) the golden ratio.

$$x=\frac{4\pm 2\sqrt{2}}{2} \qquad \sqrt{16-8}=\sqrt{8}=2\sqrt{2}$$

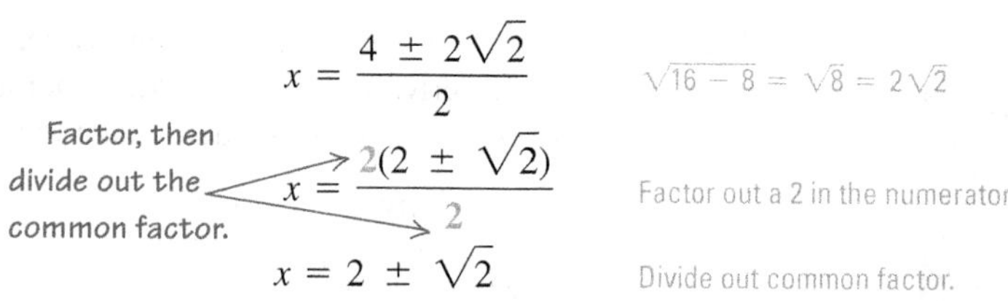


$$x=\frac{2(2\pm\sqrt{2})}{2} \qquad \text{Factor out a 2 in the numerator.}$$

$$x=2\pm\sqrt{2} \qquad \text{Divide out common factor.}$$

The solution set is $\{2+\sqrt{2}, 2-\sqrt{2}\}$, abbreviated $\{2\pm\sqrt{2}\}$.

## EXAMPLE 4 Using the Quadratic Formula

Solve $2x^2=x+4$.

**SOLUTION**

First write the equation in standard form as $2x^2-x-4=0$.

$$x=\frac{-(-1)\pm\sqrt{(-1)^2-4(2)(-4)}}{2(2)} \qquad \text{Quadratic formula with } a=2, b=-1, c=-4$$

$$x=\frac{1\pm\sqrt{1+32}}{4} \qquad \text{Simplify the radicand.}$$

$$x=\frac{1\pm\sqrt{33}}{4} \qquad \text{Add.}$$

The solution set is $\left\{\frac{1\pm\sqrt{33}}{4}\right\}$.

**Applications** When solving applied problems that lead to quadratic equations, we might get a solution that does not satisfy the physical constraints of the problem. For example, if $x$ represents a width and the two solutions of the quadratic equation are $-9$ and 1, the value $-9$ must be rejected, since a width must be a positive number.

## EXAMPLE 5 Applying a Quadratic Equation

Two cars left an intersection at the same time, one heading due north, and the other due west. Some time later, they were exactly 100 miles apart. The car headed north had gone 20 miles farther than the car headed west. How far had each car traveled?

**SOLUTION**

*Step 1* **Read** the problem carefully.

*Step 2* **Assign a variable.**

Let $x$ = the distance traveled by the car headed west;

Then $(x+20)$ = the distance traveled by the car headed north.

See Figure 16. The cars are 100 miles apart, so the hypotenuse of the right triangle equals 100.

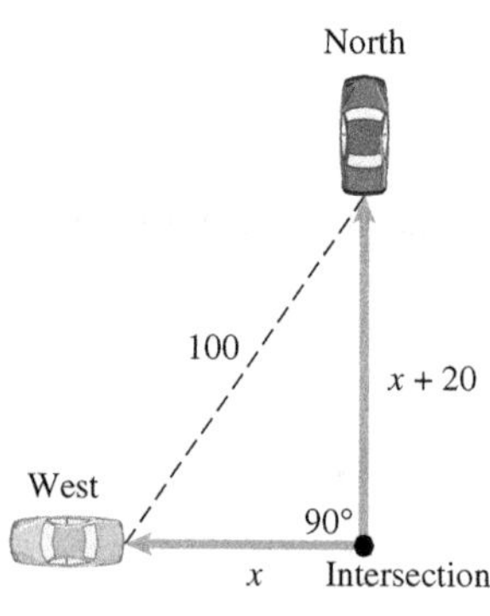


**FIGURE 16**

*Step 3* **Write an equation.**

$$c^2 = a^2 + b^2 \quad \text{Pythagorean theorem}$$
$$100^2 = x^2 + (x + 20)^2 \quad \text{Substitute.}$$

*Step 4* **Solve.**

$$10{,}000 = x^2 + x^2 + 40x + 400 \quad \text{Square the binomial.}$$
$$2x^2 + 40x - 9600 = 0 \quad \text{Standard form}$$
$$2(x^2 + 20x - 4800) = 0 \quad \text{Factor out the common factor.}$$
$$x^2 + 20x - 4800 = 0 \quad \text{Divide both sides by 2.}$$

Use the quadratic formula to find $x$.

$$x = \frac{-20 \pm \sqrt{400 - 4(1)(-4800)}}{2} \quad a = 1,\ b = 20,\ c = -4800$$
$$x = \frac{-20 \pm \sqrt{19{,}600}}{2}$$
$$x = 60 \quad \text{or} \quad x = -80 \quad \text{Use a calculator.}$$

*Step 5* **State the answer.** Since distance cannot be negative, discard the negative solution. The required distances are 60 miles and $60 + 20 = 80$ miles.

*Step 6* **Check.** Since $60^2 + 80^2 = 100^2$, the answer is correct.

## EXAMPLE 6 Applying a Quadratic Equation

If a rock on Earth is projected upward from the top of a 144-foot building with an initial velocity of 112 feet per second, its position (in feet above the ground) is given by $s = -16t^2 + 112t + 144$, where $t$ is time in seconds after it was projected. When does it hit the ground?

**SOLUTION**

When the rock hits the ground, its distance above the ground is 0. Find $t$ when $s$ is 0 by solving the following equation.

$$0 = -16t^2 + 112t + 144 \quad \text{Let } s = 0.$$
$$0 = t^2 - 7t - 9 \quad \text{Divide both sides by } -16.$$
$$t = \frac{7 \pm \sqrt{49 + 36}}{2} \quad \text{Quadratic formula}$$
$$t = \frac{7 \pm \sqrt{85}}{2} \quad \text{Add.}$$
$$t \approx 8.1 \quad \text{or} \quad t \approx -1.1 \quad \text{Use a calculator.}$$

Since time cannot be negative, discard the negative solution. The rock will hit the ground about 8.1 seconds after it is projected.

## 7.7 EXERCISES

*Fill in each blank with the correct response.*

**1.** For the quadratic equation $4x^2 + 5x - 9 = 0$, the values of $a$, $b$, and $c$ are, respectively, _____, _____, and _____.

**2.** To solve the equation $3x^2 - 5x = -2$ by the quadratic formula, the first step is to add _____ to both sides of the equation.

**3.** When using the quadratic formula, if $b^2 - 4ac$ is positive, then the equation has _________ (how many?) real solution(s).

**4.** If $a$, $b$, and $c$ are integers in $ax^2 + bx + c = 0$ and $b^2 - 4ac = 17$, then the equation has _________ (how many?) irrational solution(s).

*Solve each equation by the zero-factor property.*

**5.** $(x + 3)(x - 9) = 0$
**6.** $(m + 6)(m + 4) = 0$
**7.** $(2t - 7)(5t + 1) = 0$
**8.** $(7x - 3)(6x + 4) = 0$
**9.** $x^2 - x - 12 = 0$
**10.** $m^2 + 4m - 5 = 0$
**11.** $x^2 + 9x + 14 = 0$
**12.** $15r^2 + 7r = 2$
**13.** $12x^2 + 4x = 1$
**14.** $x(x + 3) = 4$
**15.** $(x + 4)(x - 6) = -16$
**16.** $(w - 1)(3w + 2) = 4w$

*Solve each equation by using the square root property. Give only real number solutions.*

**17.** $x^2 = 64$
**18.** $w^2 = 16$
**19.** $x^2 = 24$
**20.** $x^2 = 48$
**21.** $r^2 = -5$
**22.** $x^2 = -10$
**23.** $(x - 4)^2 = 9$
**24.** $(x + 3)^2 = 25$
**25.** $(4 - x)^2 = 3$
**26.** $(3 + x)^2 = 11$
**27.** $(2x - 5)^2 = 13$
**28.** $(4x + 1)^2 = 19$

*Solve each equation by the quadratic formula. Give only real number solutions.*

**29.** $4x^2 - 8x + 1 = 0$
**30.** $m^2 + 2m - 5 = 0$
**31.** $2x^2 = 2x + 1$
**32.** $9r^2 + 6r = 1$
**33.** $q^2 - 1 = q$
**34.** $2p^2 - 4p = 5$
**35.** $4k(k + 1) = 1$
**36.** $4r(r - 1) = 19$
**37.** $(g + 2)(g - 3) = 1$
**38.** $(x - 5)(x + 2) = 6$
**39.** $m^2 - 6m = -14$
**40.** $x^2 = 2x - 2$

**41.** Can the quadratic formula be used to solve the equation $2x^2 - 5 = 0$? Explain, and solve it if the answer is yes.

**42.** Can the quadratic formula be used to solve the equation $4x^2 + 3x = 0$? Explain, and solve it if the answer is yes.

**43.** Why can't the quadratic formula be used to solve the equation $2x^3 + 3x - 4 = 0$?

**44.** A student gave the quadratic formula incorrectly as follows: $x = -b \pm \frac{\sqrt{b^2 - 4ac}}{2a}$. What is wrong with this?

*The expression $b^2 - 4ac$, the radicand in the quadratic formula, is called the* **discriminant** *of the quadratic equation $ax^2 + bx + c = 0$, $a \neq 0$. By evaluating it we can determine, without actually solving the equation, the number and nature of the solutions of the equation. Suppose that a, b, and c are integers. Then the chart at the top of the next page shows how the discriminant can be used to analyze the solutions.*

| Discriminant | Solutions |
|---|---|
| Positive, and the square of an integer | Two different rational solutions |
| Positive, but not the square of an integer | Two different irrational solutions |
| Zero | One rational solution (a double solution) |
| Negative | No real solutions |

*In Exercises 45–50, evaluate the discriminant, and then determine whether the equation has* **(a)** *two different rational solutions,* **(b)** *two different irrational solutions,* **(c)** *one rational solution (a double solution), or* **(d)** *no real solutions.*

**45.** $x^2 + 6x + 9 = 0$

**46.** $4x^2 + 20x + 25 = 0$

**47.** $6x^2 + 7x - 3 = 0$

**48.** $2x^2 + x - 3 = 0$

**49.** $9x^2 - 30x + 15 = 0$

**50.** $2x^2 - x + 1 = 0$

*Solve each problem by using a quadratic equation. Use a calculator as necessary, and round the answer to the nearest tenth.*

**51.** ***Height of a Projectile*** The Mart Hotel in Dallas, Texas, is 400 feet high. Suppose that a ball is projected upward from the top of the Mart, and its position $s$ in feet above the ground is given by the equation $s = -16t^2 + 45t + 400$, where $t$ is the number of seconds elapsed. How long will it take for the ball to reach a height of 200 feet above the ground? (*Source: The World Almanac and Book of Facts.*)

**52.** ***Height of a Projectile*** The Toronto Dominion Center in Winnipeg, Manitoba, is 407 feet high. Suppose that a ball is projected upward from the top of the Center, and its position $s$ in feet above the ground is given by the equation $s = -16t^2 + 75t + 407$, where $t$ is the number of seconds elapsed. How long will it take for the ball to reach a height of 450 feet above the ground? (*Source: The World Almanac and Book of Facts.*)

**53.** ***Height of a Projectile*** Refer to the equations in Exercises 51 and 52. Suppose that the first sentence in each problem did not give the height of the building. How could you use the equation to determine the height of the building?

**54.** ***Position of a Searchlight Beam*** A searchlight beam moves horizontally back and forth along a wall with the distance of the light from a starting point at $t$ minutes given by $s = 100t^2 - 300t$. How long will it take before the light returns to the starting point?

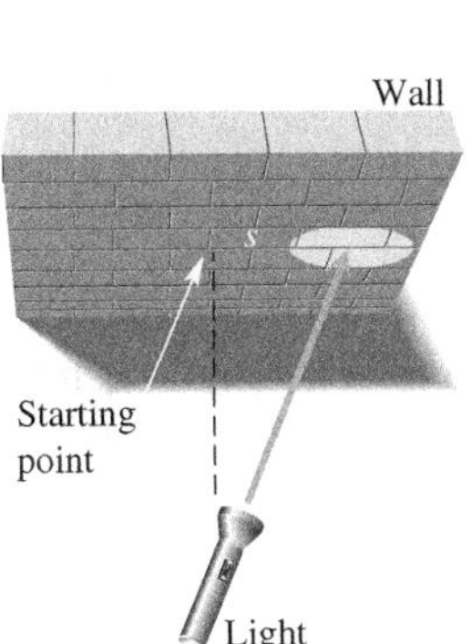


**55.** ***Height of a Projectile*** An object is projected directly upward from the ground. After $t$ seconds its distance in feet above the ground is $s = 144t - 16t^2$.

**(a)** After how many seconds will the object be 128 feet above the ground? (*Hint:* Look for a common factor before solving the equation.)

**(b)** When does the object strike the ground?

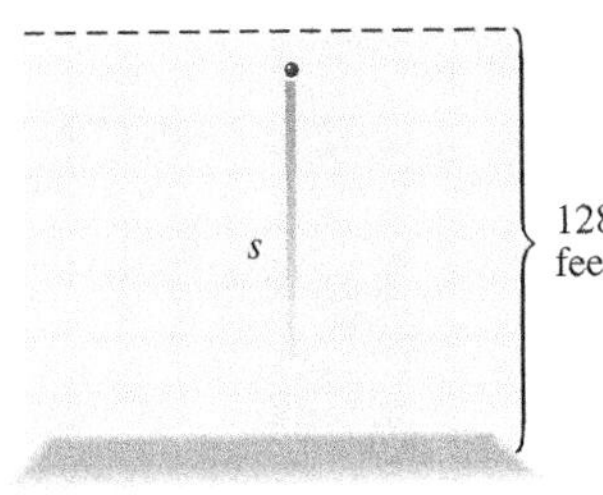


**56.** ***Distance of a Skid*** The formula $D = 100t - 13t^2$ gives the distance in feet a car going approximately 68 miles per hour will skid in $t$ seconds. Find the time it would take for the car to skid 190 feet. (*Hint:* Your answer must be less than the time it takes the car to stop, which is 3.8 seconds.)

57. ***Side Lengths of a Triangle*** Find the lengths of the sides of the triangle.

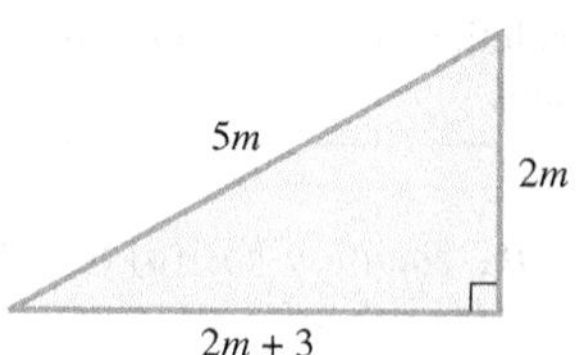


58. ***Side Lengths of a Triangle*** Find the lengths of the sides of the triangle.

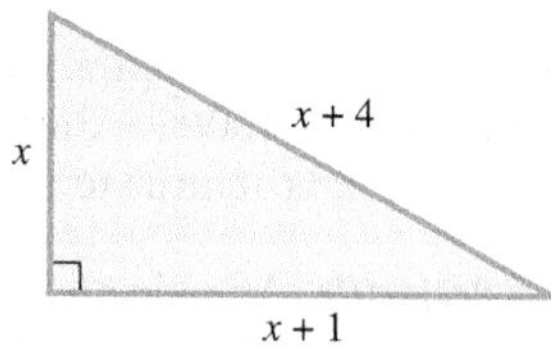


59. ***Length of a Wire*** Refer to Exercise 51. Suppose that a wire is attached to the top of the Mart and pulled tight. It is attached to the ground 100 feet from the base of the building, as shown in the figure. How long is the wire?

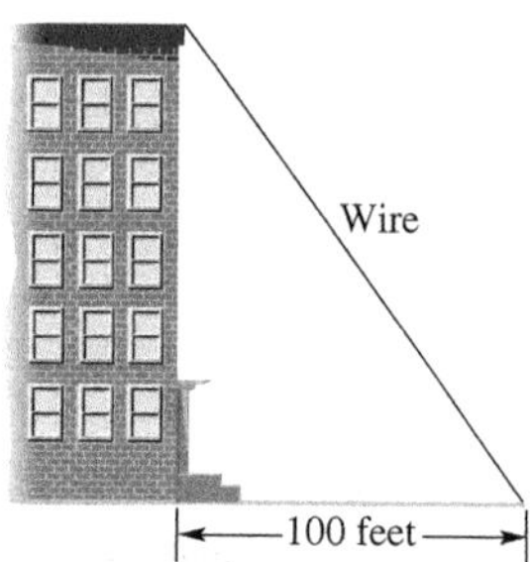


60. ***Length of a Wire*** Refer to Exercise 52. Suppose that a wire is attached to the top of the Center and pulled tight. The length of the wire is twice the distance between the base of the Center and the point on the ground where the wire is attached. How long is the wire?

61. ***Distances Traveled by Ships*** Two ships leave port at the same time, one heading due south and the other heading due east. (See the top of the next column.) Several hours later, they are 170 miles apart. If the ship traveling south travels 70 miles farther than the other, how many miles does each travel?

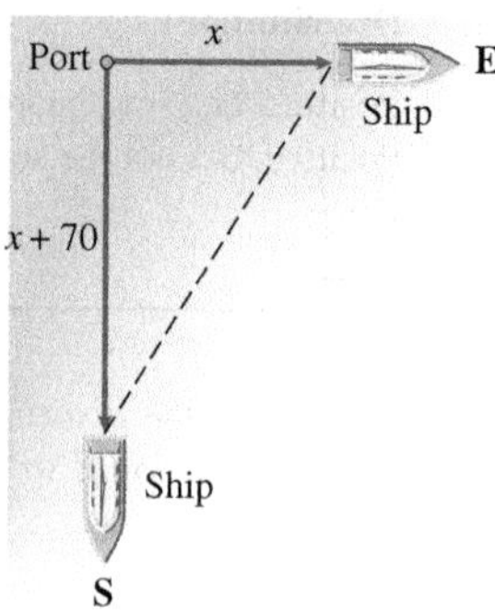


62. ***Height of a Kite*** Kim Hobbs is flying a kite that is 30 feet farther above her hand than its horizontal distance from her. The string from her hand to the kite is 150 feet long. How far is the kite above her hand?

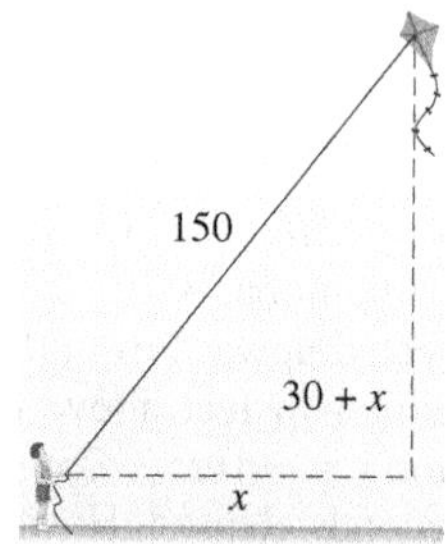


63. ***Size of a Toy Piece*** A toy manufacturer needs a piece of plastic in the shape of a right triangle with the longer leg 2 centimeters more than twice as long as the shorter leg, and the hypotenuse 1 centimeter more than the longer leg. How long should the three sides of the triangular piece be?

64. ***Size of a Developer's Property*** Michael Cardella, a developer, owns a piece of land enclosed on three sides by streets, giving it the shape of a right triangle. The hypotenuse is 8 meters longer than the longer leg, and the shorter leg is 9 meters shorter than the hypotenuse. Find the lengths of the three sides of the property.

65. ***Dimensions of Puzzle Pieces*** Two pieces of a large wooden puzzle fit together to form a rectangle with a length 1 centimeter less than twice the width. The diagonal, where the two pieces meet, is 2.5 centimeters in length. Find the length and width of the rectangle.

66. ***Leaning Ladder*** A 13-foot ladder is leaning against a house. The distance from the bottom of the ladder to the house is 7 feet less than the distance from the top of the ladder to the ground. How far is the bottom of the ladder from the house?

67. ***Dimensions of a Strip of Flooring Around a Rug*** Catarina and José want to buy a rug for a room that is 15 feet by 20 feet. They want to leave an even strip of flooring uncovered around the edges of the room. How wide a strip will they have if they buy a rug with an area of 234 square feet?

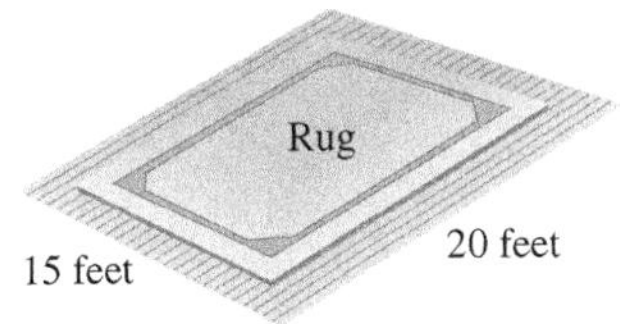


68. ***Dimensions of a Border Around a Pool*** A club swimming pool is 30 feet wide and 40 feet long. The club members want an exposed aggregate border in a strip of uniform width around the pool. They have enough material for 296 square feet. How wide can the strip be?

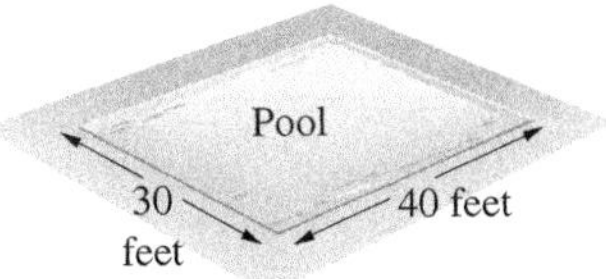


69. ***Dimensions of a Garden*** Arif's backyard is 20 meters by 30 meters. He wants to put a flower garden in the middle of the backyard, leaving a strip of grass of uniform width around the flower garden. Arif must have 184 square meters of grass. Under these conditions, what will the length and width of the garden be?

70. ***Interest Rate*** The formula $A = P(1 + r)^2$ gives the amount $A$ in dollars that $P$ dollars will grow to in 2 years at interest rate $r$ (where $r$ is given as a decimal), using compound interest. What interest rate will cause \$2000 to grow to \$2142.25 in 2 years?

71. ***Dimensions of a Piece of Sheet Metal*** A rectangular piece of sheet metal has a length that is 4 inches less than twice the width. A square piece 2 inches on a side is cut from each corner. The sides are then turned up to form an uncovered box of volume 256 cubic inches. Find the length and width of the original piece of metal.

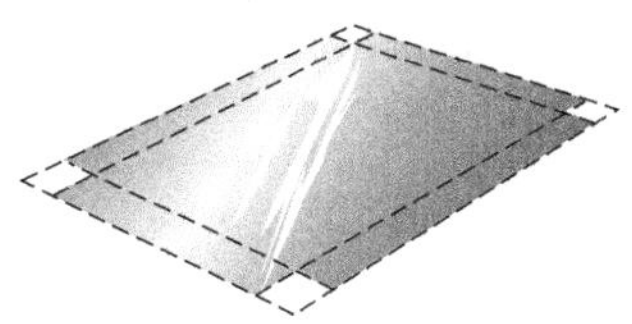

72. ***Cardboard Box Dimensions*** If a square piece of cardboard has 3-inch squares cut from its corners and then has the flaps folded up to form an open-top box, the volume of the box is given by the formula $V = 3(x - 6)^2$, where $x$ is the length of each side of the original piece of cardboard in inches. What original length would yield a box with a volume of 432 cubic inches?

73. ***Supply and Demand for Bran Muffins*** A certain bakery has found that the daily demand for bran muffins is $\frac{3200}{p}$ where $p$ is the price of a muffin in cents. The daily supply is $3p - 200$. Find the price at which supply and demand are equal.

74. ***Supply and Demand for Compact Discs*** In one area the demand for compact discs is $\frac{700}{P}$ per day, where $P$ is the price in dollars per disc. The supply is $5P - 1$ per day. At what price does supply equal demand?

***Froude Number*** *William Froude was a 19th-century naval architect who used the expression* $\frac{v^2}{g\ell}$ *in shipbuilding. This expression, known as the Froude number, was also used by R. McNeill Alexander in his research on dinosaurs. (See "How Dinosaurs Ran," in* Scientific American, *April 1991, pp. 130–136.)*

*In Exercises 75 and 76, find the value of $v$ (in meters per second) given that $g = 9.8$ meters per second squared.*

**75.** Rhinoceros: $\ell = 1.2$; Froude number $= 2.57$

**76.** Triceratops: $\ell = 2.8$; Froude number $= .16$

*Recall that the corresponding sides of similar triangles are proportional. (Refer to Section 7.3 Exercises 53–56.) Use this fact to find the lengths of the indicated sides of each pair of similar triangles. Check all possible solutions in both triangles. Sides of a triangle cannot be negative.*

**77.** Side $AC$

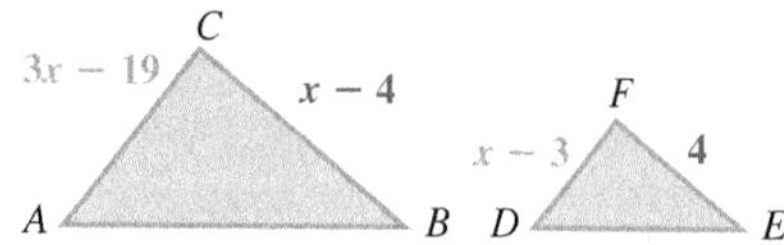


**78.** Side $RQ$

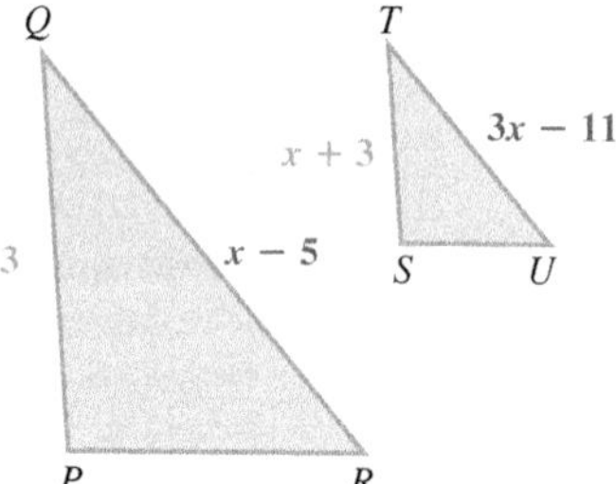


**79.** For centuries mathematicians wrestled with finding a formula that could solve cubic (third-degree) equations. A story from sixteenth-century Italy concerns two main characters, Girolamo Cardano and Niccolo Tartaglia. In those days, mathematicians often participated in contests. Tartaglia had developed a method of solving a cubic equation of the form $x^3 + mx = n$ and had used it in one of these contests. Cardano begged to know Tartaglia's method and after he was told, he was sworn to secrecy. Nonetheless, Cardano published Tartaglia's method in his 1545 work *Ars Magna* (although he did give Tartaglia credit).

The formula for finding one real solution of the above equation is

$$x = \sqrt[3]{\frac{n}{2} + \sqrt{\left(\frac{n}{2}\right)^2 + \left(\frac{m}{3}\right)^3}} - \sqrt[3]{-\left(\frac{n}{2}\right) + \sqrt{\left(\frac{n}{2}\right)^2 + \left(\frac{m}{3}\right)^3}}.$$

Solve $x^3 + 9x = 26$ using this formula.

# COLLABORATIVE INVESTIGATION

## How Does Your Walking Rate Compare to That of Olympic Race-Walkers?

Race-walking at speeds exceeding 8 miles per hour is a high fitness, long-distance competitive sport. The table below contains gold medal winners in the 2004 Olympic Games race-walking competition.

**A.** Complete the table by applying the proportion given below to find the race-walker's steps per minute. **Use 10 km ≈ 6.21 miles.** (Round all answers except those for steps per minute to the nearest thousandth. Round steps per minute to the nearest whole number.)

$$\frac{70 \text{ steps per minute}}{2 \text{ miles per hour}} = \frac{x \text{ steps per minute}}{y \text{ miles per hour}}$$

| Event | Gold Medal Winner | Country | Time in Hours: Minutes: Seconds | Time in Minutes | Time in Hours | *y* Miles per Hour | *x* Steps per Minute |
|---|---|---|---|---|---|---|---|
| 20-km Walk, Women | Athanasia Tsoumeleka | Greece | 1:29:12 | | | | |
| 20-km Walk, Men | Ivano Brugnatti | Italy | 1:19:40 | | | | |
| 50-km Walk, Men | Robert Korzeniowski | Poland | 3:38:48 | | | | |

*Source: The World Almanac and Book of Facts 2006.*

**B.** Using a stopwatch, take turns counting how many steps each member of the group takes in one minute while walking at a normal pace. Record the results in the table below. Then do it again at a fast pace. Record these results.

**C.** Use the proportion from part A to convert the numbers from part B to miles per hour and complete the chart.

1. Find the average speed for the group at a normal pace and at a fast pace.
2. What is the minimum number of steps per minute you would have to take to be a race-walker?
3. At a fast pace, did anyone in the group walk fast enough to be a race-walker? Explain how you decided.

| | Normal Pace | | Fast Pace | |
|---|---|---|---|---|
| Name | *x* Steps per Minute | *y* Miles per Hour | *x* Steps per Minute | *y* Miles per Hour |
| | | | | |
| | | | | |
| | | | | |
| | | | | |

# CHAPTER 7 TEST

*Solve each equation.*

1. $5x - 3 + 2x = 3(x - 2) + 11$

2. $\dfrac{2p - 1}{3} + \dfrac{p + 1}{4} = \dfrac{43}{12}$

3. Decide whether the equation

$$3x - (2 - x) + 4x = 7x - 2 - (-x)$$

is conditional, an identity, or a contradiction. Give its solution set.

4. Solve for $v$: $S = vt - 16t^2$.

*Solve each application.*

5. ***Areas of Hawaiian Islands*** Three islands in the Hawaiian island chain are Hawaii (the Big Island), Maui, and Kauai. Together, their areas total 5300 square miles. The island of Hawaii is 3293 square miles larger than the island of Maui, and Maui is 177 square miles larger than Kauai. What is the area of each island?

6. ***Chemical Mixture*** How many liters of a 20% solution of a chemical should Tippy Hurst mix with 10 liters of a 50% solution to obtain a mixture that is 40% chemical?

7. ***Speeds of Trains*** A passenger train and a freight train leave a town at the same time and travel in opposite directions. Their speeds are 60 mph and 75 mph, respectively. How long will it take for them to be 297 miles apart?

8. ***Merchandise Pricing*** Which is the better buy for processed cheese slices: 8 slices for \$2.19 or 12 slices for \$3.30?

9. ***Distance Between Cities*** The distance between Milwaukee and Boston is 1050 miles. On a certain map this distance is represented by 21 inches. On the same map Seattle and Cincinnati are 46 inches apart. What is the actual distance between Seattle and Cincinnati?

10. ***Current in a Circuit*** The current in a simple electrical circuit is inversely proportional to the resistance. If the current is 80 amps when the resistance is 30 ohms, find the current when the resistance is 12 ohms.

*Solve each inequality. Give the solution set in both interval and graph forms.*

11. $-4x + 2(x - 3) \geq 4x - (3 + 5x) - 7$

12. $-10 < 3k - 4 \leq 14$

13. Which one of the following inequalities is equivalent to $x < -3$?
    A. $-3x < 9$ B. $-3x > -9$
    C. $-3x > 9$ D. $-3x < -9$

14. ***Grade Average*** Paul Lorio has scores of 83, 76, and 79 on his first three tests in Math 1031 (Survey of Mathematics). If he wants an average of at least 80 after his fourth test, what are the possible scores he can make on his fourth test?

*Evaluate each exponential expression.*

15. $\left(\dfrac{4}{3}\right)^2$

16. $-(-2)^6$

17. $\left(\dfrac{3}{4}\right)^{-3}$

18. $-5^0 + (-5)^0$

*Use the properties of exponents to simplify each expression. Write answers with positive exponents only. Assume that all variables represent nonzero real numbers.*

19. $9(4p^3)(6p^{-7})$

20. $\dfrac{m^{-2}(m^3)^{-3}}{m^{-4}m^7}$

21. Write each number in standard notation.
    (a) $6.93 \times 10^8$
    (b) $1.25 \times 10^{-7}$

22. Use scientific notation to evaluate

$$\frac{(2{,}500{,}000)(.00003)}{(.05)(5{,}000{,}000)}.$$

Leave the answer in scientific notation.

23. ***Time Traveled for a Radio Signal*** The mean distance to Earth from the planet Pluto is $4.58 \times 10^9$ kilometers. The first U.S. space probe to Pluto, Pioneer 10, transmitted radio signals from Pluto to Earth at the speed of light, $3.00 \times 10^5$ kilometers per second. How long (in seconds) did it take for the signals to reach Earth?

*Perform the indicated operations.*

**24.** $(3k^3 - 5k^2 + 8k - 2) - (3k^3 - 9k^2 + 2k - 12)$

**25.** $(5x + 2)(3x - 4)$

**26.** $(4x^2 - 3)(4x^2 + 3)$

**27.** $(x + 4)(3x^2 + 8x - 9)$

**28.** Give an example of a polynomial in the variable $t$, such that it is fifth degree, in descending powers of the variable, with exactly six terms, and having a negative coefficient for its second degree term.

*Factor each polynomial completely.*

**29.** $2p^2 - 5pq + 3q^2$

**30.** $100x^2 - 49y^2$

**31.** $27y^3 - 125x^3$

**32.** $4x + 4y - mx - my$

*Solve each quadratic equation.*

**33.** $6x^2 + 7x - 3 = 0$

**34.** $x^2 - 13 = 0$

**35.** $x^2 - x = 7$

**36.** ***Time an Object Has Descended*** The equation

$$s = 16t^2 + 15t$$

gives the distance $s$ in feet an object thrown off a building has descended in $t$ seconds. Find the time $t$ when the object has descended 25 feet. Use a calculator and round the answer to the nearest hundredth.

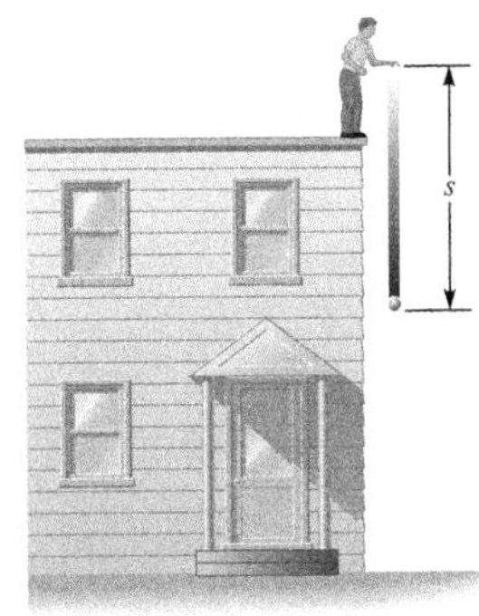

# GRAPHS, FUNCTIONS, AND SYSTEMS OF EQUATIONS AND INEQUALITIES

During the seasons of 1969–70 and 1970–71, the NBC television network aired *The Bill Cosby Show,* in which the popular comedian played Chet Kincaid, a Los Angeles high school physical education teacher. In one of the first season episodes, Chet has to substitute for the algebra teacher one Friday. He and the entire class are stumped by the following problem:

> *How many pounds of candy that sells for \$.75 per pound must be mixed with candy that sells for \$1.25 per pound to obtain 9 pounds of a mixture that should sell for \$.96 per pound.*

Chet learns that he will have to teach the class again on Monday, and he spends his weekend trying to solve this problem. (The title of the episode is "Let *x* Equal a Lousy Weekend.") He even visits the local candy store, where the owner says that in order to solve the problem, "you have to know algebra." On Monday, the smartest student in the class, Eddie Tucker, is able to solve the problem correctly using a system of equations. Can you do this as well? See page 508 for Eddie's answer.

# 8.1 The Rectangular Coordinate System and Circles

**Rectangular Coordinates • Distance Formula • Midpoint Formula • Circles**

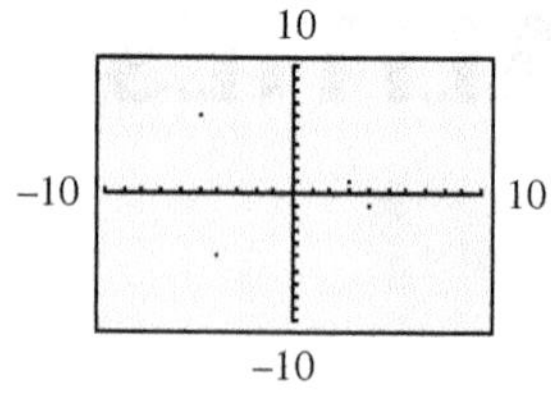


The points in Figure 2 are plotted on this calculator screen. Why is $E(-5, 0)$ not visible?

## Rectangular Coordinates

Each of the pairs of numbers (1, 2), (−1, 5), and (3, 7) is an example of an **ordered pair**—a pair of numbers written within parentheses in which the order of the numbers is important. The two numbers are the **components** of the ordered pair. An ordered pair is graphed using two number lines that intersect at right angles at the zero points, as shown in Figure 1. The common zero point is called the **origin.** The horizontal line, the **x-axis,** represents the first number in an ordered pair, and the vertical line, the **y-axis,** represents the second. The $x$-axis and the $y$-axis make up a **rectangular** (or **Cartesian**) **coordinate system.** The axes form four **quadrants,** numbered I, II, III, and IV as shown in Figure 2. (A point on an axis is not considered to be in any of the four quadrants.)

**Double Descartes** After the French postal service issued the above stamp in honor of **René Descartes,** sharp eyes noticed that the title of Descartes's most famous book was wrong. Thus a second stamp (see facing page) was issued with the correct title. The book in question, *Discourse on Method,* appeared in 1637. In it Descartes rejected traditional Aristotelian philosophy, outlining a universal system of knowledge that was to have the certainty of mathematics. For Descartes, method was *analysis,* going from self-evident truths step-by-step to more distant and more general truths. One of these truths is his famous statement, "I think, therefore I am." (Thomas Jefferson, also a rationalist, began the *Declaration* with the words, "We hold these truths to be self-evident.")

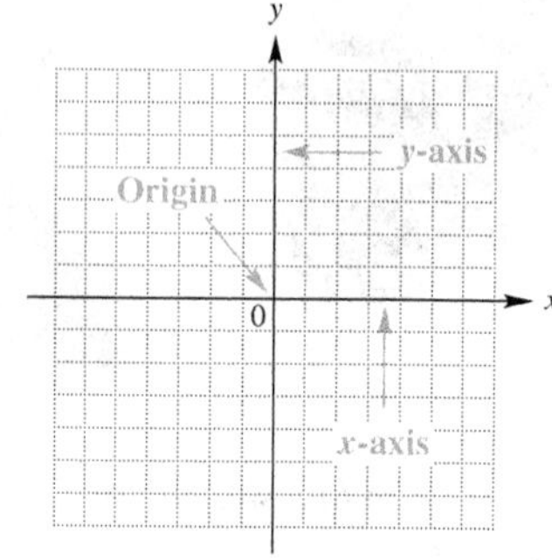


**FIGURE 1**

**FIGURE 2**

We locate, or **plot,** the point on the graph that corresponds to the ordered pair (3, 1) by going three units from zero to the right along the $x$-axis, and then one unit up parallel to the $y$-axis. The point corresponding to the ordered pair (3, 1) is labeled $A$ in Figure 2. The phrase "the point corresponding to the ordered pair (3, 1)" often is abbreviated "the point (3, 1)." The numbers in an ordered pair are called the **coordinates** of the corresponding point.

The parentheses used to represent an ordered pair also are used to represent an open interval (introduced in an earlier chapter). The context of the discussion tells us whether we are discussing ordered pairs or open intervals.

## Distance Formula

Suppose that we wish to find the distance between two points, say (3, −4) and (−5, 3). The Pythagorean theorem allows us to do this. In Figure 3 on the next page, we see that the vertical line through (−5, 3) and the horizontal line through (3, −4) intersect at the point (−5, −4). Thus, the point (−5, −4) becomes the vertex of the right angle in a right triangle. By the Pythagorean theorem, the square of the length of the hypotenuse, $d$, of the right triangle in Figure 3 is equal to the sum of the squares of the lengths of the two legs $a$ and $b$:

$$d^2 = a^2 + b^2.$$

The length $a$ is the distance between the endpoints of that leg. Since the $x$-coordinate of both points is $-5$, the side is vertical, and we can find $a$ by finding the difference between the $y$-coordinates. Subtract $-4$ from 3 to get a positive value of $a$. Similarly, find $b$ by subtracting $-5$ from 3.

$$a = 3 - (-4) = 7 \qquad \text{Use parentheses when}$$
$$b = 3 - (-5) = 8 \qquad \text{subtracting a negative number.}$$

Substituting these values into the formula, we have

$$d^2 = a^2 + b^2$$
$$d^2 = 7^2 + 8^2 \qquad \text{Let } a = 7 \text{ and } b = 8.$$
$$d^2 = 49 + 64$$
$$d^2 = 113$$
$$d = \sqrt{113}. \qquad \text{Square root property, } d > 0$$

Therefore, the distance between $(-5, 3)$ and $(3, -4)$ is $\sqrt{113}$.

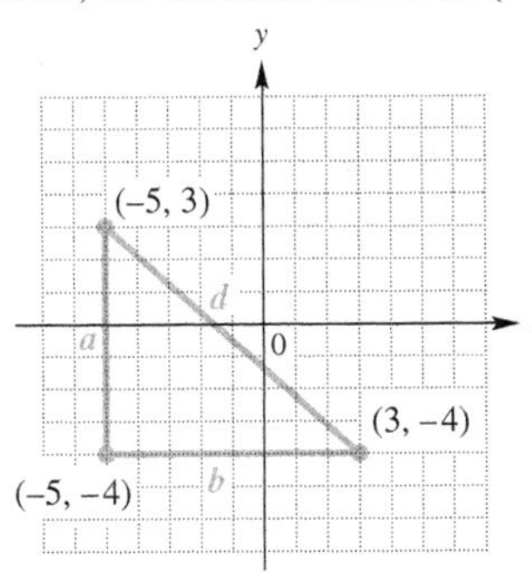


FIGURE 3

FIGURE 4

This result can be generalized. Figure 4 shows the two different points $(x_1, y_1)$ and $(x_2, y_2)$. To find a formula for the distance $d$ between these two points, notice that the distance between $(x_2, y_2)$ and $(x_2, y_1)$ is given by $a = y_2 - y_1$, and the distance between $(x_1, y_1)$ and $(x_2, y_1)$ is given by $b = x_2 - x_1$. From the Pythagorean theorem,

$$d^2 = (x_2 - x_1)^2 + (y_2 - y_1)^2,$$

and by using the square root property, we obtain the distance formula.

**Descartes** wrote his *Geometry* as an application of his method; it was published as an appendix to the *Discourse*. His attempts to unify algebra and geometry influenced the creation of what became coordinate geometry and influenced the development of calculus by Newton and Leibniz in the next generation.

In 1649 Descartes went to Sweden to tutor Queen Christina. She preferred working in the unheated castle in the early morning; Descartes was used to staying in bed until noon. The rigors of the Swedish winter proved too much for him, and he died less than a year later.

### Distance Formula

The distance between the points $(x_1, y_1)$ and $(x_2, y_2)$ is

$$d = \sqrt{(x_2 - x_1)^2 + (y_2 - y_1)^2}.$$

This result is called the **distance formula.**

The small numbers 1 and 2 in the ordered pairs $(x_1, y_1)$ and $(x_2, y_2)$ are called **subscripts.** We read $x_1$ as "$x$ sub 1." Subscripts are used to distinguish between different values of a variable that have a common property. For example, in the ordered pairs $(-3, 5)$ and $(6, 4)$, $-3$ can be designated as $x_1$ and 6 as $x_2$. Their common property is that they are both $x$ components of ordered pairs. This idea is used in the following example.

```
X1=
?-3
Y1=
?5
X2=
?6
Y2=
?4
```

```
D=SQUARE ROOT OF
              82
OR
     9.055385138
            Done
```

A program can be written for the distance formula. This one supports the result in Example 1, since $\sqrt{82} \approx 9.055385138$.

### EXAMPLE 1 Finding the Distance Between Two Points

Find the distance between $(-3, 5)$ and $(6, 4)$.

**SOLUTION**

When using the distance formula to find the distance between two points, designating the points as $(x_1, y_1)$ and $(x_2, y_2)$ is arbitrary. Let us choose $(x_1, y_1) = (-3, 5)$ and $(x_2, y_2) = (6, 4)$.

$$d = \sqrt{(x_2 - x_1)^2 + (y_2 - y_1)^2}$$

$$= \sqrt{(6 - (-3))^2 + (4 - 5)^2} \quad x_2 = 6,\ y_2 = 4,\ x_1 = -3,\ y_1 = 5$$

Begin with the x- and y- values of the same point.

$$= \sqrt{9^2 + (-1)^2}$$

$$= \sqrt{82}$$

## Midpoint Formula

**Midpoint Formula** The **midpoint** of a line segment is the point on the segment that is equidistant from both endpoints. Given the coordinates of the two end-points of a line segment, we can find the coordinates of the midpoint of the segment.

### Midpoint Formula

The coordinates of the midpoint of the segment with endpoints $(x_1, y_1)$ and $(x_2, y_2)$ are

$$\left(\frac{x_1 + x_2}{2}, \frac{y_1 + y_2}{2}\right).$$

In words, the coordinates of the midpoint of a line segment are found by calculating the averages of the $x$- and $y$-coordinates of the endpoints.

### EXAMPLE 2 Finding the Midpoint of a Segment

Find the coordinates of the midpoint of the line segment with endpoints $(8, -4)$ and $(-9, 6)$.

**SOLUTION**

Using the midpoint formula, we find that the coordinates of the midpoint are

$$\left(\frac{8 + (-9)}{2}, \frac{-4 + 6}{2}\right) = \left(-\frac{1}{2}, 1\right).$$

### EXAMPLE 3 Applying the Midpoint Formula to Data

Figure 5 on the next page depicts how the number of McDonald's restaurants worldwide increased from 1995 through 2001. Use the midpoint formula and the two given points to estimate the number of restaurants in 1998, and compare it to the actual (rounded) figure of 24,000.

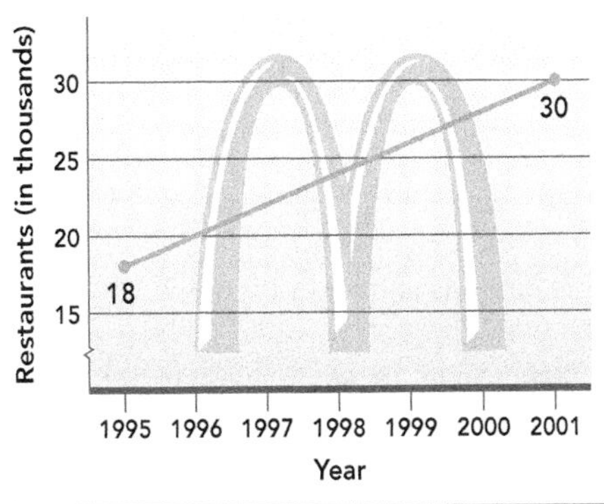


*Source:* McDonald's Corp.; Yahoo.com.

**FIGURE 5**

**SOLUTION**

The year 1998 lies halfway between 1995 and 2001, so we must find the coordinates of the midpoint of the segment that has endpoints (1995, 18) and (**2001**, **30**). (Here, $y$ is in thousands.) By the midpoint formula, this is

$$\left(\frac{1995 + \mathbf{2001}}{2}, \frac{18 + \mathbf{30}}{2}\right) = (1998, 24)$$

Thus, our estimate is 24,000 restaurants in 1998, which matches the actual (rounded) figure.

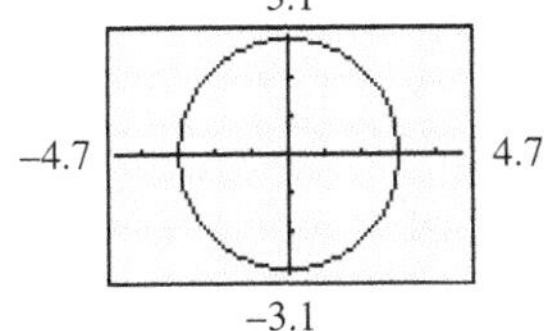


To graph $x^2 + y^2 = 9$, we solve for $y$ to get $y_1 = \sqrt{9 - x^2}$ and $y_2 = -\sqrt{9 - x^2}$. Then we graph both in a square window.

**Circles** An application of the distance formula leads to one of the most familiar shapes in geometry, the circle. A **circle** is the set of all points in a plane that lie a fixed distance from a fixed point. The fixed point is called the **center** and the fixed distance is called the **radius.**

### EXAMPLE 4 Finding an Equation of a Circle

Find an equation of the circle with radius 3 and center at (0, 0), and graph the circle.

**SOLUTION**

If the point $(x, y)$ is on the circle, the distance from $(x, y)$ to the center (0, 0) is 3, as shown in Figure 6.

$$\sqrt{(x_2 - x_1)^2 + (y_2 - y_1)^2} = d \quad \text{Distance formula}$$

$$\sqrt{(x - 0)^2 + (y - 0)^2} = 3 \quad x_1 = 0, y_1 = 0, x_2 = x, y_2 = y, d = 3$$

$$x^2 + y^2 = 9 \quad \text{Square both sides.}$$

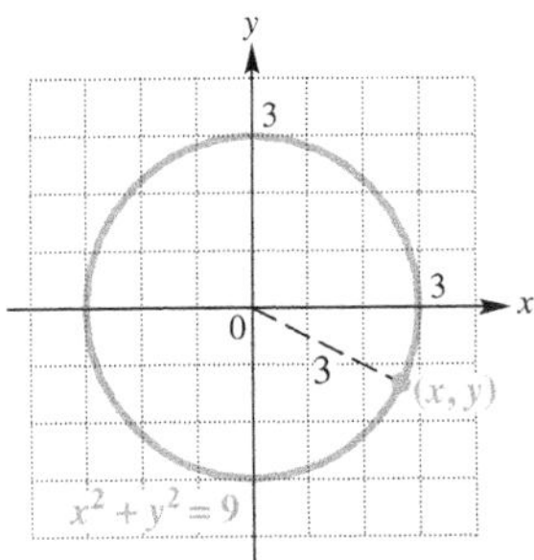


**FIGURE 6**

An equation of this circle is $x^2 + y^2 = 9$. It can be graphed by locating all points three units from the origin.

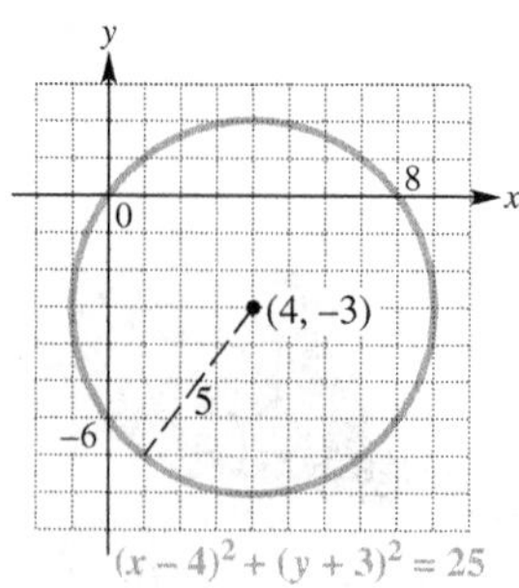


**FIGURE 7**

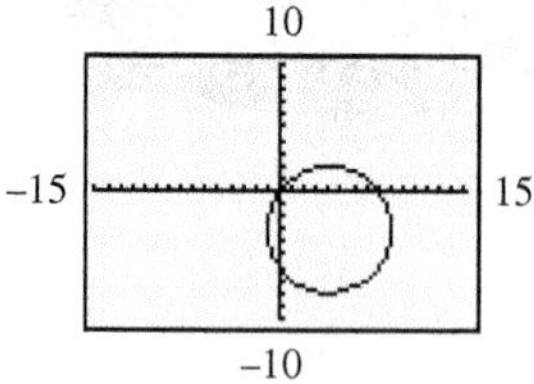


A circle can be "drawn" by using the appropriate command, entering the coordinates of the center and the radius. Compare with Example 5 and Figure 7.

## EXAMPLE 5 Finding an Equation of a Circle and Graphing

Find an equation for the circle that has its center at $(4, -3)$ and radius 5, and graph the circle.

**SOLUTION**

$$\sqrt{(x-4)^2+[y-(-3)]^2} = 5 \quad \text{Substitute in the distance formula.}$$

$$(x-4)^2+(y+3)^2 = 25 \quad \text{Square both sides.}$$

The graph of this circle is shown in Figure 7. ■

Examples 4 and 5 can be generalized to get an equation of a circle with radius $r$ and center at $(h, k)$. If $(x, y)$ is a point on the circle, the distance from the center $(h, k)$ to the point $(x, y)$ is $r$. Then by the distance formula, $\sqrt{(x-h)^2+(y-k)^2} = r$. Squaring both sides gives the following equation of a circle.

### Equation of a Circle

The equation of a circle of radius $r$ with center at $(h, k)$ is

$$(x-h)^2+(y-k)^2 = r^2.$$

In particular, a circle of radius $r$ with center at the origin has equation

$$x^2+y^2=r^2.$$

## EXAMPLE 6 Finding an Equation of a Circle

Find an equation of the circle with center at $(-1, 2)$ and radius 4.

**SOLUTION**

$$(x-h)^2+(y-k)^2 = r^2$$

$$[x-(-1)]^2+(y-2)^2 = 4^2 \quad \text{Let } h=-1,\ k=2, \text{ and } r=4.$$

$$(x+1)^2+(y-2)^2 = 16$$

■

In the equation found in Example 5, multiplying out $(x-4)^2$ and $(y+3)^2$ and then combining like terms gives

$$(x-4)^2+(y+3)^2 = 25$$

$$x^2-8x+16+y^2+6y+9 = 25$$

$$x^2+y^2-8x+6y = 0$$

This result suggests that an equation that has both $x^2$- and $y^2$-terms with equal coefficients may represent a circle. The next example shows how to tell, using the method of **completing the square.**

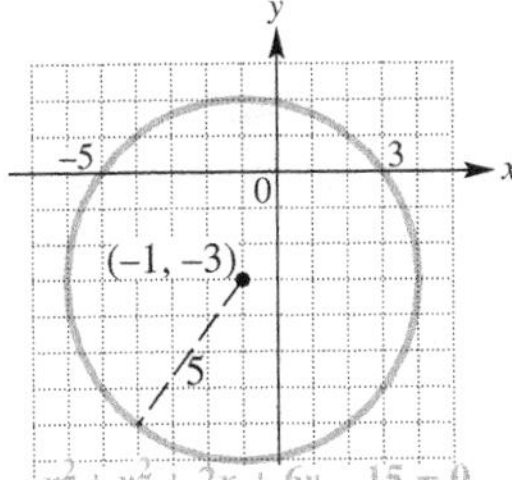


**FIGURE 8**

## EXAMPLE 7 Completing the Square and Graphing a Circle

Graph $x^2 + y^2 + 2x + 6y - 15 = 0$.

**SOLUTION**

Since the equation has $x^2$- and $y^2$-terms with equal coefficients, its graph might be that of a circle. To find the center and radius, complete the squares in $x$ and $y$ as follows. (See page 418, where completing the square is introduced.)

$$x^2 + y^2 + 2x + 6y = 15 \quad \text{Add 15 to both sides.}$$

$$(x^2 + 2x \quad\quad ) + (y^2 + 6y \quad\quad ) = 15 \quad \text{Rewrite in anticipation of completing the square.}$$

$$(x^2 + 2x + 1) + (y^2 + 6y + 9) = 15 + 1 + 9 \quad \text{Complete the squares in both } x \text{ and } y.$$

$$(x + 1)^2 + (y + 3)^2 = 25 \quad \text{Factor on the left and add on the right.}$$

The final equation shows that the graph is a circle with center at $(-1, -3)$ and radius 5. The graph is shown in Figure 8.

The final example in this section shows how equations of circles can be used in locating the epicenter of an earthquake.

## EXAMPLE 8 Locating the Epicenter of an Earthquake

Seismologists can locate the epicenter of an earthquake by determining the intersection of three circles. The radii of these circles represent the distances from the epicenter to each of three receiving stations. The centers of the circles represent the receiving stations.

Suppose receiving stations $A$, $B$, and $C$ are located on a coordinate plane at the points $(1, 4)$, $(-3, -1)$, and $(5, 2)$. Let the distances from the earthquake epicenter to the stations be 2 units, 5 units, and 4 units, respectively. See Figure 9. Where on the coordinate plane is the epicenter located?

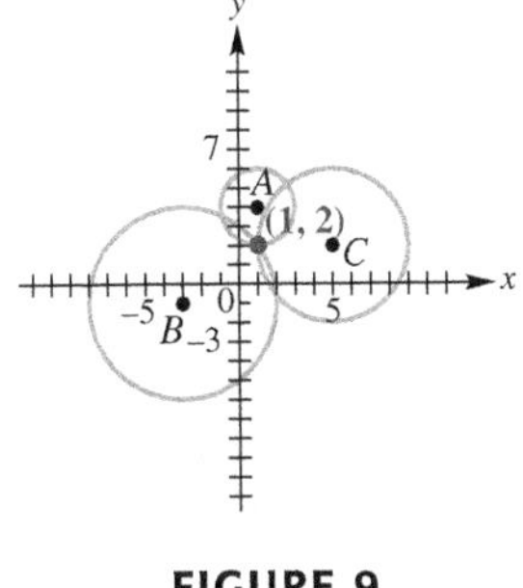


**FIGURE 9**

**SOLUTION**

Graphically, it appears that the epicenter is located at $(1, 2)$. To check this algebraically, determine the equation for each circle and substitute $x = 1$ and $y = 2$.

*Station A*

$$(x - 1)^2 + (y - 4)^2 = 4$$
$$(1 - 1)^2 + (2 - 4)^2 = 4$$
$$0 + 4 = 4$$
$$4 = 4$$

*Station B*

$$(x + 3)^2 + (y + 1)^2 = 25$$
$$(1 + 3)^2 + (2 + 1)^2 = 25$$
$$16 + 9 = 25$$
$$25 = 25$$

*Station C*

$$(x - 5)^2 + (y - 2)^2 = 16$$
$$(1 - 5)^2 + (2 - 2)^2 = 16$$
$$16 + 0 = 16$$
$$16 = 16$$

Thus, we can be sure that the epicenter lies at $(1, 2)$.

## 8.1 EXERCISES

*In Exercises 1 and 2, answer each question by locating ordered pairs on the graphs.*

1. ***Women in Mathematics or Computer Science*** The graph shows the percent of women in mathematics or computer science professions since 1970.

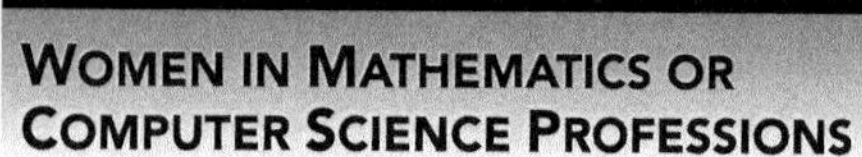


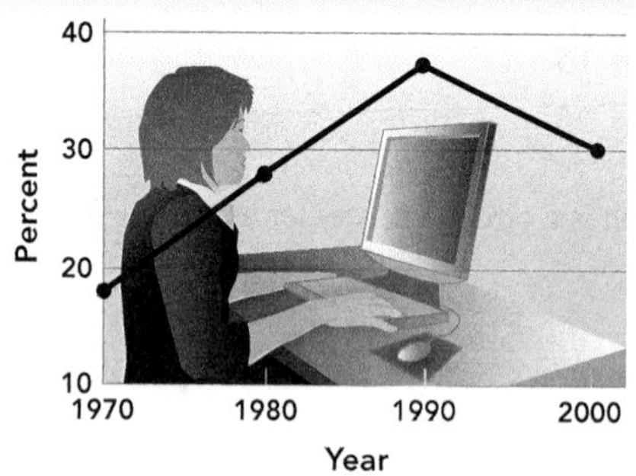


*Source:* U.S. Bureau of the Census and Bureau of Labor Statistics.

(a) If $(x, y)$ represents a point on the graph, what does $x$ represent? What does $y$ represent?
(b) In what decade (10-year period) did the percent of women in mathematics or computer science professions decrease?
(c) When did the percent of women in mathematics or computer science professions reach a maximum?
(d) In what year was the percent of women in mathematics or computer science professions about 27%?

2. ***Federal Government Tax Revenues*** The graph shows federal government tax revenues in billions of dollars.

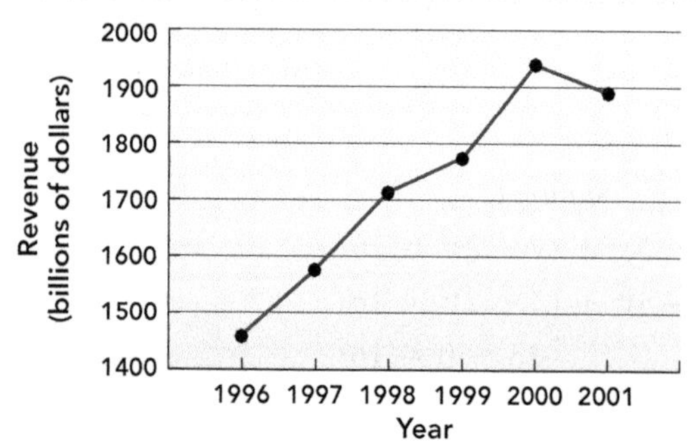


*Source:* U.S. Office of Management and Budget.

(a) If $(x, y)$ represents a point on the graph, what does $x$ represent? What does $y$ represent?
(b) What was the revenue in 1999?
(c) In what year was revenue about \$1700 billion?

*Fill in each blank with the correct response.*

3. For any value of $x$, the point $(x, 0)$ lies on the ______ -axis.

4. For any value of $y$, the point $(0, y)$ lies on the ______ -axis.

5. The circle $x^2 + y^2 = 9$ has the point ____ as its center.

6. The point (___, 0) is the center of the circle

$$(x - 2)^2 + y^2 = 16.$$

*Name the quadrant, if any, in which each point is located.*

7. (a) $(1, 6)$
(b) $(-4, -2)$
(c) $(-3, 6)$
(d) $(7, -5)$
(e) $(-3, 0)$

8. (a) $(-2, -10)$
(b) $(4, 8)$
(c) $(-9, 12)$
(d) $(3, -9)$
(e) $(0, -8)$

9. Use the given information to determine the possible quadrants in which the point $(x, y)$ must lie.
(a) $xy > 0$
(b) $xy < 0$
(c) $\frac{x}{y} < 0$
(d) $\frac{x}{y} > 0$

10. What must be true about one of the coordinates of any point that lies along an axis?

*Locate the following points on the rectangular coordinate system, using a graph similar to Figure 2.*

11. $(2, 3)$

12. $(-1, 2)$

13. $(-3, -2)$

14. $(1, -4)$

15. $(0, 5)$

16. $(-2, -4)$

17. $(-2, 4)$

18. $(3, 0)$

19. $(-2, 0)$

20. $(3, -3)$

*Find*
**(a)** *the distance between the pair of points, and*
**(b)** *the coordinates of the midpoint of the segment having the points as endpoints.*

21. $(3, 4)$ and $(-2, 1)$

22. $(-2, 1)$ and $(3, -2)$

23. $(-2, 4)$ and $(3, -2)$

24. $(1, -5)$ and $(6, 3)$

25. $(-3, 7)$ and $(2, -4)$

26. $(0, 5)$ and $(-3, 12)$

*In Exercises 27–30, match each center-radius form of the equation of a circle with the correct graph from choices A–D.*

**A.**

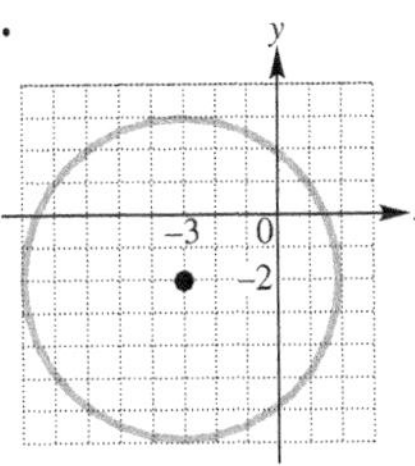


**B.**

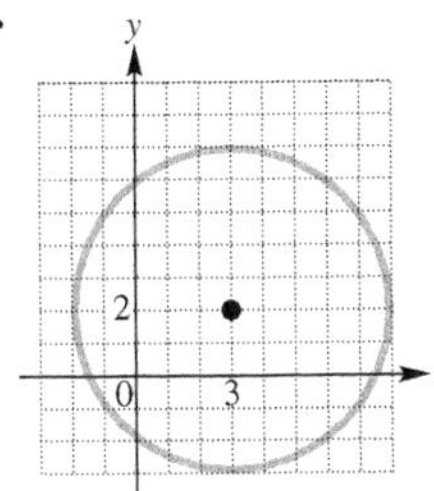


**C.**

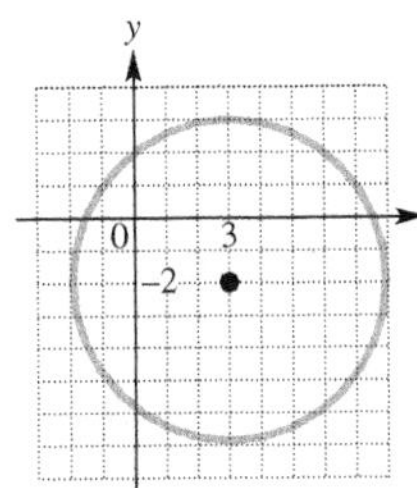


**D.**

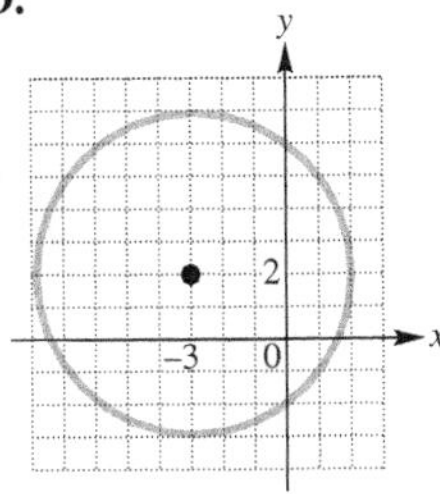


27. $(x - 3)^2 + (y - 2)^2 = 25$

28. $(x - 3)^2 + (y + 2)^2 = 25$

29. $(x + 3)^2 + (y - 2)^2 = 25$

30. $(x + 3)^2 + (y + 2)^2 = 25$

*Write an equation of the circle with the given center and radius.*

31. $(0, 0)$; $r = 6$

32. $(0, 0)$; $r = 5$

33. $(-1, 3)$; $r = 4$

34. $(2, -2)$; $r = 3$

35. $(0, 4)$; $r = \sqrt{3}$

36. $(-2, 0)$; $r = \sqrt{5}$

37. Suppose that a circle has an equation of the form $x^2 + y^2 = r^2$, $r > 0$. What is the center of the circle? What is the radius of the circle?

38. **(a)** How many points are there on the graph of $(x - 4)^2 + (y - 1)^2 = 0$? Explain your answer.
**(b)** How many points are there on the graph of $(x - 4)^2 + (y - 1)^2 = -1$? Explain your answer.

*Find the center and the radius of each circle. (Hint: In Exercises 43 and 44 divide both sides by the greatest common factor.)*

39. $x^2 + y^2 + 4x + 6y + 9 = 0$

40. $x^2 + y^2 - 8x - 12y + 3 = 0$

41. $x^2 + y^2 + 10x - 14y - 7 = 0$

42. $x^2 + y^2 - 2x + 4y - 4 = 0$

43. $3x^2 + 3y^2 - 12x - 24y + 12 = 0$

44. $2x^2 + 2y^2 + 20x + 16y + 10 = 0$

*Graph each circle.*

45. $x^2 + y^2 = 36$

46. $x^2 + y^2 = 81$

47. $(x - 2)^2 + y^2 = 36$

48. $x^2 + (y + 3)^2 = 49$

49. $(x + 2)^2 + (y - 5)^2 = 16$

50. $(x - 4)^2 + (y - 3)^2 = 25$

51. $(x + 3)^2 + (y + 2)^2 = 36$

52. $(x - 5)^2 + (y + 4)^2 = 49$

*Find* **(a)** *the distance between P and Q and* **(b)** *the coordinates of the midpoint of the segment joining P and Q.*

**53.** **54.**

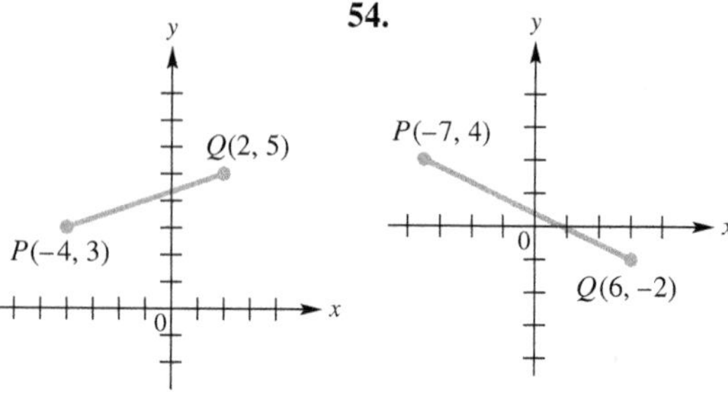


**55.** ***(Modeling) Tuition and Fees*** From 1998–2004, the average annual cost (in dollars) of tuition and fees at private four-year colleges rose in an approximately linear fashion. The graph depicts this growth with a line segment. Use the midpoint formula to approximate the cost during the year 2001.

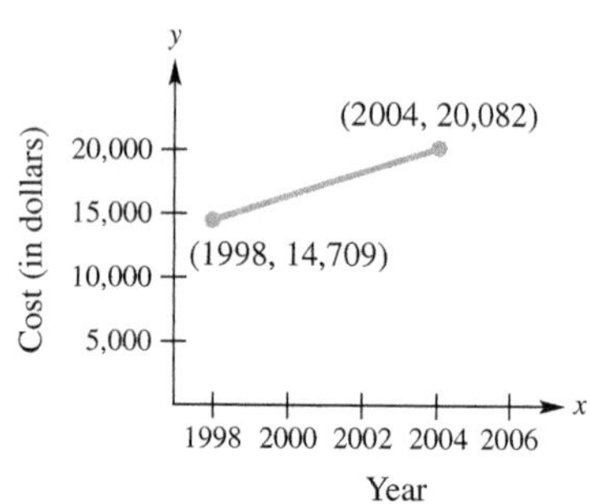


*Source*: The College Board.

**56.** ***(Modeling) Two-Year College Enrollment*** Projected enrollments in two-year colleges for 2005, 2007, and 2009 are shown in the table. Use the midpoint formula to estimate the enrollments for 2006 and 2008.

| Year | Enrollment (in thousands) |
|---|---|
| 2005 | 6038 |
| 2007 | 6146 |
| 2009 | 6257 |

*Source: Statistical Abstract of the United States.*

**57.** ***(Modeling) Poverty-Level Income Cutoffs*** The table at the top of the next column lists poverty-level income cutoffs for a family of four since 1983. Use the midpoint formula to estimate the poverty-level cutoffs (rounded to the nearest dollar) in 1988 and 1998.

| Year | Income (in dollars) |
|---|---|
| 1983 | 10,178 |
| 1993 | 14,763 |
| 2003 | 18,810 |

*Source:* U.S. Census Bureau.

**58.** An alternative form of the distance formula is

$$d = \sqrt{(x_1 - x_2)^2 + (y_1 - y_2)^2}.$$

Compare this to the form given in this section, and explain why the two forms are equivalent.

**59.** A student was asked to find the distance between the points (5, 8) and (2, 14), and wrote the following:

$$d = \sqrt{(5 - 8)^2 + (2 - 14)^2}.$$

Explain why this is incorrect.

**60.** A circle can be drawn on a piece of posterboard by fastening one end of a string, pulling the string taut with a pencil, and tracing a curve as shown in the figure. Explain why this method works.

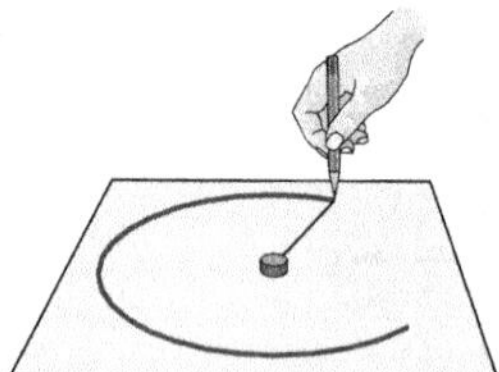

**61.** ***Crawfish Racing*** This figure shows how the crawfish race is held at the Crawfish Festival in Breaux Bridge, Louisiana. Explain why a circular "race-track" is appropriate for such a race.

**62.** ***Epicenter of an Earthquake*** Show algebraically that if three receiving stations at $(1, 4)$, $(-6, 0)$, and $(5, -2)$ record distances to an earthquake epicenter of 4 units, 5 units, and 10 units, respectively, the epicenter would lie at $(-3, 4)$.

**63.** ***Epicenter of an Earthquake*** Three receiving stations record the presence of an earthquake. The locations of the receiving stations and the distances to the epicenter are contained in the following three equations: $(x-2)^2+(y-1)^2=25$, $(x+2)^2+(y-2)^2=16$, and $(x-1)^2+(y+2)^2=9$. Graph the circles and determine the location of the earthquake epicenter.

**64.** Without actually graphing, state whether the graphs of $x^2+y^2=4$ and $x^2+y^2=25$ will intersect. Explain your answer.

**65.** Can a circle have its center at $(2, 4)$ and be tangent to both axes? (*Tangent to* means touching in one point.) Explain.

**66.** Suppose that the endpoints of a line segment have coordinates $(x_1, y_1)$ and $(x_2, y_2)$.

**(a)** Show that the distance between $(x_1, y_1)$ and $\left(\frac{x_1+x_2}{2}, \frac{y_1+y_2}{2}\right)$ is the same as the distance between $(x_2, y_2)$ and $\left(\frac{x_1+x_2}{2}, \frac{y_1+y_2}{2}\right)$.

**(b)** Show that the sum of the distances between $(x_1, y_1)$ and $\left(\frac{x_1+x_2}{2}, \frac{y_1+y_2}{2}\right)$, and $(x_2, y_2)$ and $\left(\frac{x_1+x_2}{2}, \frac{y_1+y_2}{2}\right)$ is equal to the distance between $(x_1, y_1)$ and $(x_2, y_2)$.

**(c)** From the results of parts (a) and (b), what conclusion can be made?

**67.** If the coordinates of one endpoint of a line segment $(3, -8)$ and the coordinates of the midpoint of the segment are $(6, 5)$, what are the coordinates of the other endpoint?

**68.** Which one of the following has a circle as its graph?

**A.** $x^2-y^2=9$ **B.** $x^2=9-y^2$

**C.** $y^2-x^2=9$ **D.** $-x^2-y^2=9$

**69.** For the three choices that are not circles in Exercise 68, explain why their equations are not those of circles.

**70.** An *isosceles triangle* has at least two sides of equal length. Determine whether the triangle with vertices $(0, 0)$, $(3, 4)$, and $(7, 1)$ is isosceles.

# 8.2 Lines, Slope, and Average Rate of Change

**Linear Equations in Two Variables • Intercepts • Slope • Parallel and Perpendicular Lines • Average Rate of Change**

## Linear Equations in Two Variables

In the previous chapter, we studied linear equations in a single variable. The solution of such an equation is a real number. A linear equation in *two* variables will have solutions written as ordered pairs. Unlike linear equations in a single variable, equations with two variables will, in general, have an infinite number of solutions.

To find ordered pairs that satisfy the equation, select any number for one of the variables, substitute it into the equation for that variable, and then solve for the other variable. For example, suppose $x = 0$ in the equation $2x + 3y = 6$. Then

$$\begin{aligned} 2x + 3y &= 6 \\ 2(0) + 3y &= 6 \quad \text{Let } x = 0. \\ 0 + 3y &= 6 \\ 3y &= 6 \\ y &= 2, \end{aligned}$$

| X | Y1 |
|---|---|
| 0 | 2 |
| 1 | 1.3333 |
| 2 | .66667 |
| 3 | 0 |
| 4 | -.6667 |
| 5 | -1.333 |
| 6 | -2 |

Y1■(6-2X)/3

Graphing calculators can generate tables of ordered pairs. Here is an example for $2x + 3y = 6$. We must solve for $y$ to get $Y_1 = (6 - 2X)/3$ before generating the table.

giving the ordered pair (0, 2). Other ordered pairs satisfying $2x + 3y = 6$ include $(6, -2)$, $(3, 0)$, $(-3, 4)$, and $(9, -4)$.

The equation $2x + 3y = 6$ is graphed by first plotting all the ordered pairs mentioned above. These are shown in Figure 10(a). The resulting points appear to lie on a straight line. If all the ordered pairs that satisfy the equation $2x + 3y = 6$ were graphed, they would form a straight line. In fact, the graph of any first-degree equation in two variables is a straight line. The graph of $2x + 3y = 6$ is the line shown in Figure 10(b).

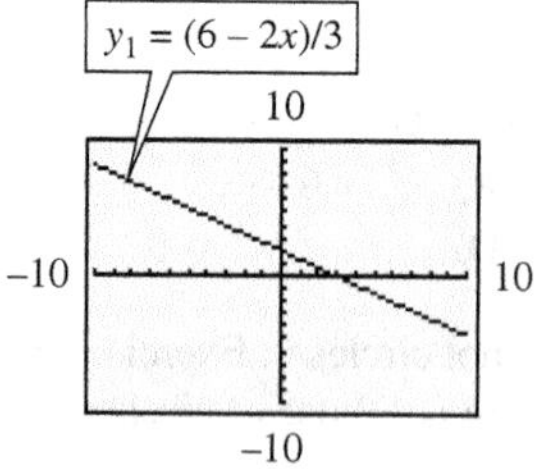


This is a calculator graph of the line shown in Figure 10(b).

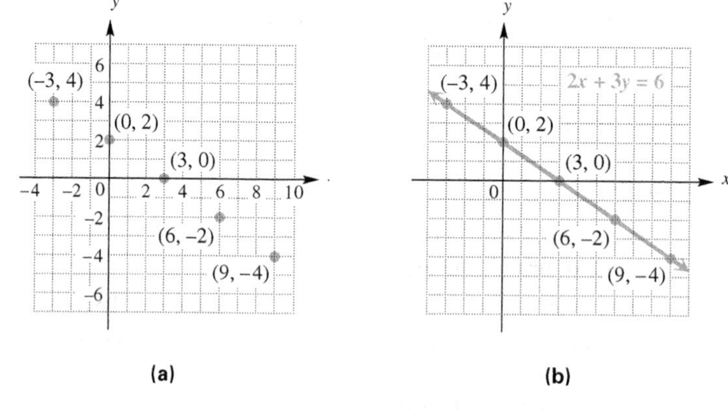


**FIGURE 10**

### Linear Equation in Two Variables

An equation that can be written in the form

$$Ax + By = C \quad \text{(where } A \text{ and } B \text{ are not both 0)}$$

is a **linear equation in two variables.** This form is called **standard form.**

All first-degree equations with two variables have straight-line graphs. Since a straight line is determined if any two different points on the line are known, finding two different points is sufficient to graph the line.

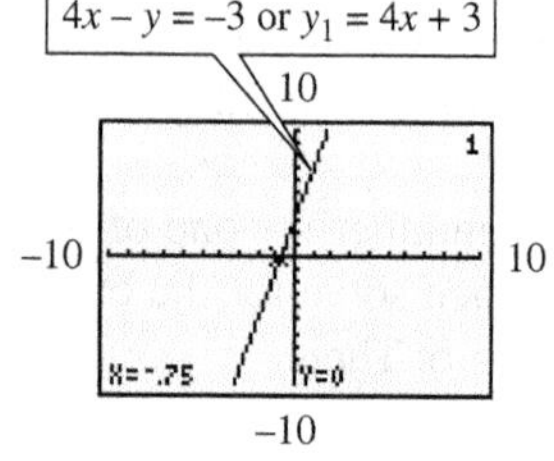


The display at the bottom of the screen supports the fact that $(-\frac{3}{4}, 0)$ is the $x$-intercept of the line in Figure 11 on the next page. We could locate the $y$-intercept similarly.

**Intercepts** Two points that are useful for graphing lines are the $x$- and $y$-intercepts. The ***x*-intercept** is the point (if any) where the line crosses the $x$-axis, and the ***y*-intercept** is the point (if any) where the line crosses the $y$-axis. (*Note:* In many texts, the intercepts are defined as numbers, and not points. However, in this book we will refer to intercepts as points.) Intercepts can be found as follows.

### Intercepts

To find the $x$-intercept of the graph of a linear equation, let $y = 0$ and solve for $x$.

To find the $y$-intercept, let $x = 0$ and solve for $y$.

### EXAMPLE 1 Graphing an Equation Using Intercepts

Find the $x$- and $y$-intercepts of $4x - y = -3$, and graph the equation.

**SOLUTION**

To find the $x$-intercept, let $y = 0$.

$$4x - 0 = -3 \quad \text{Let } y = 0.$$
$$4x = -3$$
$$x = -\frac{3}{4} \quad x\text{-intercept is } \left(-\tfrac{3}{4}, 0\right).$$

To find the $y$-intercept, let $x = 0$.

$$4(0) - y = -3 \quad \text{Let } x = 0.$$
$$-y = -3$$
$$y = 3 \quad y\text{-intercept is } (0, 3).$$

The intercepts are the two points $\left(-\frac{3}{4}, 0\right)$ and $(0, 3)$. Use these two points to draw the graph, as shown in Figure 11.

**FIGURE 11**

A line may not have an $x$-intercept, or it may not have a $y$-intercept.

### EXAMPLE 2 Graphing Lines with a Single Intercept

Graph each line.

**(a)** $y = 2$ **(b)** $x = -1$

**SOLUTION**

**(a)** Writing $y = 2$ as $0x + 1y = 2$ shows that any value of $x$, including $x = 0$, gives $y = 2$, making the $y$-intercept $(0, 2)$. Since $y$ is always 2, there is no value of $x$ corresponding to $y = 0$, and so the graph has no $x$-intercept. The graph, shown in Figure 12(a), is a horizontal line.

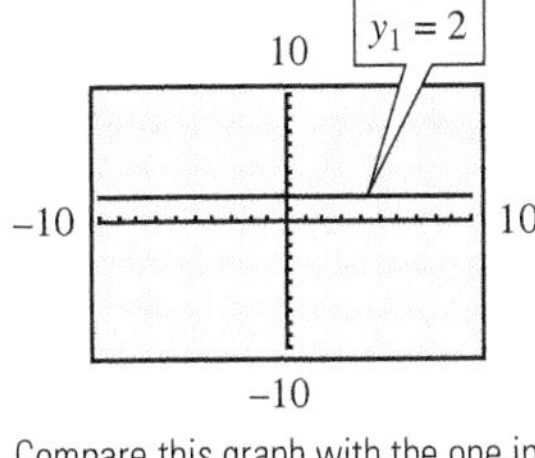

Compare this graph with the one in Figure 12(a).

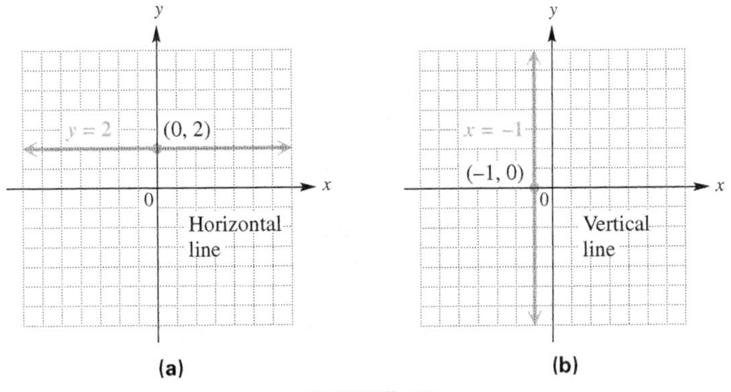

**FIGURE 12**

**(b)** In this equation, for all $x$, $x = -1$. No value of $y$ makes $x = 0$. The graph has no $y$-intercept. The only way a straight line can have no $y$-intercept is to be vertical, as shown in Figure 12(b).

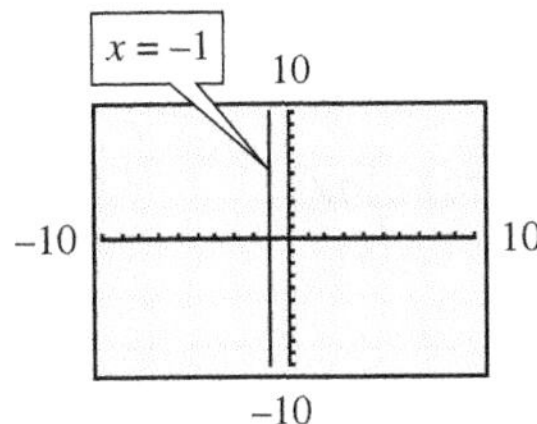

This vertical line is not an example of a *function* (see Section 8.4), so we must use a *draw* command to obtain it. Compare with Figure 12(b).

**Slope** Two distinct points determine a unique line. A line also can be determined by a point on the line and some measure of the "steepness" of the line. The measure of the steepness of a line is called the *slope* of the line. One way to get a measure of the steepness of a line is to compare the vertical change in the line (the *rise*) to the horizontal change (the *run*) while moving along the line from one fixed point to another.

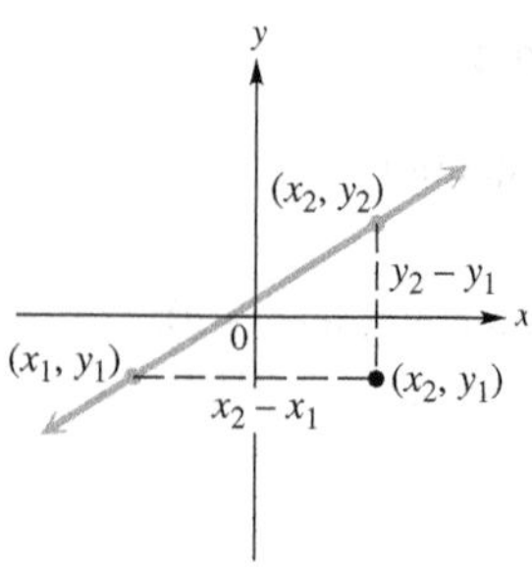


**FIGURE 13**

Suppose that $(x_1, y_1)$ and $(x_2, y_2)$ are two different points on a line. Then, going along the line from $(x_1, y_1)$ to $(x_2, y_2)$, the $y$-value changes from $y_1$ to $y_2$, an amount equal to $y_2 - y_1$. As $y$ changes from $y_1$ to $y_2$, the value of $x$ changes from $x_1$ to $x_2$ by the amount $x_2 - x_1$. See Figure 13. The ratio of the change in $y$ to the change in $x$ is called the **slope** of the line. The letter $m$ is used to denote the slope.

## Slope

If $x_1 \neq x_2$, the slope of the line through the distinct points $(x_1, y_1)$ and $(x_2, y_2)$ is

$$m = \frac{\textbf{rise}}{\textbf{run}} = \frac{\textbf{change in } y}{\textbf{change in } x} = \frac{y_2 - y_1}{x_2 - x_1}.$$

### EXAMPLE 3 Using the Slope Formula

Find the slope of the line that passes through the points $(2, -1)$ and $(-5, 3)$.

**SOLUTION**

If $(2, -1) = (x_1, y_1)$ and $(-5, 3) = (x_2, y_2)$, then

$$m = \frac{y_2 - y_1}{x_2 - x_1} = \frac{3 - (-1)}{-5 - 2} = \frac{4}{-7} = -\frac{4}{7}.$$

Start with the x- and y-values of the same point.

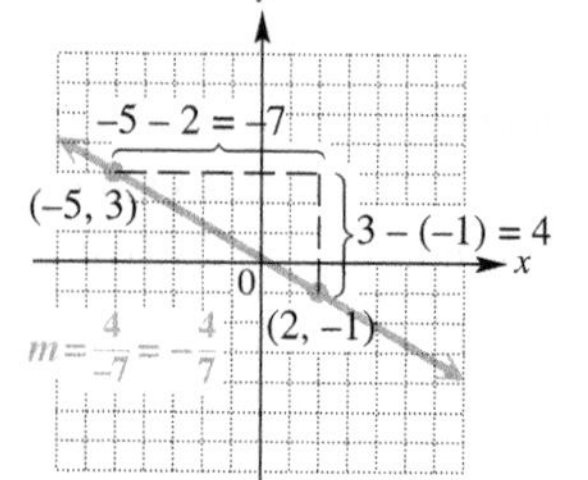


**FIGURE 14**

See Figure 14. On the other hand, if $(2, -1) = (x_2, y_2)$ and $(-5, 3) = (x_1, y_1)$, the slope would be

$$m = \frac{-1 - 3}{2 - (-5)} = \frac{-4}{7} = -\frac{4}{7},$$

the same answer. This example suggests that the slope is the same no matter which point is considered first. Also, using similar triangles from geometry, it can be shown that the slope is the same for *any* two different points chosen on the line.

If we apply the slope formula to a vertical or a horizontal line, we find that either the numerator or denominator in the fraction is 0.

### EXAMPLE 4 Finding Slopes of Vertical and Horizontal Lines

Find the slope, if possible, of each of the following lines.

**(a)** $x = -3$ **(b)** $y = 5$

**SOLUTION**

**(a)** By inspection, $(-3, 5)$ and $(-3, -4)$ are two points that satisfy the equation $x = -3$. Use these two points to find the slope.

$$m = \frac{-4 - 5}{-3 - (-3)} = \frac{-9}{0} \quad \text{Undefined slope}$$

Since division by zero is undefined, the slope is undefined. This is why the definition of slope includes the restriction that $x_1 \neq x_2$.

**Highway slopes** are measured in percent. For example, a slope of 8% means that the road gains 8 feet in altitude for each 100 feet that the road travels horizontally. Interstate highways cannot exceed a slope of 6%. While this may not seem like much of a slope, there are probably stretches of interstate highways that would be hard work for a distance runner.

**(b)** Find the slope by selecting two different points on the line, such as $(3, 5)$ and $(-1, 5)$, and by using the definition of slope.

$$m = \frac{5 - 5}{3 - (-1)} = \frac{0}{4} = 0 \quad \text{Zero slope}$$

In Example 2, $x = -1$ has a graph that is a vertical line, and $y = 2$ has a graph that is a horizontal line. Generalizing from those results and the results of Example 4, we can make the following statements about vertical and horizontal lines.

### Vertical and Horizontal Lines

A vertical line has an equation of the form $x = a$, where $a$ is a real number, and its slope is undefined. A horizontal line has an equation of the form $y = b$, where $b$ is a real number, and its slope is 0.

If we know the slope of a line and a point contained on the line, then we can graph the line using the method shown in the next example.

### EXAMPLE 5 Graphing a Line Using Slope and a Point

Graph the line that has slope $\frac{2}{3}$ and passes through the point $(-1, 4)$.

**SOLUTION**

First locate the point $(-1, 4)$ on a graph as shown in Figure 15. Then,

$$m = \frac{\text{change in } y}{\text{change in } x} = \frac{2}{3}. \quad \text{Definition of slope}$$

Move *up* 2 units in the $y$-direction and then 3 units to the *right* in the $x$-direction to locate another point on the graph (labeled $P$). The line through $(-1, 4)$ and $P$ is the required graph.

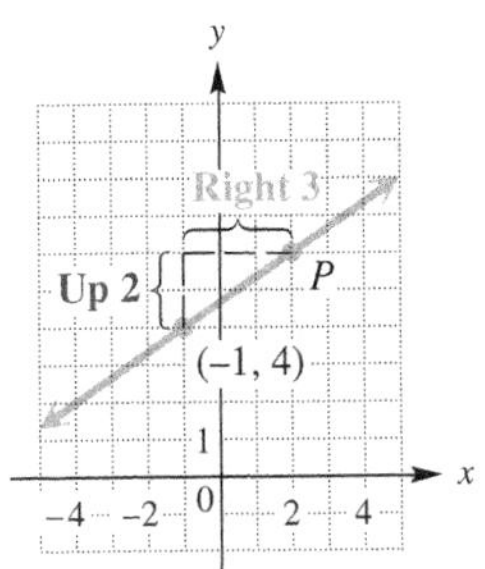


FIGURE 15

The line graphed in Figure 14 has a negative slope, $-\frac{4}{7}$, and the line *falls* from left to right. In contrast, the line graphed in Figure 15 has a positive slope, $\frac{2}{3}$ and it *rises* from left to right. These ideas can be generalized. (Figure 16 shows lines of positive, zero, negative, and undefined slopes.)

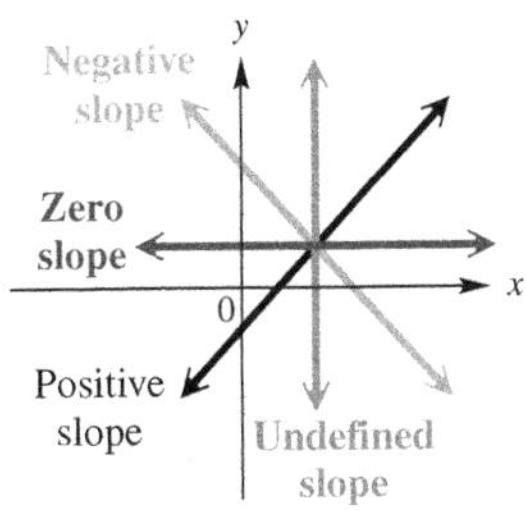


FIGURE 16

### Positive and Negative Slopes

A line with a positive slope rises from left to right, while a line with a negative slope falls from left to right.

**Parallel and Perpendicular Lines** The slopes of a pair of parallel or perpendicular lines are related in a special way. The slope of a line measures the steepness of the line. Since parallel lines have equal steepness, their slopes also must be equal. Also, lines with the same slope are parallel.

**Slopes of Parallel Lines**

Two nonvertical lines with the same slope are parallel. Two nonvertical parallel lines have the same slope. Furthermore, any two vertical lines are parallel.

### EXAMPLE 6 Determining Whether Two Lines Are Parallel

Determine whether the lines $L_1$, through $(-2, 1)$ and $(4, 5)$, and $L_2$, through $(3, 0)$ and $(0, -2)$, are parallel.

**SOLUTION**

The slope of $L_1$ is $\quad m_1 = \dfrac{5 - 1}{4 - (-2)} = \dfrac{4}{6} = \dfrac{2}{3}.$

The slope of $L_2$ is $\quad m_2 = \dfrac{-2 - 0}{0 - 3} = \dfrac{-2}{-3} = \dfrac{2}{3}.$

Because the slopes are equal, the lines are parallel. ■

Perpendicular lines are lines that meet at right angles. It can be shown that the slopes of perpendicular lines have a product of $-1$, provided that neither line is vertical. For example, if the slope of a line is $\frac{3}{4}$, then any line perpendicular to it has slope $-\frac{4}{3}$, because $\left(\frac{3}{4}\right)\left(-\frac{4}{3}\right) = -1$.

**Slopes of Perpendicular Lines**

If neither is vertical, two perpendicular lines have slopes that are negative reciprocals—that is, their product is $-1$. Also, two lines with slopes that are negative reciprocals are perpendicular. Every vertical line is perpendicular to every horizontal line.

### EXAMPLE 7 Determining Whether Two Lines Are Perpendicular

Determine whether the lines $L_1$, through $(0, -3)$ and $(2, 0)$, and $L_2$, through $(-3, 0)$ and $(0, -2)$, are perpendicular.

**SOLUTION**

The slope of $L_1$ is $\quad m_1 = \dfrac{0 - (-3)}{2 - 0} = \dfrac{3}{2}.$

The slope of $L_2$ is $\quad m_2 = \dfrac{-2 - 0}{0 - (-3)} = -\dfrac{2}{3}.$

Because the product of the slopes of the two lines is $\frac{3}{2}\left(-\frac{2}{3}\right) = -1$, the lines are perpendicular. ■

**Average Rate of Change** We have seen how the slope of a line is the ratio of the change in $y$ (vertical change) to the change in $x$ (horizontal change). This idea can be extended to real-life situations as follows: the slope gives the average rate of change of $y$ per unit of change in $x$, where the value of $y$ *is dependent upon the value of* $x$. The next example illustrates this idea of average rate of change. We assume a linear relationship between $x$ and $y$.

### EXAMPLE 8 Finding Average Rate of Change

Figure 17 depicts how the purchasing power of the dollar declined from 1990 to 2000, based on changes in the Consumer Price Index. In this model, the base period is 1982–1984. For example, it would have cost \$1.00 to purchase in 1990 what \$.766 would have purchased during the base period. Find the average rate of change in the purchasing power of the dollar during the decade.

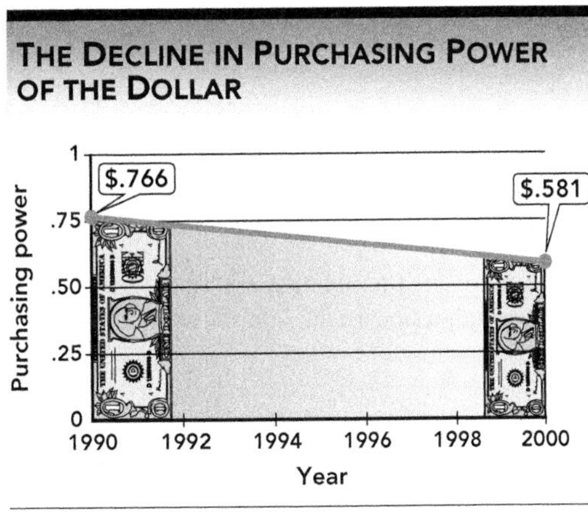


**FIGURE 17**

**SOLUTION**

The average rate of change is found by determining the slope of the line segment. Using $x$ for year and $y$ for purchasing power, the two points indicated are (1990, .766) and (2000, .581). By the slope formula,

$$\text{average rate of change} = \frac{y_2 - y_1}{x_2 - x_1} = \frac{.766 - .581}{1990 - 2000} = \frac{.185}{-10} = -.0185.$$

Because $-.0185$ is approximately $-.02$, we can say that on the average, the purchasing power *dropped* by about 2 cents per year during the decade.

## 8.2 EXERCISES

*Complete the given ordered pairs for each equation. Then graph the equation.*

1. $2x + y = 5$; (0, ), ( , 0), (1, ), ( ,1)
2. $3x - 4y = 24$; (0, ), ( , 0), (6, ), ( , −3)
3. $x - y = 4$; (0, ), ( , 0), (2, ), ( , −1)
4. $x + 3y = 12$; (0, ), ( ,0), (3, ), ( , 6)
5. $4x + 5y = 20$; (0, ), ( , 0), (3, ), ( , 2)
6. $2x - 5y = 12$; (0, ), ( , 0), ( , −2), (−2, )

**7.** $3x + 2y = 8$

| $x$ | $y$ |
|---|---|
| 0 | |
| | 0 |
| 2 | |
| | $-2$ |

**8.** $5x + y = 12$

| $x$ | $y$ |
|---|---|
| 0 | |
| | 0 |
| | $-3$ |
| 2 | |

**9.** Explain how to find the $x$-intercept of a linear equation in two variables.

**10.** Explain how to find the $y$-intercept of a linear equation in two variables.

**11.** Which has a horizontal line as its graph?
**A.** $2y = 6$ **B.** $2x = 6$
**C.** $x - 4 = 0$ **D.** $x + y = 0$

**12.** What is the minimum number of points that must be determined in order to graph a linear equation in two variables?

*For each equation, give the x-intercept and the y-intercept. Then graph the equation.*

**13.** $3x + 2y = 12$ **14.** $2x + 5y = 10$

**15.** $5x + 6y = 10$ **16.** $3y + x = 6$

**17.** $2x - y = 5$ **18.** $3x - 2y = 4$

**19.** $x - 3y = 2$ **20.** $y - 4x = 3$

**21.** $y + x = 0$ **22.** $2x - y = 0$

**23.** $3x = y$ **24.** $x = -4y$

**25.** $x = 2$ **26.** $y = -3$

**27.** $y = 4$ **28.** $x = -2$

*In Exercises 29–36, match the equation with the figure in choices A–D in the next column that most closely resembles its graph.*

**29.** $y + 2 = 0$ **30.** $y + 4 = 0$

**31.** $x + 3 = 0$ **32.** $x + 7 = 0$

**33.** $y - 2 = 0$ **34.** $y - 4 = 0$

**35.** $x - 3 = 0$ **36.** $x - 7 = 0$

**A.** 
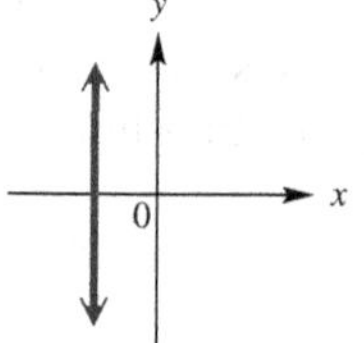

**B.** 
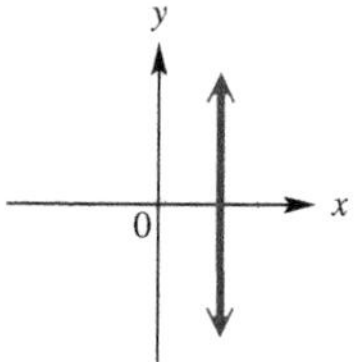

**C.**
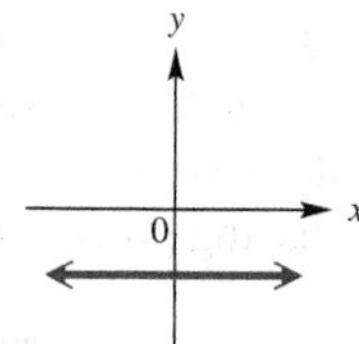

**D.**
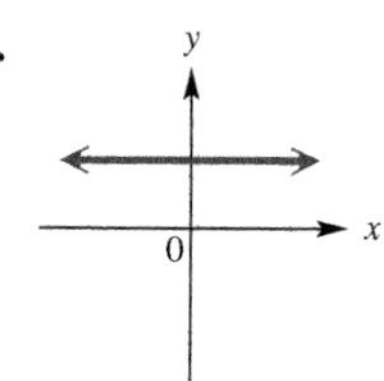

**37.** What is the slope (or pitch) of this roof?

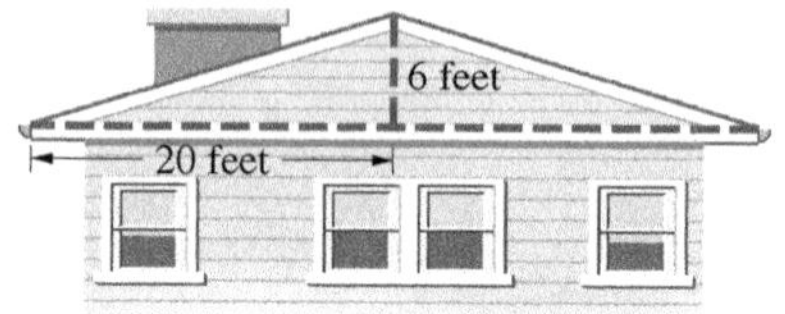


**38.** What is the slope (or grade) of this hill?

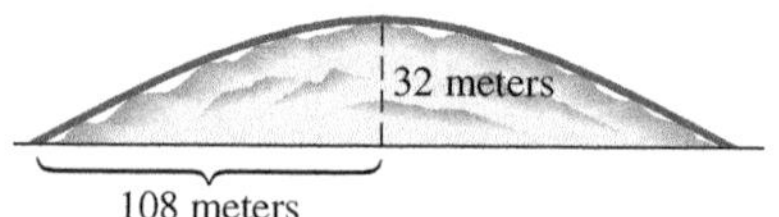


**39.** Use the coordinates of the indicated points to find the slope of each line.

**(a)**
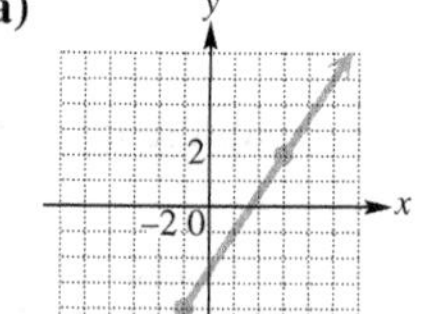

**(b)**
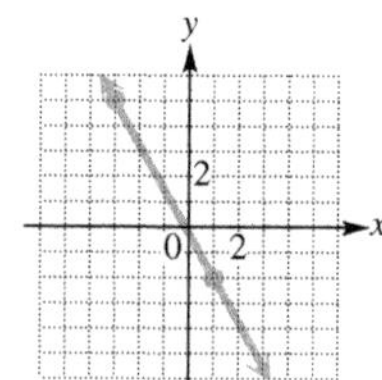

**40.** Tell whether the slope of the given line in (a) – (d) is positive, negative, zero, or undefined.

**(a)**
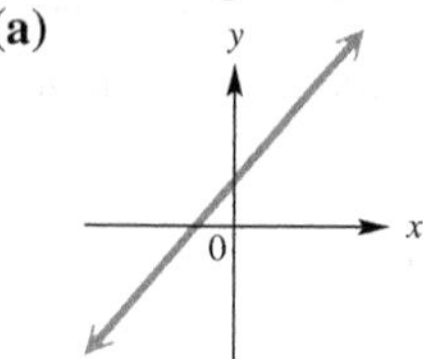

**(b)**
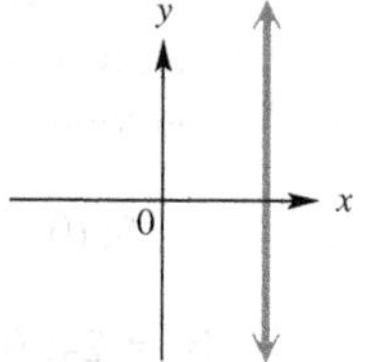

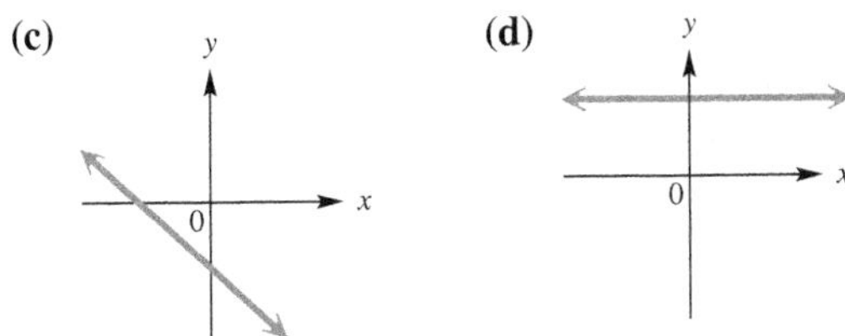


*Find the slope of the line through each pair of points by using the slope formula.*

**41.** $(-2, -3)$ and $(-1, 5)$

**42.** $(-4, 3)$ and $(-3, 4)$

**43.** $(8, 1)$ and $(2, 6)$

**44.** $(13, -3)$ and $(5, 6)$

**45.** $(2, 4)$ and $(-4, 4)$

**46.** $(-6, 3)$ and $(2, 3)$

**47.** ***Public School Data*** Figure A depicts public school enrollment (in thousands) in grades 9–12 in the United States. Figure B in the next column gives the (average) number of public school students per computer.

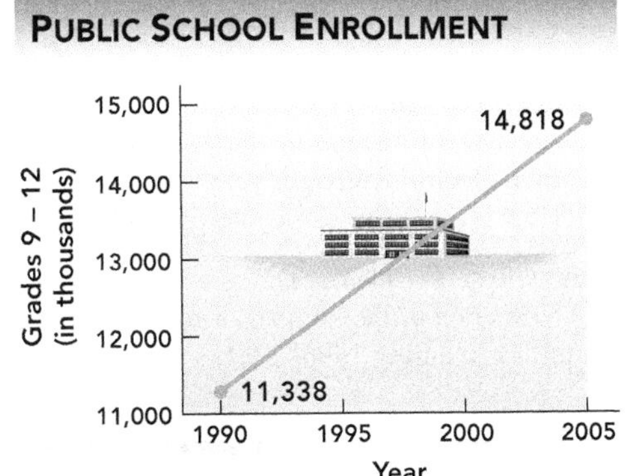


Source: *Digest of Educational Statistics,* annual; and *Projections of Educational Statistics,* annual.

**FIGURE A**

(a) Use the ordered pairs (1990, 11,338) and (2005, 14,818) to find the slope of the line in Figure A.

(b) The slope of the line in Figure A is ________ (positive/negative).
This means that during the period represented, enrollment ____________ (increased/decreased).

(c) The slope of a line represents its *rate of change.* Based on Figure A, what was the increase in students *per year* during the period shown?

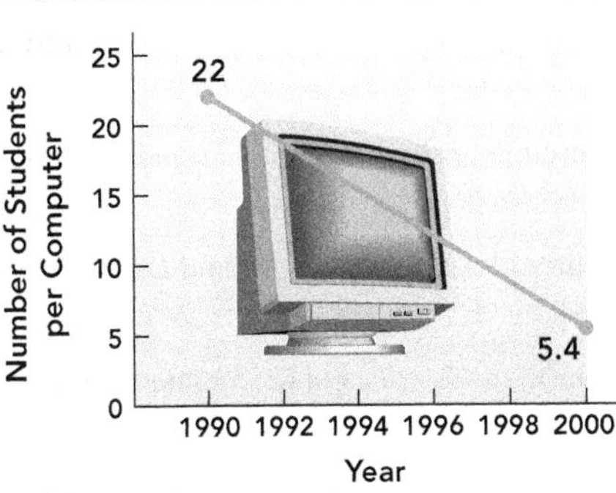


Source: *Quality Education Data.*

**FIGURE B**

(d) Use the given ordered pairs to find the slope of the line in Figure B.

(e) The slope of the line in Figure B is ________ (positive/negative).
This means that during the period represented, the number of students per computer ___________ (increased/decreased).

(f) Based on Figure B, what was the decrease in students per computer *per year* during the period shown?

**48.** Use the results of Exercise 47 to make a connection between the sign of the slope of a line and the increase or decrease in the quantity represented by $y$.

*Use the method of Example 5 to graph each of the following lines.*

**49.** $m = \frac{1}{2}$, through $(-3, 2)$

**50.** $m = \frac{2}{3}$, through $(0, 1)$

**51.** $m = -\frac{5}{4}$, through $(-2, -1)$

**52.** $m = -\frac{3}{2}$, through $(-1, -2)$

**53.** $m = -2$, through $(-1, -4)$

**54.** $m = 3$, through $(1, 2)$

**55.** $m = 0$, through $(2, -5)$

**56.** undefined slope, through $(-3, 1)$

*Determine whether the lines described are* parallel, perpendicular, *or* neither parallel nor perpendicular.

57. $L_1$ through (4, 6) and (−8, 7), and $L_2$ through (7, 4) and (−5, 5)

58. $L_1$ through (9, 15) and (−7, 12), and $L_2$ through (−4, 8) and (−20, 5)

59. $L_1$ through (2, 0) and (5, 4), and $L_2$ through (6, 1) and (2, 4)

60. $L_1$ through (0, −7) and (2, 3), and $L_2$ through (0, −3) and (1, −2)

61. $L_1$ through (0, 1) and (2, −3), and $L_2$ through (10, 8) and (5, 3)

62. $L_1$ through (1, 2) and (−7, −2), and $L_2$ through (1, −1) and (5, −9)

*Use the concept of slope to solve each problem.*

63. ***Steepness of an Upper Deck*** The upper deck at U.S. Cellular Field in Chicago has produced, among other complaints, displeasure with its steepness. It has been compared to a ski jump. It is 160 ft from home plate to the front of the upper deck and 250 ft from home plate to the back. The top of the upper deck is 63 ft above the bottom. What is its slope?

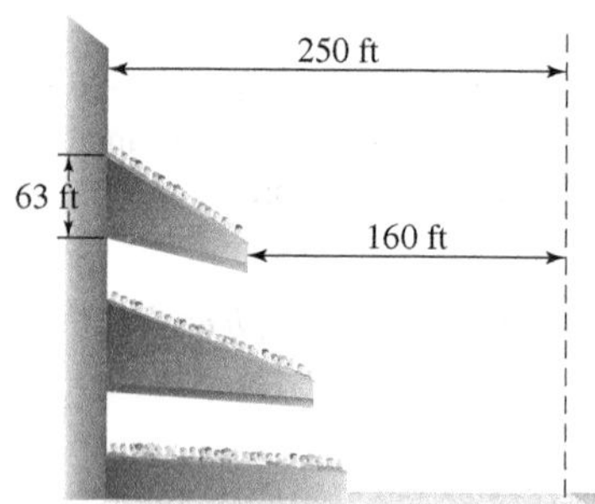


64. ***Grade (Slope) of a Ramp*** When designing the new TD Banknorth Garden arena in Boston to replace the old Boston Garden, architects were careful to design the ramps leading up to the entrances so that circus elephants would be able to walk up the ramps. The maximum grade (or slope) that an elephant will walk on is 13%. Suppose that such a ramp was constructed with a horizontal run of 150 ft. What would be the maximum vertical rise the architects could use?

*Use the idea of average rate of change to solve each problem.*

65. ***Electronic Filing of Tax Returns*** The percent of tax returns filed electronically for the years 1997–2002 is shown in the graph.

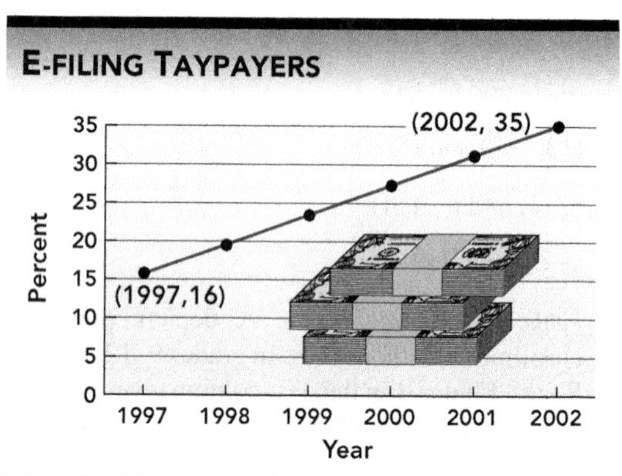


*Source:* Internal Revenue Service.

(a) Use the given ordered pairs to determine the average rate of change in the percent of tax returns filed electronically per year.
(b) How is a positive slope interpreted here?

66. ***Food Stamp Recipients*** The graph provides a good approximation of the number of food stamp recipients (in millions) during 1996–2001.

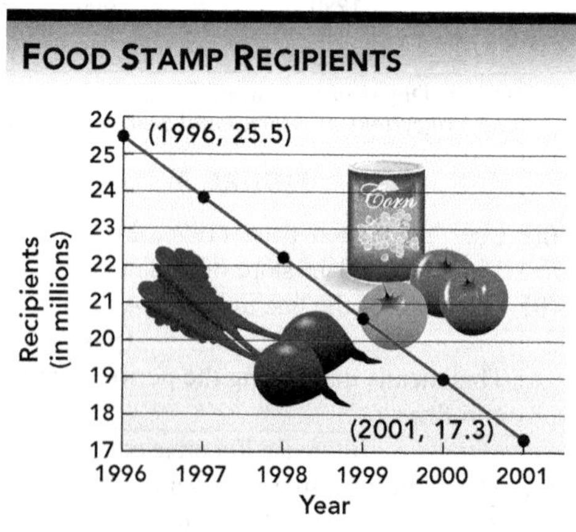


*Source:* U.S. Department of Agriculture.

(a) Use the given ordered pairs to find the average rate of change in food stamp recipients per year during this period.
(b) Interpret the meaning of a negative slope in this situation.

67. ***Book Sales*** The table gives book publishers' revenue for the period 1999–2002.

**Book Publishers' Revenue**

| Year | Revenue (in millions) |
|---|---|
| 1999 | 24,000 |
| 2000 | 25,000 |
| 2001 | 26,000 |
| 2002 | 27,000 |

*Source:* U.S. Census Bureau.

Find the average rate of change for 1999–2000; 2000–2001; 2001–2002. What do you notice about your answers? What does this tell you?

68. ***Cellular Telephone Subscribers*** The table in the next column gives the number of cellular telephone subscribers from 1999 through 2003.

**Cellular Telephone Subscribers**

| Year | Subscribers (in thousands) |
|---|---|
| 1999 | 86,047 |
| 2000 | 109,478 |
| 2001 | 128,375 |
| 2002 | 140,766 |
| 2003 | 158,722 |

*Source:* Cellular Telecommunications Industry Association, Washington, D.C. *State of the Cellular Industry* (Annual).

(a) Find the average rate of change in subscribers from 1999 to 2003.

(b) Is the average rate of change in successive years approximately the same? If the ordered pairs in the table were plotted, could an approximately straight line be drawn through them?

69. Explain the meaning of *slope*. Give examples showing cases of positive, negative, zero, and undefined slope.

70. Explain how the *grade* of a highway corresponds to the slope concept.

# 8.3 Equations of Lines and Linear Models

**Point-Slope Form • Slope-Intercept Form • Summary of Forms of Linear Equations • Linear Models**

## Point-Slope Form

If the slope of a line and a particular point on the line are known, it is possible to find an equation of the line. Suppose that the slope of a line is $m$ and $(x_1, y_1)$ is a particular point on the line. Let $(x, y)$ be any other point on the line. Then, by the definition of slope,

$$m = \frac{y - y_1}{x - x_1}.$$

Multiplying both sides by $x - x_1$ gives the *point-slope form* of the equation of the line.

### Point-Slope Form

The equation of the line through $(x_1, y_1)$ with slope $m$ is written in **point-slope form** as

$$y - y_1 = m(x - x_1).$$

**Maria Gaetana Agnesi** (1719–1799) did much of her mathematical work in coordinate geometry. She grew up in a scholarly atmosphere; her father was a mathematician on the faculty at the University of Bologna. In a larger sense she was an heir to the long tradition of Italian mathematicians.

Maria Agnesi was fluent in several languages by age 13, but she chose mathematics over literature. The curve shown below, called the **witch of Agnesi,** is studied in analytic geometry courses.

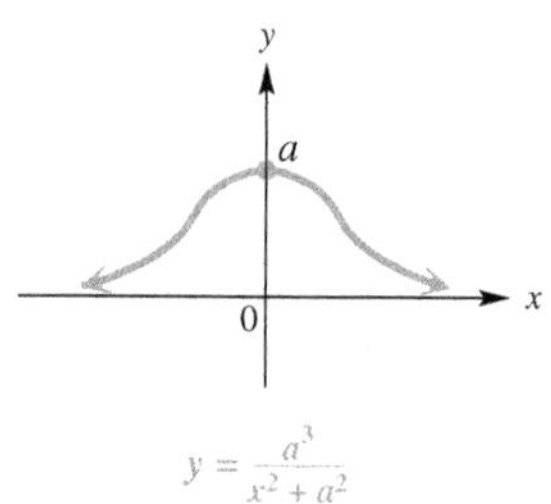


## EXAMPLE 1 Finding an Equation Given the Slope and a Point

Find the standard form of an equation of the line with slope $\frac{1}{3}$, passing through the point $(-2, 5)$.

**SOLUTION**

$$y - y_1 = m(x - x_1) \quad \text{Point-slope form}$$

$$y - 5 = \frac{1}{3}[x - (-2)] \quad \text{Let } (x_1, y_1) = (-2, 5) \text{ and } m = \tfrac{1}{3}.$$

Substitute carefully.

$$y - 5 = \frac{1}{3}(x + 2)$$

$$3y - 15 = x + 2 \quad \text{Multiply by 3.}$$

$$x - 3y = -17 \quad \text{Standard form}$$

If two points on a line are known, it is possible to find an equation of the line. First, find the slope using the slope formula, and then use the slope with one of the given points in the point-slope form.

## EXAMPLE 2 Finding an Equation Given Two Points

Find the standard form of an equation of the line passing through the points $(-4, 3)$ and $(5, -7)$.

**SOLUTION**

First find the slope, using the definition.

$$m = \frac{-7 - 3}{5 - (-4)} = -\frac{10}{9}$$

Either $(-4, 3)$ or $(5, -7)$ may be used as $(x_1, y_1)$ in the point-slope form of the equation of the line. If $(-4, 3)$ is used, then $-4 = x_1$ and $3 = y_1$.

$$y - y_1 = m(x - x_1) \quad \text{Point-slope form}$$

$$y - 3 = -\frac{10}{9}[x - (-4)] \quad (x_1, y_1) = (-4, 3) \text{ and } m = -\tfrac{10}{9}$$

$$y - 3 = -\frac{10}{9}(x + 4)$$

$$9(y - 3) = -10(x + 4) \quad \text{Multiply by 9.}$$

$$9y - 27 = -10x - 40 \quad \text{Distributive property}$$

$$10x + 9y = -13 \quad \text{Standard form}$$

**Slope-Intercept Form** Suppose that the slope $m$ of a line is known, and the $y$-intercept of the line has coordinates $(0, b)$. Then,

$$y - y_1 = m(x - x_1) \quad \text{Point-slope form}$$

$$y - b = m(x - 0) \quad \text{Let } (x_1, y_1) = (0, b).$$

$$y - b = mx$$

$$y = mx + b. \quad \text{Add } b \text{ to both sides.}$$

This last result is known as the *slope-intercept form* of the equation of the line.

### Slope-Intercept Form

The equation of a line with slope $m$ and $y$-intercept $(0, b)$ is written in **slope-intercept form** as

$$y = mx + b.$$

Slope ($m$); $y$-intercept is $(0, b)$.

The importance of the slope-intercept form of a linear equation cannot be overemphasized. First, every linear equation (of a nonvertical line) has a *unique* (one and only one) slope-intercept form. Second, in the next section we will study *linear functions,* where the slope-intercept form is necessary in specifying such functions.

## EXAMPLE 3 Writing an Equation in Slope-Intercept Form

Write each of the following equations in slope-intercept form.

**(a)** the line described in Example 1 **(b)** the line described in Example 2

**SOLUTION**

**(a)** We determined the standard form of the equation of the line to be $x - 3y = -17$. Solve for $y$ to obtain the slope-intercept form.

$$-3y = -x - 17 \quad \text{Subtract } x.$$

$$y = \frac{1}{3}x + \frac{17}{3} \quad \text{Multiply by } -\frac{1}{3}.$$

The slope is $\frac{1}{3}$ and the $y$-intercept is $(0, \frac{17}{3})$.

**(b)** The equation determined in Example 2 is $10x + 9y = -13$.

$$9y = -10x - 13 \quad \text{Subtract } 10x.$$

$$y = -\frac{10}{9}x - \frac{13}{9} \quad \text{Divide by 9.}$$

The slope is $-\frac{10}{9}$ and the $y$-intercept is $(0, -\frac{13}{9})$.

If the slope-intercept form of the equation of a line is known, the method of graphing described in Example 5 of Section 8.2 can be used to graph the line.

## EXAMPLE 4 Graphing a Line Using Slope and $y$-Intercept

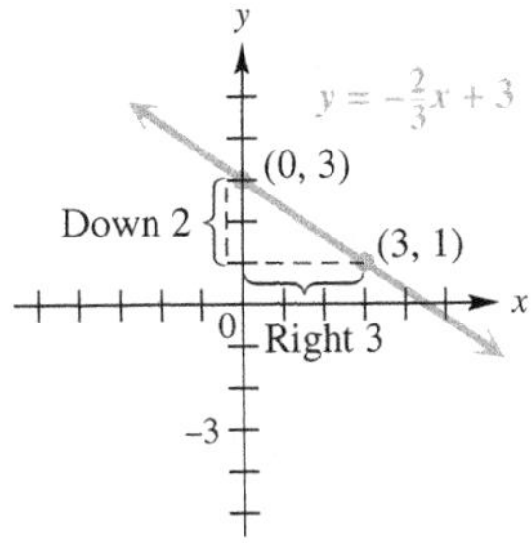


**FIGURE 18**

Graph the line with the equation $y = -\frac{2}{3}x + 3$.

**SOLUTION**

Because the equation is given in slope-intercept form, we can easily see that the slope is $-\frac{2}{3}$ and the $y$-intercept is $(0, 3)$. For now, interpret $-\frac{2}{3}$ as $\frac{-2}{3}$. Plot the point $(0, 3)$, and then, using the "rise over run" interpretation of slope, move *down* 2 units (because of the $-2$ in the numerator of the slope) and to the *right* 3 units (because of the 3 in the denominator). We arrive at the point $(3, 1)$. Plot the point $(3, 1)$, and join the two points with a line, as shown in Figure 18. (We could also have interpreted $-\frac{2}{3}$ as $\frac{2}{-3}$ and obtained a different second point; however, the line would be the same.)

As mentioned in the previous section, parallel lines have the same slope and perpendicular lines have slopes that are negative reciprocals of each other.

### EXAMPLE 5 Finding an Equation Using a Slope Relationship (Parallel Lines)

Find the slope-intercept form of the equation of the line parallel to the graph of $2x + 3y = 6$, passing through the point $(-4, 5)$.

**SOLUTION**

The slope of the line $2x + 3y = 6$, shown in Figure 19, can be found by solving for $y$.

$$2x + 3y = 6$$

$$3y = -2x + 6 \quad \text{Subtract } 2x.$$

$$y = -\frac{2}{3}x + 2 \quad \text{Divide by 3.}$$

↑ Slope

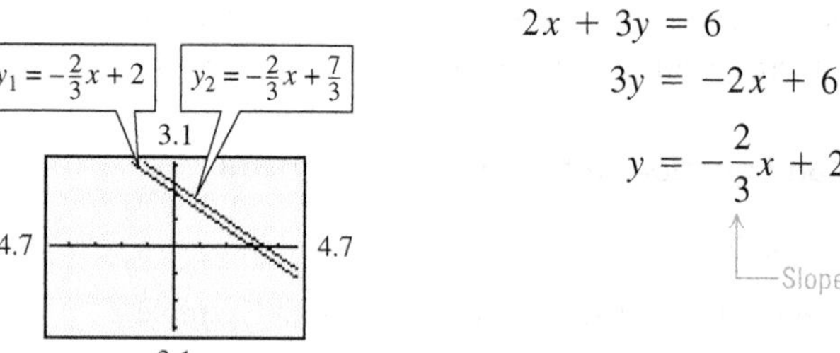


This screen gives support to the result in Example 5.

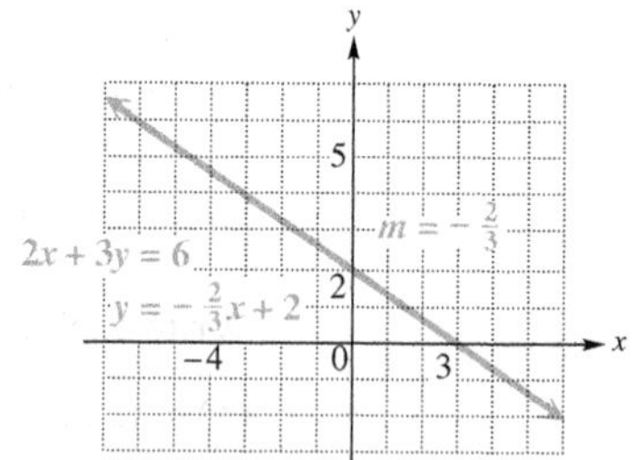


**FIGURE 19**

The slope is given by the coefficient of $x$, so $m = -\frac{2}{3}$. The required equation of the line through $(-4, 5)$ and parallel to $2x + 3y = 6$ must also have slope $-\frac{2}{3}$. To find the required equation, use the point-slope form, with $(x_1, y_1) = (-4, 5)$ and $m = -\frac{2}{3}$.

$$y - 5 = -\frac{2}{3}[x - (-4)] \quad y_1 = 5,\ m = -\frac{2}{3},\ x_1 = -4$$

$$y - 5 = -\frac{2}{3}(x + 4)$$

$$y - 5 = -\frac{2}{3}x - \frac{8}{3} \quad \text{Distributive property}$$

$$y = -\frac{2}{3}x - \frac{8}{3} + \frac{15}{3} \quad \text{Add } 5 = \frac{15}{3}.$$

$$y = -\frac{2}{3}x + \frac{7}{3} \quad \text{Combine like terms.}$$

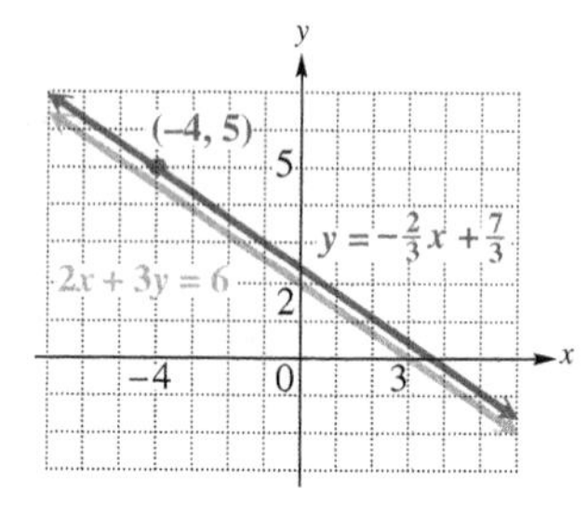


**FIGURE 20**

We did not clear fractions after the substitution step here because we want the equation in slope-intercept form—that is, solved for $y$. Both lines are shown in Figure 20.

### EXAMPLE 6 Finding an Equation Using a Slope Relationship (Perpendicular Lines)

Find the slope-intercept form of the equation of the line perpendicular to the graph of $2x + 3y = 6$, passing through the point $(-4, 5)$.

**SOLUTION**

In Example 5 we found that the slope of the line $2x + 3y = 6$ is $-\frac{2}{3}$. To be perpendicular to it, a line must have a slope that is the negative reciprocal of $-\frac{2}{3}$, which is $\frac{3}{2}$. Use the point $(-4, 5)$ and slope $\frac{3}{2}$ in the point-slope form to obtain the equation of the perpendicular line shown in Figure 21 on the next page.

$$y - 5 = \frac{3}{2}[x - (-4)] \quad y_1 = 5, m = \frac{3}{2}, x_1 = -4$$

$$y - 5 = \frac{3}{2}(x + 4)$$

$$y - 5 = \frac{3}{2}x + 6 \quad \text{Distributive property}$$

$$y = \frac{3}{2}x + 11 \quad \text{Add 5.}$$

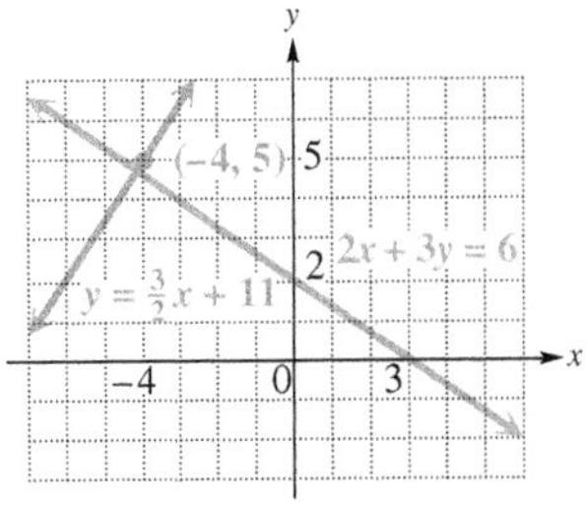

**FIGURE 21**

**Summary of Forms of Linear Equations** A summary of the various forms of linear equations from this section and the previous one follows.

### Summary of Forms of Linear Equations

| | |
|---|---|
| $Ax + By = C$ | **Standard form** (Neither $A$ nor $B$ is 0.) |
| $x = a$ | **Vertical line** Undefined slope and the $x$-intercept is $(a, 0)$. |
| $y = b$ | **Horizontal line** Slope is 0 and the $y$-intercept is $(0, b)$. |
| $y = mx + b$ | **Slope-intercept form** Slope is $m$ and the $y$-intercept is $(0, b)$. |
| $y - y_1 = m(x - x_1)$ | **Point-slope form** Slope is $m$ and the line passes through $(x_1, y_1)$. |

**Linear Models** Earlier examples and exercises gave equations that described real data. Now we show how such equations can be found. The process of writing an equation to fit a graph is called *curve-fitting*. The next example illustrates this concept for a straight line. The resulting equation is called a **linear model.**

**TABLE 1**

| Year | Cost (in billions) |
|---|---|
| 2002 | 264 |
| 2003 | 281 |
| 2004 | 299 |
| 2005 | 318 |
| 2006 | 336 |
| 2007 | 354 |

*Source:* U.S. Center for Medicare and Medicaid Services.

### EXAMPLE 7 Modeling Medicare Costs

Estimates for Medicare costs (in billions of dollars) are shown in Table 1.

**(a)** Graph the data. Let $x = 0$ correspond to 2002, $x = 1$ to 2003, and so on. What type of equation might model the data?

**(b)** Find a linear equation that models the data.

**(c)** Use the equation from part (b) to predict Medicare costs in 2010.

**SOLUTION**

**(a)** Because $x = 0$ corresponds to 2002, $x = 1$ corresponds to 2003, and so on, the data points can be expressed as the ordered pairs

$$(0, 264), \quad (1, 281), \quad (2, 299), \quad (3, 318), \quad (4, 336), \quad \text{and} \quad (5, 354).$$

The data are graphed in Figure 22 and appear to be approximately linear, so a linear equation is appropriate.

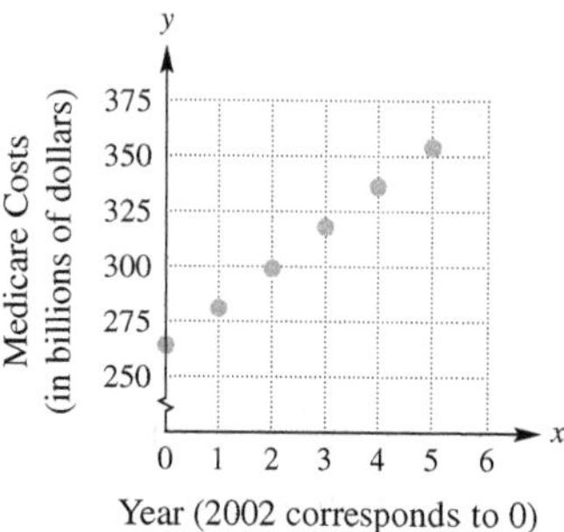


**FIGURE 22**

**(b)** We start by choosing two data points that the line should pass through. For example, if we use (0, 264) and (3, 318), then the slope of the line is

Start with the x- and y-values of the same point.

$$m = \frac{318 - 264}{3 - 0} = 18.$$

The point (0, 264) indicates that the value of $b$ is **264**. Thus,

$$y = 18x + \mathbf{264}.$$

The slope $m = 18$ indicates that Medicare costs might increase, on average, by \$18 billion per year.

**(c)** The value $x = 8$ corresponds to the year 2010. When $x = 8$,

$$y = 18(8) + 264 = \mathbf{408}.$$

This model predicts that Medicare costs will reach \$408 billion in 2010.

The equation $y = 18x + 264$ found in Example 7 is not unique. If two different points are chosen, a different equation may result. However, all such equations should be in approximate agreement for linear data points.

## 8.3 EXERCISES

*Match each equation in Column I with the correct description given in Column II.*

| I | II |
|---|---|
| **1.** $y = 4x$ | **A.** slope $= -2$, through the point (4, 1) |
| **2.** $y = \frac{1}{4}x$ | **B.** slope $= -2$, $y$-intercept (0, 1) |
| **3.** $y = -2x + 1$ | **C.** passing through the points (0, 0) and (4, 1) |
| **4.** $y - 1 = -2(x - 4)$ | **D.** passing through the points (0, 0) and (1, 4) |

*Use the geometric interpretation of slope* (rise *divided by* run) *to find the slope of each line. Then, by identifying the y-intercept from the graph, write the slope-intercept form of the equation of the line.*

**5.**

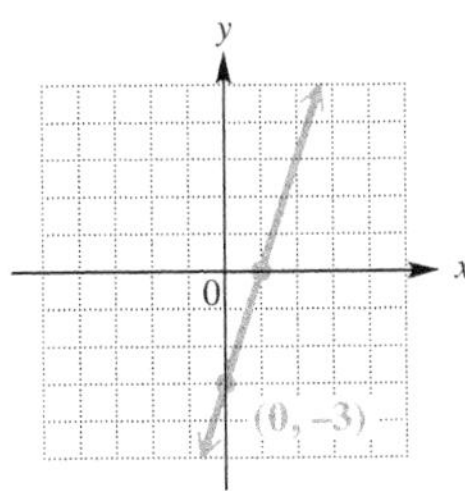


**6.**

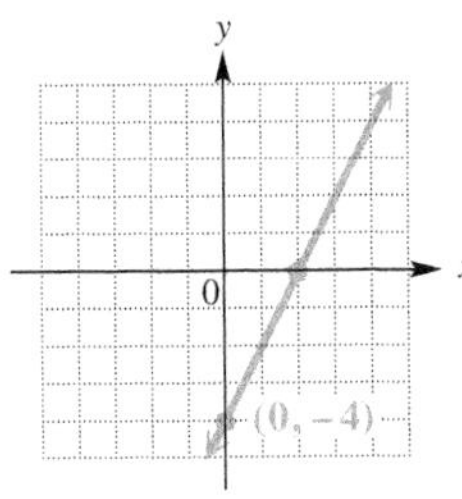


**7.**

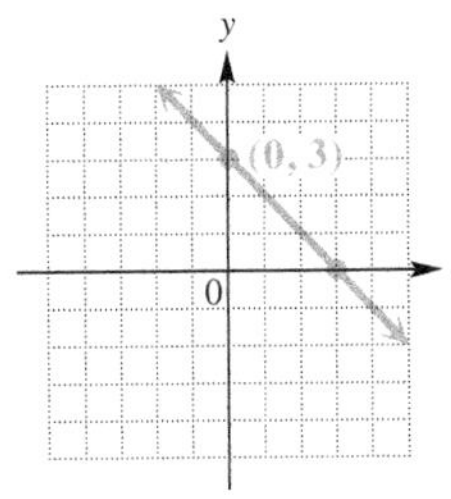


**8.**

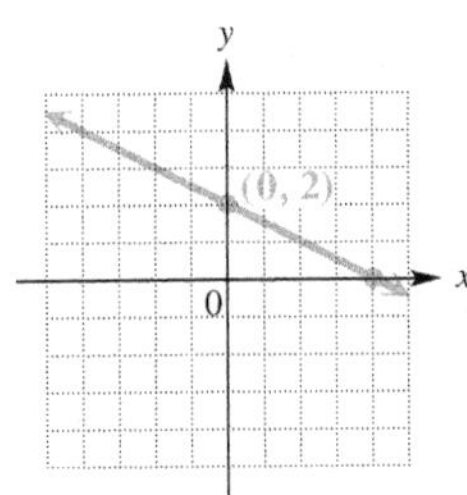


*In Exercises 9–16, match each equation with the graph that it most closely resembles in Choices A–H. (Hint: Determining the signs of m and b will help you make your decision.)*

**9.** $y = 2x + 3$ **10.** $y = -2x + 3$ **11.** $y = -2x - 3$ **12.** $y = 2x - 3$

**13.** $y = 2x$ **14.** $y = -2x$ **15.** $y = 3$ **16.** $y = -3$

**A.**

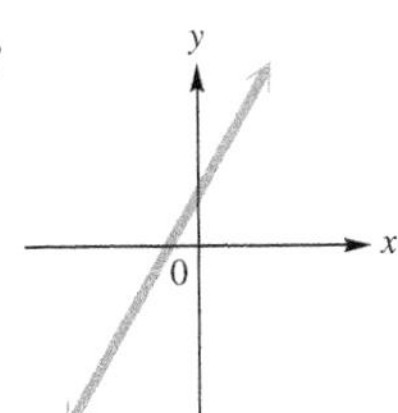

**B.**

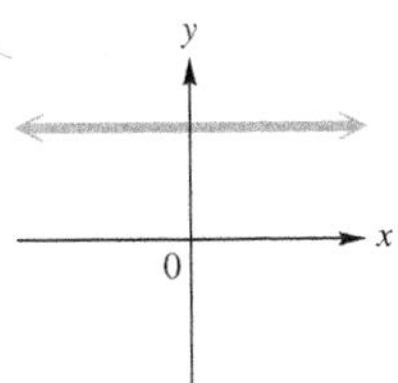

**C.**

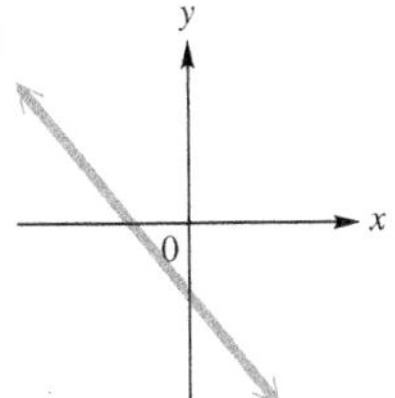

**D.**

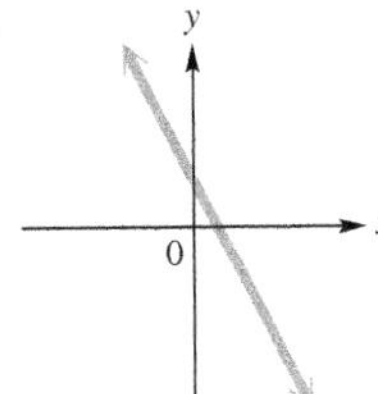

**E.**

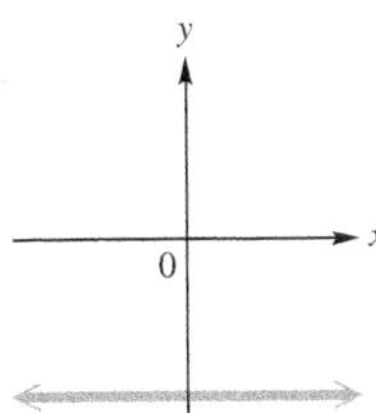

**F.**

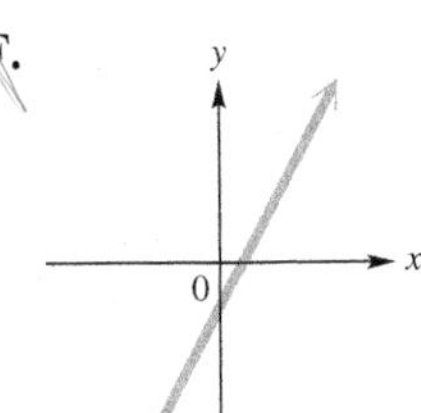

**G.**

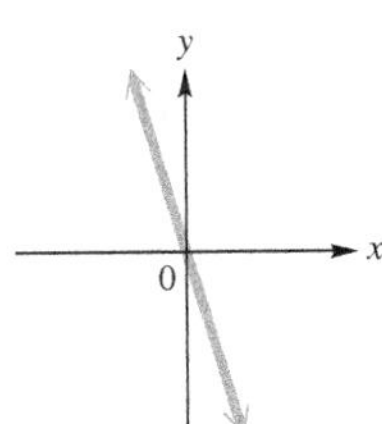

**H.**

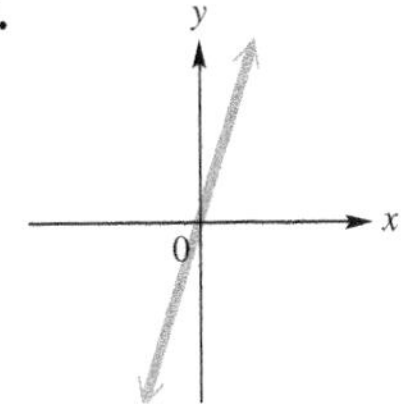

*Write the slope-intercept form of the equation of the line satisfying the given conditions.*

**17.** Through $(-2, 4)$; slope $-\frac{3}{4}$

**18.** Through $(-1, 6)$; slope $-\frac{5}{6}$

**19.** Through $(5, 8)$; slope $-2$

**20.** Through $(12, 10)$; slope 1

**21.** Through $(-5, 4)$; slope $\frac{1}{2}$

**22.** Through $(7, -2)$; slope $\frac{1}{4}$

**23.** $x$-intercept $(3, 0)$; slope 4

**24.** $x$-intercept $(-2, 0)$; slope $-5$

*Write an equation for a line that satisfies the given conditions.*

**25.** Through $(9, 5)$; slope 0

**26.** Through $(-4, -2)$; slope 0

**27.** Through $(9, 10)$; undefined slope

**28.** Through $(-2, 8)$; undefined slope

**29.** Through (.5, .2); vertical

**30.** Through $\left(\frac{5}{8}, \frac{2}{9}\right)$; vertical

**31.** Through $(-7, 8)$; horizontal

**32.** Through (2, 7); horizontal

*Write the equation, in slope-intercept form if possible, of the line passing through the two points.*

**33.** (3, 4) and (5, 8)

**34.** $(5, -2)$ and $(-3, 14)$

**35.** (6, 1) and $(-2, 5)$

**36.** $(-2, 5)$ and $(-8, 1)$

**37.** $\left(-\frac{2}{5}, \frac{2}{5}\right)$ and $\left(\frac{4}{3}, \frac{2}{3}\right)$

**38.** $\left(\frac{3}{4}, \frac{8}{3}\right)$ and $\left(\frac{2}{5}, \frac{2}{3}\right)$

**39.** (2, 5) and (1, 5)

**40.** $(-2, 2)$ and (4, 2)

**41.** (7, 6) and $(7, -8)$

**42.** (13, 5) and $(13, -1)$

**43.** $(1, -3)$ and $(-1, -3)$

**44.** $(-4, 6)$ and (5, 6)

*Find the equation in slope-intercept form of the line satisfying the given conditions.*

**45.** $m = 5$; $b = 15$

**46.** $m = -2$; $b = 12$

**47.** $m = -\frac{2}{3}$; $b = \frac{4}{5}$

**48.** $m = -\frac{5}{8}$; $b = -\frac{1}{3}$

**49.** Slope $\frac{2}{5}$; $y$-intercept (0, 5)

**50.** Slope $-\frac{3}{4}$; $y$-intercept (0, 7)

**51.** Explain why the point-slope form of an equation cannot be used to find the equation of a vertical line.

**52.** Which one of the following equations is in standard form, according to the definition of standard form given in this text?
**A.** $3x + 2y - 6 = 0$ **B.** $y = 5x - 12$
**C.** $2y = 3x + 4$ **D.** $6x - 5y = 12$

*For each equation* **(a)** *write in slope-intercept form,* **(b)** *give the slope of the line, and* **(c)** *give the y-intercept.*

**53.** $x + y = 12$

**54.** $x - y = 14$

**55.** $5x + 2y = 20$

**56.** $6x + 5y = 40$

**57.** $2x - 3y = 10$

**58.** $4x - 3y = 10$

*Write the equation in slope-intercept form of the line satisfying the given conditions.*

**59.** Through (7, 2); parallel to $3x - y = 8$

**60.** Through (4, 1); parallel to $2x + 5y = 10$

**61.** Through $(-2, -2)$; parallel to $-x + 2y = 10$

**62.** Through $(-1, 3)$; parallel to $-x + 3y = 12$

**63.** Through (8, 5); perpendicular to $2x - y = 7$

**64.** Through $(2, -7)$; perpendicular to $5x + 2y = 18$

**65.** Through $(-2, 7)$; perpendicular to $x = 9$

**66.** Through (8, 4); perpendicular to $x = -3$

*Solve each problem.*

67. ***Private 4-year College Costs*** The table lists the average annual cost (in dollars) of tuition and fees at private 4-year colleges for selected years, where year 0 represents 1990, year 5 represents 1995, and so on.

**Private College Costs**

| Year | Cost (in dollars) |
|---|---|
| 0 | 9391 |
| 5 | 12,432 |
| 9 | 15,380 |
| 14 | 20,082 |

*Source:* The College Board.

(a) Plot the four ordered pairs (year, cost). Do the points lie in approximately a straight line?
(b) Use the ordered pairs (0, 9391) and (14, 20,082) to find the equation of a line that approximates the data. Write the equation in slope-intercept form. (Round the slope to the nearest tenth.)
(c) Use the equation from part (b) to estimate the average annual cost at private 4-year colleges in 2008.

68. ***Nuclear Waste*** The table gives the heavy metal nuclear waste (in thousands of metric tons) from spent reactor fuel stored temporarily at reactor sites, awaiting permanent storage. (*Source*: "Burial of Radioactive Nuclear Waste under the Seabed," *Scientific American*, January 1998, p. 62.)

**Heavy Metal Nuclear Waste**

| Year $x$ | Waste $y$ |
|---|---|
| 1995 | 32 |
| 2000* | 42 |
| 2010* | 61 |
| 2020* | 76 |

*Estimates by the U.S. Department of Energy.

Let $x = 0$ represent 1995, $x = 5$ represent 2000 (since $2000 - 1995 = 5$), and so on.
(a) Plot the ordered pairs $(x, y)$. Do the points lie approximately in a line?
(b) Use the ordered pairs (0, 32) and (25, 76) to find the equation of a line that approximates the other ordered pairs. Use the form $y = mx + b$.
(c) Use the equation from part (b) to estimate the amount of nuclear waste in 2008.

69. ***U.S. Post Offices*** The number of post offices in the United States has been declining. Use the information given on the bar graph for the years 1990 and 2000, letting $x = 0$ represent the year 1990 and $y$ represent the number of post offices.

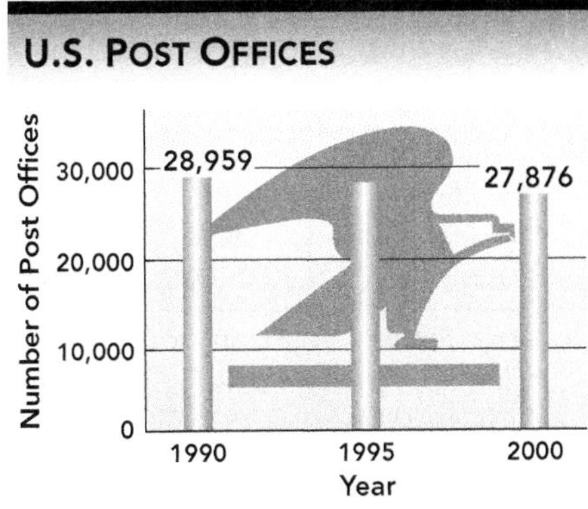


*Source:* U.S. Postal Service, *Annual Report of the Postmaster General.*

(a) Find a linear equation that models the data. Write it in slope-intercept form.
(b) Predict the number of post offices in 2005 using the model for part (a).

70. ***Air Conditioner Choices*** The graph shows the recommended air conditioner size (in British thermal units) for selected room sizes in square feet. Use the information given for rooms of 150 square feet and 1400 square feet. Let $x$ represent the number of square feet and $y$ represent the corresponding Btu size air conditioner. Find a linear equation that models the data. Write it in slope-intercept form.

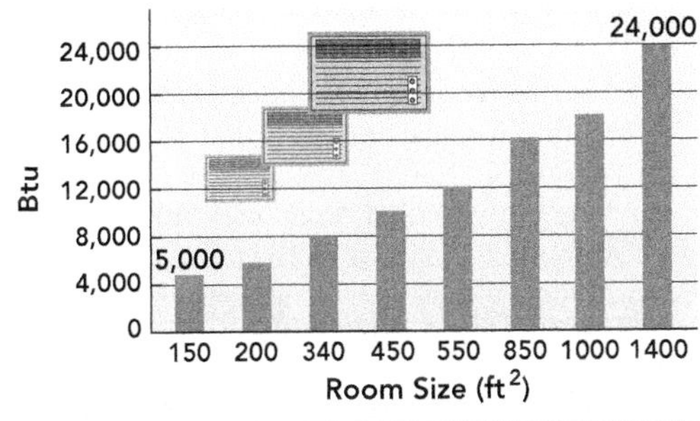


*Source:* Carey, Morris and James, *Home Improvement for Dummies*, IDG Books.

71. ***Distant Galaxies*** In the late 1920s, the famous observational astronomer Edwin P. Hubble (1889–1953) determined the distances to several galaxies and the velocities at which they were receding from Earth. Four galaxies with their distances in light-years and velocities in miles per second are listed in the table.

| Galaxy | Distance | Velocity |
|---|---|---|
| Virgo | 50 | 990 |
| Ursa Minor | 650 | 9,300 |
| Corona Borealis | 950 | 15,000 |
| Bootes | 1,700 | 25,000 |

*Source:* Sharov, A., and I. Novikov, *Edwin Hubble, the Discoverer of the Big Bang Universe,* Cambridge University Press, 1993.

(a) Let $x$ represent distance and $y$ represent velocity. Use the data for Virgo and Bootes to find an equation of a line that models the data.

(b) If the galaxy Hydra is receding at a speed of 37,000 miles per second, estimate its distance from Earth, using the equation from part (a).

72. ***Heights and Weights of Men*** A sample of 10 adult men gave the following data on their heights and weights:

| Height, $x$ (in inches) | Weight, $y$ (in pounds) |
|---|---|
| 61 | 120 |
| 62 | 140 |
| 63 | 130 |
| 65 | 150 |
| 66 | 142 |
| 67 | 130 |
| 68 | 135 |
| 69 | 175 |
| 70 | 149 |
| 72 | 168 |

(a) Use the data for the shortest and tallest two men to find a linear equation that models height vs. weight.

(b) Use the equation from part (a) to predict the weight of a man 74 inches tall.

73. ***Fahrenheit-Celsius Relationship*** If we think of ordered pairs of the form (C, F), then the two most common methods of measuring temperature, Celsius and Fahrenheit, can be related as follows: When C = 0, F = 32, and when C = 100, F = 212. This exercise explains how this information is used to find the formula that relates the two temperature scales.

(a) There is a linear relationship between Celsius and Fahrenheit temperatures. When C = 0°, F = ___, and when C = 100°, F = ____.

(b) Think of ordered pairs of temperatures (C, F), where C and F represent corresponding Celsius and Fahrenheit temperatures. The equation that relates the two scales has a straight-line graph that contains the two points determined in part (a). What are these two points?

(c) Find the slope of the line described in part (b).

(d) Think of the point-slope form of the equation in terms of C and F, where C replaces $x$ and F replaces $y$. Use the slope from part (c) and one of the two points determined earlier to find the equation that gives F in terms of C.

(e) To obtain another form of the formula, use the equation you found in part (d) and solve for C in terms of F.

(f) The equation found in part (d) is graphed on the graphing calculator screen shown here. Observe the display at the bottom, and interpret it in the context of this exercise.

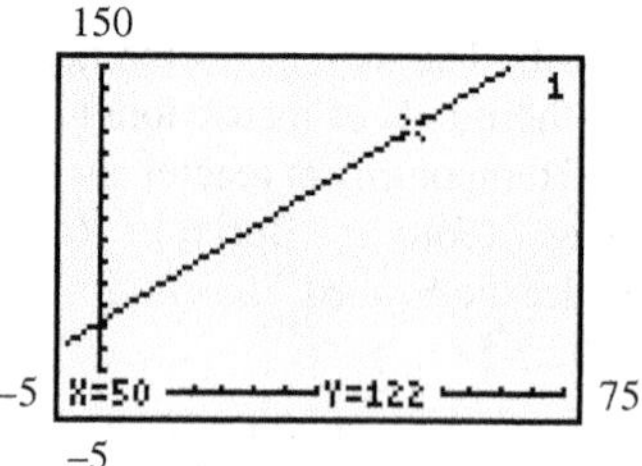


74. A table of points, generated by a graphing calculator, is shown for a line $Y_1$. Use any two points to find the equation of each line in slope-intercept form.

(a)

| X | $Y_1$ |
|---|---|
| -2 | -.5 |
| -1 | .25 |
| 0 | 1 |
| 1 | 1.75 |
| 2 | 2.5 |
| 3 | 3.25 |
| 4 | 4 |

X= -2

(b)

| X | $Y_1$ |
|---|---|
| -4 | 14 |
| -3 | 10 |
| -2 | 6 |
| -1 | 2 |
| 0 | -2 |
| 1 | -6 |
| 2 | -10 |

X= -4

# 8.4 An Introduction to Functions: Linear Functions, Applications, and Models

**Relations and Functions • Domain and Range • Graphs of Relations • Graphs of Functions • Function Notation • Linear Functions • Modeling with Linear Functions**

## Relations and Functions

We often describe one quantity in terms of another; for example, the growth of a plant is related to the amount of light it receives, the demand for a product is related to the price of the product, the cost of a trip is related to the distance traveled, and so on. To represent these corresponding quantities, we can use ordered pairs.

For example, suppose that it is time to fill up your car's tank with gasoline. At your local station, 89-octane gas is selling for \$3.10 per gallon. Experience has taught you that the final price you pay is determined by the number of gallons you buy multiplied by the price per gallon (in this case, \$3.10). As you pump the gas, two sets of numbers spin by: the number of gallons pumped and the price for that number of gallons. Table 2 uses ordered pairs to illustrate this situation.

**TABLE 2**

| Number of Gallons Pumped | Price for This Number of Gallons |
|---|---|
| 0 | \$0.00 = 0 (\$3.10) |
| 1 | \$3.10 = 1 (\$3.10) |
| 2 | \$6.20 = 2 (\$3.10) |
| 3 | \$9.30 = 3 (\$3.10) |
| 4 | \$12.40 = 4 (\$3.10) |

If we let $x$ denote the number of gallons pumped, then the price $y$ in dollars can be found by the linear equation $y = 3.10x$. Theoretically, there are infinitely many ordered pairs $(x, y)$ that satisfy this equation, but in this application we are limited to nonnegative values for $x$, since we cannot have a negative number of gallons. There also is a practical maximum value for $x$ in this situation, which varies from one car to another. What determines this maximum value?

In this example, the total price depends on the amount of gasoline pumped. For this reason, price is called the *dependent variable*, and the number of gallons is called the *independent variable*. Generalizing, if the value of the variable $y$ depends on the value of the variable $x$, then $y$ is the **dependent variable** and $x$ the **independent variable.**

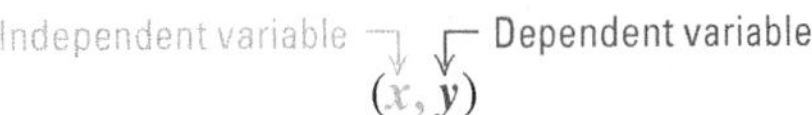


Because related quantities can be written using ordered pairs, the concept of *relation* can be defined as follows.

**Relation**

A **relation** is a set of ordered pairs.

For example, the sets

$$F = \{(1, 2), (-2, 5), (3, -1)\} \quad \text{and} \quad G = \{(-4, 1), (-2, 1), (-2, 0)\}$$

both are relations. A special kind of relation, called a *function*, is very important in mathematics and its applications.

**Function**

A **function** is a relation in which for each value of the first component of the ordered pairs there is *exactly one value* of the second component.

Of the two examples of a relation just given, only set $F$ is a function, because for each $x$-value, there is exactly one $y$-value. In set $G$, the last two ordered pairs have the same $x$-value paired with two different $y$-values, so $G$ is a relation, but not a function.

$$F = \{(1, 2), (-2, 5), (3, -1)\} \quad \text{Function}$$

Different $x$-values

$$G = \{(-4, 1), (-2, 1), (-2, 0)\} \quad \text{Not a function}$$

Same $x$-values

***In a function, there is exactly one value of the dependent variable, the second component, for each value of the independent variable, the first component.***

Another way to think of a functional relationship is to think of the independent variable as an input and the dependent variable as an output. A calculator is an input-output machine, for example. To find $8^2$, we must input 8, press the squaring key, and see that the output is 64. Inputs and outputs also can be determined from a graph or a table.

A third way to describe a function is to give a rule that tells how to determine the dependent variable for a specific value of the independent variable. Suppose the rule is given in words as "the dependent variable is twice the independent variable." As an equation, this can be written

$$y = 2x.$$

Dependent variable ($y$) — Independent variable ($x$)

## EXAMPLE 1 Determining Independent and Dependent Variables

Determine the independent and dependent variables for each of the following functions. Give an example of an ordered pair belonging to the function.

**(a)** The years and locations of the three summer Olympic Games prior to the 2004 games by the relation $\{(1992, \text{Barcelona}), (1996, \text{Atlanta}), (2000, \text{Sydney})\}$

**(b)** The procedure by which someone uses a calculator that finds square roots

**TABLE 3**

**U.S. Refined Petroleum Product Imports**

| Year | Imports (millions of barrels) |
|---|---|
| 1998 | 731 |
| 1999 | 775 |
| 2000 | 872 |
| 2001 | 928 |
| 2002 | 844 |

*Source:* American Petroleum Institute.

(c) The graph in Figure 23 that shows the relationship between the number of gallons of water in a small swimming pool and time in hours

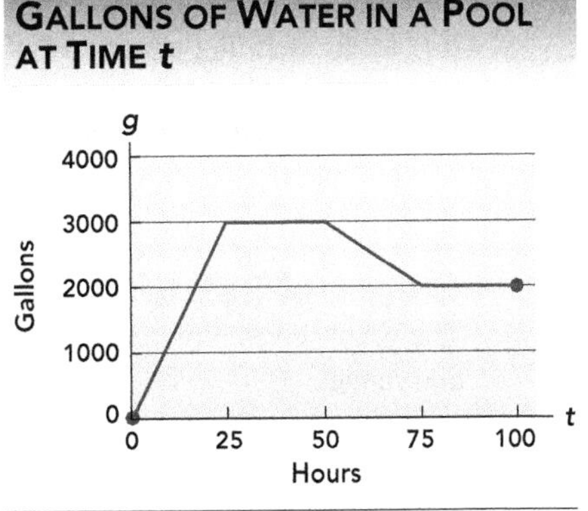


**FIGURE 23**

(d) The table of petroleum imports shown in Table 3

(e) $y = 3x + 4$

**SOLUTION**

(a) The independent variable (the first component in each ordered pair) is the year. The dependent variable (the second component) is the city. For example, (1996, Atlanta) belongs to this function.

(b) The independent variable (the input) is a nonnegative real number, because the square root of a negative number is not a real number. The dependent variable (the output) is the nonnegative square root. For example, (81, 9) belongs to this function.

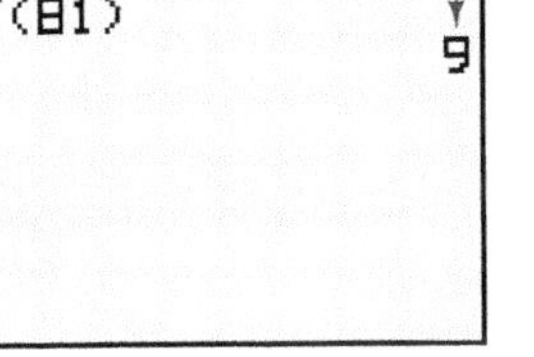


(c) The independent variable is time, in hours, and the dependent variable is the number of the gallons of water in the pool. One ordered pair is (25, 3000).

(d) The independent variable is the year and the dependent variable is the number of millions of barrels. An example of an ordered pair is (2000, 872).

(e) The independent variable is $x$, and the dependent variable is $y$. One ordered pair is (1, 7).

## Domain and Range

**Domain and Range**

In a relation, the set of all values of the independent variable ($x$) is the **domain.** The set of all values of the dependent variable ($y$) is the **range.**

### EXAMPLE 2 Determining Domain and Range

Give the domain and range of each function in Example 1.

**SOLUTION**

(a) The domain is the set of years, {1992, 1996, 2000}, and the range is the set of cities, {Barcelona, Atlanta, Sydney}.

(b) The domain is restricted to nonnegative numbers: $[0, \infty)$. The range also is $[0, \infty)$.

**(c)** The domain is all possible values of $t$, the time in hours, which is the interval [0, 100]. The range is the number of gallons at time $t$, the interval [0, 3000].

**(d)** The domain is the set of years, {1998, 1999, 2000, 2001, 2002}. The range is the set of import values (in millions of barrels), {731, 775, 872, 928, 844}.

**(e)** In the defining equation (or rule), $y = 3x + 4$, $x$ can be any real number, so the domain is $\{x|x \text{ is a real number}\}$, or $(-\infty, \infty)$. Because every real number $y$ can be produced by some value of $x$, the range also is the set $\{y|y \text{ is a real number}\}$, or $(-\infty, \infty)$.

## Graphs of Relations

The **graph of a relation** is the graph of its ordered pairs. The graph gives a picture of the relation, which can be used to determine its domain and range.

### EXAMPLE 3 Determining Domain and Range

Give the domain and range of each relation.

**(a)**

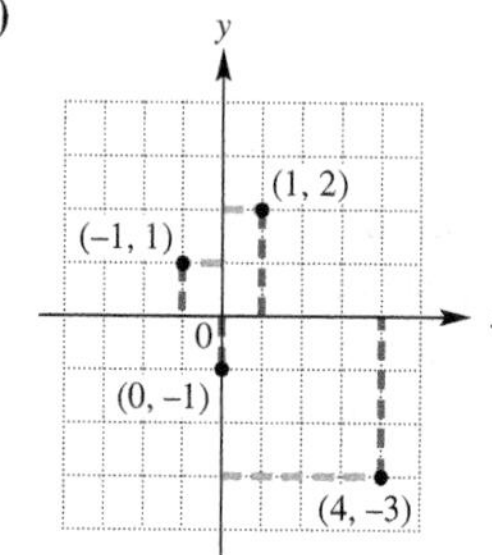


**(b)**

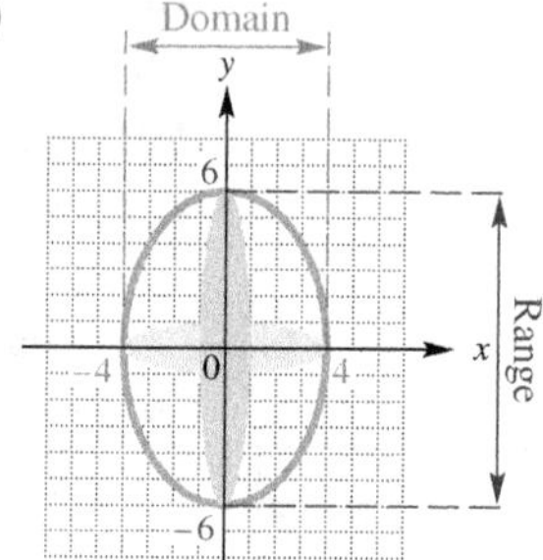


**(c)**

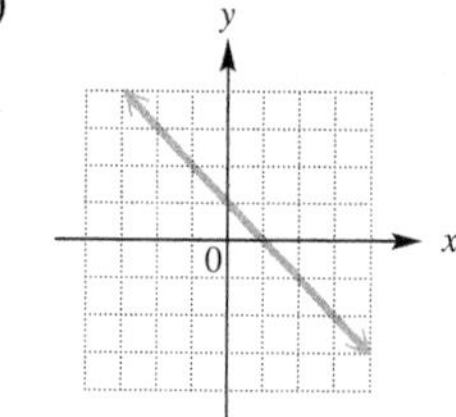


**(d)**

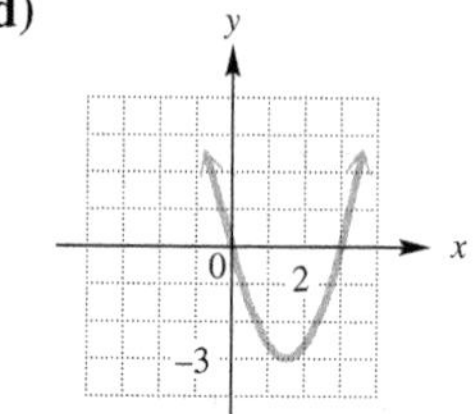


**SOLUTION**

**(a)** The domain is the set of $x$-values, $\{-1, 0, 1, 4\}$, and the range is the set of $y$-values, $\{-3, -1, 1, 2\}$.

**(b)** The $x$-values of the points on the graph include all numbers between $-4$ and 4, inclusive. The $y$-values include all numbers between $-6$ and 6, inclusive. Using interval notation, the domain is $[-4, 4]$ and the range is $[-6, 6]$.

**(c)** The arrowheads indicate that the line extends indefinitely left and right, as well as up and down. Therefore, both the domain and the range are the set of all real numbers, written $(-\infty, \infty)$.

**(d)** The arrowheads indicate that the graph extends indefinitely left and right, as well as upward. The domain is $(-\infty, \infty)$. Because there is a least $y$-value, $-3$, the range includes all real numbers greater than or equal to $-3$, written $[-3, \infty)$.

We have seen that relations can be defined by equations, such as $y = 2x + 3$ and $y^2 = x$. It is sometimes necessary to determine the domain of a relation from its equation. In this book, the following agreement on the domain of a relation is assumed.

**Agreement on Domain**

The domain of a relation is assumed to be all real numbers that produce real numbers when substituted for the independent variable.

To illustrate this agreement, because any real number can be used as a replacement for $x$ in $y = 2x + 3$, the domain of this function is the set of real numbers. As another example, the function defined by $y = \frac{1}{x}$ has all real numbers except 0 as domain, because $y$ is undefined only if $x = 0$. In general, the domain of a function defined by an algebraic expression is all real numbers, except those numbers that lead to division by 0 or an even root of a negative number.

## Graphs of Functions

Most of the relations we have seen in the examples are functions—that is, each $x$-value corresponds to exactly one $y$-value. Now we look at ways to determine whether a given relation, defined algebraically, is a function.

In a function each value of $x$ leads to only one value of $y$, so any vertical line drawn through the graph of a function must intersect the graph in at most one point. This is the **vertical line test for a function.**

**Vertical Line Test**

If a vertical line intersects the graph of a relation in more than one point, then the relation is not a function.

For example, the graph shown in Figure 24(a) is not the graph of a function, since a vertical line can intersect the graph in more than one point, while the graph in Figure 24(b) does represent a function.

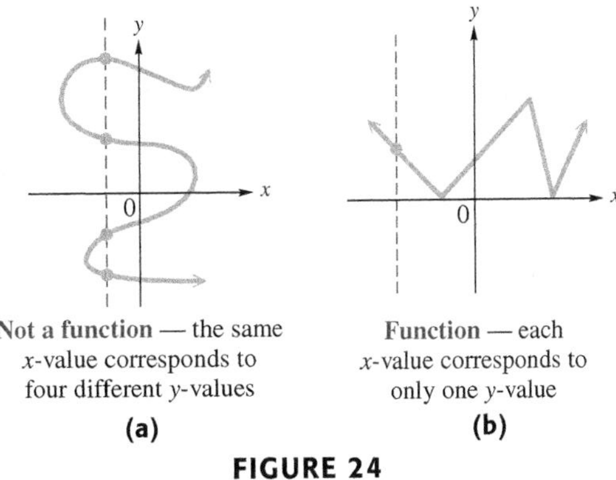


**Not a function** — the same $x$-value corresponds to four different $y$-values

**(a)**

**Function** — each $x$-value corresponds to only one $y$-value

**(b)**

**FIGURE 24**

The vertical line test is a simple method for identifying a function defined by a graph. It is more difficult to decide whether a relation defined by an equation is a function. The next example gives some hints that may help.

### EXAMPLE 4 Determining Whether a Relation is a Function

Decide whether each equation defines a function, and give the domain.

**(a)** $y = \sqrt{2x - 1}$ **(b)** $y^2 = x$

**(c)** $y \leq x - 1$ **(d)** $y = \dfrac{5}{x - 1}$

**SOLUTION**

**(a)** In the equation $y = \sqrt{2x - 1}$, for any choice of $x$ in the domain, there is exactly one corresponding value for $y$ (the radical is a nonnegative number). Thus, this equation defines a function. Because the radicand cannot be negative,

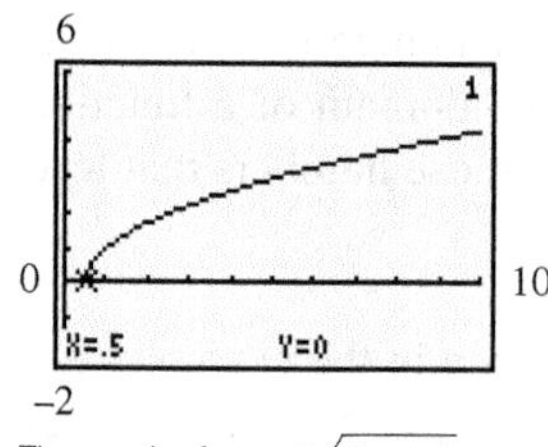

The graph of $y = \sqrt{2x - 1}$ supports the result in Example 4(a). The domain is $\left[\frac{1}{2}, \infty\right)$.

$$\begin{aligned} 2x - 1 &\geq 0 \\ 2x &\geq 1 \quad \text{Add 1.} \\ x &\geq \frac{1}{2}. \quad \text{Divide by 2.} \end{aligned}$$

The domain is $\left[\frac{1}{2}, \infty\right)$.

**(b)** The ordered pairs $(16, 4)$ and $(16, -4)$ both satisfy the equation $y^2 = x$. Since one value of $x$, 16, corresponds to two values of $y$, 4 and $-4$, this equation does not define a function. Solving $y^2 = x$ for $y$ gives

$$y = \sqrt{x} \quad \text{or} \quad y = -\sqrt{x},$$

which shows that two values of $y$ correspond to each positive value of $x$. Because $x$ is equal to the square of $y$, the values of $x$ must always be nonnegative. The domain of the relation is $[0, \infty)$.

**(c)** By definition, $y$ is a function of $x$ if every value of $x$ leads to exactly one value of $y$. In the inequality

$$y \leq x - 1,$$

a particular value of $x$, say 1, corresponds to many values of $y$. The ordered pairs $(1, 0)$, $(1, -1)$, $(1, -2)$, $(1, -3)$, and so on, all satisfy the inequality. For this reason, the inequality does not define a function. Any number can be used for $x$, so the domain is the set of real numbers $(-\infty, \infty)$.

**(d)** For the equation $y = \frac{5}{x - 1}$, given any value of $x$ in the domain, we find $y$ by subtracting 1, then dividing the result into 5. This process produces exactly one value of $y$ for each value in the domain, so this equation defines a function. The domain includes all real numbers except those that make the denominator 0. We find these numbers by setting the denominator equal to 0 and solving for $x$.

$$\begin{aligned} x - 1 &= 0 \\ x &= 1 \end{aligned}$$

Thus, the domain includes all real numbers except 1. In interval notation this is written as $(-\infty, 1) \cup (1, \infty)$. ■

In summary, three variations of the definition of function are given here.

## Variations of the Definition of Function

1. A **function** is a relation in which for each value of the first component of the ordered pairs there is exactly one value of the second component.
2. A **function** is a set of distinct ordered pairs in which no first component is repeated.
3. A **function** is a rule or correspondence that assigns exactly one range value to each domain value.

**Function Notation** When a function $f$ is defined with a rule or an equation using $x$ and $y$ for the independent and dependent variables, we say "$y$ is a function of $x$" to emphasize that $y$ *depends on* $x$. We use the notation

$$y = f(x),$$

called **function notation,** to express this and read $f(x)$ as "$f$ of $x$." (In this notation the parentheses do not indicate multiplication.) For example, if $y = 2x - 7$, we write

Do not read f(x) as "f times x." → $f(x) = 2x - 7.$

***Note that f(x) is just another name for the dependent variable y.*** For example, if $y = f(x) = 9x - 5$, and $x = 2$, then we find $y$, or $f(2)$, by replacing $x$ with 2.

$$y = f(2)$$
$$y = 9 \cdot 2 - 5 = 18 - 5 = 13.$$

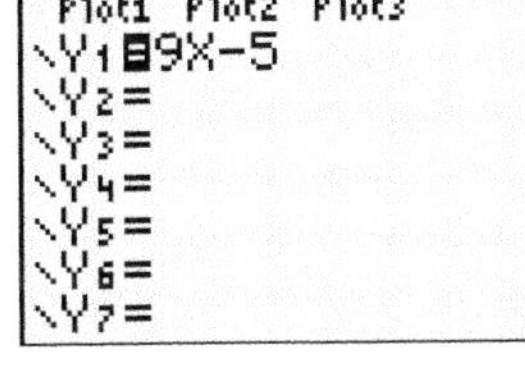


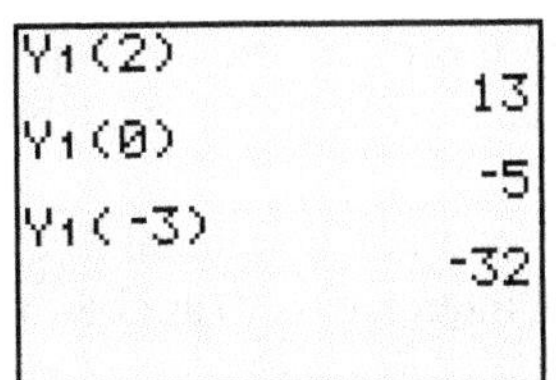


For $Y_1 = 9X - 5$, function notation capability of the TI-83/84 Plus supports the discussion here.

The statement "if $x = 2$, then $y = 13$" is abbreviated with function notation as

$$f(2) = 13.$$

Read $f(2)$ as "$f$ of 2" or "$f$ at 2." Also,

$$f(0) = 9 \cdot 0 - 5 = -5, \quad \text{and} \quad f(-3) = 9(-3) - 5 = -32.$$

These ideas and the symbols used to represent them can be explained as follows.

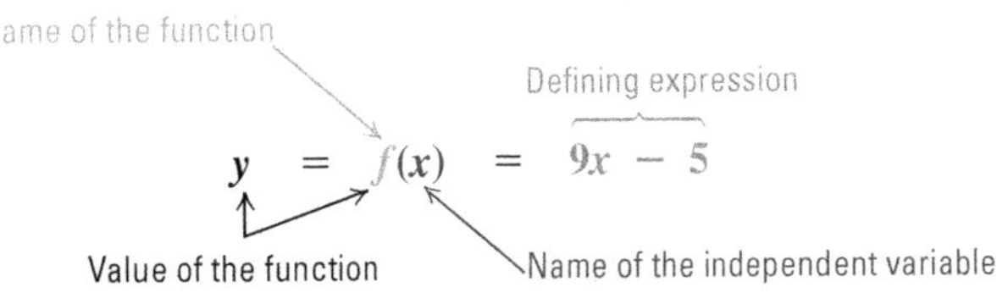


### EXAMPLE 5 Using Function Notation

Let $f(x) = -x^2 + 5x - 3$. Find the following.

**(a)** $f(2)$ **(b)** $f(-1)$ **(c)** $f(2x)$

**SOLUTION**

**(a)** $f(x) = -x^2 + 5x - 3$

$f(2) = -2^2 + 5 \cdot 2 - 3$ Replace $x$ with 2.

$= -4 + 10 - 3$

$= 3$

$-2^2$ means $-(2^2) = -4$.

**(b)** $f(-1) = -(-1)^2 + 5(-1) - 3$
$= -1 - 5 - 3 = -9$

**(c)** $f(2x) = -(2x)^2 + 5(2x) - 3$ Replace $x$ with $2x$.
$= -4x^2 + 10x - 3$

**Linear Functions** An important type of elementary function is the *linear function.*

**Linear Function**

A function that can be written in the form

$$f(x) = mx + b$$

for real numbers $m$ and $b$ is a **linear function.**

Notice that the form $f(x) = mx + b$ defining a linear function is the same as that of the slope-intercept form of the equation of a line, first seen in the previous section. We know that the graph of $f(x) = mx + b$ will be a line with slope $m$ and $y$-intercept $(0, b)$.

**EXAMPLE 6 Graphing Linear Functions**

Graph each linear function.

**(a)** $f(x) = -2x + 3$ **(b)** $f(x) = 3$

**SOLUTION**

**(a)** To graph the function, locate the $y$-intercept, $(0, 3)$. From this point, use the slope $-2 = \frac{-2}{1}$ to go down 2 and right 1. This second point is used to obtain the graph in Figure 25(a).

**(b)** From the previous section, we know that the graph of $y = 3$ is a horizontal line. Therefore, the graph of $f(x) = 3$ is a horizontal line with $y$-intercept $(0, 3)$ as shown in Figure 25(b).

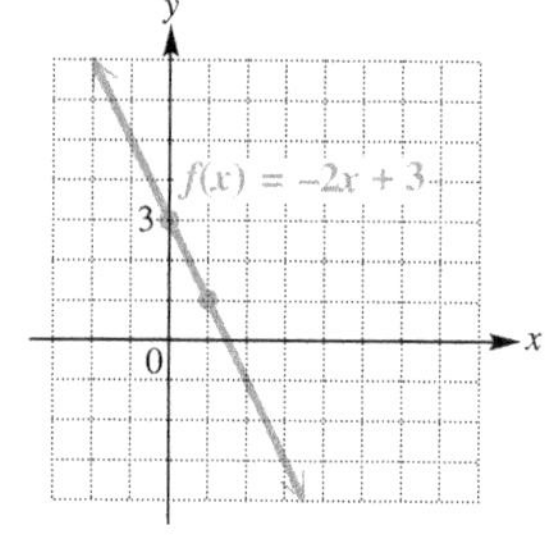


(a)

(b)

FIGURE 25

The function defined in Example 6(b) and graphed in Figure 25(b) is an example of a constant function. A **constant function** is a linear function of the form $f(x) = b$, where $b$ is a real number. The domain of any linear function is $(-\infty, \infty)$. The range of a nonconstant linear function (like in Example 6(a)) is also $(-\infty, \infty)$, while the range of the constant function $f(x) = b$ is $\{b\}$.

**Modeling with Linear Functions** A company's cost of producing a product and the revenue from selling the product can be expressed as linear functions. The idea of **break-even analysis** then can be explained using the graphs of these functions. When cost is greater than revenue earned, the company loses money. When cost is less than revenue the company makes money, and when cost equals revenue the company breaks even.

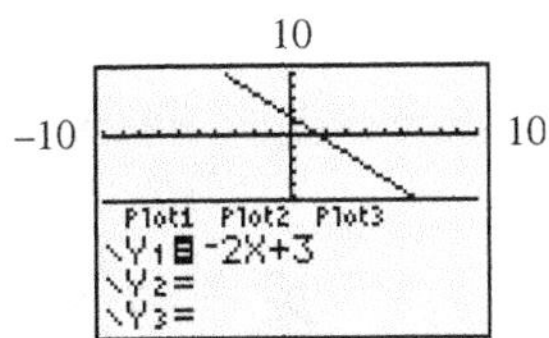


Compare with Example 6(a) and Figure 25(a).

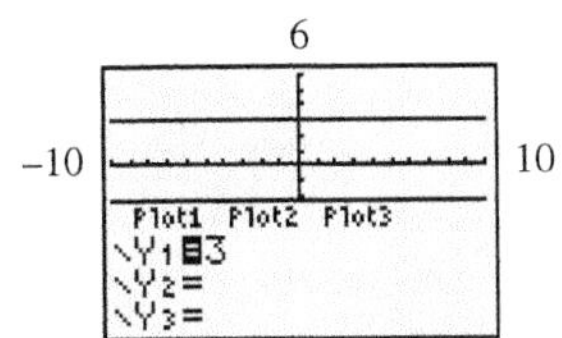


Compare with Example 6(b) and Figure 25(b).

## EXAMPLE 7 Analyzing Cost, Revenue, and Profit

Peripheral Visions, Inc., produces studio quality DVDs of live concerts. The company places an ad in a trade newsletter. The cost of the ad is \$100. Each DVD costs \$20 to produce, and the company charges \$24 per disk.

**(a)** Express the cost $C$ as a function of $x$, the number of DVDs produced.

**(b)** Express the revenue $R$ as a function of $x$, the number of DVDs sold.

**(c)** When will the company break even? That is, for what value of $x$ does revenue equal cost?

**(d)** Graph the cost and revenue functions on the same coordinate system, and interpret the graph.

**SOLUTION**

**(a)** The *fixed cost* is \$100, and for each DVD produced, the *variable cost* is \$20. Therefore, the cost $C$ can be expressed as a function of $x$, the number of DVDs produced:

$$C(x) = 20x + 100 \quad (C \text{ in dollars}).$$

**(b)** Each DVD sells for \$24, so the revenue $R$ is given by

$$R(x) = 24x \quad (R \text{ in dollars}).$$

**(c)** The company will just break even (no profit and no loss) as long as revenue just equals cost, or $R(x) = C(x)$. This is true whenever

$$
\begin{aligned}
R(x) &= C(x) \\
24x &= 20x + 100 && \text{Substitute for } R(x) \text{ and } C(x). \\
4x &= 100 && \text{Subtract } 20x. \\
x &= 25. && \text{Divide by 4.}
\end{aligned}
$$

If 25 DVDs are produced and sold, the company will break even.

**(d)** Figure 26 shows the graphs of the two functions. At the break-even point, we see that when 25 DVDs are produced and sold, both the cost and the revenue are \$600. If fewer than 25 DVDs are produced and sold (that is, when $x < 25$), the company loses money. When more than 25 DVDs are produced and sold (that is, when $x > 25$), there is a profit.

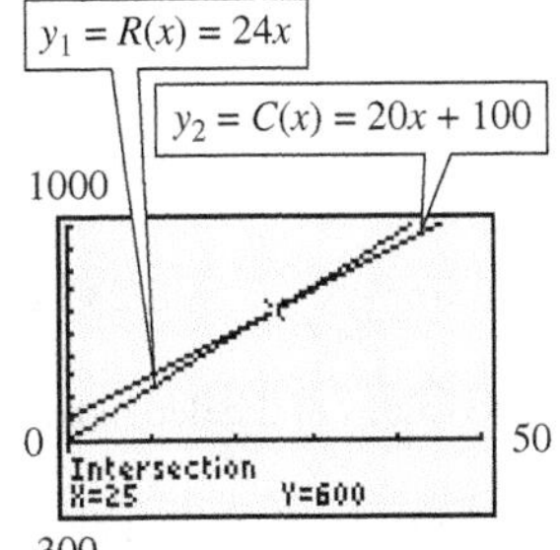


The break-even point is (25, 600), as indicated at the bottom of the screen. The calculator can find the point of intersection of the graphs. Compare with Figure 26.

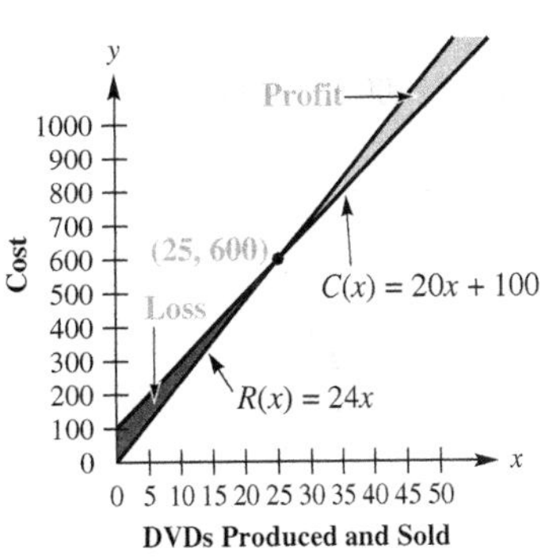


**FIGURE 26**

## 8.4 Exercises

1. In your own words, define *function* and give an example.

2. In your own words, define *domain of a function* and give an example.

3. In an ordered pair of a relation, is the first element a value of the independent or the dependent variable?

*For each relation, decide whether it is a function, and give the domain and range.*

4. $\{(1, 1), (1, -1), (2, 4), (2, -4), (3, 9), (3, -9)\}$

5. $\{(2, 5), (3, 7), (4, 9), (5, 11)\}$

6. The set containing certain countries and their predicted life expectancy estimates for persons born in 2050 is {(United States, 83.9), (Japan, 90.91), (Canada, 85.26), (Britain, 83.79), (France, 87.01), (Germany, 83.12), (Italy, 82.26)}. (*Source:* Shripad Tuljapurkar, Mountain View Research, Los Altos, California.)

7. An input–output machine accepts positive real numbers as input, and outputs both their positive and negative square roots.

8.

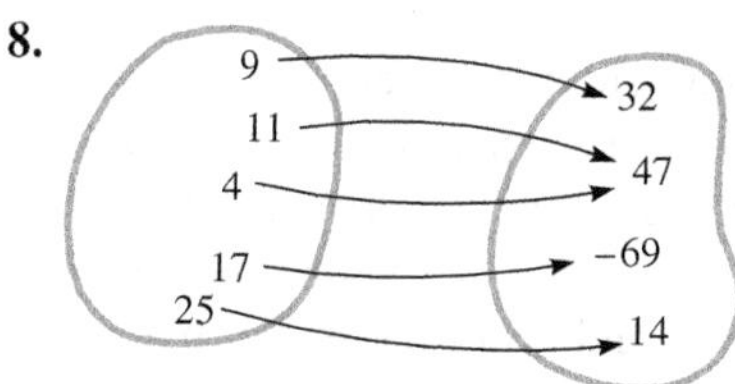


9. **U.S. Voting-Age Population in 2000 (in millions)**

| | |
|---|---|
| Hispanic | 21.3 |
| Native American | 1.6 |
| Asian American | 8.2 |
| African American | 24.6 |
| White | 152.0 |

*Source:* U.S. Bureau of the Census.

10. $\{(x, y) \mid x = |y|\}$

11.

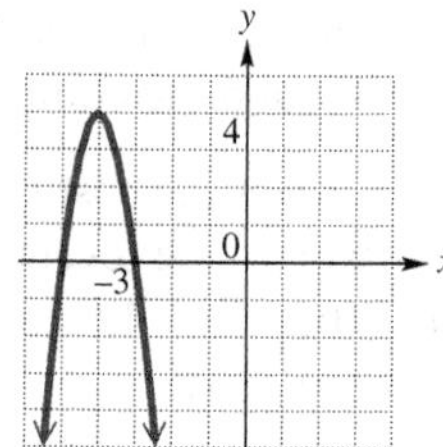


12.

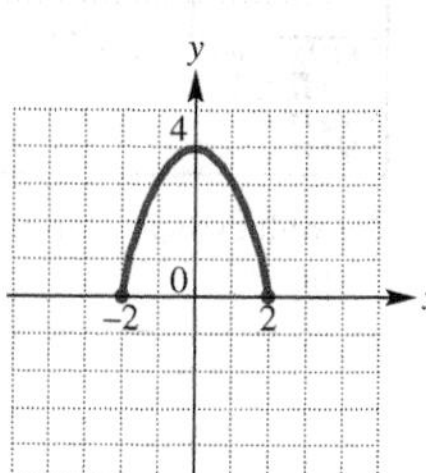


13.

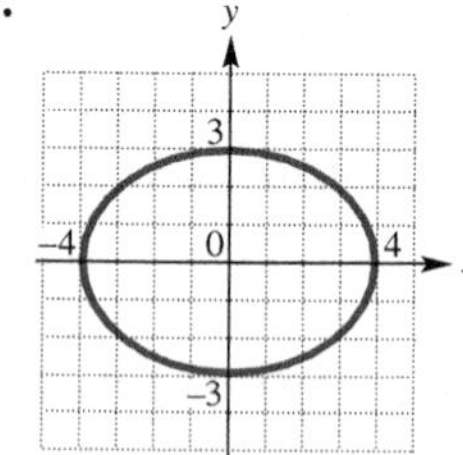


14.

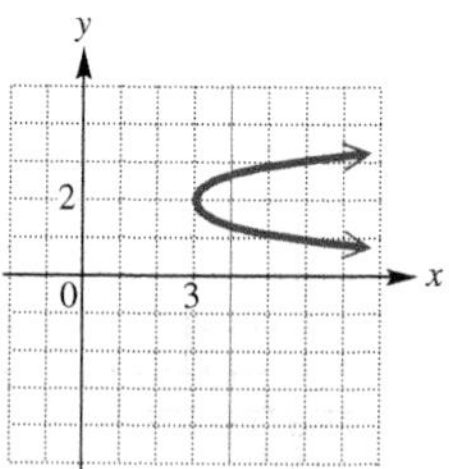


*Decide whether the given relation defines y as a function of x. Give the domain.*

15. $y = x^2$

16. $y = x^3$

17. $x = y^2$

18. $x = y^4$

19. $x + y < 4$

20. $x - y < 3$

21. $y = \sqrt{x}$

22. $y = -\sqrt{x}$

23. $xy = 1$

24. $xy = -3$

25. $y = \sqrt{4x + 2}$

26. $y = \sqrt{9 - 2x}$

27. $y = \dfrac{2}{x - 9}$

28. $y = \dfrac{-7}{x - 16}$

29. ***Pool Water Level*** Refer to Example 1, Figure 23, to answer the questions.
   (a) What numbers are possible values of the dependent variable?
   (b) For how long is the water level increasing? Decreasing?
   (c) How many gallons are in the pool after 90 hours?
   (d) Call this function $g$. What is $g(0)$? What does it mean in this example?

**30.** ***Electricity Consumption*** The graph shows the megawatts of electricity used on a record-breaking summer day in Sacramento, California.

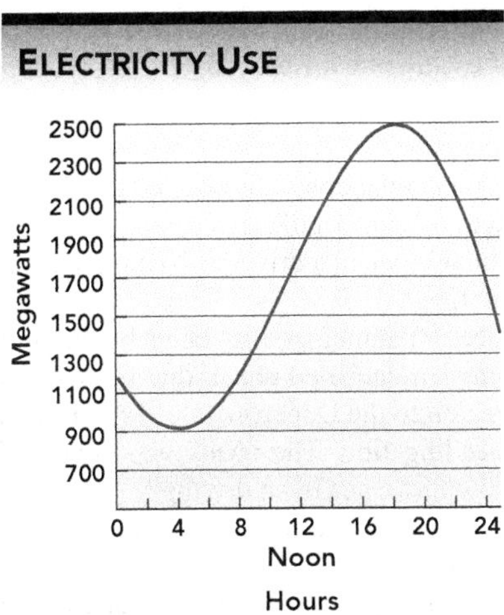


*Source:* Sacramento Municipal Utility District.

(a) Is this the graph of a function?
(b) What is the domain?
(c) Estimate the number of megawatts of electricity use at 8 A.M.
(d) At what time was the most electricity used? The least electricity?

**31.** Give an example of a function from everyday life. (*Hint:* Fill in the blanks: ______ depends on ______, so ______ is a function of ______.)

**32.** Choose the correct response. The notation $f(3)$ means

**A.** the variable $f$ times 3, or $3f$.
**B.** the value of the dependent variable when the independent variable is 3.
**C.** the value of the independent variable when the dependent variable is 3.
**D.** $f$ equals 3.

*Let $f(x) = 3 + 2x$ and $g(x) = x^2 - 2$. Find each function value.*

**33.** $f(1)$ **34.** $f(4)$ **35.** $g(2)$

**36.** $g(0)$ **37.** $g(-1)$ **38.** $g(-3)$

**39.** $f(-8)$ **40.** $f(-5)$

*Sketch the graph of each linear function. Give the domain and range.*

**41.** $f(x) = -2x + 5$ **42.** $g(x) = 4x - 1$

**43.** $h(x) = \frac{1}{2}x + 2$ **44.** $F(x) = -\frac{1}{4}x + 1$

**45.** $G(x) = 2x$ **46.** $H(x) = -3x$

**47.** $f(x) = 5$ **48.** $g(x) = -4$

*An equation that defines y as a function of x is given.* **(a)** *Solve for y in terms of x, and replace y with the function notation f(x).* **(b)** *Find f(3).*

**49.** $y + 2x^2 = 3$ **50.** $y - 3x^2 = 2$

**51.** $4x - 3y = 8$ **52.** $-2x + 5y = 9$

**53.** Fill in the blanks with the correct responses. The equation $2x + y = 4$ has a straight ____ as its graph. One point that lies on the line is (3, ____). If we solve the equation for $y$ and use function notation, we have a linear function $f(x) =$ ________. For this function, $f(3) =$ ____, meaning that the point (____, ____) lies on the graph of the function.

**54.** Which one of the following defines a linear function?

**A.** $y = \frac{x-5}{4}$ **B.** $y = \frac{1}{x}$

**C.** $y = x^2$ **D.** $y = \sqrt{x}$

**55.** ***Taxi Fares***

(a) Suppose that a taxicab driver charges \$1.50 per mile. Fill in the chart with the correct response for the price $f(x)$ she charges for a trip of $x$ miles.

| $x$ | $f(x)$ |
|---|---|
| 0 | |
| 1 | |
| 2 | |
| 3 | |

(b) The linear function that gives a rule for the amount charged is $f(x) =$ ______.
(c) Graph this function for the domain $\{0, 1, 2, 3\}$.

**56.** ***Cost to Mail a Package*** Suppose that a package weighing $x$ pounds costs $f(x)$ dollars to mail to a given location, where $f(x) = 2.75x$.

(a) What is the value of $f(3)$?

**(b)** Describe what 3 and the value $f(3)$ mean in part (a), using the terminology *independent variable* and *dependent variable.*

**(c)** How much would it cost to mail a 5-lb package? Write the answer using function notation.

**57.** ***Forensic Studies*** Forensic scientists use the lengths of the tibia ($t$), the bone from the ankle to the knee, and the femur ($r$), the bone from the knee to the hip socket, to calculate the height of a person. A person's height ($h$) is determined from the lengths of these bones using functions defined by the following formulas. All measurements are in centimeters.

*For men:*

$$h(r) = 69.09 + 2.24r$$

or $h(t) = 81.69 + 2.39t$

*For women:*

$$h(r) = 61.41 + 2.32r$$

or $h(t) = 72.57 + 2.53t$

**(a)** Find the height of a man with a femur measuring 56 centimeters.

**(b)** Find the height of a man with a tibia measuring 40 centimeters.

**(c)** Find the height of a woman with a femur measuring 50 centimeters.

**(d)** Find the height of a woman with a tibia measuring 36 centimeters.

**58.** ***Pool Size for Sea Otters*** Federal regulations set standards for the size of the quarters of marine mammals. A pool to house sea otters must have a volume of "the square of the sea otter's average adult length (in meters) multiplied by 3.14 and by .91 meter." If $x$ represents the sea otter's average adult length and $f(x)$ represents the volume of the corresponding pool size, this formula can be written as $f(x) = (.91)(3.14)x^2$.

Find the volume of the pool for each of the following adult lengths (in meters). Round answers to the nearest hundredth.

**(a)** .8
**(b)** 1.0
**(c)** 1.2
**(d)** 1.5

**59.** ***Speeding Fines*** Suppose that speeding fines are determined by the linear function

$$f(x) = 10(x - 65) + 50, \quad x > 65,$$

where $f(x)$ is the cost in dollars of the fine if a person is caught driving $x$ miles per hour.

**(a)** Radar clocked a driver at 76 mph. How much was the fine?

**(b)** While balancing his checkbook, Johnny ran across a canceled check that his wife Gwen had written to the Department of Motor Vehicles for a speeding fine. The check was written for \$100. How fast was Gwen driving?

**(c)** At what whole-number speed are tickets first given?

**(d)** For what speeds is the fine greater than \$200?

**60.** ***Expansion and Contraction of Gases*** In 1787, Jacques Charles noticed that gases expand when heated and contract when cooled. Suppose that a particular gas follows the model

$$f(x) = \frac{5}{3}x + 455,$$

where $x$ is the temperature in Celsius and $f(x)$ is the volume in cubic centimeters. (*Source:* Bushaw, D., et al., *A Sourcebook of Applications of School Mathematics*, MAA, 1980. Reprinted with permission.)

**(a)** What is the volume when the temperature is 27°C?

**(b)** What is the temperature when the volume is 605 cubic centimeters?

**(c)** Determine what temperature gives a volume of 0 cubic centimeters (that is, absolute zero, or the coldest possible temperature).

***Cost and Revenue Models*** *In each of the following,* **(a)** *express the cost C as a function of x, where x represents the quantity of items as given;* **(b)** *express the revenue R as a function of x;* **(c)** *determine the value of x for which revenue equals cost;* **(d)** *graph $y = C(x)$ and $y = R(x)$ on the same axes, and interpret the graph.*

**61.** Perian Herring stuffs envelopes for extra income during her spare time. Her initial cost to obtain the necessary information for the job was \$200.00. Each envelope costs \$.02 and she gets paid \$.04 per envelope stuffed. Let $x$ represent the number of envelopes stuffed.

62. Brent Labatut runs a copying service in his home. He paid \$3500 for the copier and a lifetime service contract. Each sheet of paper he uses costs \$.01, and he gets paid \$.05 per copy he makes. Let $x$ represent the number of copies he makes.

63. Roy Pollina operates a delivery service in a southern city. His start-up costs amounted to \$2300. He estimates that it costs him (in terms of gasoline, wear and tear on his car, etc.) \$3.00 per delivery. He charges \$5.50 per delivery. Let $x$ represent the number of deliveries he makes.

64. Katie Simon bakes cakes and sells them at county fairs. Her initial cost for the St. Charles Parish fair this year was \$40.00. She figures that each cake costs \$2.50 to make, and she charges \$6.50 per cake. Let $x$ represent the number of cakes sold. (Assume that there were no cakes left over.)

# 8.5 Quadratic Functions, Graphs, and Models

**Quadratic Functions and Parabolas • Graphs of Quadratic Functions • Vertex of a Parabola • General Graphing Guidelines • A Model for Optimization**

## Quadratic Functions and Parabolas

In the previous section, we discussed linear functions, those that are defined by first-degree polynomials. We now look at *quadratic functions,* those defined by second-degree polynomials.

### Quadratic Function

A function $f$ is a **quadratic function** if

$$f(x) = ax^2 + bx + c,$$

where $a$, $b$, and $c$ are real numbers, with $a \neq 0$.

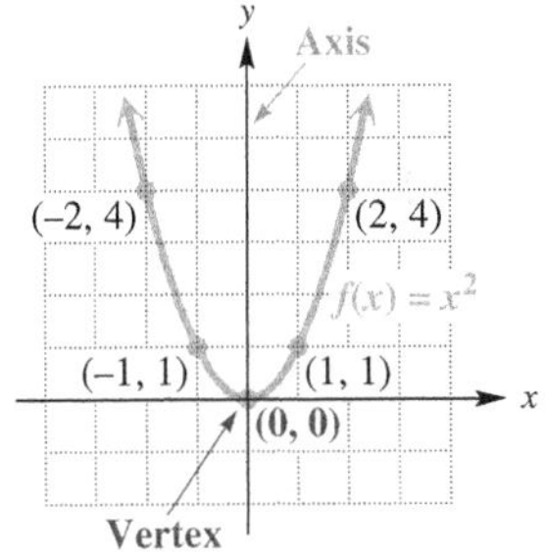


**FIGURE 27**

The simplest quadratic function is defined by $f(x) = x^2$. This function can be graphed by finding several ordered pairs that satisfy the equation: for example, (0, 0), (1, 1), $(-1, 1)$, (2, 4), $(-2, 4)$, $\left(\frac{1}{2}, \frac{1}{4}\right)$, $\left(-\frac{1}{2}, \frac{1}{4}\right)$, $\left(\frac{3}{2}, \frac{9}{4}\right)$, and $\left(-\frac{3}{2}, \frac{9}{4}\right)$. Plotting these points and drawing a smooth curve through them gives the graph shown in Figure 27. This graph is called a **parabola.** Every quadratic function has a graph that is a parabola.

Parabolas are symmetric about a line (the $y$-axis in Figure 27.) Intuitively, this means that if the graph were folded along the line of symmetry, the two sides would coincide. The line of symmetry for a parabola is called the **axis** of the parabola. The point where the axis intersects the parabola is the **vertex** of the parabola. The vertex is the lowest (or highest) point of a vertical parabola.

Parabolas have many practical applications. For example, the reflectors of solar ovens and flashlights are made by revolving a parabola about its axis. The **focus** of a parabola is a point on its axis that determines the curvature. See Figure 28. When the parabolic reflector of a solar oven is aimed at the sun, the light rays bounce off the reflector and collect at the focus, creating intense heat at that point. In contrast, when a lightbulb is placed at the focus of a parabolic reflector, light rays reflect out parallel to the axis.

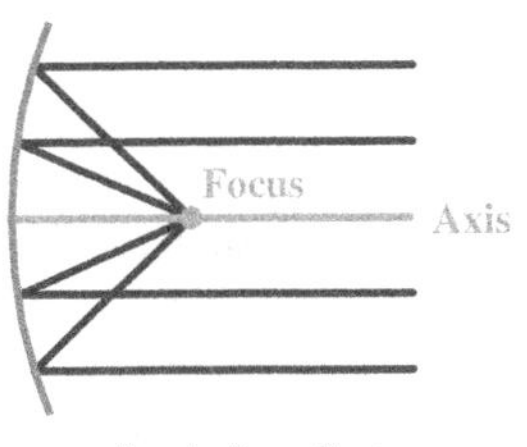


Parabolic reflector

**FIGURE 28**

## Graphs of Quadratic Functions

The first example shows how the constant $a$ affects the graph of a function of the form $g(x) = ax^2$.

## EXAMPLE 1 Graphing Quadratic Functions ($g(x) = ax^2$)

Graph the functions defined as follows.

**(a)** $g(x) = -x^2$ **(b)** $g(x) = \frac{1}{2}x^2$

**SOLUTION**

**(a)** For a given value of $x$, the corresponding value of $g(x)$ will be the negative of what it was for $f(x) = x^2$. (See the table of values with Figure 29(a).) Because of this, the graph of $g(x) = -x^2$ is the same shape as that of $f(x) = x^2$, but opens downward. See Figure 29(a). This is generally true; the graph of $f(x) = ax^2 + bx + c$ opens downward whenever $a < 0$.

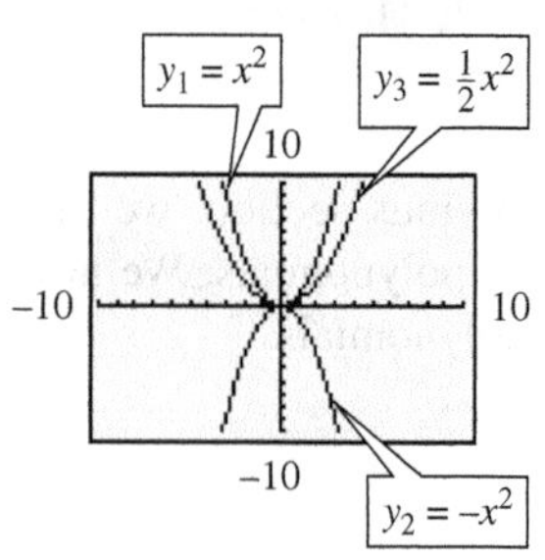


The screen illustrates the three graphs considered in Example 1 and Figures 29(a) and 29(b).

| $x$ | $y$ |
|---|---|
| $-2$ | $-4$ |
| $-1$ | $-1$ |
| 0 | 0 |
| 1 | $-1$ |
| 2 | $-4$ |

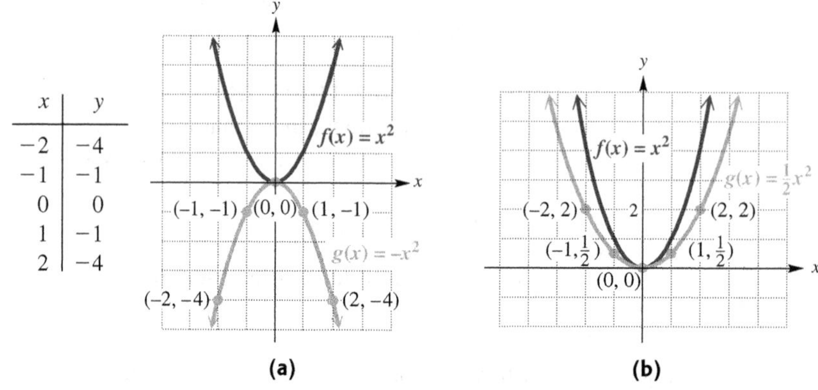


**FIGURE 29**

**(b)** Choose a value of $x$, and then find $g(x)$. The coefficient $\frac{1}{2}$ will cause the resulting value of $g(x)$ to be less than that of $f(x) = x^2$, making the parabola wider than the graph of $f(x) = x^2$. See Figure 29(b). In both parabolas of this example, the axis is the vertical line $x = 0$ and the vertex is the origin (0, 0).

The next few examples show the results of horizontal and vertical shifts, called **translations,** of the graph of $f(x) = x^2$.

## EXAMPLE 2 Graphing a Quadratic Function (Vertical Shift)

Graph $g(x) = x^2 - 4$.

**SOLUTION**

By comparing the tables of values for $g(x) = x^2 - 4$ and $f(x) = x^2$ shown with Figure 30 on the next page, we can see that for corresponding $x$-values, the $y$-values of $g$ are each 4 less than those for $f$. This leads to a *vertical shift*. Thus, the graph of $g(x) = x^2 - 4$ is the same as that of $f(x) = x^2$, but translated 4 units down. See Figure 30. The vertex of this parabola (here the lowest point) is at $(0, -4)$. The axis of the parabola is the vertical line $x = 0$.

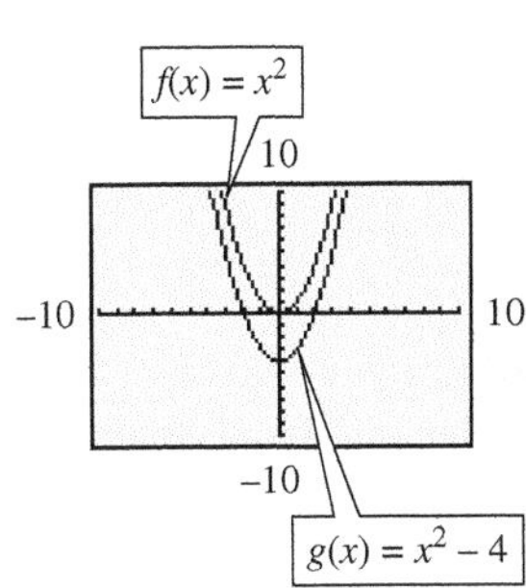


Compare with Figure 30.

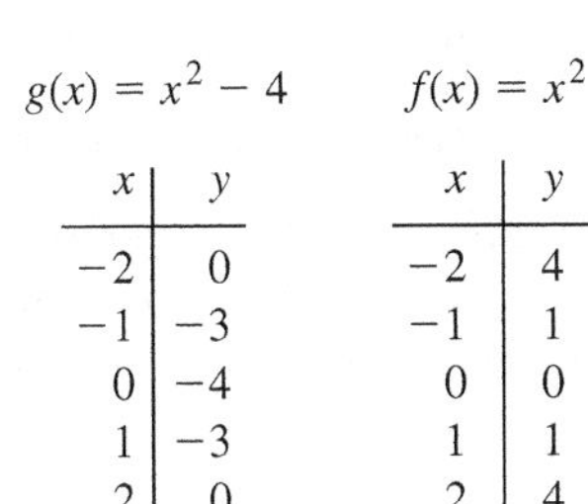

$g(x) = x^2 - 4$

| $x$ | $y$ |
|---|---|
| −2 | 0 |
| −1 | −3 |
| 0 | −4 |
| 1 | −3 |
| 2 | 0 |

$f(x) = x^2$

| $x$ | $y$ |
|---|---|
| −2 | 4 |
| −1 | 1 |
| 0 | 0 |
| 1 | 1 |
| 2 | 4 |

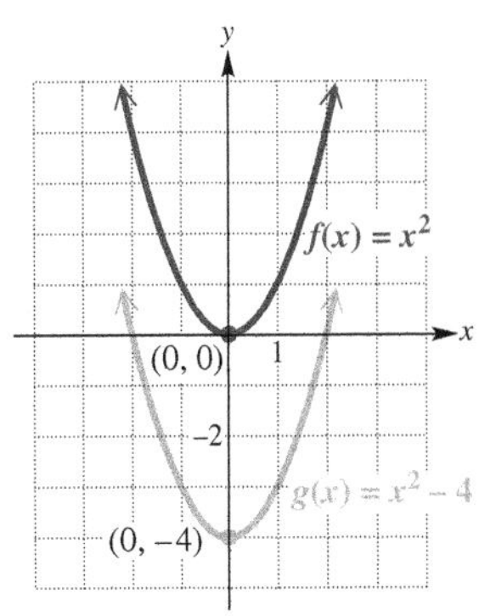


**FIGURE 30**

## EXAMPLE 3 Graphing a Quadratic Function (Horizontal Shift)

Graph $g(x) = (x - 4)^2$.

**SOLUTION**

Comparing the tables of values shown with Figure 31 shows that the graph of $g(x) = (x - 4)^2$ is the same as that of $f(x) = x^2$, but translated 4 units to the right. This is a *horizontal shift*. The vertex is at (4, 0). As shown in Figure 31, the axis of this parabola is the vertical line $x = 4$.

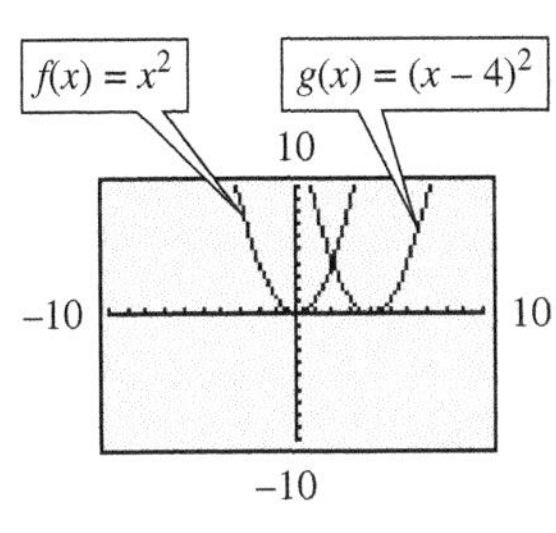


Compare with Figure 31.

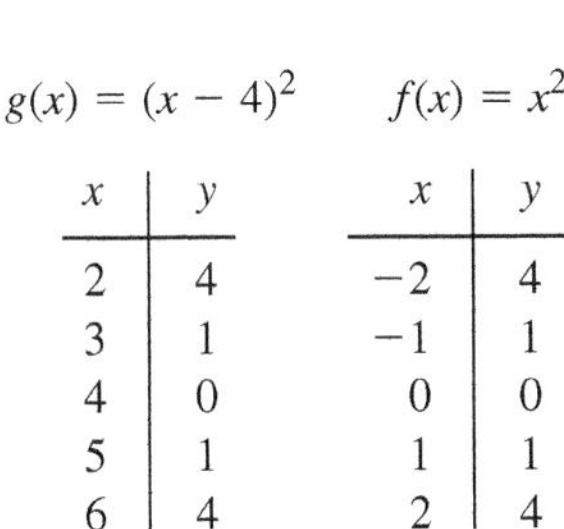

$g(x) = (x - 4)^2$

| $x$ | $y$ |
|---|---|
| 2 | 4 |
| 3 | 1 |
| 4 | 0 |
| 5 | 1 |
| 6 | 4 |

$f(x) = x^2$

| $x$ | $y$ |
|---|---|
| −2 | 4 |
| −1 | 1 |
| 0 | 0 |
| 1 | 1 |
| 2 | 4 |

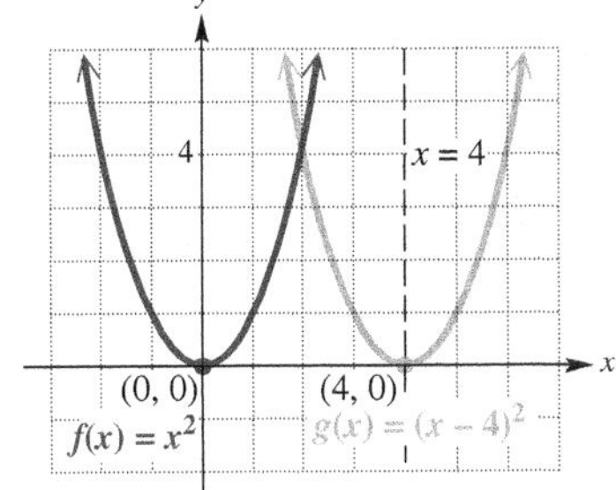


**FIGURE 31**

Pay close attention to this warning. ⟶ ***Errors frequently occur when horizontal shifts are involved.*** To determine the direction and magnitude of horizontal shifts, find the value of $x$ that would cause the expression $x - h$ to equal 0. For example, the graph of

$$f(x) = (x - 5)^2$$

would be shifted 5 units to the *right*, because $x = +5$ would cause $x - 5$ to equal 0. On the other hand, the graph of

$$f(x) = (x + 4)^2$$

would be shifted 4 units to the *left*, because $x = -4$ would cause $x + 4$ to equal 0.

The following general principles apply for graphing functions of the form $f(x) = a(x - h)^2 + k$.

**General Principles for Graphs of Quadratic Functions**

1. The graph of the quadratic function defined by

$$f(x) = a(x - h)^2 + k, \quad a \neq 0,$$

is a parabola with vertex $(h, k)$, and the vertical line $x = h$ as axis.
2. The graph opens upward if $a$ is positive and downward if $a$ is negative.
3. The graph is wider than that of $f(x) = x^2$ if $0 < |a| < 1$. The graph is narrower than that of $f(x) = x^2$ if $|a| > 1$.

### EXAMPLE 4 Graphing a Quadratic Function Using General Principles

Graph $f(x) = -2(x + 3)^2 + 4$.

**SOLUTION**

The parabola opens downward (because $a < 0$), and is narrower than the graph of $f(x) = x^2$, since $a = -2$, and $|-2| > 1$. This parabola has vertex at $(-3, 4)$, as shown in Figure 32. To complete the graph, we plotted the additional ordered pairs $(-4, 2)$ and $(-2, 2)$.

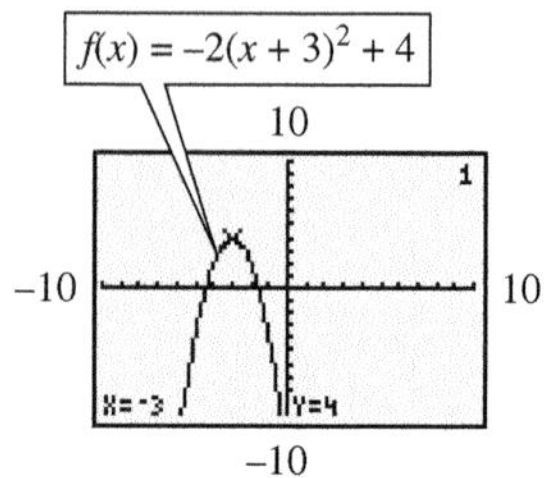

Compare with Figure 32. The vertex is $(-3, 4)$.

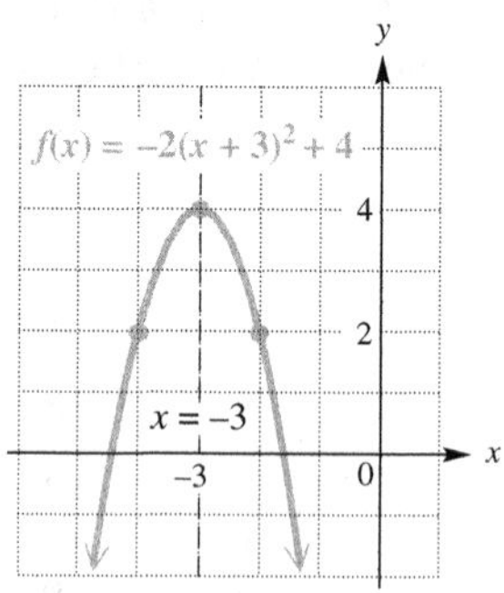

**FIGURE 32**

## Vertex of a Parabola

When the equation of a parabola is given in the form $f(x) = ax^2 + bx + c$, it is necessary to locate the vertex in order to sketch an accurate graph. This can be done in two ways. The first is by completing the square, as shown in Example 5. The second is by using a formula which can be derived by completing the square.

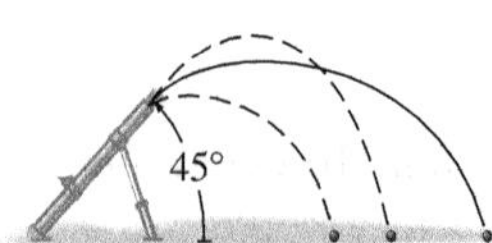

The trajectory of a shell fired from a cannon is a **parabola.** To reach the maximum range with a cannon, it is shown in calculus that the muzzle must be set at 45°. If the muzzle is elevated above 45°, the shell goes too high and falls too soon. If the muzzle is set below 45°, the shell is rapidly pulled to Earth by gravity.

### EXAMPLE 5 Finding the Vertex by Completing the Square

Find the vertex of the graph of $f(x) = x^2 - 4x + 5$.

**SOLUTION**

To find the vertex, we need to express $x^2 - 4x + 5$ in the form $(x - h)^2 + k$. This is done by completing the square. (See pages 418 and 437.) To simplify the notation, replace $f(x)$ by $y$.

$$\begin{aligned} y &= x^2 - 4x + 5 \\ y - 5 &= x^2 - 4x && \text{Transform so that the constant term is on the left.} \\ y - 5 + 4 &= x^2 - 4x + 4 && \text{Half of } -4 \text{ is } -2;\ (-2)^2 = 4. \text{ Add 4 to both sides.} \\ y - 1 &= (x - 2)^2 && \text{Combine terms on the left and factor on the right.} \\ y &= (x - 2)^2 + 1 && \text{Add 1 to both sides.} \end{aligned}$$

Now write the original equation as $f(x) = (x - 2)^2 + 1$. As shown earlier, the vertex of this parabola is (2, 1). ■

**Johann Kepler** (1571–1630) established the importance of a curve called an **ellipse** in 1609, when he discovered that the orbits of the planets around the sun were elliptical, not circular. The orbit of Halley's comet, shown here, also is elliptical.

See For Further Thought at the end of this section for more on ellipses.

A formula for the vertex of the graph of the quadratic function $y = ax^2 + bx + c$ can be found by completing the square for the general form of the equation. In doing so, we begin by dividing by $a$, since the coefficient of $x^2$ must be 1.

$$\begin{aligned} y &= ax^2 + bx + c \quad (a \neq 0) \\ \frac{y}{a} &= x^2 + \frac{b}{a}x + \frac{c}{a} && \text{Divide by } a. \\ \frac{y}{a} - \frac{c}{a} &= x^2 + \frac{b}{a}x && \text{Subtract } \frac{c}{a}. \\ \frac{y}{a} - \frac{c}{a} + \frac{b^2}{4a^2} &= x^2 + \frac{b}{a}x + \frac{b^2}{4a^2} && \text{Add } \left(\frac{1}{2} \cdot \frac{b}{a}\right)^2 = \frac{b^2}{4a^2}. \\ \frac{y}{a} + \frac{b^2 - 4ac}{4a^2} &= \left(x + \frac{b}{2a}\right)^2 && \text{Combine terms on the left and factor on the right.} \\ \frac{y}{a} &= \left(x + \frac{b}{2a}\right)^2 - \frac{b^2 - 4ac}{4a^2} && \text{Transform so that the } y\text{-term is alone on the left.} \\ y &= a\left(x + \frac{b}{2a}\right)^2 + \frac{4ac - b^2}{4a} && \text{Multiply by } a. \\ y &= a\Bigg[x - \underbrace{\left(-\frac{b}{2a}\right)}_{h}\Bigg]^2 + \underbrace{\frac{4ac - b^2}{4a}}_{k} \end{aligned}$$

The final equation shows that the vertex $(h, k)$ can be expressed in terms of $a$, $b$, and $c$. However, it is not necessary to memorize the expression for $k$, because it can be obtained by replacing $x$ by $-\frac{b}{2a}$.

**Vertex Formula**

The vertex of the graph of $f(x) = ax^2 + bx + c\ (a \neq 0)$ has coordinates

$$\left(-\frac{b}{2a},\ f\left(-\frac{b}{2a}\right)\right).$$

## EXAMPLE 6 Finding the Vertex by Using the Formula

Use the vertex formula to find the vertex of the graph of the function

$$f(x) = x^2 - x - 6.$$

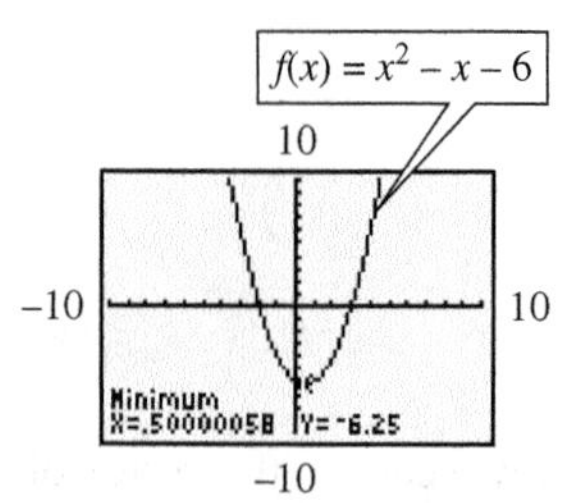


Notice the slight discrepancy when we instruct the calculator to find the vertex (a *minimum* here). This reinforces the fact that *we must understand the concepts and not totally rely on technology!*

**SOLUTION**

For this function, $a = 1$, $b = -1$, and $c = -6$. The $x$-coordinate of the vertex of the parabola is given by

$$-\frac{b}{2a} = -\frac{(-1)}{2(1)} = \frac{1}{2}.$$

The $y$-coordinate is $f\left(-\frac{b}{2a}\right) = f\left(\frac{1}{2}\right)$.

$$f\left(\frac{1}{2}\right) = \left(\frac{1}{2}\right)^2 - \frac{1}{2} - 6 = \frac{1}{4} - \frac{1}{2} - 6 = -\frac{25}{4}$$

Finally, the vertex is $\left(\frac{1}{2}, -\frac{25}{4}\right)$.

## General Graphing Guidelines

A general approach to graphing quadratic functions using intercepts and the vertex is now given.

### Graphing a Quadratic Function $f(x) = ax^2 + bx + c$

*Step 1* **Decide whether the graph opens upward or downward.** Determine whether the graph opens upward (if $a > 0$) or opens downward (if $a < 0$) to aid in the graphing process.

*Step 2* **Find the vertex.** Find the vertex either by using the formula or by completing the square.

*Step 3* **Find the $y$-intercept.** Find the $y$-intercept by evaluating $f(0)$.

*Step 4* **Find the $x$-intercepts.** Find the $x$-intercepts, if any, by solving $f(x) = 0$.

*Step 5* **Complete the graph.** Find and plot additional points as needed, using the symmetry about the axis.

### EXAMPLE 7 Graphing a Quadratic Function Using General Guidelines

Graph the quadratic function $f(x) = x^2 - x - 6$.

**SOLUTION**

*Step 1* From the equation, $a = 1 > 0$, so the graph of the function opens up.

*Step 2* The vertex, $\left(\frac{1}{2}, -\frac{25}{4}\right)$, was found in Example 6 using the vertex formula.

*Step 3* To find the $y$-intercept, evaluate $f(0)$.

$$f(x) = x^2 - x - 6$$
$$f(0) = 0^2 - 0 - 6 \quad \text{Let } x = 0.$$
$$f(0) = -6$$

The $y$-intercept is $(0, -6)$.

*Step 4* Find any $x$-intercepts. Because the vertex, $\left(\frac{1}{2}, -\frac{25}{4}\right)$, is in quadrant IV and the graph opens up, there will be two $x$-intercepts. To find them, let $f(x) = 0$ and solve.

$$f(x) = x^2 - x - 6$$
$$0 = x^2 - x - 6 \quad \text{Let } f(x) = 0.$$
$$0 = (x - 3)(x + 2) \quad \text{Factor.}$$
$$x - 3 = 0 \quad \text{or} \quad x + 2 = 0 \quad \text{Zero-factor property}$$
$$x = 3 \quad \text{or} \quad x = -2$$

The $x$-intercepts are $(3, 0)$ and $(-2, 0)$.

*Step 5* Plot the points found so far, and plot any additional points as needed. The symmetry of the graph is helpful here. The graph is shown in Figure 33.

**FIGURE 33**

## A Model for Optimization

As we have seen, the vertex of a vertical parabola is either the highest or the lowest point of the parabola. The $y$-value of the vertex gives the maximum or minimum value of $y$, while the $x$-value tells where that maximum or minimum occurs. Often a model can be constructed so that $y$ can be *optimized*.

**PROBLEM-SOLVING HINT** In some practical problems we want to know the least or greatest value of some quantity. When that quantity can be expressed using a quadratic function $f(x) = ax^2 + bx + c$, as in the next example, the vertex can be used to find the desired value.

### EXAMPLE 8 Finding a Maximum Area

A farmer has 120 feet of fencing. He wants to put a fence around three sides of a rectangular plot of land, with the side of a barn forming the fourth side. Find the maximum area he can enclose. What dimensions give this area?

| X | $Y_1$ |
|---|---|
| -2 | 0 |
| -1 | -4 |
| 0 | -6 |
| 1 | -6 |
| 2 | -4 |
| 3 | 0 |
| 4 | 6 |

$Y_1 = X^2 - X - 6$

This table provides other points on the graph of

$$Y_1 = X^2 - X - 6.$$

**Galileo Galilei** (1564–1642) died in the year Newton was born; his work was important in Newton's development of calculus. The idea of **function** is implicit in Galileo's analysis of the parabolic path of a projectile, where height and range are functions (in our terms) of the angle of elevation and the initial velocity.

According to legend, Galileo dropped objects of different weights from the tower of Pisa to disprove the Aristotelian view that heavier objects fall faster than lighter objects. He developed a formula for freely falling objects that is described by

$$d = 16t^2,$$

where $d$ is the distance in feet that a given object falls (discounting air resistance) in a given time $t$, in seconds, regardless of weight.

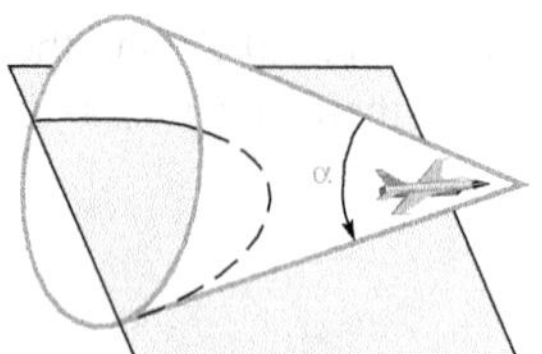

A sonic boom is a loud explosive sound caused by the shock wave that accompanies an aircraft traveling at supersonic speed. The sonic boom shock wave has the shape of a cone, and it intersects the ground in one branch of a curve known as a **hyperbola.** Everyone located along the hyperbolic curve on the ground hears the sound at the same time.

See For Further Thought on the next page for more on hyperbolas.

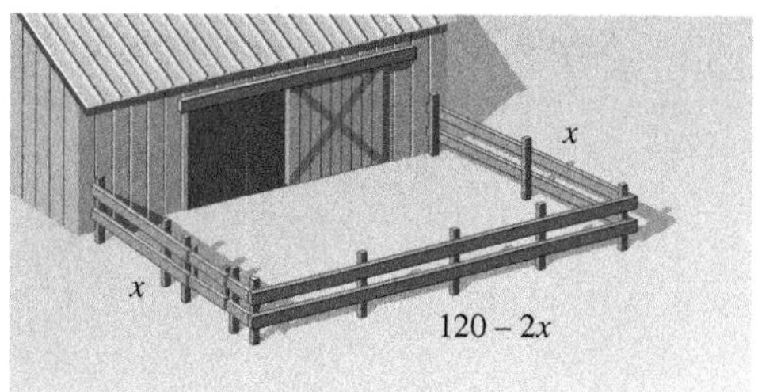


**FIGURE 34**

**SOLUTION**

Figure 34 shows the plot. Let $x$ represent its width. Then, since there are 120 feet of fencing,

$$x + x + \text{length} = 120 \qquad \text{Sum of the three fenced sides is 120 feet.}$$
$$2x + \text{length} = 120 \qquad \text{Combine terms.}$$
$$\text{length} = 120 - 2x. \qquad \text{Subtract } 2x.$$

The area is modeled by the product of the length and width, or

$$A(x) = (120 - 2x)x = 120x - 2x^2.$$

To make $120x - 2x^2$ (and thus the area) as large as possible, first find the vertex of the graph of the function $A(x) = 120x - 2x^2$.

$$A(x) = -2x^2 + 120x \qquad \text{Standard form}$$

Here we have $a = -2$ and $b = 120$. The $x$-coordinate of the vertex is

$$-\frac{b}{2a} = -\frac{120}{2(-2)} = 30.$$

$A(x) = 120x - 2x^2$

2000

−10 60

Maximum
X=30.000003 Y=1800

−400

The vertex is (30, 1800), supporting the analytic result in Example 8.

The vertex is a maximum point (since $a = -2 < 0$), so the maximum area that the farmer can enclose is

$$A(30) = -2(30)^2 + 120(30) = 1800 \text{ square feet.}$$

The farmer can enclose a maximum area of 1800 square feet, when the width of the plot is 30 feet and the length is $120 - 2(30) = 60$ feet.

As seen in Example 8, be careful when interpreting the meanings of the coordinates of the vertex in problems involving maximum or minimum values. The first coordinate, $x$, gives the value for which the *function value* is a maximum or a minimum. Read the problem carefully to determine whether you are asked to find the value of the independent variable, the dependent variable (that is, the function value), or both.

## For Further Thought

### The Conic Sections

The circle, introduced in the first section of this chapter, the parabola, the ellipse, and the hyperbola are known as **conic sections.** As seen in the figure below, each of these geometric shapes can be obtained by intersecting a plane and an infinite cone (made up of two *nappes*).

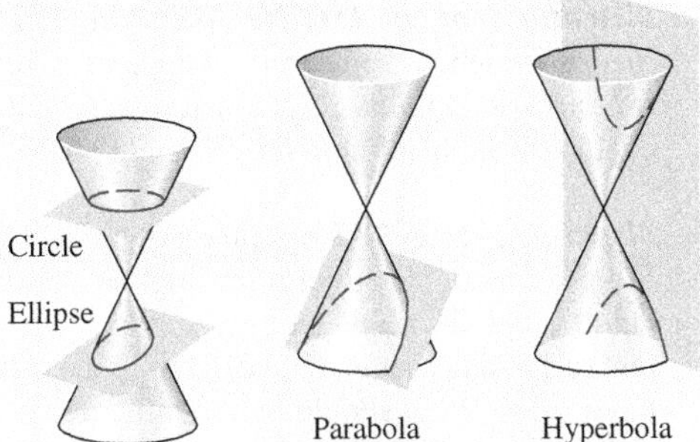


The Greek geometer Apollonius (c. 225 B.C.) was also an astronomer, and his classic work *Conic Sections* thoroughly investigated these figures. Apollonius is responsible for the names "ellipse," "parabola," and "hyperbola." The margin notes in this section show some ways that these figures appear in the world around us.

### For Group Discussion or Individual Investigation

1. The terms *ellipse, parabola,* and *hyperbola* are similar to the terms *ellipsis, parable*, and *hyperbole*. What do these latter three terms mean? You might want to do some investigation as to the similarities between the mathematical terminology and these language-related terms.
2. Identify some places in the world around you where conic sections are encountered.
3. The accompanying figure shows how an ellipse can be drawn using tacks and string. Have a class member volunteer to go to the board and using string and chalk, modify the method to draw a circle. Then have two class members work together to draw an ellipse. (*Hint:* Press hard!)

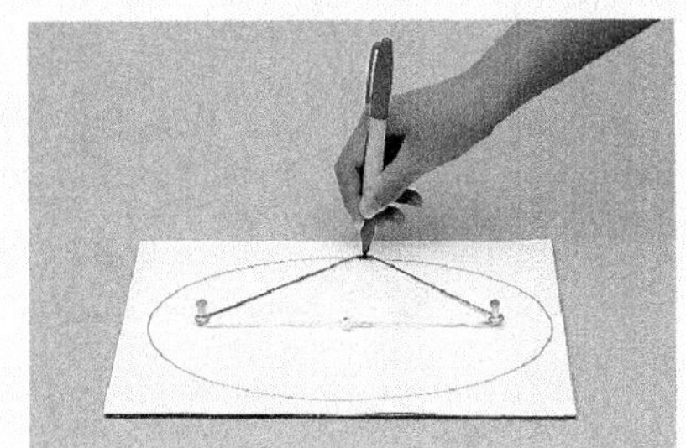

## 8.5 Exercises

*In Exercises 1–6, match each equation with the figure in A–F that most closely resembles its graph.*

A.

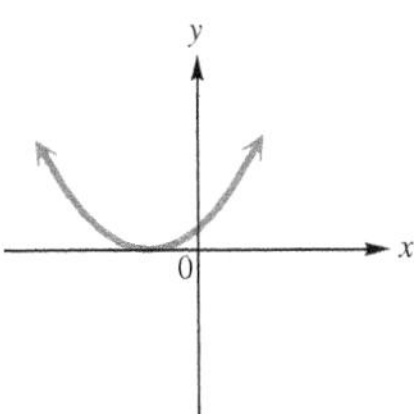

B.

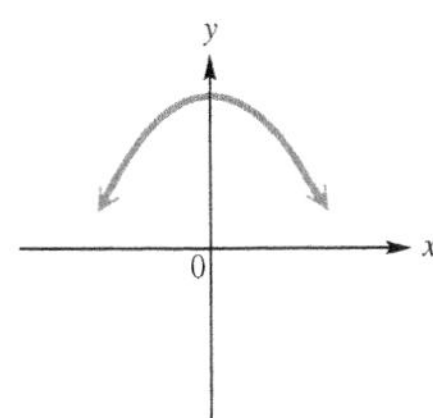

C.

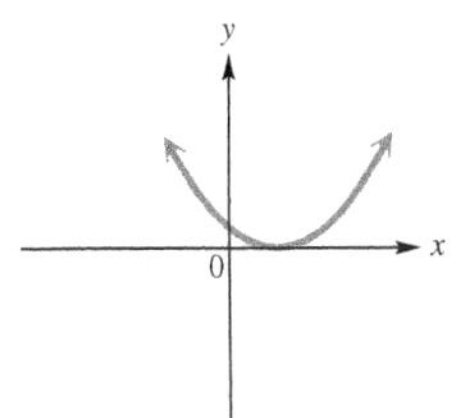

D.

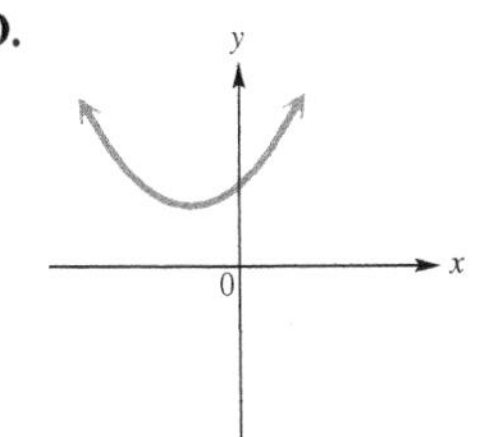

E.

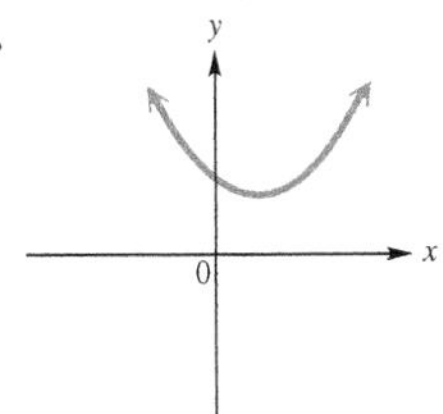

F.

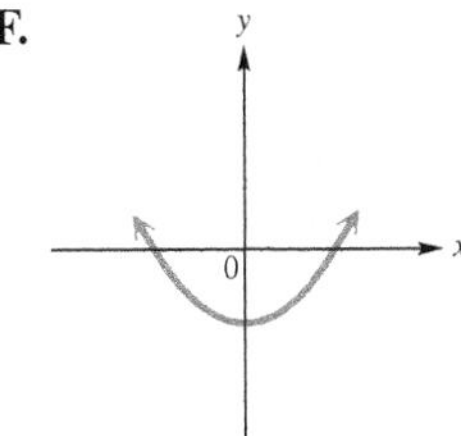

1. $g(x) = x^2 - 5$
2. $h(x) = -x^2 + 4$
3. $F(x) = (x - 1)^2$
4. $G(x) = (x + 1)^2$
5. $H(x) = (x - 1)^2 + 1$
6. $K(x) = (x + 1)^2 + 1$
7. Explain in your own words the meaning of each term.
   (a) vertex of a parabola (b) axis of a parabola
8. Explain why the axis of the graph of a quadratic function cannot be a horizontal line.

*Identify the vertex of the graph of each quadratic function.*

**9.** $f(x) = -3x^2$

**10.** $f(x) = -.5x^2$

**11.** $f(x) = x^2 + 4$

**12.** $f(x) = x^2 - 4$

**13.** $f(x) = (x - 1)^2$

**14.** $f(x) = (x + 3)^2$

**15.** $f(x) = (x + 3)^2 - 4$

**16.** $f(x) = (x - 5)^2 - 8$

**17.** Describe how the graph of each parabola in Exercises 15 and 16 is shifted compared to the graph of $y = x^2$.

*For each quadratic function, tell whether the graph opens upward or downward, and tell whether the graph is wider, narrower, or the same as the graph of $f(x) = x^2$.*

**18.** $f(x) = -2x^2$

**19.** $f(x) = -3x^2 + 1$

**20.** $f(x) = .5x^2$

**21.** $f(x) = \frac{2}{3}x^2 - 4$

**22.** What does the value of $a$ in $f(x) = a(x - h)^2 + k$ tell you about the graph of the function compared to the graph of $y = x^2$?

**23.** For $f(x) = a(x - h)^2 + k$, in what quadrant is the vertex if:
**(a)** $h > 0, k > 0$; **(b)** $h > 0, k < 0$;
**(c)** $h < 0, k > 0$; **(d)** $h < 0, k < 0$?

**24.** **(a)** What is the value of $h$ if the graph of $f(x) = a(x - h)^2 + k$ has vertex on the $y$-axis?
**(b)** What is the value of $k$ if the graph of $f(x) = a(x - h)^2 + k$ has vertex on the $x$-axis?

*Sketch the graph of each quadratic function using the methods described in this section. Indicate two points on each graph.*

**25.** $f(x) = 3x^2$

**26.** $f(x) = -2x^2$

**27.** $f(x) = -\frac{1}{4}x^2$

**28.** $f(x) = \frac{1}{3}x^2$

**29.** $f(x) = x^2 - 1$

**30.** $f(x) = x^2 + 3$

**31.** $f(x) = -x^2 + 2$

**32.** $f(x) = -x^2 - 4$

**33.** $f(x) = 2x^2 - 2$

**34.** $f(x) = -3x^2 + 1$

**35.** $f(x) = (x - 4)^2$

**36.** $f(x) = (x - 3)^2$

**37.** $f(x) = 3(x + 1)^2$

**38.** $f(x) = -2(x + 1)^2$

**39.** $f(x) = (x + 1)^2 - 2$

**40.** $f(x) = (x - 2)^2 + 3$

*Sketch the graph of each quadratic function. Indicate the coordinates of the vertex of the graph.*

**41.** $f(x) = x^2 + 8x + 14$

**42.** $f(x) = x^2 + 10x + 23$

**43.** $f(x) = x^2 + 2x - 4$

**44.** $f(x) = 3x^2 - 9x + 8$

**45.** $f(x) = -2x^2 + 4x + 5$

**46.** $f(x) = -5x^2 - 10x + 2$

*Solve each problem.*

**47.** ***Dimensions of an Exercise Run*** Rick Pal has 100 meters of fencing material to enclose a rectangular exercise run for his dog. What width will give the enclosure the maximum area?

**48.** ***Dimensions of a Parking Lot*** Morgan's Department Store wants to construct a rectangular parking lot on land bordered on one side by a highway. It has 280 feet of fencing that is to be used to fence off the other three sides. What should be the dimensions of the lot if the enclosed area is to be a maximum? What is the maximum area?

**49.** ***Height of a Projected Object*** If an object on Earth is projected upward with an initial velocity of 32 feet per second, then its height after $t$ seconds is given by

$$h(t) = 32t - 16t^2.$$

Find the maximum height attained by the object and the number of seconds it takes to hit the ground.

**50.** ***Height of a Projected Object*** A projectile on Earth is fired straight upward so that its distance (in feet) above the ground $t$ seconds after firing is given by

$$s(t) = -16t^2 + 400t.$$

Find the maximum height it reaches and the number of seconds it takes to reach that height.

**51.** ***Height of a Projected Object*** If air resistance is neglected, a projectile on Earth shot straight upward with an initial velocity of 40 meters per second will be at a height $s$ in meters given by the function

$$s(t) = -4.9t^2 + 40t,$$

where $t$ is the number of seconds elapsed after projection. After how many seconds will it reach its maximum height, and what is this maximum height? Round your answers to the nearest tenth.

**52.** ***Height of a Projected Object*** A space robot is projected from the moon with its distance in feet given by

$$f(x) = 1.727x - .0013x^2$$

feet, where $x$ is time in seconds. Find the maximum height the robot can reach, and the time it takes to get there. Round answers to the nearest tenth.

**53.** ***Carbon Monoxide Exposure*** Carbon monoxide (CO) combines with the hemoglobin of the blood to form carboxyhemoglobin (COHb), which reduces the transport of oxygen to tissues. Smokers routinely have a 4% to 6% COHb level in their blood, which can cause symptoms such as blood flow alterations, visual impairment, and poorer vigilance. The quadratic function defined by

$$T(x) = .00787x^2 - 1.528x + 75.89$$

approximates the exposure time in hours necessary to reach this 4% to 6% level, where $50 \le x \le 100$ is the amount of carbon monoxide present in the air in parts per million (ppm). (*Source: Indoor Air Quality Environmental Information Handbook: Combustion Sources*, U.S. Department of Energy, 1985.)

**(a)** A kerosene heater or a room full of smokers is capable of producing 50 ppm of carbon monoxide. How long would it take for a nonsmoking person to start feeling the symptoms mentioned?

**(b)** Find the carbon monoxide concentration necessary for a person to reach the 4% to 6% COHb level in 3 hours.

**54.** ***Carbon Monoxide Exposure*** Refer to Exercise 53. High concentrations of carbon monoxide (CO) can cause coma and death. The time required for a person to reach a COHb level capable of causing a coma can be approximated by

$$T(x) = .0002x^2 - .316x + 127.9,$$

where $T$ is the exposure time in hours necessary to reach that level and $500 \le x \le 800$ is the amount of carbon monoxide in parts per million (ppm). (*Source: Indoor Air Quality Environmental Information Handbook: Combustion Sources*, U.S. Department of Energy, 1985.)

**(a)** What is the exposure time when $x = 600$ ppm?

**(b)** Estimate the concentration of CO necessary to produce a coma in 4 hours.

**55.** ***Automobile Stopping Distance*** Selected values of the stopping distance $y$ in feet of a car traveling $x$ mph are given in the table.

| Speed (in mph) | Stopping Distance (in feet) |
|---|---|
| 20 | 46 |
| 30 | 87 |
| 40 | 140 |
| 50 | 240 |
| 60 | 282 |
| 70 | 371 |

*Source: National Safety Institute Student Workbook*, 1993, p. 7.

The quadratic function defined by

$$f(x) = .056057x^2 + 1.06657x$$

is one model of the data. Find and interpret $f(45)$.

**56.** ***Investment Portfolio Mixtures*** The graph, which appears to be a portion of a parabola opening to the *right*, shows the performance of investment portfolios with different mixtures of U.S. and foreign investments for the period January 1, 1971, to December 31, 1996.

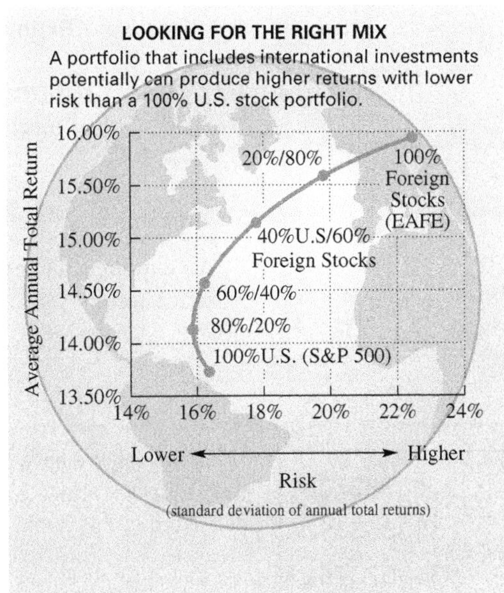


*Source: Financial Ink* Newsletter, Investment Management and Research, Inc., Feb. 1998. Thanks to David Van Geffen for this information.

Use the graph to answer the following questions.

**(a)** Is this the graph of a function? Explain.

(b) What investment mixture shown on the graph appears to represent the vertex? What relative amount of risk does this point represent? What return on investment does it provide?
(c) Which point on the graph represents the riskiest investment mixture? What return on investment does it provide?

57. ***Maximum Airline Revenue*** A charter flight charges a fare of \$200 per person, plus \$4 per person for each unsold seat on the plane. If the plane holds 100 passengers and if $x$ represents the number of unsold seats, find the following.
(a) An expression for the total revenue $R(x)$ received for the flight (*Hint*: Multiply the number of people flying, $100 - x$, by the price per ticket.)
(b) The graph for the function of part (a)
(c) The number of unsold seats that will produce the maximum revenue
(d) The maximum revenue

58. ***Maximum Bus Fare Revenue*** For a trip to a resort, a charter bus company charges a fare of \$48 per person, plus \$2 per person for each unsold seat on the bus. If the bus has 42 seats and $x$ represents the number of unsold seats, find the following.
(a) An expression that defines the total revenue, $R(x)$, from the trip (*Hint:* Multiply the total number riding, $42 - x$, by the price per ticket, $48 + 2x$.)
(b) The graph of the function from part (a)
(c) The number of unsold seats that produces the maximum revenue
(d) The maximum revenue

## 8.6 Exponential and Logarithmic Functions, Applications, and Models

**Exponential Functions and Applications • Logarithmic Functions and Applications • Exponential Models in Nature**

### Exponential Functions and Applications

In this section we introduce two new types of functions.

**Exponential Function**

An **exponential function** with base $b$, where $b > 0$ and $b \neq 1$, is a function of the form

$$f(x) = b^x, \quad \text{where } x \text{ is any real number.}$$

```
2^(9/7)
            2.438027308
(1/2)^1.5
            .3535533906
10^√(3)
            53.95737429
```

Compare with the discussion in the text.

Thus far, we have defined only integer exponents. In the definition of exponential function, we allow $x$ to take on any real number value. By using methods not discussed in this book, expressions such as

$$2^{9/7}, \quad \left(\frac{1}{2}\right)^{1.5}, \quad \text{and} \quad 10^{\sqrt{3}}$$

can be approximated. A scientific or graphing calculator is capable of determining approximations for these numbers. See the screen in the margin.

***Notice that in the definition of exponential function, the base b is restricted to positive numbers, with b ≠ 1.***

The graphs of $f(x) = 2^x$, $g(x) = \left(\frac{1}{2}\right)^x$, and $h(x) = 10^x$ are shown in Figure 35(a), (b), and (c). In each case, a table of selected points is given. The points are joined with a smooth curve, typical of the graphs of exponential functions. For each graph, the curve approaches but does not intersect the $x$-axis. For this reason, the $x$-axis is called the **horizontal asymptote** of the graph.

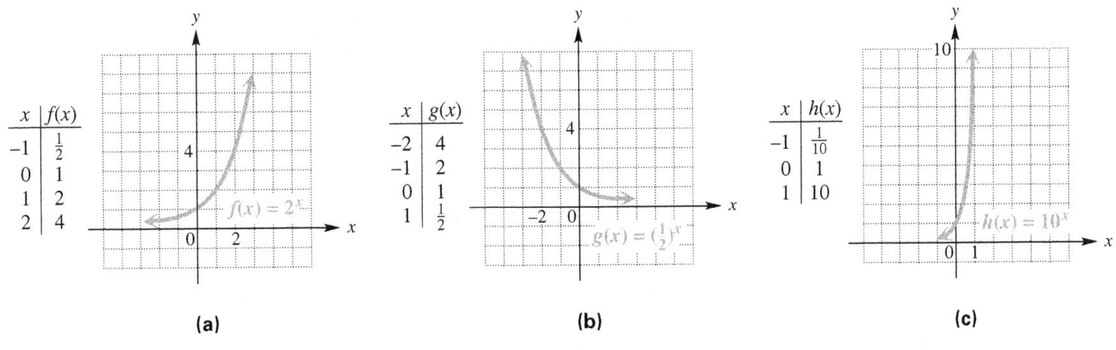

| $x$ | $f(x)$ |
|---|---|
| $-1$ | $\frac{1}{2}$ |
| 0 | 1 |
| 1 | 2 |
| 2 | 4 |

| $x$ | $g(x)$ |
|---|---|
| $-2$ | 4 |
| $-1$ | 2 |
| 0 | 1 |
| 1 | $\frac{1}{2}$ |

| $x$ | $h(x)$ |
|---|---|
| $-1$ | $\frac{1}{10}$ |
| 0 | 1 |
| 1 | 10 |



**FIGURE 35**

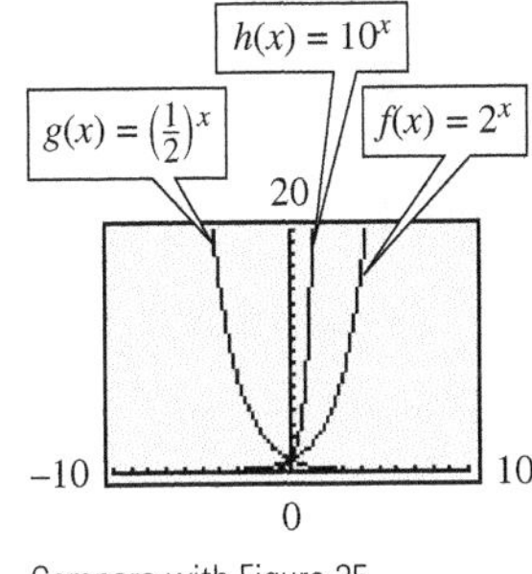


Compare with Figure 35.

This discussion illustrates the following facts about the graph of an exponential function.

## Graph of $f(x) = b^x$

1. The graph always will contain the point $(0, 1)$, because $b^0 = 1$.
2. When $b > 1$, the graph will *rise* from left to right (as in the illustrations of Figures 35(a) and (c) above, with $b = 2$ and $b = 10$). When $0 < b < 1$, the graph will *fall* from left to right (as in the illustration of Figure 35(b), with $b = \frac{1}{2}$).
3. The $x$-axis is the horizontal asymptote.
4. The domain is $(-\infty, \infty)$ and the range is $(0, \infty)$.

Probably the most important exponential function has the base $e$. (See Section 6.4.) The number $e$ is named after Leonhard Euler (1707–1783), and is approximately 2.718281828. It is an irrational number, and its value is approached by the expression

$$\left(1 + \frac{1}{n}\right)^n$$

as $n$ takes on larger and larger values. We write

$$\text{as } n \to \infty, \quad \left(1 + \frac{1}{n}\right)^n \to e \approx 2.718281828.$$

| X | Y1 |
|---|---|
| 1 | 2 |
| 10 | 2.5937 |
| 100 | 2.7048 |
| 1000 | 2.7169 |
| 10000 | 2.7181 |
| 100000 | 2.7183 |
| 1E6 | 2.7183 |

Y1=(1+1/X)^X

This table shows selected values for $Y_1 = \left(1 + \frac{1}{X}\right)^X$. Compare with Table 4.

See Table 4.

**TABLE 4**

| $n$ | Approximate Value of $\left(1 + \frac{1}{n}\right)^n$ |
|---|---|
| 1 | 2 |
| 100 | 2.70481 |
| 1000 | 2.71692 |
| 10,000 | 2.71815 |
| 1,000,000 | 2.71828 |

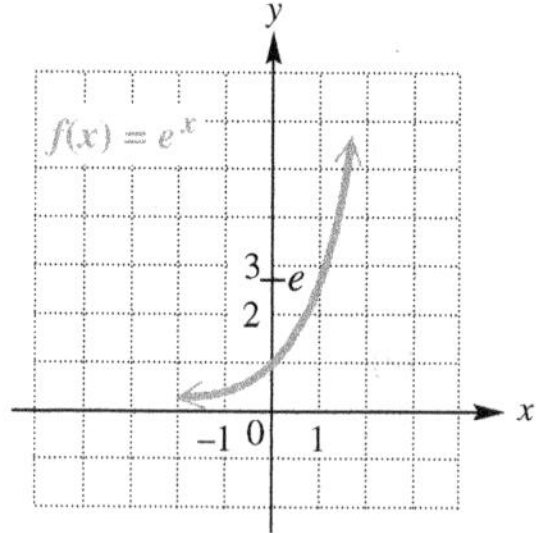


**FIGURE 36**

Powers of $e$ can be approximated on a scientific or graphing calculator. Some powers of $e$ obtained on a calculator are

$$e^{-2} \approx .1353352832, \qquad e^{1.3} \approx 3.669296668, \qquad e^4 \approx 54.59815003.$$

The graph of the function $f(x) = e^x$ is shown in Figure 36.

A real-life application of exponential functions occurs in the computation of **compound interest.**

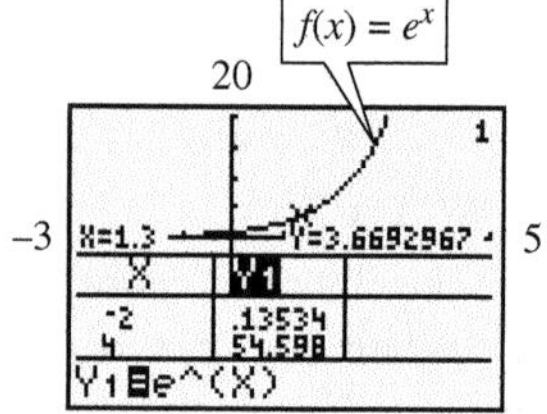


The values for $e^{-2}$, $e^{1.3}$, and $e^4$ are approximated in this split-screen graph of $f(x) = e^x$.

## Compound Interest Formula

Suppose that a principal of $P$ dollars is invested at an annual interest rate $r$ (in percent, expressed as a decimal), compounded $n$ times per year. Then the amount $A$ accumulated after $t$ years is given by the formula

$$A = P\left(1 + \frac{r}{n}\right)^{nt}.$$

## EXAMPLE 1 Applying the Compound Interest Formula

Suppose that \$1000 is invested at an annual rate of 8%, compounded quarterly (four times per year). Find the total amount in the account after ten years if no withdrawals are made.

**SOLUTION**

$$A = P\left(1 + \frac{r}{n}\right)^{nt} \qquad \text{Compound interest formula}$$

$$A = 1000\left(1 + \frac{.08}{4}\right)^{4 \cdot 10} \qquad P = 1000,\ r = .08,\ n = 4,\ t = 10$$

$$A = 1000(1.02)^{40}$$

$$A \approx 1000(2.20804) \qquad \text{Evaluate } 1.02^{40} \text{ with a calculator.}$$

$$A = 2208.04. \qquad \text{To the nearest cent}$$

≈ means "approximately equal to."

There would be \$2208.04 in the account at the end of ten years.

Following her success in *I Love Lucy*, **Lucille Ball** starred in *The Lucy Show* which aired for six seasons on CBS in the 1960s. She worked for Mr. Mooney (Gale Gordon), who was very careful with his money. In the September 26, 1966, show "Lucy, the Bean Queen," Lucy learned a lesson about **exponential growth.** Mr. Mooney had refused to lend her $1500 to buy furniture, because he claimed she did not know the value of money. He explained to her that if she were to save one penny on Day 1, two pennies on Day 2, four pennies on Day 3, and so on, she would have more than enough money to buy her furniture after only nineteen days. (You might want to verify this on your own.)

The compounding formula given earlier applies if the financial institution compounds interest for a finite number of compounding periods annually. Theoretically, the number of compounding periods per year can get larger and larger (quarterly, monthly, daily, etc.), and if $n$ is allowed to approach infinity, we say that interest is compounded *continuously*. The formula for **continuous compounding** involves the number $e$.

### Continuous Compound Interest Formula

Suppose that a principal of $P$ dollars is invested at an annual interest rate $r$ (in percent, expressed as a decimal), compounded continuously. Then the amount $A$ accumulated after $t$ years is given by the formula

$$A = Pe^{rt}.$$

### EXAMPLE 2 Applying the Continuous Compound Interest Formula

Suppose that $5000 is invested at an annual rate of 6.5%, compounded continuously. Find the total amount in the account after four years if no withdrawals are made.

**SOLUTION**

$$A = Pe^{rt} \qquad \text{Continuous compound interest formula}$$
$$A = 5000e^{.065(4)} \qquad P = 5000,\ r = .065,\ t = 4$$
$$A = 5000e^{.26}$$
$$A \approx 5000(1.29693) \qquad \text{Use the } e^x \text{ key on a calculator.}$$
$$A = 6484.65$$

There will be $6484.65 in the account after four years. ■

The continuous compound interest formula is an example of an **exponential growth function.** In situations involving growth or decay of a quantity, the amount or number present at time $t$ can often be approximated by a function of the form

$$A(t) = A_0e^{kt},$$

where $A_0$ represents the amount or number present at time $t = 0$, and $k$ is a constant. If $k > 0$, there is exponential growth; if $k < 0$, there is exponential decay.

## Logarithmic Functions and Applications

Consider the equation

$$2^3 = 8.$$

Here 3 is the exponent (or power) to which 2 must be raised in order to obtain 8. The exponent 3 is called the *logarithm* to the base 2 of 8, and this is written

$$3 = \log_2 8.$$

A variation of **exponential growth** is found in the legend of a Persian king, who wanted to please his executive officer, the Grand Vizier, with a gift of his choice. The Grand Vizier explained that he would like to be able to use his chessboard to accumulate wheat. A single grain of wheat would be received for the first square on the board, two grains would be received for the second square, four grains for the third, and so on, doubling the number of grains for each of the 64 squares on the board. As unlikely as it may seem, the number of grains would total 18.5 quintillion! Even with today's methods of production, this amount would take 150 years to produce. The Grand Vizier evidently knew his mathematics.

In general, we have the following relationship.

### Definition of $\log_b x$

For $b > 0$, $b \neq 1$,

$$\text{if } b^y = x, \quad \text{then} \quad y = \log_b x.$$

Table 5 illustrates the relationship between exponential equations and logarithmic equations.

**TABLE 5**

| Exponential Equation | Logarithmic Equation |
|---|---|
| $3^4 = 81$ | $4 = \log_3 81$ |
| $10^5 = 100{,}000$ | $5 = \log_{10} 100{,}000$ |
| $\left(\frac{1}{2}\right)^{-4} = 16$ | $-4 = \log_{1/2} 16$ |
| $10^0 = 1$ | $0 = \log_{10} 1$ |
| $4^{-3} = \frac{1}{64}$ | $-3 = \log_4 \frac{1}{64}$ |

The concept of inverse functions (studied in more advanced algebra courses) leads us to the definition of the logarithmic function with base $b$.

$F(x) = \log_2 x$ $H(x) = \log_{10} x$

10

−2 10

−5

$G(x) = \log_{1/2} x$

Compare with Figure 37. Graphs of logarithmic functions with bases other than 10 and $e$ are obtained with the use of the change-of-base rule from algebra:

$$\log_a x = \frac{\log x}{\log a} = \frac{\ln x}{\ln a}.$$

Alternatively, they can be drawn by using the capability that allows the user to obtain the graph of the inverse.

### Logarithmic Function

A **logarithmic function with base $b$,** where $b > 0$ and $b \neq 1$, is a function of the form

$$g(x) = \log_b x, \qquad \text{where } x > 0.$$

***The graph of the function $g(x) = \log_b x$ can be found by interchanging the roles of $x$ and $y$ in the function $f(x) = b^x$. Geometrically, this is accomplished by reflecting the graph of $f(x) = b^x$ about the line $y = x$.***

The graphs of

$$F(x) = \log_2 x, \quad G(x) = \log_{1/2} x, \quad \text{and} \quad H(x) = \log_{10} x$$

are shown in Figure 37(a), (b), and (c) on the next page. In each case, a table of selected points is given. These points were obtained by interchanging the roles of $x$ and $y$ in the tables of points given in Figure 35. The points are joined with a smooth curve, typical of the graphs of logarithmic functions. For each graph, the curve approaches but does not intersect the $y$-axis. Thus, the $y$-axis is called the **vertical asymptote** of the graph.

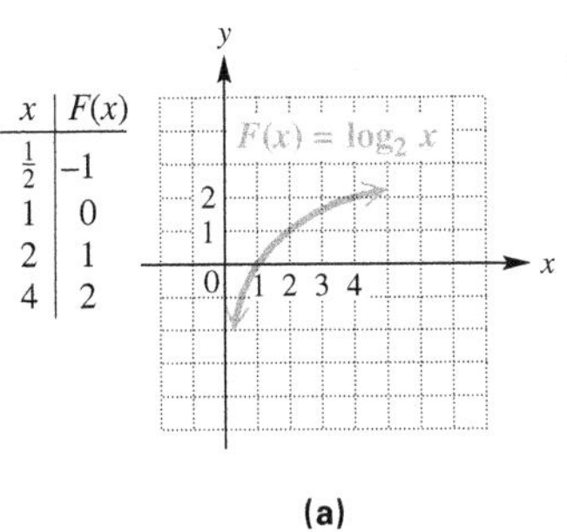

| $x$ | $F(x)$ |
|---|---|
| $\frac{1}{2}$ | $-1$ |
| 1 | 0 |
| 2 | 1 |
| 4 | 2 |



(a)

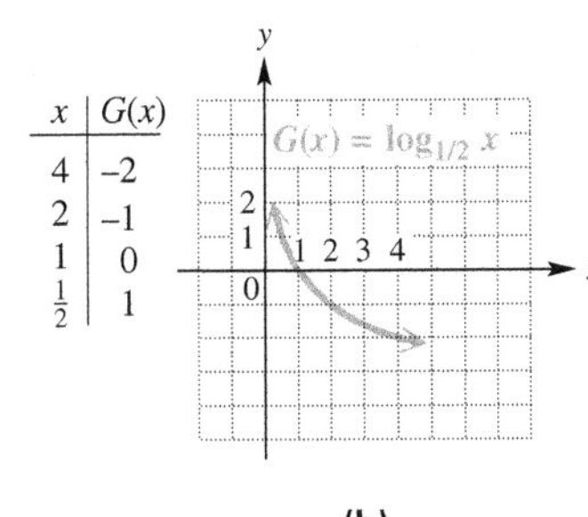

| $x$ | $G(x)$ |
|---|---|
| 4 | $-2$ |
| 2 | $-1$ |
| 1 | 0 |
| $\frac{1}{2}$ | 1 |



(b)

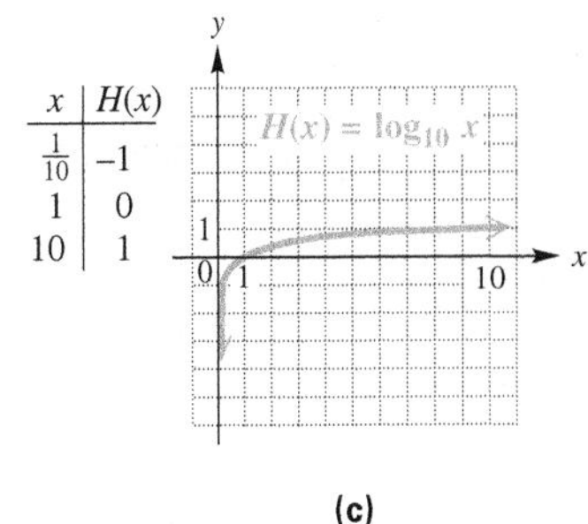

| $x$ | $H(x)$ |
|---|---|
| $\frac{1}{10}$ | $-1$ |
| 1 | 0 |
| 10 | 1 |



(c)

**FIGURE 37**

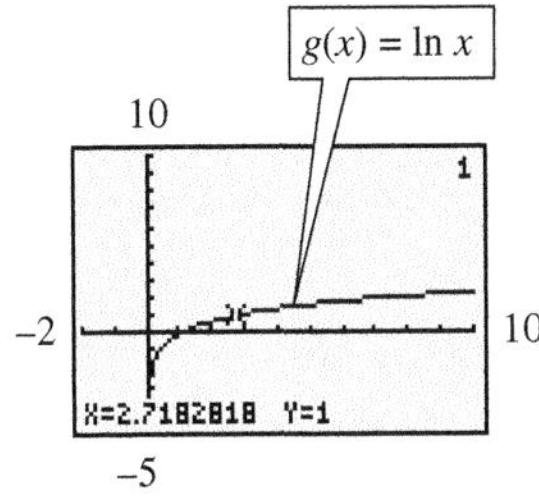



Notice that when

$x = e \approx 2.7182818,$

$y = \ln e = 1.$

## Graph of $g(x) = \log_b x$

1. The graph will always contain the point $(1, 0)$, because $\log_b 1 = 0$.
2. When $b > 1$, the graph will *rise* from left to right, from the fourth quadrant to the first (as in the illustrations of Figure 37(a) and (c) above, with $b = 2$ and $b = 10$). When $0 < b < 1$, the graph will *fall* from left to right, from the first quadrant to the fourth (as in the illustration of Figure 37(b), with $b = \frac{1}{2}$).
3. The $y$-axis is the vertical asymptote.
4. The domain is $(0, \infty)$ and the range is $(-\infty, \infty)$.

An important logarithmic function is the function with base $e$. If we interchange the roles of $x$ and $y$ in the graph of $f(x) = e^x$ (Figure 36), we obtain the graph of $g(x) = \log_e x$. There is a special symbol for $\log_e x$: it is $\ln x$. That is,

$$\ln x = \log_e x.$$

Figure 38 shows the graph of $g(x) = \ln x$, called the **natural logarithmic function.**

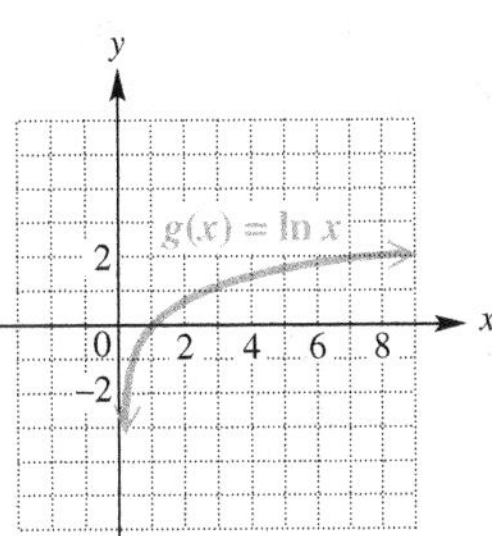



**FIGURE 38**

The expression $\ln e^k$ is the exponent to which the base $e$ must be raised in order to obtain $e^k$. There is only one such number that will do this, and it is $k$. Thus, for all real numbers $k$,

$$\ln e^k = k.$$

**The number *e*** is named in honor of Leonhard Euler (1707–1783), the prolific Swiss mathematician. The value of *e* can be expressed as an **infinite series.**

$$e = 1 + \frac{1}{1} + \frac{1}{1 \cdot 2} + \frac{1}{1 \cdot 2 \cdot 3} + \frac{1}{1 \cdot 2 \cdot 3 \cdot 4} + \cdots$$

It can also be expressed in two ways using **continued fractions.**

$$e = 2 + \cfrac{1}{1 + \cfrac{1}{2 + \cfrac{1}{1 + \cfrac{1}{1 + \cfrac{1}{4 + \cdots}}}}}$$

$$e = 2 + \cfrac{1}{1 + \cfrac{1}{2 + \cfrac{2}{3 + \cfrac{3}{4 + \cfrac{4}{\cdots}}}}}$$

### EXAMPLE 3 Finding the Time for an Amount to Triple

Suppose that a certain amount $P$ is invested at an annual rate of 6.5%, compounded continuously. How long will it take for the amount to triple?

**SOLUTION**

We wish to find the value of $t$ in the continuous compound interest formula that will make the amount $A$ equal to $3P$ (since we want the initial investment, $P$, to triple).

$$A = Pe^{rt}$$

$$3P = Pe^{.065t} \quad \text{Substitute } 3P \text{ for } A \text{ and } .065 \text{ for } r.$$

$$3 = e^{.065t} \quad \text{Divide both sides by } P.$$

$$\ln 3 = \ln e^{.065t} \quad \text{Take the natural logarithm of both sides.}$$

$$\ln 3 = .065t \quad \text{Use the fact that } \ln e^k = k.$$

$$t = \frac{\ln 3}{.065} \quad \text{Divide both sides by .065.}$$

A calculator shows that $\ln 3 \approx 1.098612289$. Dividing this by .065 gives

$$t \approx 16.9$$

to the nearest tenth. Therefore, it would take about 16.9 years for any initial investment $P$ to triple under the given conditions. (The amount of time it would take for a given amount to double under given conditions is called **doubling time.** The doubling time for this example is $\frac{\ln 2}{.065} \approx 10.66$ years.)

## Exponential Models in Nature

### EXAMPLE 4 Modeling the Greenhouse Effect

The *greenhouse effect* refers to the phenomenon whereby emissions of gases such as carbon dioxide, methane, and chlorofluorocarbons (CFCs) have the potential to alter the climate of the earth and destroy the ozone layer. Concentrations of CFC-12, used in refrigeration technology, in parts per billion (ppb) can be modeled by the exponential function defined by

$$f(x) = .48e^{.04x},$$

where $x = 0$ represents 1990, $x = 1$ represents 1991, and so on. Use this function to approximate the concentration in 1998.

**SOLUTION**

Because $x = 0$ represents 1990, $x = 8$ represents 1998. Evaluate $f(8)$ using a calculator.

$$f(8) = .48e^{.04(8)} = .48e^{.32} \approx .66$$

In 1998, the concentration of CFC-12 was about .66 ppb.

Radioactive materials disintegrate according to exponential decay functions. The **half-life** of a quantity that decays exponentially is the amount of time that it takes for any initial amount to decay to half its initial value.

## EXAMPLE 5 Carbon 14 Dating

Carbon 14 is a radioactive form of carbon that is found in all living plants and animals. After a plant or animal dies, the radiocarbon disintegrates. Scientists determine the age of the remains by comparing the amount of carbon 14 present with the amount found in living plants and animals. The amount of carbon 14 present after $t$ years is modeled by the exponential equation $y = y_0 e^{-.0001216t}$, where $y_0$ represents the initial amount. **(a)** What is the half-life of carbon 14? **(b)** If an initial sample contains 1 gram of carbon 14, how much will be left after 10,000 years?

**SOLUTION**

**(a)** To find the half-life, let $y = \frac{1}{2}y_0$ in the equation.

$$\frac{1}{2}y_0 = y_0 e^{-.0001216t}$$

$$\frac{1}{2} = e^{-.0001216t} \quad \text{Divide by } y_0.$$

$$\ln\left(\frac{1}{2}\right) = -.0001216t \quad \text{Take the natural logarithm of both sides.}$$

$$t \approx 5700 \quad \text{Use a calculator.}$$

The half-life of carbon 14 is about 5700 years.

**(b)** Evaluate $y$ for $t = 10{,}000$ and $y_0 = 1$.

$$y = 1e^{-.0001216(10{,}000)} \approx .30 \quad \text{Use a calculator.}$$

There will be about .30 grams remaining. ■

---

If you were to travel back in time to a period before the availability of handheld calculators, your study of logarithms would probably focus on how they can be used to perform calculations. **Tables of logarithms** were routinely included in mathematics textbooks. Properties of logarithms allow us to multiply by adding, divide by subtracting, and raise to powers and take roots by simple multiplications and divisions.

To get an idea of what computing with logarithms involved, look at the photo above. It shows a homework problem from May 15, 1930, where the student was required to calculate

$$\sqrt[5]{\frac{3.1416 \times 4771.21 \times 2.7183^{1/2}}{30.103^4 \times .4343^{1/2} \times 69.897^4}}.$$

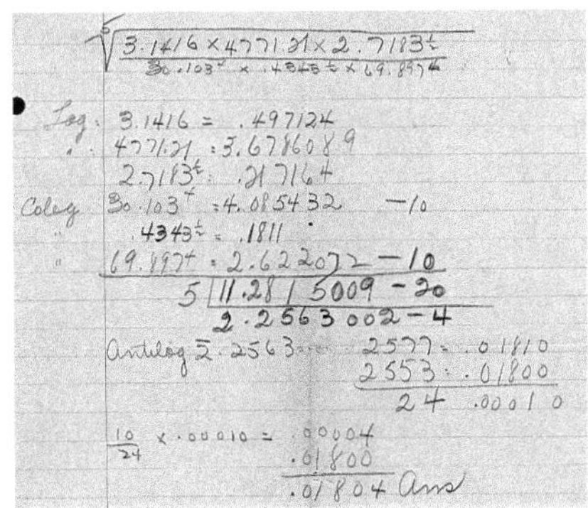

It was found on a well-preserved sheet of paper stuck inside an old mathematics text purchased in a used-book store in New Orleans. The student's answer .01804 is correct. Doesn't this make you appreciate your calculator?

A **common,** or **base ten logarithm,** of a positive number $x$ is the exponent to which 10 must be raised in order to obtain $x$. Symbolically, we simply write $\log x$ to denote $\log_{10} x$. Common logarithms are still used in certain applications in science. For example, the **pH** of a substance is the negative of the common logarithm of the hydronium ion concentration in moles per liter. The pH value is a measure of the acidity or alkalinity of a solution. If pH $> 7.0$, the solution is alkaline; if pH $< 7.0$, it is acidic. The **Richter scale,** used to measure the intensity of earthquakes, is based on logarithms, and sound intensities, measured in decibels, also have a logarithmic basis.

## 8.6 EXERCISES

*Fill in each blank with the correct response.*

1. For an exponential function $f(x) = a^x$, if $a > 1$, the graph ________ (rises/falls) from left to right. If $0 < a < 1$, the graph ________ (rises/falls) from left to right.

2. The $y$-intercept of the graph of $y = a^x$ is ______.

3. The graph of the exponential function $f(x) = a^x$ ____________ (does/does not) have an $x$-intercept.

4. The point (2, ______) is on the graph of $f(x) = 3^{4x-3}$.

5. For a logarithmic function $g(x) = \log_a x$, if $a > 1$, the graph ________ (rises/falls) from left to right. If $0 < a < 1$, the graph ________ (rises/falls) from left to right.

6. The $x$-intercept of the graph of $y = \log_a x$ is ______.

7. The graph of the exponential function $g(x) = \log_a x$ ____________ (does/does not) have a $y$-intercept.

8. The point (98, ______) lies on the graph of $g(x) = \log_{10}(x + 2)$.

*Use a calculator to find an approximation for each number. Give as many digits as the calculator displays.*

9. $9^{3/7}$

10. $14^{2/7}$

11. $(.83)^{-1.2}$

12. $(.97)^{3.4}$

13. $(\sqrt{6})^{\sqrt{5}}$

14. $(\sqrt{7})^{\sqrt{3}}$

15. $\left(\frac{1}{3}\right)^{9.8}$

16. $\left(\frac{2}{5}\right)^{8.1}$

*Sketch the graph of each function.*

17. $f(x) = 3^x$

18. $f(x) = 5^x$

19. $f(x) = \left(\frac{1}{4}\right)^x$

20. $f(x) = \left(\frac{1}{3}\right)^x$

*Use a calculator to approximate each number. Give as many digits as the calculator displays.*

21. $e^3$

22. $e^4$

23. $e^{-4}$

24. $e^{-3}$

*In Exercises 25–28, rewrite the exponential equation as a logarithmic equation. In Exercises 29–32, rewrite the logarithmic equation as an exponential equation.*

25. $4^2 = 16$

26. $5^3 = 125$

27. $\left(\frac{2}{3}\right)^{-3} = \frac{27}{8}$

28. $\left(\frac{1}{10}\right)^{-4} = 10{,}000$

29. $5 = \log_2 32$

30. $3 = \log_4 64$

31. $1 = \log_3 3$

32. $0 = \log_{12} 1$

*Use a calculator to approximate each number. Give as many digits as the calculator displays.*

33. $\ln 4$

34. $\ln 6$

35. $\ln .35$

36. $\ln 2.45$

**Global Warming** *This figure appeared in the October 1990 issue of* National Geographic. *It shows projected temperature increases using two graphs: one an exponential-type curve, and the other linear. From the figure, approximate the increase* **(a)** *for the exponential curve, and* **(b)** *for the linear graph for each of the years in Exercises 37–40.*

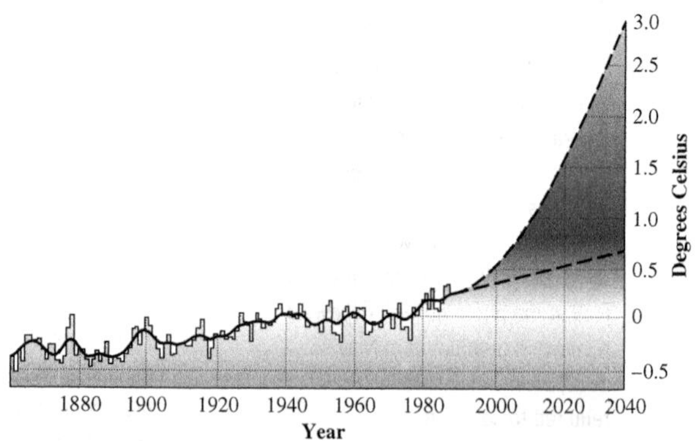


*Source:* "Zero Equals Average Global Temperature for the Period 1950–1979" by Dale D. Glasgow from *National Geographic*, October 1990. Reprinted by permission of the National Geographic Society.

**37.** 2000 **38.** 2010

**39.** 2020 **40.** 2040

*Sketch the graph of each function. (Hint: Use the graphs of the exponential functions in Exercises 17–20 to help.)*

**41.** $g(x) = \log_3 x$ **42.** $g(x) = \log_5 x$

**43.** $g(x) = \log_{1/4} x$ **44.** $g(x) = \log_{1/3} x$

***Investment*** *Determine the amount of money that will be accumulated in an account that pays compound interest, given the initial principal in each of the following.*

**45.** \$20,000 invested at 3% annual interest for 4 years compounded **(a)** annually; **(b)** semiannually

**46.** \$35,000 invested at 4.2% annual interest for 3 years compounded **(a)** annually; **(b)** quarterly

**47.** \$27,500 invested at 3.95% annual interest for 5 years compounded **(a)** daily ($n = 365$); **(b)** continuously

**48.** \$15,800 invested at 4.6% annual interest for 6.5 years compounded **(a)** quarterly; **(b)** continuously

***Comparing Investment Plans*** *In Exercises 49 and 50, decide which of the two plans will provide a better yield. (Interest rates stated are annual rates.)*

**49.** Plan A: \$40,000 invested for 3 years at 4.5%, compounded quarterly
Plan B: \$40,000 invested for 3 years at 4.4%, compounded continuously

**50.** Plan A: \$50,000 invested for 10 years at 4.75%, compounded daily ($n = 365$)
Plan B: \$50,000 invested for 10 years at 4.7%, compounded continuously

*Solve each problem.*

**51.** ***Atmospheric Pressure*** The atmospheric pressure $f$ (in millibars) at a given altitude $x$ (in meters) is approximated by the function

$$f(x) = 1013e^{-.0001341x}.$$

**(a)** Predict the pressure at 1500 meters.
**(b)** Predict the pressure at 11,000 meters.

**52.** ***World Population Growth*** World population in millions closely fits the exponential function defined by

$$y = 5282e^{.01405x},$$

where $x$ is the number of years since 1990. (*Source*: U.S. Census Bureau.)
**(a)** The world population was about 6080 million in 2000. How closely does the function approximate this value?
**(b)** Use this model to approximate the population in 2005.
**(c)** Use the model to predict the population in 2010.

**53.** ***Population of Pakistan*** The U.S. Census Bureau projects that the approximate population of Pakistan will grow according to the function

$$f(x) = 146{,}250(2)^{.0176x},$$

where $x = 0$ represents the year 2000, $x = 25$ represents 2025, and $x = 50$ represents 2050.
**(a)** According to this model, what was the population of Pakistan in 2000?
**(b)** What will the population be in 2025?
**(c)** How will the population in 2025 compare to the population in 2000?

**54.** ***Population of Brazil*** The U.S. Census Bureau projects that the approximate population of Brazil will grow according to the function

$$f(x) = 176{,}000(2)^{.008x},$$

where $x = 0$ represents the year 2000, $x = 25$ represents 2025, and $x = 50$ represents 2050.
**(a)** According to this model, what was the population of Brazil in 2000?
**(b)** What will the population be in 2025?
**(c)** How will the population in 2025 compare to the population in 2000?

55. ***Decay of Lead*** A sample of 500 grams of radioactive lead 210 decays to polonium 210 according to the function defined by

$$A(t) = 500e^{-.032t},$$

where $t$ is time in years. Find the amount of the sample remaining after
(a) 4 years
(b) 8 years
(c) 20 years
(d) Find the half-life.

56. ***Decay of Plutonium*** Repeat Exercise 55 for 500 grams of plutonium 241, which decays according to the function defined as follows, where $t$ is time in years.

$$A(t) = A_0e^{-.053t}$$

57. ***Decay of Radium*** Find the half-life of radium 226, which decays according to the function defined as follows, where $t$ is time in years.

$$A(t) = A_0e^{-.00043t}$$

58. ***Decay of Iodine*** How long will it take any quantity of iodine 131 to decay to 25% of its initial amount, knowing that it decays according to the function defined as follows, where $t$ is time in days?

$$A(t) = A_0e^{-.087t}$$

59. ***Carbon 14 Dating*** Suppose an Egyptian mummy is discovered in which the amount of carbon 14 present is only about one-third the amount found in living human beings. About how long ago did the Egyptian die?

60. ***Carbon 14 Dating*** A sample from a refuse deposit near the Strait of Magellan had 60% of the carbon 14 of a contemporary living sample. How old was the sample?

61. ***Carbon 14 Dating*** Estimate the age of a specimen that contains 20% of the carbon 14 of a comparable living specimen.

62. ***Value of a Copier*** A small business estimates that the value $V(t)$ of a copier is decreasing according to the function defined by

$$V(t) = 5000(2)^{-.15t},$$

where $t$ is the number of years that have elapsed since the machine was purchased, and $V(t)$ is in dollars.

(a) What was the original value of the machine?
(b) What is the value of the machine 5 years after purchase? Give your answer to the nearest dollar.
(c) What is the value of the machine 10 years after purchase? Give your answer to the nearest dollar.

***Earthquake Intensity*** *In the United States, the intensity of an earthquake is rated using the Richter scale. The Richter scale rating of an earthquake in intensity x is given by*

$$R = \log_{10}\frac{x}{x_0},$$

*where $x_0$ is the intensity of an earthquake of a certain (small) size. The figure shows Richter scale ratings for major Southern California earthquakes since 1920. As the figure indicates, earthquakes "come in bunches" and the 1990s were an especially busy time.*

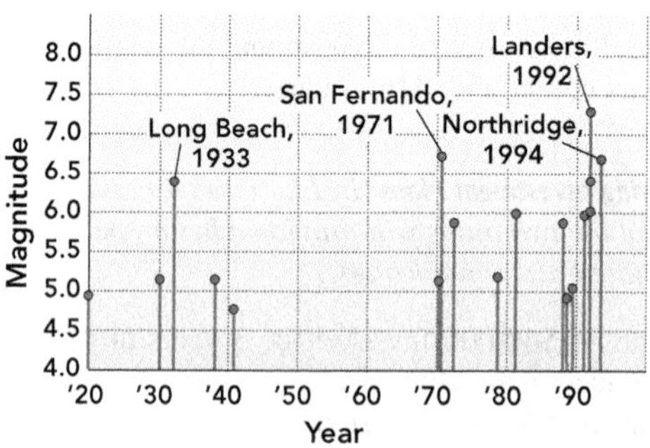


*Source:* Caltech; U.S. Geological Survey.

*Writing the logarithmic equation just given in exponential form, we get*

$$10^R = \frac{x}{x_0} \quad \text{or} \quad x = 10^R x_0.$$

*The 1994 Northridge earthquake had a Richter scale rating of* 6.7; *the Landers earthquake had a rating of* 7.3.

63. How many times as powerful was the Landers earthquake compared to the Northridge earthquake?

64. Compare the smallest rated earthquake in the graph (at 4.8) with the Landers quake. How many times as powerful was the Landers quake?

# 8.7 Systems of Equations and Applications

**Linear Systems in Two Variables • Elimination Method • Substitution Method • Linear Systems in Three Variables • Applications of Linear Systems**

## Linear Systems in Two Variables

During the 1990s, the audiocassette as a medium of recorded music began its demise, while compact discs gained in popularity. Figure 39 shows these trends. With $x = 0$ representing 1990 and $x = 10$ representing 2000, the two equations

$$y = 74.523x + 289.3 \quad \text{Compact discs}$$
$$y = -34.107x + 434.49 \quad \text{Audiocassettes}$$

provide good models for the growth in sales of CDs and decline in sales of cassettes, where $y$ is in millions of dollars. The two equations here are considered together, and such a set of equations is called a **system of equations.** The point where the graphs in Figure 39 intersect is a solution of each of the individual equations. It is also the solution of the system of equations. From the figure we see that in 1991, both CDs and cassettes had sales of about \$400 million.

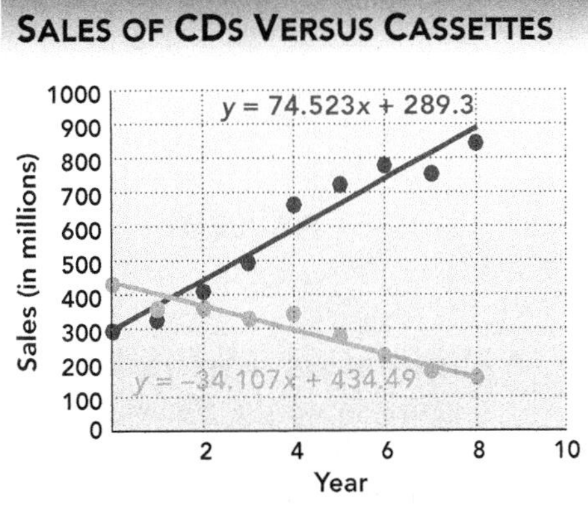


*Source: World Almanac and Book of Facts.*

**FIGURE 39**

The definition of a linear equation given earlier can be extended to more variables. Any equation of the form

$$a_1x_1 + a_2x_2 + \cdots + a_nx_n = b$$

for real numbers $a_1, a_2, \ldots, a_n$ (not all of which are 0), and $b$, is a **linear equation in $n$ variables.** If all the equations in a system are linear, the system is a **system of linear equations,** or a **linear system.**

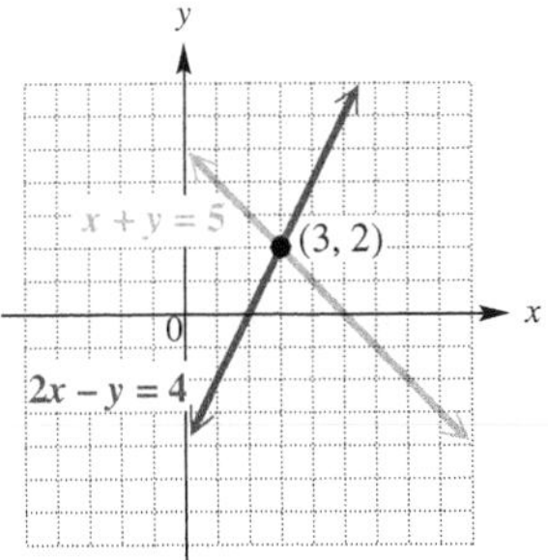


**FIGURE 40**

In Figure 40, the two linear equations $x + y = 5$ and $2x - y = 4$ are graphed in the same coordinate system. Notice that they intersect at the point (3, 2). Because (3, 2) is the only ordered pair that satisfies both equations at the same time, we say that $\{(3, 2)\}$ is the solution set of the system

$$x + y = 5$$
$$2x - y = 4$$

Because the graph of a linear equation is a straight line, there are three possibilities for the number of solutions in the solution set of a system of two linear equations, as shown in Figures 41–43.

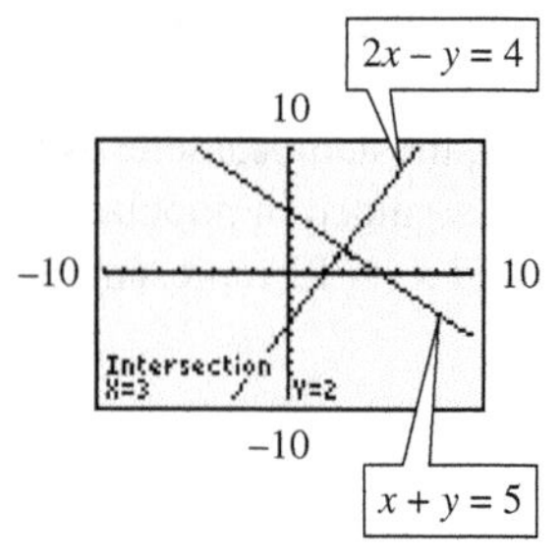


A graphing calculator supports our statement that (3, 2) is the solution of the system

$$x + y = 5$$
$$2x - y = 4.$$

### Graphs of a Linear System (The Three Possibilities)

1. The two graphs intersect in a single point. The coordinates of this point give the only solution of the system. In this case, the system is **consistent** and the equations are **independent.** This is the most common case. See Figure 41.
2. The graphs are parallel lines. In this case, the system is **inconsistent** and the equations are **independent.** That is, there is no solution common to both equations of the system, and the solution set is $\emptyset$. See Figure 42.
3. The graphs are the same line. In this case, the system is **consistent** and the equations are **dependent,** because any solution of one equation of the system is also a solution of the other. The solution set is an infinite set of ordered pairs representing the points on the line. See Figure 43.

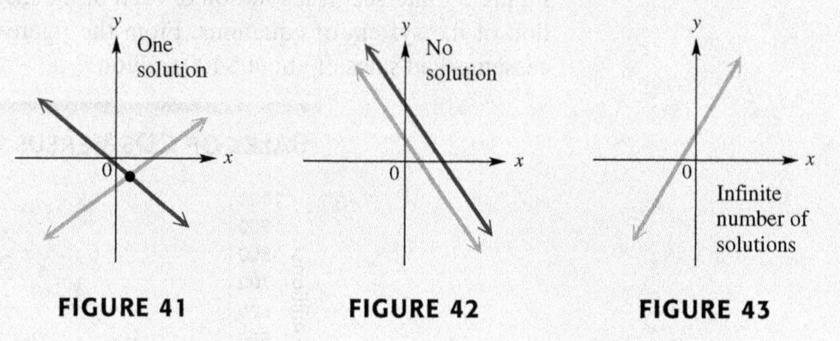


**FIGURE 41** **FIGURE 42** **FIGURE 43**

**Elimination Method** In most cases, we cannot rely on graphing to solve systems, so we use algebraic methods. One such method is called the **elimination method.** The elimination method involves combining the two equations of the system so that one variable is eliminated. This is done using the following fact.

**If $a = b$ and $c = d$, then $a + c = b + d$.**

The method of solving a system by elimination is summarized as follows.

The solution of **systems of equations** of graphs more complicated than straight lines is the principle behind the **mattang** (shown on this stamp), a stick chart used by the people of the Marshall Islands in the Pacific. A mattang is made of roots tied together with coconut fibers, and it shows the wave patterns found when approaching an island.

### Solving Linear Systems by Elimination

*Step 1* **Write both equations in standard form $Ax + By = C$.**

*Step 2* **Make the coefficients of one pair of variable terms opposites.** Multiply one or both equations by appropriate numbers so that the sum of the coefficients of either $x$ or $y$ is zero.

*Step 3* **Add** the new equations to eliminate a variable. The sum should be an equation with just one variable.

*Step 4* **Solve** the equation from Step 3.

*(continued)*

*Step 5* **Find the other value.** Substitute the result of Step 4 into either of the given equations and solve for the other variable.

*Step 6* **Find the solution set.** Check the solution in both of the given equations. Then write the solution set.

## EXAMPLE 1 Solving a System by Elimination (Two Variables)

Solve the system.

$$5x - 2y = 4 \quad (1)$$
$$2x + 3y = 13 \quad (2)$$

**SOLUTION**

*Step 1* Both equations are already in standard form.

*Step 2* Our goal is to add the two equations so that one of the variables is eliminated. Suppose we wish to eliminate the variable $x$. Since the coefficients of $x$ are *not* opposites, we must first transform one or both equations so that the coefficients *are* opposites. Then, when we combine the equations, the term with $x$ will have a coefficient of 0, and we will be able to solve for $y$. We begin by multiplying equation (1) by 2 and equation (2) by $-5$.

$$10x - 4y = 8 \quad \text{2 times each side of equation (1)}$$
$$-10x - 15y = -65 \quad \text{−5 times each side of equation (2)}$$

*Step 3* Now add the two equations to eliminate $x$.

$$\begin{aligned} 10x - 4y &= 8 \\ -10x - 15y &= -65 \\ \hline -19y &= -57 \quad \text{Add.} \end{aligned}$$

*Step 4* Solve the equation from Step 3 to get $y = 3$.

*Step 5* To find $x$, we substitute 3 for $y$ in either of the original equations.

$$\begin{aligned} 2x + 3y &= 13 && \text{We use equation (2).} \\ 2x + 3(3) &= 13 && \text{Let } y = 3. \\ 2x + 9 &= 13 \\ 2x &= 4 && \text{Subtract 9.} \\ x &= 2 && \text{Divide by 2.} \end{aligned}$$

Write the x-value first.

*Step 6* The solution appears to be (2, 3). To check, substitute 2 for $x$ and 3 for $y$ in both of the original equations.

$$\begin{aligned} 5x - 2y &= 4 && (1) \\ 5(2) - 2(3) &= 4 && ? \\ 10 - 6 &= 4 && ? \\ 4 &= 4 && \text{True} \end{aligned}$$

$$\begin{aligned} 2x + 3y &= 13 && (2) \\ 2(2) + 3(3) &= 13 && ? \\ 4 + 9 &= 13 && ? \\ 13 &= 13 && \text{True} \end{aligned}$$

The solution set is $\{(2, 3)\}$.

5x − 2y = 4
10
−10
10
Intersection X=2 Y=3
−10
2x + 3y = 13

The solution in Example 1 is supported by a graphing calculator. We solve each equation for $y$, graph them both, and find the point of intersection of the two lines: (2, 3).

**Substitution Method** Linear systems can also be solved by the **substitution method.** This method is most useful for solving linear systems in which one variable has coefficient 1 or $-1$. As shown in more advanced algebra courses, the substitution method also is the best choice for solving many *nonlinear* systems.

**Solving Linear Systems by Substitution**

*Step 1* **Solve for one variable in terms of the other.** Solve one of the equations for either variable. (If one of the variables has coefficient 1 or $-1$, choose it, since the substitution method is usually easier this way.)

*Step 2* **Substitute** for that variable in the other equation. The result should be an equation with just one variable.

*Step 3* **Solve** the equation from Step 2.

*Step 4* **Find the other value.** Substitute the result from Step 3 into the equation from Step 1 to find the value of the other variable.

*Step 5* **Find the solution set.** Check the solution in both of the given equations. Then write the solution set.

## EXAMPLE 2 Solving a System by Substitution (Two Variables)

Solve the system.

$$3x + 2y = 13 \quad (1)$$
$$4x - y = -1 \quad (2)$$

**SOLUTION**

*Step 1* To use the substitution method, first solve one of the equations for either $x$ or $y$. Since the coefficient of $y$ in equation (2) is $-1$, it is easiest to solve for $y$ in equation (2).

$$-y = -1 - 4x \quad \text{Equation (2) rearranged}$$
$$y = 1 + 4x$$

*Step 2* Substitute $1 + 4x$ for $y$ in equation (1) to obtain an equation in $x$.

$$3x + 2y = 13 \quad (1)$$
$$3x + 2(1 + 4x) = 13 \quad \text{Let } y = 1 + 4x.$$

*Step 3* Solve for $x$ in the equation just obtained.

$$3x + 2 + 8x = 13 \quad \text{Distributive property}$$
$$11x = 11 \quad \text{Combine terms; subtract 2.}$$
$$x = 1 \quad \text{Divide by 11.}$$

*Step 4* Now solve for $y$. Because $y = 1 + 4x$, $y = 1 + 4(1) = 5$.

*Step 5* Check to see that the ordered pair $(1, 5)$ satisfies both equations. The solution set is $\{(1, 5)\}$.

The next example illustrates special cases that may result when systems are solved. (We will use the elimination method, but the same conclusions will follow when the substitution method is used.)

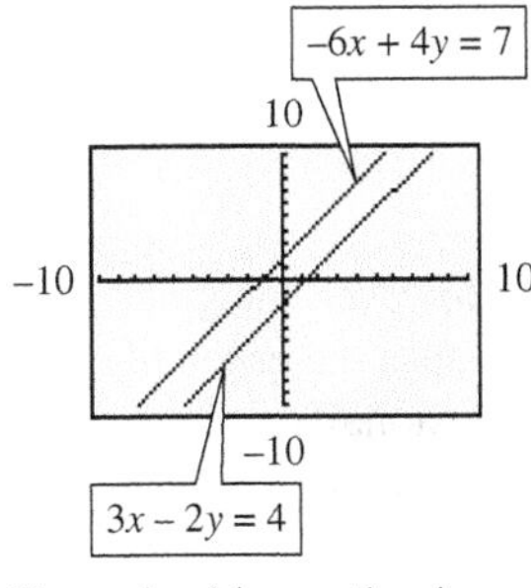


The graphs of the equations in Example 3(a) are parallel. There are no solutions.

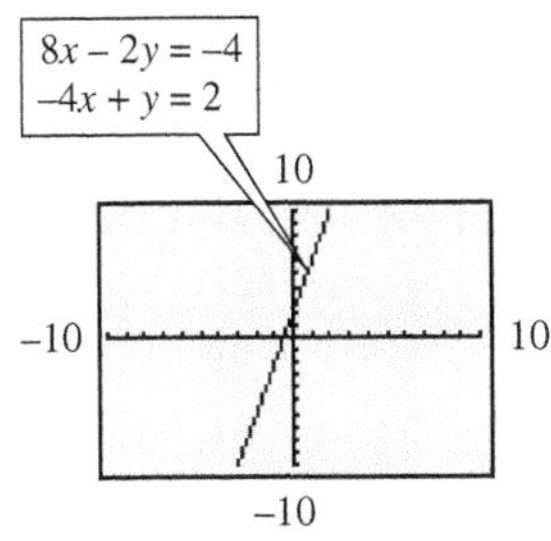


The graphs of the equations in Example 3(b) coincide. We see only one line. There are infinitely many solutions.

## EXAMPLE 3 Solving Systems of Special Cases

Solve each system.

**(a)** $3x - 2y = 4$ (1) **(b)** $-4x + y = 2$ (3)

$-6x + 4y = 7$ (2) $8x - 2y = -4$ (4)

**SOLUTION**

**(a)** Eliminate $x$ by multiplying both sides of equation (1) by 2 and then adding.

$$\begin{aligned} 6x - 4y &= 8 \quad \text{2 times equation (1)} \\ -6x + 4y &= 7 \quad \text{(2)} \\ \hline \mathbf{0} &= \mathbf{15} \quad \text{False} \end{aligned}$$

Both variables were eliminated here, leaving the false statement $0 = 15$, indicating that these two equations have no solutions in common. The system is inconsistent, with the empty set $\emptyset$ as the solution set.

**(b)** Eliminate $x$ by multiplying both sides of equation (3) by 2 and then adding the result to equation (4).

$$\begin{aligned} -8x + 2y &= 4 \quad \text{2 times equation (3)} \\ 8x - 2y &= -4 \quad \text{(4)} \\ \hline 0 &= 0 \quad \text{True} \end{aligned}$$

This true statement, $0 = 0$, indicates that a solution of one equation is also a solution of the other, so the solution set is an infinite set of ordered pairs. The two equations are dependent.

We write the solution set of a system of dependent equations as a set of ordered pairs by expressing $x$ in terms of $y$ as follows. Choose either equation and solve for $x$. Choosing equation (3) gives

$$-4x + y = 2 \quad \text{(3)}$$

$$x = \frac{2 - y}{-4} = \frac{y - 2}{4}.$$

The solution set is written as

$$\left\{ \left( \frac{y - 2}{4}, y \right) \right\}.$$

By selecting values for $y$ and calculating the corresponding values for $x$, individual ordered pairs of the solution set can be found. For example, if $y = -2$, $x = \frac{-2-2}{4} = -1$ and the ordered pair $(-1, -2)$ is a solution.

**Linear Systems in Three Variables** A solution of an equation in three variables, such as $2x + 3y - z = 4$, is called an **ordered triple** and is written $(x, y, z)$. For example, the ordered triples $(1, 1, 1)$ and $(10, -3, 7)$ are both solutions of the equation $2x + 3y - z = 4$, because the numbers in these ordered triples satisfy the equation when used as replacements for $x$, $y$, and $z$, respectively. The methods of solving systems of two equations in two variables can be extended to solving systems of equations in three variables such as

$$\begin{aligned} 4x + 8y + z &= 2 \\ x + 7y - 3z &= -14 \\ 2x - 3y + 2z &= 3. \end{aligned}$$

Theoretically, a system of this type can be solved by graphing. However, the graph of a linear equation with three variables is a *plane* and not a line. Because the graph of each equation of the system is a plane, which requires three-dimensional graphing, this method is not practical. However, it does illustrate the number of solutions possible for such systems, as Figure 44 shows.

### Possibilities for Graphs of Linear Systems in Three Variables

1. The three planes may meet at a single, common point that forms the solution set of the system. See Figure 44(a).
2. The three planes may have the points of a line in common so that the set of points along that line is the solution set of the system. See Figure 44(b).
3. The three planes may coincide so that the solution set of the system is the set of all points on that plane. See Figure 44(c).
4. The planes may have no points common to all three so that there is no solution for the system. See Figure 44(d), (e), and (f).

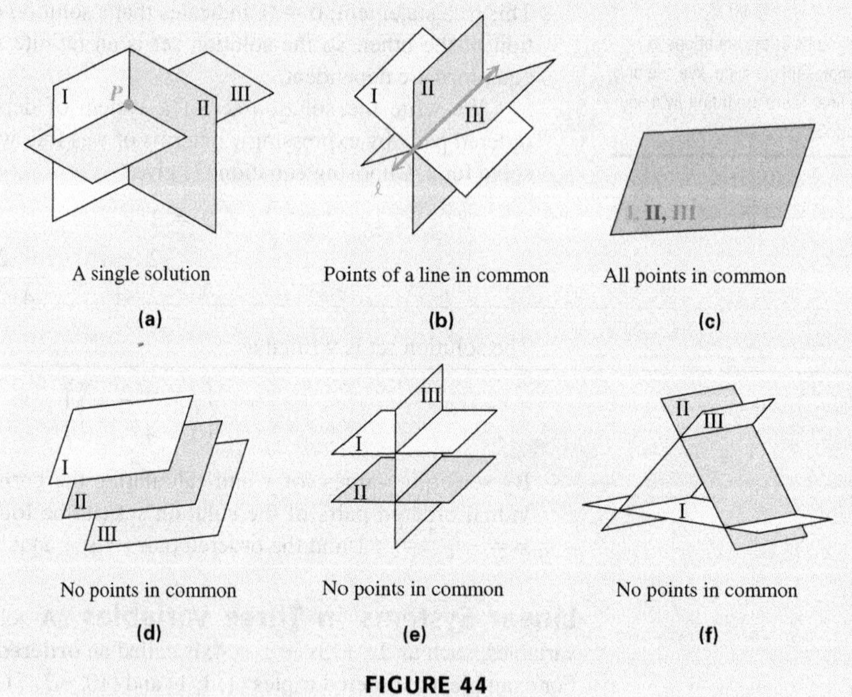


A single solution (a)

Points of a line in common (b)

All points in common (c)

No points in common (d)

No points in common (e)

No points in common (f)

**FIGURE 44**

Because graphing to find the solution set of a system of three equations in three variables is impractical, these systems are solved with an extension of the elimination method, summarized as follows.

### Solving Linear Systems in Three Variables by Elimination

*Step 1* **Eliminate a variable.** Use the elimination method to eliminate any variable using any two of the given equations. The result is an equation in two variables.

*Step 2* **Eliminate the same variable again.** Eliminate the *same* variable using any *other* two equations. The result is an equation in the same two variables as in Step 1.

*Step 3* **Eliminate a different variable and solve.** Use the elimination method to eliminate a second variable using the two equations in two variables that result from Steps 1 and 2. The result is an equation in one variable that gives the value of that variable.

*Step 4* **Find a second value.** Substitute the value of the variable found in Step 3 into either of the equations in two variables to find the value of the second variable.

*Step 5* **Find a third value.** Use the values of the two variables from Steps 3 and 4 to find the value of the third variable by substituting into any of the original equations.

*Step 6* **Find the solution set.** Check the solution in all of the original equations. Then write the solution set.

## EXAMPLE 4 Solving a System (Three Variables)

Solve the system.

$$\begin{aligned} 4x + 8y + z &= 2 && (1) \\ x + 7y - 3z &= -14 && (2) \\ 2x - 3y + 2z &= 3 && (3) \end{aligned}$$

**SOLUTION**

*Step 1* The choice of which variable to eliminate is arbitrary. Suppose we decide to begin by eliminating $z$. To do this, multiply both sides of equation (1) by 3 and then add the result to equation (2).

$$\begin{aligned} 12x + 24y + 3z &= 6 && \text{Multiply both sides of equation (1) by 3.} \\ x + 7y - 3z &= -14 && (2) \\ \hline 13x + 31y &= -8 && \text{Add.} \end{aligned}$$

*Step 2* The new equation has only two variables. To get another equation without $z$, multiply both sides of equation (1) by $-2$ and add the result to equation (3). ***It is essential at this point to eliminate the same variable, z.***

$$\begin{aligned} -8x - 16y - 2z &= -4 && \text{Multiply both sides of equation (1) by } -2. \\ 2x - 3y + 2z &= 3 && (3) \\ \hline -6x - 19y \quad &= -1 && \text{Add.} \end{aligned}$$

*Step 3* Now solve the system of equations from Steps 1 and 2 for $x$ and $y$. (This step is possible only if the *same* variable is eliminated in the first two steps.)

$$\begin{aligned} 78x + 186y &= -48 && \text{Multiply both sides of } 13x + 31y = -8 \text{ by 6.} \\ -78x - 247y &= -13 && \text{Multiply both sides of } -6x - 19y = -1 \text{ by 13.} \\ \hline -61y &= -61 && \text{Add.} \\ y &= 1 \end{aligned}$$

*Step 4* Substitute 1 for $y$ in either equation from Steps 1 and 2. Choosing $-6x - 19y = -1$ gives

$$\begin{aligned} -6x - 19y &= -1 \\ -6x - 19(1) &= -1 && \text{Let } y = 1. \\ -6x - 19 &= -1 \\ -6x &= 18 \\ x &= -3. \end{aligned}$$

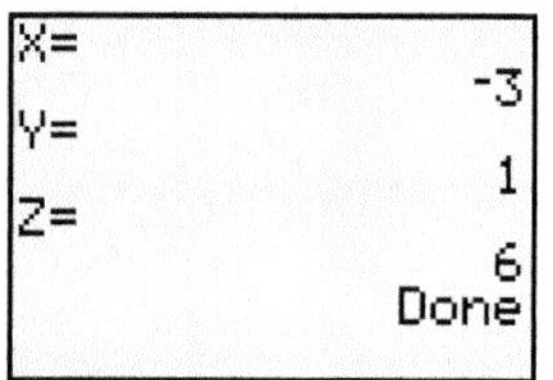


A graphing calculator can be *programmed* to solve a system such as the one in Example 4. Compare the result here to the solution in the text.

*Step 5* Substitute $-3$ for $x$ and 1 for $y$ in any one of the three given equations to find $z$. Choosing equation (1) gives

$$\begin{aligned} 4x + 8y + z &= 2 \\ 4(-3) + 8(1) + z &= 2 && \text{Let } x = -3 \text{ and } y = 1. \\ z &= 6. \end{aligned}$$

*Step 6* It appears that the ordered triple $(-3, 1, 6)$ is the only solution of the system. Check that the solution satisfies all three equations of the system. We show the check here only for equation (1).

$$\begin{aligned} 4x + 8y + z &= 2 && (1) \\ 4(-3) + 8(1) + 6 &= 2 && ? \\ -12 + 8 + 6 &= 2 && ? \\ 2 &= 2 && \text{True} \end{aligned}$$

Because $(-3, 1, 6)$ also satisfies equations (2) and (3), the solution set is $\{(-3, 1, 6)\}$.

## Applications of Linear Systems

**PROBLEM-SOLVING HINT** Many problems involve more than one unknown quantity. Although some problems with two unknowns can be solved using just one variable, many times it is easier to use two variables. To solve a problem with two unknowns, we write two equations that relate the unknown quantities. The system formed by the pair of equations then can be solved using the methods of this section.

**Just for Fun** Here is a way to find a person's age and the date of his or her birth. Ask the person to do the following.

1. Multiply the number of the month of birth by *100*.
2. Add the date of the month.
3. Multiply the sum by *2*.
4. Add *8*.
5. Multiply this result by *5*.
6. Add *4*.
7. Multiply by *10*.
8. Add *4*.
9. Add the person's age to this.

Ask the person the number obtained. You should then subtract *444* from the number you are given. The final two figures give the age, the next figure (or figures) will identify the date of the month, and the first figure (or figures) will give the number of the month.

The following steps, based on the six-step problem-solving method first introduced in Chapter 7, give a strategy for solving problems using more than one variable.

### Solving an Applied Problem by Writing a System of Equations

*Step 1* **Read** the problem carefully until you understand what is given and what is to be found.

*Step 2* **Assign variables** to represent the unknown values, using diagrams or tables as needed. *Write down* what each variable represents.

*Step 3* **Write a system of equations** that relates the unknowns.

*Step 4* **Solve** the system of equations.

*Step 5* **State the answer** to the problem. Does it seem reasonable?

*Step 6* **Check** the answer in the words of the original problem.

Problems about the perimeter of a geometric figure often involve two unknowns and can be solved using systems of equations.

### EXAMPLE 5 Solving a Perimeter Problem

A rectangular soccer field may have a width between 50 and 100 yards and a length between 50 and 100 yards. Suppose that one particular field has a perimeter of 320 yards. Its length measures 40 yards more than its width. What are the dimensions of this field? (*Source: Microsoft Encarta Encyclopedia.*)

**SOLUTION**

*Step 1* **Read** the problem again. We are asked to find the dimensions of the field.

*Step 2* **Assign variables.** Let $L =$ the length and $W =$ the width.

*Step 3* **Write a system of equations.** Because the perimeter is 320 yards, we find one equation by using the perimeter formula:

$$2L + 2W = 320.$$

Because the length is 40 yards more than the width, we have

$$L = W + 40.$$

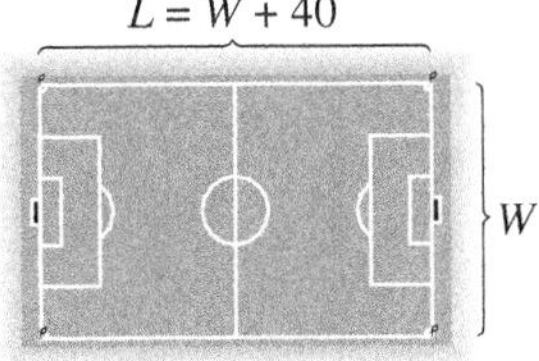


**FIGURE 45**

See Figure 45. The system is, therefore,

$$\begin{aligned} 2L + 2W &= 320 \quad (1) \\ L &= W + 40. \quad (2) \end{aligned}$$

*Step 4* **Solve** the system of equations. Since equation (2) is solved for $L$, we can substitute $W + 40$ for $L$ in equation (1), and solve for $W$.

$$\begin{aligned} 2L + 2W &= 320 && (1) \\ 2(W + 40) + 2W &= 320 && L = W + 40 \\ 2W + 80 + 2W &= 320 && \text{Distributive property} \\ 4W + 80 &= 320 && \text{Combine like terms.} \\ 4W &= 240 && \text{Subtract 80.} \\ W &= 60 && \text{Divide by 4.} \end{aligned}$$

Let $W = 60$ in the equation $L = W + 40$ to find $L$.

$$L = 60 + 40 = 100$$

*Step 5* **State the answer.** The length is 100 yards, and the width is 60 yards. Both dimensions are within the ranges given in the problem.

*Step 6* **Check.** The answer is correct, because the perimeter of this soccer field is

$$2(100) + 2(60) = 320 \text{ yards,}$$

and the length, 100 yards, is indeed 40 yards more than the width, because

$$100 - 40 = 60.$$

Professional sport ticket prices increase annually. Average per-ticket prices in three of the four major sports (football, basketball, and hockey) now exceed \$30.00.

## EXAMPLE 6 Solving a Problem About Ticket Prices

During recent National Hockey League and National Basketball Association seasons, two hockey tickets and one basketball ticket purchased at their average prices would have cost \$110.40. One hockey ticket and two basketball tickets would have cost \$106.32. What were the average ticket prices for the two sports? (*Source:* Team Marketing Report, Chicago.)

**SOLUTION**

*Step 1* **Read** the problem again. There are two unknowns.

*Step 2* **Assign variables.** Let $h$ represent the average price for a hockey ticket and $b$ represent the average price for a basketball ticket.

*Step 3* **Write a system of equations.** Because two hockey tickets and one basketball ticket cost a total of \$110.40, one equation for the system is

$$2h + b = 110.40.$$

By similar reasoning, the second equation is

$$h + 2b = 106.32.$$

Therefore, the system is

$$\begin{aligned} 2h + b &= 110.40 \quad (1) \\ h + 2b &= 106.32. \quad (2) \end{aligned}$$

*Step 4* **Solve** the system of equations. We eliminate $h$.

$$\begin{aligned} 2h + b &= 110.40 && (1) \\ -2h - 4b &= -212.64 && \text{Multiply each side of (2) by } -2. \\ \hline -3b &= -102.24 && \text{Add.} \\ b &= 34.08 && \text{Divide by } -3. \end{aligned}$$

To find the value of $h$, let $b = 34.08$ in equation (2).

$$\begin{aligned} h + 2b &= 106.32 && (2) \\ h + 2(34.08) &= 106.32 && \text{Let } b = 34.08. \\ h + 68.16 &= 106.32 && \text{Multiply.} \\ h &= 38.16 && \text{Subtract 68.16.} \end{aligned}$$

*Step 5* **State the answer.** The average price for one basketball ticket was \$34.08. For one hockey ticket, the average price was \$38.16.

*Step 6* **Check** that these values satisfy the conditions stated in the problem.

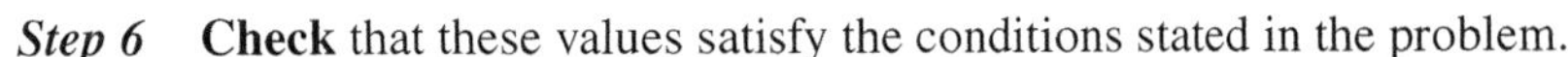

We solved mixture problems earlier using one variable. Another approach is to use two variables and a system of equations.

Problems that can be solved by writing a **system of equations** have been of interest historically. The following problem first appeared in a **Hindu** work that dates back to about A.D. 850.

*The mixed price of 9 citrons [a lemonlike fruit shown in the photo] and 7 fragrant wood apples is 107; again, the mixed price of 7 citrons and 9 fragrant wood apples is 101. O you arithmetician, tell me quickly the price of a citron and the price of a wood apple here, having distinctly separated those prices well.*

Use a system to solve this problem. The answer can be found at the end of the exercises for this section on page 514.

## EXAMPLE 7 Solving a Mixture Problem

How many ounces each of 5% hydrochloric acid and 20% hydrochloric acid must be combined to get 10 oz of solution that is 12.5% hydrochloric acid?

**SOLUTION**

*Step 1* **Read** the problem. Two solutions of different strengths are being mixed together to get a specific amount of a solution with an "in-between" strength.

*Step 2* **Assign variables.** Let $x$ represent the number of ounces of 5% solution and $y$ represent the number of ounces of 20% solution. Summarize the information from the problem in a table.

| Percent (as a decimal) | Ounces of Solution | Ounces of Pure Acid |
|---|---|---|
| $5\% = .05$ | $x$ | $.05x$ |
| $20\% = .20$ | $y$ | $.20y$ |
| $12.5\% = .125$ | $10$ | $(.125)10$ |

Figure 46 also illustrates what is happening in the problem.

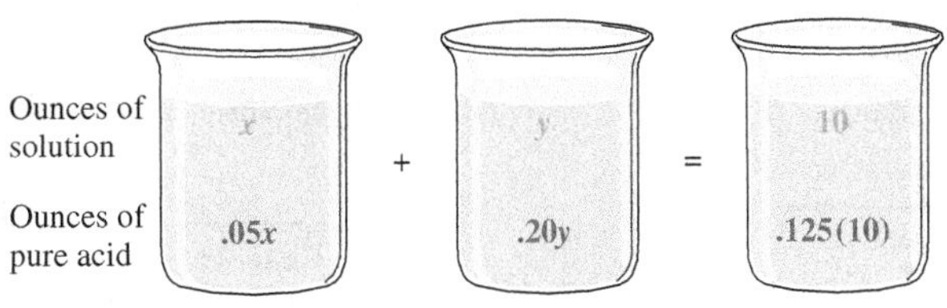


**FIGURE 46**

*Step 3* **Write a system of equations.** When $x$ ounces of 5% solution and $y$ ounces of 20% solution are combined, the total number of ounces is 10, so

$$x + y = 10. \quad (1)$$

The ounces of pure acid in the 5% solution ($.05x$) plus the ounces of pure acid in the 20% solution ($.20y$) should equal the total ounces of pure acid in the mixture, which is $(.125)10$, or 1.25. That is,

$$.05x + .20y = 1.25. \quad (2)$$

Notice that these equations can be quickly determined by reading down in the table or using the labels in Figure 46.

*Step 4* **Solve** the system of equations (1) and (2). We eliminate $x$.

$$\begin{aligned} 5x + 20y &= 125 && \text{Multiply each side of (2) by 100.} \\ -5x - 5y &= -50 && \text{Multiply each side of (1) by } -5. \\ \hline 15y &= 75 && \text{Add.} \\ y &= 5 \end{aligned}$$

Because $y = 5$ and $x + y = 10$, $x$ is also 5.

*Step 5* **State the answer.** The desired mixture will require 5 ounces of the 5% solution and 5 ounces of the 20% solution.

*Step 6* **Check** that these values satisfy both equations of the system.

Problems that use the distance formula $d = rt$ were first introduced in Chapter 7. In many cases, these problems can be solved with systems of two linear equations. Keep in mind that setting up a table and drawing a sketch will help you solve such problems.

**François Viète,** a mathematician of sixteenth-century France, did much for the symbolism of mathematics. Before his time, different symbols were often used for different powers of a quantity. Viète used the same letter with a description of the power and the coefficient. According to Howard Eves in *An Introduction to the History of Mathematics*, Viète would have written

$$5BA^2 - 2CA + A^3 = D$$

as

*B*5 in *A* quad − *C* plano 2 in
*A* + *A* cub aequatur *D* solido.

## EXAMPLE 8 Solving a Motion Problem

Two executives in cities 400 miles apart drive to a business meeting at a location on the line between their cities. They meet after 4 hours. Find the speed of each car if one car travels 20 miles per hour faster than the other.

**SOLUTION**

*Step 1* **Read** the problem carefully.

*Step 2* **Assign variables.**

$$\text{Let } x = \text{the speed of the faster car,}$$
$$\text{and } y = \text{the speed of the slower car.}$$

We use the formula $d = rt$. Each car travels for 4 hours, so the time, $t$, for each car is 4, as shown in the table. The distance is found by using the formula $d = rt$ and the expressions already entered in the table.

| | $r$ | $t$ | $d$ |
|---|---|---|---|
| Faster car | $x$ | 4 | $4x$ |
| Slower car | $y$ | 4 | $4y$ |

Find $d$ from $d = rt$.

Sketch what is happening in the problem. See Figure 47.

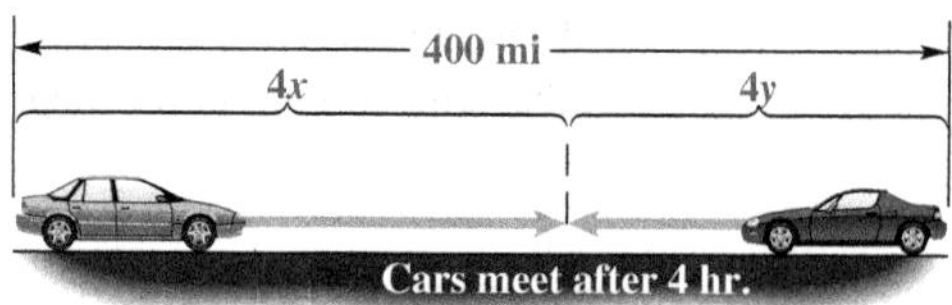


**FIGURE 47**

*Step 3* **Write two equations.** As shown in the figure, because the total distance traveled by both cars is 400 miles, one equation is

$$4x + 4y = 400.$$

Because the faster car goes 20 miles per hour faster than the slower car, the second equation is

$$x = 20 + y.$$

*Step 4* **Solve.** This system of equations,

$$\begin{aligned} 4x + 4y &= 400 \quad (1) \\ x &= 20 + y, \quad (2) \end{aligned}$$

can be solved by substitution. Replace $x$ with $20 + y$ in equation (1) and solve for $y$.

$$\begin{aligned} 4(20 + y) + 4y &= 400 \quad \text{Let } x = 20 + y. \\ 80 + 4y + 4y &= 400 \quad \text{Distributive property} \\ 80 + 8y &= 400 \quad \text{Combine like terms.} \\ 8y &= 320 \quad \text{Subtract 80.} \\ y &= 40 \quad \text{Divide by 8.} \end{aligned}$$

Since $x = 20 + y$, and $y = 40$,

$$x = 20 + 40 = 60.$$

*Step 5* **State the answer.** The speeds of the two cars are 40 miles per hour and 60 miles per hour.

*Step 6* **Check** the answer. Because each car travels for 4 hours, the total distance traveled is

$$4(60) + 4(40) = 240 + 160 = 400 \text{ miles}, \quad \text{as required.}$$

The final example shows how a system in three variables is used to solve a problem.

## EXAMPLE 9 Solving a Problem Involving Prices

At Panera Bread, a loaf of honey wheat bread costs \$2.40, a loaf of pumpernickel bread costs \$3.35, and a loaf of French bread costs \$2.10. On a recent day, three times as many loaves of honey wheat were sold as pumpernickel. The number of loaves of French bread sold was 5 less than the number of loaves of honey wheat sold. Total receipts for these breads were \$56.90. How many loaves of each type of bread were sold? (*Source:* Panera Bread menu.)

**SOLUTION**

*Step 1* **Read** the problem again. There are three unknowns in this problem.

*Step 2* **Assign variables** to represent the three unknowns.

Let $x$ = the number of loaves of honey wheat,

$y$ = the number of loaves of pumpernickel,

and $z$ = the number of loaves of French bread.

*Step 3* **Write a system of three equations** using the information in the problem. Because three times as many loaves of honey wheat were sold as pumpernickel,

$$x = 3y, \quad \text{or} \quad x - 3y = 0. \quad (1)$$

**Solution to the Chapter Opener Problem** Let $x$ represent the number of pounds of $.75 candy, and let $y$ represent the number of pounds of $1.25 candy. The system to solve is

$$x + y = 9$$
$$.75x + 1.25y = .96(9).$$

Using the methods of this section, we find that there should be 5.22 pounds at $.75 per pound and 3.78 pounds at $1.25 per pound.

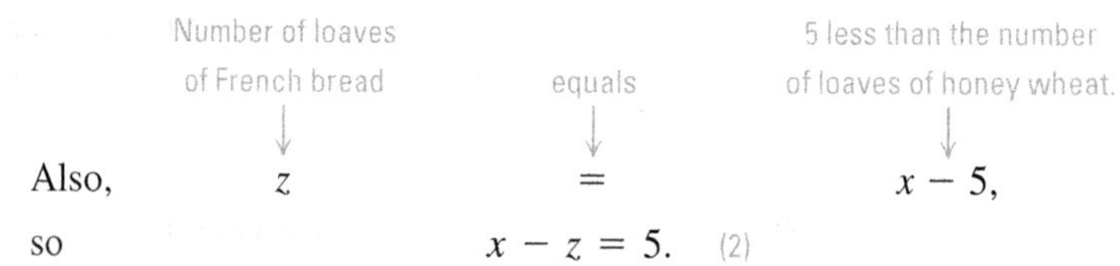


Also, $z = x - 5,$

so $x - z = 5.$ (2)

Multiplying the cost of a loaf of each kind of bread by the number of loaves of that kind sold and adding gives the total receipts.

$$2.40x + 3.35y + 2.10z = 56.90$$

Multiply each side of this equation by 100 to clear it of decimals.

$$240x + 335y + 210z = 5690 \quad (3)$$

*Step 4* **Solve** the system of three equations.

$$x - 3y = 0 \quad (1)$$
$$x - z = 5 \quad (2)$$
$$240x + 335y + 210z = 5690 \quad (3)$$

using the method of this section to find that the solution set is $\{(12, 4, 7)\}$.

*Step 5* **State the answer.** The answer is 12 loaves of honey wheat, 4 loaves of pumpernickel, and 7 loaves of French bread were sold.

*Step 6* **Check.** Because $12 = 3 \cdot 4$, the number of loaves of honey wheat is three times the number of loaves of pumpernickel. Also, $12 - 7 = 5$, so the number of loaves of French bread is 5 less than the number of loaves of honey wheat. Multiply the appropriate cost per loaf by the number of loaves sold and add the results to check that total receipts were $56.90.

## 8.7 Exercises

*Answer the questions in Exercises 1 and 2 by observing the graphs provided.*

1. ***Music Format Sales*** The graph shows how the production of vinyl LPs, audiocassettes, and compact discs (CDs) changed over the years from 1986 through 1998.

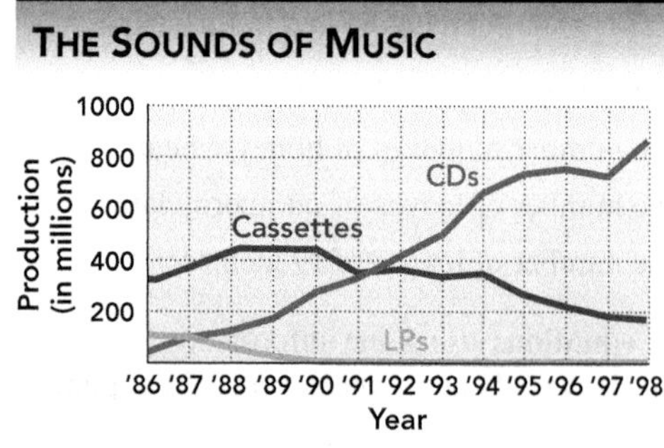


*Source:* Recording Industry Association of America.

(a) In what year did cassette production and CD production reach equal levels? What was that level?
(b) Express the point of intersection of the graphs of LP production and CD production as an ordered pair of the form (year, production level).
(c) Between what years did cassette production first stabilize and remain fairly constant?
(d) Describe the trend in CD production from 1986 through 1998. If a straight line were used to approximate its graph, would the line have positive, negative, or 0 slope?
(e) If a straight line were used to approximate the graph of cassette production from 1990 through 1998, would the line have positive, negative, or 0 slope? Why?

2. ***Network News Programs*** The graph on the next page shows network share (the percentage of TV sets in use) for the early evening news programs for three major broadcast networks for 1986–2000.

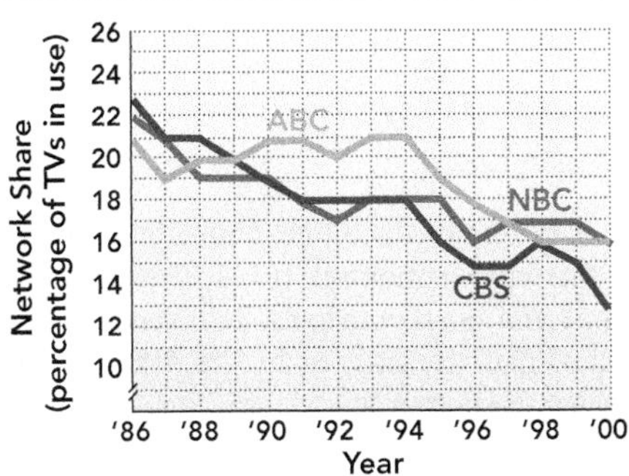


*Source:* Nielson Media Research.

(a) Between what years did the ABC early evening news dominate?

(b) During what year did ABC's dominance end? Which network equaled ABC's share that year? What was that share?

(c) During what years did ABC and CBS have equal network share? What was the share for each of these years?

(d) Which networks most recently had equal share? Write their share as an ordered pair of the form (year, share).

(e) Describe the general trend in viewership for the three major networks during these years.

*Decide whether the ordered pair is a solution of the given system.*

**3.** $x + y = 6$ $(5, 1)$
$x - y = 4$

**4.** $x - y = 17$ $(8, -9)$
$x + y = -1$

**5.** $2x - y = 8$ $(5, 2)$
$3x + 2y = 20$

**6.** $3x - 5y = -12$ $(-1, 2)$
$x - y = 1$

*Solve each system by graphing.*

**7.** $x + y = 4$
$2x - y = 2$

**8.** $x + y = -5$
$-2x + y = 1$

*Solve each system by elimination.*

**9.** $2x - 5y = 11$
$3x + y = 8$

**10.** $-2x + 3y = 1$
$-4x + y = -3$

**11.** $3x + 4y = -6$
$5x + 3y = 1$

**12.** $4x + 3y = 1$
$3x + 2y = 2$

**13.** $3x + 3y = 0$
$4x + 2y = 3$

**14.** $8x + 4y = 0$
$4x - 2y = 2$

**15.** $7x + 2y = 6$
$-14x - 4y = -12$

**16.** $x - 4y = 2$
$4x - 16y = 8$

**17.** $\frac{x}{2} + \frac{y}{3} = -\frac{1}{3}$
$\frac{x}{2} + 2y = -7$

**18.** $\frac{x}{5} + y = \frac{6}{5}$
$\frac{x}{10} + \frac{y}{3} = \frac{5}{6}$

**19.** $5x - 5y = 3$
$x - y = 12$

**20.** $2x - 3y = 7$
$-4x + 6y = 14$

*Solve each system by substitution.*

**21.** $4x + y = 6$
$y = 2x$

**22.** $2x - y = 6$
$y = 5x$

**23.** $3x - 4y = -22$
$-3x + y = 0$

**24.** $-3x + y = -5$
$x + 2y = 0$

**25.** $-x - 4y = -14$
$2x = y + 1$

**26.** $-3x - 5y = -17$
$4x = y - 8$

**27.** $5x - 4y = 9$
$3 - 2y = -x$

**28.** $6x - y = -9$
$4 + 7x = -y$

**29.** $x = 3y + 5$
$x = \frac{3}{2}y$

**30.** $x = 6y - 2$
$x = \frac{3}{4}y$

**31.** $\frac{1}{2}x + \frac{1}{3}y = 3$
$y = 3x$

**32.** $\frac{1}{4}x - \frac{1}{5}y = 9$
$y = 5x$

**33.** Explain what the following statement means: The solution set of the system

$$\begin{aligned} 2x + y + z &= 3 \\ 3x - y + z &= -2 \\ 4x - y + 2z &= 0 \end{aligned} \quad \text{is } \{(-1, 2, 3)\}.$$

**34.** Write a system of three linear equations in three variables that has solution set $\{(3, 1, 2)\}$. Then solve the system. (*Hint:* Start with the solution and make up three equations that are satisfied by the solution. There are many ways to do this.)

*Solve each system of equations in three variables.*

**35.** $3x + 2y + z = 8$
$2x - 3y + 2z = -16$
$x + 4y - z = 20$

**36.** $-3x + y - z = -10$
$-4x + 2y + 3z = -1$
$2x + 3y - 2z = -5$

**37.** $2x + 5y + 2z = 0$
$4x - 7y - 3z = 1$
$3x - 8y - 2z = -6$

**38.** $5x - 2y + 3z = -9$
$4x + 3y + 5z = 4$
$2x + 4y - 2z = 14$

**39.** $x + y - z = -2$
$2x - y + z = -5$
$-x + 2y - 3z = -4$

**40.** $x + 2y + 3z = 1$
$-x - y + 3z = 2$
$-6x + y + z = -2$

**41.** $2x - 3y + 2z = -1$
$x + 2y + z = 17$
$2y - z = 7$

**42.** $2x - y + 3z = 6$
$x + 2y - z = 8$
$2y + z = 1$

**43.** $4x + 2y - 3z = 6$
$x - 4y + z = -4$
$-x + 2z = 2$

**44.** $2x + 3y - 4z = 4$
$x - 6y + z = -16$
$-x + 3z = 8$

**45.** $2x + y = 6$
$3y - 2z = -4$
$3x - 5z = -7$

**46.** $4x - 8y = -7$
$4y + z = 7$
$-8x + z = -4$

*Solve each problem involving two unknowns.*

**47.** ***Win–Loss Record*** During the 2005 Major League Baseball regular season, the St. Louis Cardinals played 162 games. They won 38 more games than they lost. What was their win–loss record that year?

**2005 MLB FINAL STANDINGS NATIONAL LEAGUE CENTRAL**

| Team | W | L |
|---|---|---|
| St. Louis | — | — |
| Houston | 89 | 73 |
| Milwaukee | 81 | 81 |
| Chicago | 79 | 83 |
| Cincinnati | 73 | 89 |
| Pittsburgh | — | — |

*Source:* mlb.com.

**48.** ***Win–Loss Record*** Refer to Exercise 47. During the same 162-game season, the Pittsburgh Pirates lost 28 more games than they won. What was the team's win–loss record?

**49.** ***Dimensions of a Basketball Court*** LeBron and Yao found that the width of their basketball court was 44 feet less than the length. If the perimeter was 288 feet, what were the length and the width of their court?

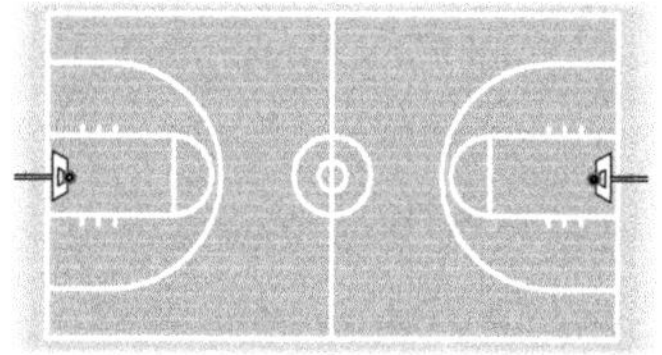

**50.** ***Dimensions of a Tennis Court*** Venus and Serena measured a tennis court and found that it was 42 feet longer than it was wide and had a perimeter of 228 feet. What were the length and the width of the tennis court?

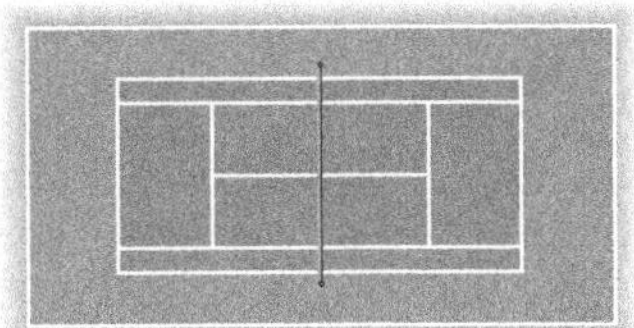

51. ***Car Rental*** On a 6-day business trip, Jerome Dugas rented a car for \$53 per day at weekday rates and \$35 per day at weekend rates. If his total rental bill was \$264, how many days did he rent at each rate? (*Source:* Enterprise.)

52. ***Popular Fiction*** A popular leisure activity of Americans is reading. In a recent year, two popular fiction titles were *How Stella Got Her Groove Back* by Terry McMillan and *The Deep End of the Ocean* by Jacquelyn Mitchard. Together, these two titles sold 1,622,962 copies. The Mitchard book sold 57,564 more copies than the McMillan book. How many copies of each title were sold? (*Source: Publishers Weekly.*)

53. ***Dimensions of a Square and a Triangle*** The side of a square is 4 centimeters longer than the side of an equilateral triangle. The perimeter of the square is 24 centimeters more than the perimeter of the triangle. Find the lengths of a side of the square and a side of the triangle.

54. ***Dimensions of a Rectangle*** The length of a rectangle is 7 feet more than the width. If the length were decreased by 3 feet and the width were increased by 2 feet, the perimeter would be 32 feet. Find the length and width of the original rectangle.

55. ***Coffee Prices*** At a business meeting at Panera Bread, the bill for two cappuccinos and three house lattes was \$10.95. At another table, the bill for one cappuccino and two house lattes was \$6.65. How much did each type of beverage cost? (*Source:* Panera Bread menu.)

56. ***Cost of Art Supplies*** For an art project Margaret Maggio bought 8 sheets of colored paper and 3 marker pens for \$6.50. She later needed 2 sheets of colored paper and 2 marker pens. These items cost \$3.00. Find the cost of 1 marker pen and 1 sheet of colored paper.

***Fan Cost Index*** *The Fan Cost Index (FCI) represents the cost of four average-price tickets, four small soft drinks, two small beers, four hot dogs, parking for one car, two game programs, and two souvenir caps to a sporting event. For example, in 2005, the FCI for Major League Baseball was \$164.43. This was by far the least for the four major professional sports. (Source:* www.teammarketing.com.*) Use the concept of FCI in Exercises 57 and 58.*

57. The FCI prices for the National Hockey League and the National Basketball Association totaled \$514.69. The hockey FCI was \$20.05 less than that of basketball. What were the FCIs for these sports?

58. The FCI prices for Major League Baseball and the National Football League totaled \$494.25. The football FCI was \$165.39 more than that of baseball. What were the FCIs for these sports?

59. ***Travel Costs*** Tokyo and New York are among the most expensive cities worldwide for business travelers. Using average costs per day for each city (which includes room, meals, laundry, and two taxi fares), 2 days in Tokyo and 3 days in New York cost \$2015. Four days in Tokyo and 2 days in New York cost \$2490. What is the average cost per day for each city? (*Source:* ECA International.)

60. ***Prices at Wendy's*** Andrew McGinnis works at Wendy's Old Fashioned Hamburgers. During one particular lunch hour, he sold 15 single hamburgers and 10 double hamburgers, totaling \$63.25. Another lunch hour, he sold 30 singles and 5 doubles, totaling \$78.65. How much did each type of burger cost? (*Source*: Wendy's Old Fashioned Hamburgers menu.)

61. ***Cost of Clay*** For his art class, Bryce bought 2 kilograms of dark clay and 3 kilograms of light clay, paying \$22 for the clay. He later needed 1 kilogram of dark clay and 2 kilograms of light clay, costing \$13 altogether. What was the cost per kilogram for each type of clay?

62. ***Yarn and Thread Production*** A factory makes use of two basic machines, $A$ and $B$, which turn out two different products, yarn and thread. Each unit of yarn requires 1 hour on machine $A$ and 2 hours on machine $B$, while each unit of thread requires 1 hour on $A$ and 1 hour on $B$. Machine $A$ runs 8 hours per day, while machine $B$ runs 14 hours per day. How many units per day of yarn and thread should the factory make to keep its machines running at capacity?

***Formulas*** *The formulas $p = br$ (percentage = base × rate) and $I = prt$ (simple interest = principal × rate × time) are used in the applications in Exercises 67–76. To prepare to use these formulas, answer the questions in Exercises 63–66.*

**63.** If a container of liquid contains 120 oz of solution, what is the number of ounces of pure acid if the given solution contains the following acid concentrations?
(a) 10% (b) 25%
(c) 40% (d) 50%

**64.** If \$50,000 is invested in an account paying simple annual interest, how much interest will be earned during the first year at the following rates?
(a) 2% (b) 3%
(c) 4% (d) 3.5%

**65.** If a pound of turkey costs \$1.29, give an expression for the cost of $x$ pounds.

**66.** If a ticket to the movie *Ice Age 2: The Meltdown* costs \$9 and $y$ tickets are sold, give an expression for the amount collected.

**67. *Acid Mixture*** How many liters each of 15% acid and 33% acid should be mixed to obtain 40 liters of 21% acid?

| Kind of Solution | Liters of Solution | Amount of Pure Acid |
|---|---|---|
| .15 | $x$ | |
| .33 | $y$ | |
| .21 | 40 | |

**68. *Alcohol Mixture*** How many gallons each of 25% alcohol and 35% alcohol should be mixed to obtain 20 gallons of 32% alcohol?

| Kind of Solution | Gallons of Solution | Amount of Pure Alcohol |
|---|---|---|
| .25 | $x$ | $.25x$ |
| .35 | $y$ | $.35y$ |
| .32 | 20 | .32(20) |

**69. *Antifreeze Mixture*** A truck radiator holds 18 liters of fluid. How much pure antifreeze must be added to a mixture that is 4% antifreeze in order to fill the radiator with a mixture that is 20% antifreeze?

**70. *Acid Mixture*** Pure acid is to be added to a 10% acid solution to obtain 27 liters of a 20% acid solution. What amounts of each should be used?

**71. *Fruit Drink Mixture*** A popular fruit drink is made by mixing fruit juices. Such a mixture with 50% juice is to be mixed with another mixture that is 30% juice to get 200 liters of a mixture that is 45% juice. How much of each should be used?

| Kind of Juice | Number of Liters | Amount of Pure Juice |
|---|---|---|
| .50 | $x$ | $.50x$ |
| .30 | $y$ | |
| .45 | | |

**72. *Candy Mixture*** Lauren plans to mix pecan clusters that sell for \$3.60 per pound with chocolate truffles that sell for \$7.20 per pound to get a mixture that she can sell in Valentine boxes for \$4.95 per pound. How much of the \$3.60 clusters and the \$7.20 truffles should she use to create 80 pounds of the mix?

| | Number of Pounds | Price per Pound | Value of Candy |
|---|---|---|---|
| Clusters | $x$ | 3.60 | $3.60x$ |
| Truffles | $y$ | 7.20 | $7.20y$ |
| Mixture | 80 | 4.95 | 4.95(80) |

**73. *Candy Mixture*** A grocer plans to mix candy that sells for \$1.20 per pound with candy that sells for \$2.40 per pound to get a mixture that he plans to sell for \$1.65 per pound. How much of the \$1.20 and \$2.40 candy should he use if he wants 160 pounds of the mix?

**74. *Ticket Sales*** Tickets to a production of *Oklahoma* at Northeastern State University cost \$2.50 for general admission or \$2.00 with student identification. If 184 people paid to see a performance and \$406 was collected, how many of each type of admission were sold?

**75. *Investment Mixture*** An investor must invest a total of \$15,000 in two accounts, one paying 4% simple annual interest, and the other 3%. If he wants to earn \$550 annual interest, how much should he invest at each rate?

| Principal | Rate | Interest |
|---|---|---|
| $x$ | .04 | |
| $y$ | .03 | |
| 15,000 | | |

**76. *Investment Mixture*** A total of \$3000 is invested, part at 2% simple interest and part at 4%. If the total annual return from the two investments is $100, how much is invested at each rate?

| Principal | Rate | Interest |
|---|---|---|
| $x$ | .02 | $.02x$ |
| $y$ | .04 | $.04y$ |
| 3000 | | 100 |

77. ***Speeds of Trains*** A train travels 150 kilometers in the same time that a plane covers 400 kilometers. If the speed of the plane is 20 kilometers per hour less than 3 times the speed of the train, find both speeds.

78. ***Speeds of Trains*** A freight train and an express train leave towns 390 kilometers apart, traveling toward one another. The freight train travels 30 kilometers per hour slower than the express train. They pass one another 3 hours later. What are their speeds?

79. ***Speeds of Boat and Current*** In his motorboat, Nguyen travels upstream at top speed to his favorite fishing spot, a distance of 36 miles, in two hours. Returning, he finds that the trip downstream, still at top speed, takes only 1.5 hours. Find the speed of Nguyen's boat and the speed of the current.

80. ***Speeds of Snow Speeder and Wind*** Braving blizzard conditions on the planet Hoth, Luke Skywalker sets out at top speed in his snow speeder for a rebel base 3600 miles away. He travels into a steady headwind, and makes the trip in 2 hours. Returning, he finds that the trip back, still at top speed but now with a tailwind, takes only 1.5 hours. Find the top speed of Luke's snow speeder and the speed of the wind.

*Solve each problem involving three unknowns.*

81. ***Olympic Gold Medals*** In the 2004 Olympics in Athens, Greece, the United States earned 4 fewer gold medals than silver. The number of bronze medals earned was 49 less than twice the number of silver medals. The United States earned a total of 103 medals. How many of each kind of medal did the United States earn? (*Source: World Almanac and Book of Facts.*)

82. ***Voter Affiliations*** In a random sample of 100 Americans of voting age, 10 more Americans identify themselves as Independents than Republicans. Six fewer Americans identify themselves as Republicans than Democrats. Assuming that all of those sampled are Republican, Democrat, or Independent, how many of those in the sample identify themselves with each political affiliation? (*Source:* The Gallup Organization.)

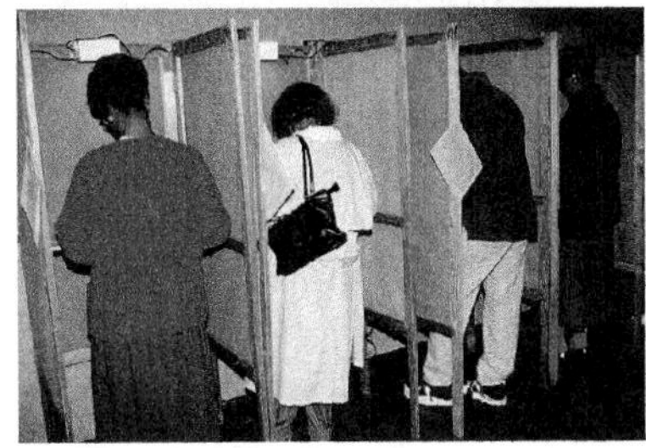

83. ***Dimensions of a Triangle*** The perimeter of a triangle is 56 inches. The longest side measures 4 inches less than the sum of the other two sides. Three times the shortest side is 4 inches more than the longest side. Find the lengths of the three sides.

84. ***Dimensions of a Triangle*** The perimeter of a triangle is 70 centimeters. The longest side is 4 centimeters less than the sum of the other two sides. Twice the shortest side is 9 centimeters less than the longest side. Find the length of each side of the triangle.

85. ***Hardware Production*** A hardware supplier manufactures three kinds of clamps, types A, B, and C. Production restrictions require it to make 10 units more type C clamps than the total of the other types and twice as many type B clamps as type A. The shop must produce a total of 490 units of clamps per day. How many units of each type can be made per day?

86. ***Television Production*** A company produces three color television sets, models X, Y, and Z. Each model X set requires 2 hr of electronics work, 2 hr of assembly time, and 1 hr of finishing time. Each model Y requires 1, 3, and 1 hr of electronics, assembly, and finishing time, respectively. Each model Z requires 3, 2, and 2 hr of the same work, respectively. There are 100 hr available for electronics, 100 hr available for assembly, and 65 hr available for finishing per week. How many of each model should be produced each week if all available time must be used?

87. ***Globetrotter Ticket Prices*** Tickets for one show on the Harlem Globetrotters' 75th Anniversary Tour cost \$10, \$18, or, for VIP seats, \$30. So far, five times as many \$18 tickets have been sold as VIP tickets. The number of \$10 tickets equals the number of \$18 tickets plus twice the number of VIP tickets. Sales of these tickets total \$9500. How many of each kind of ticket have been sold? (*Source:* www.ticketmaster.com)

88. ***Concert Ticket Prices*** Three kinds of tickets are available for a Third Day concert: "up close," "in the middle," and "far out." "Up close" tickets cost \$10 more than "in the middle" tickets, while "in the middle" tickets cost \$10 more than "far out" tickets. Twice the cost of an "up close" ticket is \$20 more than 3 times the cost of a "far out" seat. Find the price of each kind of ticket.

***Answer to Margin Note problem on page 505:*** price of a citron: 8; price of a wood apple: 5

## EXTENSION

# Using Matrix Row Operations to Solve Systems

The elimination method used to solve systems introduced in the previous section can be streamlined into a systematic method by using *matrices* (singular: *matrix*). Matrices can be used to solve linear systems and matrix methods are particularly suitable for computer solutions of large systems of equations having many unknowns.

To begin, consider a system of three equations and three unknowns such as

$$\begin{aligned} a_1x + b_1y + c_1z &= d_1 \\ a_2x + b_2y + c_2z &= d_2, \\ a_3x + b_3y + c_3z &= d_3 \end{aligned} \quad \text{written in an abbreviated form as} \quad \begin{bmatrix} a_1 & b_1 & c_1 & d_1 \\ a_2 & b_2 & c_2 & d_2 \\ a_3 & b_3 & c_3 & d_3 \end{bmatrix}.$$

Such a rectangular array of numbers enclosed by brackets is called a **matrix.** Each number in the array is an **element** or **entry.** The matrix above has three **rows** (horizontal) and four **columns** (vertical) of entries, and is called a $3 \times 4$ (read "3 by 4") matrix. The constants in the last column of the matrix can be set apart from the coefficients of the variables by using a vertical line, as shown in the following **augmented matrix.**

$$\text{Rows} \rightarrow \left[\begin{array}{ccc|c} a_1 & b_1 & c_1 & d_1 \\ a_2 & b_2 & c_2 & d_3 \\ a_3 & b_3 & c_3 & d_3 \end{array}\right] \quad \text{Augmented matrix}$$

Columns

NAMES MATH EDIT
0↑cumSum(
A:ref(
B:rref(
C:rowSwap(
D:row+(
E:*row(
F:*row+(

Choices C, D, E, and F provide the user of the TI-83/84 Plus calculator a means of performing row operations on matrices.

The rows of this augmented matrix can be treated the same as the equations of a system of equations, since the augmented matrix is actually a short form of the system. Any transformation of the matrix that will result in an equivalent system is permitted. The following **matrix row operations** produce such transformations.

### Matrix Row Operations

For any real number $k$ and any augmented matrix of a system of linear equations, the following operations will produce the matrix of an *equivalent system*—that is, another system with the same solution set.

1. **Interchange any two rows of a matrix.**
2. **Multiply the elements of any row of a matrix by the same nonzero number $k$.**
3. **Add a common multiple of the elements of one row to the corresponding elements of another row.**

If the word "row" is replaced by "equation," it can be seen that the three row operations also apply to a system of equations, so that a system of equations can be solved by transforming its corresponding matrix into the matrix of an equivalent, simpler system. The goal is a matrix in the form

$$\left[\begin{array}{cc|c} 1 & 0 & a \\ 0 & 1 & b \end{array}\right] \quad \text{or} \quad \left[\begin{array}{ccc|c} 1 & 0 & 0 & a \\ 0 & 1 & 0 & b \\ 0 & 0 & 1 & c \end{array}\right]$$

for systems with two or three equations respectively. Notice that on the left of the vertical bar there are ones down the diagonal from upper left to lower right and zeros elsewhere in the matrices. When these matrices are rewritten as systems of equations, the values of the variables are known. The **Gauss-Jordan method** is a systematic way of using the matrix row operations to change the augmented matrix of a system into the form that shows its solution. The following examples will illustrate this method.

### EXAMPLE 1 Solving a Linear System Using Gauss-Jordan (Two Unknowns)

Solve the linear system.

$$\begin{aligned} 3x - 4y &= 1 \\ 5x + 2y &= 19 \end{aligned}$$

**SOLUTION**

The equations should all be in the same form, with the variable terms in the same order on the left, and the constant term on the right. Begin by writing the augmented matrix.

$$\left[\begin{array}{cc|c} 3 & -4 & 1 \\ 5 & 2 & 19 \end{array}\right]$$

The goal is to transform this augmented matrix into one in which the values of the variables will be easy to see. That is, since each column in the matrix represents the coefficients of one variable, the augmented matrix should be transformed so that it is of the form

$$\left[\begin{array}{cc|c} 1 & 0 & k \\ 0 & 1 & j \end{array}\right]$$

for real numbers $k$ and $j$. Once the augmented matrix is in this form, the matrix can be rewritten as a linear system to get

$$\begin{aligned} x &= k \\ y &= j. \end{aligned}$$

The necessary transformations are performed as follows. It is best to work in columns beginning in each column with the element that is to become 1. In the augmented matrix,

$$\left[\begin{array}{cc|c} 3 & -4 & 1 \\ 5 & 2 & 19 \end{array}\right]$$

there is a 3 in the first row, first column position. Use row operation 2, multiplying each entry in the first row by $\frac{1}{3}$ to get a 1 in this position. (This step is abbreviated as $\frac{1}{3}$ R1.)

$$\left[\begin{array}{cc|c} 1 & -\frac{4}{3} & \frac{1}{3} \\ 5 & 2 & 19 \end{array}\right] \quad \tfrac{1}{3}\text{R1}$$

Introduce 0 in the second row, first column by multiplying each element of the first row by $-5$ and adding the result to the corresponding element in the second row, using row operation 3.

$$\left[\begin{array}{cc|c} 1 & -\frac{4}{3} & \frac{1}{3} \\ 0 & \frac{26}{3} & \frac{52}{3} \end{array}\right] \quad -5\text{R1} + \text{R2}$$

Obtain 1 in the second row, second column by multiplying each element of the second row by $\frac{3}{26}$, using row operation 2.

$$\left[\begin{array}{cc|c} 1 & -\frac{4}{3} & \frac{1}{3} \\ 0 & 1 & 2 \end{array}\right] \quad \tfrac{3}{26}\text{R2}$$

Finally, obtain 0 in the first row, second column by multiplying each element of the second row by $\frac{4}{3}$ and adding the result to the corresponding element in the first row.

$$\left[\begin{array}{cc|c} 1 & 0 & 3 \\ 0 & 1 & 2 \end{array}\right] \quad \tfrac{4}{3}\text{R2} + \text{R1}$$

This last matrix corresponds to the system

$$\begin{aligned} x &= 3 \\ y &= 2, \end{aligned}$$

that has the solution set $\{(3, 2)\}$. This solution could have been read directly from the third column of the final matrix. ■

A linear system with three equations is solved in a similar way. Row operations are used to get 1s down the diagonal from left to right and 0s above and below each 1.

## EXAMPLE 2 Solving a System Using Gauss-Jordan (Three Unknowns)

Use the Gauss-Jordan method to solve the system.

$$\begin{aligned} x - y + 5z &= -6 \\ 3x + 3y - z &= 10 \\ x + 3y + 2z &= 5 \end{aligned}$$

### SOLUTION

Because the system is in proper form, begin by writing the augmented matrix of the linear system.

$$\left[\begin{array}{rrr|r} 1 & -1 & 5 & -6 \\ 3 & 3 & -1 & 10 \\ 1 & 3 & 2 & 5 \end{array}\right]$$

The final matrix is to be of the form

$$\left[\begin{array}{rrr|r} 1 & 0 & 0 & m \\ 0 & 1 & 0 & n \\ 0 & 0 & 1 & p \end{array}\right],$$

where $m$, $n$, and $p$ are real numbers. This final form of the matrix gives the system $x = m$, $y = n$, and $z = p$, so the solution set is $\{(m, n, p)\}$.

There is already a 1 in the first row, first column. Introduce a 0 in the second row of the first column by multiplying each element in the first row by $-3$ and adding the result to the corresponding element in the second row, using row operation 3.

$$\left[\begin{array}{rrr|r} 1 & -1 & 5 & -6 \\ 0 & 6 & -16 & 28 \\ 1 & 3 & 2 & 5 \end{array}\right] \quad -3R1 + R2$$

Now, to change the last element in the first column to 0, use row operation 3. Multiply each element of the first row by $-1$, then add the results to the corresponding elements of the third row.

$$\left[\begin{array}{rrr|r} 1 & -1 & 5 & -6 \\ 0 & 6 & -16 & 28 \\ 0 & 4 & -3 & 11 \end{array}\right] \quad -1R1 + R3$$

The same procedure is used to transform the second and third columns. For both of these columns, first perform the step of getting 1 in the appropriate position of each column. Do this by multiplying the elements of the row by the reciprocal of the number in that position.

$$\left[\begin{array}{rrr|r} 1 & -1 & 5 & -6 \\ 0 & 1 & -\frac{8}{3} & \frac{14}{3} \\ 0 & 4 & -3 & 11 \end{array}\right] \quad \tfrac{1}{6}R2$$

$$\left[\begin{array}{ccc|c} 1 & 0 & \frac{7}{3} & -\frac{4}{3} \\ 0 & 1 & -\frac{8}{3} & \frac{14}{3} \\ 0 & 4 & -3 & 11 \end{array}\right] \quad \text{R2 + R1}$$

$$\left[\begin{array}{ccc|c} 1 & 0 & \frac{7}{3} & -\frac{4}{3} \\ 0 & 1 & -\frac{8}{3} & \frac{14}{3} \\ 0 & 0 & \frac{23}{3} & -\frac{23}{3} \end{array}\right] \quad -4\text{R2 + R3}$$

$$\left[\begin{array}{ccc|c} 1 & 0 & \frac{7}{3} & -\frac{4}{3} \\ 0 & 1 & -\frac{8}{3} & -\frac{14}{3} \\ 0 & 0 & 1 & -1 \end{array}\right] \quad \tfrac{3}{23}\text{R3}$$

$$\left[\begin{array}{ccc|c} 1 & 0 & 0 & 1 \\ 0 & 1 & -\frac{8}{3} & \frac{14}{3} \\ 0 & 0 & 1 & -1 \end{array}\right] \quad -\tfrac{7}{3}\text{R3 + R1}$$

$$\left[\begin{array}{ccc|c} 1 & 0 & 0 & 1 \\ 0 & 1 & 0 & 2 \\ 0 & 0 & 1 & -1 \end{array}\right] \quad \tfrac{8}{3}\text{R3 + R2}$$

The linear system associated with this final matrix is

$$\begin{aligned} x &= 1 \\ y &= 2 \\ z &= -1 \end{aligned}\text{, and the solution set is } \{(1, 2, -1)\}.$$

## EXTENSION EXERCISES

*Use the Gauss-Jordan method to solve each system of equations.*

1. $\begin{aligned} x + y &= 5 \\ x - y &= -1 \end{aligned}$

2. $\begin{aligned} x + 2y &= 5 \\ 2x + y &= -2 \end{aligned}$

3. $\begin{aligned} x + y &= -3 \\ 2x - 5y &= -6 \end{aligned}$

4. $\begin{aligned} 3x - 2y &= 4 \\ 3x + y &= -2 \end{aligned}$

5. $\begin{aligned} 2x - 3y &= 10 \\ 2x + 2y &= 5 \end{aligned}$

6. $\begin{aligned} 4x + y &= 5 \\ 2x + y &= 3 \end{aligned}$

7. $\begin{aligned} 3x - 7y &= 31 \\ 2x - 4y &= 18 \end{aligned}$

8. $\begin{aligned} 5x - y &= 14 \\ x + 8y &= 11 \end{aligned}$

9. $\begin{aligned} x + y - z &= 6 \\ 2x - y + z &= -9 \\ x - 2y + 3z &= 1 \end{aligned}$

10. $\begin{aligned} x + 3y - 6z &= 7 \\ 2x - y + 2z &= 0 \\ x + y + 2z &= -1 \end{aligned}$

11. $\begin{aligned} 2x - y + 3z &= 0 \\ x + 2y - z &= 5 \\ 2y + z &= 1 \end{aligned}$

12. $\begin{aligned} 4x + 2y - 3z &= 6 \\ x - 4y + z &= -4 \\ -x + 2z &= 2 \end{aligned}$

13. $\begin{aligned} -x + y &= -1 \\ y - z &= 6 \\ x + z &= -1 \end{aligned}$

14. $\begin{aligned} x + y &= 1 \\ 2x - z &= 0 \\ y + 2z &= -2 \end{aligned}$

15. $\begin{aligned} 2x - y + 4z &= -1 \\ -3x + 5y - z &= 5 \\ 2x + 3y + 2z &= 3 \end{aligned}$

16. $\begin{aligned} 5x - 3y + 2z &= -5 \\ 2x + 2y - z &= 4 \\ 4x - y + z &= -1 \end{aligned}$

17. $\begin{aligned} x + y - 2z &= 1 \\ 2x - y - 4z &= -4 \\ 3x - 2y + z &= -7 \end{aligned}$

18. $\begin{aligned} x + 3y - 6z &= -26 \\ 3x + y - z &= -10 \\ 2x - y - 3z &= -16 \end{aligned}$

# 8.8 Linear Inequalities, Systems, and Linear Programming

**Linear Inequalities in Two Variables • Systems of Inequalities • Linear Programming**

## Linear Inequalities in Two Variables

Linear inequalities with one variable were graphed on the number line in an earlier chapter. In this section linear inequalities in two variables are graphed in a rectangular coordinate system.

### Linear Inequality in Two Variables

An inequality that can be written as

$$Ax + By < C \quad \text{or} \quad Ax + By > C,$$

where $A$, $B$, and $C$ are real numbers and $A$ and $B$ are not both 0, is a **linear inequality in two variables.** The symbols $\leq$ and $\geq$ may replace $<$ and $>$ in this definition.

A line divides the plane into three regions: the line itself and the two half-planes on either side of the line. Recall that the graphs of linear inequalities in one variable are intervals on the number line that sometimes include an endpoint. The graphs of linear inequalities in two variables are *regions* in the real number plane and may include a *boundary line*. The **boundary line** for the inequality $Ax + By < C$ or $Ax + By > C$ is the graph of the *equation* $Ax + By = C$. To graph a linear inequality, we follow these steps.

### Graphing a Linear Inequality

*Step 1* **Draw the boundary.** Draw the graph of the straight line that is the boundary. Make the line solid if the inequality involves $\leq$ or $\geq$; make the line dashed if the inequality involves $<$ or $>$.

*Step 2* **Choose a test point.** Choose any point not on the line as a test point.

*Step 3* **Shade the appropriate region.** Shade the region that includes the test point if it satisfies the original inequality; otherwise, shade the region on the other side of the boundary line.

### EXAMPLE 1 Graphing a Linear Inequality

Graph $3x + 2y \geq 6$.

**SOLUTION**

First graph the straight line $3x + 2y = 6$. The graph of this line, the boundary of the graph of the inequality, is shown in Figure 48 on the next page. The graph of

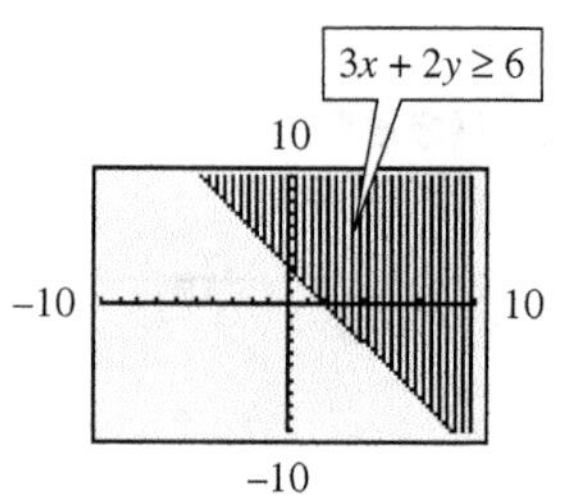


The TI-83/84 Plus allows us to shade the appropriate region for an inequality. Compare with Figure 48.

the inequality $3x + 2y \geq 6$ includes the points of the line $3x + 2y = 6$, and either the points *above* the line $3x + 2y = 6$ or the points *below* that line. To decide which, select any point not on the line $3x + 2y = 6$ as a test point. The origin, (0, 0), often is a good choice. Substitute the values from the test point (0, 0) for $x$ and $y$ in the inequality $3x + 2y \geq 6$.

$$3(0) + 2(0) \geq 6 \quad ?$$
$$0 \geq 6 \quad \text{False}$$

Because the result is false, (0, 0) does not satisfy the inequality, and so the solution set includes all points on the other side of the line. This region is shaded in Figure 48.

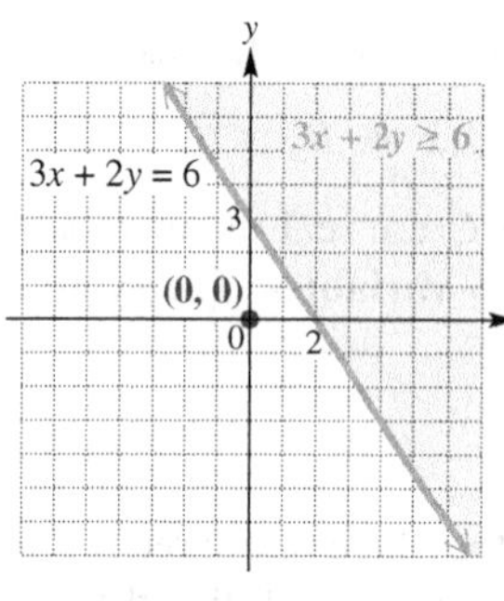


FIGURE 48

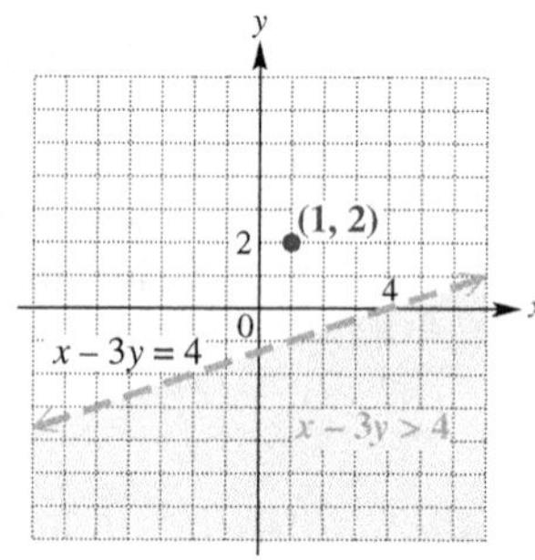


FIGURE 49

## EXAMPLE 2 Graphing a Linear Inequality

Graph $x - 3y > 4$.

**SOLUTION**

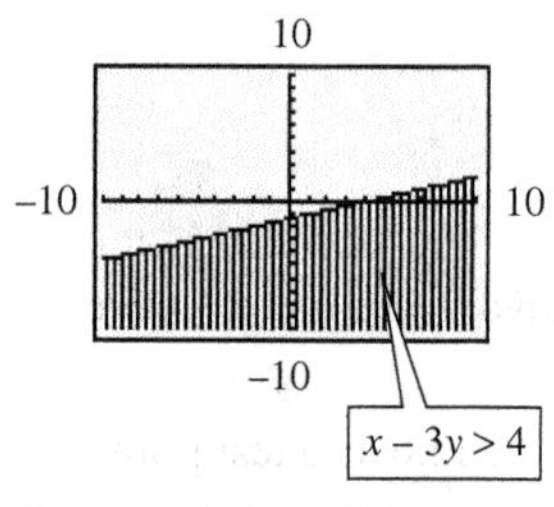


Compare with Figure 49. Can you tell from the calculator graph whether points on the boundary line are included in the solution set of the inequality?

First graph the boundary line, $x - 3y = 4$. The graph is shown in Figure 49. The points of the boundary line do not belong to the inequality $x - 3y > 4$ (since the inequality symbol is $>$ and not $\geq$). For this reason, the line is dashed. To decide which side of the line is the graph of the solution set, choose any point that is not on the line, say (1, 2). Substitute 1 for $x$ and 2 for $y$ in the original inequality.

$$1 - 3(2) > 4 \quad ?$$
$$-5 > 4 \quad \text{False}$$

Because of this false result, the solution set lies on the side of the boundary line that does *not* contain the test point (1, 2). The solution set, graphed in Figure 49, includes only those points in the shaded region (not those on the line).

**Systems of Inequalities** Methods of solving systems of *equations* were discussed in the previous section. System of inequalities with two variables may be solved by graphing. A system of linear inequalities consists of two or more such inequalities, and the solution set of such a system consists of all points that make all the inequalities true at the same time.

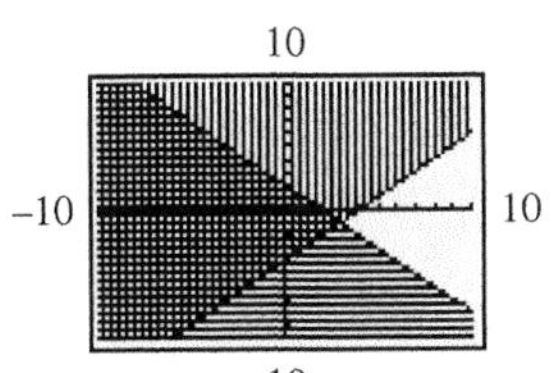


The cross-hatched region shows the solution set of the system

$$y > x - 4$$
$$y < -x + 2.$$

## Graphing a System of Linear Inequalities

*Step 1* **Graph each inequality in the same coordinate system.** Graph each inequality in the system, using the method described in Examples 1 and 2.

*Step 2* **Find the intersection of the regions of solutions.** Indicate the intersection of the regions of solutions of the individual inequalities. This is the solution set of the system.

### EXAMPLE 3 Graphing a System of Inequalities

Graph the solution set of the linear system.

$$3x + 2y \le 6$$
$$2x - 5y \ge 10$$

**SOLUTION**

Begin by graphing $3x + 2y \le 6$. To do this, graph $3x + 2y = 6$ as a solid line. Since (0, 0) makes the inequality true, shade the region containing (0, 0), as shown in Figure 50.

Now graph $2x - 5y \ge 10$. The solid line boundary is the graph of $2x - 5y = 10$. Since (0, 0) makes the inequality false, shade the region that does not contain (0, 0), as shown in Figure 51.

The solution set of the system is given by the intersection (overlap) of the regions of the graphs in Figures 50 and 51. The solution set is the shaded region in Figure 52, and includes portions of the two boundary lines.

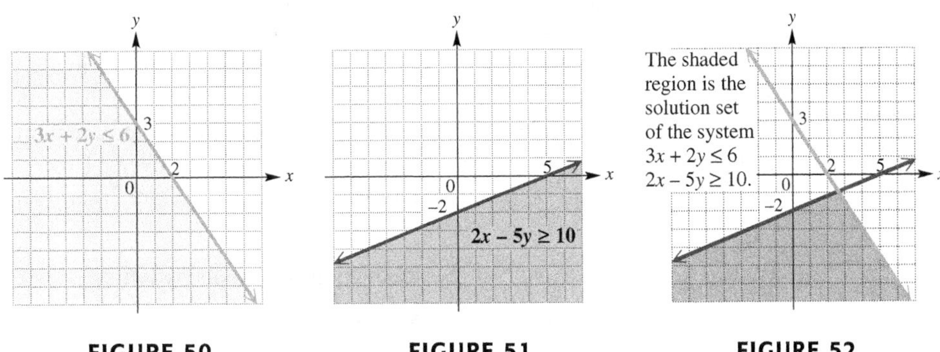


**FIGURE 50** **FIGURE 51** **FIGURE 52**

In practice, we usually do all the work in one coordinate system at the same time. In the following example, only one graph is shown.

### EXAMPLE 4 Graphing a System of Inequalities

Graph the solution set of the linear system.

$$2x + 3y \ge 12$$
$$7x + 4y \ge 28$$
$$y \le 6$$
$$x \le 5$$

**SOLUTION**

Graph the four inequalities in one coordinate system and shade the region common to all four as shown in Figure 53. As shown, the boundary lines are all solid.

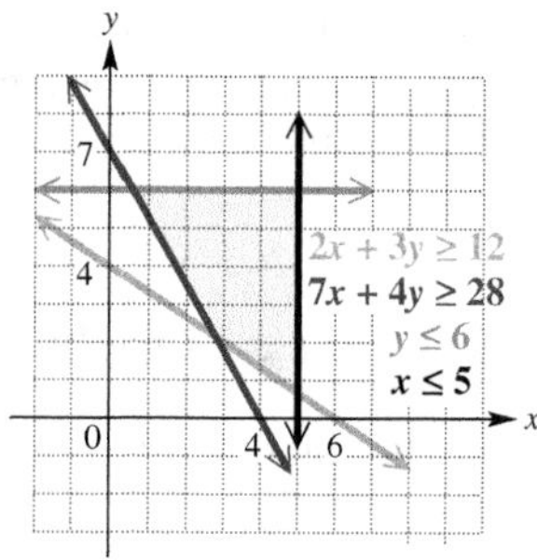


**FIGURE 53**

**George B. Dantzig** (1914–2005) of Stanford University was one of the key people behind **operations research** (OR). As a management science, OR is not a single discipline, but draws from mathematics, probability theory, statistics, and economics. The name given to this "multiplex" shows its historical origins in World War II, when operations of a military nature called forth the efforts of many scientists to research their fields for applications to the war effort and to solve tactical problems.

Operations research is an approach to problem solving and decision making. First of all, the problem has to be clarified. Quantities involved have to be designated as variables, and the objectives as functions. Use of **models** is an important aspect of OR.

**Linear Programming** A very important application of mathematics to business and social science is called **linear programming.** Linear programming is used to find an optimum value, for example, minimum cost or maximum profit. Procedures for solving linear programming problems were developed in 1947 by George Dantzig, while he was working on a problem of allocating supplies for the Air Force in a way that minimized total cost.

### EXAMPLE 5 Maximizing Profit

The Smartski Company makes two products, DVD recorders and MP-3 players. Each DVD recorder gives a profit of \$3, while each MP-3 player gives a profit of \$7. The company must manufacture at least 1 DVD recorder per day to satisfy one of its customers, but no more than 5 because of production problems. Also, the number of MP-3 players produced cannot exceed 6 per day. As a further requirement, the number of DVD recorders cannot exceed the number of MP-3 players. How many of each should the company manufacture in order to obtain the maximum profit?

**SOLUTION**

We translate the statements of the problem into symbols by letting

$x$ = number of DVD recorders to be produced daily

$y$ = number of MP-3 players to be produced daily.

According to the statement of the problem, the company must produce at least one DVD recorder (one or more), so

$$x \geq 1.$$

No more than 5 DVD recorders may be produced:

$$x \leq 5.$$

No more than 6 MP-3 players may be made in one day:

$$y \leq 6.$$

The number of DVD recorders may not exceed the number of MP-3 players:

$$x \leq y.$$

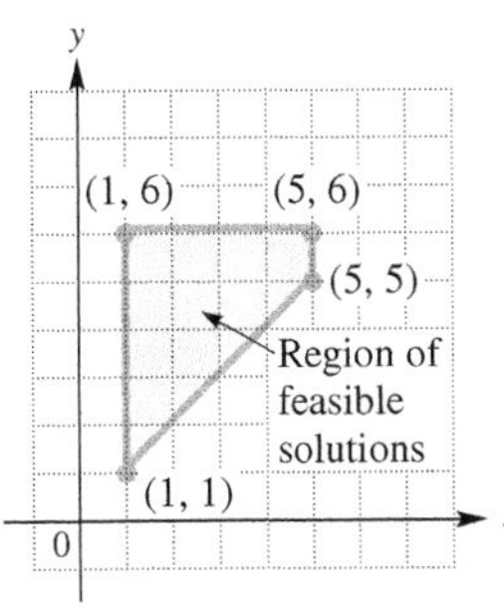


FIGURE 54

The number of DVD recorders and of MP-3 players cannot be negative:

$$x \geq 0 \quad \text{and} \quad y \geq 0.$$

All restrictions, or **constraints,** that are placed on production can now be summarized:

$$x \geq 1, \quad x \leq 5, \quad y \leq 6, \quad x \leq y, \quad x \geq 0, \quad y \geq 0.$$

The maximum possible profit that the company can make, subject to these constraints, is found by sketching the graph of the solution set of the system. See Figure 54. The only feasible values of $x$ and $y$ are those that satisfy all constraints. These values correspond to points that lie on the boundary or in the shaded region, called the **region of feasible solutions.**

Because each DVD recorder gives a profit of \$3, the daily profit from the production of $x$ DVD recorders is $3x$ dollars. Also, the profit from the production of $y$ MP-3 players will be $7y$ dollars per day. The total daily profit is thus given by the following **objective function:**

$$\text{Profit} = 3x + 7y.$$

The problem may now be stated as follows: find values of $x$ and $y$ in the region of feasible solutions as shown in Figure 54 that will produce the maximum possible value of $3x + 7y$. It can be shown that any optimum value (maximum or minimum) will always occur at a **vertex** (or **corner point**) of the region of feasible solutions. Locate the point $(x, y)$ that gives the maximum profit by checking the coordinates of the vertices, shown in Figure 54 and in Table 6. Find the profit that corresponds to each coordinate pair and choose the one that gives the maximum profit.

**It Pays to Do Your Homework**

George Dantzig, profiled on the previous page, was interviewed in the September 1986 issue of the *College Mathematics Journal.* In the interview he relates the story of how he obtained his degree without actually writing a thesis.

One day Dantzig arrived late to one of his classes and on the board were two problems. Assuming that they were homework problems, he worked on them and handed them in a few days later, apologizing to his professor for taking so long to do them. Several weeks later he received an early morning visit from his professor. The problems had not been intended as homework problems; they were actually two famous *unsolved* problems in statistics! Later, when Dantzig began to think about a thesis topic, his professor told him that the two solutions would serve as his thesis.

**TABLE 6**

| Point | Profit = $3x + 7y$ | |
|---|---|---|
| (1,1) | $3(1) + 7(1) = 10$ | |
| (1,6) | $3(1) + 7(6) = 45$ | |
| (5,6) | $3(5) + 7(6) = 57$ | ← Maximum |
| (5,5) | $3(5) + 7(5) = 50$ | |

The maximum profit of \$57 is obtained when 5 DVD recorders and 6 MP-3 players are produced each day.

To solve a linear programming problem in general, use the following steps.

**Solving a Linear Programming Problem**

***Step 1*** Write all necessary constraints and the objective function.

***Step 2*** Graph the region of feasible solutions.

***Step 3*** Identify all vertices.

***Step 4*** Find the value of the objective function at each vertex.

***Step 5*** The solution is given by the vertex producing the optimum value of the objective function.

## 8.8 Exercises

*In Exercises 1–4, match each system of inequalities with the correct graph from choices A–D.*

**A.**

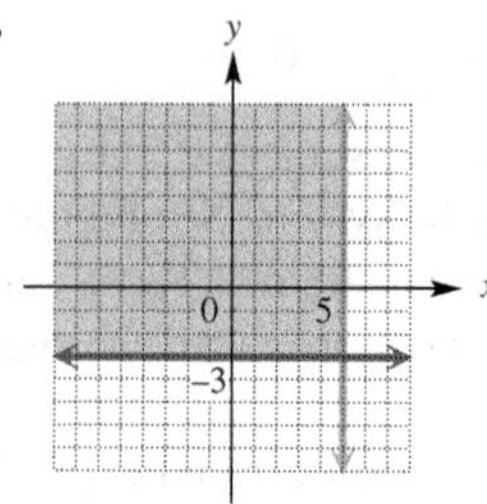

**B.**

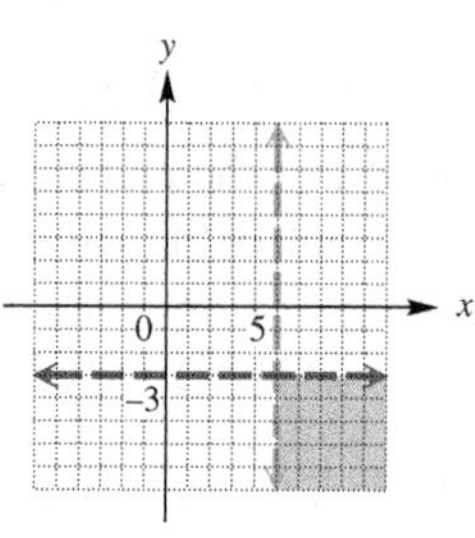

**C.**

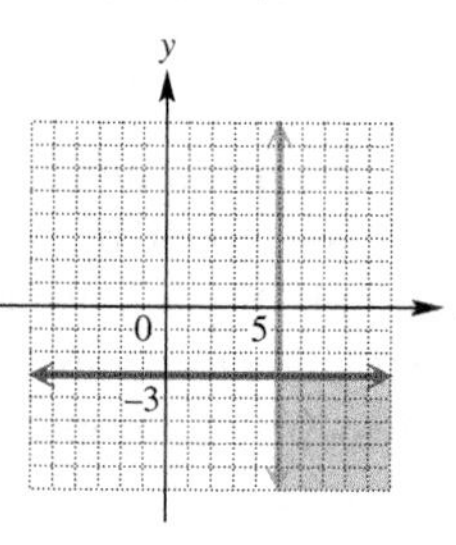

**D.**

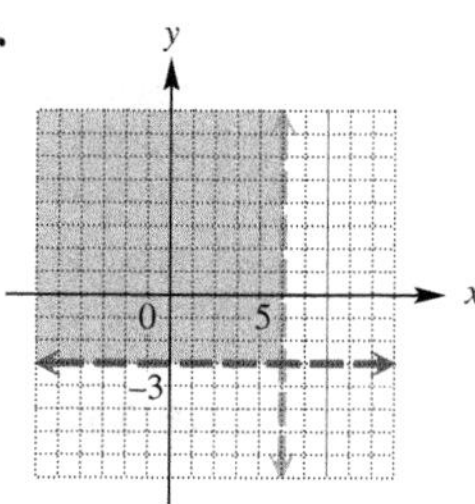

**1.** $x \geq 5$
$y \leq -3$

**2.** $x \leq 5$
$y \geq -3$

**3.** $x > 5$
$y < -3$

**4.** $x < 5$
$y > -3$

*Graph each linear inequality.*

**5.** $x + y \leq 2$

**6.** $x - y \geq -3$

**7.** $4x - y \leq 5$

**8.** $3x + y \geq 6$

**9.** $x + 3y \geq -2$

**10.** $4x + 6y \leq -3$

**11.** $x + 2y \leq -5$

**12.** $2x - 4y \leq 3$

**13.** $4x - 3y < 12$

**14.** $5x + 3y > 15$

**15.** $y > -x$

**16.** $y < x$

*Graph each system of inequalities.*

**17.** $x + y \leq 1$
$x \geq 0$

**18.** $3x - 4y \leq 6$
$y \geq 1$

**19.** $2x - y \geq 1$
$3x + 2y \geq 6$

**20.** $x + 3y \geq 6$
$3x - 4y \leq 12$

**21.** $-x - y < 5$
$x - y \leq 3$

**22.** $6x - 4y < 8$
$x + 2y \geq 4$

*Exercises 23 and 24 show regions of feasible solutions. Find the maximum and minimum values of the given expressions.*

**23.** $3x + 5y$

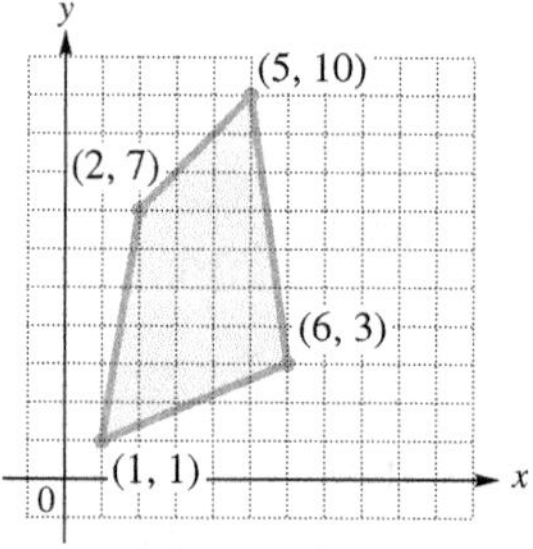


**24.** $40x + 75y$

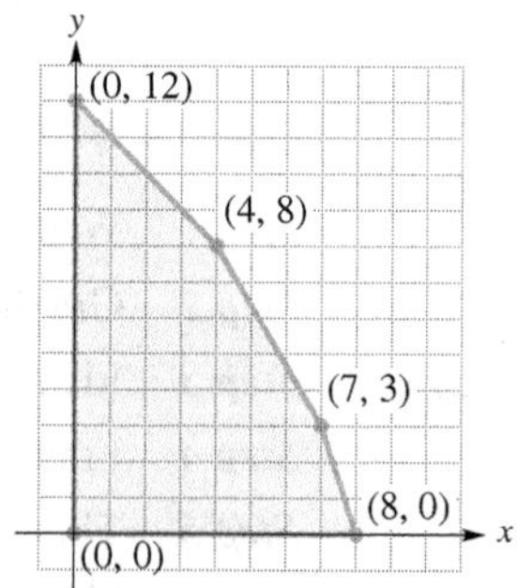

*Use graphical methods to find values of x and y satisfying the given conditions. (It may be necessary to solve a system of equations in order to find vertices.) Find the value of the maximum or minimum.*

**25.** Find $x \geq 0$ and $y \geq 0$ such that

$$2x + 3y \leq 6$$
$$4x + y \leq 6$$

and $5x + 2y$ is maximized.

**26.** Find $x \geq 0$ and $y \geq 0$ such that

$$x + y \leq 10$$
$$5x + 2y \geq 20$$
$$2y \geq x$$

and $x + 3y$ is minimized.

**27.** Find $x \geq 2$ and $y \geq 5$ such that

$$3x - y \geq 12$$
$$x + y \leq 15$$

and $2x + y$ is minimized.

**28.** Find $x \geq 10$ and $y \geq 20$ such that

$$2x + 3y \leq 100$$
$$5x + 4y \leq 200$$

and $x + 3y$ is maximized.

*Solve each linear programming problem.*

**29.** ***Refrigerator Shipping Costs*** A manufacturer of refrigerators must ship at least 100 refrigerators to its two West coast warehouses. Each warehouse holds a maximum of 100 refrigerators. Warehouse A holds 25 refrigerators already, while warehouse B has 20 on hand. It costs \$12 to ship a refrigerator to warehouse A and \$10 to ship one to warehouse B. How many refrigerators should be shipped to each warehouse to minimize cost? What is the minimum cost?

**30.** ***Food Supplement Costs*** Bonnie, who is dieting, requires two food supplements, I and II. She can get these supplements from two different products, A and B. Product A provides 3 grams per serving of supplement I and 2 grams per serving of supplement II. Product B provides 2 grams per serving of supplement I and 4 grams per serving of supplement II. Her dietician, Dr. Dawson, has recommended that she include at least 15 grams of each supplement in her daily diet. If product A costs 25¢ per serving and product B costs 40¢ per serving, how can she satisfy her requirements most economically?

**31.** ***Vitamin Pill Costs*** Elizabeth Lamulle takes vitamin pills. Each day, she must have at least 16 units of Vitamin A, at least 5 units of Vitamin $B_1$, and at least 20 units of Vitamin C. She can choose between red pills costing 10¢ each that contain 8 units of A, 1 of $B_1$, and 2 of C; and blue pills that cost 20¢ each and contain 2 units of A, 1 of $B_1$, and 7 of C. How many of each pill should she take in order to minimize her cost and yet fulfill her daily requirements?

**32.** ***Bolt Costs*** A machine shop manufactures two types of bolts. Each can be made on any of three groups of machines, but the time required on each group differs, as shown in the table in the next column.

| | | Machine Groups | | |
|---|---|---|---|---|
| | | I | II | III |
| Bolts | Type A | .1 min | .1 min | .1 min |
| | Type B | .1 min | .4 min | .5 min |

Production schedules are made up one day at a time. In a day there are 240, 720, and 160 minutes available, respectively, on these machines. Type A bolts sell for 10¢ and type B bolts for 12¢. How many of each type of bolt should be manufactured per day to maximize revenue? What is the maximum revenue?

**33.** ***Gasoline and Fuel Oil Costs*** A manufacturing process requires that oil refineries manufacture at least 2 gallons of gasoline for each gallon of fuel oil. To meet the winter demand for fuel oil, at least 3 million gallons a day must be produced. The demand for gasoline is no more than 6.4 million gallons per day. If the price of gasoline is \$1.90 per gallon and the price of fuel oil is \$1.50 per gallon, how much of each should be produced to maximize revenue?

**34.** ***Cake and Cookie Production*** A bakery makes both cakes and cookies. Each batch of cakes requires two hours in the oven and three hours in the decorating room. Each batch of cookies needs one and a half hours in the oven and two-thirds of an hour in the decorating room. The oven is available no more than 15 hours a day, while the decorating room can be used no more than 13 hours a day. How many batches of cakes and cookies should the bakery make in order to maximize profits if cookies produce a profit of \$20 per batch and cakes produce a profit of \$30 per batch?

35. ***Aid to Earthquake Victims*** Earthquake victims in China need medical supplies and bottled water. Each medical kit measures 1 cubic foot and weighs 10 pounds. Each container of water is also 1 cubic foot and weighs 20 pounds. The plane can only carry 80,000 pounds with a total volume of 6000 cubic feet. Each medical kit will aid 6 people, while each container of water will serve 10 people. How many of each should be sent in order to maximize the number of people aided?

36. ***Aid to Earthquake Victims*** If each medical kit could aid 4 people instead of 6, how would the results in Exercise 35 change?

# COLLABORATIVE INVESTIGATION

## Living with AIDS

The graph here shows a comparison of the number of African Americans and Whites living with AIDS in the United States during 1993–2000. Form groups of 2–3 students each to work the following.

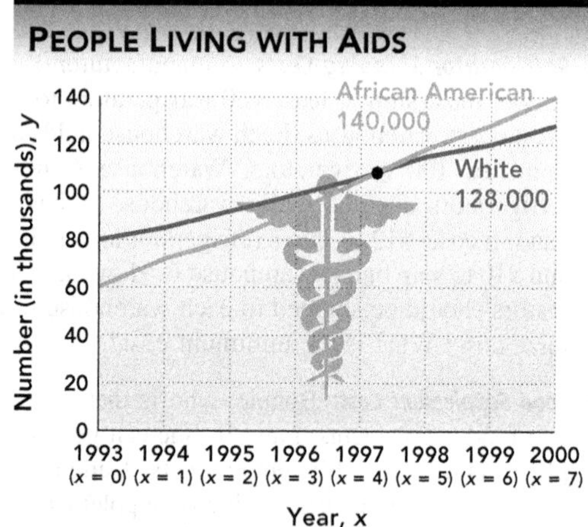


*Source:* U.S. Centers for Disease Control.

### Topics for Discussion

1. The two lines were obtained by joining the data points that are of the form

(year, number of people in thousands).

Let $x = 0$ represent the year 1993, $x = 1$ represent 1994, and so on, and approximate the value of $y$ for each year for African Americans. Estimate the missing values, and fill in the table. Remember that $y$ is in thousands.

| Year | Number of African Americans with AIDS ($y$, in thousands) |
|---|---|
| 1993 ($x = 0$) | 60 |
| 1994 ($x = 1$) | |
| 1995 ($x = 2$) | |
| 1996 ($x = 3$) | |
| 1997 ($x = 4$) | |
| 1998 ($x = 5$) | |
| 1999 ($x = 6$) | |
| 2000 ($x = 7$) | 140 |

Now use any two data points to find an equation of the line describing this data.

2. Repeat the procedure from part 1, applying the data from the line for Whites living with AIDS.

| Year | Number of Whites with AIDS ($y$, in thousands) |
|---|---|
| 1993 ($x = 0$) | 80 |
| 1994 ($x = 1$) | |
| 1995 ($x = 2$) | |
| 1996 ($x = 3$) | |
| 1997 ($x = 4$) | |
| 1998 ($x = 5$) | |
| 1999 ($x = 6$) | |
| 2000 ($x = 7$) | 128 |

Now use any two data points to find an equation of the line describing this data.

3. The two equations from parts 1 and 2 form a system of two linear equations in two variables. Solve this system using any method you wish.

4. The $x$-coordinate of the solution of the system in part 3 should correspond to the year in which the two lines intersect. Look at the graph again. Does your $x$-value correspond the way it should?

5. Discuss why results of this activity might vary among groups performing it.

# CHAPTER 8 TEST

1. Find the distance between the points $(-3, 5)$ and $(2, 1)$.

2. Find an equation of the circle whose center has coordinates $(-1, 2)$, with radius 3. Sketch its graph.

3. Find the $x$- and $y$-intercepts of the graph of $3x - 2y = 8$, and graph the equation.

4. Find the slope of the line passing through the points $(6, 4)$ and $(-1, 2)$.

5. Find the slope-intercept form of the equation of the line described.
   (a) passing through the point $(-1, 3)$, with slope $-\frac{2}{5}$
   (b) passing through $(-7, 2)$ and perpendicular to $y = 2x$
   (c) the line shown in the figures below (Look at the displays at the bottom.)

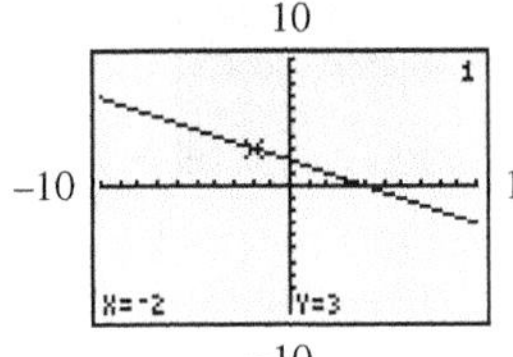


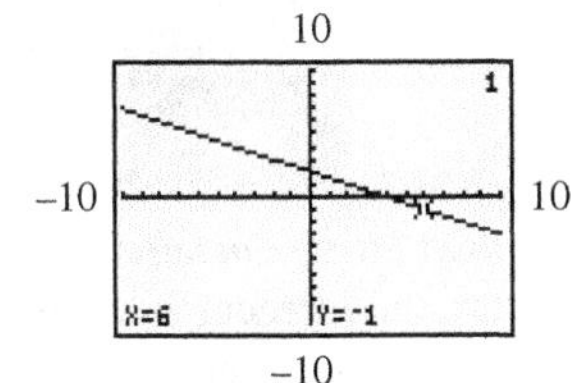


6. Which one of the following has positive slope and negative $y$-coordinate for its $y$-intercept?

A.
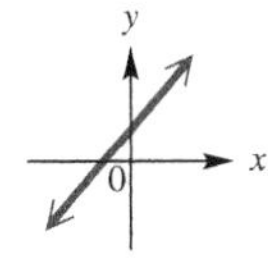

B.
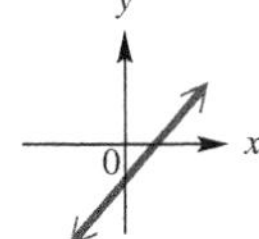


C.
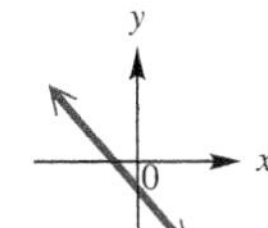


D.
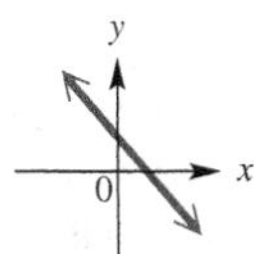


7. ***Income for Americans*** Median household income of Americans is shown in the graph in the next column.

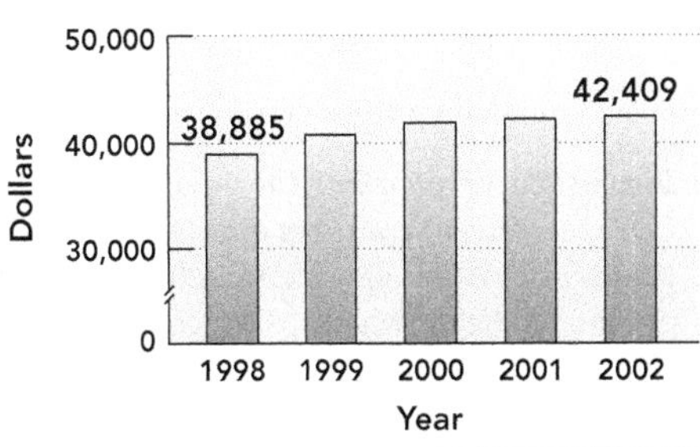


*Source:* U.S. Bureau of the Census.

   (a) Use the information given for the years 1998 and 2002, letting $x = 0$ represent 1998, $x = 4$ represent 2002, and $y$ represent the median income, to write an equation that models median household income.

   (b) Use the equation to approximate the median income for 2001. How does your result compare to the actual income, \$42,228?

8. ***Library Fines*** It costs a borrower \$.05 per day for an overdue book, plus a flat \$.50 charge for all books borrowed. Let $x$ represent the number of days the book is overdue, so $y$ represents the total fine to the tardy user. Write an equation in the form $y = mx + b$ for this situation. Then give three ordered pairs with $x$-values of 1, 5, and 10 that satisfy the equation.

9. Write the slope-intercept form of the equation of the line shown.

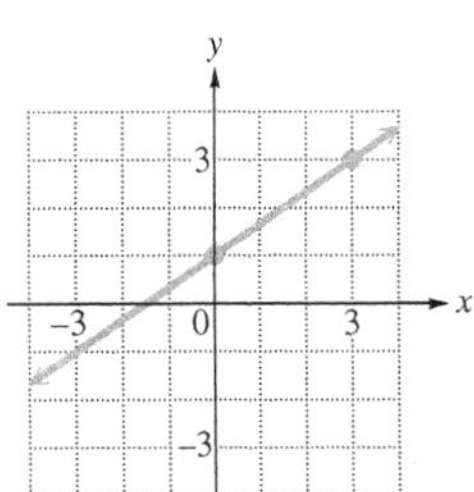

**10.** For the function $f(x) = x^2 - 3x + 12$,
**(a)** give its domain. **(b)** find $f(-2)$.

**11.** Give the domain of the function defined by

$$f(x) = \frac{2}{x - 3}.$$

**12.** ***Calculator Production*** If the cost to produce $x$ units of calculators is $C(x) = 50x + 5000$ dollars, while the revenue is $R(x) = 60x$ dollars, find the number of units of calculators that must be produced in order to break even. What is the revenue at the break-even point?

**13.** Graph the quadratic function

$$f(x) = -(x + 3)^2 + 4.$$

Give the axis, the vertex, the domain, and the range.

**14.** ***Dimensions of a Parking Lot*** Miami-Dade Community College wants to construct a rectangular parking lot on land bordered on one side by a highway. It has 320 ft of fencing with which to fence off the other three sides. What should be the dimensions of the lot if the enclosed area is to be a maximum?

**15.** Use a scientific calculator to find an approximation of each of the following. Give as many digits as the calculator displays.
**(a)** $5.1^{4.7}$
**(b)** $e^{-1.85}$
**(c)** $\ln 23.56$

**16.** Which one of the following is a false statement?
**A.** The domain of the function $f(x) = \log_2 x$ is $(-\infty, \infty)$.
**B.** The graph of $F(x) = 3^x$ intersects the $y$-axis.
**C.** The graph of $G(x) = \log_3 x$ intersects the $x$-axis.
**D.** The expression $\ln x$ represents the exponent to which $e$ must be raised in order to obtain $x$.

**17.** ***Investment*** Suppose that \$12,000 is invested in an account that pays 4% annual interest, and is left untouched for 3 years. How much will be in the account if
**(a)** interest is compounded quarterly (four times per year);
**(b)** interest is compounded continuously?

**18.** ***Decay of Plutonium-241*** Suppose that the amount, in grams, of plutonium-241 present in a given sample is determined by the function defined by

$$A(t) = 2.00e^{-.053t},$$

where $t$ is measured in years. Find the amount present in the sample after the given number of years.

**(a)** 4 **(b)** 10
**(c)** 20
**(d)** What was the initial amount present?

*Solve each system by using elimination, substitution, or a combination of the two methods.*

**19.** $$\begin{aligned} 2x + 3y &= 2 \\ 3x - 4y &= 20 \end{aligned}$$

**20.** $$\begin{aligned} 2x + y + z &= 3 \\ x + 2y - z &= 3 \\ 3x - y + z &= 5 \end{aligned}$$

**21.** $$\begin{aligned} 2x + 3y - 6z &= 11 \\ x - y + 2z &= -2 \\ 4x + y - 2z &= 7 \end{aligned}$$

*Solve each problem by using a system of equations.*

**22.** ***Julia Roberts' Box Office Hits*** Julia Roberts is one of the biggest box-office stars in Hollywood. As of April 2006, her two top-grossing domestic films, *Pretty Woman* and *Ocean's Eleven*, together earned \$914.1 million in worldwide revenues. If *Ocean's Eleven* grossed \$12.7 million less than *Pretty Woman*, how much did each film gross? (*Source:* ACNielsen EDI.)

**23.** ***Real Estate Commission*** Keshon Grant sells real estate. On three recent sales, he made 10% commission, 6% commission, and 5% commission. His total commissions on these sales were \$17,000, and he sold property worth \$280,000. If the 5% sale amounted to the sum of the other two, what were the three sales' prices?

**24.** Graph the solution set of the system of inequalities.

$$\begin{aligned} x + y &\leq 6 \\ 2x - y &\geq 3 \end{aligned}$$

**25.** ***Ring Sales*** The Alessi company designs and sells two types of rings: the VIP and the SST. The company can produce up to 24 rings each day using up to 60 total hours of labor. It takes 3 hours to make one VIP ring, and 2 hours to make one SST ring. How many of each type of ring should be made daily in order to maximize profit, if profit on a VIP ring is \$30 and profit on an SST ring is \$40? What is the profit?

# GEOMETRY

Director Robert Zemeckis' *Cast Away* was one of the top films of 2000. It stars Tom Hanks as Chuck Noland, a Federal Express employee who, as the only survivor in a plane crash, is stranded for 4 years alone on a tropical island. Not long after the crash, speaking to his "friend" Wilson, a volleyball that had washed ashore, he used geometry to assess their chances of being found. Sketching a circle and performing an arithmetic calculation on the side of a rock, Chuck realizes their futility.

> *So, Wilson. We were en route from Memphis for eleven and a half hours at about 475 miles an hour. They think that we are right here. But we went out of radio contact and flew around that storm for about an hour. So that's a distance of what, 400 miles? Four hundred miles squared, that's 160,000, times pi, 3.14, . . .*

Chuck's calculation for the size of the search area is an application of the formula for the area of a circle, $A = \pi r^2$. He looks to Wilson, and sighs,

> *. . . That's twice the size of Texas. They may never find us.*

What was Chuck's answer? The land area of Texas is 261,797 square miles. Was he correct? The answer can be found on page 559.

# 9.1 Points, Lines, Planes, and Angles

**The Geometry of Euclid • Points, Lines, and Planes • Angles**

Euclid's *Elements* as translated by Billingsley appeared in 1570 and was the first English language translation of the text—the most influential geometry text ever written.

Unfortunately, no copy of *Elements* exists that dates back to the time of Euclid (circa 300 B.C.), and most current translations are based upon a revision of the work prepared by Theon of Alexandria.

Although *Elements* was only one of several works of Euclid, it is, by far, the most important. It ranks second only to the Bible as the most published book in history.

## The Geometry of Euclid

*Let no one unversed in geometry enter here.*
—Motto over the door of Plato's Academy

To the ancient Greeks, mathematics meant geometry above all—a rigid kind of geometry from a modern-day point of view. The Greeks studied the properties of figures identical in shape and size (congruent figures) as well as figures identical in shape but not necessarily in size (similar figures). They absorbed ideas about area and volume from the Egyptians and Babylonians and established general formulas. The Greeks were the first to insist that statements in geometry be given rigorous proof.

The Greek view of geometry (and other mathematical ideas) was summarized in *Elements,* written by Euclid about 300 B.C. The influence of this book has been extraordinary; it has been studied virtually unchanged to this day as a geometry textbook and as *the* model of deductive logic.

The most basic ideas of geometry are **point, line,** and **plane.** In fact, it is not really possible to define them with other words. Euclid defined a point as "that which has no part," but this definition is so vague as to be meaningless. Do you think you could decide what a point is from this definition? But from your experience in saying "this point in time" or in sharpening a pencil, you have an idea of what he was getting at. Even though we don't try to define *point,* we do agree that, intuitively, a point has no magnitude and no size.

Euclid defined a line as "that which has breadthless length." Again, this definition is vague. Based on our experience, however, we know what Euclid meant. The drawings that we use for lines have properties of no thickness and no width, and they extend indefinitely in two directions.

What do you visualize when you read Euclid's definition of a plane: "a surface which lies evenly with the straight lines on itself"? Do you think of a flat surface, such as a tabletop or a page in a book? That is what Euclid intended.

The geometry of Euclid is a model of deductive reasoning. In this chapter, we will present geometry from an inductive viewpoint, using objects and situations found in the world around us as models for study.

**Points, Lines, and Planes** There are certain universally accepted conventions and symbols used to represent points, lines, planes, and angles. A capital letter usually represents a point. A line may be named by two capital letters representing points that lie on the line, or by a single (usually lowercase) letter, such as $\ell$. Subscripts are sometimes used to distinguish one line from another when a lowercase letter is used. For example, $\ell_1$ and $\ell_2$ would represent two distinct lines. A plane may be named by three capital letters representing points that lie in the plane, or by a letter of the Greek alphabet, such as $\alpha$ (alpha), $\beta$ (beta), or $\gamma$ (gamma).

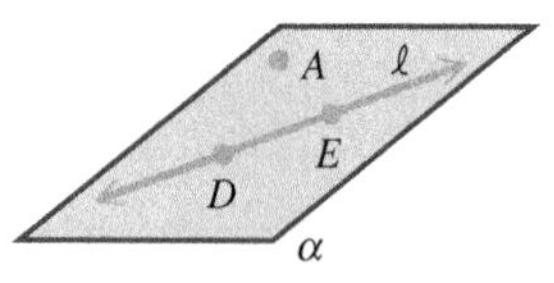


**FIGURE 1**

Figure 1 depicts a plane that may be represented either as $\alpha$ or as plane *ADE*. Contained in the plane is the line *DE* (or, equivalently, line *ED*), which is also labeled $\ell$ in the figure.

Selecting any point on a line divides the line into three parts: the point itself, and two **half-lines,** one on each side of the point. For example point *A* divides the line shown in Figure 2 into three parts, *A* itself and two half-lines. Point *A* belongs to neither half-line. As the figure suggests, each half-line extends indefinitely in the direction opposite the other half-line.

**Given any three points** that are not in a straight line, a plane can be passed through the points. That is why **camera tripods** have three legs—no matter how irregular the surface, the tips of the three legs determine a plane. On the other hand, a camera support with four legs would wobble unless all four legs were carefully extended just the right amount.

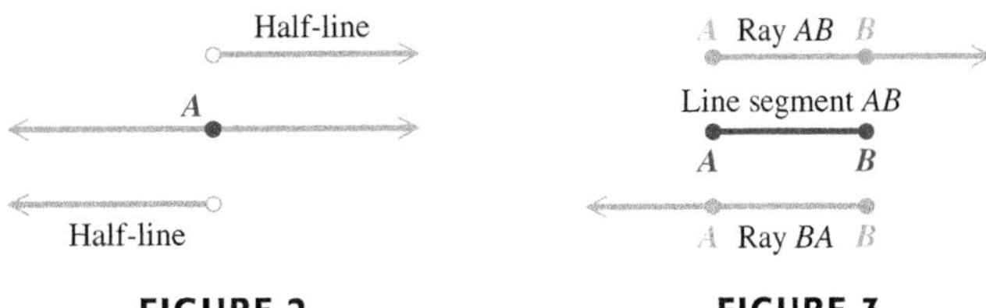


**FIGURE 2** **FIGURE 3**

Including an initial point with a half-line gives a **ray.** A ray is named with two letters, one for the initial point of the ray, and one for another point contained in the half-line. For example, in Figure 3 ray *AB* has initial point *A* and extends in the direction of *B*. On the other hand, ray *BA* has *B* as its initial point and extends in the direction of *A*.

A **line segment** includes both endpoints and is named by its endpoints. Figure 3 shows line segment *AB*, which may also be designated as line segment *BA*.

Table 1 shows these figures along with the symbols used to represent them.

**TABLE 1**

| Name | Figure | Symbol |
|---|---|---|
| Line *AB* or line *BA* | A B | $\overleftrightarrow{AB}$ or $\overleftrightarrow{BA}$ |
| Half-line *AB* | A B | $\overset{\circ\!\!\rightarrow}{AB}$ |
| Half-line *BA* | A B | $\overset{\circ\!\!\rightarrow}{BA}$ |
| Ray *AB* | A B | $\overset{\bullet\!\!\rightarrow}{AB}$ |
| Ray *BA* | A B | $\overset{\bullet\!\!\rightarrow}{BA}$ |
| Segment *AB* or segment *BA* | A B | $\overset{\bullet\!-\!\bullet}{AB}$ or $\overset{\bullet\!-\!\bullet}{BA}$ |

For a line, the symbol above the two letters shows two arrowheads, indicating that the line extends indefinitely in both directions. For half-lines and rays, only one arrowhead is used because these extend in only one direction. An open circle is used for a half-line to show that the endpoint is not included, while a solid circle is used for a ray to indicate the inclusion of the endpoint. Since a segment includes both endpoints and does not extend in either direction, solid circles are used to indicate endpoints of line segments.

The geometric definitions of "parallel" and "intersecting" apply to two or more lines or planes. (See Figure 4 on the next page.) **Parallel lines** lie in the same plane and never meet, no matter how far they are extended. However, **intersecting lines** do meet. If two distinct lines intersect, they intersect in one and only one point.

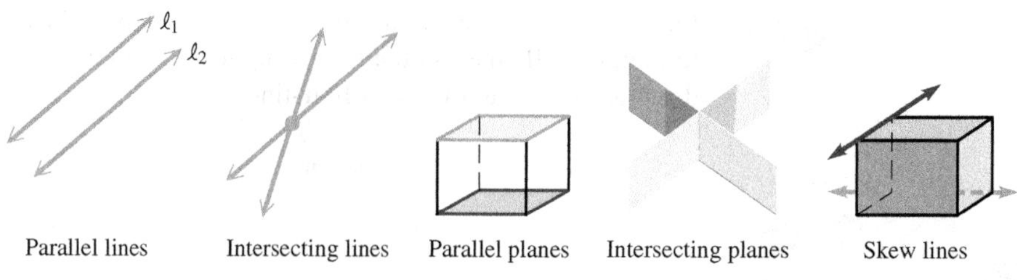


**FIGURE 4**

We use the symbol $\parallel$ to denote parallelism. If $\ell_1$ and $\ell_2$ are parallel lines, as in Figure 4, then this may be indicated as $\ell_1 \parallel \ell_2$.

**Parallel planes** also never meet, no matter how far they are extended. Two distinct **intersecting planes** form a straight line, the one and only line they have in common. **Skew lines** do not lie in the same plane, and they never meet, no matter how far they are extended.

## Angles

An **angle** is the union of two rays that have a common endpoint, as shown in Figure 5. It is important to remember that the angle is formed by points on the rays themselves, and no other points. In Figure 5, point $X$ is *not* a point on the angle. (It is said to be in the *interior* of the angle.) Notice that "angle" is the first basic term in this section that is actually defined, using the undefined terms *ray* and *endpoint*.

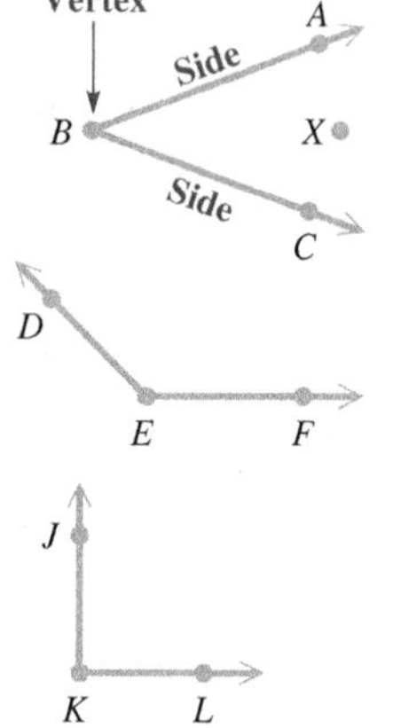


**FIGURE 5**

The rays forming an angle are called its **sides.** The common endpoint of the rays is the **vertex** of the angle. There are two standard ways of naming angles using letters. If no confusion will result, an angle can be named with the letter marking its vertex. Using this method, the angles in Figure 5 can be named, respectively, angle $B$, angle $E$, and angle $K$. Angles also can be named with three letters: the first letter names a point on one side of the angle; the middle letter names the vertex; the third names a point on the other side of the angle. In this system, the angles in the figure can be named angle $ABC$, angle $DEF$, and angle $JKL$. The symbol for representing an angle is $\measuredangle$. Rather than writing "angle $ABC$," we may write "$\measuredangle ABC$."

An angle can be associated with an amount of rotation. For example, in Figure 6(a), we let $\overleftrightarrow{BA}$ first coincide with $\overleftrightarrow{BC}$—as though they were the same ray. We then rotate $\overleftrightarrow{BA}$ (the endpoint remains fixed) in a counterclockwise direction to form $\measuredangle ABC$.

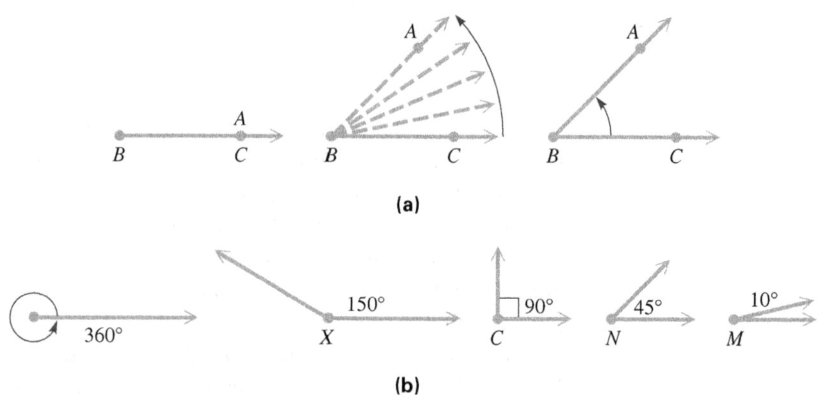


**FIGURE 6**

**Why 360?** The use of the number 360 goes back to the Babylonian culture. There are several theories regarding why 360 was chosen for the number of degrees in a complete rotation around a circle. One says that 360 was chosen because it is close to the number of days in a year, and is conveniently divisible by 2, 3, 4, 5, 6, 8, 9, 10, 12, and other numbers.

Angles are measured by the amount of rotation, using a system that dates back to the Babylonians some two centuries before Christ. Babylonian astronomers chose the number 360 to represent the amount of rotation of a ray back onto itself. Using 360 as the amount of rotation of a ray back onto itself, **one degree,** written $1°$, is defined to be $\frac{1}{360}$ of a complete rotation. Figure 6(b) shows angles of various degree measures.

Angles are classified and named with reference to their degree measures. An angle whose measure is between $0°$ and $90°$ is called an **acute angle.** Angles *M* and *N* in Figure 6(b) are acute. An angle that measures $90°$ is called a **right angle.** Angle *C* in the figure is a right angle. The squared symbol ⏋ at the vertex denotes a right angle. Angles that measure more than $90°$ but less than $180°$ are said to be **obtuse angles** (angle *X*, for example). An angle that measures $180°$ is a **straight angle.** Its sides form a straight line.

Angles are the key to the study of **geodesy,** the measurement of distances on the earth's surface.

Our work in this section will be devoted primarily to angles whose measures are less than or equal to $180°$. Angles whose measures are greater than $180°$ are discussed in Chapter 10 and are studied in more detail in trigonometry courses.

A tool called a **protractor** can be used to measure angles. Figure 7 shows a protractor measuring an angle. To use a protractor, position the hole (or dot) of the protractor on the vertex of the angle. The 0-degree measure on the protractor should be placed on one side of the angle, while the other side should extend to the degree measure of the angle. The figure indicates an angle whose measure is $135°$.

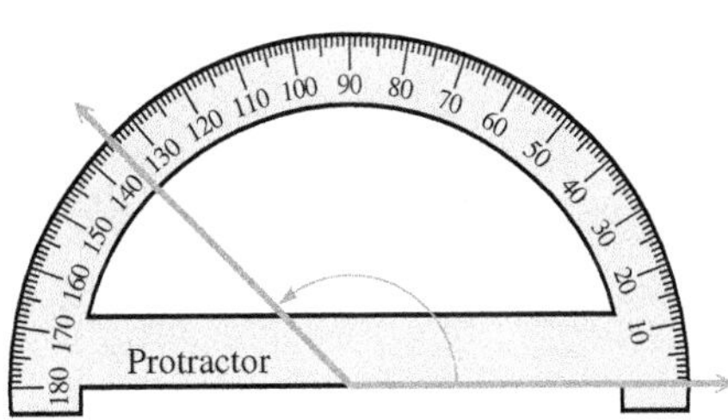


**FIGURE 7**

When two lines intersect to form right angles they are called **perpendicular lines.** Our sense of *vertical* and *horizontal* depends on perpendicularity.

In Figure 8, the sides of $\measuredangle NMP$ have been extended to form another angle, $\measuredangle RMQ$. The pair $\measuredangle NMP$ and $\measuredangle RMQ$ are called **vertical angles.** Another pair of vertical angles have been formed at the same time. They are $\measuredangle NMQ$ and $\measuredangle PMR$.

An important property of vertical angles follows.

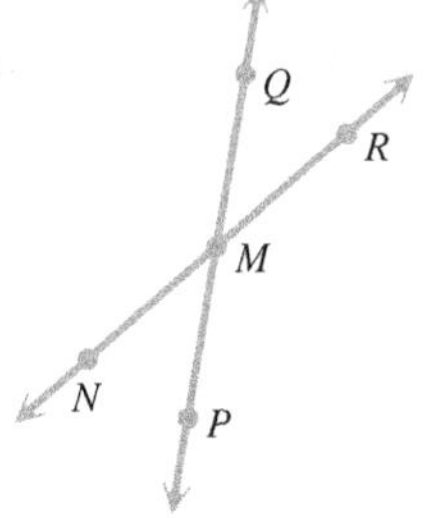


**FIGURE 8**

### Property of Vertical Angles

Vertical angles have equal measures.

For example, $\measuredangle NMP$ and $\measuredangle RMQ$ in Figure 8 have equal measures. What other pair of angles in the figure have equal measures?

## EXAMPLE 1 Finding Angle Measures

Find the measure of each marked angle in the given figure.

**(a)** Figure 9 **(b)** Figure 10

**SOLUTION**

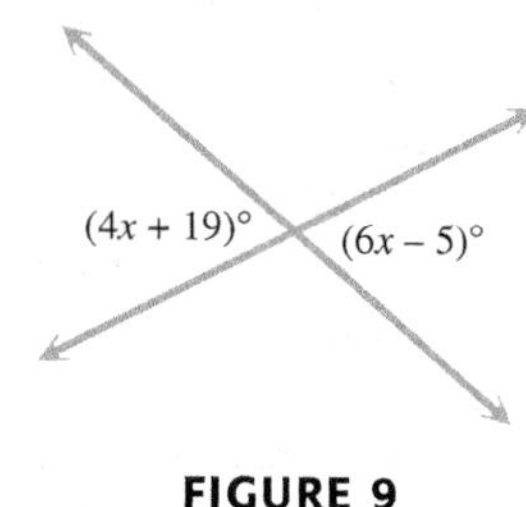


FIGURE 9

**(a)** Because the marked angles are vertical angles, they have the same measure. So,

$$4x + 19 = 6x - 5$$
$$4x + 19 - 4x = 6x - 5 - 4x \quad \text{Subtract } 4x.$$
$$19 = 2x - 5 \quad \text{Combine like terms.}$$
$$19 + 5 = 2x - 5 + 5 \quad \text{Add 5.}$$
$$24 = 2x$$
Don't stop here. ⟶ $$\mathbf{12} = x. \quad \text{Divide by 2.}$$

Since $x = 12$, one angle has measure $4(\mathbf{12}) + 19 = 67$ degrees. The other has the same measure, because $6(\mathbf{12}) - 5 = 67$ as well. Each angle measures 67°.

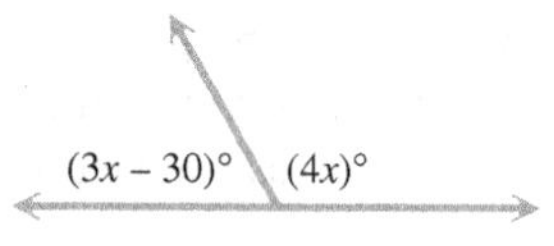


FIGURE 10

**(b)** The measures of the marked angles must add to 180° because together they form a straight angle.

$$(3x - 30) + 4x = 180 \quad \text{The angle sum is 180.}$$
$$7x - 30 = 180 \quad \text{Combine like terms.}$$
$$7x - 30 + 30 = 180 + 30 \quad \text{Add 30.}$$
$$7x = 210$$
Don't stop here. ⟶ $$x = \mathbf{30} \quad \text{Divide by 7.}$$

To find the measures of the angles, replace $x$ with 30 in the two expressions.

$$3x - 30 = 3(\mathbf{30}) - 30 = 90 - 30 = 60$$
$$4x = 4(\mathbf{30}) = 120$$

The two angle measures are 60° and 120°. ■

If the sum of the measures of two acute angles is 90°, the angles are said to be **complementary,** and each is called the *complement* of the other. For example, angles measuring 40° and 50° are complementary angles, because 40° + 50° = 90°. If two angles have a sum of 180°, they are **supplementary.** The *supplement* of an angle whose measure is 40° is an angle whose measure is 140°, because 40° + 140° = 180°.

***If x represents the degree measure of an angle, 90 − x represents the measure of its complement, and 180 − x represents the measure of its supplement.***

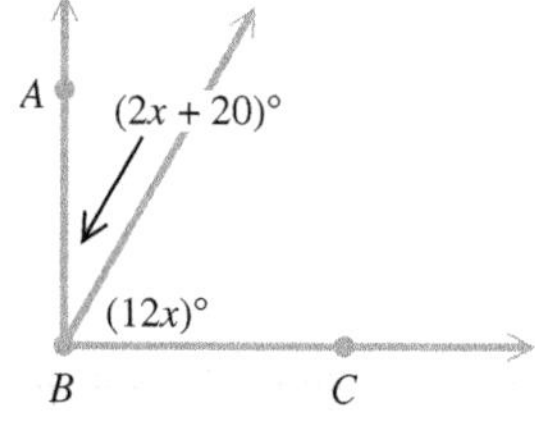


FIGURE 11

## EXAMPLE 2 Finding Angle Measures

Find the measures of the angles in Figure 11, given that $\measuredangle ABC$ is a right angle.

**SOLUTION**

The sum of the measures of the two acute angles is 90° (that is, they are complementary), because they form a right angle. We add their measures to obtain a sum of 90 and solve the resulting equation.

$$
\begin{aligned}
(2x + 20) + 12x &= 90 \\
14x + 20 &= 90 \quad \text{Combine like terms.} \\
14x &= 70 \quad \text{Subtract 20.} \\
x &= 5 \quad \text{Divide by 14.}
\end{aligned}
$$

The value of $x$ is 5. Therefore, replace $x$ with 5 in the two expressions.

$$2x + 20 = 2(5) + 20 = 30.$$

$$12x = 12(5) = 60$$

The measures of the two angles are 30° and 60°.

## EXAMPLE 3 Using Complementary and Supplementary Angles

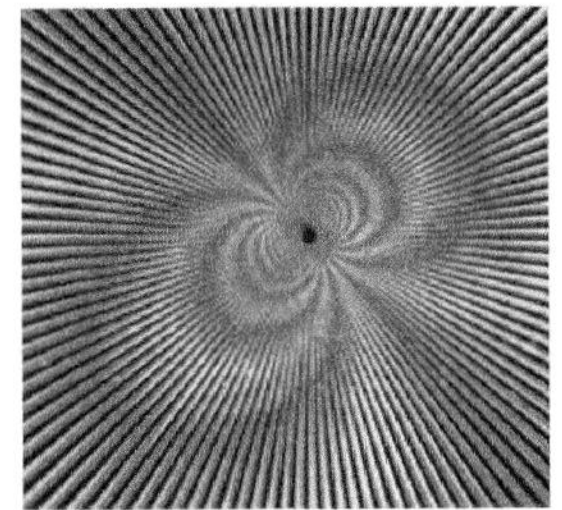

A set of parallel lines with equidistant spacing intersects an identical set, but at a small angle. The result is a **moiré pattern,** named after the fabric *moiré* ("watered") *silk*. You often see similar effects looking through window screens with bulges. Moiré patterns are related to **periodic functions,** which describe regular recurring phenomena (wave patterns such as heartbeats or business cycles). Moirés thus apply to the study of electromagnetic, sound, and water waves, to crystal structure, and to other wave phenomena.

The supplement of an angle measures 10° more than three times its complement. Find the measure of the angle.

**SOLUTION**

Let $x =$ the degree measure of the angle.

Then $180 - x =$ the degree measure of its supplement,

and $90 - x =$ the degree measure of its complement.

Now use the words of the problem to write the equation.

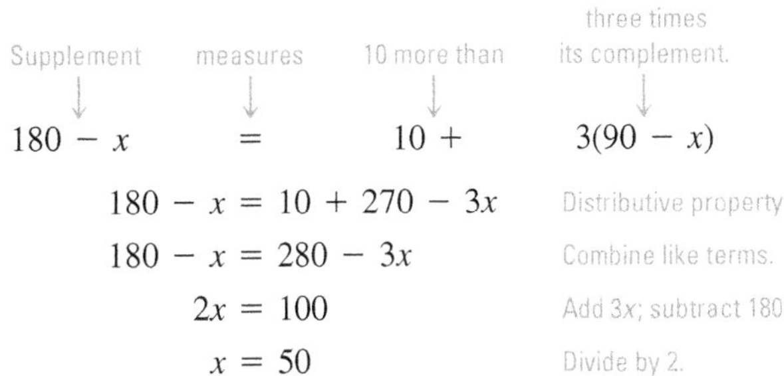


$$180 - x \quad = \quad 10 + \quad 3(90 - x)$$

$$
\begin{aligned}
180 - x &= 10 + 270 - 3x \quad \text{Distributive property} \\
180 - x &= 280 - 3x \quad \text{Combine like terms.} \\
2x &= 100 \quad \text{Add } 3x\text{; subtract 180.} \\
x &= 50 \quad \text{Divide by 2.}
\end{aligned}
$$

The angle measures 50°. Because its supplement (130°) is 10° more than three times its complement (40°) (that is, $130 = 10 + 3(40)$ is true) the answer checks.

**Parallel lines** are lines that lie in the same plane and do not intersect. Figure 12 shows parallel lines $m$ and $n$. When a line $q$ intersects two parallel lines, $q$ is called a **transversal.** In Figure 12, the transversal intersecting the parallel lines forms eight angles, indicated by numbers. Angles 1 through 8 in the figure possess some special properties regarding their degree measures, as shown in Table 2 on the next page.

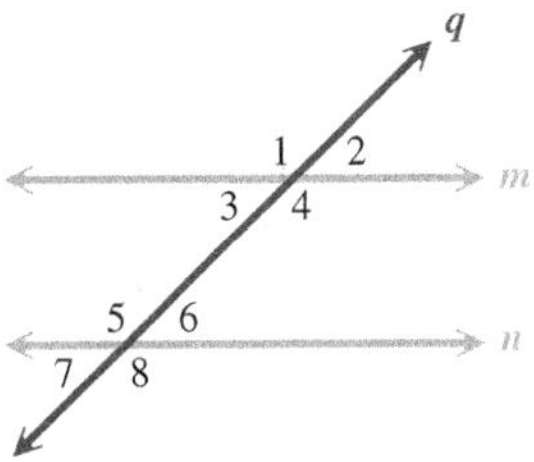


**FIGURE 12**

**TABLE 2**

| Name | Figure | Rule |
|---|---|---|
| **Alternate interior angles** | (also 3 and 6) | Angle measures are equal. |
| **Alternate exterior angles** | (also 2 and 7) | Angle measures are equal. |
| **Interior angles on same side of transversal** | (also 3 and 5) | Angle measures add to 180°. |
| **Corresponding angles** | (also 1 and 5, 3 and 7, 4 and 8) | Angle measures are equal. |

The converses of the above also are true. That is, if alternate interior angles are equal, then the lines are parallel, with similar results valid for alternate exterior angles, interior angles on the same side of a transversal, and corresponding angles.

## EXAMPLE 4 Finding Angle Measures

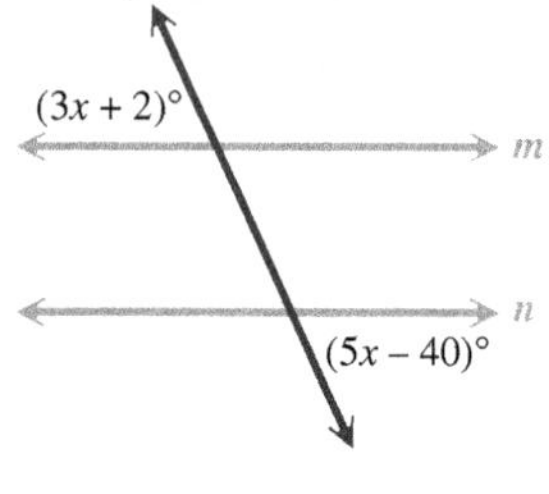


**FIGURE 13**

Find the measure of each marked angle in Figure 13, given that lines $m$ and $n$ are parallel.

**SOLUTION**

The marked angles are alternate exterior angles, which are equal. This gives

$$3x + 2 = 5x - 40$$
$$42 = 2x \quad \text{Subtract } 3x\text{; add 40.}$$
$$21 = x. \quad \text{Divide by 2.}$$

Because $3x + 2 = 3 \cdot 21 + 2 = 65$ and $5x - 40 = 5 \cdot 21 - 40 = 65$, both angles measure 65°.

## 9.1 EXERCISES

*Fill in each blank with the correct response.*

1. The sum of the measures of two complementary angles is _____ degrees.

2. The sum of the measures of two supplementary angles is _____ degrees.

3. The measures of two vertical angles are _____.
(equal/not equal)

4. The measures of _____ right angles add up to the measure of a straight angle.

*Decide whether each statement is* true *or* false.

5. A line segment has two endpoints.

6. A ray has one endpoint.

7. If $A$ and $B$ are distinct points on a line, then ray $AB$ and ray $BA$ represent the same set of points.

8. If two lines intersect, they lie in the same plane.

9. If two lines are parallel, they lie in the same plane.

10. If two lines do not intersect, they must be parallel.

11. Segment $AB$ and segment $BA$ represent the same set of points.

12. There is no angle that is its own complement.

13. There is no angle that is its own supplement.

14. The origin of the use of the degree as a unit of measure of an angle goes back to the Egyptians.

*Exercises 15–24 name portions of the line shown. For each exercise,* **(a)** *give the symbol that represents the portion of the line named, and* **(b)** *draw a figure showing just the portion named, including all labeled points.*

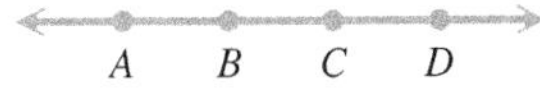


15. line segment $AB$
16. ray $BC$
17. ray $CB$
18. line segment $AD$
19. half-line $BC$
20. half-line $AD$
21. ray $BA$
22. ray $DA$
23. line segment $CA$
24. line segment $DA$

*Match the symbol in Column I with the symbol in Column II that names the same set of points, based on the figure.*

| I | | II | |
|---|---|---|---|
| **25.** $\overline{PQ}$ | **26.** $\overset{\circ\!\!\rightarrow}{QR}$ | **A.** $\overset{\circ\!\!\rightarrow}{QS}$ | **B.** $\overrightarrow{RQ}$ |
| **27.** $\overrightarrow{QR}$ | **28.** $\overleftrightarrow{PQ}$ | **C.** $\overset{\circ\!\!\rightarrow}{SR}$ | **D.** $\overrightarrow{QS}$ |
| **29.** $\overrightarrow{RP}$ | **30.** $\overset{\circ\!\!\rightarrow}{SQ}$ | **E.** $\overline{SP}$ | **F.** $\overline{QP}$ |
| **31.** $\overline{PS}$ | **32.** $\overset{\circ\!\!\rightarrow}{PS}$ | **G.** $\overleftrightarrow{RS}$ | **H.** none of these |

*Lines, rays, half-lines, and segments may be considered sets of points. The* **intersection** *(symbolized ∩) of two sets is composed of all elements common to both sets, while the* **union** *(symbolized ∪) of two sets is composed of all elements found in at least one of the two sets. Based on the figure below, specify each of the sets given in Exercises 33–40 in a simpler way.*

33. $\overline{MN} \cup \overline{NO}$
34. $\overline{MN} \cap \overline{NO}$
35. $\overrightarrow{MO} \cap \overrightarrow{OM}$
36. $\overrightarrow{MO} \cup \overrightarrow{OM}$
37. $\overset{\circ\!\!\rightarrow}{OP} \cap O$
38. $\overset{\circ\!\!\rightarrow}{OP} \cup O$
39. $\overline{NP} \cap \overline{OP}$
40. $\overline{NP} \cup \overline{OP}$

*Give the measure of the complement of each angle.*

**41.** 28° **42.** 32° **43.** 89° **44.** 45° **45.** $x°$ **46.** $(90 - x)°$

*Give the measure of the supplement of each angle.*

**47.** 132° **48.** 105° **49.** 26° **50.** 90° **51.** $y°$ **52.** $(180 - y)°$

*Name all pairs of vertical angles in each figure.*

**53.**

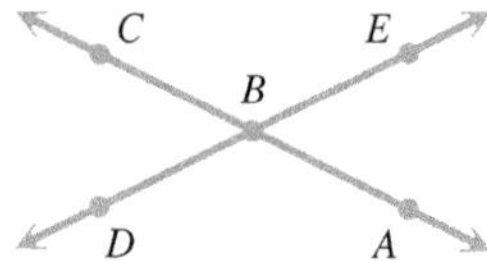


**54.**

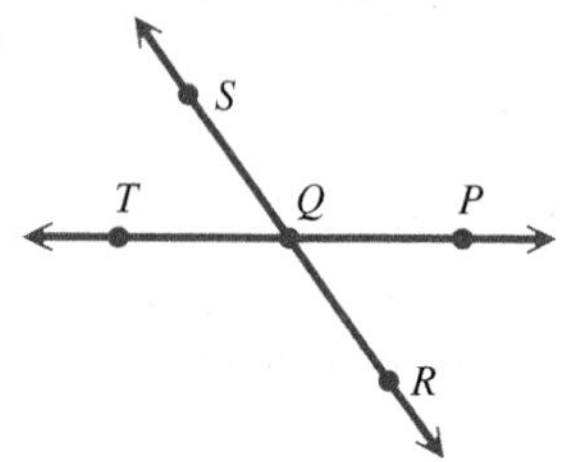


**55.** In Exercise 53, if $\measuredangle ABE$ has a measure of 52°, find the measures of the angles.
**(a)** $\measuredangle CBD$
**(b)** $\measuredangle CBE$

**56.** In Exercise 54, if $\measuredangle SQP$ has a measure of 126°, find the measures of the angles.
**(a)** $\measuredangle TQR$
**(b)** $\measuredangle PQR$

*Find the measure of each marked angle.*

**57.**

(10x + 7)° (7x + 3)°

**58.**

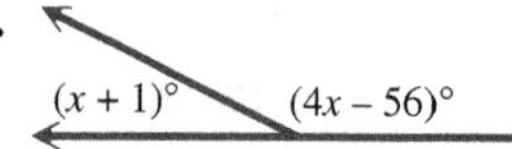


**59.**

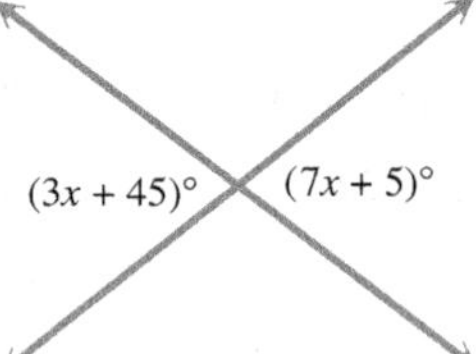


**60.**

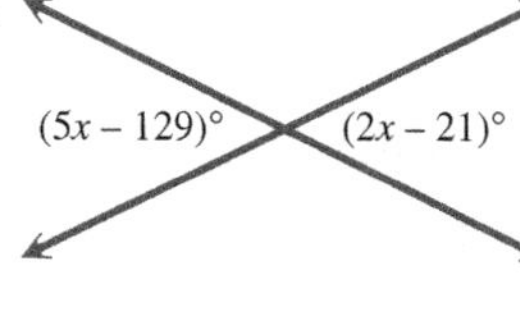


**61.**

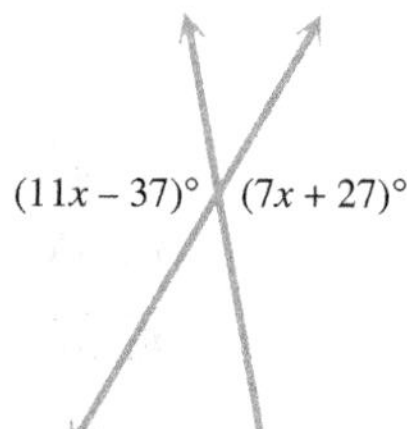


**62.**

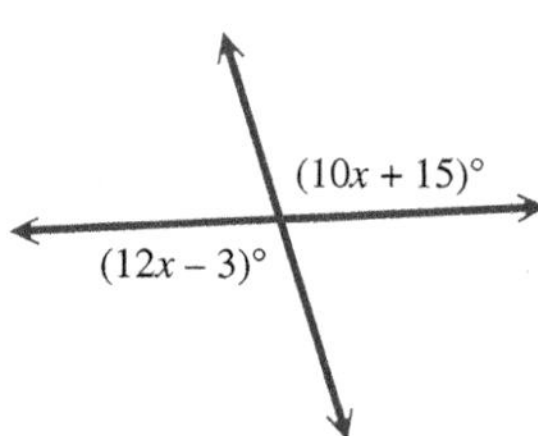


**63.**

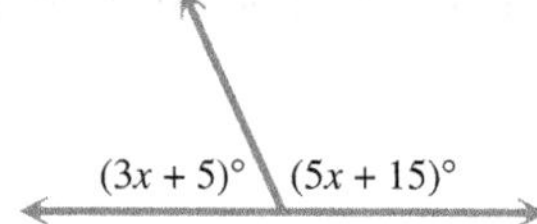


**64.**

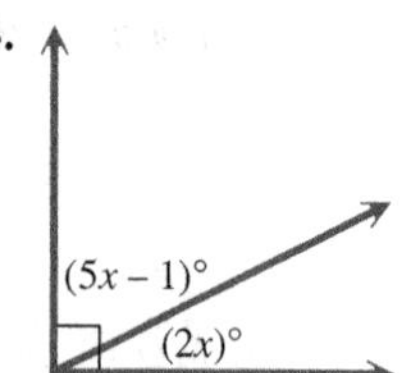


**65.**

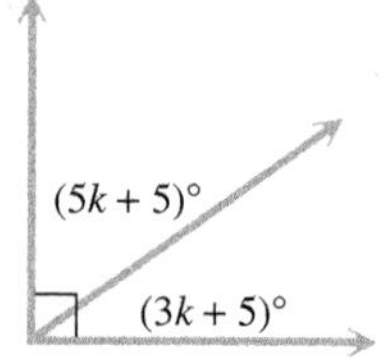

*In Exercises 66–69, assume that lines m and n are parallel, and find the measure of each marked angle.*

**66.**

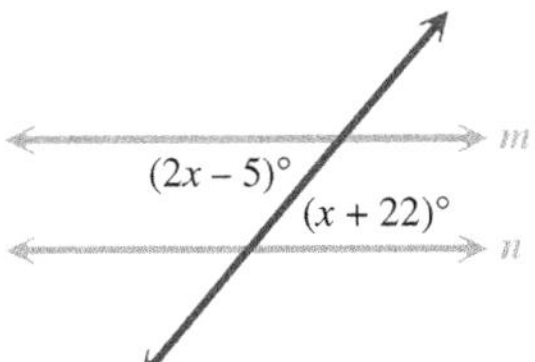


**67.**

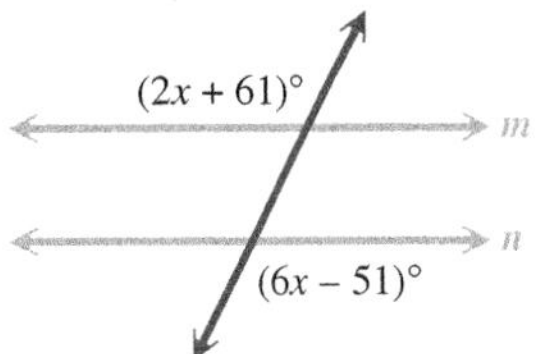


**68.**

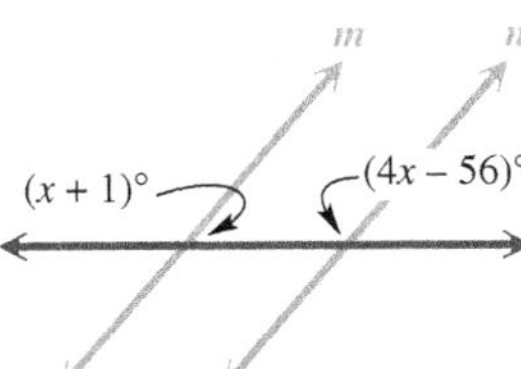


**69.**

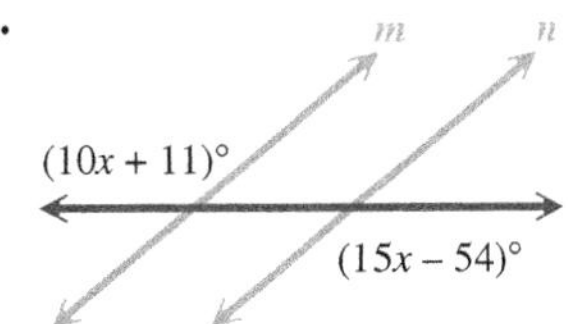


***Complementary and Supplementary Angles*** *Solve each problem in Exercises 70–73.*

**70.** The supplement of an angle measures 25° more than twice its complement. Find the measure of the angle.

**71.** The complement of an angle measures 10° less than one-fifth of its supplement. Find the measure of the angle.

**72.** The supplement of an angle added to the complement of the angle gives 210°. What is the measure of the angle?

**73.** Half the supplement of an angle is 12° less than twice the complement of the angle. Find the measure of the angle.

**74.** The sketch shows parallel lines $m$ and $n$ cut by a transversal $q$. Using the figure, complete the steps to prove that alternate exterior angles have the same measure.

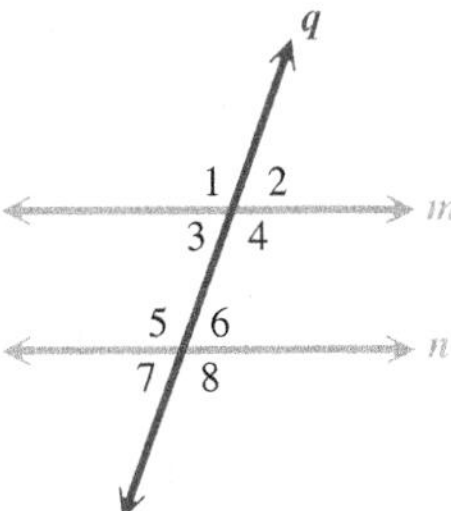


**(a)** Measure of ∡2 = measure of ∡ _____, since they are vertical angles.

**(b)** Measure of ∡3 = measure of ∡ _____, since they are alternate interior angles.

**(c)** Measure of ∡6 = measure of ∡ _____, since they are vertical angles.

**(d)** By the results of parts (a), (b), and (c), the measure of ∡2 must equal the measure of ∡ _____, showing that alternate ________ angles have equal measures.

**75.** Use the sketch to find the measure of each numbered angle. Assume that $m \parallel n$.

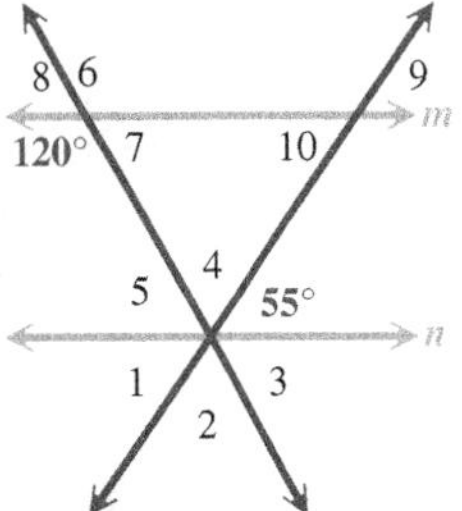


**76.** Complete these steps in the proof that vertical angles have equal measures. In this exercise, m(∡$x$) means "the measure of the angle $x$." Use the figure at the right.

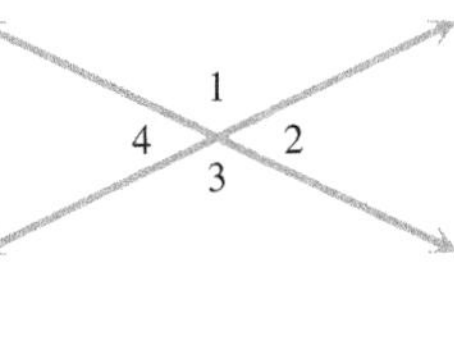


**(a)** m(∡1) + m(∡2) = _____°

**(b)** m(∡2) + m(∡3) = _____°

**(c)** Subtract the equation in part (b) from the equation in part (a) to get [m(∡1) + m(∡2)] − [m(∡2) + m(∡3)] = _____° − _____°.

**(d)** m(∡1) + m(∡2) − m(∡2) − m(∡3) = ___°

**(e)** m(∡1) − m(∡3) = _____°

**(f)** m(∡1) = m(∡ _____)

77. Use the approach of Exercise 74 to prove that interior angles on the same side of a transversal are supplementary.

78. Find the values of $x$ and $y$ in the figure, given that $x + y = 40$.

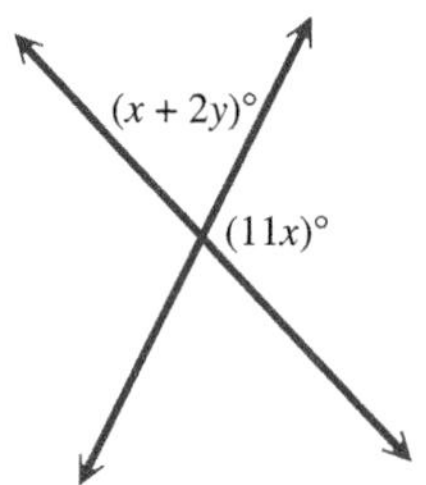


## 9.2 Curves, Polygons, and Circles

**Curves • Triangles and Quadrilaterals • Circles**

**Curves** The basic undefined term *curve* is used for describing figures in the plane. (See Figure 14.)

Simple; closed

Simple; not closed

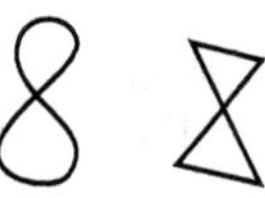

Not simple; closed

Not simple; not closed

**FIGURE 14**

### Simple Curve; Closed Curve

A **simple curve** can be drawn without lifting the pencil from the paper, and without passing through any point twice.

A **closed curve** has its starting and ending points the same, and is also drawn without lifting the pencil from the paper.

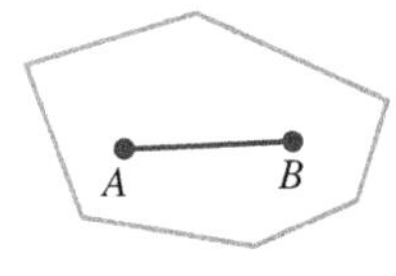


Convex

(a)

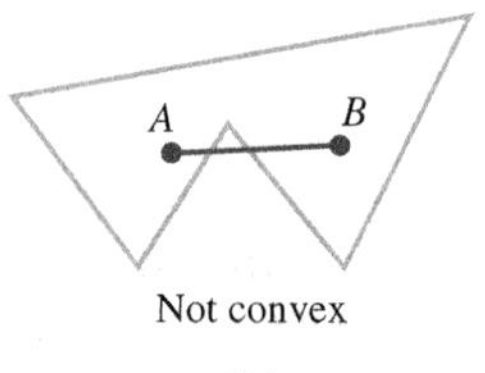


Not convex

(b)

**FIGURE 15**

A figure is said to be **convex** if, for any two points $A$ and $B$ inside the figure, the line segment $AB$ (that is, $\overleftrightarrow{AB}$) is always completely inside the figure. Figure 15(a) shows a convex figure and (b) shows one that is not convex.

Among the most common types of curves in mathematics are those that are both simple and closed, and perhaps the most important of these are *polygons*. A **polygon** is a simple closed curve made up only of straight line segments. The line segments are called the *sides,* and the points at which the sides meet are called *vertices* (singular: *vertex*). Polygons are classified according to the number of line segments used as sides. Table 3 on the next page gives the special names. In general, if a polygon has $n$ sides, and no particular value of $n$ is specified, it is called an $n$-gon.

Some examples of polygons are shown in Figure 16. A polygon may or may not be convex. Polygons with all sides equal and all angles equal are **regular polygons.**

**TABLE 3**
Classification of Polygons According to Number of Sides

| Number of Sides | Name |
|---|---|
| 3 | triangle |
| 4 | quadrilateral |
| 5 | pentagon |
| 6 | hexagon |
| 7 | heptagon |
| 8 | octagon |
| 9 | nonagon |
| 10 | decagon |

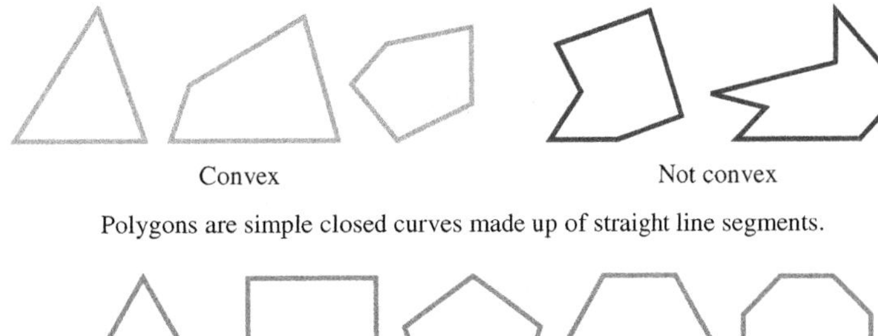


Polygons are simple closed curves made up of straight line segments.

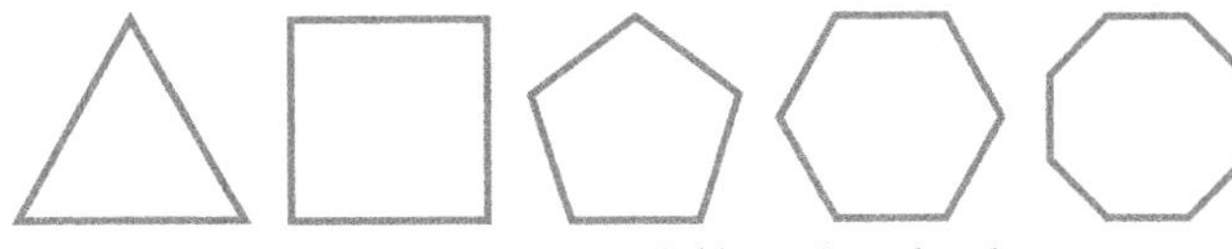

Regular polygons have equal sides and equal angles.

**FIGURE 16**

The puzzle-game above comes from China, where it has been a popular amusement for centuries. The figure on the left is a **tangram.** Any tangram is composed of the same set of seven tans (the pieces making up the square are shown on the right).

Mathematicians have described various properties of tangrams. While each tan is convex, only 13 convex tangrams are possible. All others, like the figure on the left, are not convex.

**Triangles and Quadrilaterals** Two of the most common types of polygons are triangles and quadrilaterals. Triangles are classified by measures of angles as well as by number of equal sides, as shown in the following box. (Notice that tick marks are used in the bottom three figures to show how side lengths are related.)

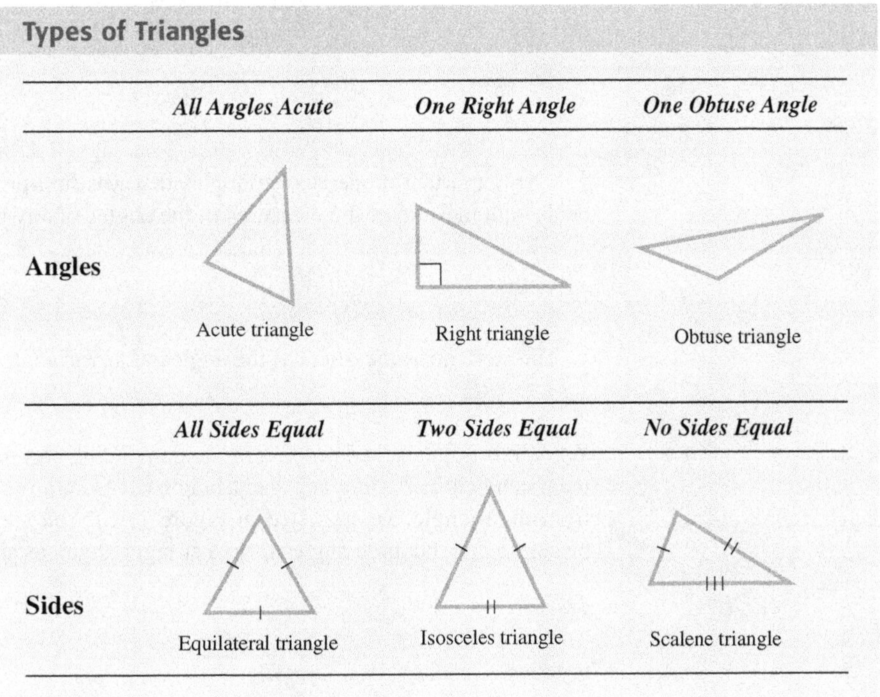


Quadrilaterals are classified by sides and angles. It can be seen in the box at the top of the next page that an important distinction involving quadrilaterals is whether one or more pairs of sides are parallel.

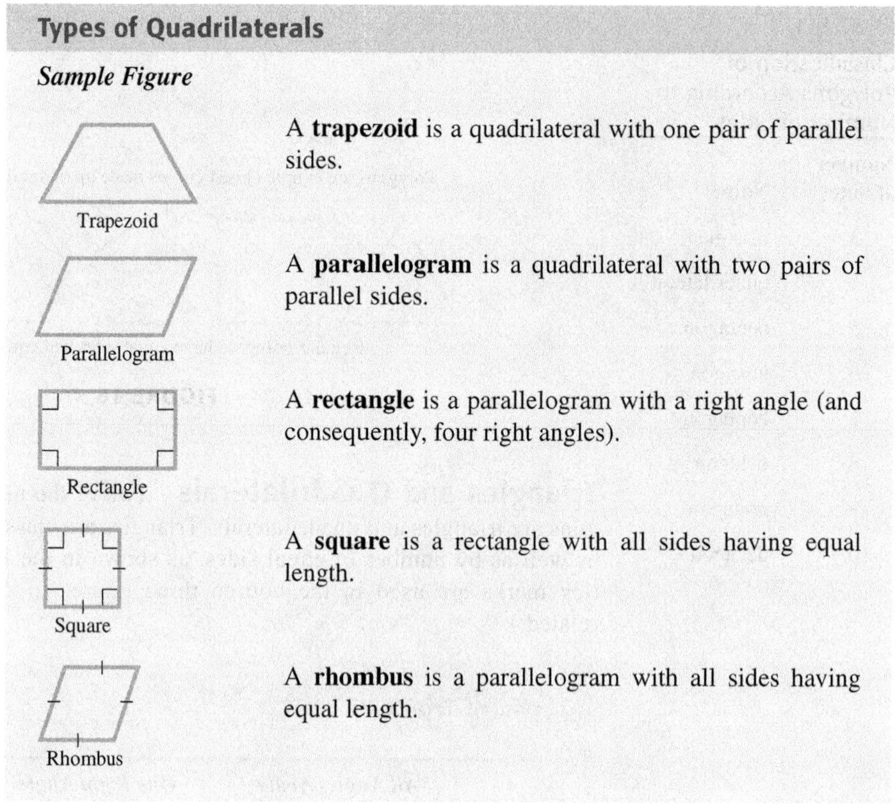

### Types of Quadrilaterals

***Sample Figure***

Trapezoid — A **trapezoid** is a quadrilateral with one pair of parallel sides.

Parallelogram — A **parallelogram** is a quadrilateral with two pairs of parallel sides.

Rectangle — A **rectangle** is a parallelogram with a right angle (and consequently, four right angles).

Square — A **square** is a rectangle with all sides having equal length.

Rhombus — A **rhombus** is a parallelogram with all sides having equal length.

An important property of triangles that was first proved by the Greek geometers deals with the sum of the measures of the angles of any triangle.

### Angle Sum of a Triangle

The sum of the measures of the angles of any triangle is 180°.

While it is not an actual proof, a rather convincing argument for the truth of this statement can be given using any size triangle cut from a piece of paper. Tear each corner from the triangle, as suggested in Figure 17(a). You should be able to rearrange the pieces so that the three angles form a straight angle, as shown in Figure 17(b).

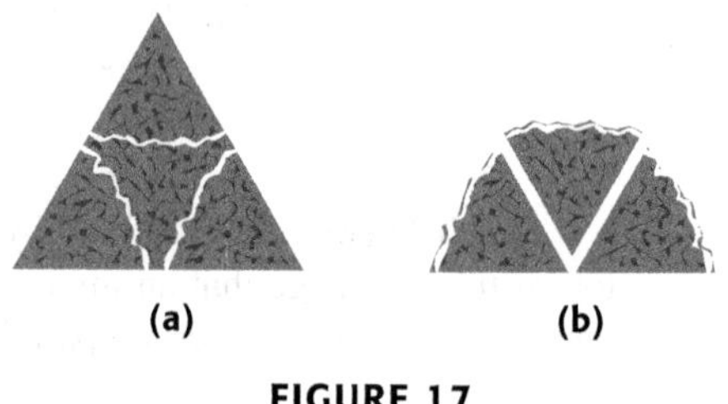


**FIGURE 17**

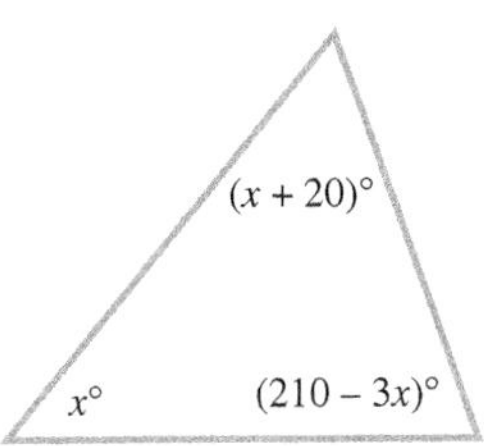


FIGURE 18

## EXAMPLE 1 Finding Angle Measures in a Triangle

Find the measure of each angle in the triangle of Figure 18.

**SOLUTION**

By the angle sum relationship, the three angle measures must add up to 180°.

$$x + (x + 20) + (210 - 3x) = 180$$

$$-x + 230 = 180 \quad \text{Combine like terms.}$$

$$-x = -50 \quad \text{Subtract 230.}$$

There are two more values to find. ⟶ $x = 50$ Divide by $-1$.

Because $x = 50$, $x + 20 = 50 + 20 = 70$ and $210 - 3x = 210 - 3(50) = 60$. Thus the measures of the three angles are 50°, 70°, and 60°. Because $50° + 70° + 60° = 180°$, the answers satisfy the angle sum relationship.

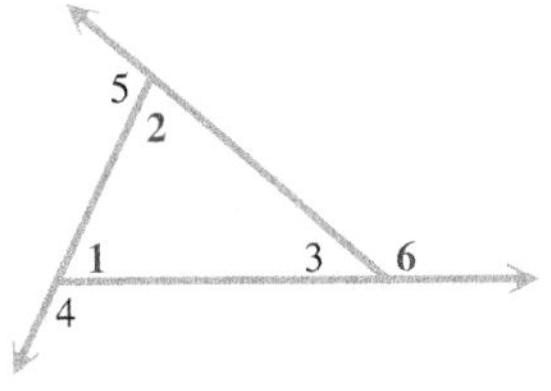


FIGURE 19

In the triangle shown in Figure 19, angles 1, 2, and 3 are called **interior angles,** while angles 4, 5, and 6 are called **exterior angles** of the triangle. Using the fact that the sum of the angle measures of any triangle is 180°, and a straight angle also measures 180°, the following property may be deduced.

### Exterior Angle Measure

The measure of an exterior angle of a triangle is equal to the sum of the measures of the two opposite interior angles.

In Figure 19, the measure of angle 6 is equal to the sum of the measures of angles 1 and 2. Two other such statements can be made.

## EXAMPLE 2 Finding Interior and Exterior Angle Measures

Find the measures of interior angles $A$, $B$, and $C$ of the triangle in Figure 20, and the measure of exterior angle $BCD$.

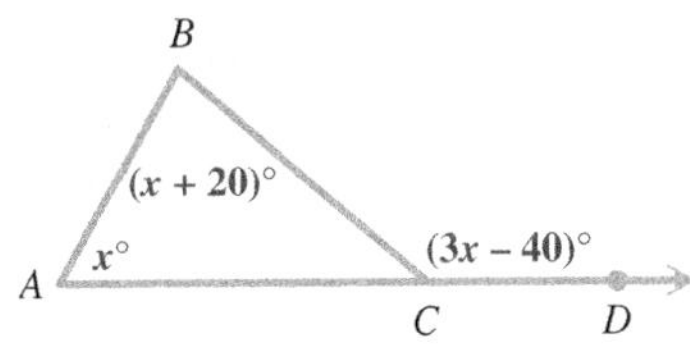


FIGURE 20

**SOLUTION**

By the property concerning exterior angles, the sum of the measures of interior angles $A$ and $B$ must equal the measure of angle $BCD$. Thus,

$$x + (x + 20) = 3x - 40$$

$$2x + 20 = 3x - 40 \quad \text{Combine like terms.}$$

$$-x = -60 \quad \text{Subtract } 3x\text{; subtract 20.}$$

$$x = 60. \quad \text{Divide by } -1.$$

Because the value of $x$ is 60,

$$\begin{aligned} m(\text{Interior angle } A) &= 60^\circ \\ m(\text{Interior angle } B) &= (60 + 20)^\circ = 80^\circ \\ m(\text{Interior angle } C) &= 180^\circ - (60^\circ + 80^\circ) = 40^\circ \\ m(\text{Exterior angle } BCD) &= [3(60) - 40]^\circ = 140^\circ. \end{aligned}$$

**Circles** One of the most important plane curves is the circle. It is a simple closed curve defined as follows.

**Circle**

A **circle** is a set of points in a plane, each of which is the same distance from a fixed point.

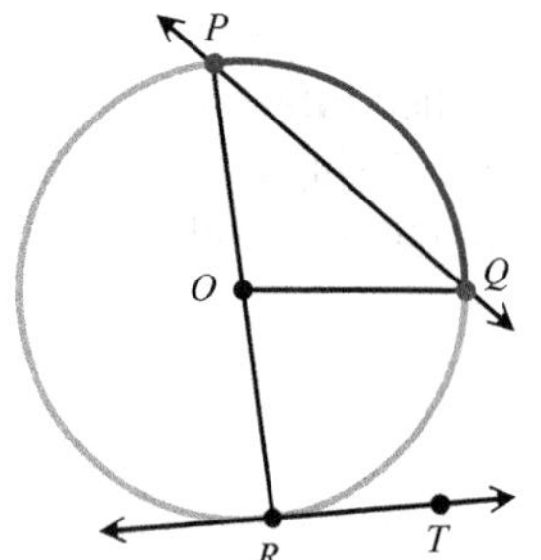


**FIGURE 21**

A circle may be physically constructed with compasses, where the spike leg remains fixed and the other leg swings around to construct the circle. A string may also be used to draw a circle. For example, loop a piece of chalk on one end of a piece of string. Hold the other end in a fixed position on a chalkboard, and pull the string taut. Then swing the chalk end around to draw a circle.

A circle, along with several lines and segments, is shown in Figure 21. The points $P$, $Q$, and $R$ lie on the circle. Each lies the same distance from point $O$, which is called the **center** of the circle. (It is the "fixed point" referred to in the definition.) $\overline{OP}$, $\overline{OQ}$, and $\overline{OR}$ are segments whose endpoints are the center and a point on the circle. Each is called a **radius** of the circle (plural: **radii**). $\overline{PQ}$ is a segment whose endpoints both lie on the circle and is an example of a **chord.** The segment $\overline{PR}$ is a chord that passes through the center and is called a **diameter** of the circle. Notice that the measure of a diameter is twice that of a radius. A diameter such as $\overline{PR}$ in Figure 21 divides a circle into two parts of equal size, each of which is called a **semicircle.**

$\overleftrightarrow{RT}$ is a line that touches (intersects) the circle in only one point, $R$, and is called a **tangent** to the circle. $R$ is the point of tangency. $\overleftrightarrow{PQ}$, which intersects the circle in two points, is called a **secant** line. (What is the distinction between a chord and a secant?)

The portion of the circle shown in red in Figure 21 is an **arc** of the circle. It consists of two endpoints ($P$ and $Q$) and all points on the circle "between" these endpoints. The colored portion is called arc $PQ$ (or $QP$), denoted in symbols as $\overset{\frown}{PQ}$ (or $\overset{\frown}{QP}$).

The Greeks were the first to insist that all propositions, or **theorems,** about geometry be given a rigorous proof before being accepted. According to tradition, the first theorem to receive such a proof was the following.

**Thales** made his fortune merely to prove how easy it is to become wealthy; he cornered all the oil presses during a year of an exceptionally large olive crop. Legend records that Thales studied for a time in Egypt and then introduced geometry to Greece, where he attempted to apply the principles of Greek logic to his newly learned subject.

**Inscribed Angle**

Any angle inscribed in a semicircle must be a right angle.

To be **inscribed** in a semicircle, the vertex of the angle must be on the circle with the sides of the angle going through the endpoints of the diameter at the base of the semicircle. (See Figure 22 on the next page.) This first proof was said to have been given by the Greek philosopher Thales.

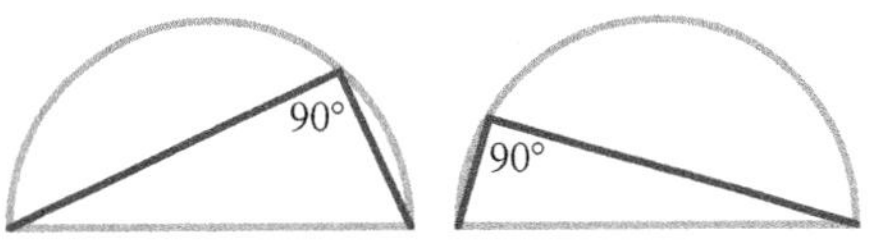


**FIGURE 22**

The result illustrated in Figure 22 is a special case of a more general theorem: The measure of an angle inscribed in a *circle* is one-half the measure of the intercepted arc.

## 9.2 EXERCISES

*Fill in each blank with the correct response.*

**1.** A segment joining two points on a circle is called a(n) ______.

**2.** A segment joining the center of a circle and a point on the circle is called a(n) ______ .

**3.** A regular triangle is called a(n) ____________ triangle.

**4.** A chord that contains the center of a circle is called a(n) _______.

*Decide whether each statement is* true *or* false.

**5.** A rhombus is an example of a regular polygon.

**6.** If a triangle is isosceles, then it is not scalene.

**7.** A triangle can have more than one obtuse angle.

**8.** A square is both a rectangle and a parallelogram.

**9.** A square must be a rhombus.

**10.** A rhombus must be a square.

**11.** In your own words, explain the distinction between a square and a rhombus.

**12.** What common traffic sign in the U.S. is in the shape of an octagon?

*Identify each curve as* simple, closed, both, *or* neither.

**13.**

**14.**

**15.**

**16.**

**17.**

**18.**

**19.**

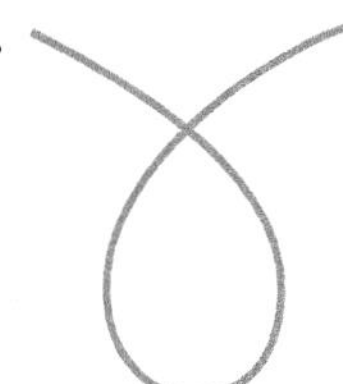

**20.**

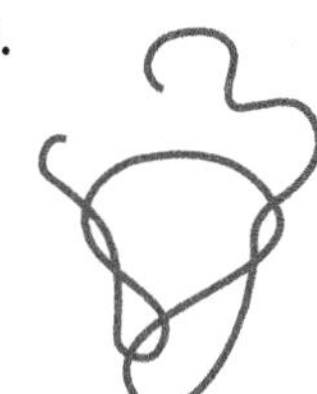

*Decide whether each figure is* convex *or* not convex.

**21.** 

**22.** 

**23.** 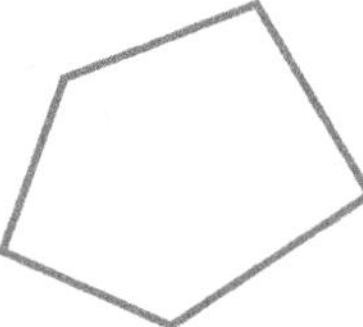

**24.** 

**25.** 

**26.** 

*Classify each triangle as* acute, right, *or* obtuse. *Also classify each as* equilateral, isosceles, *or* scalene.

**27.** 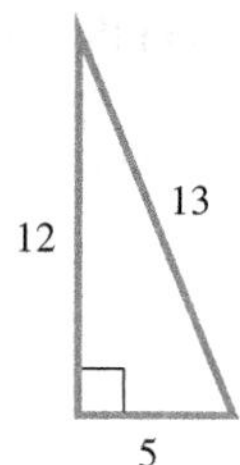


**28.** 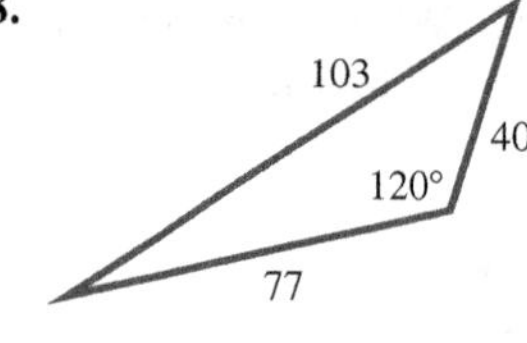


**29.** 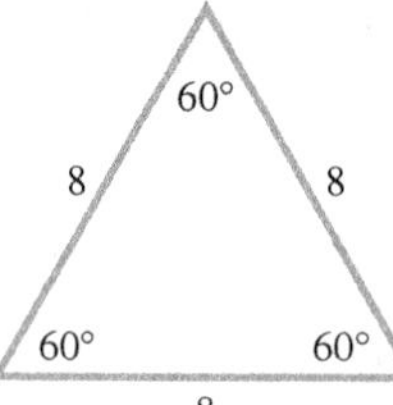


**30.** 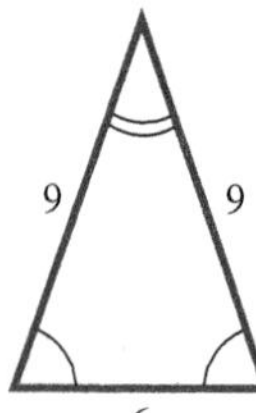


**31.** 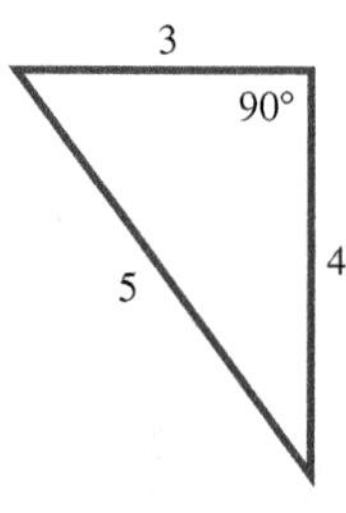


**32.** 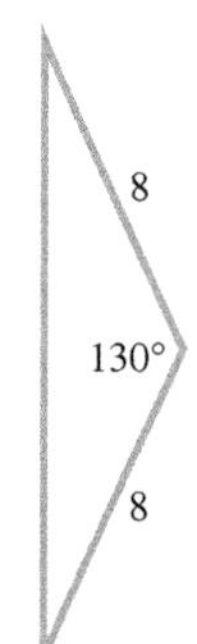


**33.** 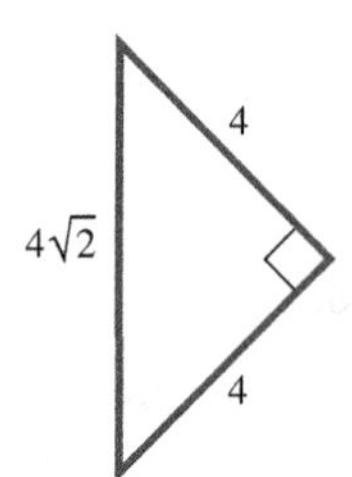


**34.** 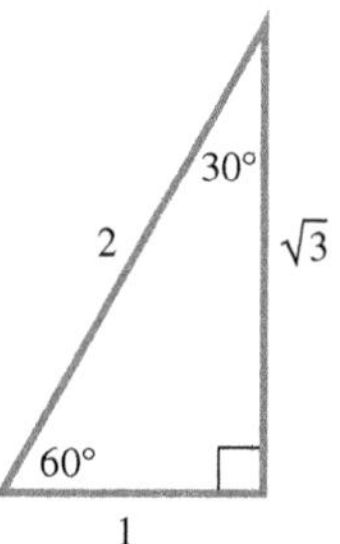

35.

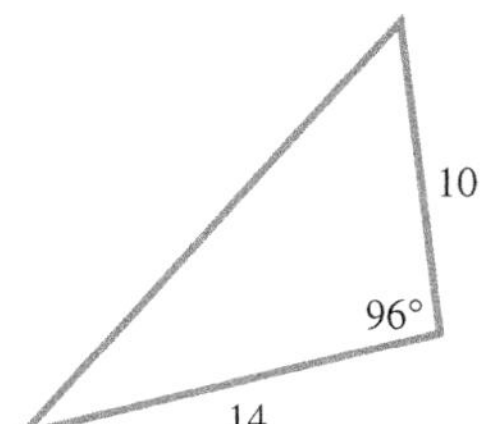


36.

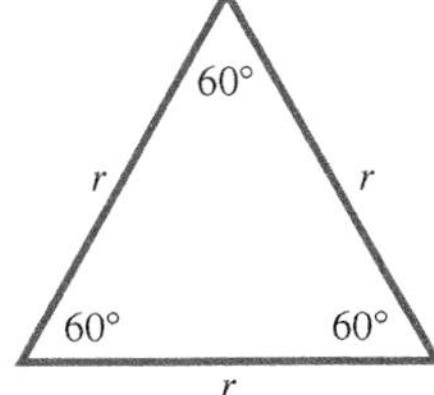


37.

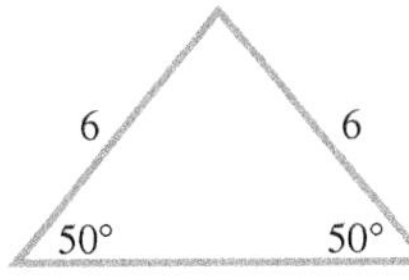


38.

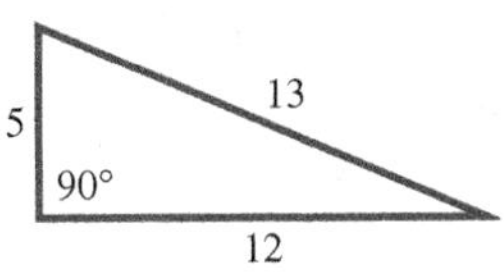


39. Write a definition of *isosceles right triangle.*

40. Explain why the sum of the lengths of any two sides of a triangle must be greater than the length of the third side.

41. Can a triangle be both right and obtuse? Explain.

42. In the classic 1939 movie *The Wizard of Oz*, the Scarecrow, upon getting a brain, says the following: "The sum of the square roots of any two sides of an isosceles triangle is equal to the square root of the remaining side." Give an example to show that his statement is incorrect.

*Find the measure of each angle in triangle ABC.*

43.

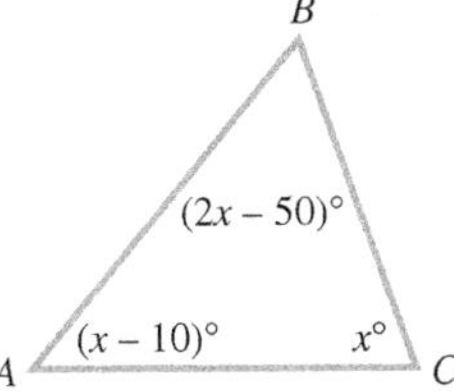


44.

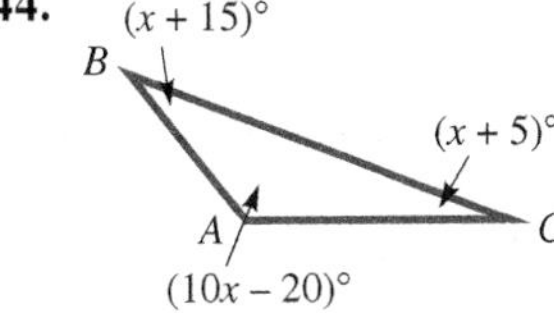


45.

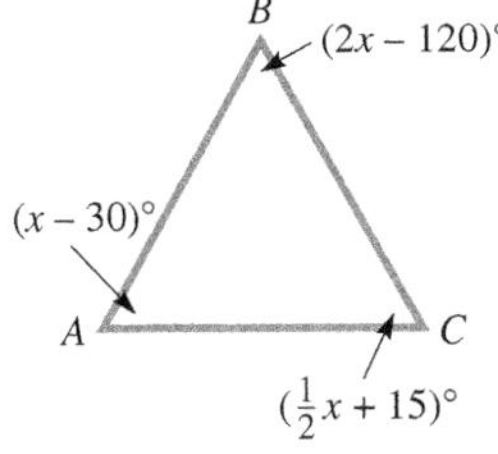


46.

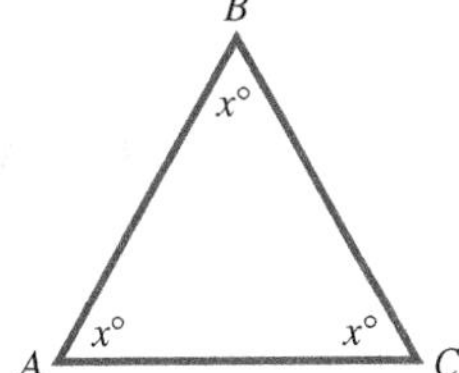


47. ***Angle Measures*** In triangle $ABC$, angles $A$ and $B$ have the same measure, while the measure of angle $C$ is 24 degrees larger than the measure of each of $A$ and $B$. What are the measures of the three angles?

48. ***Angle Measures*** In triangle $ABC$, the measure of angle $A$ is 30 degrees more than the measure of angle $B$. The measure of angle $B$ is the same as the measure of angle $C$. Find the measure of each angle.

*In each triangle, find the measure of exterior angle BCD.*

**49.**

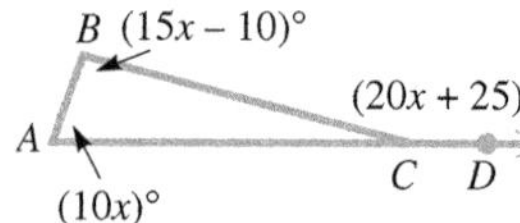


**50.**

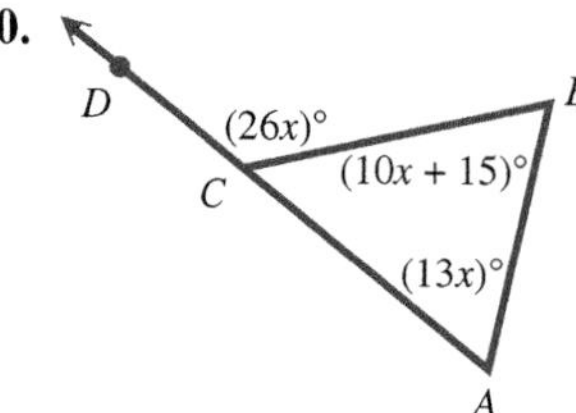


**51.**

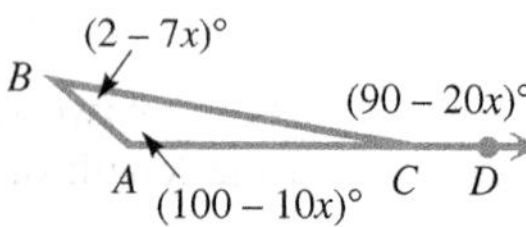


**52.**

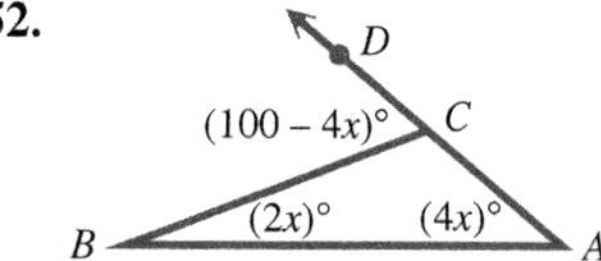


**53.** Using the points, segments, and lines in the figure, list all parts of the circle.

**(a)** center
**(b)** radii
**(c)** diameters
**(d)** chords
**(e)** secants
**(f)** tangents

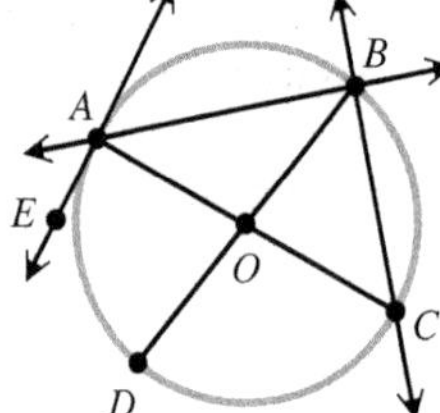


**54.** Refer to angles 1, 2, and 6 in the figure. Prove that the sum of the measures of angles 1 and 2 is equal to the measure of angle 6.

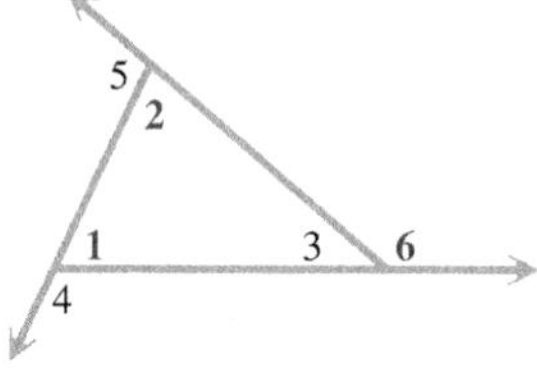


**55.** Go through the following argument provided by Richard Crouse in a letter to the editor of *Mathematics Teacher* in the February 1988 issue.

**(a)** Place the eraser end of a pencil on vertex $A$ of the triangle and let the pencil coincide with side $AC$ of the triangle.
**(b)** With the eraser fixed at $A$, rotate the pencil counterclockwise until it coincides with side $AB$.
**(c)** With the pencil fixed at point $B$, rotate the eraser end counterclockwise until the pencil coincides with side $BC$.
**(d)** With the eraser fixed at point $C$ (slide the pencil to this position), rotate the point end of the pencil counterclockwise until the pencil coincides with side $AC$.
**(e)** Notice that the pencil is now pointing in the opposite direction. What concept from this section does this exercise reinforce?

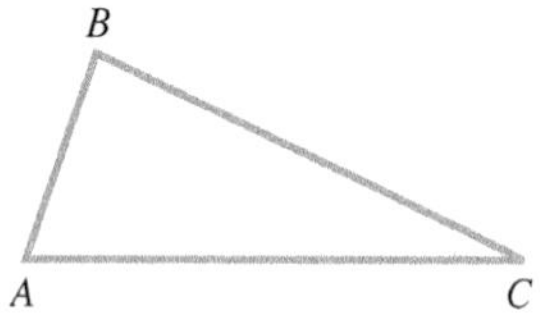


## EXTENSION

### Geometric Constructions

The Greeks did not study algebra as we do. To them geometry was the highest expression of mathematical science; their geometry was an abstract subject. Any practical application resulting from their work was nice but held no great importance. To the Greeks, a geometrical construction also needed abstract beauty. A construction could not be polluted with such practical instruments as a ruler. The Greeks permitted only two tools in geometrical construction: compasses for drawing circles and arcs of circles, and a straightedge for drawing straight line segments. The straightedge, unlike a ruler, could have no marks on it. It was not permitted to line up points by eye.

In his first effort as a director, Mel Gibson starred in the 1993 movie *The Man Without a Face.* As disfigured former teacher Justin McLeod, he tutors teenager Chuck Norstadt (portrayed by Nick Stahl) who has hopes of attending a boarding school. In one scene, McLeod explains to Norstadt how to find the center of a circle using any three points on the circle as he sketches the diagram on a windowpane. Although his explanation has some flaws, it conveys the general idea of how to perform this **construction.** It is based on the fact that the **perpendicular bisector** of any chord of a circle passes through the center of the circle.

Suppose the points on the circle are *A, B,* and *C.* Draw the chord *AB,* and construct its perpendicular bisector. Then draw *BC,* and construct its perpendicular bisector. The point of intersection of the two perpendicular bisectors is the center of the circle.

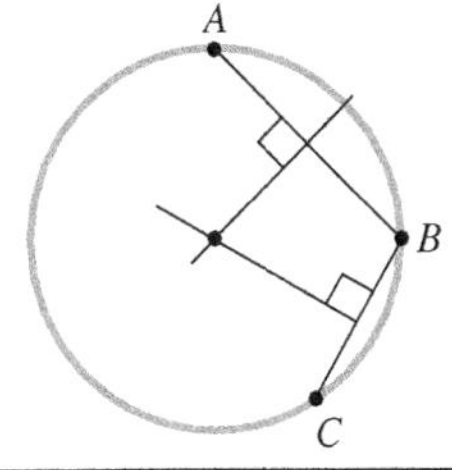


Here are four basic constructions. Their justifications are based on the *congruence properties* of Section 9.4.

**Construction 1** Construct the perpendicular bisector of a given line segment.

Let the segment have endpoints $A$ and $B$. Adjust the compasses for any radius greater than half the length of $AB$. Place the point of the compasses at $A$ and draw an arc, then draw another arc of the same size at $B$. The line drawn through the points of intersection of these two arcs is the desired perpendicular bisector. See Figure 23.

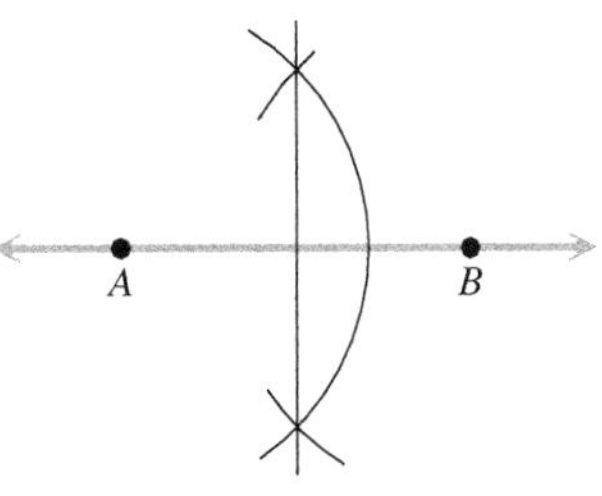


**FIGURE 23**

**Construction 2** Construct a perpendicular from a point off a line to the line.

1. Let $A$ be the point, $r$ the line. Place the point of the compasses at $A$ and draw an arc, cutting $r$ in two points.
2. Swing arcs of equal radius from each of the two points on $r$ which were constructed in (1). The line drawn through the intersection of the two arcs and point $A$ is perpendicular to $r$. See Figure 24.

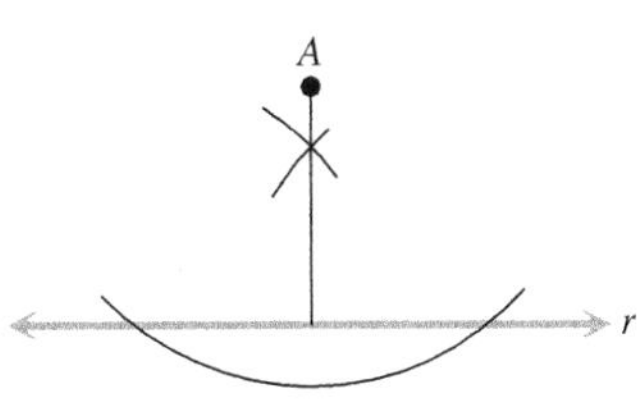


**FIGURE 24**

**Construction 3** Construct a perpendicular to a line at some given point on the line.

1. Let $r$ be the line and $A$ the point. Using any convenient radius on the compasses, place the compass point at $A$ and swing arcs that intersect $r$, as in Figure 25.

**FIGURE 25**

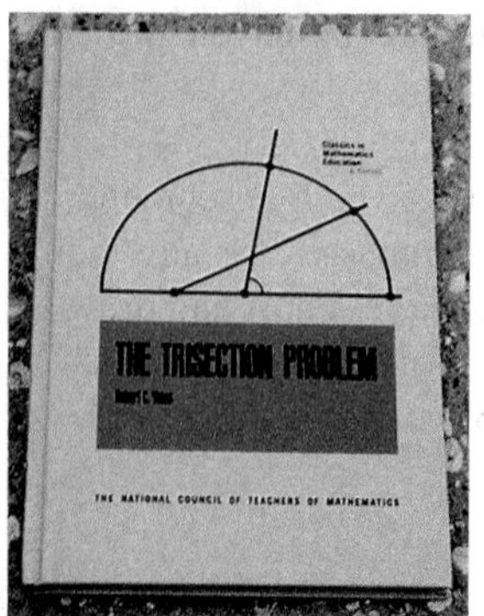


**Euclidean tools,** the compasses and unmarked straightedge, proved to be sufficient for Greek geometers to accomplish a great number of geometric constructions. Basic constructions such as copying an angle, constructing the perpendicular bisector of a segment, and bisecting an angle are easily performed and verified.

There were, however, three constructions that the Greeks were not able to accomplish with these tools. Now known as the *three famous problems of antiquity,* they are:

1. To trisect an arbitrary angle;
2. To construct the length of the edge of a cube having twice the volume of a given cube;
3. To construct a square having the same area as that of a given circle.

In the nineteenth century it was learned that these constructions are, in fact, impossible to accomplish with Euclidean tools. Over the years other methods have been devised to accomplish them. For example, trisecting an arbitrary angle can be accomplished if one allows the luxury of marking on the straightedge! But this violates the rules followed by the Greeks.

2. Increase the radius of the compasses, place the point of the compasses on the points obtained in (1) and draw arcs. A line through $A$ and the intersection of the two arcs is perpendicular to $r$. See Figure 26.

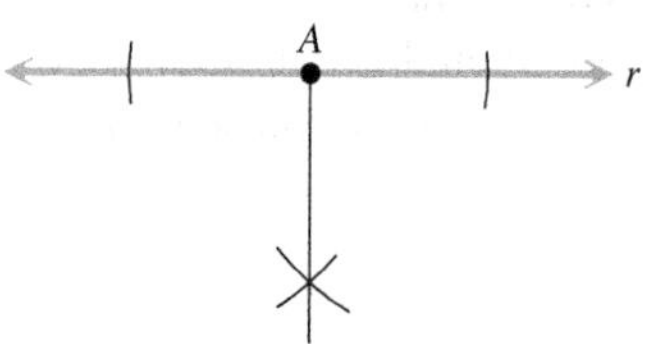


**FIGURE 26**

**Construction 4** Copy an angle.

1. In order to copy an angle $ABC$ on line $r$, place the point of the compasses at $B$ and draw an arc. Then place the point of the compasses on $r'$ at some point $P$ and draw the same arc, as in Figure 27.

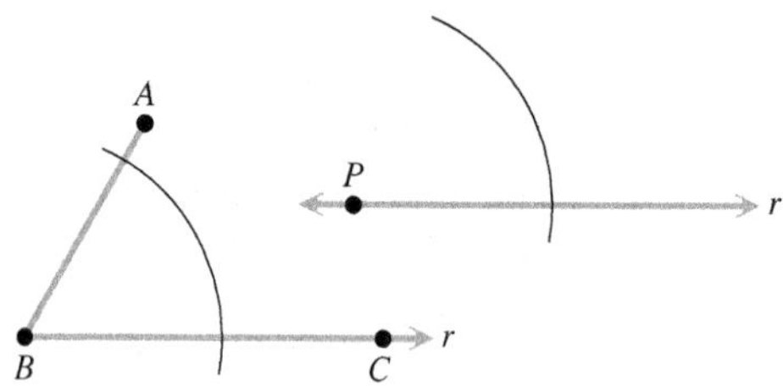


**FIGURE 27**

2. Measure, with your compasses, the distance between the points where the arc intersects the angle, and transfer this distance, as shown in Figure 28. Use a straightedge to join $P$ to the point of intersection. The angle is now copied.

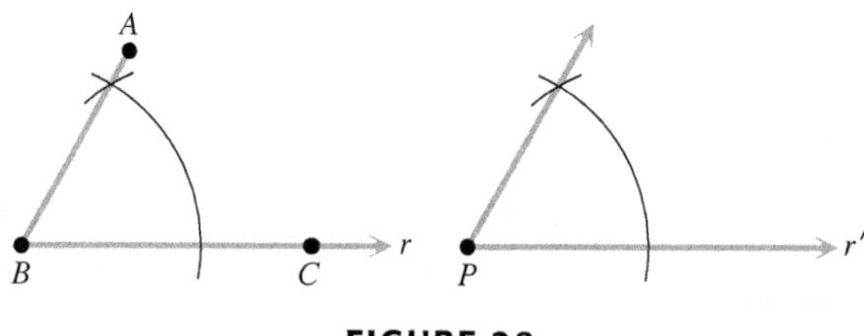


**FIGURE 28**

There are other basic constructions that can be found in books on plane geometry.

## EXTENSION EXERCISES

*In Exercises 1 and 2, use Construction 1 to construct the perpendicular bisector of segment PQ.*

**1.** P Q r

**2.**

*In Exercises 3 and 4, use Construction 2 to construct a perpendicular from P to the line r.*

**3.**

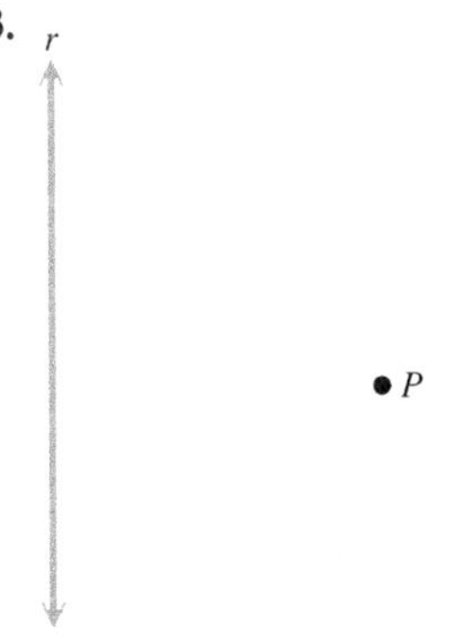


**4.**

*In Exercises 5 and 6, use Construction 3 to construct a perpendicular to the line r at P.*

**5.** P r

**6.** r P

*In Exercises 7 and 8, use Construction 4 to copy the given angle.*

**7.**

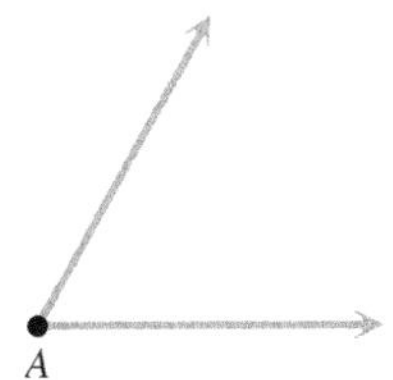


**8.**

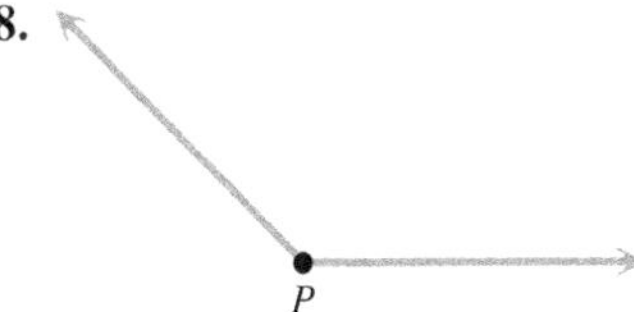


**9.** Construct a 45° angle.

**10.** It is impossible to trisect the general angle using only Euclidean tools. Investigate this fact, and write a short report on it. Include in your report information on the construction tool called a *tomahawk*.

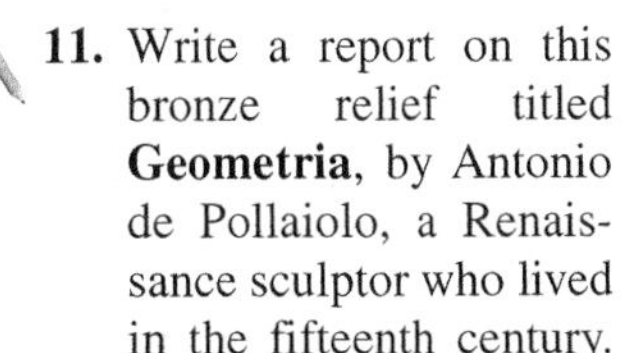

**11.** Write a report on this bronze relief titled **Geometria**, by Antonio de Pollaiolo, a Renaissance sculptor who lived in the fifteenth century.

# 9.3 Perimeter, Area, and Circumference

**Perimeter of a Polygon • Area of a Polygon • Circumference of a Circle • Area of a Circle**

To construct a **golden rectangle,** one in which the ratio of the length to the width is equal to the ratio of the length plus the width to the length, begin with a square $ABCD$. With the point of the compasses at $M$, the midpoint of $\overleftrightarrow{AD}$, swing an arc of radius $MC$ to intersect the extension of $\overleftrightarrow{AD}$ at $F$. Construct a perpendicular at $F$, and have it intersect the extension of $\overleftrightarrow{BC}$ at $E$. Then $ABEF$ is a golden rectangle with ratio $(1 + \sqrt{5})/2$. (See Section 5.4 for more on the golden ratio.)

To verify this construction, let $AM = x$, so that $AD = CD = 2x$. Then, by the Pythagorean theorem,

$$MC = \sqrt{x^2 + (2x)^2} = \sqrt{x^2 + 4x^2} = \sqrt{5x^2}.$$

Because $CF$ is an arc of the circle with radius $MC$, $MF = MC = \sqrt{5x^2}$. Then the ratio of length $AF$ to width $EF$ is

$$\frac{AF}{EF} = \frac{x + \sqrt{5x^2}}{2x} = \frac{x + x\sqrt{5}}{2x} = \frac{x(1 + \sqrt{5})}{2x} = \frac{1 + \sqrt{5}}{2}.$$

Similarly, it can be shown that

$$\frac{AF + EF}{AF} = \frac{1 + \sqrt{5}}{2}.$$

## Perimeter of a Polygon

When working with a polygon, we are sometimes required to find the "distance around," or *perimeter,* of the polygon.

### Perimeter

The **perimeter** of any polygon is the sum of the measures of the line segments that form its sides. Perimeter is measured in *linear units.*

The simplest polygon is a triangle. If a triangle has sides of lengths $a$, $b$, and $c$, then to find its perimeter we simply find the sum of $a$, $b$, and $c$, as shown below.

### Perimeter of a Triangle

The perimeter $P$ of a triangle with sides of lengths $a$, $b$, and $c$ is given by the formula

$$P = a + b + c.$$

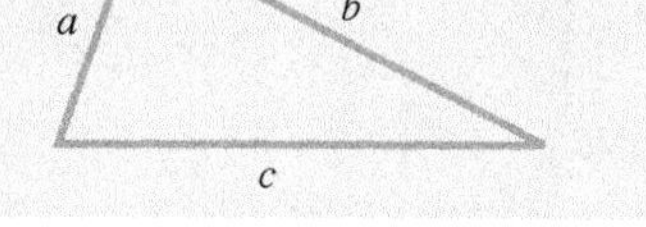


Because a rectangle is made up of two pairs of sides with the two sides in each pair equal in length, the formula for the perimeter of a rectangle may be stated as follows.

### Perimeter of a Rectangle

The perimeter $P$ of a rectangle with length $\ell$ and width $w$ is given by the formula

$$P = 2\ell + 2w,$$

or equivalently,

$$P = 2(\ell + w).$$

### EXAMPLE 1 Using Perimeter to Determine Amount of Fencing Needed

A plot of land is in the shape of a rectangle. If it has length 50 feet and width 26 feet, how much fencing would be needed to completely enclose the plot?

**SOLUTION**

Since we must find the distance around the plot of land, the formula for the perimeter of a rectangle is needed.

$$P = 2\ell + 2w$$
$$P = 2(50) + 2(26) \quad \ell = 50, w = 26$$
$$P = 100 + 52 \quad \text{Multiply.}$$
$$P = 152 \quad \text{Add.}$$

The perimeter is 152 feet, so 152 feet of fencing is required.

A square is a rectangle with four sides of equal length. The formula for the perimeter of a square is a special case of the formula for the perimeter of a rectangle.

### Perimeter of a Square

The perimeter $P$ of a square with all sides of length $s$ is given by the formula

$$P = 4s.$$

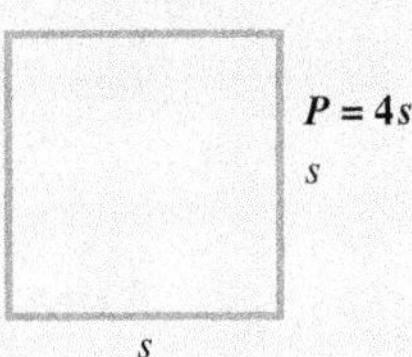


### EXAMPLE 2 Using the Formula for Perimeter of a Square

A square has perimeter 54 inches. What is the length of each side?

**SOLUTION**

$$P = 4s$$
$$54 = 4s \quad P = 54$$
$$s = 13.5 \quad \text{Divide by 4.}$$

Each side has a measure of 13.5 inches.

**PROBLEM-SOLVING HINT** The six-step method of solving an applied problem from Section 7.2 can be used to solve problems involving geometric figures.

### EXAMPLE 3 Finding Length and Width of a Rectangle

The length of a rectangular-shaped label is 1 centimeter more than twice the width. The perimeter is 110 centimeters. Find the length and the width.

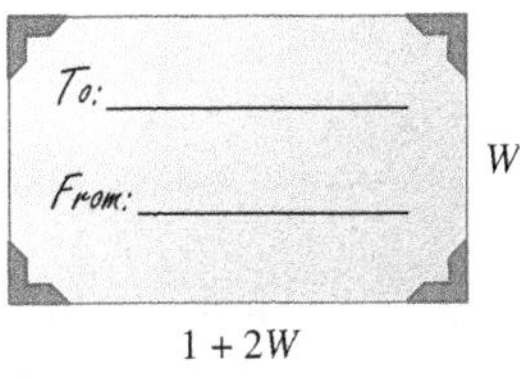


**FIGURE 29**

**SOLUTION**

*Step 1* **Read the problem.** We must find the length and the width.

*Step 2* **Assign a variable.** Let $W$ represent the width. Then $1 + 2W$ can represent the length, because the length is 1 centimeter more than twice the width. Figure 29 shows a diagram of the label.

*Step 3* **Write an equation.** In the formula $P = 2\ell + 2w$, replace $w$ with $W$, $\ell$ with $1 + 2W$, and $P$ with 110, because the perimeter is 110 centimeters.

$$110 = 2(1 + 2W) + 2W$$

*Step 4* **Solve the equation.**

$$110 = 2 + 4W + 2W \quad \text{Distributive property}$$
$$110 = 2 + 6W \quad \text{Combine like terms.}$$
$$108 = 6W \quad \text{Subtract 2.}$$
$$18 = W \quad \text{Divide by 6.}$$

*Step 5* **State the answer.** Because $W = 18$, the width is 18 centimeters and the length is $1 + 2W = 1 + 2(18) = 37$ centimeters.

*Step 6* **Check.** Because 37 is 1 more than twice 18, and because the perimeter is $2(37) + 2(18) = 110$, the answers are correct.

## Area of a Polygon

**Area**

The amount of plane surface covered by a polygon is called its **area.** Area is measured in *square units.*

Defining the **area** of a figure requires a basic *unit of area.* One that is commonly used is the *square centimeter,* abbreviated $cm^2$. One square centimeter, or 1 $cm^2$, is the area of a square one centimeter on a side. In place of 1 $cm^2$, the basic unit of area could have been 1 $in.^2$, 1 $ft^2$, 1 $m^2$, or any appropriate unit.

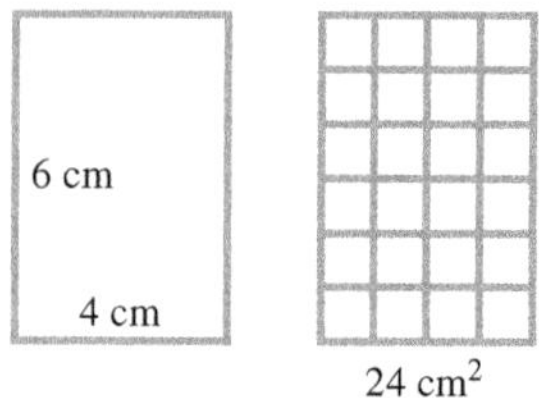


**FIGURE 30**

As an example, we calculate the area of the rectangle shown in Figure 30. Using the basic 1 $cm^2$ unit, Figure 30 shows that four squares, each 1 cm on a side, can be laid off horizontally while six such squares can be laid off vertically. A total of $24 = 4 \cdot 6$ of the small squares are needed to cover the large rectangle. Thus, the area of the large rectangle is 24 $cm^2$.

We can generalize the above illustration to obtain a formula for the area of a rectangle.

**Area of a Rectangle**

The area $A$ of a rectangle with length $\ell$ and width $w$ is given by the formula

$$A = \ell w.$$

$w$

$\ell$

$A = \ell w$

The formula for the area of a rectangle $A = \ell w$ can be used to find formulas for the areas of other figures. For example, if the letter $s$ represents the equal lengths of the sides of a square, then $A = s \cdot s = s^2$.

## Area of a Square

The area $A$ of a square with all sides of length $s$ is given by the formula

$$A = s^2.$$

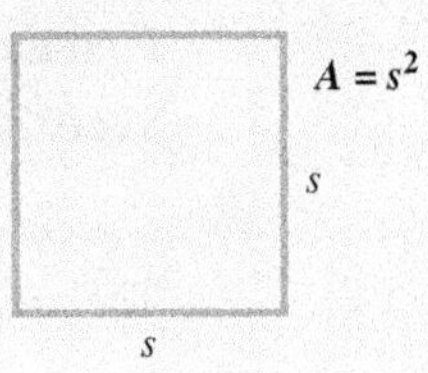


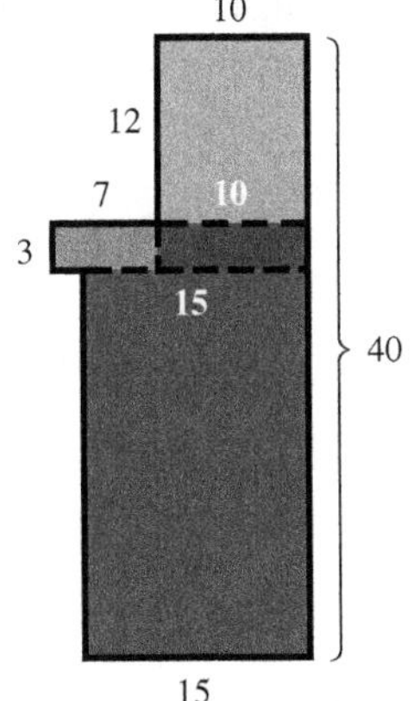


FIGURE 31

### EXAMPLE 4 Using Area to Determine Amount of Carpet Needed

Figure 31 shows the floor plan of a building, made up of various rectangles. If each length given is in meters, how many square meters of carpet would be required to carpet the building?

**SOLUTION**

The dashed lines in the figure break up the floor area into rectangles. The areas of the various rectangles that result are

$$10 \text{ m} \cdot 12 \text{ m} = 120 \text{ m}^2, \qquad 3 \text{ m} \cdot 10 \text{ m} = \mathbf{30 \text{ m}^2},$$
$$3 \text{ m} \cdot 7 \text{ m} = 21 \text{ m}^2, \qquad 15 \text{ m} \cdot 25 \text{ m} = \mathbf{375 \text{ m}^2}.$$

$40 - 12 - 3 = 25$

Because $(120 + 30 + 21 + 375) \text{ m}^2 = 546 \text{ m}^2$, the amount of carpet needed is $546 \text{ m}^2$.

As mentioned earlier in this chapter, a **parallelogram** is a four-sided figure with both pairs of opposite sides parallel. Because a parallelogram need not be a rectangle, the formula for the area of a rectangle cannot be used directly for a parallelogram. However, this formula can be used indirectly, as shown in Figure 32. Cut off the triangle in color, and attach it at the right. The resulting figure is a rectangle with the same area as the original parallelogram.

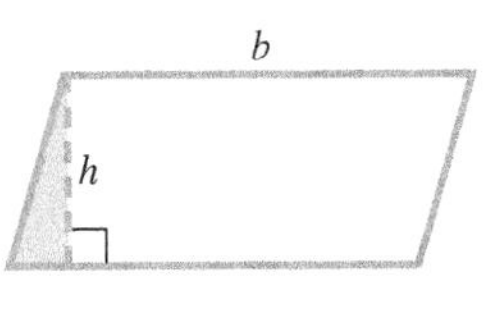


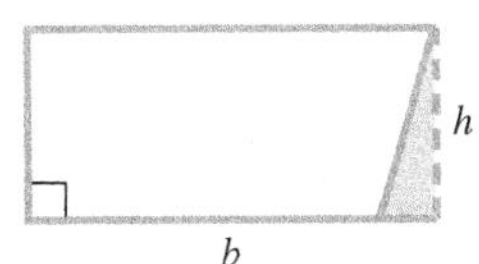


FIGURE 32

The *height* of the parallelogram is the perpendicular distance between two of the parallel sides and is denoted by $h$ in the figure. The width of the rectangle equals the height of the parallelogram, and the length of the rectangle is the base $b$ of the parallelogram, so

$$A = \text{length} \cdot \text{width} \qquad \text{becomes} \qquad A = \text{base} \cdot \text{height}.$$

## Area of a Parallelogram

The area $A$ of a parallelogram with height $h$ and base $b$ is given by the formula

$$A = bh.$$

(*Note:* $h$ is not the length of a side.)

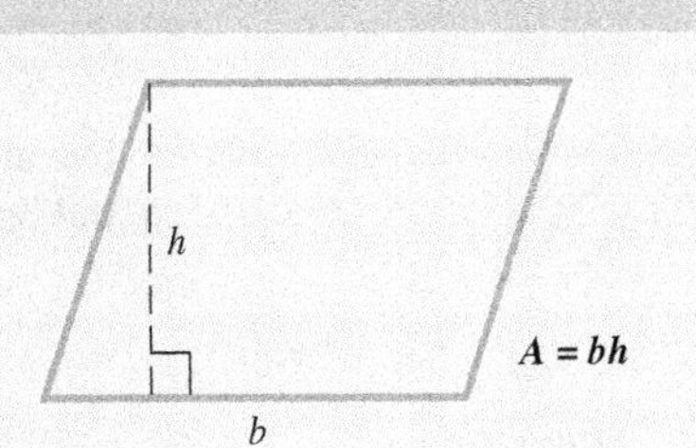

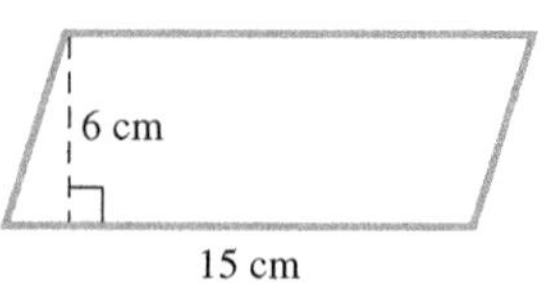

FIGURE 33

## EXAMPLE 5 Using the Formula for Area of a Parallelogram

Find the area of the parallelogram in Figure 33.

**SOLUTION**

$$A = bh = 15 \text{ cm} \cdot 6 \text{ cm} = 90 \text{ cm}^2 \quad b = 15 \text{ cm}, h = 6 \text{ cm}$$

The area is $90 \text{ cm}^2$.

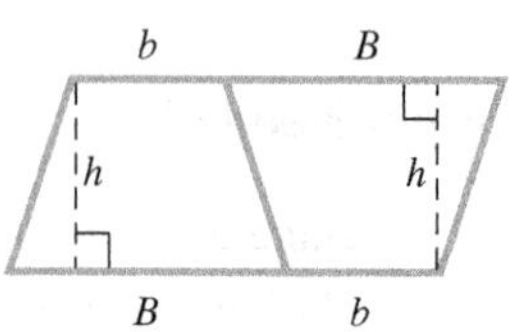

FIGURE 34

Figure 34 shows how we can find a formula for the area of a trapezoid. Notice that the figure as a whole is a parallelogram. It is made up of two trapezoids, each of which has height $h$, shorter base $b$, and longer base $B$. The area of the parallelogram is found by multiplying the height $h$ by the base of the parallelogram, $b + B$, that is, $h(b + B)$. Because the area of the parallelogram is twice the area of each trapezoid, the area of each trapezoid is *half* the area of the parallelogram.

### Area of a Trapezoid

The area $A$ of a trapezoid with parallel bases $b$ and $B$ and height $h$ is given by the formula

$$A = \frac{1}{2}h(b + B).$$

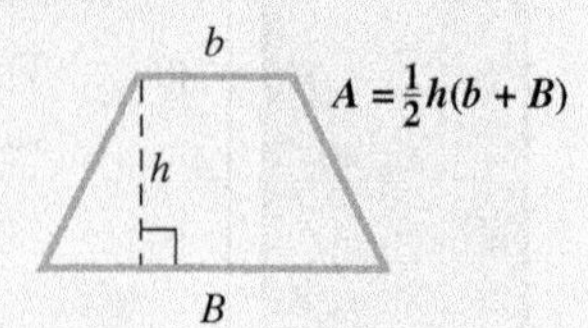


## EXAMPLE 6 Using the Formula for Area of a Trapezoid

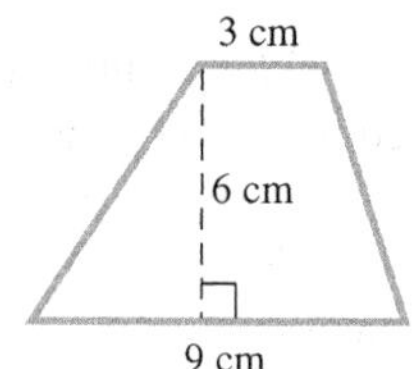

FIGURE 35

Find the area of the trapezoid in Figure 35.

**SOLUTION**

$$A = \frac{1}{2}h(B + b) = \frac{1}{2}(6 \text{ cm})(9 \text{ cm} + 3 \text{ cm}) \quad h = 6 \text{ cm}, B = 9 \text{ cm}, b = 3 \text{ cm}$$

$$= \frac{1}{2}(6 \text{ cm})(12 \text{ cm}) = 36 \text{ cm}^2$$

The area of the trapezoid is $36 \text{ cm}^2$.

The formula for the area of a triangle can be found from the formula for the area of a parallelogram. In Figure 36 the triangle with vertices $A$, $B$, and $C$ has been broken into two parts, one shown in color and one shown in gray. Repeating the part shown in color and the part in gray gives a parallelogram. The area of this parallelogram is $A = \text{base} \cdot \text{height}$, or $A = bh$. However, the parallelogram has *twice* the area of the triangle; in other words, the area of the triangle is *half* the area of the parallelogram.

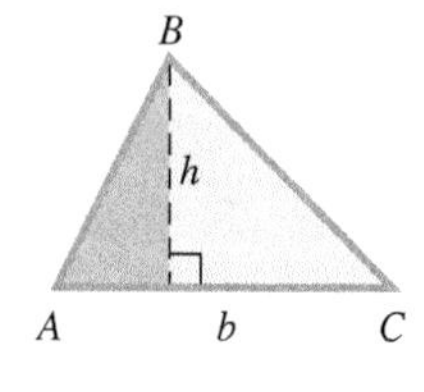

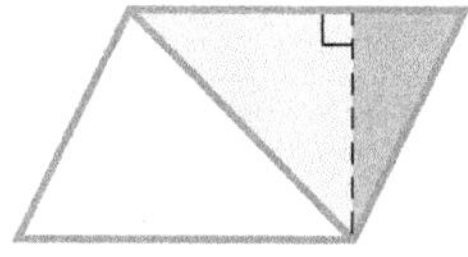
FIGURE 36

### Area of a Triangle

The area $A$ of a triangle with height $h$ and base $b$ is given by the formula

$$A = \frac{1}{2}bh.$$

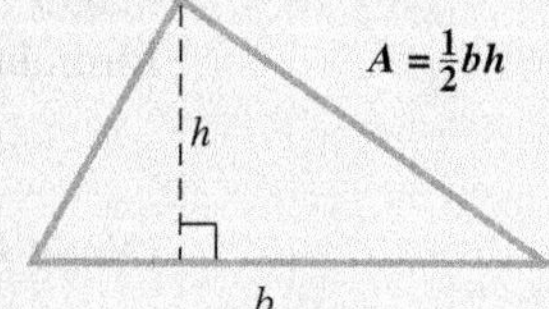

To use the formula for the area of a triangle, $A = \frac{1}{2}bh$, we must know the height from one of the sides of the triangle to the opposite vertex. Suppose that we know only the lengths of the three sides. Is there a way to determine the area from only this given information?

The answer is yes, and it leads us to the formula known as **Heron's formula.** Heron of Alexandria lived during the second half of the first century A.D., and although the formula is named after him, there is evidence that it was known to Archimedes several centuries earlier.

Let *a*, *b*, and *c* be lengths of the sides of any triangle. Let $s = \frac{1}{2}(a + b + c)$ represent the semiperimeter. Then the area *A* of the triangle is given by the formula

$$A = \sqrt{s(s-a)(s-b)(s-c)}.$$

The Vietnam Veterans' Memorial in Washington, D.C., is in the shape of an unenclosed isosceles triangle. The walls form a "V-shape," and each wall measures 246.75 feet. The distance between the ends of the walls is 438.14 feet. Use Heron's formula to find the area enclosed by the triangular shape.

When applying the formula for the area of a triangle, remember that the height is the perpendicular distance between a vertex and the opposite side (or the extension of that side). See Figure 37.

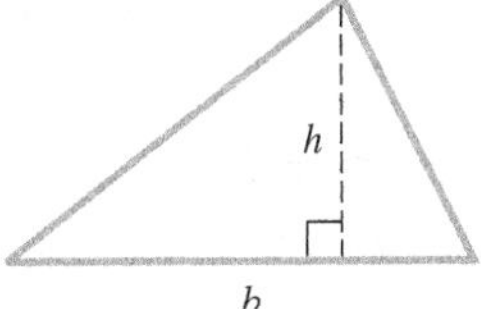


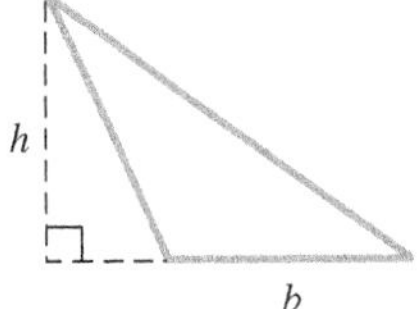


In each case, $A = \frac{1}{2}bh$.

**FIGURE 37**

## EXAMPLE 7 Finding the Height of a Triangular Sail

The area of a triangular sail of a sailboat is $126\text{ ft}^2$. The base of the sail is 12 ft. Find the height of the sail.

**FIGURE 38**

**SOLUTION**

*Step 1* **Read.** We must find the height of the triangular sail.

*Step 2* **Assign a variable.** Let $h =$ the height of the sail in feet. See Figure 38.

*Step 3* **Write an equation.** Using the information given in the problem, we substitute 126 $\text{ft}^2$ for *A* and 12 ft for *b* in the formula for the area of a triangle.

$$A = \frac{1}{2}bh$$

$$126\text{ ft}^2 = \frac{1}{2}(12\text{ ft})h \qquad A = 126\text{ ft}^2,\ b = 12\text{ ft}$$

*Step 4* **Solve.**

$$126\text{ ft}^2 = 6h\text{ ft} \qquad \text{Multiply.}$$

$$21\text{ ft} = h \qquad \text{Divide by 6 ft.}$$

*Step 5* **State the answer.** The height of the sail is 21 ft.

*Step 6* **Check** to see that the values $A = 126\text{ ft}^2$, $b = 12$ ft, and $h = 21$ ft satisfy the formula for the area of a triangle.

## Circumference of a Circle

The distance around a circle is called its **circumference** (rather than "perimeter"). To understand the formula for the circumference of a circle, use a piece of string to measure the distance around a circle. Measure its diameter and then divide the circumference by the diameter. This quotient is the same, no matter what the size of the circle. The result of this measurement is an approximation for the number $\pi$. We have

$$\pi = \frac{\text{circumference}}{\text{diameter}} = \frac{C}{d}, \quad \text{or alternatively,} \quad C = \pi d.$$

Because the diameter of a circle measures twice the radius, we have $d = 2r$. These relationships allow us to state the following formulas for the circumference of a circle.

### Circumference of a Circle

The circumference $C$ of a circle of diameter $d$ is given by the formula

$$C = \pi d.$$

Also, the circumference $C$ of a circle of radius $r$ is given by the formula

$$C = 2\pi r.$$

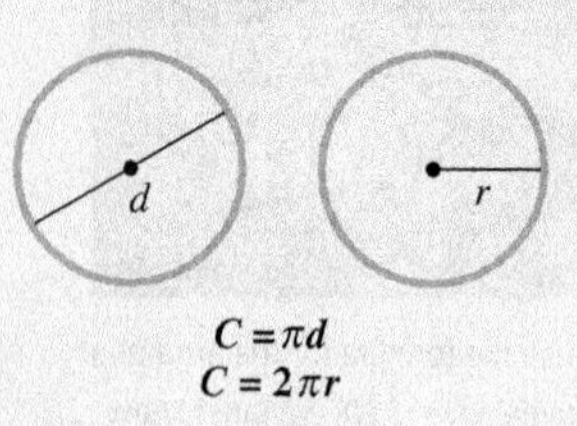


Recall that $\pi$ is not a rational number. In this chapter we will use 3.14 as an approximation for $\pi$ when one is required.

### EXAMPLE 8 Finding the Circumference of a Circle

Find the circumference of each circle described. Use $\pi \approx 3.14$.

**(a)** A circle with diameter 12.6 centimeters

**(b)** A circle with radius 1.7 meters

**SOLUTION**

**(a)** $C = \pi d \approx 3.14(12.6 \text{ cm}) = 39.564 \text{ cm}$ $\quad d = 12.6$ cm

The circumference is about 39.6 centimeters, rounded to the nearest tenth.

**(b)** $C = 2\pi r \approx 2(3.14)(1.7 \text{ m}) \approx 10.7 \text{ m}$ $\quad r = 1.7$ m

The circumference is approximately 10.7 meters.

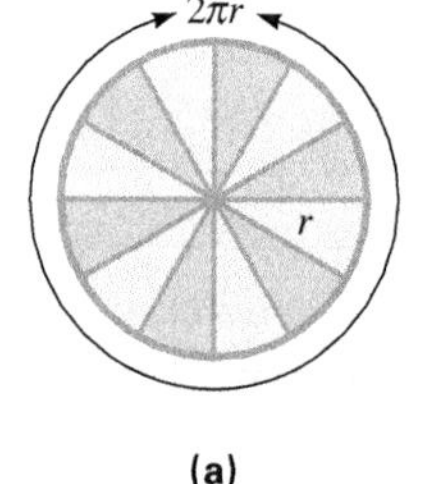


(a)

$\pi r$

$r$

$A \approx \pi r^2$

(b)

**FIGURE 39**

**Area of a Circle** Start with a circle as shown in Figure 39(a), divided into many equal pie-shaped pieces (**sectors**). Rearrange the pieces into an approximate rectangle as shown in Figure 39(b). The circle has circumference $2\pi r$, so the "length" of the approximate rectangle is one-half of the circumference, or $\frac{1}{2}(2\pi r) = \pi r$, while its "width" is $r$. The area of the approximate rectangle is length times width, or $(\pi r)r = \pi r^2$. By choosing smaller and smaller sectors, the figure becomes closer and closer to a rectangle, so its area becomes closer and closer to $\pi r^2$. This "limiting" procedure leads to the following formula.

### Area of a Circle

The area $A$ of a circle with radius $r$ is given by the formula

$$A = \pi r^2.$$

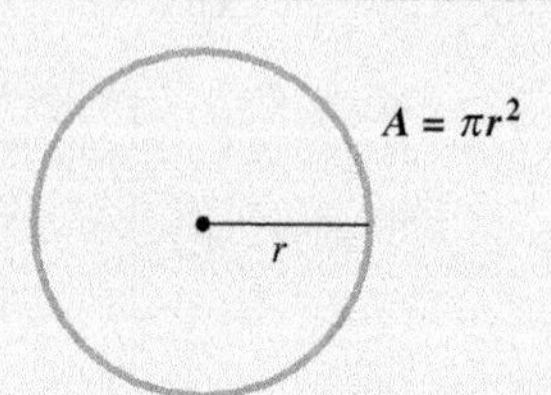

**PROBLEM-SOLVING HINT** The formula for the area of a circle can be used to determine the best value for the money the next time you purchase a pizza. The next example uses the idea of unit pricing.

**EXAMPLE 9 Using Area to Determine Better Value for Pizza**

Paw-Paw Johnny's delivers pizza. The price of an 8-inch diameter pepperoni pizza is \$6.99, while the price of a 16-inch diameter pizza is \$13.98. Which is the better buy?

**SOLUTION**

To determine which pizza is the better value for the money, we must first find the area of each, and divide the price by the area to determine the price per square inch.

$$\text{8-inch diameter pizza area} = \pi(4 \text{ in.})^2 \approx 50.24 \text{ in.}^2 \quad \text{Radius is } (\tfrac{1}{2})(8 \text{ in.}) = 4 \text{ in.}$$
$$\text{16-inch diameter pizza area} = \pi(8 \text{ in.})^2 \approx 200.96 \text{ in.}^2 \quad \text{Radius is } (\tfrac{1}{2})(16 \text{ in.}) = 8 \text{ in.}$$

The price per square inch for the 8-inch pizza is $\frac{\$6.99}{50.24} \approx 13.9¢$, while the price per square inch for the 16-inch pizza is $\frac{\$13.98}{200.96} \approx 7.0¢$. Therefore, the 16-inch pizza is the better buy, since it costs approximately half as much per square inch.

**Solution to Chapter Opener Problem** Chuck computes the approximate search area as 502,400 square miles. "Twice the size of Texas" is 2(261,797) = 523,594 square miles, so his analysis is correct.

## 9.3 EXERCISES

*In Exercises 1–5, fill in each blank with the correct response.*

**1.** The perimeter of an equilateral triangle with side length equal to _____ inches is the same as the perimeter of a rectangle with length 10 inches and width 8 inches.

**2.** A square with area 16 $\text{cm}^2$ has perimeter _____ cm.

**3.** If the area of a certain triangle is 24 square inches, and the base measures 8 inches, then the height must measure _____ inches.

**4.** If the radius of a circle is doubled, then its area is multiplied by a factor of _____.

**5.** Perimeter is to a polygon as _____________ is to a circle.

**6.** ***Perimeter or Area?*** *Decide whether perimeter or area would be used to solve a problem concerning the measure of the quantity.*

**(a)** Sod for a lawn
**(b)** Carpeting for a bedroom
**(c)** Baseboards for a living room
**(d)** Fencing for a yard
**(e)** Fertilizer for a garden
**(f)** Tile for a bathroom
**(g)** Determining the cost of planting rye grass in a lawn for the winter
**(h)** Determining the cost of replacing a linoleum floor with a wood floor

*Use the formulas of this section to find the area of each figure. In Exercises 19–22, use 3.14 as an approximation for $\pi$.*

**7.**

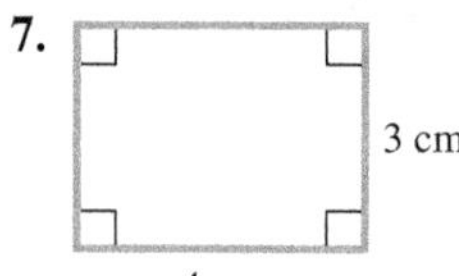


**8.**

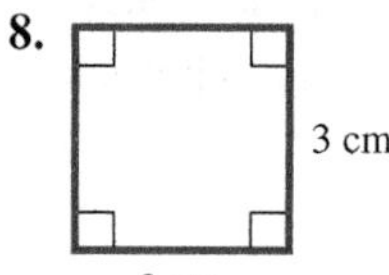


**9.**

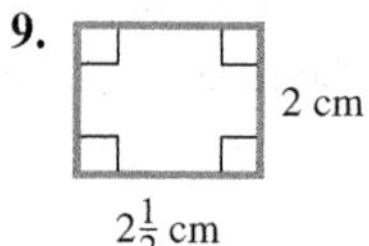


**10.**

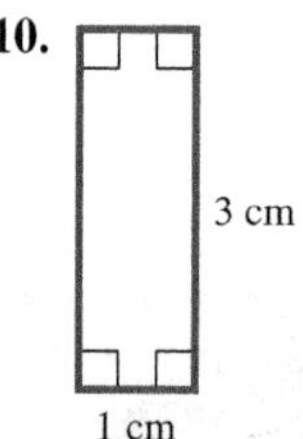


**11.**

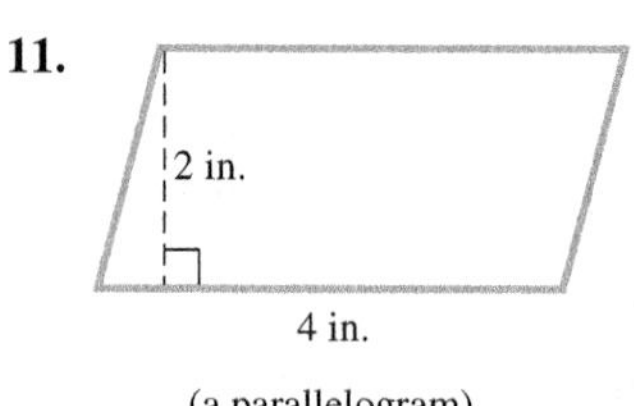


(a parallelogram)

**12.**

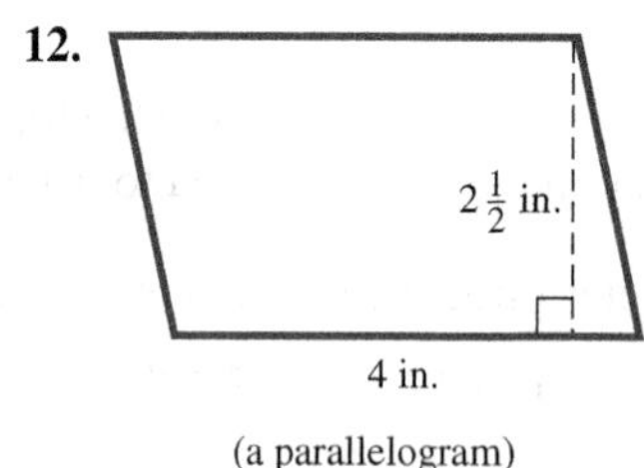


(a parallelogram)

**13.**

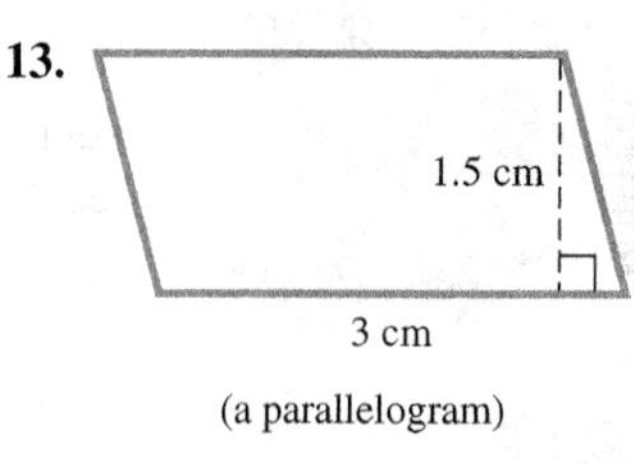


(a parallelogram)

**14.**

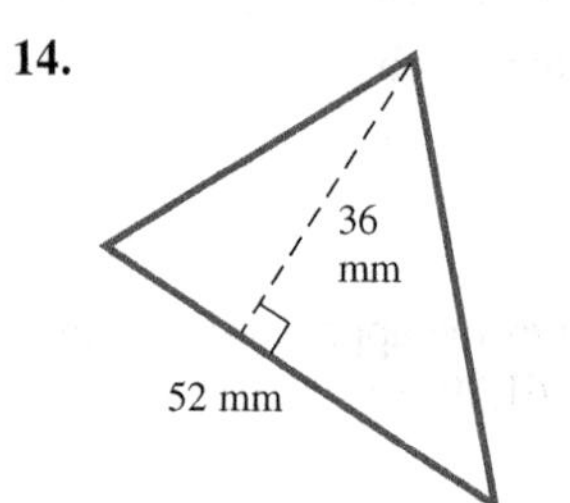


**15.**

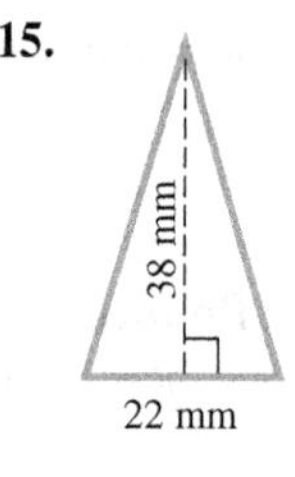


**16.**

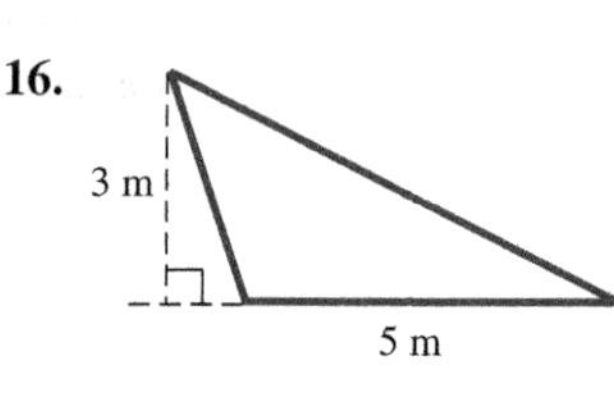


**17.**

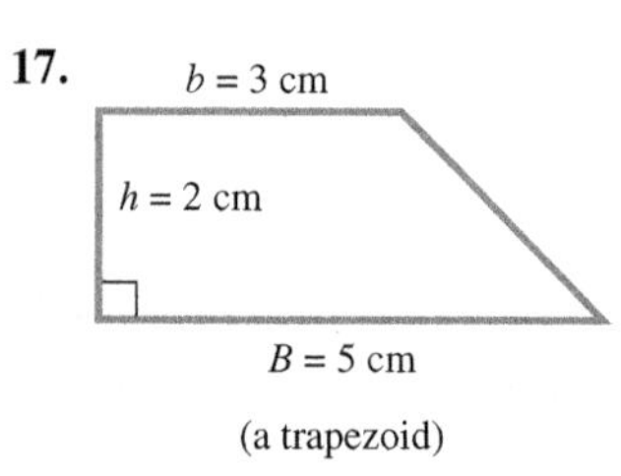


(a trapezoid)

**18.**

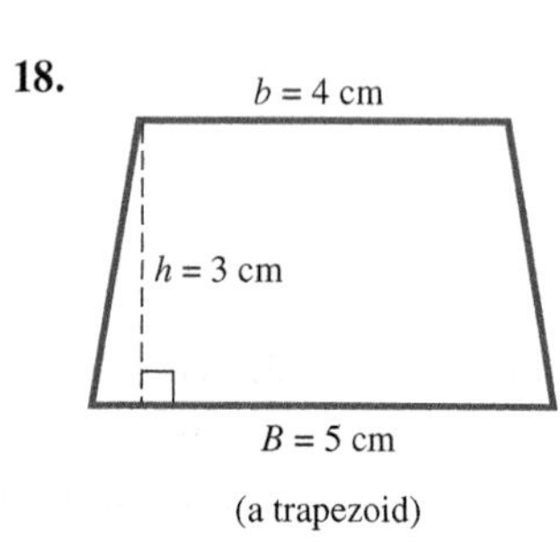


(a trapezoid)

**19.**

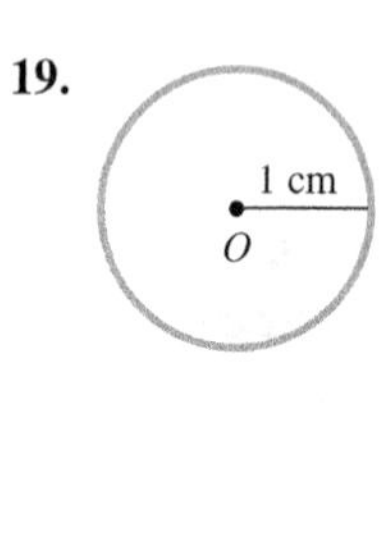


**20.**

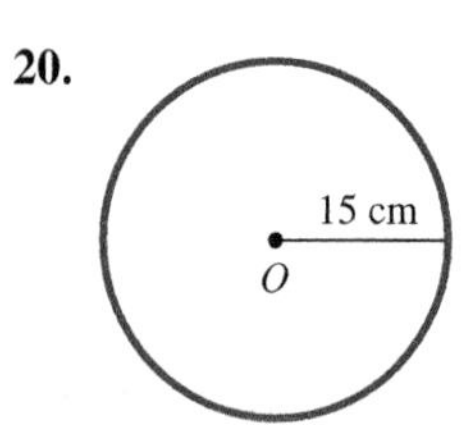


**21.**

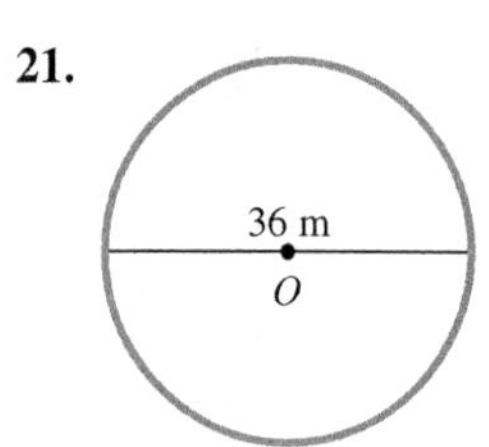


**22.**

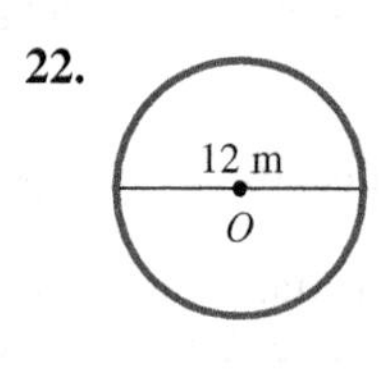

*Solve each problem.*

23. ***Window Side Length*** A stained-glass window in a church is in the shape of a square. The perimeter of the square is 7 times the length of a side in meters, decreased by 12. Find the length of a side of the window.

24. ***Dimensions of a Rectangle*** A video rental establishment displayed a rectangular cardboard stand-up advertisement for the movie *Failure to Launch*. The length was 20 in. more than the width, and the perimeter was 176 in. What were the dimensions of the rectangle?

25. ***Dimensions of a Lot*** A lot is in the shape of a triangle. One side is 100 ft longer than the shortest side, while the third side is 200 ft longer than the shortest side. The perimeter of the lot is 1200 ft. Find the lengths of the sides of the lot.

26. ***Pennant Side Lengths*** A wall pennant is in the shape of an isosceles triangle. Each of the two equal sides measures 18 in. more than the third side, and the perimeter of the triangle is 54 in. What are the lengths of the sides of the pennant?

27. ***Radius of a Circular Foundation*** A hotel is in the shape of a cylinder, with a circular foundation. The circumference of the foundation is 6 times the radius, increased by 12.88 ft. Find the radius of the circular foundation. (Use 3.14 as an approximation for $\pi$.)

28. ***Radius of a Circle*** If the radius of a certain circle is tripled, with 8.2 cm then added, the result is the circumference of the circle. Find the radius of the circle. (Use 3.14 as an approximation for $\pi$.)

29. ***Area of Two Lots*** The survey plat in the figure at the top of the next column shows two lots that form a trapezoid. The measures of the parallel sides are 115.80 ft and 171.00 ft. The height of the trapezoid is 165.97 ft. Find the combined area of the two lots. Round your answer to the nearest hundredth of a square foot.

30. ***Area of a Lot*** Lot A in the figure is in the shape of a trapezoid. The parallel sides measure 26.84 ft and 82.05 ft. The height of the trapezoid is 165.97 ft. Find the area of Lot A. Round your answer to the nearest hundredth of a square foot.

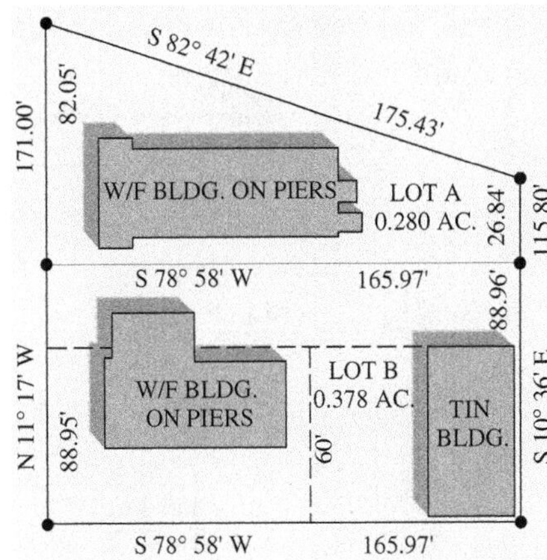


31. ***Perimeter or Area?*** In order to purchase fencing to go around a rectangular yard, would you need to use perimeter or area to decide how much to buy?

32. ***Perimeter or Area?*** In order to purchase fertilizer for the lawn of a yard, would you need to use perimeter or area to decide how much to buy?

*In the chart below, one of the values r (radius), d (diameter), C (circumference), or A (area) is given for a particular circle. Find the remaining three values. Leave $\pi$ in your answers.*

| | $r$ | $d$ | $C$ | $A$ |
|---|---|---|---|---|
| 33. | 6 in. | | | |
| 34. | 9 in. | | | |
| 35. | | 10 ft | | |
| 36. | | 40 ft | | |
| 37. | | | $12\pi$ cm | |
| 38. | | | $18\pi$ cm | |
| 39. | | | | $100\pi$ in.$^2$ |
| 40. | | | | $256\pi$ in.$^2$ |

*Each figure has perimeter as indicated. (Figures are not necessarily to scale.) Find the value of x.*

**41.** $P = 58$

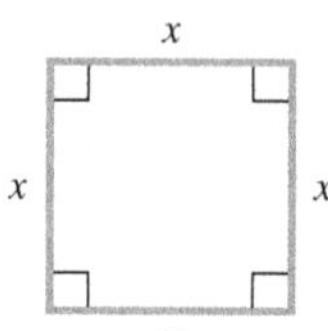


**42.** $P = 42$

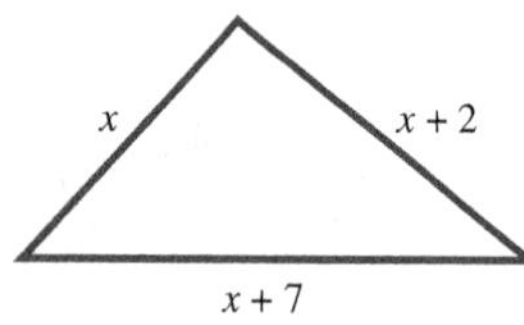


**43.** $P = 38$

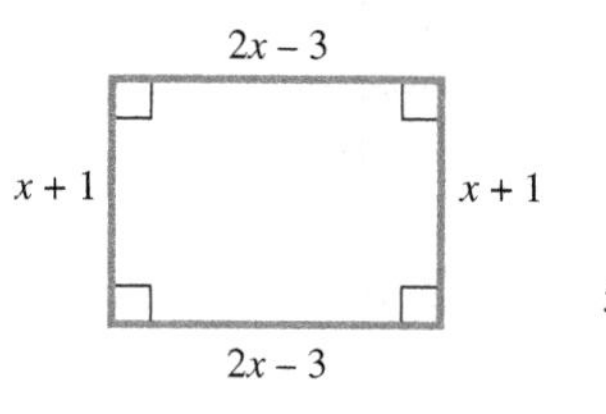


**44.** $P = 278$

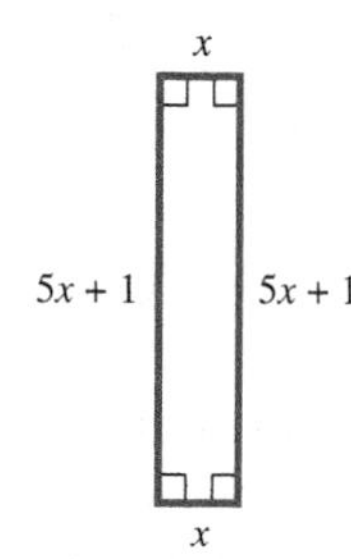


*Each figure has area as indicated. Find the value of x.*

**45.** $A = 26.01$

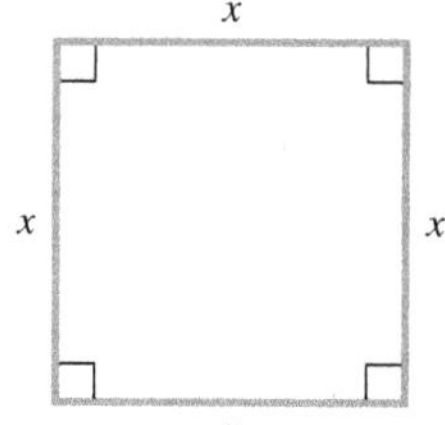


**46.** $A = 28$

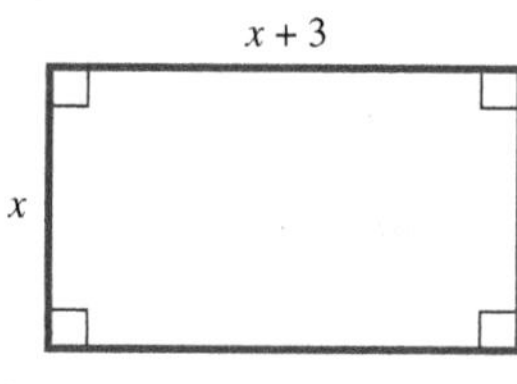


**47.** $A = 15$

x + 1

x

**48.** $A = 30$

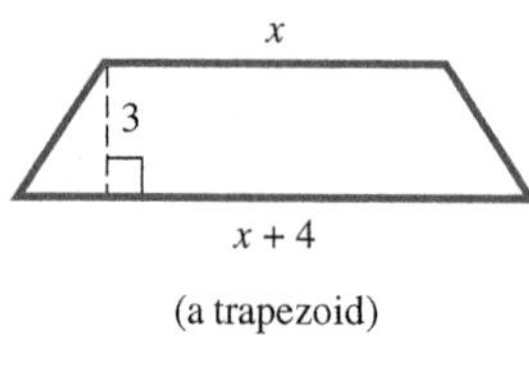


(a trapezoid)

*Each circle has circumference or area as indicated. Find the value of x. Use 3.14 as an approximation for $\pi$.*

**49.** $C = 37.68$

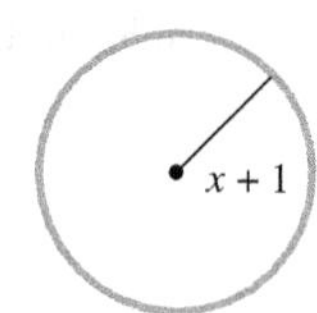


**50.** $C = 54.95$

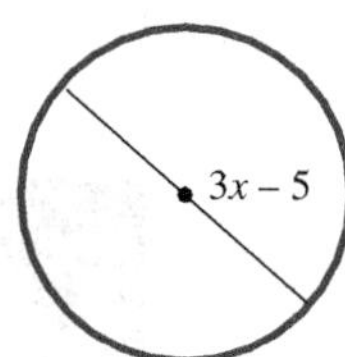


**51.** $A = 28.26$

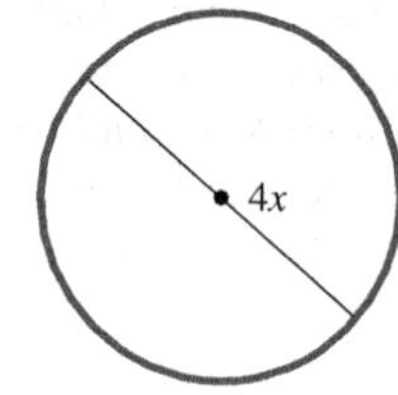


**52.** $A = 18.0864$

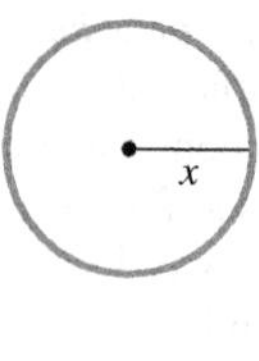


**53.** Work through the parts of this exercise in order, and use it to make a generalization concerning areas of rectangles.

**(a)** Find the area of a rectangle 4 cm by 5 cm.

**(b)** Find the area of a rectangle 8 cm by 10 cm.

**(c)** Find the area of a rectangle 12 cm by 15 cm.

**(d)** Find the area of a rectangle 16 cm by 20 cm.

**(e)** The rectangle in part (b) had sides twice as long as the sides of the rectangle in part (a). Divide the larger area by the smaller. By doubling the sides, the area increased _____ times.

**(f)** To get the rectangle in part (c), each side of the rectangle in part (a) was multiplied by _____. This made the larger area _____ times the size of the smaller area.

**(g)** To get the rectangle of part (d), each side of the rectangle of part (a) was multiplied by _____. This made the area increase to _____ times what it was originally.

**(h)** In general, if the length of each side of a rectangle is multiplied by $n$, the area is multiplied by _____.

***Job Cost*** *Use the results of Exercise 53 to solve each problem.*

54. A ceiling measuring 9 ft by 15 ft can be painted for \$60. How much would it cost to paint a ceiling 18 ft by 30 ft?

55. Suppose carpet for a 10 ft by 12 ft room costs \$200. Find the cost to carpet a room 20 ft by 24 ft.

56. A carpet cleaner charges \$80 to shampoo an area 31 ft by 31 ft. What would be the charge for an area 93 ft by 93 ft?

57. Use the logic of Exercise 53 to answer the following: If the radius of a circle is multiplied by $n$, then the area of the circle is multiplied by _____.

58. Use the logic of Exercise 53 to answer the following: If the height of a triangle is multiplied by $n$ and the base length remains the same, then the area of the triangle is multiplied by _____.

***Total Area as the Sum of Areas*** *By considering total area as the sum of the areas of all of its parts, the area of a figure such as those in Exercises 59–62 can be determined. Find the total area of each figure. Use 3.14 as an approximation for $\pi$ in Exercises 61 and 62.*

59.
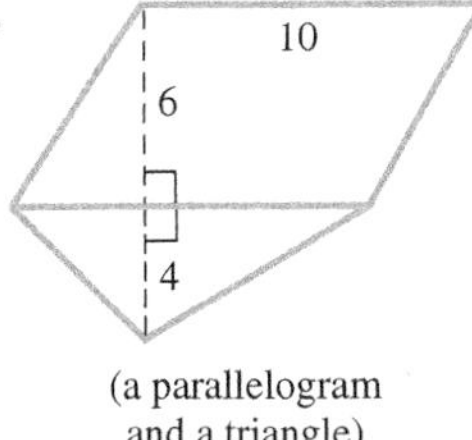

(a parallelogram and a triangle)

60.
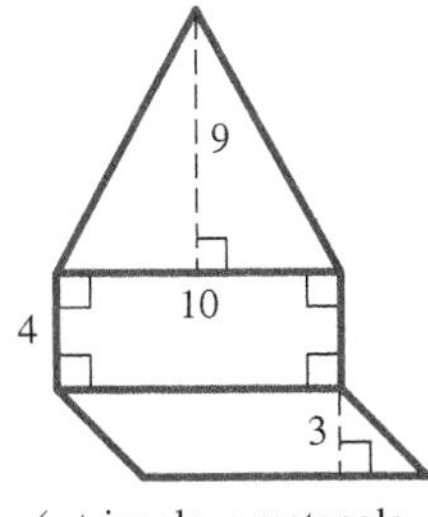

(a triangle, a rectangle, and a parallelogram)

61.
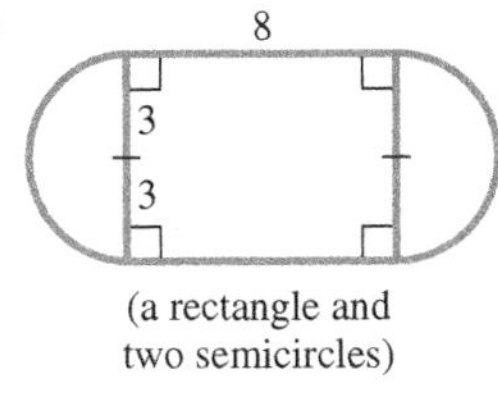

(a rectangle and two semicircles)

62.
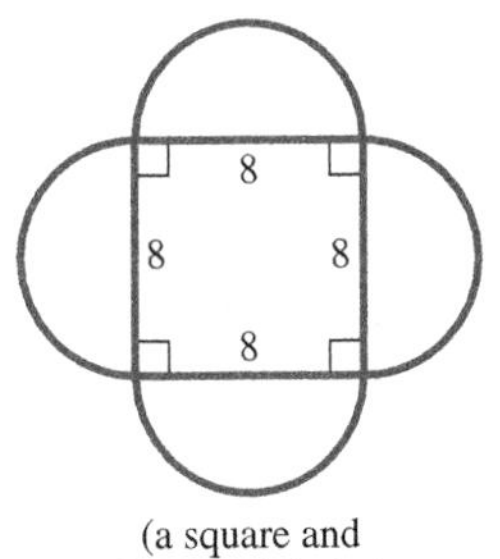

(a square and four semicircles)

***Area of a Shaded Portion of a Plane Figure*** *The shaded areas of the figures in Exercises 63–68 may be found by subtracting the area of the unshaded portion from the total area of the figure. Use this approach to find the area of the shaded portion. Use 3.14 as an approximation for $\pi$ in Exercises 66–68, and round to the nearest hundredth.*

63. 64.
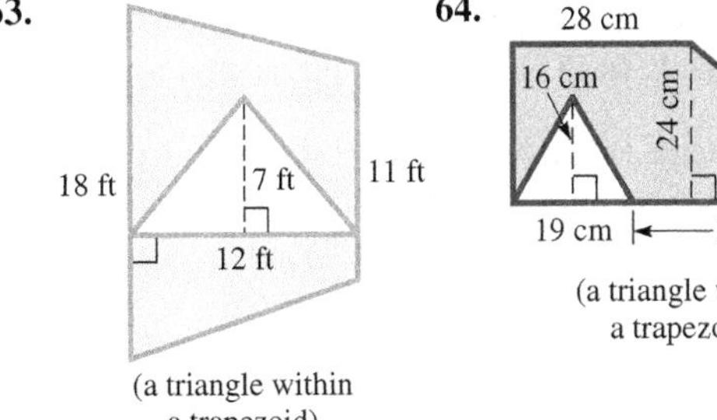

(a triangle within a trapezoid)

(a triangle within a trapezoid)

65. 66.
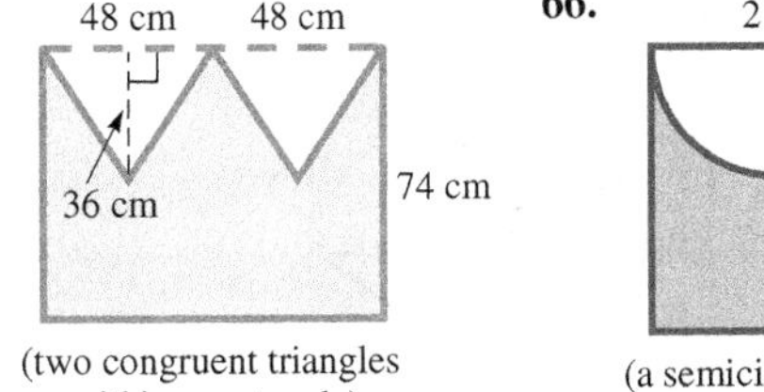

(two congruent triangles within a rectangle)

(a semicircle within a rectangle)

67.
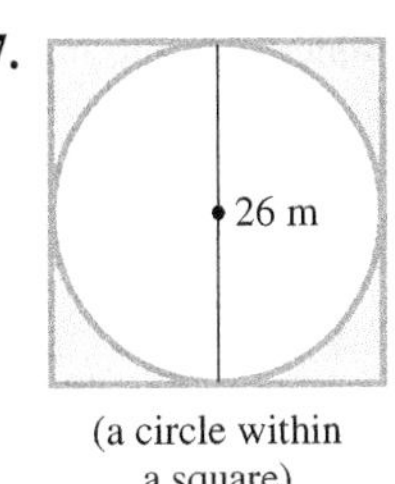

(a circle within a square)

68.
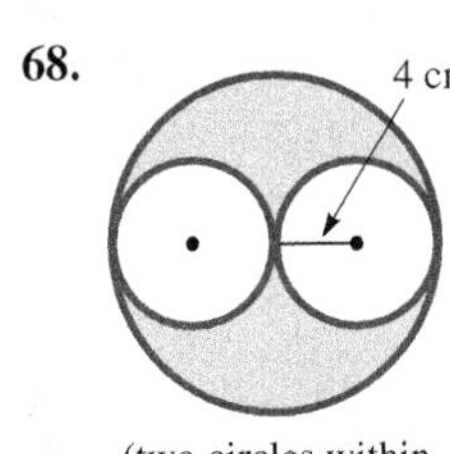

(two circles within a circle)

***Pizza Pricing*** *The following exercises show prices actually charged by Maw-Maw Gigi's, a local pizzeria. In each case, the dimension is the diameter of the pizza. Find the best buy.*

**69.** Cheese pizza: 10-in. pizza sells for \$5.99, 12-in. pizza sells for \$7.99, 14-in. pizza sells for \$8.99.

**70.** Cheese pizza with two toppings: 10-in. pizza sells for \$7.99, 12-in. pizza sells for \$9.99, 14-in. pizza sells for \$10.99.

**71.** All Feasts pizza: 10-in. pizza sells for \$9.99, 12-in. pizza sells for \$11.99, 14-in. pizza sells for \$12.99.

**72.** Extravaganza pizza: 10-in. pizza sells for \$11.99, 12-in. pizza sells for \$13.99, 14-in. pizza sells for \$14.99.

*A polygon can be inscribed within a circle or circumscribed about a circle. In the figure, triangle ABC is inscribed within the circle, while square WXYZ is circumscribed about it. These ideas will be used in some of the remaining exercises in this section and later in this chapter.*

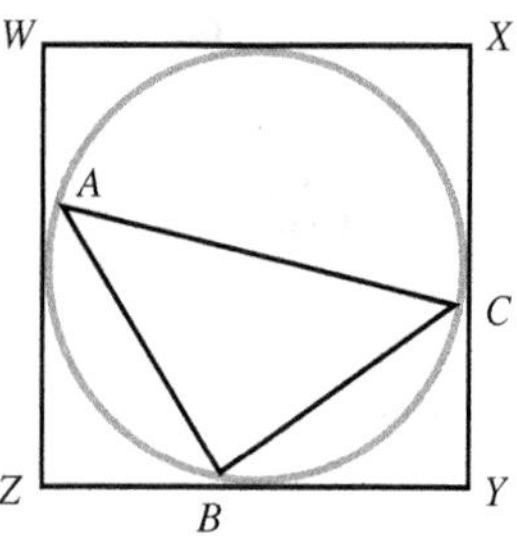


*Exercises 73–80 require some ingenuity, but all may be solved using the concepts presented so far in this chapter.*

**73. *Diameter of a Circle*** Given the circle with center $O$ and rectangle $ABCO$, find the diameter of the circle.

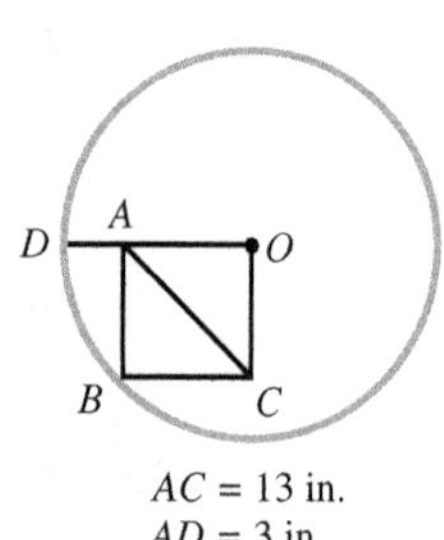


$AC = 13$ in.
$AD = 3$ in.

**74. *Perimeter of a Triangle*** What is the perimeter of $\Delta AEB$, if $AD = 20$ in., $DC = 30$ in., and $AC = 34$ in.?

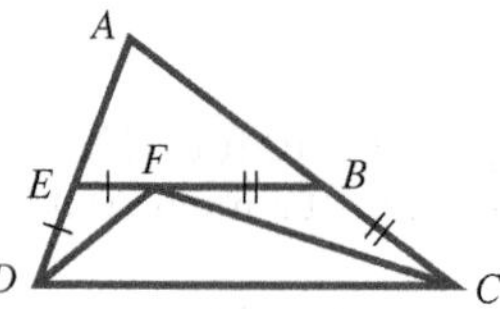


**75. *Area of a Square*** The area of square $PQRS$ is 1250 square feet. $T$, $U$, $V$, and $W$ are the midpoints of $PQ$, $QR$, $RS$, and $SP$, respectively. What is the area of square $TUVW$?

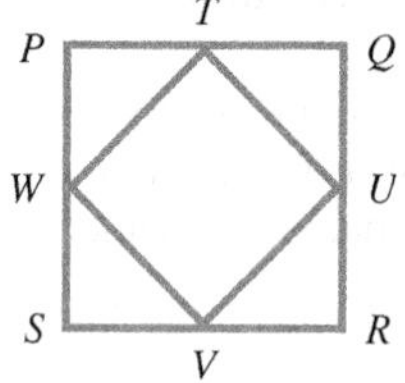


**76. *Area of a Quadrilateral*** The rectangle $ABCD$ has length twice the width. If $P$, $Q$, $R$, and $S$ are the midpoints of the sides, and the perimeter of $ABCD$ is 96 in., what is the area of quadrilateral $PQRS$?

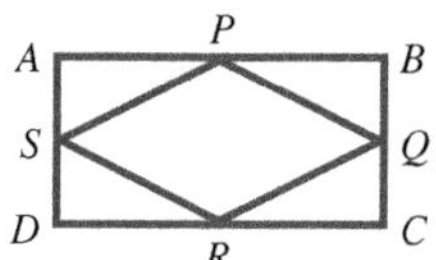


**77. *Area of a Shaded Region*** If $ABCD$ is a square with each side measuring 36 in., what is the area of the shaded region?

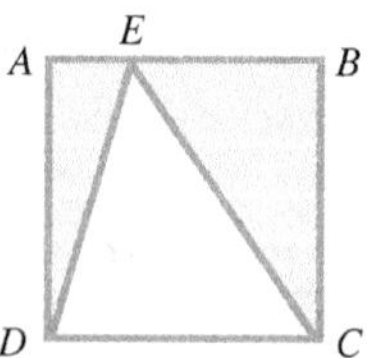


**78. *Perimeter of a Polygon*** Can the perimeter of the polygon shown be determined from the given information? If so, what is the perimeter?

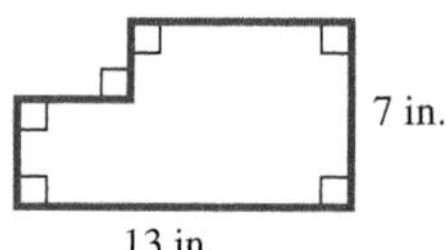

79. ***Area of a Shaded Region*** Express the area of the shaded region in terms of $r$, given that the circle is inscribed in the square.

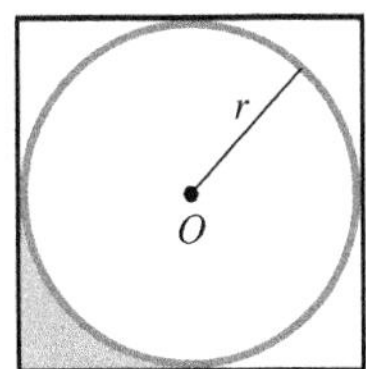


80. ***Area of a Trapezoid*** Find the area of trapezoid $ABCD$, given that the area of right triangle $ABE$ is 30 in.$^2$.

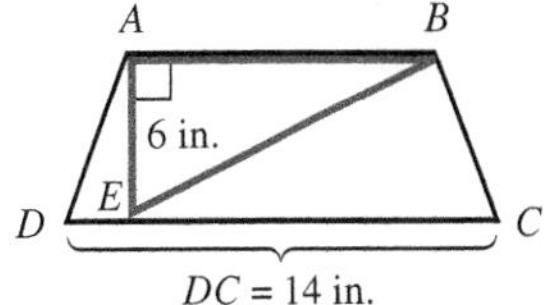

# 9.4 The Geometry of Triangles: Congruence, Similarity, and the Pythagorean Theorem

**Congruent Triangles • Similar Triangles • The Pythagorean Theorem**

## Congruent Triangles

Triangles that are both the same size and the same shape are called **congruent triangles.** Informally speaking, if two triangles are congruent, then it is possible to pick up one of them and place it on top of the other so that they coincide exactly. An everyday example of congruent triangles would be the triangular supports for a child's swing set, machine-produced with exactly the same dimensions each time.

In this section we will use the "$\triangle$" symbolism to designate triangles. Figure 40 illustrates two congruent triangles, $\triangle ABC$ and $\triangle DEF$. The symbol $\cong$ denotes congruence, so $\triangle ABC \cong \triangle DEF$. Notice how the angles and sides are marked to indicate which angles are congruent and which sides are congruent. (Using precise terminology, we refer to angles or sides as being *congruent,* while the *measures* of congruent angles or congruent sides are *equal.* We will often use the terms "equal angles" or "equal sides" to describe angles of equal measure or sides of equal measure.)

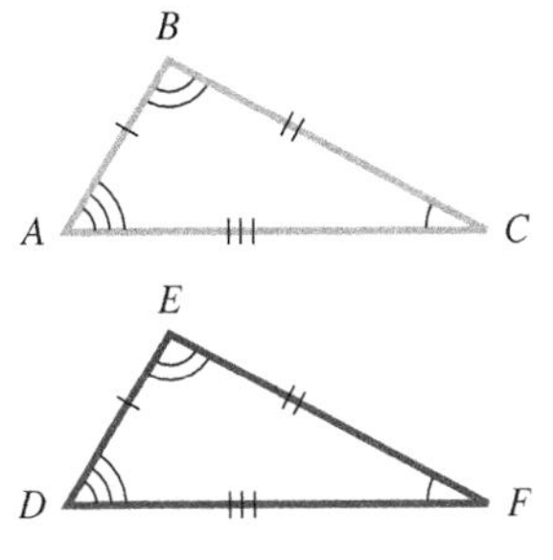


**FIGURE 40**

In geometry the following properties are used to prove that two triangles are congruent.

### Congruence Properties

**Side-Angle-Side (SAS)** If two sides and the included angle of one triangle are equal, respectively, to two sides and the included angle of a second triangle, then the triangles are congruent.

**Angle-Side-Angle (ASA)** If two angles and the included side of one triangle are equal, respectively, to two angles and the included side of a second triangle, then the triangles are congruent.

**Side-Side-Side (SSS)** If three sides of one triangle are equal, respectively, to three sides of a second triangle, then the triangles are congruent.

Examples 1–3 show how to prove statements using these properties. We use a diagram with two columns, headed by STATEMENTS and REASONS.

Our knowledge of the mathematics of the Babylonians of Mesopotamia is based largely on archaeological discoveries of thousands of clay tablets. On the tablet labeled **Plimpton 322,** there are several columns of inscriptions that represent numbers. The far right column is simply one that serves to number the lines, but two other columns represent values of hypotenuses and legs of right triangles with integer-valued sides. Thus, it seems that while the famous theorem relating right-triangle side lengths is named for the Greek Pythagoras, the relationship was known more than 1000 years prior to the time of Pythagoras.

## EXAMPLE 1 Proving Congruence

Refer to Figure 41.

*Given:* $CE = ED$

$AE = EB$

*Prove:* $\triangle ACE \cong \triangle BDE$

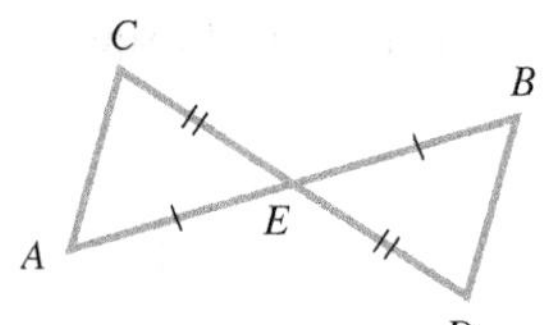


**FIGURE 41**

**PROOF**

| STATEMENTS | REASONS |
|---|---|
| **1.** $CE = ED$ | **1.** Given |
| **2.** $AE = EB$ | **2.** Given |
| **3.** $\measuredangle CEA = \measuredangle DEB$ | **3.** Vertical angles are equal. |
| **4.** $\triangle ACE \cong \triangle BDE$ | **4.** SAS congruence property |

## EXAMPLE 2 Proving Congruence

Refer to Figure 42.

*Given:* $\measuredangle ADB = \measuredangle CBD$

$\measuredangle ABD = \measuredangle CDB$

*Prove:* $\triangle ADB \cong \triangle CBD$

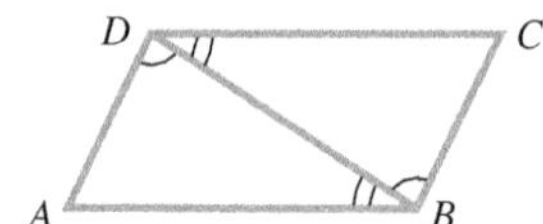


**FIGURE 42**

**PROOF**

| STATEMENTS | REASONS |
|---|---|
| **1.** $\measuredangle ADB = \measuredangle CBD$ | **1.** Given |
| **2.** $\measuredangle ABD = \measuredangle CDB$ | **2.** Given |
| **3.** $DB = DB$ | **3.** Reflexive property (a quantity is equal to itself) |
| **4.** $\triangle ADB \cong \triangle CBD$ | **4.** ASA congruence property |

## EXAMPLE 3 Proving Congruence

Refer to Figure 43.

*Given:* $AD = CD$

$AB = CB$

*Prove:* $\triangle ABD \cong \triangle CBD$

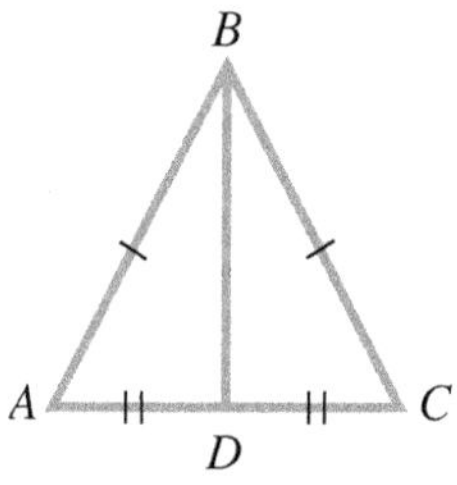


**FIGURE 43**

**PROOF**

| STATEMENTS | REASONS |
|---|---|
| **1.** $AD = CD$ | **1.** Given |
| **2.** $AB = CB$ | **2.** Given |
| **3.** $BD = BD$ | **3.** Reflexive property |
| **4.** $\triangle ABD \cong \triangle CBD$ | **4.** SSS congruence property |

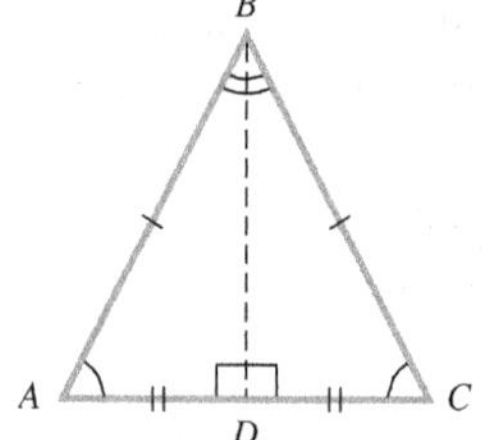


**FIGURE 44**

In Example 3, $\triangle ABC$ is an isosceles triangle. The results of that example allow us to make several important statements about an isosceles triangle. They are indicated symbolically in Figure 44 and stated in the following box.

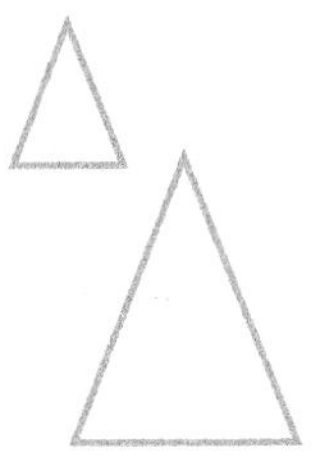

### Important Statements About Isosceles Triangles

If $\triangle ABC$ is an isosceles triangle with $AB = CB$, and if $D$ is the midpoint of the base $AC$, then the following properties hold.

1. The base angles $A$ and $C$ are equal.
2. Angles $ABD$ and $CBD$ are equal.
3. Angles $ADB$ and $CDB$ are both right angles.

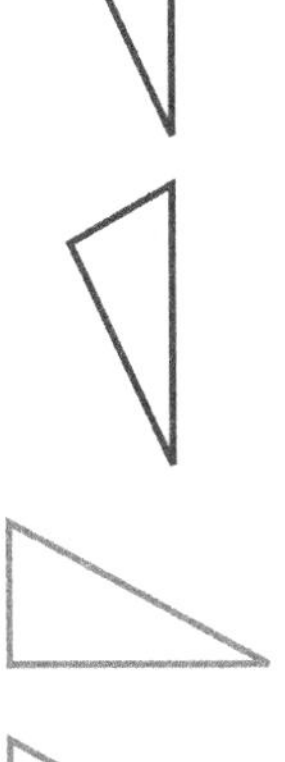

FIGURE 45

## Similar Triangles

Many of the key ideas of geometry depend on **similar triangles,** pairs of triangles that are exactly the same shape but not necessarily the same size. Figure 45 shows three pairs of similar triangles. (*Note:* The triangles do not need to be oriented in the same fashion in order to be similar.)

Suppose that a correspondence between two triangles $ABC$ and $DEF$ is set up as follows.

| | |
|---|---|
| $\measuredangle A$ corresponds to $\measuredangle D$ | side $AB$ corresponds to side $DE$ |
| $\measuredangle B$ corresponds to $\measuredangle E$ | side $BC$ corresponds to side $EF$ |
| $\measuredangle C$ corresponds to $\measuredangle F$ | side $AC$ corresponds to side $DF$ |

For triangle $ABC$ to be similar to triangle $DEF$, the following conditions must hold.

1. Corresponding angles must have the same measure.
2. The ratios of the corresponding sides must be constant; that is, the corresponding sides are proportional.

By showing that either of these conditions holds in a pair of triangles, we may conclude that the triangles are similar.

### EXAMPLE 4 Verifying Similarity

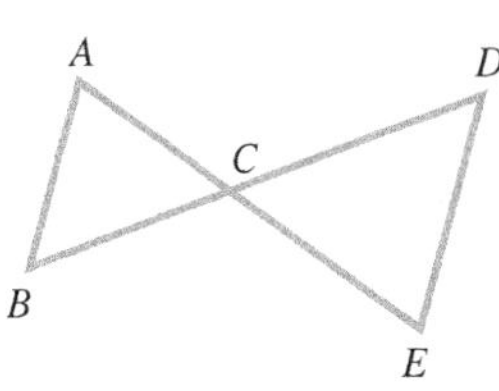


FIGURE 46

In Figure 46, $\overleftrightarrow{AB}$ is parallel to $\overleftrightarrow{ED}$. How can we verify that $\triangle ABC$ is similar to $\triangle EDC$?

**SOLUTION**

Because $\overleftrightarrow{AB}$ is parallel to $\overleftrightarrow{ED}$, the transversal $\overleftrightarrow{BD}$ forms equal alternate interior angles $ABC$ and $EDC$. Also, transversal $\overleftrightarrow{AE}$ forms equal alternate interior angles $BAC$ and $DEC$. We know that $\measuredangle ACB = \measuredangle ECD$, because they are vertical angles. Because the corresponding angles have the same measures in triangles $ABC$ and $EDC$, the triangles are similar. ■

Once we have shown that two angles of one triangle are equal to the two corresponding angles of a second triangle, it is not necessary to show the same for the third angle. Because, in any triangle, the sum of the angles equals 180°, we may conclude that the measures of the remaining angles *must* be equal. This leads to the following Angle-Angle similarity property.

### Angle-Angle (AA) Similarity Property

If the measures of two angles of one triangle are equal to those of two corresponding angles of a second triangle, then the two triangles are similar.

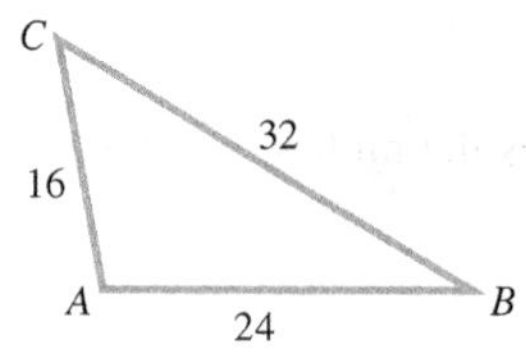


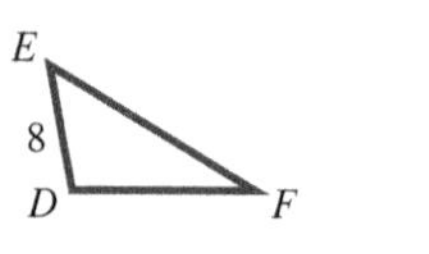


**FIGURE 47**

### EXAMPLE 5 Finding Side Lengths in Similar Triangles

In Figure 47, $\triangle EDF$ is similar to $\triangle CAB$. Find the unknown side lengths in $\triangle EDF$.

**SOLUTION**

As mentioned above, similar triangles have corresponding sides in proportion. Use this fact to find the unknown sides in the smaller triangle. Side $DF$ of the small triangle corresponds to side $AB$ of the larger one, and sides $DE$ and $AC$ correspond. This leads to the proportion

$$\frac{8}{16} = \frac{DF}{24}.$$

Using a technique from algebra, set the two cross-products equal. (As an alternative method of solution, multiply both sides by 48, the least common multiple of 16 and 24.) Setting cross-products equal gives

$$\begin{aligned} 8(24) &= 16DF \\ 192 &= 16DF \\ 12 &= DF. \end{aligned}$$

Side $DF$ has length 12.

Side $EF$ corresponds to side $CB$. This leads to another proportion.

$$\begin{aligned} \frac{8}{16} &= \frac{EF}{32} \\ \frac{1}{2} &= \frac{EF}{32} && \frac{8}{16} = \frac{1}{2} \\ 2EF &= 32 && \text{Cross-products} \\ EF &= 16 \end{aligned}$$

Side $EF$ has length 16.

### EXAMPLE 6 Finding Side Lengths and Angle Measures in Similar Triangles

Find the measures of the unknown parts of the similar triangles $STU$ and $ZXY$ in Figure 48.

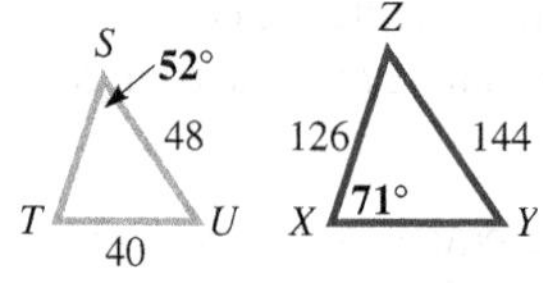


**FIGURE 48**

**SOLUTION**

Here angles $X$ and $T$ correspond, as do angles $Y$ and $U$, and angles $Z$ and $S$. Since angles $Z$ and $S$ correspond and since angle $S$ is 52°, angle $Z$ also must be 52°. The sum of the angles of any triangle is 180°. In the larger triangle $X = 71°$ and $Z = 52°$. To find $Y$, set up an equation and solve for $Y$.

$$\begin{aligned} X + Y + Z &= 180 \\ 71 + Y + 52 &= 180 \\ 123 + Y &= 180 \\ Y &= 57 \end{aligned}$$

Angle $Y$ is 57°. Because angles $Y$ and $U$ correspond, $U = 57°$ also.

The 1984 Grenada Television Ltd. production *The Return of Sherlock Holmes: The Musgrave Ritual*, stars Jeremy Brett as Sir Arthur Conan Doyle's legendary sleuth. In solving the mystery, Holmes is faced with the problem of determining where the tip end of the shadow of a tree 64 feet tall would have been on the ground. Because the tree is no longer standing, he uses **similar triangles** to solve the problem. He finds that a vertical rod of 6 feet casts a shadow of 9 feet, so he determines that at the same time of day the tree of height 64 feet would have cast a shadow of 96 feet.

Now find the unknown sides. Sides $SU$ and $ZY$ correspond, as do $TS$ and $XZ$, and $TU$ and $XY$, leading to the following proportions.

$$\frac{SU}{ZY} = \frac{TS}{XZ} \qquad \frac{XY}{TU} = \frac{ZY}{SU}$$

$$\frac{48}{144} = \frac{TS}{126} \qquad \frac{XY}{40} = \frac{144}{48}$$

$$\frac{1}{3} = \frac{TS}{126} \qquad \frac{XY}{40} = \frac{3}{1}$$

$$3TS = 126 \qquad XY = 120$$

$$TS = 42$$

Side $TS$ has length 42, and side $XY$ has length 120.

## EXAMPLE 7 Finding the Height of a Flagpole

Lucie Wanersdorfer, the Lettsworth, LA, postmaster, wants to measure the height of the office flagpole. She notices that at the instant when the shadow of the station is 18 feet long, the shadow of the flagpole is 99 feet long. The building is 10 feet high. What is the height of the flagpole?

**SOLUTION**

Figure 49 shows the information given in the problem. The two triangles shown there are similar, so that corresponding sides are in proportion, with

$$\frac{MN}{10} = \frac{99}{18}$$

$$\frac{MN}{10} = \frac{11}{2}$$

$$2MN = 110$$

$$MN = 55.$$

The flagpole is 55 feet high.

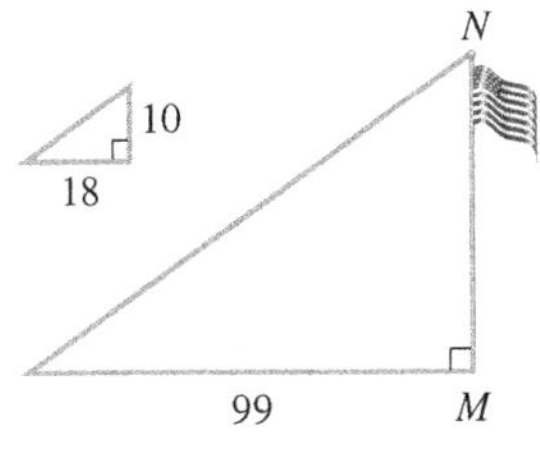


**FIGURE 49**

## The Pythagorean Theorem

We have used the Pythagorean theorem earlier in this book, and because of its importance in mathematics, we will investigate it further in this section on the geometry of triangles. Recall that in a right triangle, the side opposite the right angle (and consequently, the longest side) is called the **hypotenuse.** The other two sides, which are perpendicular, are called the **legs.**

### Pythagorean Theorem

If the two legs of a right triangle have lengths $a$ and $b$, and the hypotenuse has length $c$, then

$$a^2 + b^2 = c^2.$$

That is, the sum of the squares of the lengths of the legs is equal to the square of the hypotenuse.

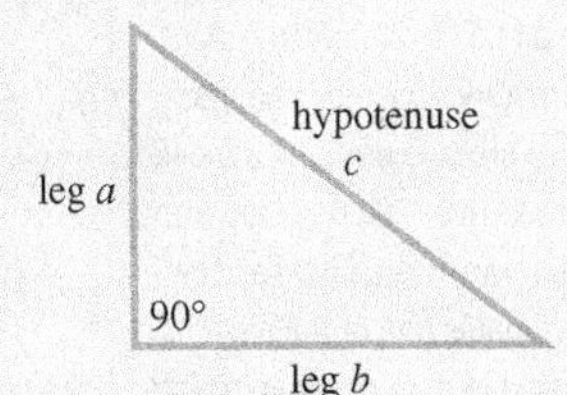

FIGURE 50

Pythagoras did not actually discover the theorem that was named after him, although legend tells that he sacrificed 100 oxen to the gods in gratitude for the discovery. There is evidence that the Babylonians knew the concept quite well. The first proof, however, may have come from Pythagoras.

Figure 50 illustrates the theorem by using a tile pattern. The side of the square along the hypotenuse measures 5 units. Those along the legs measure 3 and 4 units. If $a = 3$, $b = 4$, and $c = 5$, the equation of the Pythagorean theorem is satisfied.

$$
\begin{aligned}
a^2 + b^2 &= c^2 \\
3^2 + 4^2 &= 5^2 \\
9 + 16 &= 25 \\
25 &= 25
\end{aligned}
$$

The natural numbers (3, 4, 5) form a **Pythagorean triple,** because they satisfy the equation of the Pythagorean theorem. There are infinitely many such triples.

Probably the most famous mathematical statement in the history of motion pictures is heard in the 1939 classic *The Wizard of Oz.* Ray Bolger's character, the Scarecrow, wants a brain. When the Wizard grants him his "Th.D." (Doctor of Thinkology), the Scarecrow replies with a statement that has made mathematics teachers shudder for almost 70 years. (See Exercise 42 in Section 9.2.) His statement is quite impressive and sounds like the **Pythagorean theorem** but is totally incorrect. A triangle with sides of length 9, 9, and 4 provides a simple counterexample to his assertion.

If you watch this scene, also notice that between camera shots preceding his statement, the Scarecrow's position changes. These are two errors in a movie that has over 100 reported errors (see www.moviemistakes.com), yet remains one of the most beloved motion pictures in history.

### EXAMPLE 8 Using the Pythogorean Theorem

Find the length $a$ in the right triangle shown in Figure 51.

**SOLUTION**

$$
\begin{aligned}
a^2 + b^2 &= c^2 && \text{Pythagorean theorem} \\
a^2 + 36^2 &= 39^2 && b = 36,\ c = 39 \\
a^2 + 1296 &= 1521 \\
a^2 &= 225 && \text{Subtract 1296 from both sides.} \\
a &= 15 && \text{Choose the positive square root, because } a > 0.
\end{aligned}
$$

FIGURE 51

Verify that (15, 36, 39) is a Pythagorean triple as a check.

The next example comes from the Cairo Mathematical Papyrus, an Egyptian document that dates back to about 300 B.C.

### EXAMPLE 9 Finding a Ladder Height by Using the Pythagorean Theorem

A ladder of length 10 cubits has its foot 6 cubits from a wall. To what height does the ladder reach?

**SOLUTION**

As suggested by Figure 52, the ladder forms the hypotenuse of a right triangle, and the ground and wall form the legs. Let $x$ represent the distance from the base of the wall to the top of the ladder. Then, by the Pythagorean theorem,

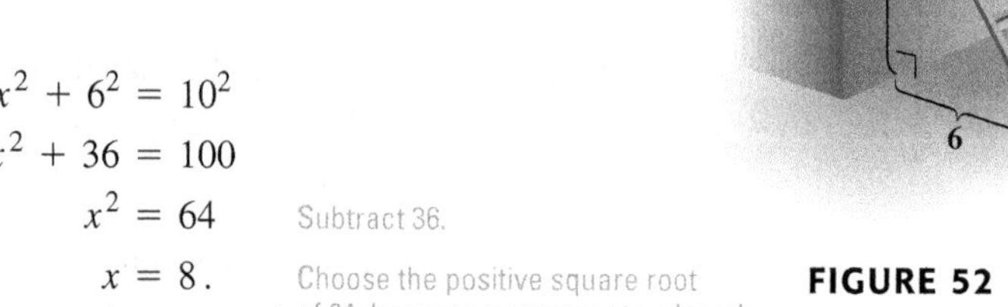

$$
\begin{aligned}
x^2 + 6^2 &= 10^2 \\
x^2 + 36 &= 100 \\
x^2 &= 64 && \text{Subtract 36.} \\
x &= 8. && \text{Choose the positive square root of 64, because } x \text{ represents a length.}
\end{aligned}
$$

FIGURE 52

The ladder reaches a height of 8 cubits.

## For Further Thought

### Proving the Pythagorean Theorem

The Pythagorean theorem has probably been proved in more different ways than any theorem in mathematics. A book titled *The Pythagorean Proposition,* by Elisha Scott Loomis, was first published in 1927. It contained more than 250 different proofs of the theorem. It was reissued in 1968 by the National Council of Teachers of Mathematics as the first title in a series of "Classics in Mathematics Education."

One of the most popular proofs of the theorem follows.

### For Group Discussion or Individual Investigation

Copy the accompanying figure. Keep in mind that the area of the large square must always be the same, no matter how it is determined. It is made up of four right triangles and a smaller square.

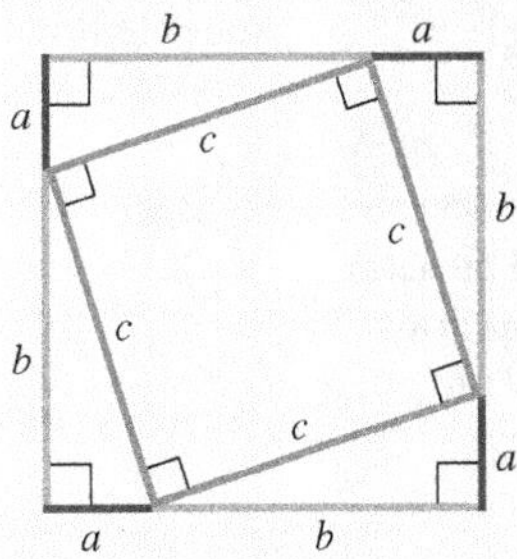


**(a)** The length of a side of the large square is _____ , so its area is (_____)$^2$ or _____.

**(b)** The area of the large square can also be found by obtaining the sum of the areas of the four right triangles and the smaller square. The area of each right triangle is _____ , so the sum of the areas of the four right triangles is _____. The area of the smaller square is _____.

**(c)** The sum of the areas of the four right triangles and the smaller square is _____.

**(d)** Since the areas in (a) and (c) represent the area of the same figure, the expressions there must be equal. Setting them equal to each other we obtain _____ = _____.

**(e)** Subtract $2ab$ from each side of the equation in (d) to obtain the desired result: _____ = _____.

Following **Hurricane Katrina** in August 2005, the pine trees of southeastern Louisiana provided thousands of examples of **right triangles.** See the photo.

Suppose the vertical distance from the base of a broken tree to the point of the break is 55 inches. The length of the broken part is 144 inches. How far along the ground is it from the base of the tree to the point where the broken part touches the ground?

The statement of the Pythagorean theorem is an *if . . . then* statement. If the antecedent (the statement following the word "if") and the consequent (the statement following the word "then") are interchanged, the new statement is called the *converse* of the original. Although the converse of a true statement may not be true, the *converse* of the Pythagorean theorem *is* also a true statement and can be used to determine if a triangle is a right triangle, given the lengths of the three sides.

### Converse of the Pythagorean Theorem

If a triangle has sides of lengths $a$, $b$, and $c$, where $c$ is the length of the longest side, and if $a^2 + b^2 = c^2$, then the triangle is a right triangle.

### EXAMPLE 10 Applying the Converse of the Pythagorean Theorem

Lee Guidroz has been contracted to complete an unfinished 8-foot-by-12-foot laundry room on an existing house. He finds that the previous contractor built the floor so that the length of its diagonal is 14 feet, 8 inches. Is the floor "squared off" properly?

**The 10 Mathematical Formulas That Changed the Face of the Earth** was the theme of ten Nicaraguan stamps commemorating mathematical formulas, including this one featuring the **Pythagorean theorem,** $a^2 + b^2 = c^2$. Notice how the compasses dominate the figure.

**SOLUTION**

Because 14 feet, 8 inches $= 14\frac{2}{3}$ feet, he must check to see whether the following statement is true.

$$8^2 + 12^2 = \left(14\frac{2}{3}\right)^2 \quad ? \quad a^2 + b^2 = c^2$$

$$8^2 + 12^2 = \left(\frac{44}{3}\right)^2 \quad ? \quad 14\tfrac{2}{3} = \tfrac{44}{3}$$

$$208 = \frac{1936}{9} \quad ? \quad \text{Simplify.}$$

$$208 \neq 215\frac{1}{9} \quad \text{False}$$

Lee needs to fix the problem, since the diagonal, which measures 14 feet, 8 inches, should actually measure $\sqrt{208} \approx 14.4 \approx 14$ feet, 5 inches. He must correct the error to avoid major problems later.

## 9.4 Exercises

*In Exercises 1–6, provide a STATEMENTS/REASONS proof similar to the ones in Examples 1–3.*

1. Given: $AC = BD$; $AD = BC$
   Prove: $\triangle ABD \cong \triangle BAC$

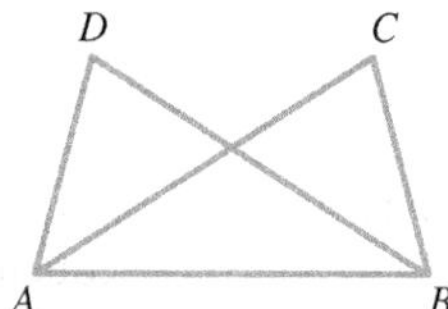


2. Given: $AC = BC$; $\measuredangle ACD = \measuredangle BCD$
   Prove: $\triangle ADC \cong \triangle BDC$

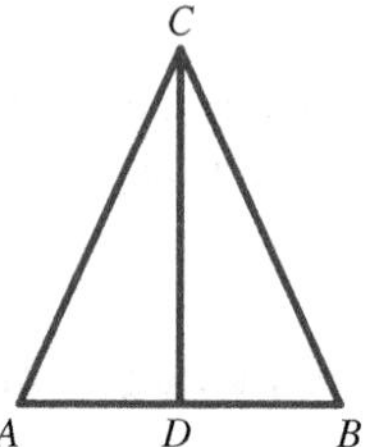


3. Given: $\overleftrightarrow{DB}$ is perpendicular to $\overleftrightarrow{AC}$; $AB = BC$
   Prove: $\triangle ABD \cong \triangle CBD$

Figure for Exercise 3

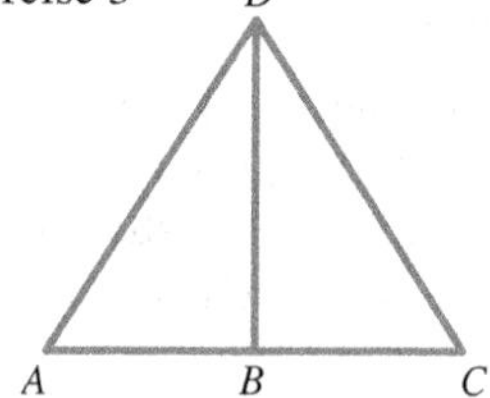


4. Given: $BC = BA$; $\measuredangle 1 = \measuredangle 2$
   Prove: $\triangle DBC \cong \triangle DBA$

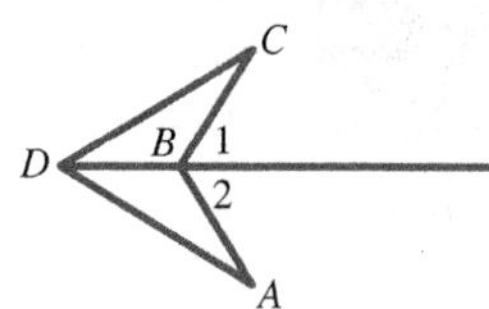


5. Given: $\measuredangle BAC = \measuredangle DAC$; $\measuredangle BCA = \measuredangle DCA$
   Prove: $\triangle ABC \cong \triangle ADC$.

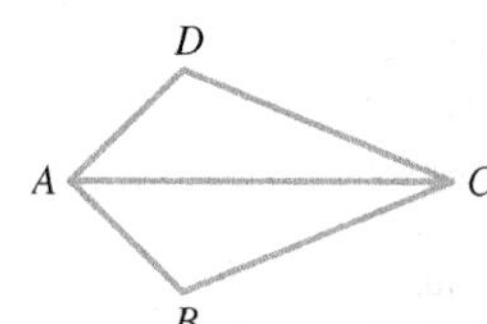

**6.** Given: $BO = OE$; $\overleftrightarrow{OB}$ is perpendicular to $\overleftrightarrow{AC}$; $\overleftrightarrow{OE}$ is perpendicular to $\overleftrightarrow{DF}$
Prove: $\triangle AOB \cong \triangle FOE$.

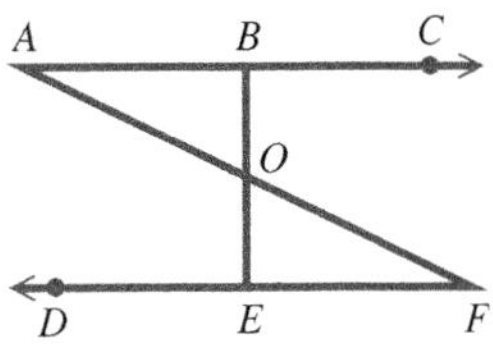


*Exercises 7–10 refer to the given figure, an isosceles triangle with AB = BC.*

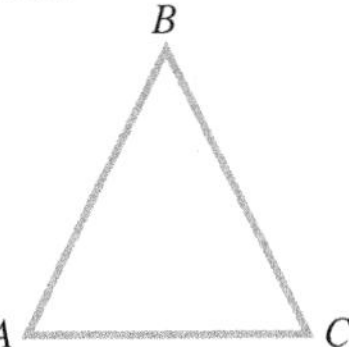


**7.** If $\measuredangle B$ measures 46°, then $\measuredangle A$ measures _____ and $\measuredangle C$ measures _____.

**8.** If $\measuredangle C$ measures 52°, what is the measure of $\measuredangle B$?

**9.** If $BC = 12$ in., and the perimeter of $\triangle ABC$ is 30 in., what is the length $AC$?

**10.** If the perimeter of $\triangle ABC = 40$ in., and $AC = 10$ in., what is the length $AB$?

**11.** Explain why all equilateral triangles must be similar.

**12.** Explain why two congruent triangles must be similar, but two similar triangles might not be congruent.

*Name the corresponding angles and the corresponding sides for each of the following pairs of similar triangles.*

**13.**

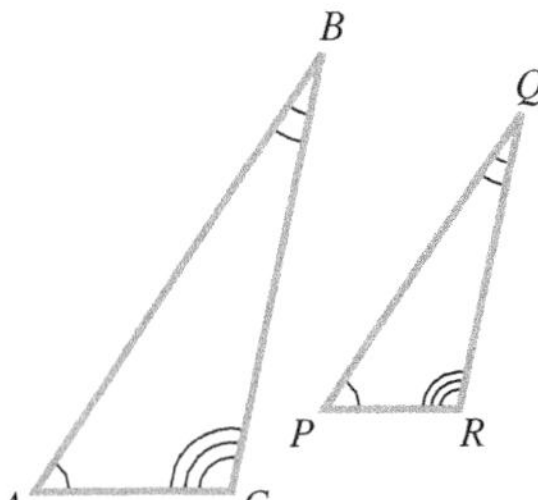


**14.**

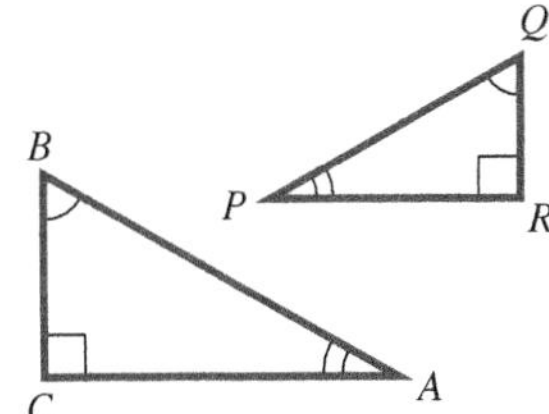


**15.**

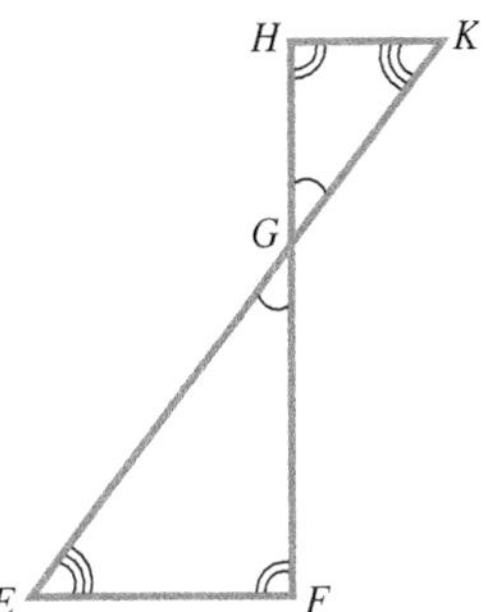


**16.**

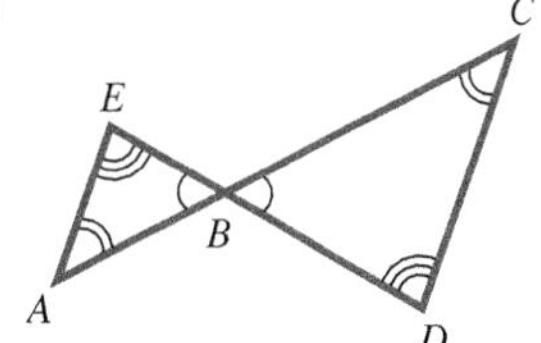


*Find all unknown angle measures in each pair of similar triangles.*

**17.**

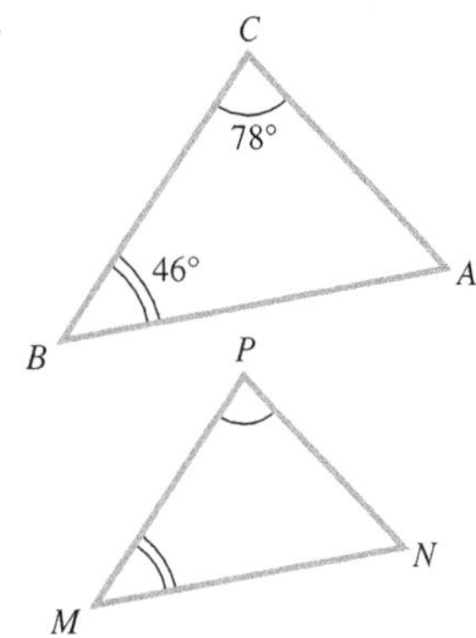


**18.**

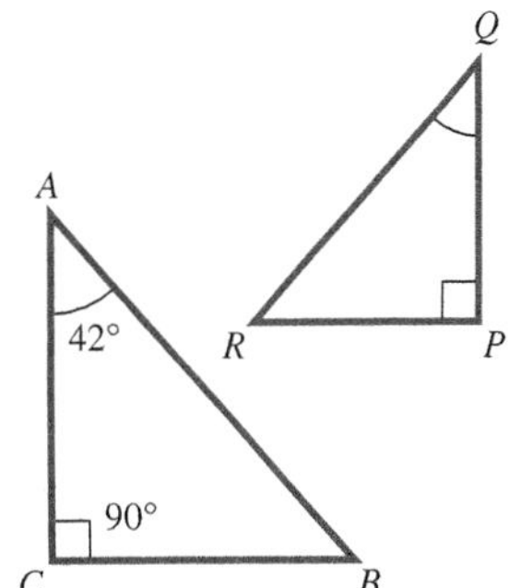

19.

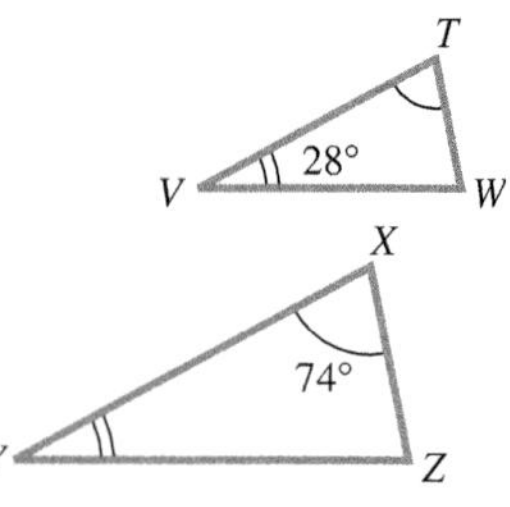


20.

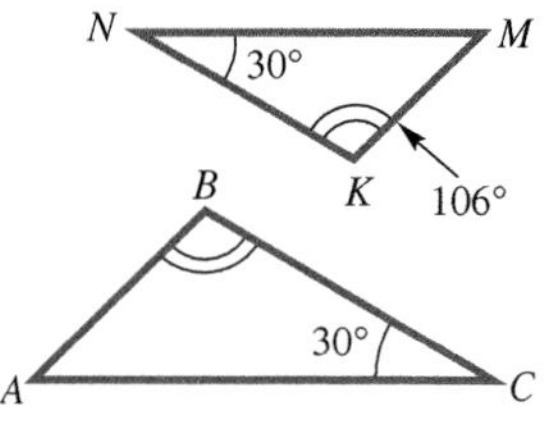


21.

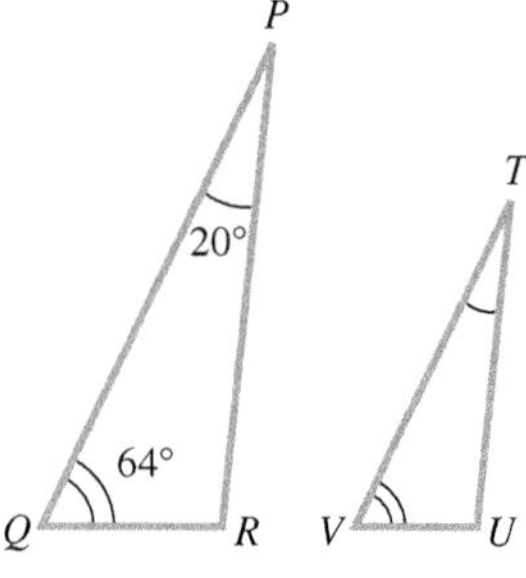


22.

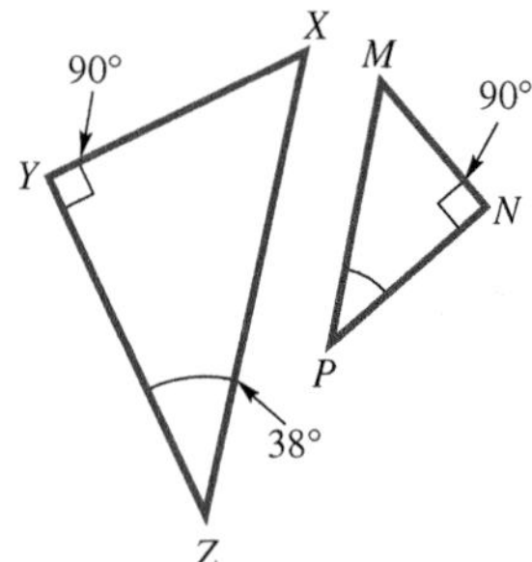


*Find the unknown side lengths in each pair of similar triangles.*

23.

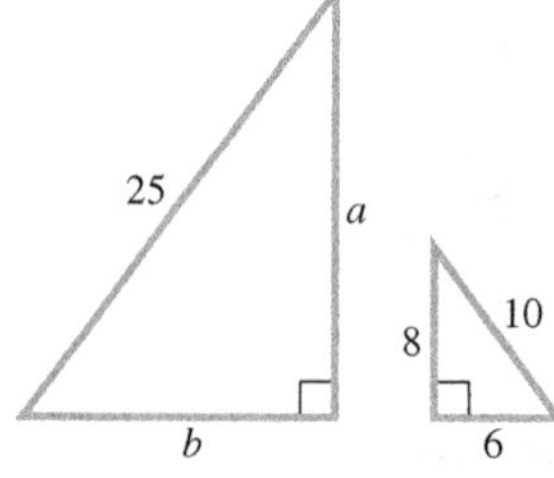


24.

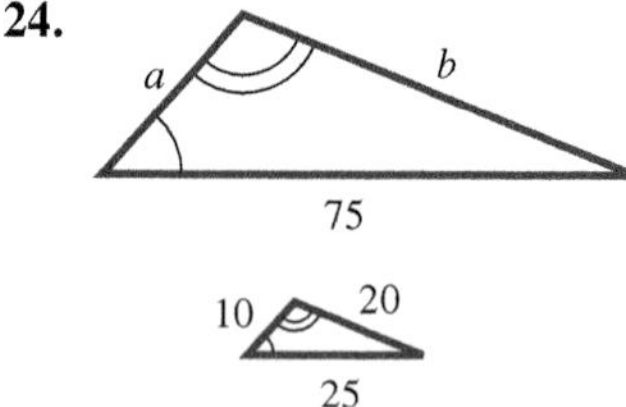


25.

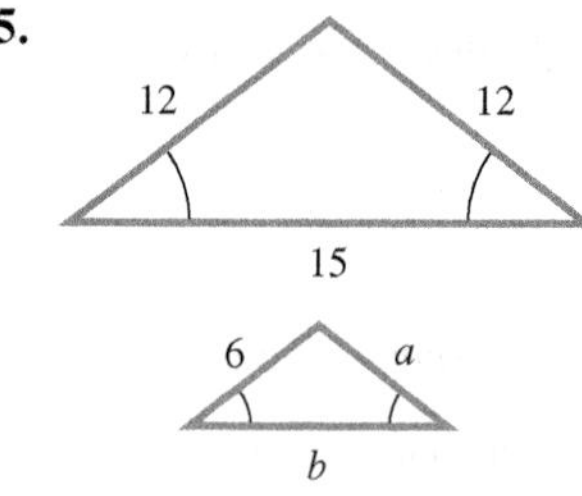


26.

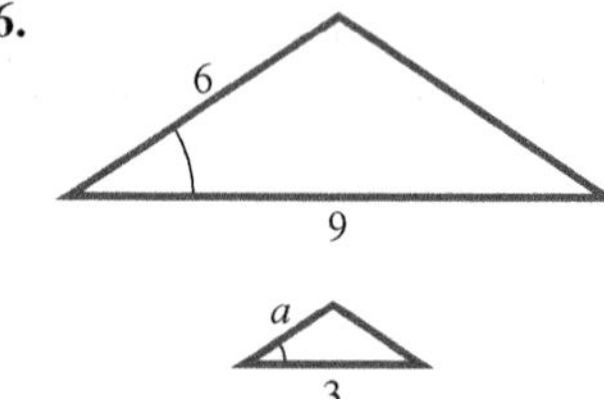


27.

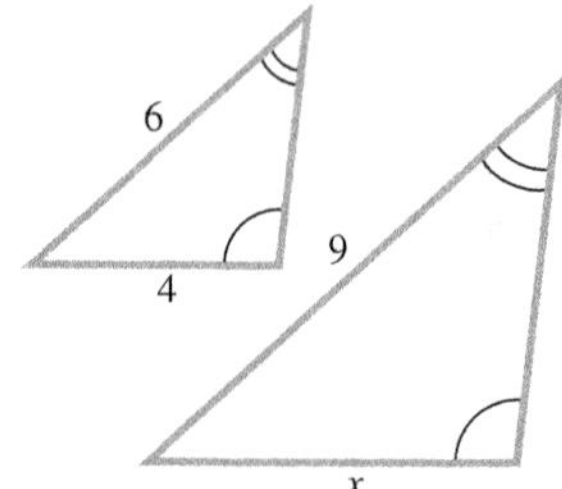

**28.**

12
14
$m$
21

*In each diagram, there are two similar triangles. Find the unknown measurement in each. (Hint: In the figure for Exercise 29, the side of length* 100 *in the smaller triangle corresponds to a side of length* $100 + 120 = 220$ *in the larger triangle.)*

**29.**

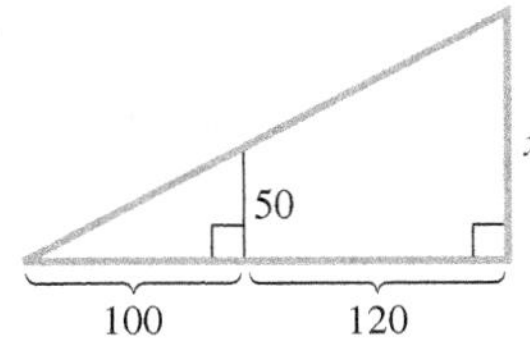


**30.**

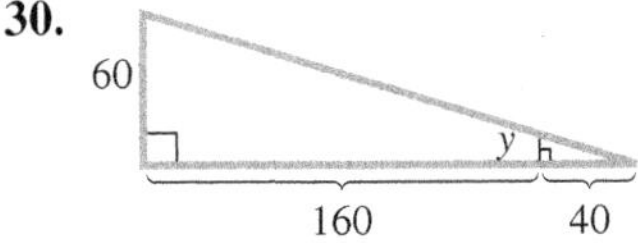


**31.**

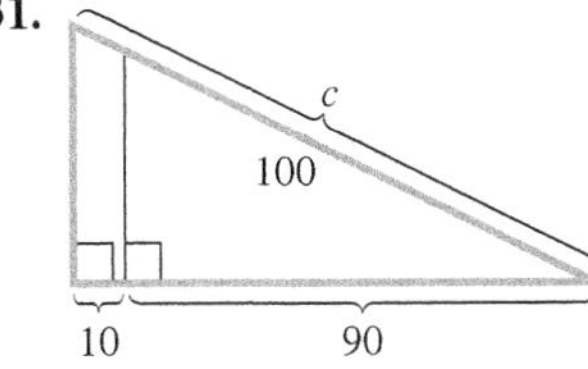


**32.**

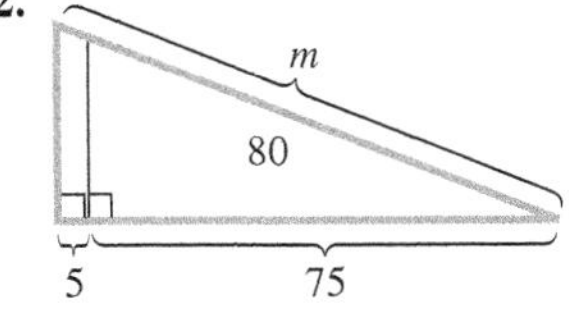


*Solve each problem.*

**33. *Height of a Tree*** A tree casts a shadow 45 m long. At the same time, the shadow cast by a vertical 2-m stick is 3 m long. Find the height of the tree.

**34. *Height of a Tower*** A forest fire lookout tower casts a shadow 180 ft long at the same time that the shadow of a 9-ft truck is 15 ft long. Find the height of the tower.

**35. *Lengths of Sides of a Photograph*** On a photograph of a triangular piece of land, the lengths of the three sides are 4 cm, 5 cm, and 7 cm, respectively. The shortest side of the actual piece of land is 400 m long. Find the lengths of the other two sides.

**36. *Height of a Lighthouse Keeper*** The Santa Cruz lighthouse is 14 m tall and casts a shadow 28 m long at 7 P.M. At the same time, the shadow of the lighthouse keeper is 3.5 m long. How tall is she?

**37. *Height of a Building*** A house is 15 ft tall. Its shadow is 40 ft long at the same time the shadow of a nearby building is 300 ft long. Find the height of the building.

**38. *Distances Between Cities*** By drawing lines on a map, a triangle can be formed by the cities of Phoenix, Tucson, and Yuma. On the map, the distance between Phoenix and Tucson is 8 cm, the distance between Phoenix and Yuma is 12 cm, and the distance between Tucson and Yuma is 17 cm. The actual straight-line distance from Phoenix to Yuma is 230 km. Find the distances between the other pairs of cities.

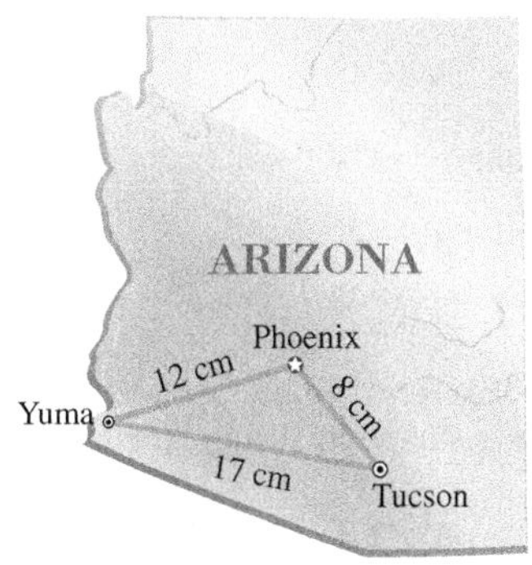


**39. *Height of the World's Tallest Human*** Robert Wadlow was the tallest human being ever recorded. When a 6-ft stick cast a shadow 24 in., Robert would cast a shadow 35.7 in. How tall was he?

**40.** ***Dimensions on Mount Rushmore*** Assume that Lincoln was $6\frac{1}{3}$ ft tall and his head $\frac{3}{4}$ ft long. Knowing that the carved head of Lincoln at Mount Rushmore is 60 ft tall, find out how tall his entire body would be if it were carved into the mountain.

*In Exercises 41–48, a and b represent the two legs of a right triangle, while c represents the hypotenuse. Find the lengths of the unknown sides.*

**41.**

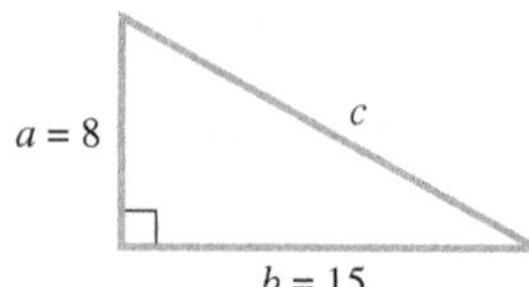


**42.**

$a = 7$, $c = 25$, $b$

**43.**

$a$, $c = 85$, $b = 84$

**44.** $a = 24$ cm; $c = 25$ cm

**45.** $a = 14$ m; $b = 48$ m

**46.** $a = 28$ km; $c = 100$ km

**47.** $b = 21$ in.; $c = 29$ in.

**48.** $b = 120$ ft; $c = 169$ ft

**49.** Refer to Exercise 42 in Section 9.2. Correct the Scarecrow's statement, using language similar to his.

**50.** Show that if $a^2 + b^2 = c^2$, then it is not necessarily true that $a + b = c$.

*There are various formulas that will generate Pythagorean triples. For example, if we choose positive integers r and s, with $r > s$, then the set of equations*

$$a = r^2 - s^2, \quad b = 2rs, \quad c = r^2 + s^2$$

*generates a Pythagorean triple (a, b, c). Use the values of r and s given in each of Exercises 51–56 to generate a Pythagorean triple using this method.*

**51.** $r = 2, s = 1$

**52.** $r = 3, s = 2$

**53.** $r = 4, s = 3$

**54.** $r = 3, s = 1$

**55.** $r = 4, s = 2$

**56.** $r = 4, s = 1$

**57.** Show that the formula given for Exercises 51–56 actually satisfies $a^2 + b^2 = c^2$.

**58.** It can be shown that if $(x, x + 1, y)$ is a Pythagorean triple, then so is

$$(3x + 2y + 1, \quad 3x + 2y + 2, \quad 4x + 3y + 2).$$

Use this idea to find three more Pythagorean triples, starting with 3, 4, 5. (*Hint:* Here, $x = 3$ and $y = 5$.)

*If m is an odd positive integer greater than 1, then*

$$\left(m, \frac{m^2 - 1}{2}, \frac{m^2 + 1}{2}\right)$$

*is a Pythagorean triple. Use this to find the Pythagorean triple generated by each value of m in Exercises 59–62.*

**59.** $m = 3$

**60.** $m = 5$

**61.** $m = 7$

**62.** $m = 9$

**63.** Show that the expressions in the directions for Exercises 59–62 actually satisfy $a^2 + b^2 = c^2$.

**64.** Show why (6, 8, 10) is the only Pythagorean triple consisting of consecutive even numbers.

*For any integer n greater than 1,*

$$(2n, n^2 - 1, n^2 + 1)$$

*is a Pythagorean triple. Use this pattern to find the Pythagorean triple generated by each value of n in Exercises 65–68.*

**65.** $n = 2$

**66.** $n = 3$

**67.** $n = 4$

**68.** $n = 5$

**69.** Show that the expressions in the directions for Exercises 65–68 actually satisfy $a^2 + b^2 = c^2$.

**70.** Can an isosceles right triangle have sides with integer lengths? Why or why not?

*Solve each problem. (You may wish to review quadratic equations from algebra.)*

**71. *Side Length of a Triangle*** If the hypotenuse of a right triangle is 1 m more than the longer leg, and the shorter leg is 7 m, find the length of the longer leg.

**72. *Side Lengths of a Triangle*** The hypotenuse of a right triangle is 1 cm more than twice the shorter leg, and the longer leg is 9 cm less than three times the shorter leg. Find the lengths of the three sides of the triangle.

**73. *Height of a Tree*** At a point on the ground 30 ft from the base of a tree, the distance to the top of the tree is 2 ft more than twice the height of the tree. Find the height of the tree.

**74. *Dimensions of a Rectangle*** The length of a rectangle is 2 in. less than twice the width. The diagonal is 5 in. Find the length and width of the rectangle.

**75. *Height of a Break in Bamboo*** (Problem of the broken bamboo, from the Chinese work *Arithmetic in Nine Sections* (1261)) There is a bamboo 10 ft high, the upper end of which, being broken, reaches the ground 3 ft from the stem. Find the height of the break.

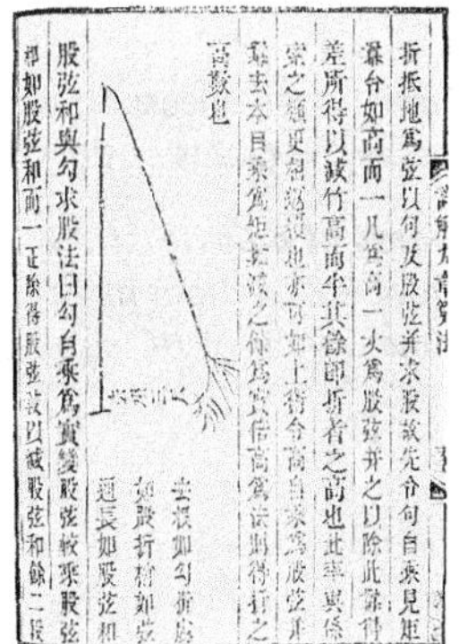

**76. *Depth of a Pond*** (Adapted from *Arithmetic in Nine Sections*) There grows in the middle of a circular pond 10 ft in diameter a reed which projects 1 ft out of the water. When it is drawn down it just reaches the edge of the pond. How deep is the water?

***Squaring Off a Floor Under Construction*** *Imagine that you are a carpenter building the floor of a rectangular room. What must the diagonal of the room measure if your floor is to be squared off properly, given the dimensions in Exercises 77–80? Give your answer to the nearest inch.*

**77.** 12 ft by 15 ft

**78.** 14 ft by 20 ft

**79.** 16 ft by 24 ft

**80.** 20 ft by 32 ft

**81. *Garfield's Proof of the Pythagorean Theorem*** James A. Garfield, the twentieth president of the United States, provided a proof of the Pythagorean theorem using the given figure. Supply the required information in each of parts (a) through (c) in order to follow his proof.

**(a)** Find the area of the trapezoid *WXYZ* using the formula for the area of a trapezoid.

**(b)** Find the area of each of the right triangles *PWX*, *PZY*, and *PXY*.

**(c)** Since the sum of the areas of the three right triangles must equal the area of the trapezoid, set the expression from part (a) equal to the sum of the three expressions from part (b). Simplify the equation as much as possible.

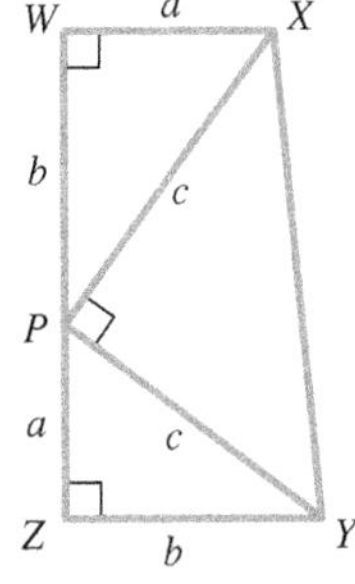


**82. *Proof of the Pythagorean Theorem by Similar Triangles*** In the figure, right triangles *ABC*, *CBD*, and *ACD* are similar. This may be used to prove the Pythagorean theorem. Fill in the blanks with the appropriate responses.

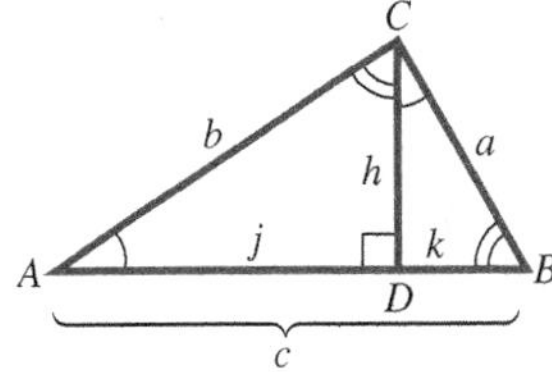


**(a)** By proportion, we have $\frac{c}{b}$ = ___$/j$.

**(b)** By proportion, we also have $\frac{c}{a} = a/$___.

**(c)** From part (a), $b^2$ = _____.

**(d)** From part (b), $a^2$ = _____.

**(e)** From the results of parts (c) and (d) and factoring, $a^2 + b^2 = c($_______$)$. Since _______ $= c$, it follows that __________.

*Exercises 83–90 require some ingenuity, but all can be solved using the concepts presented so far in this chapter.*

**83. *Area of a Quadrilateral*** Find the area of quadrilateral $ABCD$, if angles $A$ and $C$ are right angles.

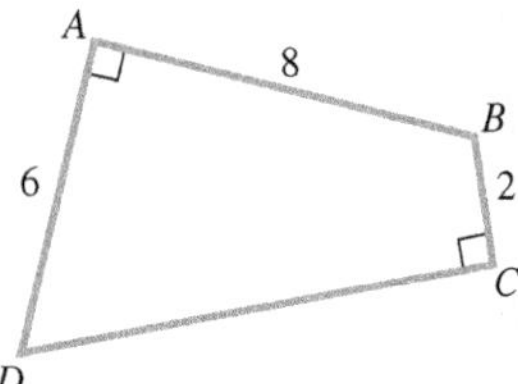


**84. *Area of a Triangle*** The perimeter of the isosceles triangle $ABC$ (with $AB = BC$) is 128 in. The altitude $BD$ is 48 in. What is the area of triangle $ABC$?

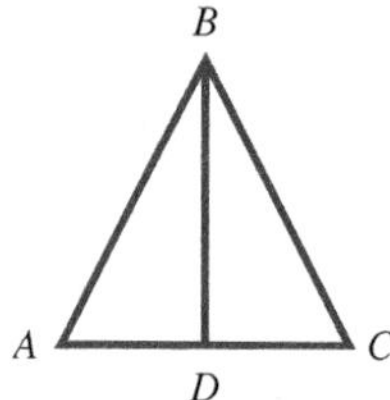


**85. *Base Measure of an Isosceles Triangle*** An isosceles triangle has a base of 24 and two sides of 13. What other base measure can an isosceles triangle with equal sides of 13 have and still have the same area as the given triangle?

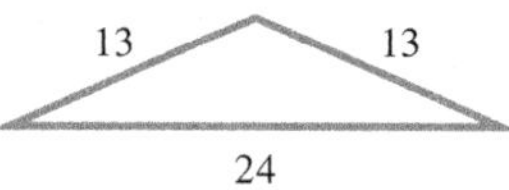


**86. *Value of a Measure in a Triangle*** In right triangle $ABC$, if $AD = DB + 8$, what is the value of $CD$?

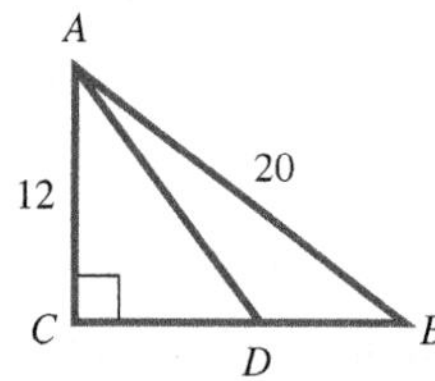


**87. *Area of a Pentagon*** In the figure at the top of the next column, pentagon $PQRST$ is formed by a square and an equilateral triangle such that $PQ = QR = RS = ST = PT$. The perimeter of the pentagon is 80. Find the area of the pentagon.

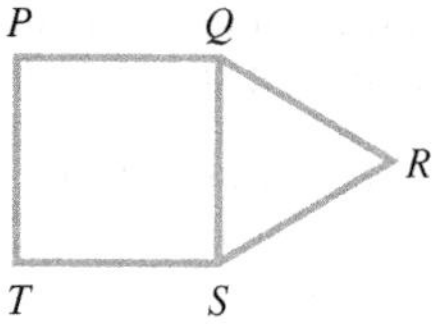


**88. *Angle Measure in a Triangle*** (A segment that *bisects* an angle divides the angle into two equal angles.) In the figure, angle $A$ measures 50°. $OB$ bisects angle $ABC$, and $OC$ bisects angle $ACB$. What is the measure of angle $BOC$?

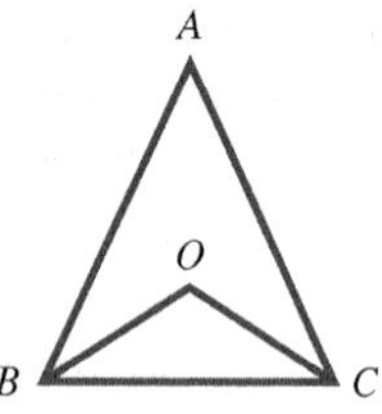


*Exercises 89 and 90 refer to the given figure. The center of the circle is O.*

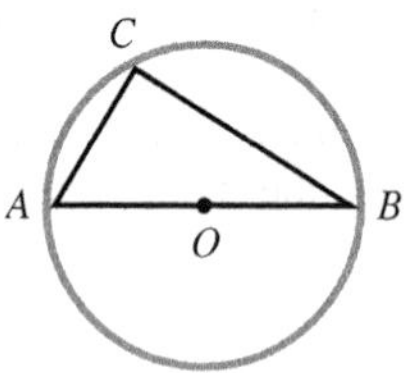


**89. *Radius of a Circle*** If $\overleftrightarrow{AC}$ measures 6 in. and $\overleftrightarrow{BC}$ measures 8 in., what is the radius of the circle?

**90. *Lengths of Chords of a Circle*** If $\overleftrightarrow{AB}$ measures 13 cm, and the length of $\overleftrightarrow{BC}$ is 7 cm more than the length of $\overleftrightarrow{AC}$, what are the lengths of $\overleftrightarrow{BC}$ and $\overleftrightarrow{AC}$?

*Verify that the following constructions from the Extension following Section 9.2 are valid. Use a STATEMENTS/REASONS proof.*

**91.** Construction 1

**92.** Construction 2

**93.** Construction 3

**94.** Construction 4

# 9.5 Space Figures, Volume, and Surface Area

## Space Figures • Volume and Surface Area of Space Figures

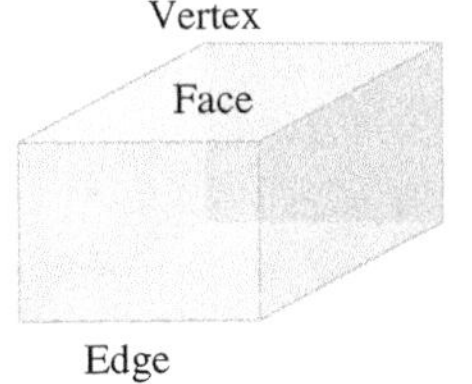


Rectangular parallelepiped (box)

**FIGURE 53**

**Space Figures** Thus far, this chapter has discussed only **plane figures**—figures that can be drawn completely in the plane of a piece of paper. However, it takes the three dimensions of space to represent the solid world around us. For example, Figure 53 shows a "box" (a **rectangular parallelepiped** in mathematical terminology). The *faces* of a box are rectangles. The faces meet at *edges;* the "corners" are called *vertices* (plural of vertex—the same word as for the "corner" of an angle).

Boxes are one kind of space figure belonging to an important group called **polyhedra,** the faces of which are made only of polygons. Perhaps the most interesting polyhedra are the *regular polyhedra.* Recall that a *regular polygon* is a polygon with all sides equal and all angles equal. A regular polyhedron is a space figure, the faces of which are only one kind of regular polygon. It turns out that there are only five different regular polyhedra. They are shown in Figure 54. A **tetrahedron** is composed of four equilateral triangles, each three of which meet in a point. Use the figure to verify that there are four faces, four vertices, and six edges.

Tetrahedron

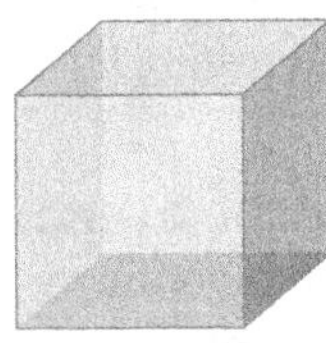

Hexahedron (cube)

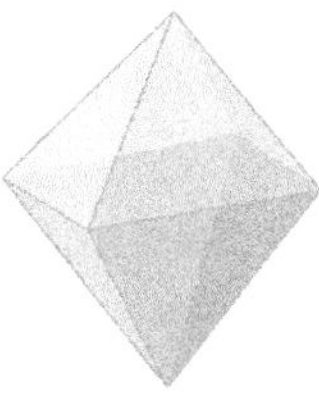

Octahedron

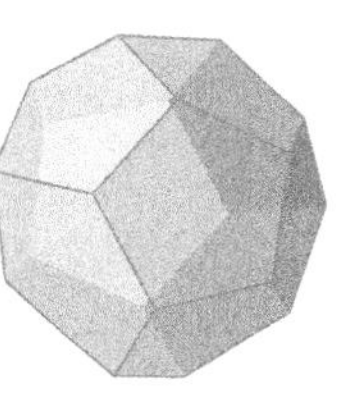

Dodecahedron

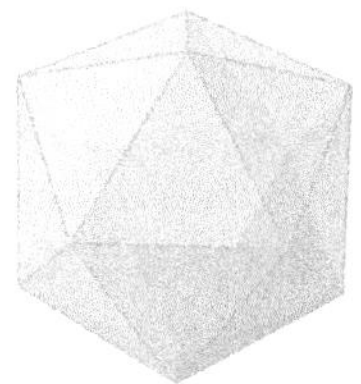

Icosahedron

**FIGURE 54**

A regular quadrilateral is called a square. Six squares, each three of which meet at a point, form a **hexahedron,** or **cube**. Again, use Figure 54 to verify that a cube has 6 faces, 8 vertices, and 12 edges.

The three remaining regular polyhedra are the **octahedron,** the **dodecahedron,** and the **icosahedron.** The octahedron is composed of groups of four regular triangles (i.e., equilateral) meeting at a point. The dodecahedron is formed by groups of three regular pentagons, while the icosahedron is made up of groups of five regular triangles. The five regular polyhedra are also known as **Platonic solids,** named for the Greek philosopher Plato. He considered them as "building blocks" of nature and assigned fire to the tetrahedron, earth to the cube, air to the octahedron, and water to the icosahedron. Because the dodecahedron is different from the others because of its pentagonal faces, he assigned to it the cosmos (stars and planets). (*Source:* www.mathacademy.com)

Two other types of polyhedra are familiar space figures: pyramids and prisms. **Pyramids** are made of triangular sides and a polygonal base. **Prisms** have two faces in parallel planes; these faces are congruent polygons. The remaining faces of a prism are all parallelograms. (See Figure 55(a) and (b) on the next page.) By this definition, a box is also a prism.

Tetrahedron

Hexahedron (cube)

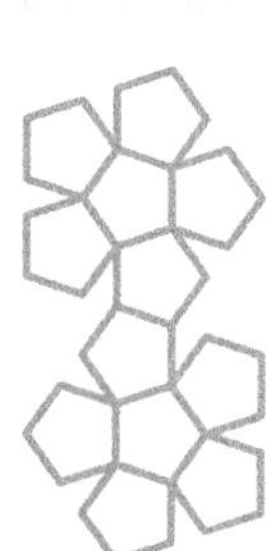

Octahedron

Dodecahedron

Icosahedron

Patterns such as these may be used to actually construct three-dimensional models of the **regular polyhedra.**

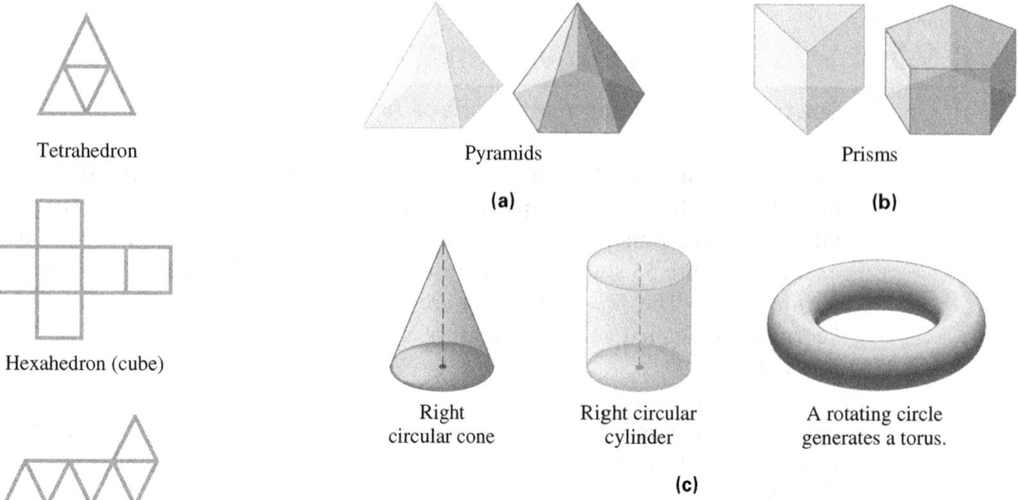


**FIGURE 55**

The circle, although a plane figure, is not a polygon. (Why?) Figure 55(c) shows space figures made up in part of circles, including *right circular cones* and *right circular cylinders.* The figure also shows how a circle can generate a *torus,* a doughnut-shaped solid that has interesting topological properties. See Section 9.7.

### Volume and Surface Area of Space Figures

While area is a measure of surface covered by a plane figure, **volume** is a measure of capacity of a space figure. Volume is measured in *cubic* units. For example, a cube with edge measuring 1 cm has volume 1 cubic cm, which is also written as 1 $\text{cm}^3$, or 1 cc. The **surface area** is the total area that would be covered if the space figure were "peeled" and the peel laid flat. Surface area is measured in *square* units.

#### Volume and Surface Area of a Box

Suppose that a box has length $\ell$, width $w$, and height $h$. Then the volume $V$ and the surface area $S$ are given by the formulas

$$V = \ell wh \quad \text{and} \quad S = 2\ell w + 2\ell h + 2hw.$$

In particular, if the box is a cube with edge of length $s$,

$$V = s^3 \quad \text{and} \quad S = 6s^2.$$

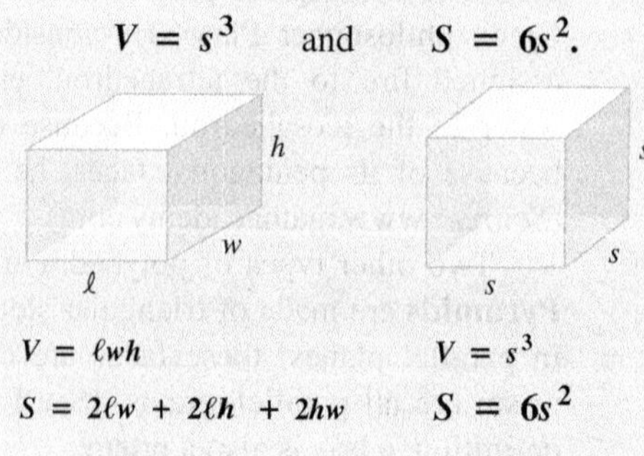

**John Conway** of Princeton University offered a reward in the 1990s to anyone producing a **holyhedron,** a polyhedron with a finite number of faces and with a hole in every face. At the time, no one knew whether such an object could exist. When graduate student **Jade Vinson** arrived at Princeton, he immediately took up the challenge and in 2000 produced (at least the proof of the theoretical existence of) a holyhedron with 78,585,627 faces. The reward offered ($10,000 divided by the number of faces) earned Vinson $.0001. Subsequently, **Don Hatch** produced one with 492 faces, good for a prize of $20.33. Conway had predicted that someone will eventually find a holyhedron with fewer than 100 faces. For more details, including references, images, and an online talk on holyhedra by Vinson, start at www.hadron.org/~hatch/

## EXAMPLE 1 Using the Formulas for a Box

Find the volume $V$ and the surface area $S$ of the box shown in Figure 56.

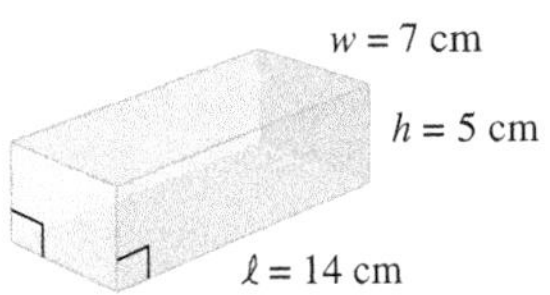


**FIGURE 56**

**SOLUTION**

$$V = \ell wh = 14 \cdot 7 \cdot 5 = 490 \qquad \ell = 14,\ w = 7,\ h = 5$$

Volume is measured in cubic units, so the volume of the box is 490 cubic centimeters, or 490 $\text{cm}^3$.

To find the surface area, use the formula $S = 2\ell w + 2\ell h + 2hw$.

$$\begin{aligned} S &= 2(14)(7) + 2(14)(5) + 2(5)(7) \\ &= 196 + 140 + 70 \\ &= 406 \end{aligned}$$

Like areas of plane figures, surface areas of space figures are measured in square units, so the surface area of the box is 406 square centimeters, or 406 $\text{cm}^2$.

A typical tin can is an example of a **right circular cylinder.**

### Volume and Surface Area of a Right Circular Cylinder

If a right circular cylinder has height $h$ and radius of its base equal to $r$, then the volume $V$ and the surface area $S$ are given by the formulas

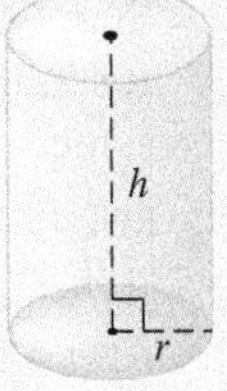


$V = \pi r^2 h$
$S = 2\pi rh + 2\pi r^2$

$$V = \pi r^2 h$$

and

$$S = 2\pi rh + 2\pi r^2.$$

(In the formula for $S$, the areas of the top and bottom are included.)

h
r = 6 in

Right circular cylinder

**FIGURE 57**

## EXAMPLE 2 Using the Formulas for a Right Circular Cylinder

In Figure 57, the right circular cylinder has surface area $288\pi$ square inches, and the radius of its base is 6 inches. Find each measure.

**(a)** the height of the cylinder
**(b)** the volume of the cylinder

On April 30, 2006, Episode 19 of the seventeenth season of the Fox television series *The Simpsons* dealt with the issue of gender, expectations, and curriculum in schools. In "Girls Just Want to Have Sums," Lisa Simpson's school is divided in two: she must attend the girls' school, where her mathematics class no longer poses a challenge. She disguises herself as a boy and infiltrates the boys' school and proves that she can handle the more difficult classes offered there.

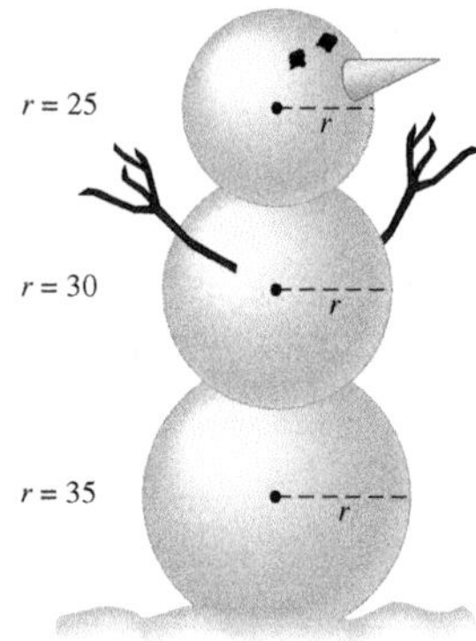


In one scene, the boys are asked by their teacher to determine the **volume of a snowman.** (See the figure above.) One boy responds to add the volumes of the spheres, because the radii are known. But Lisa corrects him, saying that he forgot the volume of the carrot nose: "one-third base times height" and gleefully follows with "Oh math, I have missed you!"

**SOLUTION**

**(a)**

$$\begin{aligned} S &= 2\pi rh + 2\pi r^2 \\ 288\pi &= 2\pi(6)h + 2\pi(6)^2 && S = 288\pi,\ r = 6 \\ 288\pi &= 12\pi h + 72\pi \\ 216\pi &= 12\pi h && \text{Subtract } 72\pi. \\ h &= 18 && \text{Divide by } 12\pi. \end{aligned}$$

The height is 18 inches.

**(b)**

$$V = \pi r^2 h = \pi(6)^2(18) = 648\pi \qquad r = 6,\ h = 18$$

The exact volume is $648\pi$ cubic inches, or approximately 2034.72 cubic inches, using $\pi \approx 3.14$.

The three-dimensional analogue of a circle is a **sphere.** It is defined by replacing the word "plane" with "space" in the definition of a circle (Section 9.2).

### Volume and Surface Area of a Sphere

If a sphere has radius $r$, then the volume $V$ and the surface area $S$ are given by the formulas

$$V = \frac{4}{3}\pi r^3 \quad \text{and} \quad S = 4\pi r^2.$$

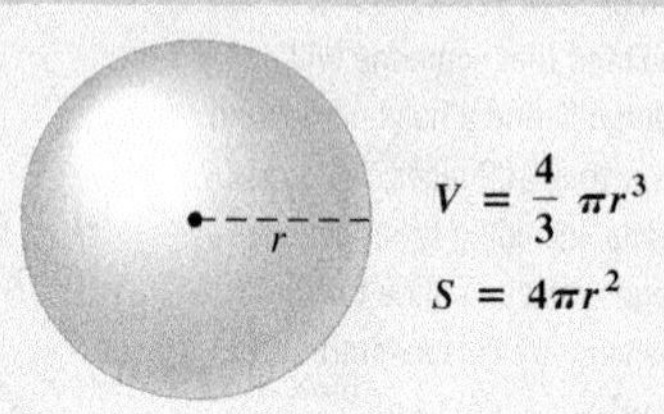


### EXAMPLE 3 Using the Volume Formula for a Sphere

Suppose that a spherical tank having radius 3 meters can be filled with liquid fuel for \$200. How much will it cost to fill a spherical tank of radius 6 meters with the same fuel?

**SOLUTION**

We must first find the volume of the tank with radius 3 meters. Call it $V_1$.

$$V_1 = \frac{4}{3}\pi r^3 = \frac{4}{3}\pi(3)^3 = \frac{4}{3}\pi(27) = 36\pi \qquad r = 3$$

Now find $V_2$, the volume of the tank having radius 6 meters.

$$V_2 = \frac{4}{3}\pi(6)^3 = \frac{4}{3}\pi(216) = 288\pi \qquad r = 6$$

Notice that by doubling the radius of the sphere from 3 meters to 6 meters, the volume has increased 8 times, because

$$V_2 = 288\pi = 8V_1 = 8(36\pi).$$

Therefore, the cost to fill the larger tank is eight times the cost to fill the smaller one: 8(\$200) = \$1600.

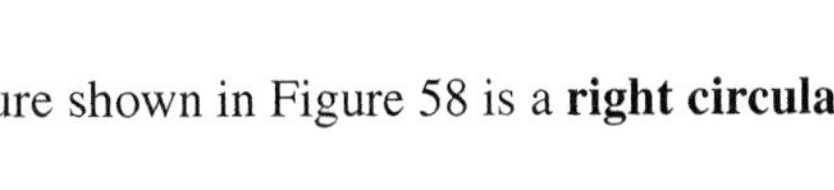

The space figure shown in Figure 58 is a **right circular cone.**

Right circular cone

**FIGURE 58**

### Volume and Surface Area of a Right Circular Cone

If a right circular cone has height $h$ and the radius of its circular base is $r$, then the volume $V$ and the surface area $S$ are given by the formulas

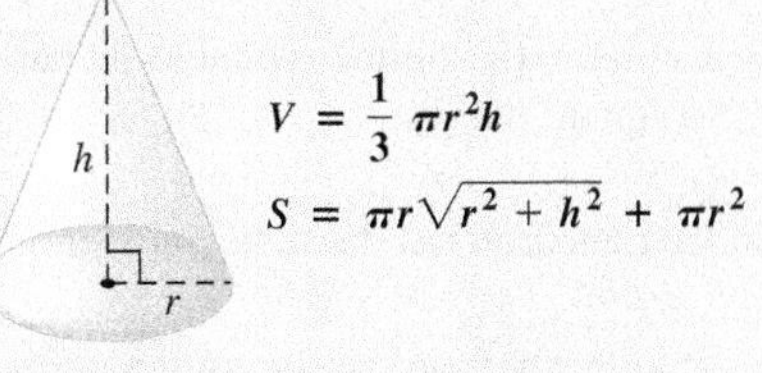


$$V = \frac{1}{3}\pi r^2 h$$

and $S = \pi r\sqrt{r^2 + h^2} + \pi r^2$.

(In the formula for $S$, the area of the bottom is included.)

A **pyramid** is a space figure having a polygonal base and triangular sides. Figure 59 shows a pyramid with a square base.

Pyramid

**FIGURE 59**

### Volume of a Pyramid

If $B$ represents the area of the base of a pyramid, and $h$ represents the height (that is, the perpendicular distance from the top, or apex, to the base), then the volume $V$ is given by the formula

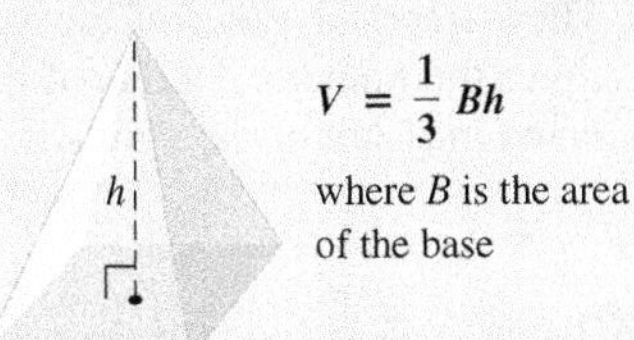


$$V = \frac{1}{3}Bh.$$

The **Transamerica Tower** in San Francisco is a pyramid with a square base. Each side of the base has a length of 52 meters, while the height of the building is 260 meters. The formula for the volume of a pyramid indicates that the volume of the building is about 234,000 cubic meters.

### EXAMPLE 4 Comparing Volumes Using Ratios

What is the ratio of the volume of a right circular cone with radius of base $r$ and height $h$ to the volume of a pyramid having a square base, with each side of length $r$, and height $h$?

**SOLUTION**

Using the formula for the volume of a cone, we have

$$V_1 = \text{Volume of the cone} = \frac{1}{3}\pi r^2 h.$$

Because the pyramid has a square base, the area $B$ of its base is $r^2$. Using the formula for the volume of a pyramid, we get

$$V_2 = \text{Volume of the pyramid} = \frac{1}{3}Bh = \frac{1}{3}(r^2)h.$$

The ratio of the first volume to the second is

$$\frac{V_1}{V_2} = \frac{\frac{1}{3}\pi r^2 h}{\frac{1}{3}r^2 h} = \pi.$$

## 9.5 Exercises

*Decide whether each of the following statements is* true *or* false.

1. A cube with volume 64 cubic inches has surface area 96 square inches.

2. A tetrahedron has the same number of faces as vertices.

3. A dodecahedron can be used as a model for a calendar for a given year, where each face of the dodecahedron contains a calendar for a single month, and there are no faces left over.

4. Each face of an octahedron is an octagon.

5. If you double the length of the edge of a cube, the new cube will have a volume that is twice the volume of the original cube.

6. The numerical value of the volume of a sphere is $\frac{r}{3}$ times the numerical value of its surface area, where $r$ is the measure of the radius.

*Find* **(a)** *the volume and* **(b)** *the surface area of each space figure. When necessary, use 3.14 as an approximation for* $\pi$*, and round answers to the nearest hundredth.*

**7.**

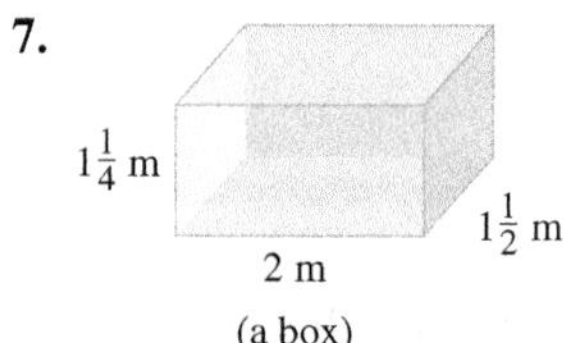

(a box)

**8.**

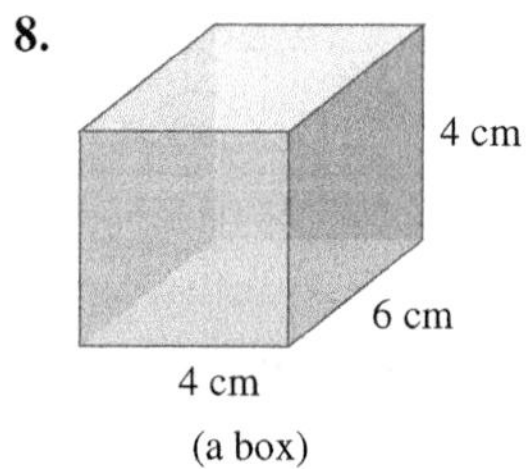

(a box)

**9.**

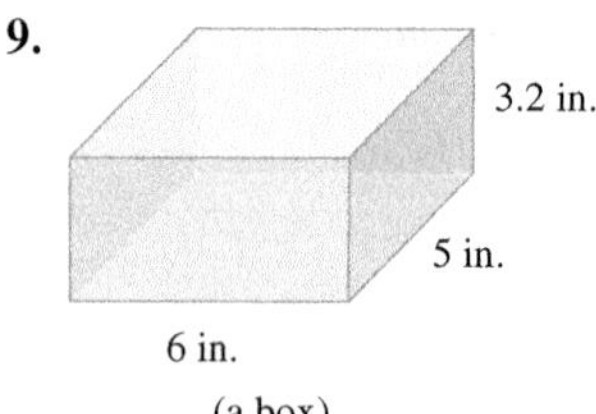

(a box)

**10.**

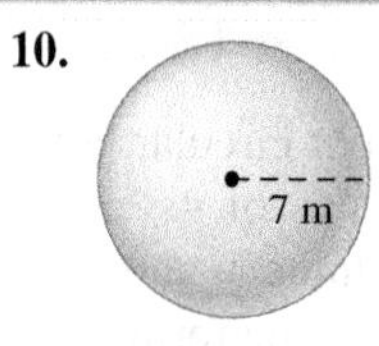

(a sphere)

**11.**

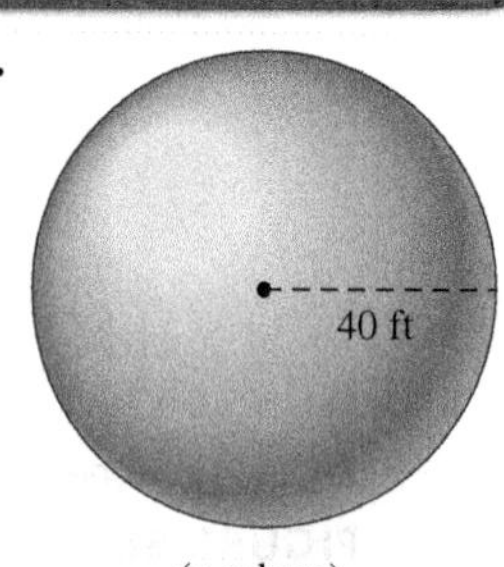

(a sphere)

**12.**

14.8 cm

(a sphere)

**13.**

5 cm

7 cm

(a right circular cylinder)

**14.**

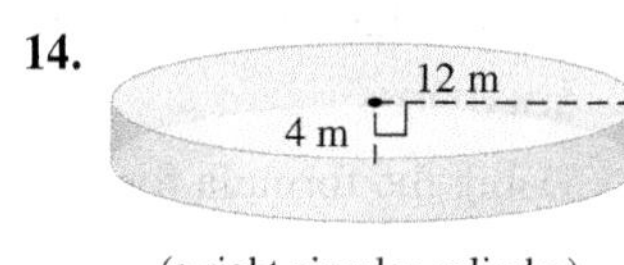

(a right circular cylinder)

**15.**

3 m

7 m

(a right circular cone)

**16.**

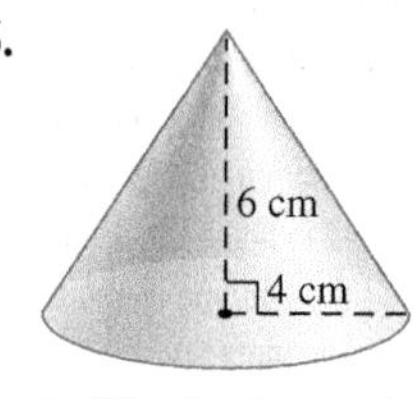

(a right circular cone)

*Find the volume of each pyramid. In each case, the base is a rectangle.*

**17.**

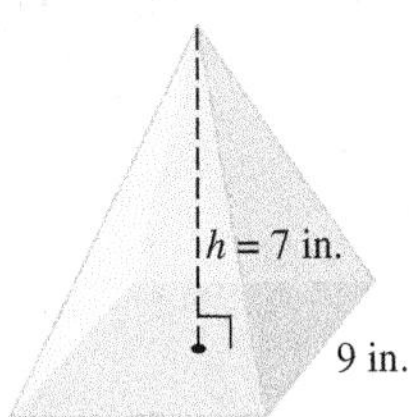


**18.**

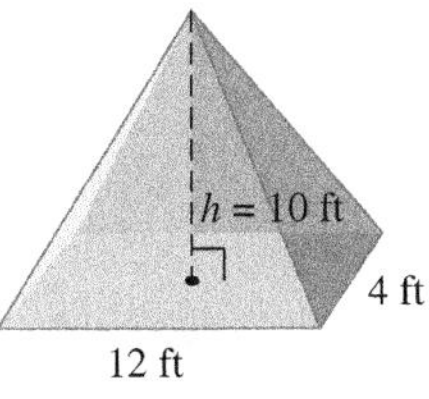


***Volumes of Common Objects*** *Find each volume. Use 3.14 as an approximation for $\pi$ when necessary.*

**19.** a coffee can, radius 6.3 cm and height 15.8 cm

**20.** a soup can, radius 3.2 cm and height 9.5 cm

**21.** a pork-and-beans can, diameter 7.2 cm and height 10.5 cm

**22.** a cardboard mailing tube, diameter 2 in. and height 40 in.

**23.** a coffee mug, diameter 9 cm and height 8 cm

**24.** a bottle of typewriter correction fluid, diameter 3 cm and height 4.3 cm

**25.** the Great Pyramid of Cheops, near Cairo—its base is a square 230 m on a side, while the height is 137 m

**26.** a hotel in the shape of a cylinder with a base radius of 46 m and a height of 220 m

**27.** a road construction marker, a cone with height 2 m and base radius $\frac{1}{2}$ m

**28.** the conical portion of a witch's hat for a Halloween costume, with height 12 in. and base radius 4 in.

*In the chart at the top of the next column, one of the values r (radius), d (diameter), V (volume), or S (surface area) is given for a particular sphere. Find the remaining three values. Leave $\pi$ in your answers.*

| | $r$ | $d$ | $V$ | $S$ |
|---|---|---|---|---|
| **29.** | 6 in. | | | |
| **30.** | 9 in. | | | |
| **31.** | | 10 ft | | |
| **32.** | | 40 ft | | |
| **33.** | | | $\frac{32}{3}\pi$ cm$^3$ | |
| **34.** | | | $\frac{256}{3}\pi$ cm$^3$ | |
| **35.** | | | | $4\pi$ m$^2$ |
| **36.** | | | | $144\pi$ m$^2$ |

*Solve each problem.*

**37. *Volume or Surface Area?*** In order to determine the amount of liquid a spherical tank will hold, would you need to use volume or surface area?

**38. *Volume or Surface Area?*** In order to determine the amount of leather it would take to manufacture a basketball, would you need to use volume or surface area?

**39. *Side Length of a Cube*** One of the three famous construction problems of Greek mathematics required the construction of an edge of a cube with twice the volume of a given cube. If the length of each side of the given cube is $x$, what would be the length of each side of a cube with twice the original volume?

**40.** Work through the parts of this exercise in order, and use them to make a generalization concerning volumes of spheres. Leave answers in terms of $\pi$.

(a) Find the volume of a sphere having a radius of 1 m.

(b) Suppose the radius is doubled to 2 m. What is the volume?

(c) When the radius was doubled, by how many times did the volume increase? (To find out, divide the answer for part (b) by the answer for part (a).)

(d) Suppose the radius of the sphere from part (a) is tripled to 3 m. What is the volume?

(e) When the radius was tripled, by how many times did the volume increase?

(f) In general, if the radius of a sphere is multiplied by $n$, the volume is multiplied by _____.

***Cost to Fill a Spherical Tank*** *If a spherical tank* 2 m *in diameter can be filled with a liquid for* \$300, *find the cost to fill tanks of each diameter.*

**41.** 6 m **42.** 8 m **43.** 10 m

44. Use the logic of Exercise 40 to answer the following: If the radius of a sphere is multiplied by $n$, then the surface area of the sphere is multiplied by _____.

*Each of the following figures has volume as indicated. Find the value of x.*

45. $V = 60$

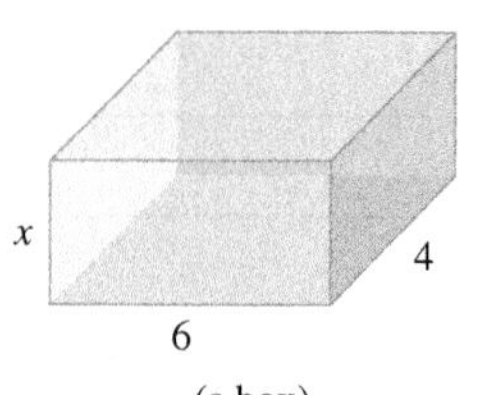

(a box)

46. $V = 450$

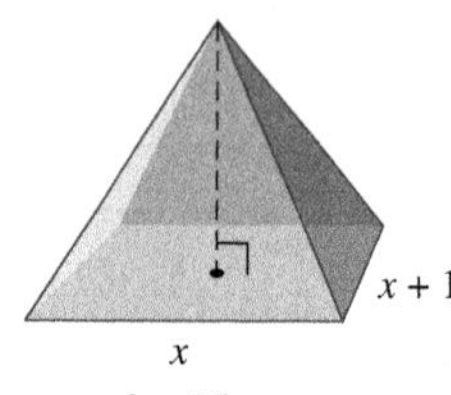

$h = 15$
Base is a rectangle.
(a pyramid)

47. $V = 36\pi$

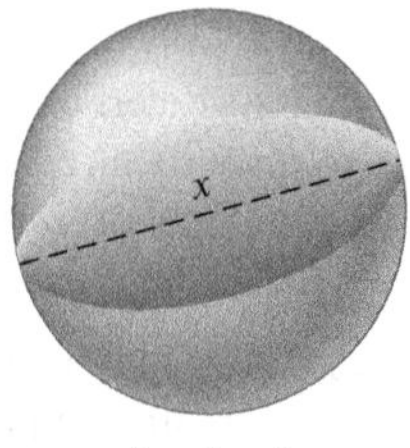

(a sphere)

48. $V = 245\pi$

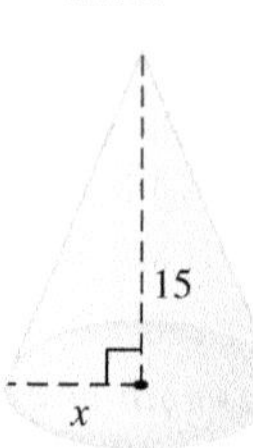

(a right circular cone)

*Exercises 49–56 require some ingenuity, but all can be solved using the concepts presented so far in this chapter.*

49. ***Volume of a Box*** The areas of the sides of a rectangular box are 30 in.$^2$, 35 in.$^2$, and 42 in.$^2$. What is the volume of the box?

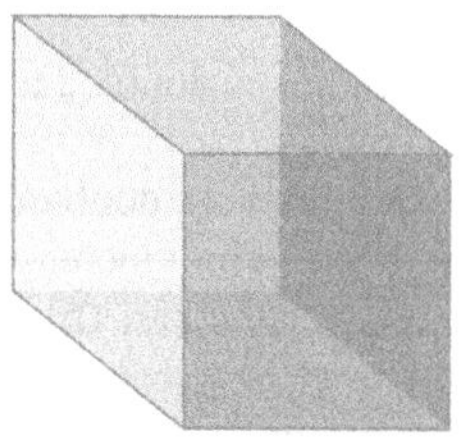

50. ***Ratios of Volumes*** In the figure, a right circular cone is inscribed in a hemisphere. What is the ratio of the volume of the cone to the volume of the hemisphere?

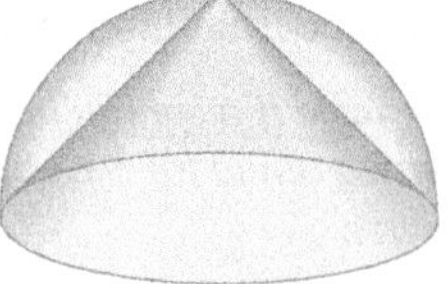

51. ***Volume of a Sphere*** A plane intersects a sphere to form a circle as shown in the figure. If the area of the circle formed by the intersection is $576\pi$ in.$^2$, what is the volume of the sphere?

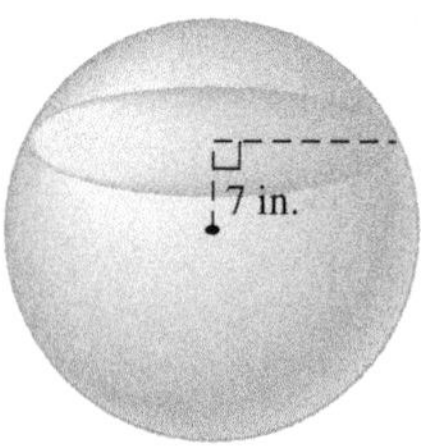


52. ***Change in Volume*** If the height of a right circular cylinder is halved and the diameter is tripled, how is the volume changed?

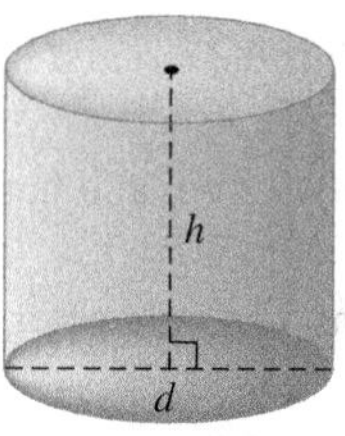


53. ***Ratio of Area*** What is the ratio of the area of the circumscribed square to the area of the inscribed square?

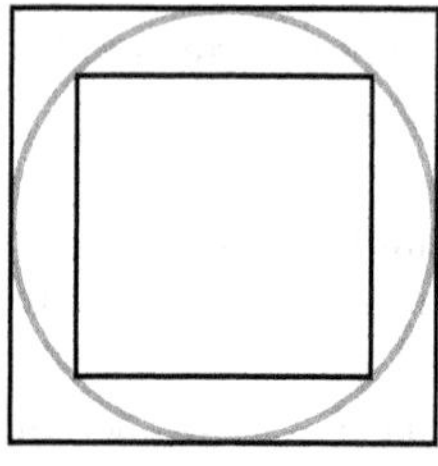

54. ***Perimeter of a Square*** Suppose the diameter of the circle shown is 8 in. What is the perimeter of the inscribed square $ABCD$?

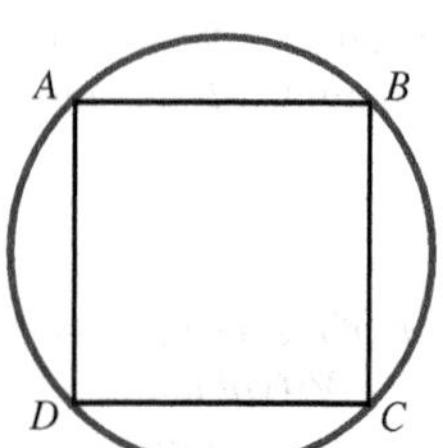

**55.** ***Value of a Sum*** In the circle shown with center $O$, the radius is 6. $QTSR$ is an inscribed square. Find the value of $PQ^2 + PT^2 + PR^2 + PS^2$.

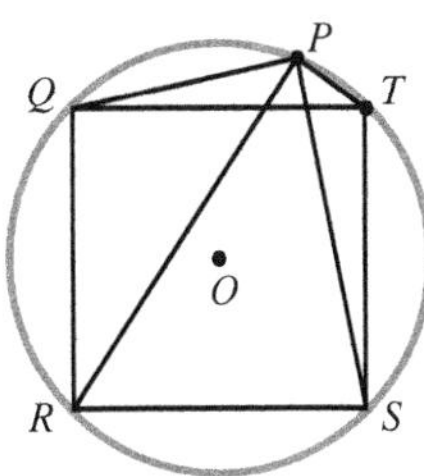


**56.** ***Ratio of Side Lengths*** The square $JOSH$ is inscribed in a semicircle. What is the ratio of $x$ to $y$?

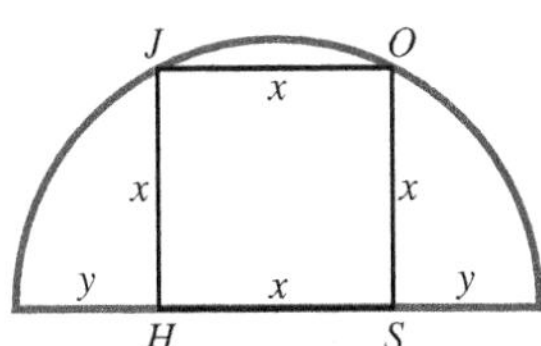


***Euler's Formula*** *Many crystals and some viruses are constructed in the shapes of regular polyhedra. On the left in the next column is a polio virus, based on an icosahedron, and on the right is radiolara, a group of microorganisms, based on a tetrahedron.*

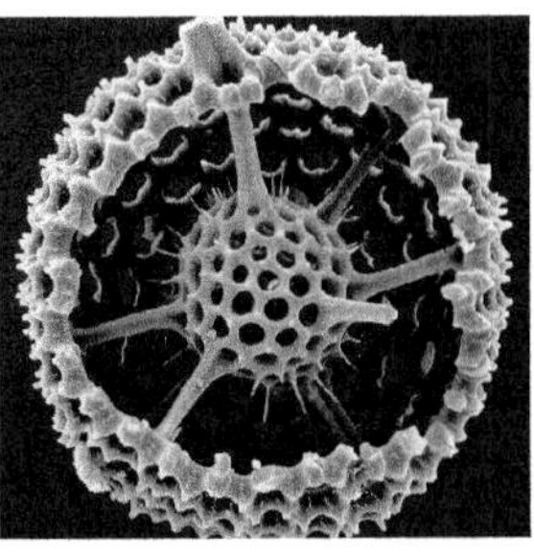

*Leonhard Euler investigated a remarkable relationship among the numbers of faces (F), vertices (V) and edges (E) for the five regular polyhedra. Complete the chart in Exercises 57–61, and then draw a conclusion in Exercise 62.*

| | Polyhedron | Faces (F) | Vertices (V) | Edges (E) | Value of $F + V - E$ |
|---|---|---|---|---|---|
| **57.** | Tetrahedron | | | | |
| **58.** | Hexahedron (Cube) | | | | |
| **59.** | Octahedron | | | | |
| **60.** | Dodecahedron | | | | |
| **61.** | Icosahedron | | | | |

**62.** Euler's formula is $F + V - E =$ _____.

# 9.6 Transformational Geometry

**Reflections • Translations and Rotations • Size Transformations**

There are many branches of geometry. In this chapter we have studied concepts of Euclidean geometry. One particular branch of geometry, known as **transformational geometry,** investigates how one geometric figure can be transformed into another. In transformational geometry we are required to reflect, rotate, and change the size of figures using concepts that we now discuss.

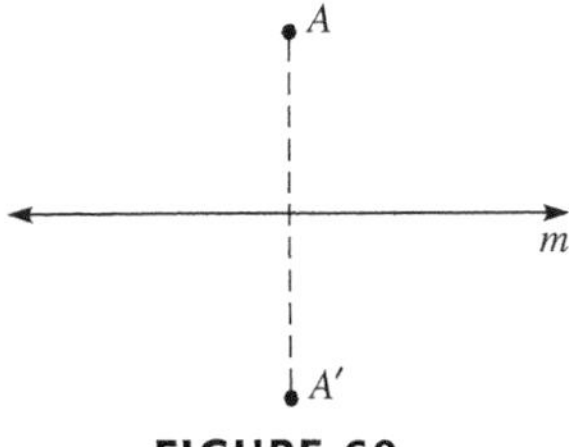


**FIGURE 60**

**Reflections** One way to transform one geometric figure into another is by reflection. In Figure 60, line $m$ is perpendicular to the line segment $AA'$ and also bisects this line segment. We call point $A'$ the **reflection image** of point $A$ about line $m$. Line $m$ is called the **line of reflection** for points $A$ and $A'$. In the figure, we use a dashed line to connect points $A$ and $A'$ to show that these two points are images of each other under this transformation.

Point $A'$ is the reflection image of point $A$ only for line $m$; if a different line were used, $A$ would have a different reflection image. Think of the reflection image of a point $A$ about a line $m$ as follows: Place a drop of ink at point $A$, and fold the paper along line $m$. The spot made by the ink on the other side of $m$ is the reflection image of $A$. If $A'$ is the image of $A$ about line $m$, then $A$ is the image of $A'$ about the same line $m$.

To find the reflection image of a figure, find the reflection image of each point of the figure. The set of all reflection images of the points of the original figure is called the **reflection image** of the figure. Figure 61 shows several figures (in black) and their reflection images (in color) about the lines shown.

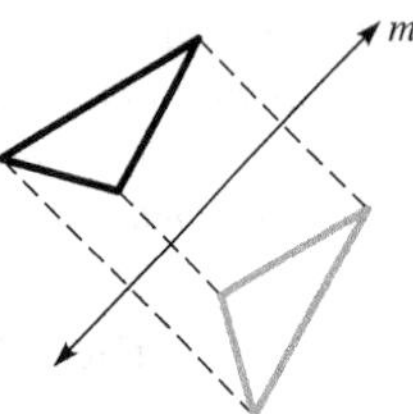

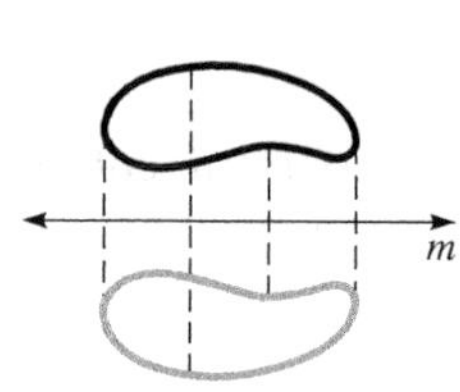

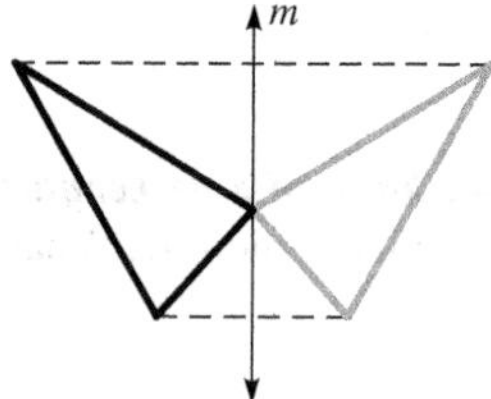


**FIGURE 61**

By the definition of reflection given above, each point in a plane has exactly one reflection image point with respect to a given line of reflection. Also, each reflection image point has exactly one original point. Thus, two distinct points cannot have the same reflection image. This means there is a *1-to-1 correspondence* between the set of points of the plane and the image points with respect to a given line of reflection. Any operation, such as reflection, in which there is a 1-to-1 correspondence between the points of the plane and their image points is called a **transformation;** we can call reflection about a line the **reflection transformation.**

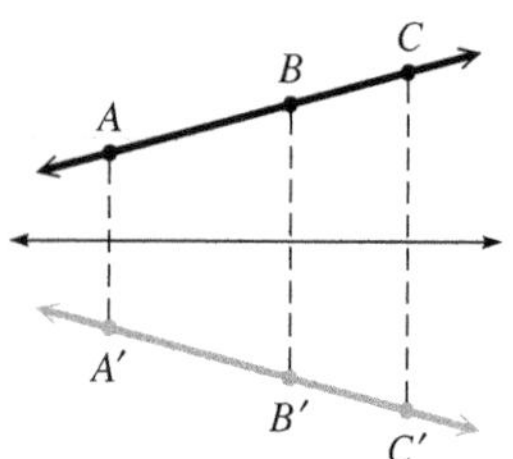


**FIGURE 62**

If a point $A$ and its image, $A'$, under a certain transformation are the same point, then point $A$ is called an **invariant point** of the transformation. The only invariant points of the reflection transformation are the points of the line of reflection.

Three points that lie on the same straight line are called **collinear.** In Figure 62, points $A$, $B$, and $C$ are collinear, and it can be shown that the reflection images $A'$, $B'$, and $C'$, are also collinear. Thus, the reflection image of a line is also a line. We express this by saying that **reflection preserves collinearity.**

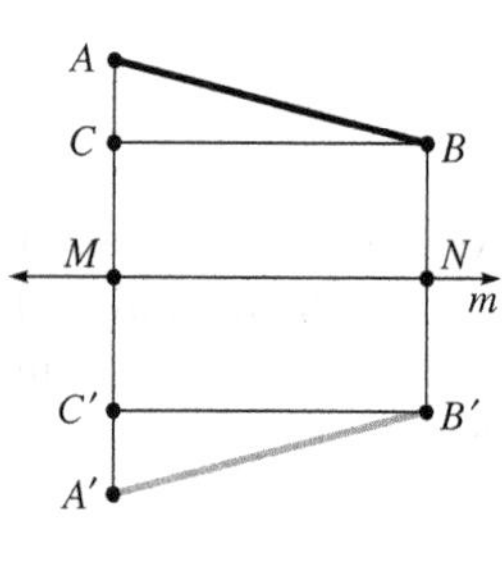


**FIGURE 63**

Distance is also preserved by the reflection transformation. Thus, in Figure 63, the distance between points $A$ and $B$, written $|AB|$, is equal to the distance between the reflection images $A'$ and $B'$, or

$$|AB| = |A'B'|.$$

To prove this, we can use the definition of reflection image to verify that $|AM| = |MA'|$, and $|BN| = |NB'|$. Construct segments $CB$ and $C'B'$, each perpendicular to $BB'$. Note that $CBB'C'$ is a rectangle. Because the opposite sides of a rectangle are equal and parallel, we have

$$|CB| = |C'B'|. \qquad \text{(Side)} \qquad \textbf{(1)}$$

Because $CBB'C'$ is a rectangle, we can also say

$$m\measuredangle ACB = m\measuredangle A'C'B' = 90^\circ \qquad \text{(Angle)} \qquad \textbf{(2)}$$

where we use $m\measuredangle ACB$ to represent the measure of angle $ACB$.

This playful little beagle, D'Artagnan, is owned by Finley Westmoreland. Notice that the markings on his face are **symmetric with respect to a vertical line** through his cold, wet, little nose.

An example of a **reflection**.

We know $|AM| = |MA'|$ and can show $|CM| = |MC'|$, so that

$$|AC| = |A'C'|. \qquad \text{(Side)} \qquad \mathbf{(3)}$$

From statements (1), (2), and (3) above, we conclude that in triangles $ABC$ and $A'B'C'$, two sides and the included angle of one are equal in measure to the corresponding two sides and angle of the other, and thus are congruent by SAS (Section 9.4). Because corresponding sides of congruent triangles are equal in length, we have

$$|AB| = |A'B'|,$$

which is what we wanted to show. Hence, the distance between two points equals the distance between their reflection images, and thus, reflection preserves distance. (The proof we have given is not really complete, because we have tacitly assumed that $AB$ is not parallel to $A'B'$, and that $A$ and $B$ are on the same side of the line of reflection. Some modification would have to be made in the proof above to include these other cases.)

The figures shown in Figure 64 are their own reflection images about the lines of reflection shown. In this case, the line of reflection is called a **line of symmetry** for the figure. Figure 64(a) has three lines of symmetry. A circle has every line through its center as a line of symmetry.

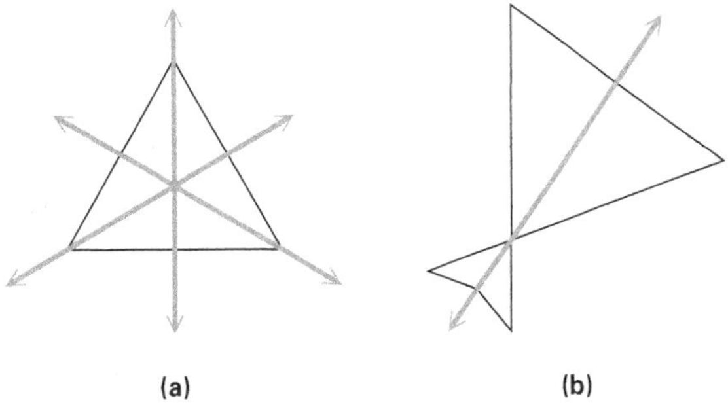


**FIGURE 64**

## Translations and Rotations

We shall use the symbol $r_m$ to represent a reflection about line $m$, and let us use $r_n \cdot r_m$ to represent a reflection about line $m$ followed by a reflection about line $n$. We call $r_n \cdot r_m$ the **composition,** or **product,** of the two reflections $r_n$ and $r_m$. Figure 65 on the next page shows two examples of the composition of two reflections. In Figure 65(a), lines $m$ and $n$ are parallel, while they intersect in Figure 65(b).

In Figure 65(a) both the original figure and its image under the composition of the two reflections appear to be oriented the same way and to have the same "tilt." In fact, it appears that the original figure could be slid along the dashed lines of Figure 65(a), with no rotation, so as to cover the image. This composite transformation is called a **translation.** Figure 66, also on the next page, shows a translation, and the image can be obtained as a composition of two reflections about parallel lines. Check that the distance between a point and its image under a translation is twice the distance between the two parallel lines. The distance between a point and its image under a translation is called the **magnitude** of the translation.

A translation of magnitude 0 leaves every point of the plane unchanged, and thus is called the **identity translation.** A translation of magnitude $k$, followed by a similar translation of magnitude $k$ but of opposite direction, returns a point to its original

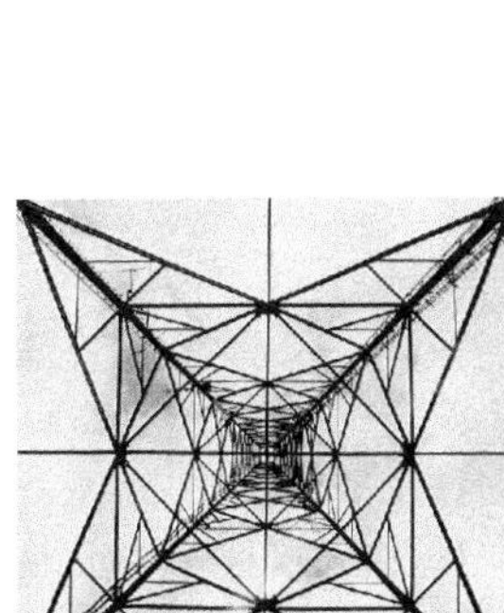

How many kinds of **symmetry** do you see here?

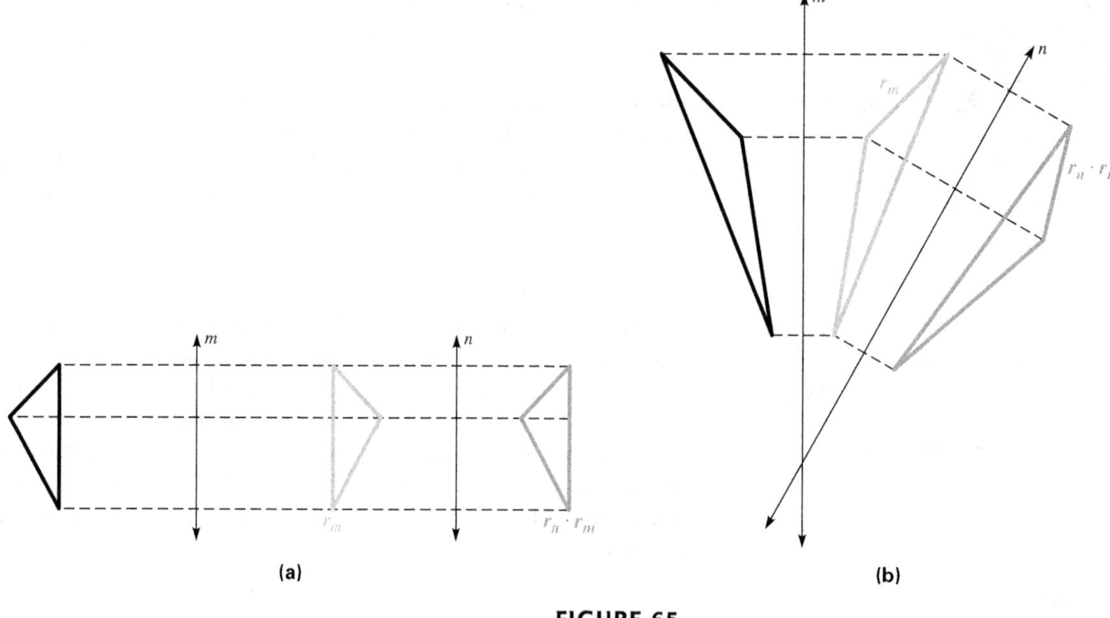


**FIGURE 65**

position, and thus, these two translations are called **inverses** of each other. Check that there are no invariant points in a translation of magnitude $k > 0$.

A translation preserves collinearity (three points on the same line have image points that also lie on a line) and distance (the distance between two points is the same as the distance between the images of the points).

In Figure 65(b), the original figure could be rotated so as to cover the image. Hence, we call the composition of two reflections about nonparallel lines a **rotation.** The point of intersection of these two nonparallel lines is called the **center of rotation.** The black triangle of Figure 67 was reflected about line $m$ and then reflected about line $n$, resulting in a rotation with center at $B$. The dashed lines in color represent the paths of the vertices

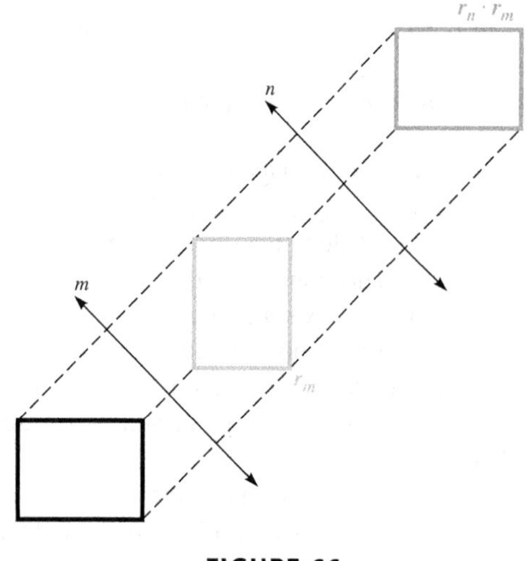

**FIGURE 66**

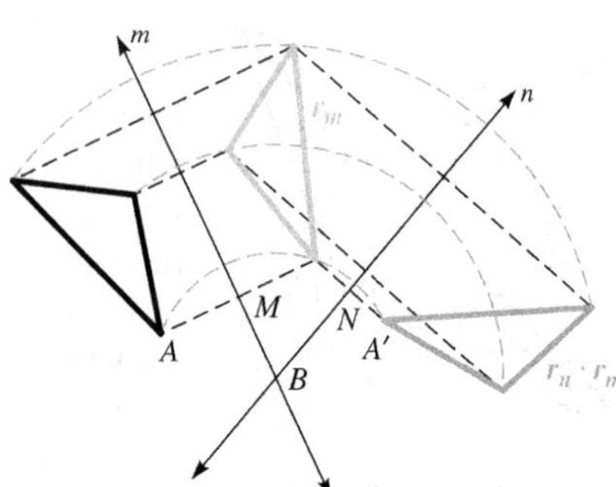


**FIGURE 67**

of the triangle under the rotation. It is shown in the exercises that $m\measuredangle ABA'$ is twice as large as $m\measuredangle MBN$. The measure of angle $ABA'$ is called the **magnitude** of the rotation.

Rotations also preserve collinearity and distance. The identity transformation here is a rotation of 0° or 360°, and rotations of, say, 240° and 120° (or in general, $x°$ and $360° - x°$, $0 \leq x \leq 360°$) are inverses of each other. The center of rotation is the only invariant point of any rotation except the identity rotation.

We have defined rotations as the composition of two reflections about nonparallel lines of reflection. We could also define a rotation by specifying its center, the angle of rotation, and a direction of rotation, as shown by the following example.

## EXAMPLE 1 Finding an Image Under a Rotation

Find the image of a point $P$ under a rotation transformation having center at a point $Q$ and magnitude 135° clockwise.

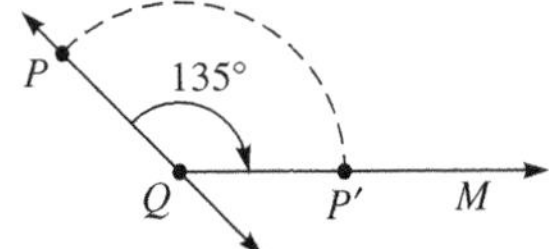


FIGURE 68

### SOLUTION

To find $P'$, the image of $P$, first draw angle $PQM$ having measure 135°. Then draw an arc of a circle with center at $Q$ and radius $|PQ|$. The point where this arc intersects side $QM$ is $P'$. See Figure 68.

Figure 69 shows a rotation transformation having center $Q$ and magnitude 180° clockwise. Point $Q$ bisects the line segment from a point $A$ to its image $A'$, and for this reason this rotation is sometimes called a **point reflection.**

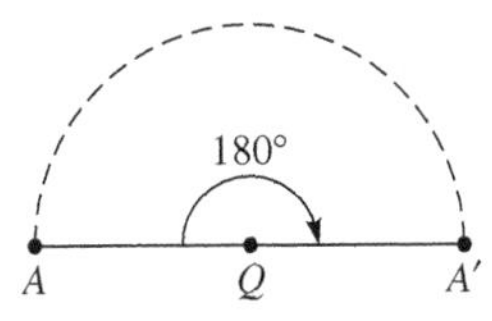


FIGURE 69

## EXAMPLE 2 Finding Point Reflections

Find the point reflection images about point $Q$ for each of the following figures.

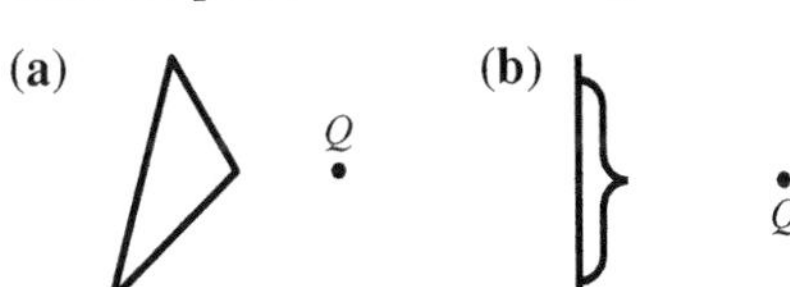


### SOLUTION

The point reflection images are shown in color.

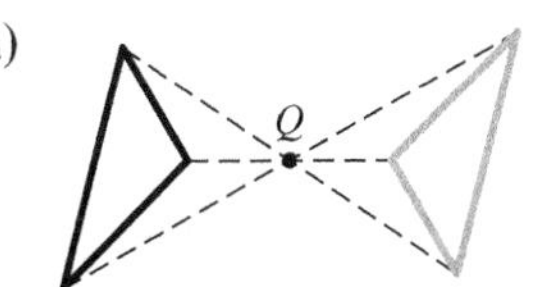


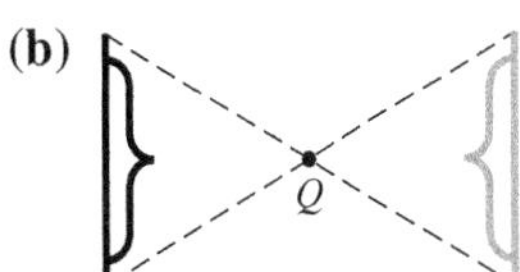

This creature exhibits **bilateral symmetry.** This kind of symmetry is often found in living organisms.

Let $r_m$ be a reflection about line $m$, and let $T$ be a translation having nonzero magnitude and a direction parallel to $m$. Then the composition of $T$ and $r_m$ is called a **glide reflection,** as seen in Figure 70 on the next page. Here a reflection followed by a translation is the same as a translation followed by a reflection, so that in this case

$$T \cdot r_m = r_m \cdot T.$$

Because a translation is the composition of *two* reflections, a glide reflection is the composition of *three* reflections. Because it is required that the translation have nonzero magnitude, there is no identity glide transformation.

**M.C. Escher** (1898–1972) was a Dutch graphic artist, most recognized for spatial illusions, impossible buildings, repeating geometric patterns (tessellations), and his incredible techniques in woodcutting and lithography.

Escher was a man studied and greatly appreciated by respected mathematicians, scientists, and crystallographers, yet he had no formal training in math or science. He was a humble man who considered himself neither an artist nor a mathematician.

Intricate repeating patterns, mathematically complex structures, and spatial perspectives all require a 'second look.' In Escher's work what you see the first time is most certainly not all there is to see." (*Sources:* M. C. Escher's Symmetry Drawing (Smaller and Smaller) and Waterfall © 2003 Cordon Art B.V., Baarn, Holland. All rights reserved; www.worldofescher.com.)

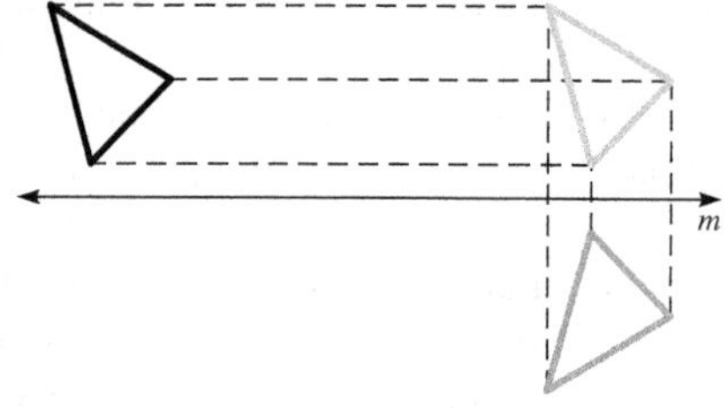

**FIGURE 70**

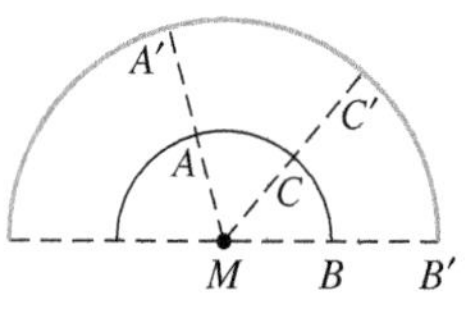


**FIGURE 71**

All the transformations of this section discussed so far are **isometries,** or transformations in which the image of a figure has the same size and shape as the original figure. Any isometry is either a reflection or the composition of two or more reflections.

## Size Transformations

Figure 71 shows a semicircle in black, a point $M$, and an image semicircle in color. Distance $A'M$ is twice the distance $AM$ and distance $B'M$ is twice the distance $BM$. In fact, all the points of the image semicircle, such as $C'$, were obtained by drawing a line through $M$ and $C$, and then locating $C'$ such that $|MC'| = 2|MC|$. Such a transformation is called a **size transformation** with center $M$ and magnitude 2. We shall assume that a size transformation can have any positive real number $k$ as magnitude. A size transformation having magnitude $k > 1$ is called a **dilatation,** or **stretch;** while a size transformation having magnitude $k < 1$ is called a **contraction,** or **shrink.**

### EXAMPLE 3 Applying Size Transformations

Apply a size transformation with center $M$ and magnitude $\frac{1}{3}$ to the two triangles shown in black in Figure 72.

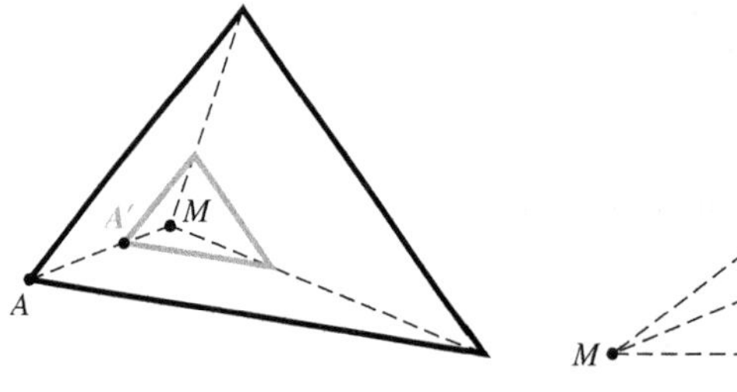


**FIGURE 72**

**SOLUTION**

To find the images of these triangles, we can find the image points of some sample points. For example, if we select point $A$ on each of the original triangles, we can find the image points by drawing a line through $A$ and $M$, and locating a point $A'$ such that $|MA'| = \frac{1}{3}|MA|$. By doing this for all points of each of the black triangles, we get the images shown in color in Figure 72.

The identity transformation is a size transformation of magnitude 1, while size transformations of magnitude $k$ and $\frac{1}{k}$, having the same center, are inverses of each other. The only invariant point of a size transformation of magnitude $k \neq 1$ is the center of the transformation.

### EXAMPLE 4 Investigating Size Transformations

Does a size transformation **(a)** preserve collinearity? **(b)** preserve distance?

**SOLUTION**

**(a)** Figure 73 shows three collinear points, $A$, $B$, and $C$, and their images under two different size transformations with center at $M$: one of magnitude 3 and one of magnitude $\frac{1}{3}$. In each case the image points appear to be collinear, and it can be proved that they are, using similar triangles. In fact, the image of a line not through the center of the transformation is a line parallel to the original line.

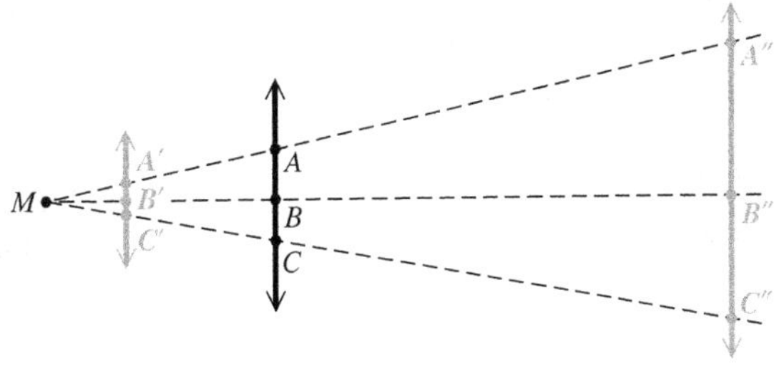


**FIGURE 73**

**(b)** As shown in Figure 73, $|AB| \neq |A'B'|$. Thus, a size transformation of magnitude $k \neq 1$ does not preserve distance and is not an isometry.

**TABLE 4** Summary of Transformations

| | Reflection | Translation | Rotation | Glide Reflection | Size Transformation |
|---|---|---|---|---|---|
| Example | | | | | |
| Preserve collinearity? | Yes | Yes | Yes | Yes | Yes |
| Preserve distance? | Yes | Yes | Yes | Yes | No |
| Identity transformation? | None | Magnitude 0 | Magnitude 360° | None | Magnitude 1 |
| Inverse transformation? | None | Same magnitude; opposite direction | Same center; magnitude $360° - x°$ | None | Same center; magnitude $\frac{1}{k}$ |
| Composition of $n$ reflections? | $n = 1$ | $n = 2$, parallel | $n = 2$, nonparallel | $n = 3$ | No |
| Isometry? | Yes | Yes | Yes | Yes | No |
| Invariant points? | Line of reflection | None | Center of rotation | None | Center of transformation |

## For Further Thought

### Tessellations

*The authors wish to thank Suzanne Alejandre for permission to reprint this article on tessellations, which first appeared at* www.mathforum.org/sum95/suzanne/whattess.html.

**tessellate** (verb), **tessellation** (noun): from Latin *tessera* "a square tablet" or "a die used for gambling." Latin tessera may have been borrowed from Greek *tessares,* meaning "four," since a square tile has four sides. The diminutive of *tessera* was *tessella,* a small, square piece of stone or a cubical tile used in mosaics. Since a mosaic extends over a given area without leaving any region uncovered, the geometric meaning of the word tessellate is "to cover the plane with a pattern in such a way as to leave no region uncovered." By extension, space or hyperspace may also be tessellated.

### Definition

A dictionary will tell you that the word "tessellate" means to form or arrange small squares in a checkered or mosaic pattern. The word "tessellate" is derived from the Ionic version of the Greek word "tesseres," which in English means "four." The first tilings were made from square tiles.

A regular polygon has 3 or 4 or 5 or more sides and angles, all equal. A **regular tessellation** means a tessellation made up of congruent regular polygons. [Remember: *Regular* means that the sides of the polygon are all the same length. *Congruent* means that the polygons that you put together are all the same size and shape.]

Only three regular polygons tessellate in the Euclidean plane: triangles, squares, or hexagons. We can't show the entire plane, but imagine that these are pieces taken from planes that have been tiled. Here are examples of

a tessellation of triangles

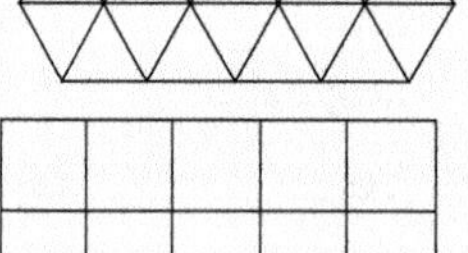

a tessellation of squares

a tessellation of hexagons

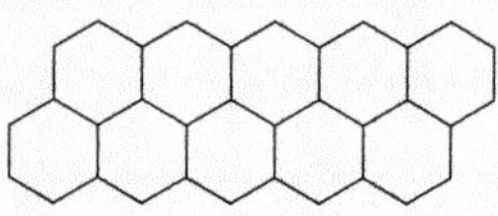

When you look at these three samples you can easily notice that the squares are lined up with each other while the triangles and hexagons are not. Also, if you look at six triangles at a time, they form a hexagon, so the tiling of triangles and the tiling of hexagons are similar and they cannot be formed by directly lining shapes up under each other–a slide (or a glide!) is involved.

You can work out the interior measure of the angles for each of these polygons:

| Shape | Angle Measure in Degrees |
|---|---|
| triangle | 60 |
| square | 90 |
| pentagon | 108 |
| hexagon | 120 |
| more than six sides | more than 120 degrees |

Since the regular polygons in a tessellation must fill the plane at each vertex, the interior angle must be an exact divisor of 360 degrees. This works for the triangle, square, and hexagon, and you can show working tessellations for these figures. For all the others, the interior angles are not exact divisors of 360 degrees, and therefore those figures cannot tile the plane.

### Naming Conventions

A tessellation of squares is named "4.4.4.4." Here's how: choose a vertex, and then look at one of the polygons that touches that vertex. How many sides does it have?

Since it's a square, it has four sides, and that's where the first "4" comes from. Now keep going around the vertex in either direction, finding the number of sides of the polygons until you get back to the polygon you started with. How many polygons did you count?

There are four polygons, and each has four sides.

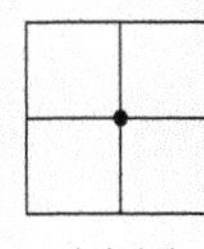

4.4.4.4

For a tessellation of regular congruent hexagons, if you choose a vertex and count the sides of the polygons that touch it, you'll see that there are three polygons and each has six sides, so this tessellation is called "6.6.6":

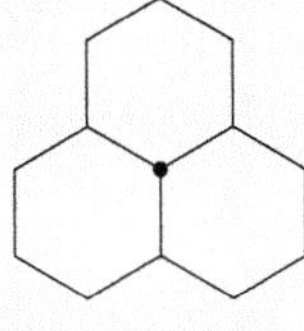

6.6.6

A tessellation of triangles has six polygons surrounding a vertex, and each of them has three sides: "3.3.3.3.3.3."

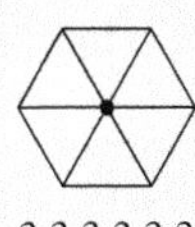

3.3.3.3.3.3

## Semi-regular Tessellations

You can also use a variety of regular polygons to make **semi-regular tessellations.**

A semi-regular tessellation has two properties, which are:

1. It is formed by regular polygons.
2. The arrangement of polygons at every vertex point is identical.

Here are the **eight** semi-regular tessellations:

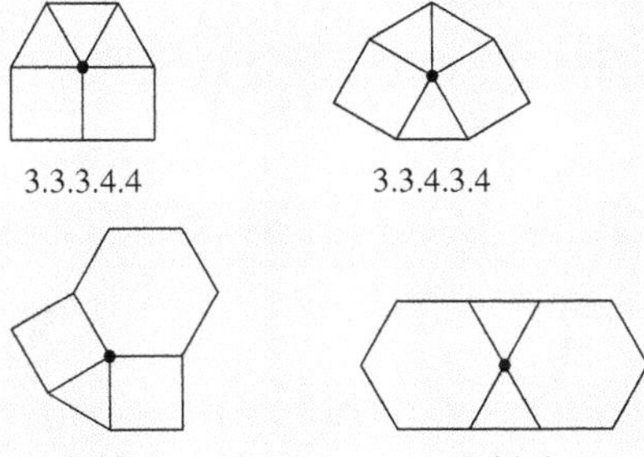

3.3.3.4.4 3.3.4.3.4

3.4.6.4 3.6.3.6

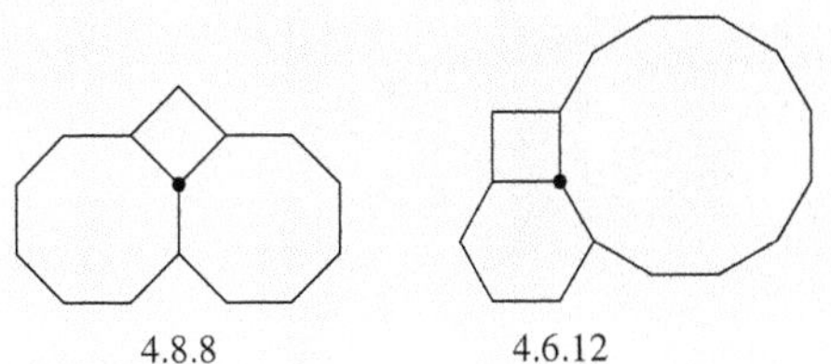

4.8.8 4.6.12

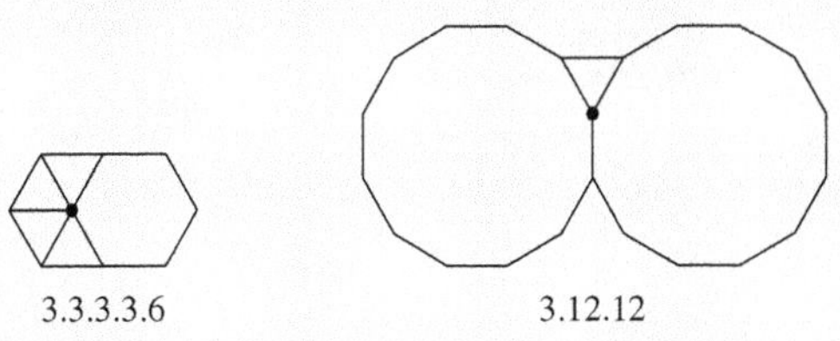

3.3.3.3.6 3.12.12

Interestingly there are other combinations that seem like they should tile the plane because the arrangements of the regular polygons fill the space around a point. For example:

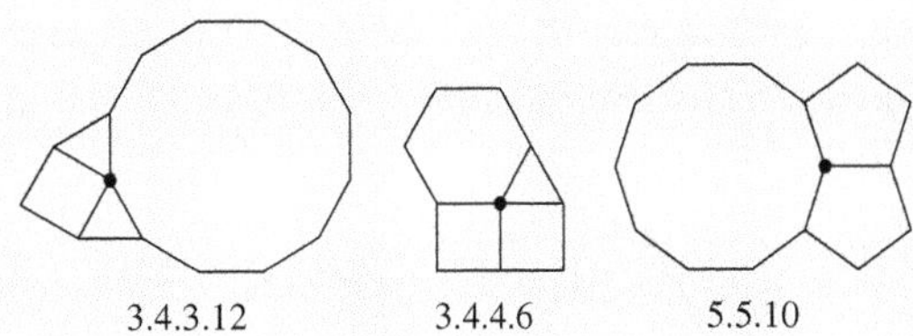

3.4.3.12 3.4.4.6 5.5.10

If you try tiling the plane with these units of tessellation you will find that they cannot be extended infinitely.

There is an infinite number of tessellations that can be made of patterns that do not have the same combination of angles at every vertex point. There are also tessellations made of polygons that do not share common edges and vertices.

## For Group Discussion or Individual Investigation

1. Use the naming conventions to name each of these semi-regular tessellations.

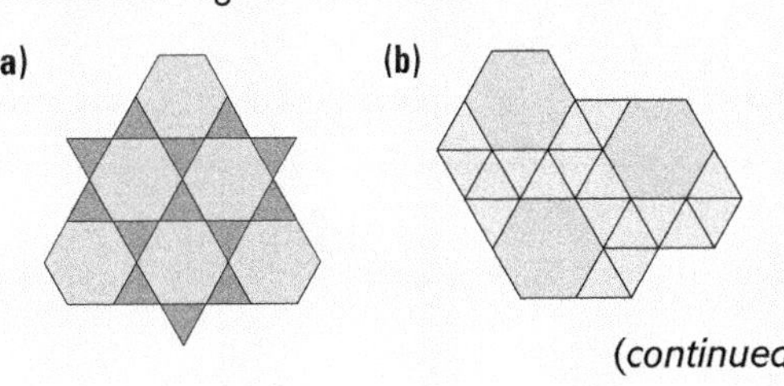

(a) (b)

*(continued)*

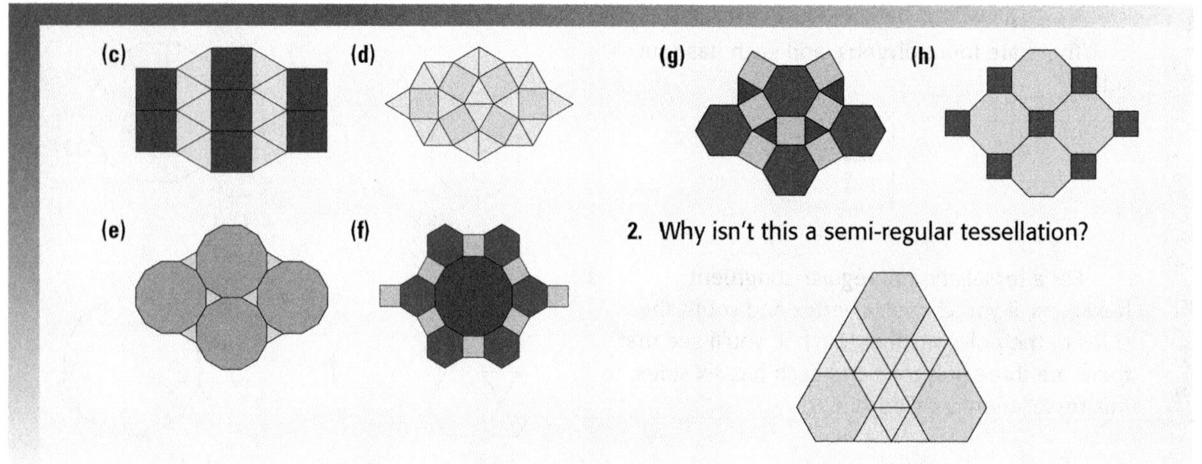


2. Why isn't this a semi-regular tessellation?

## 9.6 Exercises

*Find the reflection images of the given figures about the given lines.*

1.
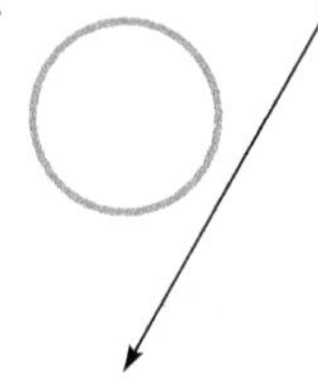

2.
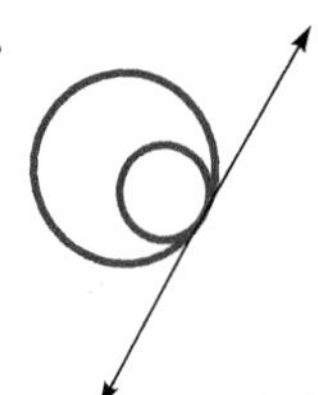

3.
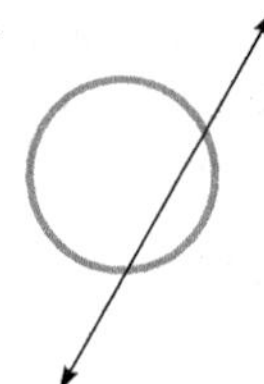

4.
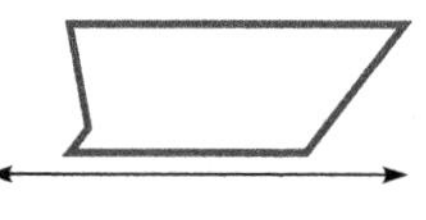

5.
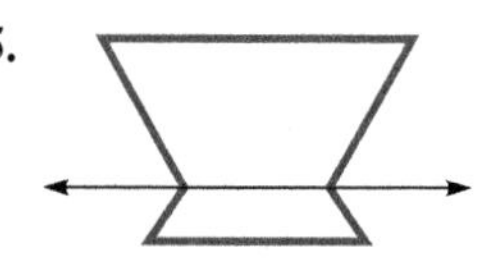

6.
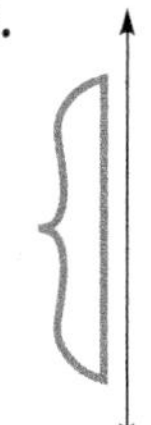

7.
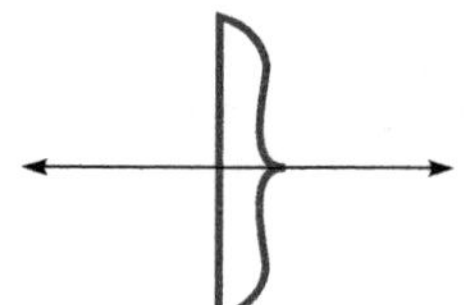

8.
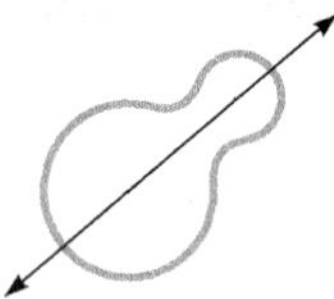

*Find any lines of symmetry of the given figures.*

9.
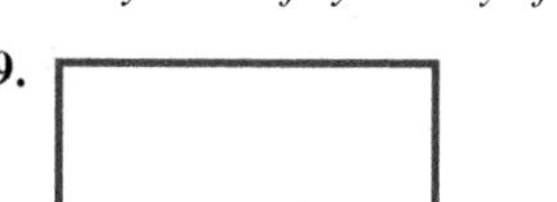

10.

11.

12.

*First reflect the given figure about line m. Then reflect about line n.*

**13.** **14.**

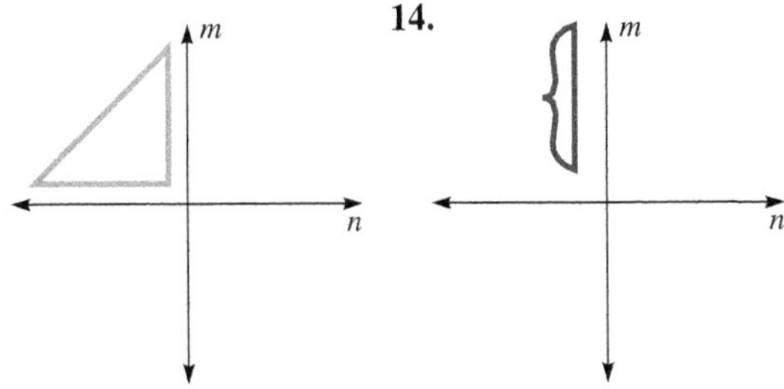


**15.** **16.**

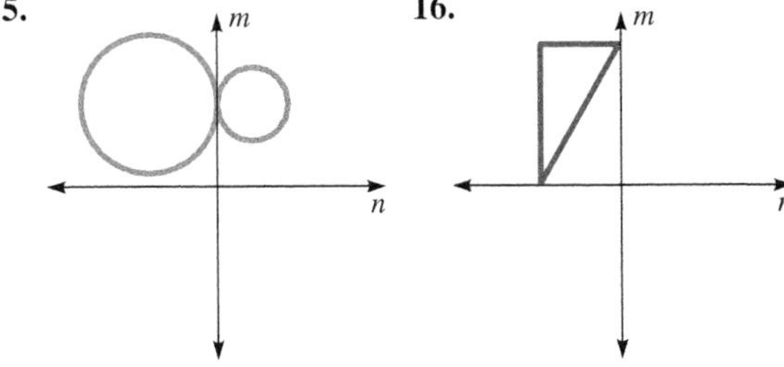


**17.**

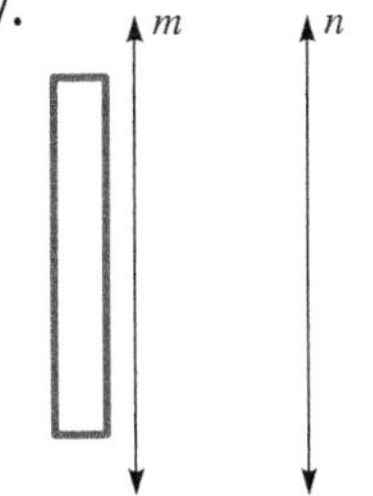


**18.**

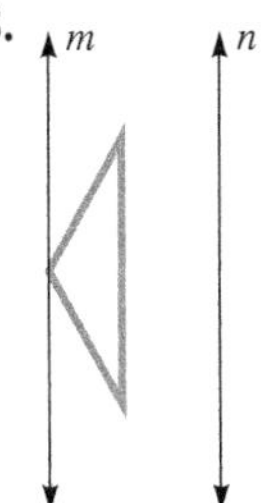


**19.**

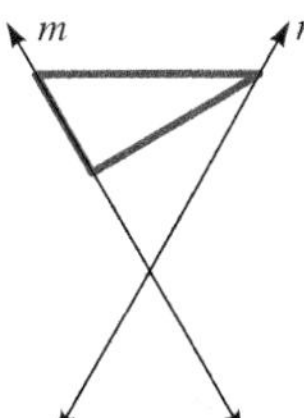


**20.**

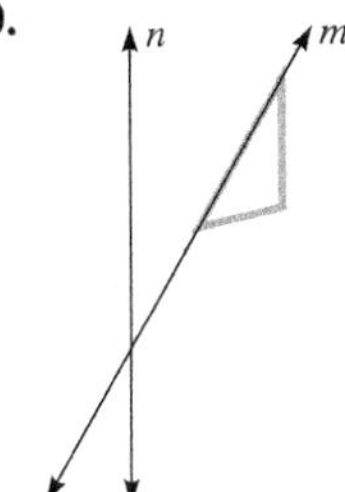


*In Exercises 21–34, let T be a translation having magnitude $\frac{3}{4}$ inch to the right in a direction parallel to the bottom edge of the page. Let $r_m$ be a reflection about line m, and let $R_p$ be a rotation about point P having magnitude 60° clockwise.*

*In each of Exercises 21–32, perform the given transformations on point A of the figure below to obtain final image point A′.*

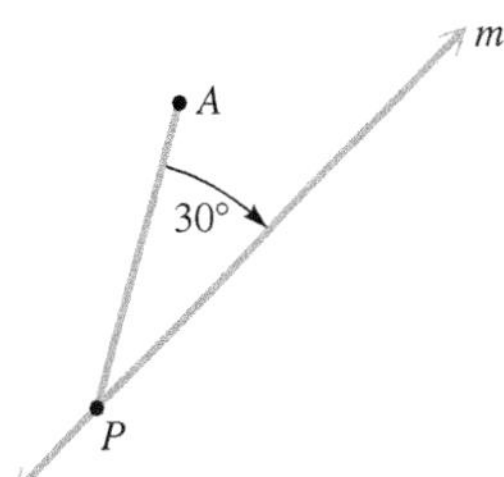


**21.** $r_m$

**22.** $R_p$

**23.** $T$

**24.** $r_m \cdot r_m$

**25.** $T \cdot T$

**26.** $R_p \cdot R_p$

**27.** $T \cdot R_p$

**28.** $T \cdot r_m$

**29.** $r_m \cdot T$

**30.** $R_P \cdot r_m$

**31.** $r_m \cdot R_P$

**32.** $R_P \cdot T$

**33.** Is $T \cdot r_m$ a glide reflection here?

**34.** Is $T \cdot r_m = r_m \cdot T$ true?

**35.** Suppose a rotation is given by $r_m \cdot r_n$, as shown in the figure below. Find the images of $A$, $B$, and $C$.

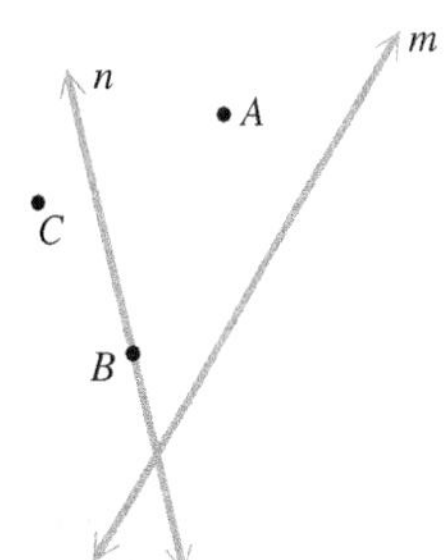


**36.** Does a glide reflection preserve
  **(a)** collinearity?
  **(b)** distance?

*Find the point reflection images of each of the following figures with the given points as center.*

**37.**

**38.**

39.

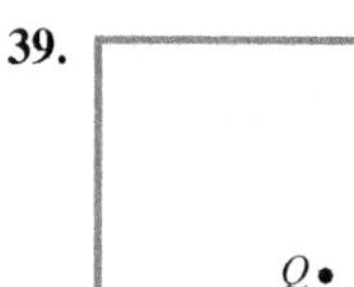


40.

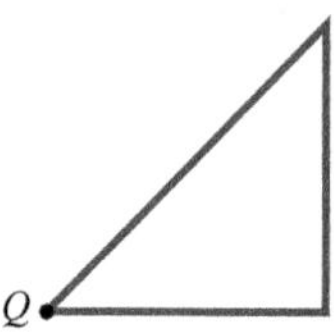


*Perform the indicated size transformation.*

41. magnitude 2; center $M$

42. magnitude $\frac{1}{2}$; center $M$

43. magnitude $\frac{1}{2}$; center $M$

44. magnitude 2; center $M$

45. magnitude $\frac{1}{3}$; center $M$

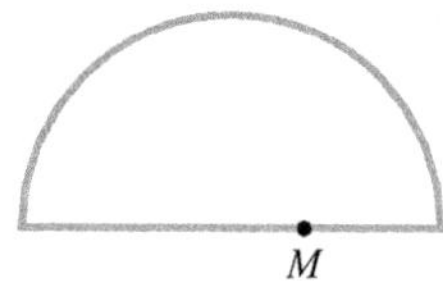


46. magnitude $\frac{1}{3}$; center $M$

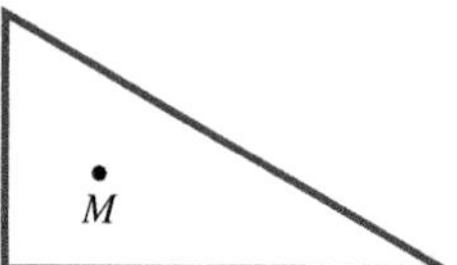


# 9.7 Non-Euclidean Geometry, Topology, and Networks

**Euclid's Postulates and Axioms • The Parallel Postulate (Euclid's Fifth Postulate) • The Origins of Non-Euclidean Geometry • Topology • Networks**

## Euclid's Postulates and Axioms

The *Elements* of Euclid is quite possibly the most influential mathematics book ever written. (See the margin note at the beginning of this chapter on page 530.) It begins with definitions of basic ideas such as point, line, and plane. Euclid then gives five postulates providing the foundation of all that follows.

Next, Euclid lists five axioms that he views as general truths and not just facts about geometry. See Table 5 on the next page. (To some of the Greek writers, postulates were truths about a particlar field, while axioms were general truths. Today, "axiom" is used in either case.)

Using only these ten statements and the basic rules of logic, Euclid was able to prove a large number of "propositions" about geometric figures.

**John Playfair** (1748–1819) wrote his *Elements of Geometry* in 1795. Playfair's Axiom is: Given a line *k* and a point *P* not on the line, there exists one and only one line *m* through *P* that is parallel to *k*. Playfair was a geologist who fostered "uniformitarianism," the doctrine that geological processes long ago gave Earth its features, and processes today are the same kind as those in the past.

**TABLE 5**

| Euclid's Postulates | Euclid's Axioms |
|---|---|
| **1.** Two points determine one and only one straight line. | **6.** Things equal to the same thing are equal to each other. |
| **2.** A straight line extends indefinitely far in either direction. | **7.** If equals are added to equals, the sums are equal. |
| **3.** A circle may be drawn with any given center and any given radius. | **8.** If equals are subtracted from equals, the remainders are equal. |
| **4.** All right angles are equal. | **9.** Figures that can be made to coincide are equal. |
| **5.** Given a line *k* and a point *P* not on the line, there exists one and only one line *m* through *P* that is parallel to *k*. | **10.** The whole is greater than any of its parts. |

The statement for Postulate 5 given above is actually known as Playfair's axiom on parallel lines, which is equivalent to Euclid's fifth postulate. To understand why this postulate caused trouble for so many mathematicians for so long, we must examine the original formulation.

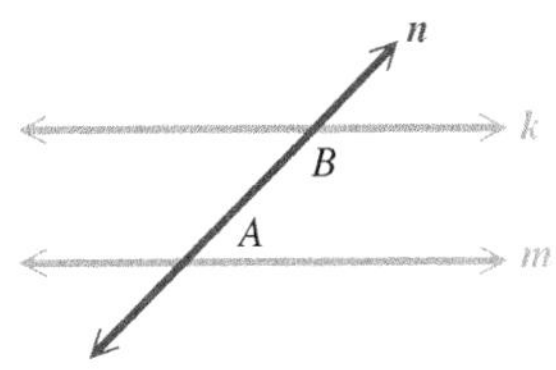


**FIGURE 74**

**The Parallel Postulate (Euclid's Fifth Postulate)** In its original form, Euclid's fifth postulate states that if two lines ($k$ and $m$ in Figure 74) are such that a third line, $n$, intersects them so that the sum of the two interior angles ($A$ and $B$) on one side of line $n$ is less than (the sum of) two right angles, then the two lines, if extended far enough, will meet on the same side of $n$ that has the sum of the interior angles less than (the sum of) two right angles.

Euclid's parallel postulate is quite different from the other nine postulates and axioms we listed. The others are simple statements that seem in complete agreement with our experience of the world around us. But the parallel postulate is long and wordy, and difficult to understand without a sketch.

The difference between the parallel postulate and the other axioms was noted by the Greeks, as well as later mathematicians. It was commonly believed that this was not a postulate at all, but a theorem to be proved. For more than 2000 years mathematicians tried repeatedly to prove it.

The most dedicated attempt came from an Italian Jesuit, Girolamo Saccheri (1667–1733). He attempted to prove the parallel postulate in an indirect way, by so-called "reduction to absurdity." He would assume the postulate to be false and then show that the assumption leads to a contradiction of something true (an absurdity). Such a contradiction would thus prove the statement true.

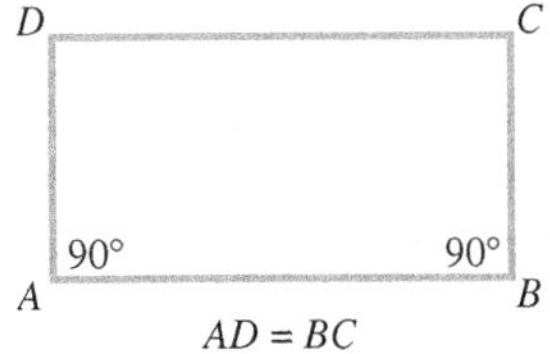


**FIGURE 75**

Saccheri began with a quadrilateral, as in Figure 75. He assumed angles $A$ and $B$ to be right angles and sides $AD$ and $BC$ to be equal. His plan was as follows:

1. To assume that angles $C$ and $D$ are obtuse angles, and to show that this leads to a contradiction.
2. To assume that angles $C$ and $D$ are acute angles, and to show that this also leads to a contradiction.

Newly Recorded...
SONGS BY
TOM LEHRER
(His Lyrics,
His Music,
His So-Called Voice
And His Piano)

Side One:
I Wanna Go Back To Dixie 1:48
The Old Dope Peddler 1:24
When You Are Old And Gray 1:50
The Wild West 1:58
Fight Fiercely Harvard 1:18
Lobachevsky 3:04

Side Two:
The Irish Ballad 1:50
The Hunting Song 2:15
My Home Town 2:38
The Wienerschnitzel Waltz 1:44
I Hold Your Hand In Mine 1:20
Be Prepared 1:26

The songs on this record are © 1952, 1953, by Tom Lehrer, and he is welcome to them. Performing rights on all selections: ASCAP. Cover Design by The Cambridge Design Group.

A song titled simply **Lobachevsky** first appeared on the LP *Songs by Tom Lehrer* (Reprise RS-6216). The liner notes indicate that the song "is a description of one way to get ahead in mathematics (which happens to be the author's own academic specialty) or any other academic field." Find a copy of the album, or the compact disc *The Remains of Tom Lehrer*, and see what Lehrer suggests!

3. Then if $C$ and $D$ can be neither acute nor obtuse angles, they must be right angles.
4. If $C$ and $D$ are both right angles, then it can be proved that the fifth postulate is true. It thus is a theorem rather than a postulate.

Saccheri had no trouble with part 1. However, he did not actually reach a contradiction in the second part, but produced some theorems so "repugnant" that he convinced himself he had vindicated Euclid. In fact, he published a book called in English *Euclid Freed of Every Flaw.*

Today we know that the fifth postulate is indeed an axiom, and not a theorem. It is *consistent* with Euclid's other axioms.

The ten axioms of Euclid describe the world around us with remarkable accuracy. We now realize that the fifth postulate is necessary in Euclidean geometry to establish *flatness.* That is, the axioms of Euclid describe the geometry of *plane surfaces.* By changing the fifth postulate, we can describe the geometry of other surfaces. So, other geometric systems exist as much as Euclidean geometry exists, and they can even be demonstrated in our world. They are just not as familiar. A system of geometry in which the fifth postulate is changed is called a **non-Euclidean geometry.**

**The Origins of Non-Euclidean Geometry** One non-Euclidean system was developed by three people working separately at about the same time. Early in the nineteenth century Carl Friedrich Gauss, one of the great mathematicians, worked out a consistent geometry replacing Euclid's fifth postulate. He never published his work, however, because he feared the ridicule of people who could not free themselves from habitual ways of thinking. Gauss first used the term "non-Euclidean." Nikolai Ivanovich Lobachevski (1793–1856) published a similar system in 1830 in the Russian language. At the same time, Janos Bolyai (1802–1860), a Hungarian army officer, worked out a similar system, which he published in 1832, not knowing about Lobachevski's work. Bolyai never recovered from the disappointment of not being the first, and did no further work in mathematics.

Lobachevski replaced Euclid's fifth postulate with:

> Angles $C$ and $D$ in the quadrilateral of Saccheri are acute angles.

This postulate of Lobachevski can be rephrased as follows:

> Through a point $P$ off a line $k$ (Figure 76), at least two different lines can be drawn parallel to $k$.

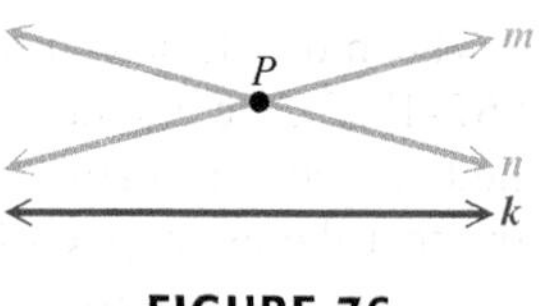


**FIGURE 76**

Compare this form of Lobachevski's postulate to the geometry of Euclid. How many lines can be drawn through $P$ and parallel to $k$ in Euclidean geometry? At first glance, the postulate of Lobachevski does not agree with what we know about the world around us. But this is only because we think of our immediate surroundings as being flat.

Many of the theorems of Euclidean geometry are valid for the geometry of Lobachevski, but many are not. For example, in Euclidean geometry, the sum of the measures of the angles in any triangle is 180°. In Lobachevskian geometry, the sum of the measures of the angles in any triangle is *less* than 180°. Also, triangles of different sizes can never have equal angles, so similar triangles do not exist.

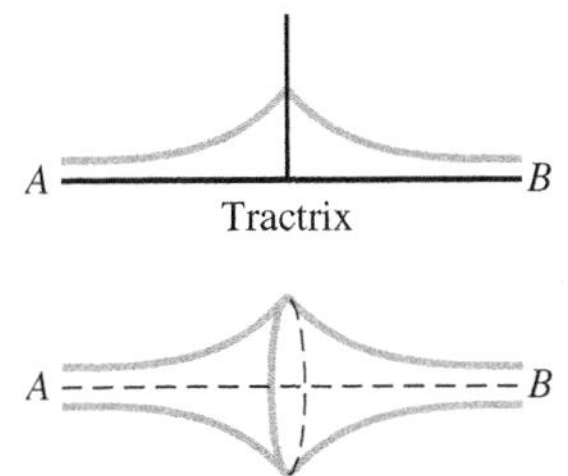


Rotating the tractrix produces the pseudosphere.

**FIGURE 77**

The geometry of Euclid can be represented on a plane. Since any portion of the earth that we are likely to see looks flat, Euclidean geometry is very useful for describing the everyday world around us. The non-Euclidean geometry of Lobachevski can be represented as a surface called a **pseudosphere.** This surface is formed by revolving a curve called a **tractrix** about the line $AB$ in Figure 77.

A second non-Euclidean system was developed by Georg Riemann (1826–1866). He pointed out the difference between a line that continues indefinitely and a line having infinite length. For example, a circle on the surface of a sphere continues indefinitely but does not have infinite length. Riemann developed the idea of geometry on a sphere and replaced Euclid's fifth postulate with:

> Angles $C$ and $D$ of the Saccheri quadrilateral are obtuse angles.

In terms of parallel lines, Riemann's postulate becomes:

> Through a point $P$ off a line $k$, no line can be drawn that is parallel to $k$.

Riemannian geometry is important in navigation. "Lines" in this geometry are really *great circles,* or circles whose centers are at the center of the sphere. The shortest distance between two points on a sphere lies along an arc of a great circle. Great circle routes on a globe don't look at all like the shortest distance when the globe is flattened out to form a map, but this is part of the distortion that occurs when the earth is represented as a flat surface. See Figure 78. The sides of a triangle drawn on a sphere would be arcs of great circles. And, in Riemannian geometry, the sum of the measures of the angles in any triangle is *more* than 180°.

**Georg Friedrich Bernhard Riemann** (1826–1866) was a German mathematician. Though he lived a short time and published few papers, his work forms a basis for much modern mathematics. He made significant contributions to the theory of functions and the study of complex numbers as well as to geometry. Most calculus books today use the idea of a "Riemann sum"in defining the integral.

Riemann achieved a complete understanding of the non-Euclidean geometries of his day, expressing them on curved surfaces and showing how to extend them to higher dimensions.

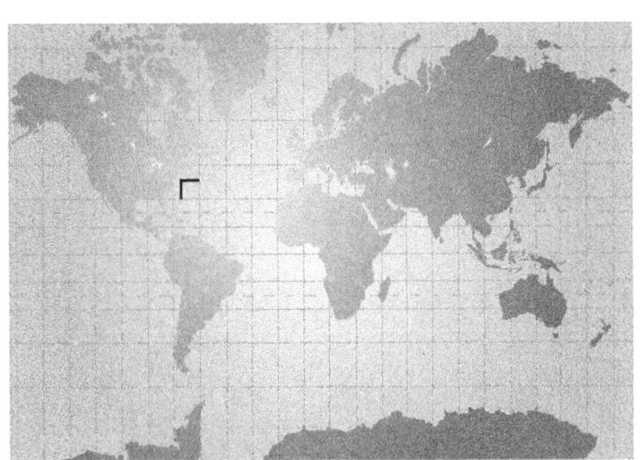

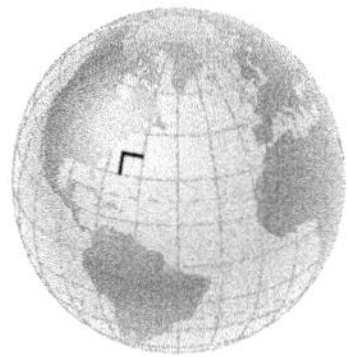

**FIGURE 78**

**Topology** This chapter began by suggesting that Euclidean geometry might seem rigid from a modern-day point of view. The plane and space figures studied in the Euclidean system are carefully distinguished by differences in size, shape, angularity, and so on. For a given figure such properties are permanent, and thus we can ask sensible questions about congruence and similarity. Suppose we studied "figures" made of rubber bands, as it were, "figures" that could be stretched, bent, or otherwise distorted without tearing or scattering. **Topology** does just that.

**Topology and geometry software,** including games for users age 10 and up, can be found at www.geometrygames.org, a site developed by Jeff Weeks. Included are Torus and Klein Bottle Games, Kali, KaleidoTile, classroom materials for teachers of grades 6 to 10, curved spaces for software developers, and research software.

Topological questions concern the basic structure of objects rather than size or arrangement. For example, a typical topological question has to do with the number of holes in an object, a basic structural property that does not change during deformation. You cannot deform a rubber ball to get a rubber band without tearing it—making a hole in it. Thus the two objects are not topologically equivalent. On the other hand, a doughnut and a coffee cup are topologically equivalent, because one could be stretched so as to form the other, without changing the basic structural property.

### EXAMPLE 1 Determining Topological Equivalence

Decide if the figures in each pair are topologically equivalent.

**(a)** a football and a cereal box
**(b)** a doughnut and an unzipped coat

**SOLUTION**

**(a)** If we assume that a football is made of a perfectly elastic substance such as rubber or dough, it could be twisted or kneaded into the same shape as a cereal box. Thus, the two figures are topologically equivalent.

**(b)** A doughnut has one hole, while the coat has two (the sleeve openings). Thus, a doughnut could not be stretched and twisted into the shape of the coat without tearing another hole in it. Because of this, a doughnut and the coat are not topologically equivalent.

In topology, figures are classified according to their **genus**—that is, the number of cuts that can be made without cutting the figures into two pieces. The genus of an object is the number of holes in it. See Figure 79.

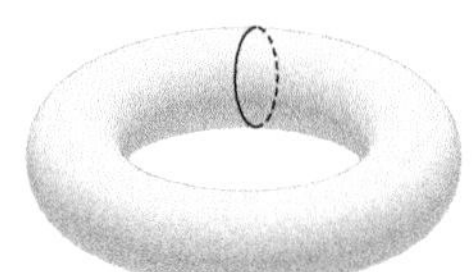

**Torus** One of the most useful figures in topology is the torus, a doughnut-like or tire-shaped surface. Its properties are different from those of a sphere, for example. Imagine a sphere covered with hair. You cannot comb the hairs in a completely smooth way; one fixed point remains, as you can find on your own head. In the same way, on the surface of Earth the winds are not a smooth system. There is a calm point somewhere. However, the hair on a torus could be combed smooth. The winds would be blowing smoothly on a planet shaped like a torus.

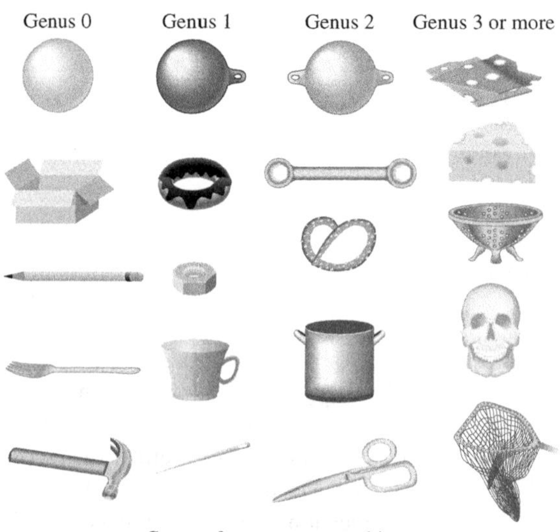

Genus of some common objects

**FIGURE 79**

## For Further Thought

### Two Interesting Topological Surfaces

Two examples of topological surfaces are the **Möbius strip** and the **Klein bottle**. The Möbius strip is a single-sided surface named after August Ferdinand Möbius (1790–1868), a pupil of Gauss.

To construct a Möbius strip, cut out a rectangular strip of paper, perhaps 3 cm by 25 cm. Paste together the two 3-cm ends after giving the paper a half-twist. To see how the strip now has only one side, mark an *x* on the strip and then mark another *x* on what appears to be the other "side." Begin at one of the *x*'s you have drawn, and trace a path along the strip. You will eventually come to the other *x* without crossing the edge of the strip.

A branch of chemistry called chemical topology studies the structures of chemical configurations. A recent advance in this area was the synthesis of the first molecular Möbius strip, which was formed by joining the ends of a double-stranded strip of carbon and oxygen atoms.

*A mathematician confided*
*That a Möbius strip is one-sided.*
*And you'll get quite a laugh*
*If you cut one in half,*
*For it stays in one piece when divided.*

Möbius strip

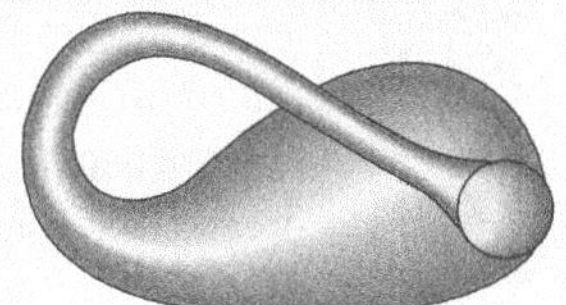

Klein bottle

Whereas a Möbius strip results from giving a paper *strip* a half-twist and then connecting it to itself, if we could do the same thing with a paper *tube* we would obtain a Klein bottle, named after Felix Klein (1849–1925). Klein produced important results in several areas, including non-Euclidean geometry and the early beginnings of group theory. (It is not possible to construct an actual Klein bottle. However, for some interesting blown glass models, see www.kleinbottle.com.)

*A mathematician named Klein*
*Thought the Möbius strip was divine.*
*Said he, "If you glue*
*The edges of two*
*You'll get a weird bottle like mine."*

### For Group Discussion or Individual Investigation

1. The Möbius strip has other interesting properties. With a pair of scissors, cut the strip lengthwise. Do you get two strips? Repeat the process with what you have obtained from the first cut. What happens?
2. Now construct another Möbius strip, and start cutting lengthwise about $\frac{1}{3}$ of the way from one edge. What happens?
3. What would be the advantage of a conveyor belt with the configuration of a Möbius strip?

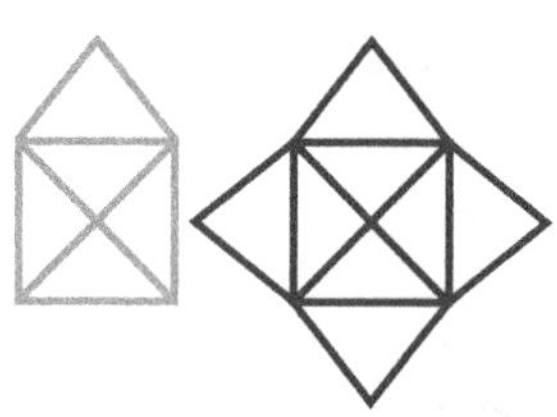

**FIGURE 80**

**Networks*** Another branch of modern geometry is *graph theory*. One topic of study in graph theory is *networks*. A **network** is a diagram showing the various paths (or **arcs**) between points (called **vertices,** or **nodes**). A network can be thought of as a set of arcs and vertices. Figure 80 shows two examples of networks. The study of networks began formally with the so-called Königsberg Bridge problem as solved by Leonhard Euler (1707–1783). In Königsberg, Germany, the River Pregel flowed through the middle of town. There were two islands in the river. During Euler's lifetime, there were seven bridges connecting the islands and the two banks of the river.

The people of the town loved Sunday strolls among the various bridges. Gradually, a competition developed to see if anyone could find a route that crossed each of the seven bridges exactly once. The problem concerns what topologists today call the *traversability* of a network. No one could find a solution. The problem became so famous that in 1735 it reached Euler, who was then at the court of the Russian empress Catherine the Great. In trying to solve the problem, Euler began by drawing a network representing the system of bridges, as in Figure 81.

How should an artist paint a realistic view of railroad tracks going off to the horizon? In reality, the tracks are always at a constant distance apart, but they cannot be drawn that way except from overhead. The artist must make the tracks converge at a point. Only in this way will the scene look "real."

Beginning in the fifteenth century, artists led by Leone Battista Alberti, Leonardo da Vinci, and Albrecht Dürer began to study the problems of representing three dimensions in two. They found geometric methods of doing this. What artists initiated, mathematicians developed into a geometry different from that of Euclid—**projective geometry.**

Gerard Desargues (1591–1661), a French architect and engineer, published in 1636 and 1639 a treatise and proposals about perspective, and had thus invented projective geometry. However, his geometric innovations were hidden for nearly 200 years. A manuscript by Desargues turned up in 1845, about 30 years after Jean-Victor Poncelet had rediscovered projective geometry.

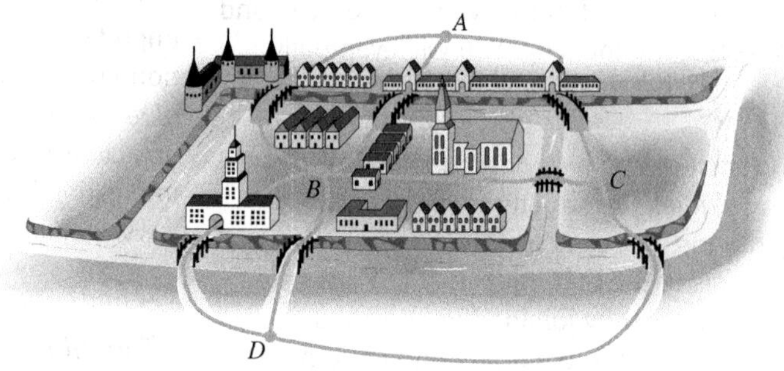


**FIGURE 81**

Euler first noticed that three routes meet at vertex $A$. Because 3 is an odd number, he called $A$ an **odd vertex.** As three routes meet at $A$, it must be a starting or an ending point for any traverse of the network. This must be true; otherwise, when you got to $A$ on your second trip there would be no way to get out. An **even vertex,** one where an even number of routes meet, need not be a starting or an ending point. (Why is this?) Three paths also meet at $C$ and $D$, with five paths meeting at $B$. Thus, $B$, $C$, and $D$ are also odd vertices. An odd vertex must be a starting or an ending point of a traverse. Thus, all four vertices $A$, $B$, $C$, and $D$ must be starting or ending points. Because a network can have only two starting or ending points (one of each), this network cannot be traversed. The residents of Königsberg were trying to do the impossible.

Euler's result can be summarized as follows.

### Results on Vertices and Traversability

1. The number of odd vertices of any network is *even.* (That is, a network must have $2n$ odd vertices, where $n = 0, 1, 2, 3, \ldots$.)
2. A network with no odd vertices or exactly two odd vertices can be traversed. In the case of exactly two, start at one odd vertex and end at the other.
3. A network with more than two odd vertices cannot be traversed.

*An entire chapter on Graph Theory, of which networks is one topic, is available from the publisher. If this chapter is not part of this book and you are interested in more information on networks, contact Addison-Wesley.

## EXAMPLE 2 Deciding Whether Networks Are Traversable

Decide whether the networks are traversable.

**(a)**

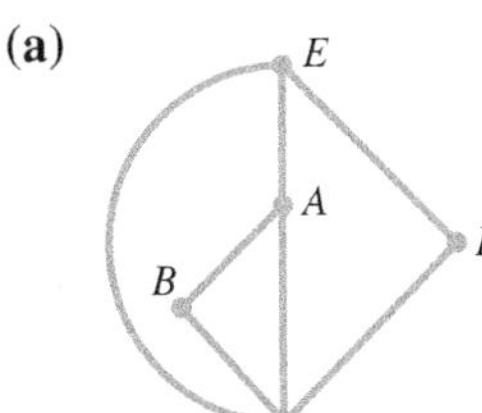


**(b)**

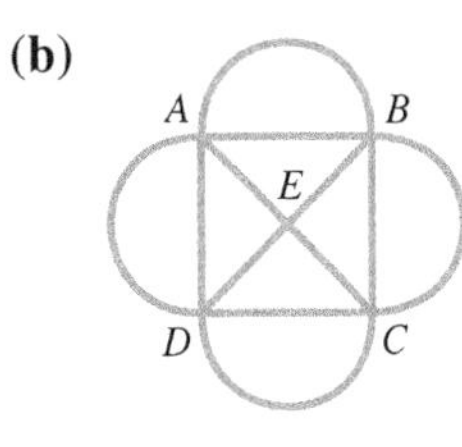


### SOLUTION

**(a)** Because there are exactly two odd vertices ($A$ and $E$) this network can be traversed. One way to traverse the network is to start at $A$, go through $B$ to $C$, then back to $A$. (It is acceptable to go through a vertex as many times as needed.) Then go to $E$, to $D$, to $C$, and finally go back to $E$. It is traversable.

**(b)** Because vertices $A$, $B$, $C$, and $D$ are all odd (five routes meet at each of them), this network is not traversable. (One of the authors of this text, while in high school, tried for hours to traverse it, not knowing he was attempting the impossible!)

## EXAMPLE 3 Applying Traversability Concepts to a Floor Plan

The figure shows the floor plan of a house. Is it possible to travel through this house, going through each door exactly once?

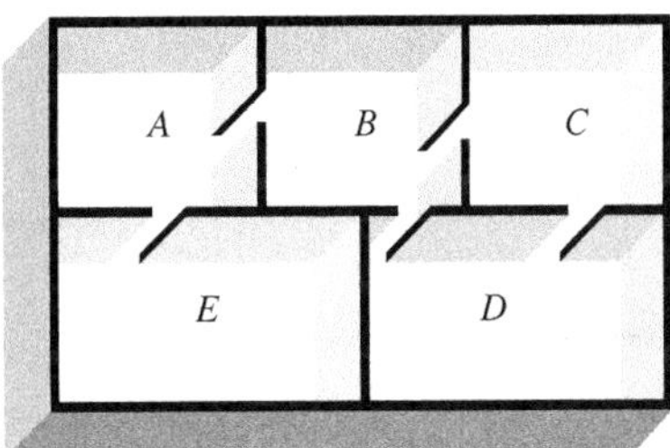


### SOLUTION

Rooms $A$, $C$, and $D$ have even numbers of doors, while rooms $B$ and $E$ have odd numbers of doors. If we think of the rooms as the vertices of a graph, then the fact that we have exactly two odd vertices means that it is possible to travel through each door of the house exactly once. One can either start in room $B$ or room $E$. The figure here shows how this can be done starting in room $E$.

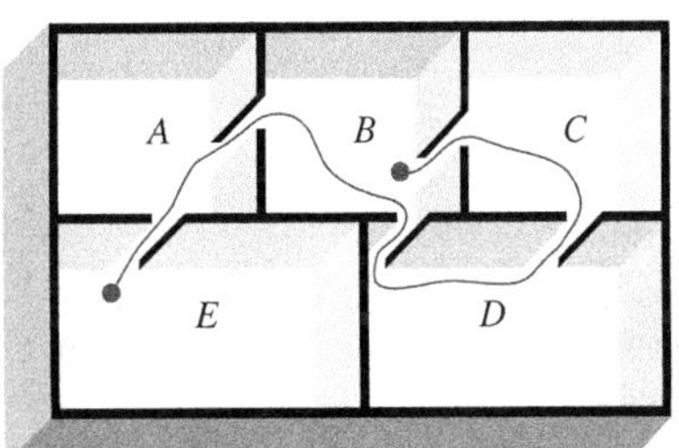

## 9.7 EXERCISES

*The chart that follows characterizes certain properties of Euclidean and non-Euclidean geometries. Study it, and use it to respond to Exercises 1–10.*

| EUCLIDEAN | NON-EUCLIDEAN | |
|---|---|---|
| **Dates back to about 300 B.C.** | **Lobachevskian (about 1830)** | **Riemannian (about 1850)** |
| Lines have *infinite* length. | | Lines have *finite* length. |
| Geometry on a plane 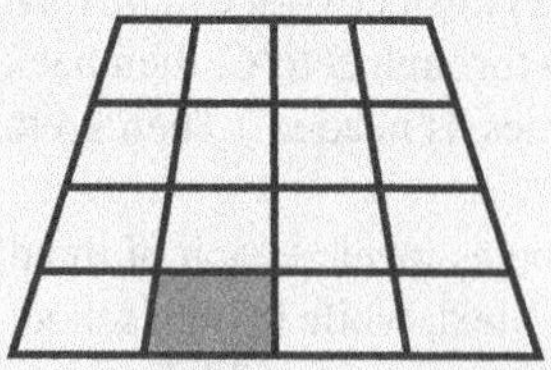 | Geometry on a surface like a pseudosphere 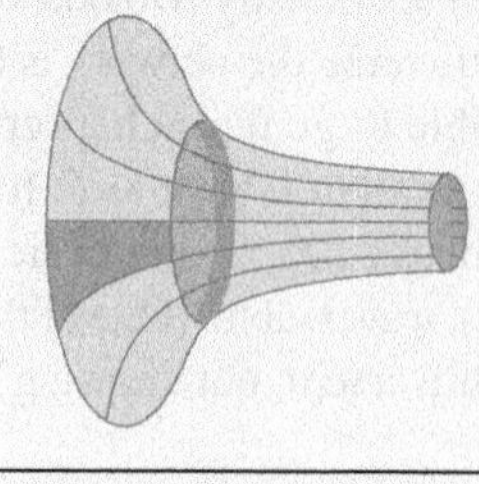 | Geometry on a sphere  |
| Angles $C$ and $D$ of a Saccheri quadrilateral are *right* angles. 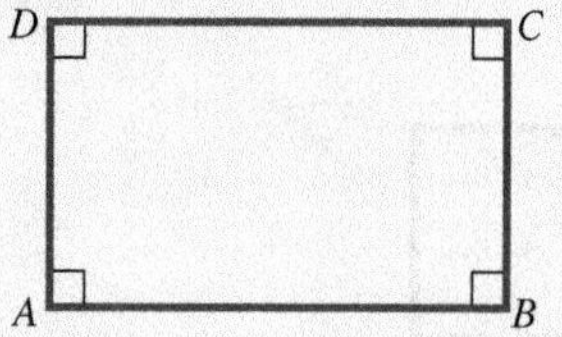 (D, C, A, B) | Angles $C$ and $D$ are *acute* angles. 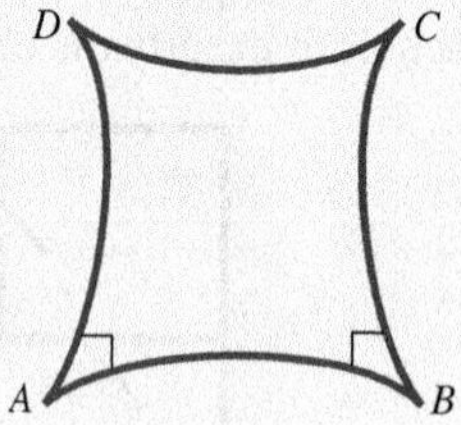 (D, C, A, B) | Angles $C$ and $D$ are *obtuse* angles. 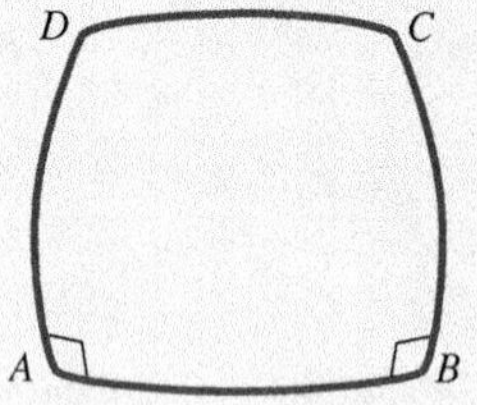 (D, C, A, B) |
| Given point $P$ off line $k$, exactly *one* line can be drawn through $P$ and parallel to $k$. | *More than one* line can be drawn through $P$ and parallel to $k$. | *No* line can be drawn through $P$ and parallel to $k$. |
| Typical triangle $ABC$ 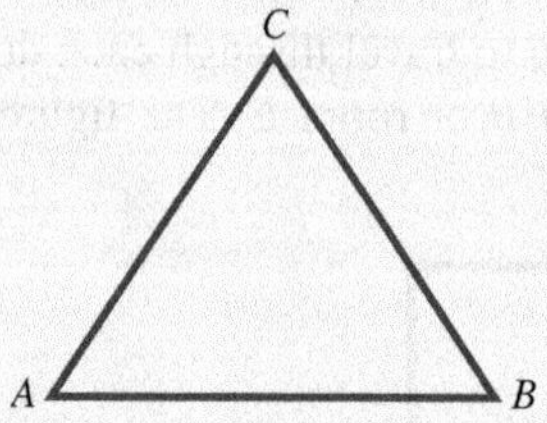 (C, A, B) | Typical triangle $ABC$ 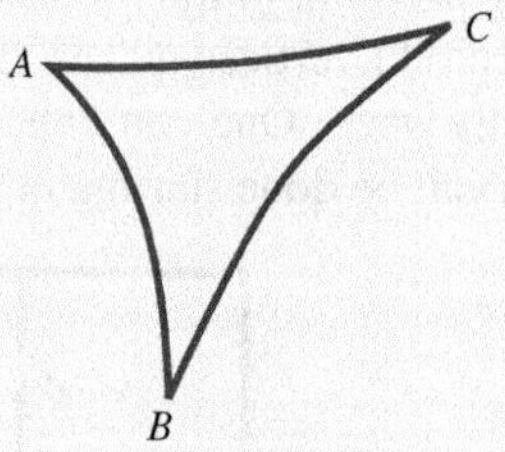 (A, C, B) | Typical triangle $ABC$ 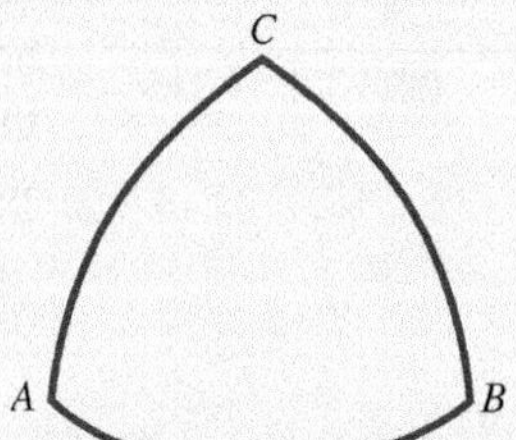 (C, A, B) |
| Two triangles can have the same size angles but different size sides (similarity as well as congruence). | Two triangles with the same size angles must have the same size sides (congruence only). | |

1. In which geometry is the sum of the measures of the angles of a triangle equal to 180°?

2. In which geometry is the sum of the measures of the angles of a triangle greater than 180°?

3. In which geometry is the sum of the measures of the angles of a triangle less than 180°?

4. In a quadrilateral *ABCD* in Lobachevskian geometry, the sum of the measures of the angles must be ________________ 360°.
(less than/greater than)

5. In a quadrilateral *ABCD* in Riemannian geometry, the sum of the measures of the angles must be ________________ 360°.
(less than/greater than)

6. Suppose that *m* and *n* represent lines through *P* that are both parallel to *k*. In which geometry is this possible?

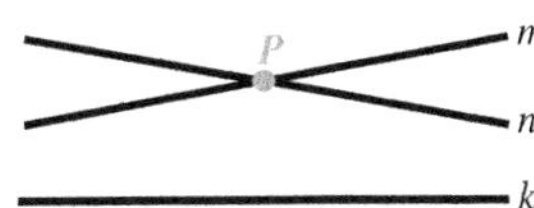


7. Suppose that *m* and *n* below *must* meet at a point. In which geometry is this possible?

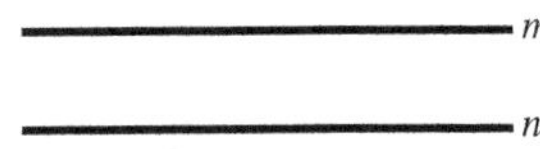


8. A globe representing the earth is a model for a surface in which geometry?

9. In which geometry is this statement possible? "Triangle *ABC* and triangle *DEF* are such that $\measuredangle A = \measuredangle D$, $\measuredangle B = \measuredangle E$, and $\measuredangle C = \measuredangle F$, and they have different areas."

10. Draw a figure (on a sheet of paper) as best you can showing the shape formed by the north pole *N* and two points *A* and *B* lying at the equator of a model of the earth.

11. Pappus, a Greek mathematician in Alexandria about A.D. 320, wrote a commentary on the geometry of the times. We will work out a theorem of his about a hexagon inscribed in two intersecting lines. First we need to define an old word in a new way: a **hexagon** consists of any six lines in a plane, no three of which meet in the same point. As the figure shows, the vertices of several hexagons are labeled with numbers. Thus 1–2 represents a line segment joining vertices 1 and 2. Segments 1–2 and 4–5 are opposite sides of a hexagon, as are 2–3 and 5–6, and 3–4 and 6–1.
   (a) Draw an angle less than 180°.
   (b) Choose three points on one side of the angle. Label them 1, 5, 3 in that order, beginning with the point nearest the vertex.
   (c) Choose three points on the other side of the angle. Label them 6, 2, 4 in that order, beginning with the point nearest the vertex.
   (d) Draw line segments 1–6 and 3–4. Draw lines through the segments so they extend to meet in a point; call it *N*.
   (e) Let lines through 1–2 and 4–5 meet in point *M*.
   (f) Let lines through 2–3 and 5–6 meet in *P*.
   (g) Draw a straight line through points *M, N,* and *P*.
   (h) Write in your own words a theorem generalizing your result.

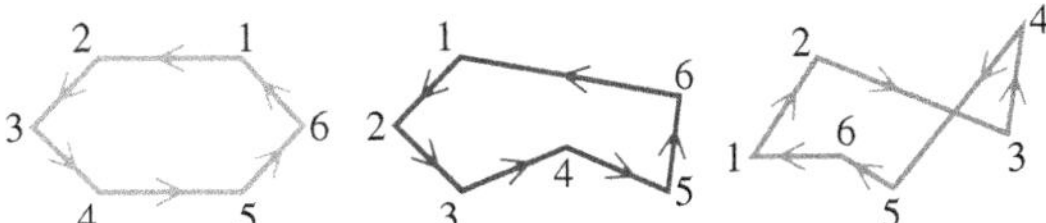


12. The following theorem comes from projective geometry:

***Theorem of Desargues in a Plane*** Desargues's theorem states that in a plane, if two triangles are placed so that lines joining corresponding vertices meet in a point, then corresponding sides, when extended, will meet in three collinear points. (*Collinear* points are points lying on the same line.)

Draw a figure that illustrates this theorem.

*In Exercises 13–20 on the next page, each figure may be topologically equivalent to none or some of the objects labeled* A–E. *List all topological equivalences (by letter) for each figure.*

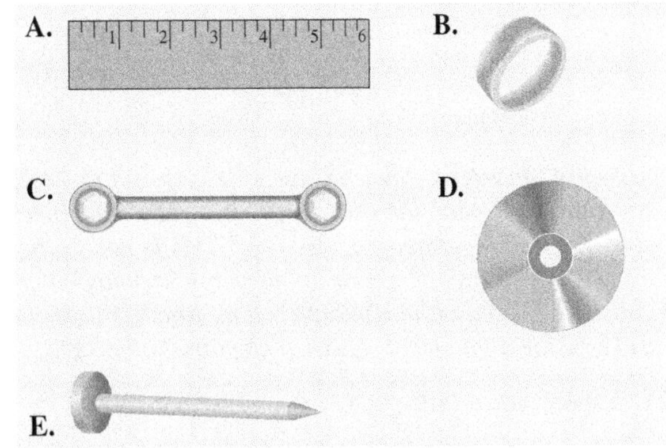

**13.**

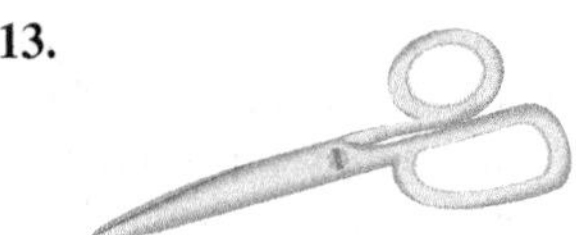

(a pair of scissors)

**14.**

(a carrot)

**15.**

(a calculator)

**16.** **17.**

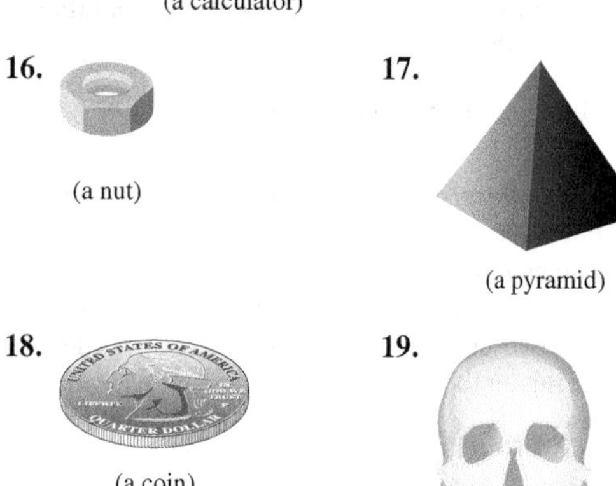

(a nut)

(a pyramid)

**18.**

(a coin)

**19.**

(a skull)

**20.**

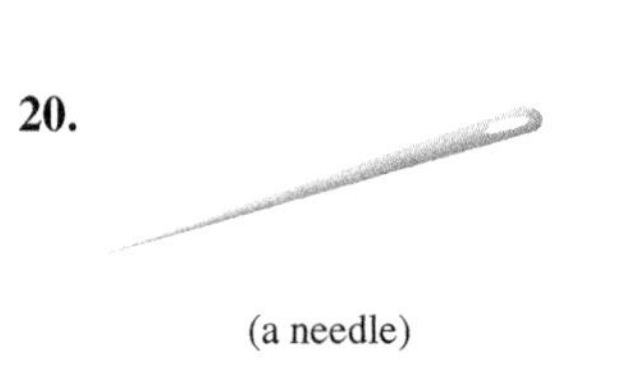

(a needle)

***Topological Equivalence*** *Someone once described a topologist as "a mathematician who doesn't know the difference between a doughnut and a coffee cup." This is due to the fact that both are of genus 1—they are topologically equivalent. Based on this interpretation, would a topologist know the difference between each pair of objects?*

**21.** a spoon and a fork

**22.** a mixing bowl and a colander

**23.** a slice of American cheese and a slice of Swiss cheese

**24.** a compact disc and a phonograph record

*Give the genus of each object.*

**25.** a compact disc

**26.** a phonograph record

**27.** a sheet of loose-leaf paper made for a three-ring binder

**28.** a sheet of loose-leaf paper made for a two-ring binder

**29.** a wedding band

**30.** a postage stamp

*For each network, decide whether each lettered vertex is* even *or* odd.

**31.**

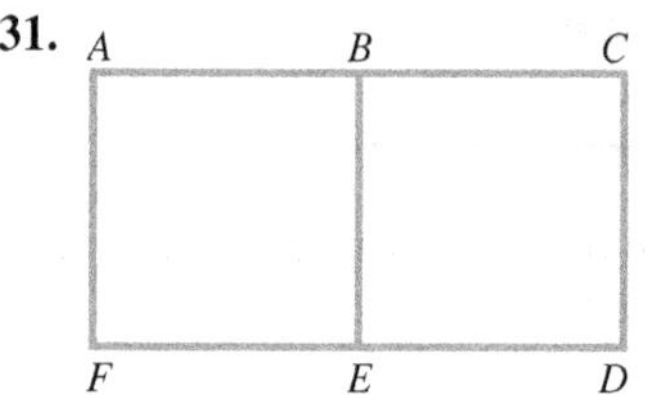



**32.**

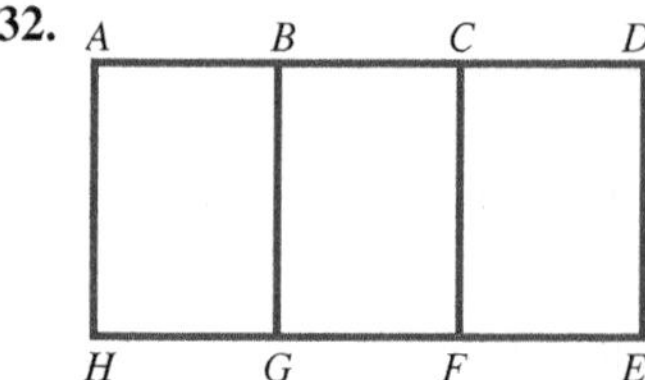



**33.**

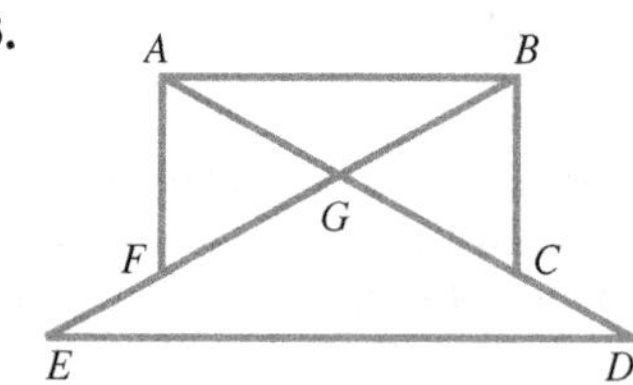



**34.**

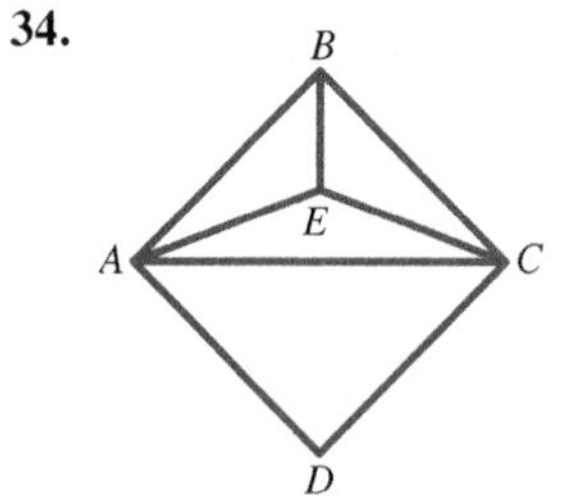

35.

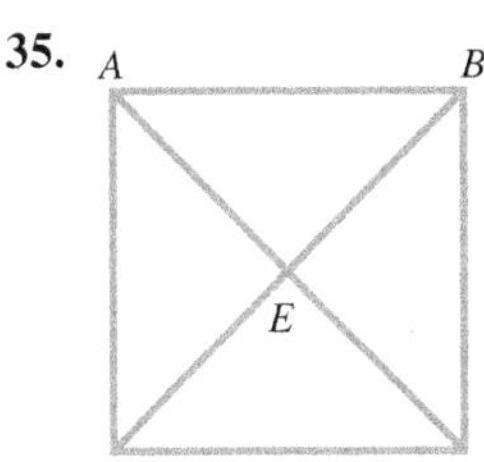


36.

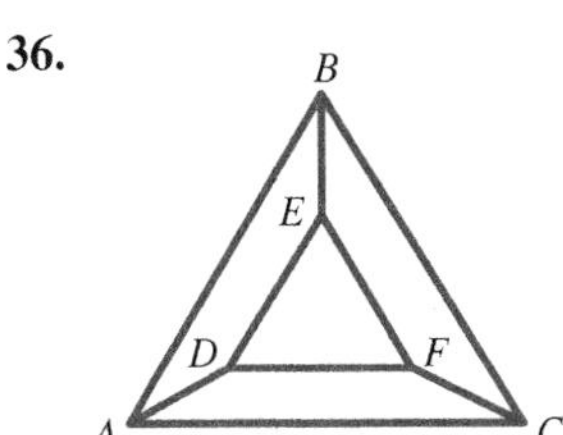


*Decide whether each network is traversable. If a network is traversable, show how it can be traversed.*

37.

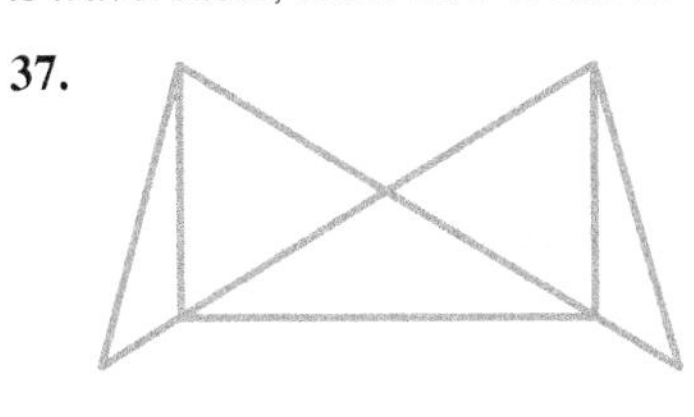

38.

39.

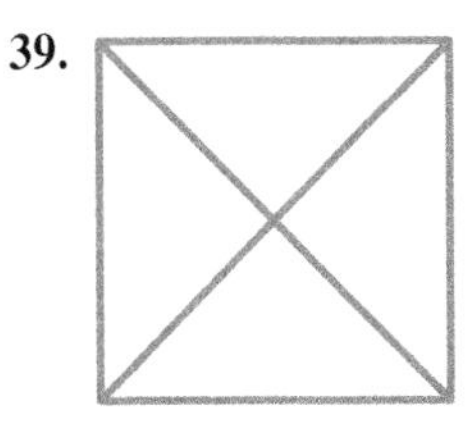

40.

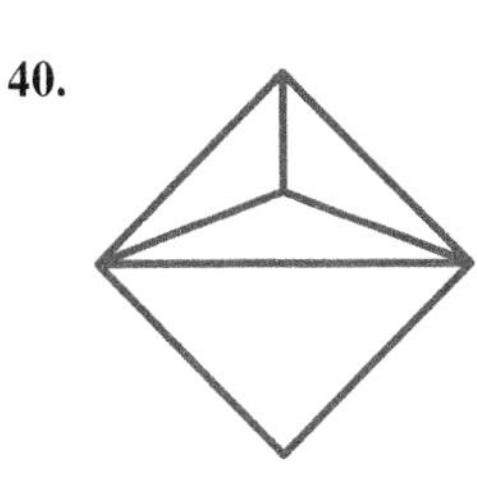

41.

42.

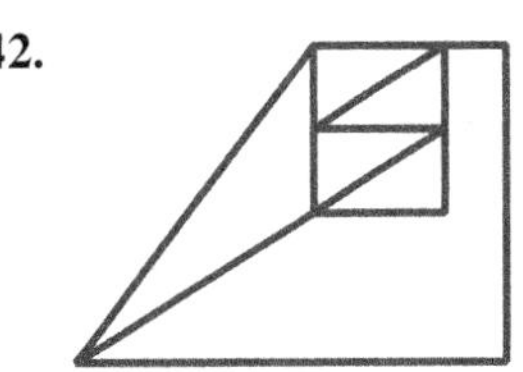

*Is it possible to walk through each door of the following houses exactly once? If the answer is "yes," show how it can be done.*

43.

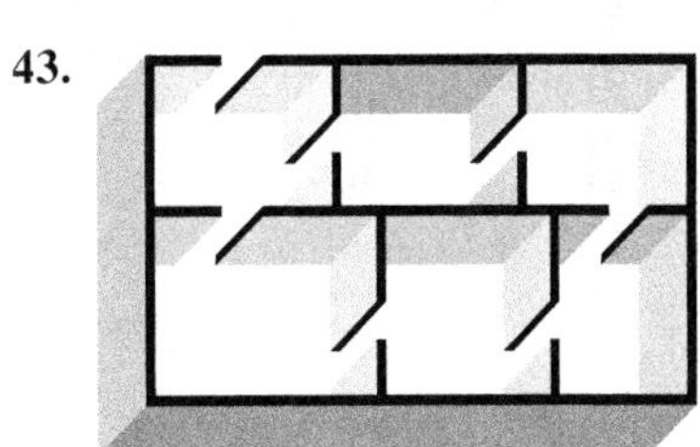

44.

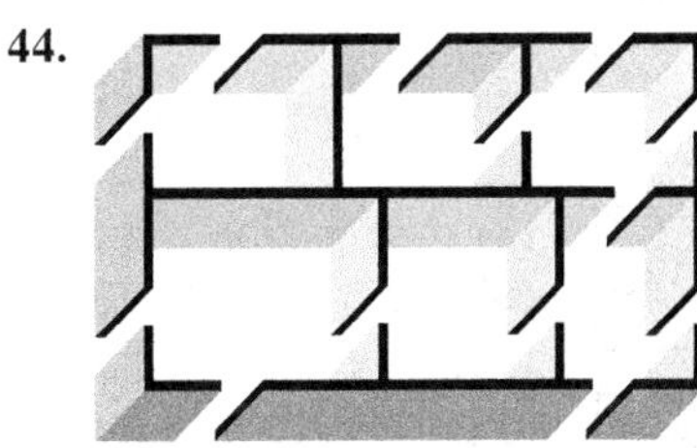

45.

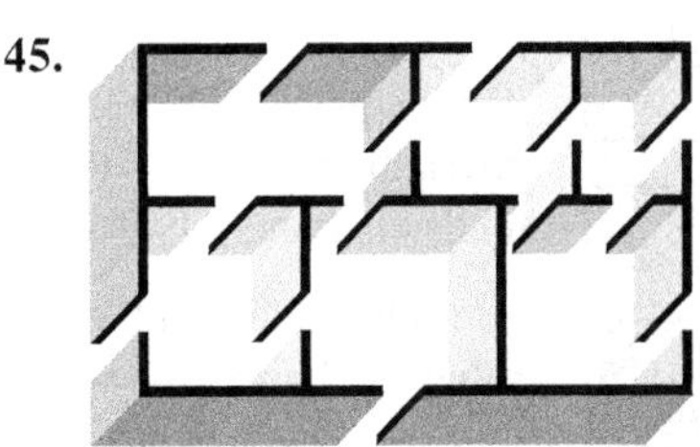

46.

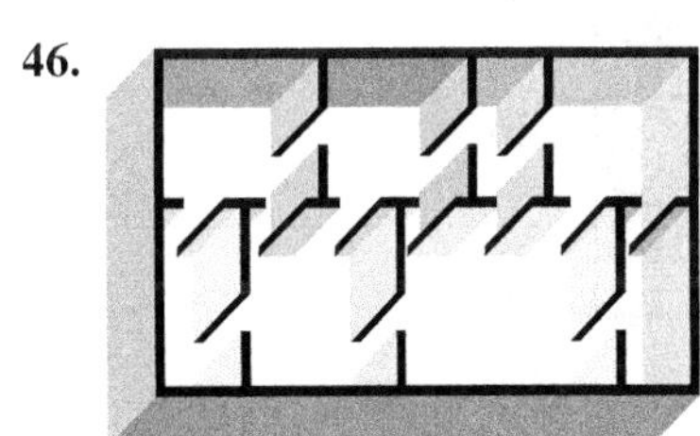

# 9.8 Chaos and Fractal Geometry

**Chaos • Fractals**

```
.8→X
                .8
2X(1-X)→X
               .32
             .4352
         .49160192
       .4998589445
```

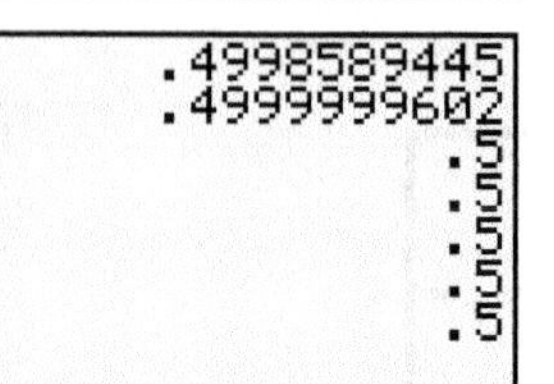


These two screens show how the TI-83/84 Plus calculator can produce the sequence described.

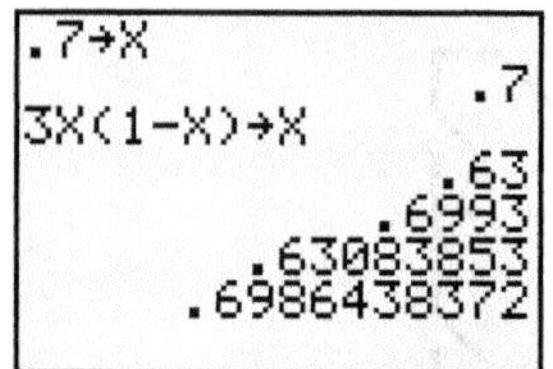


```
.6958837812
.6348886328
.6954151702
.6354387337
.6949690482
.6359612107
.6945436475
```

```
 .382819683
.8269407066
.5008842103
.8749972636
 .382819683
.8269407066
.5008842103
```

These screens support the discussion in Examples 1 and 2.

## Chaos

*Does Chaos Rule the Cosmos?*

—One of the ten great unanswered questions of science, as found in the November 1992 issue of *Discover*

Consider the equation $y = kx(1 - x)$. Choosing $k = 2$ gives the equation $y = 2x(1 - x)$, which can be "iterated" by starting with an arbitrary $x$-value between 0 and 1, calculating the resulting $y$-value, substituting that $y$-value back in as $x$, calculating the resulting $y$-value, substituting that $y$-value back in as $x$, calculating another $y$-value, and so on. For example, a starting value of $x = .8$ produces the following sequence (which you can verify with a calculator):

$$.8, .32, .435, .492, .500, .500, .500, \quad \text{and so on.}$$

The sequence seems to begin randomly but quickly stabilizes at the value .500. A different initial $x$-value would produce another sequence which would also "converge" to .500. The value .500 can be called an *attractor* for the sequence generated by the equation $y = 2x(1 - x)$. The values of the sequence are "attracted" toward .500.

### EXAMPLE 1 Finding Attractors

For the equation $y = kx(1 - x)$ with $k = 3$, begin with $x = .7$ and iterate with a calculator. What pattern emerges?

**SOLUTION**

Using a TI-83/84 Plus calculator, we find that the seventeenth through twentieth iterations give the sequence of terms

.6354387337, **.6949690482**, .6359612107, **.6945436475**.

This sequence apparently converges in a manner different from the initial discussion, alternating between values near .636 and .695. Therefore, for $k = 3$, the sequence tends alternately toward two distinct attractors. ■

It happens that the equation in Example 1 exhibits the same behavior for any initial value of $x$ between 0 and 1. You are asked to show this for several cases in the exercises.

### EXAMPLE 2 Finding Attractors

In the equation of Example 1, change the multiplier $k$ to 3.5, and find the forty-fourth through fifty-first terms. What pattern emerges?

**SOLUTION**

Again, using a TI-83/84 Plus calculator, and rounding to three decimal places, we get

$$.383, .827, .501, .875, .383, .827, .501, .875.$$

This sequence seems to stabilize around four alternating attractors, .383, .827, .501, and .875. ■

**John Nash,** a notable modern American mathematician (born in 1928), first came to the attention of the general public through his biography *A Beautiful Mind* (and the movie of the same name). In 1958 Nash narrowly lost out to René Thom (topologist and inventor of catastrophe theory, discussed on page 612) for the Fields Medal, the mathematical equivalent of the Nobel prize. Although his brilliant career was sadly interrupted by mental illness for a period of about thirty years, in 1994 Nash was awarded "the Central Bank of Sweden Prize in Economic Science in Memory of Alfred Nobel," generally regarded as equivalent to the Nobel prize. This award was for Nash's equilibrium theorem, published in his doctoral thesis in 1950. It turned out that Nash's work established a significant new way of analyzing rational conflict and cooperation in economics and other social sciences.

Notice that in our initial discussion, for $k = 2$, the sequence converged to *one* attractor. In Example 1, for $k = 3$, it converged to *two* attractors, and in Example 2, for $k = 3.5$, it converged to *four* attractors.

If $k$ is increased further, it turns out that the number of attractors doubles over and over again, more and more often. In fact, this doubling has occurred infinitely many times before $k$ even gets as large as 4. When we look closely at groups of these doublings we find that they are always similar to earlier groups but on a smaller scale. This is called *self-similarity,* or *scaling,* an idea that is not new, but which has taken on new significance in recent years. Somewhere before $k$ reaches 4, the resulting sequence becomes apparently totally random, with no attractors and no stability. This type of condition is one instance of what has come to be known in the scientific community as **chaos.** This name came from an early paper by the mathematician James A. Yorke, of the University of Maryland at College Park.

The equation $y = kx(1 - x)$ does not look all that complicated, but the intricate behavior exhibited by it and similar equations has occupied some of the brightest minds (not to mention computers) in various fields—ecology, biology, physics, genetics, economics, mathematics—since about 1960. Such an equation might represent, for example, the population of some animal species where the value of $k$ is determined by factors (such as food supply, or predators that prey on the species) that affect the increase or decrease of the population. Under certain conditions there is a long-run steady-state population (a single attractor). Under other conditions the population will eventually fluctuate between two alternating levels (two attractors), or four, or eight, and so on. But after a certain value of $k,$ the long-term population becomes totally chaotic and unpredictable.

As long as $k$ is small enough, there will be some number of attractors and the long-term behavior of the sequence (or population) is the same regardless of the initial $x$-value. But once $k$ is large enough to cause chaos, the long-term behavior of the system will change drastically when the initial $x$-value is changed only slightly. For example, consider the following two sequences, both generated from $y = 4x(1 - x)$.

$$.600, .960, .154, .520, .998, .006, .025, \ldots$$
$$.610, .952, .184, .601, .959, .157, .529, \ldots$$

The fact that the two sequences wander apart from one another is partly due to round-off errors along the way. But Yorke and others have shown that even "exact" calculations of the iterates would quickly produce divergent sequences just because of the slightly different initial values. This type of "sensitive dependence on initial conditions" was discovered (accidentally) back in the 1960s by Edward Lorenz when he was looking for an effective computerized model of weather patterns. He discerned the implication that any long-range weather predicting schemes might well be hopeless.

Patterns like those in the sequences above are more than just numerical oddities. Similar patterns apply to a great many phenomena in the physical, biological, and social sciences, many of them seemingly common natural systems that have been studied for hundreds of years. The measurement of a coastline, the description of the patterns in a branching tree, or a mountain range, or a cloud formation, or intergalactic cosmic dust, the prediction of weather patterns, the turbulent behavior of fluids of all kinds, the circulatory and neurological systems of the human body, fluctuations in populations and economic systems—these and many other phenomena remain mysteries, concealing their true nature somewhere beyond the reach of even our biggest and fastest computers.

Continuous phenomena are easily dealt with. A change in one quantity produces a predictable change in another. (For example, a little more pressure on the gas pedal produces a little more speed.) Mathematical functions that represent continuous events can be graphed by unbroken lines or curves, or perhaps smooth, gradually changing surfaces. The governing equations for such phenomena are "linear," and extensive mathematical methods of solving them have been developed. On the other hand, erratic events associated with certain other equations are harder to describe or predict. The science of chaos, made possible by modern computers, continues to open up new ways to deal with such events.

FIGURE 82

One early attempt to deal with discontinuous processes in a new way, generally acknowledged as a forerunner of chaos theory, was that of the French mathematician René Thom, who, in the 1960s, applied the methods of topology. To emphasize the feature of sudden change, Thom referred to events such as a heartbeat, a buckling beam, a stock market crash, a riot, or a tornado, as *catastrophes.* He proved that all catastrophic events (in our four-dimensional space-time) are combinations of seven elementary catastrophes. (In higher dimensions the number quickly approaches infinity.)

Each of the seven elementary catastrophes has a characteristic topological shape. Two examples are shown in Figure 82. The top figure is called a *cusp.* The bottom figure is an *elliptic umbilicus* (a belly button with an oval cross-section). Thom's work became known as **catastrophe theory.**

Computer graphics have been indispensable in the study of chaotic processes. The plotting of large numbers of points has revealed patterns that would otherwise have not been observed. (The underlying reasons for many of these patterns, however, have still not been explained.) The images shown in Figure 83 are created using chaotic processes.

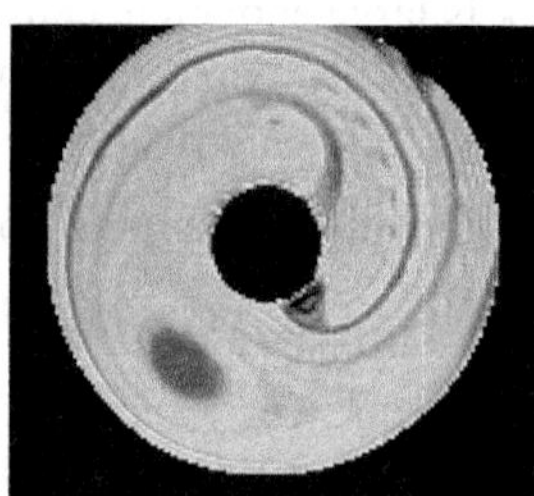

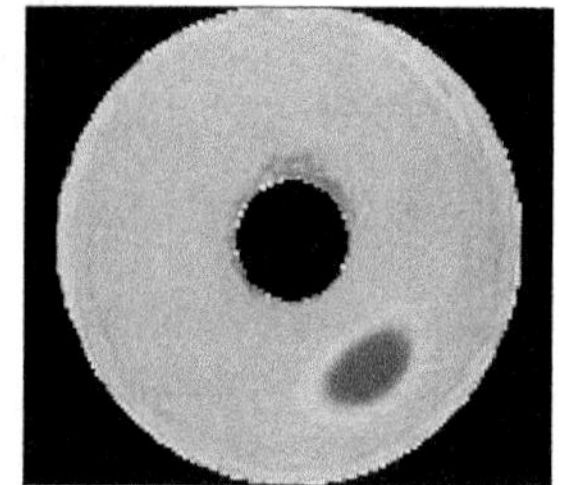

FIGURE 83

The surface of the earth, consisting of continents, mountains, oceans, valleys, and so on, has **fractal dimension** 2.2.

**Fractals** If there is one structure that has provided a key for the new study of nonlinear processes, it is **fractal geometry,** developed over a period of years mainly by the IBM mathematician Benoit Mandelbrot (1924– ). For his work in this field, and at the recommendation of the National Science Foundation, Columbia University awarded Mandelbrot the 1985 Bernard Medal for Meritorious Service to Science.

Lines have a single dimension. Plane figures have two dimensions, and we live in a three-dimensional spatial world. In a paper published in 1967, Mandelbrot investigated the idea of measuring the length of a coastline. He concluded that such a shape defies conventional Euclidean geometry and that rather than having a natural number dimension, it has a "fractional dimension." A coastline is an example of a *self-similar shape*—a shape that repeats itself over and over on different scales. From a distance, the bays and inlets cannot be individually observed, but as one moves closer they

FIGURE 84

become more apparent. The branching of a tree, from twig to limb to trunk, also exhibits a shape that repeats itself.

In the early twentieth century, the German mathematician H. von Koch investigated the so-called Koch snowflake. It is shown in Figure 84. Starting with an equilateral triangle, each side then gives rise to another equilateral triangle. The process continues over and over, indefinitely, and a curve of infinite length is produced. The mathematics of Koch's era was not advanced enough to deal with such figures. However, using Mandelbrot's theory, it is shown that the Koch snowflake has dimension of about 1.26. This figure is obtained using a formula which involves logarithms. (Logarithms were introduced briefly in Chapter 8.)

FIGURE 85

The theory of fractals is today being applied to many areas of science and technology. It has been used to analyze the symmetry of living forms, the turbulence of liquids, the branching of rivers, and price variation in economics. Hollywood has used fractals in the special effects found in some blockbuster movies. Figure 85 shows an example of a computer-generated fractal design.

An interesting account of the science of chaos is found in the popular 1987 book *Chaos,* by James Gleick. Mandelbrot has published two books on fractals. They are *Fractals: Form, Chance, and Dimension* (1975), and *The Fractal Geometry of Nature* (1982).

Aside from providing a geometric structure for chaotic processes in nature, fractal geometry is viewed by many as a significant new art form. (To appreciate why, see the 1986 publication *The Beauty of Fractals,* by H. O. Peitgen and P. H. Richter, which contains 184 figures, many in color.) Peitgen and others have also published *Fractals for the Classroom: Strategic Activities Volume One* (Springer-Verlag, 1991).

## 9.8 Exercises

*Exercises 1–25 are taken from an issue of* Student Math Notes, *published by the National Council of Teachers of Mathematics. They were written by Dr. Tami S. Martin, Mathematics Department, Illinois State University, and the authors wish to thank N.C.T.M. and Tami Martin for permission to reproduce this activity. Because the exercises should be done in numerical order, answers to all exercises (both even- and odd-numbered) appear in the answer section of this book.*

*Most of the mathematical objects you have studied have dimensions that are whole numbers. For example, such solids as cubes and icosahedrons have dimension three. Squares, triangles, and many other planar figures are two-dimensional. Lines are one-dimensional, and points have dimension zero. Consider a square with side of length one. Gather several of these squares by cutting out or using patterning blocks.*

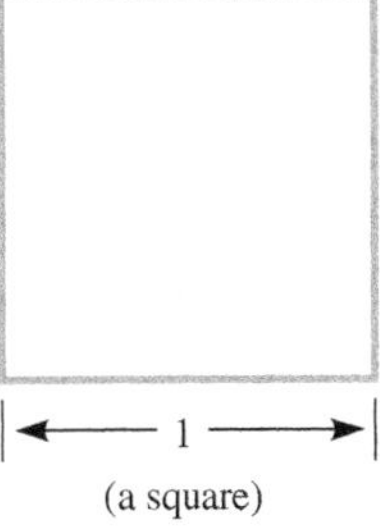


(a square)

*The size of a figure is calculated by counting the number of* replicas *(small pieces) that make it up. Here, a replica is the original square with edges of length one.*

1. What is the least number of these squares that can be put together edge to edge to form a larger square?

*The original square is made up of one small square, so its size is one.*

2. What is the size of the new square?

3. What is the length of each edge of the new square?

*Similar figures have the same shape but are not necessarily the same size. The* **scale factor** *between two similar figures can be found by calculating the ratio of corresponding edges:*

$$\frac{\text{new length}}{\text{old length}}.$$

4. What is the scale factor between the large square and the small square?

5. Find the ratio $\frac{\text{new size}}{\text{old size}}$ for the two squares.

6. Form an even larger square that is three units long on each edge. Compare this square to the small square. What is the scale factor between the two squares? What is the ratio of the new size to the old size?

7. Form an even larger square that is four units long on each edge. Compare this square to the small square. What is the scale factor between the two squares? What is the ratio of the new size to the old size?

8. Complete the table for squares.

| Scale Factor | 2 | 3 | 4 | 5 | 6 | 10 |
|---|---|---|---|---|---|---|
| Ratio of new size to old size | | | | | | |

9. How are the two rows in the table related?

*Consider an equilateral triangle. The length of an edge of the triangle is one unit. The size of this triangle is one.*

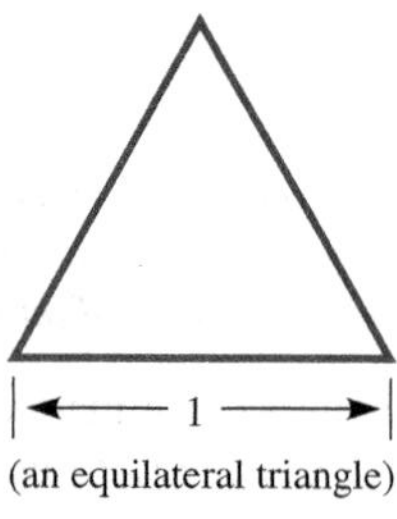

(an equilateral triangle)

10. What is the least number of equilateral triangles that can be put together edge to edge to form a similar larger triangle?

11. Complete the table for triangles.

| Scale Factor | 2 | 3 | 4 | 5 | 6 | 10 |
|---|---|---|---|---|---|---|
| Ratio of new size to old size | | | | | | |

12. How does the relationship between the two rows in this table compare with the one you found in the table for squares?

*One way to define the dimension, d, of a figure relates the scale factor, the new size, and the old size:*

$$(\text{scale factor})^d = \frac{\text{new size}}{\text{old size}}.$$

*Using a scale factor of two for squares or equilateral triangles, we can see that $2^d = \frac{4}{1}$; that is, $2^d = 4$. Because $2^2 = 4$, the dimension, d, must be two. This definition of dimension confirms what we already know—that squares and equilateral triangles are two-dimensional figures.*

13. Use this definition and your completed tables to confirm that the square and the equilateral triangle are two-dimensional figures for scale factors other than two.

*Consider a cube, with edges of length one. Let the size of the cube be one.*

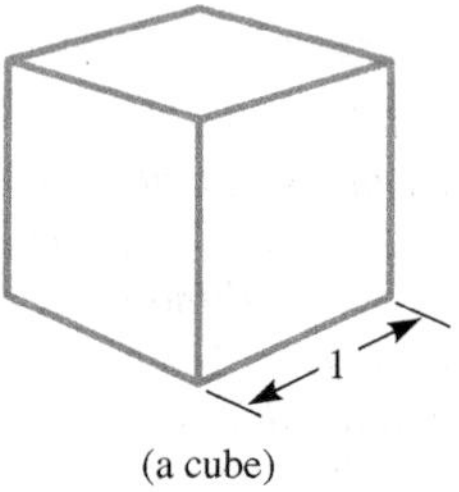

(a cube)

14. What is the least number of these cubes that can be put together face to face to form a larger cube?

15. What is the scale factor between these two cubes? What is the ratio of the new size to the old size for the two cubes?

16. Complete the table for cubes.

| Scale Factor | 2 | 3 | 4 | 5 | 6 | 10 |
|---|---|---|---|---|---|---|
| Ratio of new size to old size | | | | | | |

17. How are the two rows in the table related?

18. Use the definition of dimension and a scale factor of two to verify that a cube is a three-dimensional object.

*We have explored scale factors and sizes associated with two- and three-dimensional figures. Is it possible for mathematical objects to have fractional dimensions? Consider each figure formed by replacing the middle third of a line segment of length one by one upside-down V, each of whose two sides are equal in length to the segment removed. The first four stages in the development of this figure are shown.*

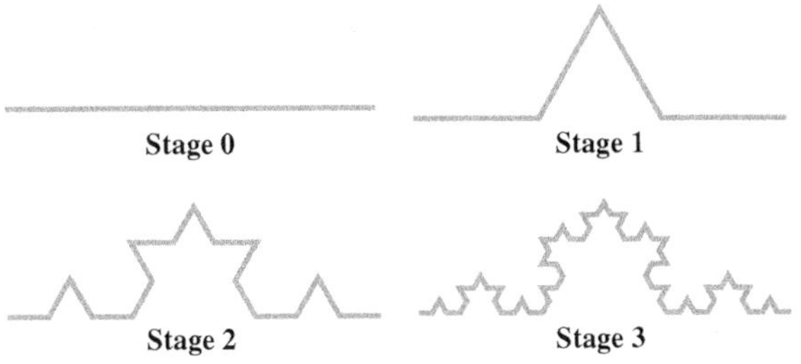


*Finding the scale factor for this sequence of figures is difficult, because the overall length of a representative portion of the figure remains the same while the number of pieces increases. To simplify the procedure, follow these steps.*

***Step 1*** *Start with any stage (e.g., Stage 1).*

***Step 2*** *Draw the next stage (e.g., Stage 2) of the sequence and "blow it up" so that it contains an exact copy of the preceding stage (in this example, Stage 1).*

*Notice that Stage 2 contains four copies, or replicas, of Stage 1 and is three times as long as Stage 1.*

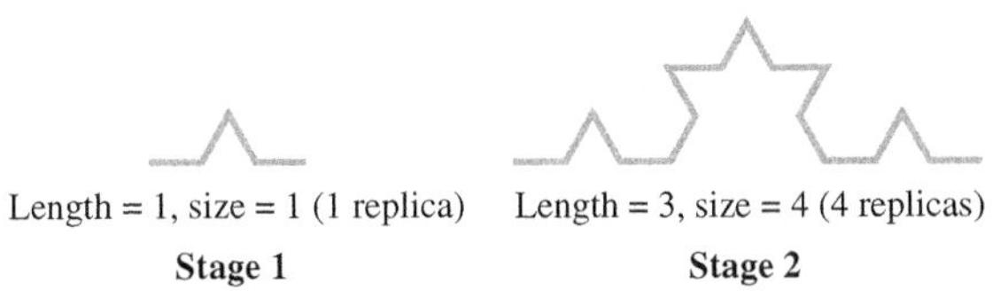


19. The scale factor is equal to the ratio $\frac{\text{new length}}{\text{old length}}$ between any two consecutive stages. The scale factor between Stage 1 and Stage 2 is _____.

20. The size can be determined by counting the number of replicas of Stage 1 found in Stage 2. Old size = 1, new size = _____.

*Use the definition of dimension to compute the dimension, d, of the figure formed by this process:* $3^d = \frac{4}{1}$; *that is,* $3^d = 4$. *Since* $3^1 = 3$ *and* $3^2 = 9$, *for* $3^d = 4$ *the dimension of the figure must be greater than one but less than two:* $1 < d < 2$.

21. Use your calculator to estimate $d$. Remember that $d$ is the exponent that makes $3^d$ equal 4. For example, because $d$ must be between 1 and 2, try $d = 1.5$. But $3^{1.5} = 5.196\ldots$, which is greater than 4; thus $d$ must be smaller than 1.5. Continue until you approximate $d$ to three decimal places. (Use logarithms for maximum accuracy.)

*The original figure was a one-dimensional line segment. By iteratively adding to the line segment, an object of dimension greater than one but less than two was generated. Objects with fractional dimension are known as* **fractals.** *Fractals are infinitely self-similar objects formed by repeated additions to, or removals from, a figure. The object attained at the limit of the repeated procedure is the fractal.*

*Next consider a two-dimensional object with sections removed iteratively. In each stage of the fractal's development, a triangle is removed from the center of each triangular region.*

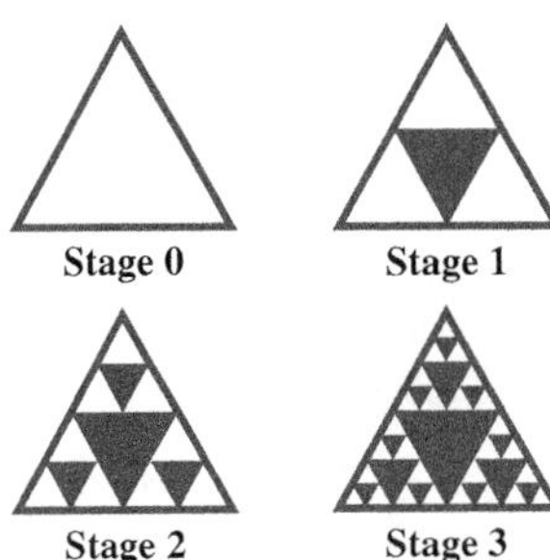


*Use the process from the last example to help answer each questions.*

22. What is the scale factor of the fractal?

23. Old size = 1, new size = _____.

24. The dimension of the fractal is between what two whole number values?

25. Use the definition of dimension and your calculator to approximate the dimension of this fractal to three decimal places.

*Use a calculator to determine the pattern of attractors for the equation* $y = kx(1 - x)$ *for the given value of k and the given initial value of x.*

26. $k = 3.25, x = .7$

27. $k = 3.4, x = .8$

28. $k = 3.55, x = .7$

# COLLABORATIVE INVESTIGATION

## Generalizing the Angle Sum Concept

In this chapter we learned that the sum of the measures of the angles of a triangle is 180°. This fact can be extended to determine a formula for the sum of the measures of the angles of any convex polygon. To begin this investigation, divide into groups of three or four students each. Prepare on a sheet of paper six figures as shown on the right.

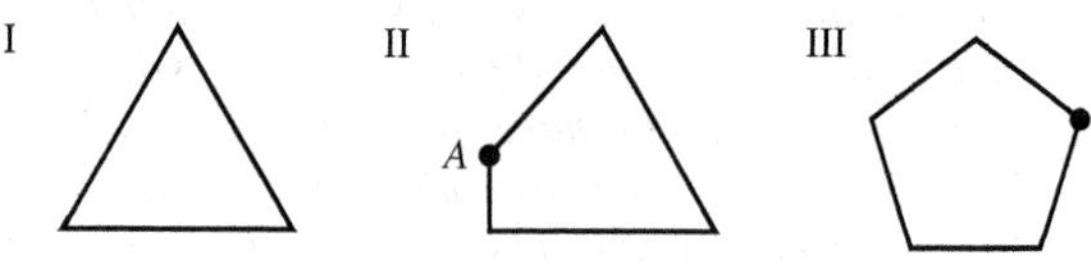


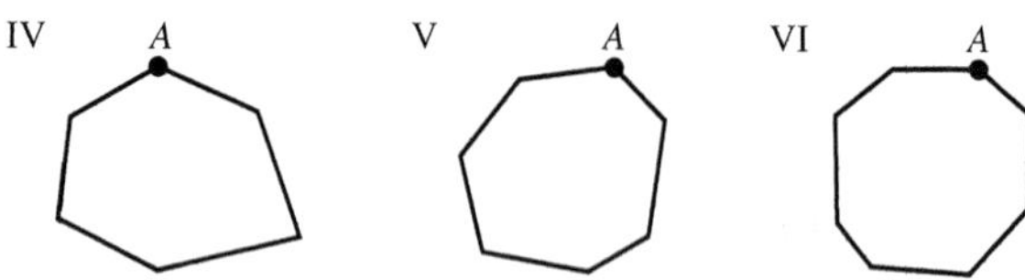


Now we define a diagonal from vertex $A$ to be a segment from $A$ to a non-adjacent vertex. The triangle in Figure I has no diagonals, but the polygons in Figures II through VI do have them.

### Topics for Discussion

1. Choose someone in the group to draw all possible diagonals from vertex A in each figure.
2. Now complete Table 6 as a group.

**TABLE 6**

| Polygon | Number of Sides | Number of Triangles, $t$ | Number of Degrees in Each Triangle | Sum of the Measures of All Angles of the Polygon, $t \cdot 180°$ |
|---|---|---|---|---|
| I | | | | |
| II | | | | |
| III | | | | |
| IV | | | | |
| V | | | | |
| VI | | | | |

3. Based on the table you completed, answer the following in order.
   (a) As suggested by the table, the number of triangles that a convex polygon can be divided into is _____ less than the number of sides.
   (b) Thus, if a polygon has $s$ sides, it can be divided into _____ triangles.
   (c) From the table we see that the sum of the measures of all the angles of a polygon can be found from the expression $t \cdot 180°$. Thus, if a polygon has $s$ sides, the sum of the measures of all the angles of the polygon is given by the expression
   (____ − _____) · ____°.
4. Use your discovery from Exercise 3(c) to find the sum of the measures of all the angles of
   (i) a nonagon (ii) a decagon
   (iii) a 12-sided polygon.

# CHAPTER 9 TEST

**1.** Consider a 38° angle. Answer each of the following.
  **(a)** What is the measure of its complement?
  **(b)** What is the measure of its supplement?
  **(c)** Classify it as acute, obtuse, right, or straight.

*Find the measure of each marked angle.*

**2.**

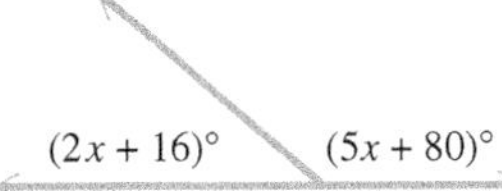


**3.**

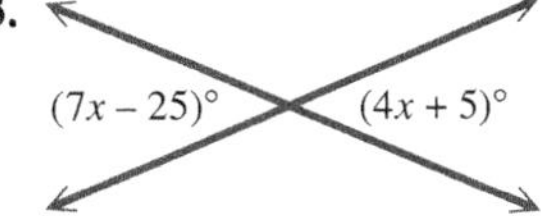


**4.**

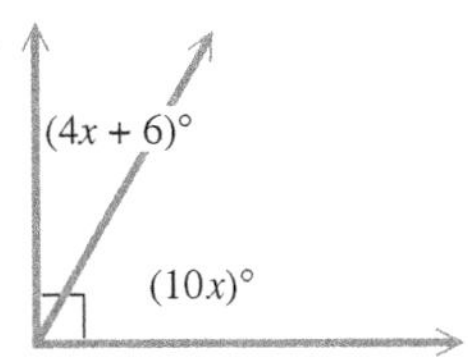


*In Exercises 5 and 6, assume that lines m and n are parallel, and find the measure of each marked angle.*

**5.**

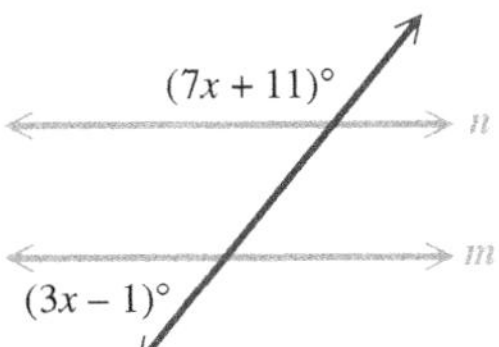


**6.**

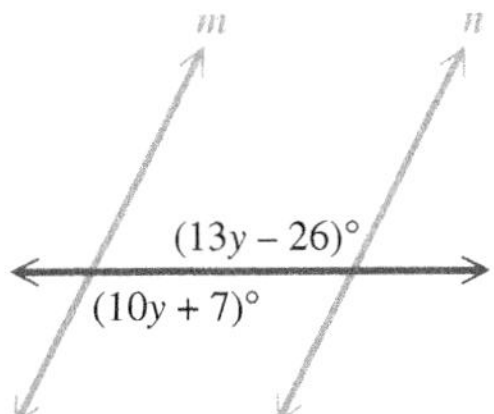


**7.** Explain why a rhombus must be a parallelogram, but a parallelogram might not be a rhombus.

**8.** Which one of the statements A–D is false?
  **A.** A square is a rhombus.
  **B.** The acute angles of a right triangle are complementary.
  **C.** A triangle may have both a right angle and an obtuse angle.
  **D.** A trapezoid may have nonparallel sides of the same length.

*Identify each of the following curves as* simple, closed, both, *or* neither.

**9.**

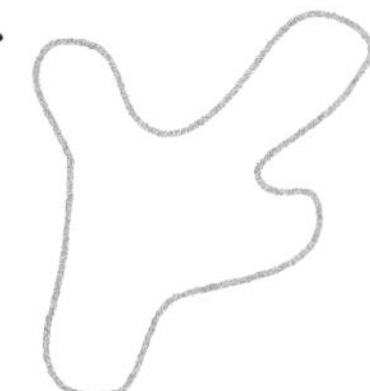

**10.**

**11.** Find the measure of each angle in the triangle.

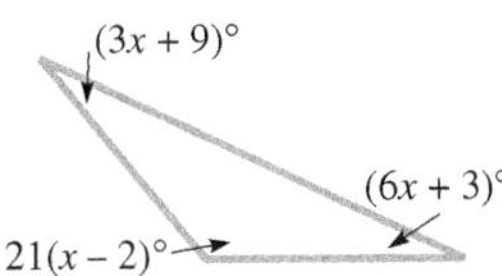


*Find the area of each of the following figures.*

**12.**

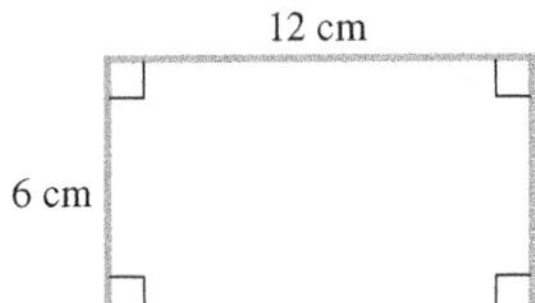


**13.**

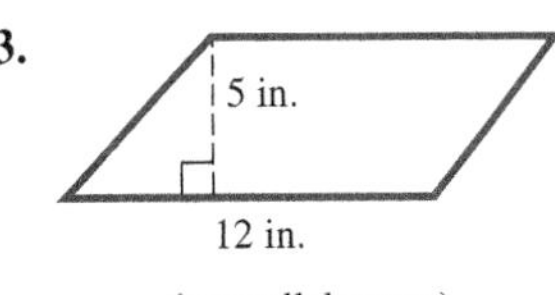


(a parallelogram)

14.

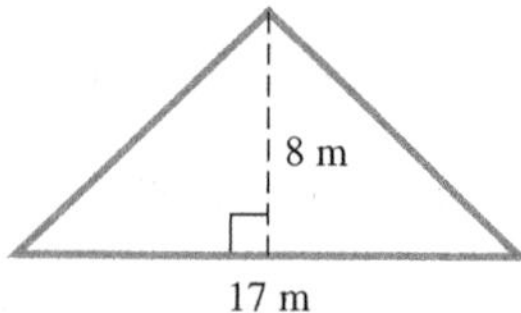


15.

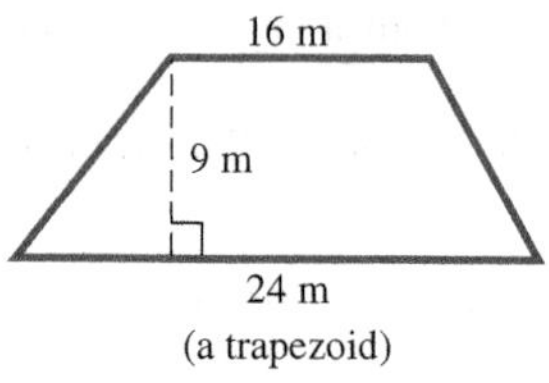

(a trapezoid)

16. If a circle has area $144\pi$ square inches, what is its circumference?

17. ***Circumference of a Dome*** The Rogers Centre in Toronto, Canada, is the first stadium with a hard-shell, retractable roof. The steel dome is 630 feet in diameter. To the nearest foot, what is the circumference of this dome?

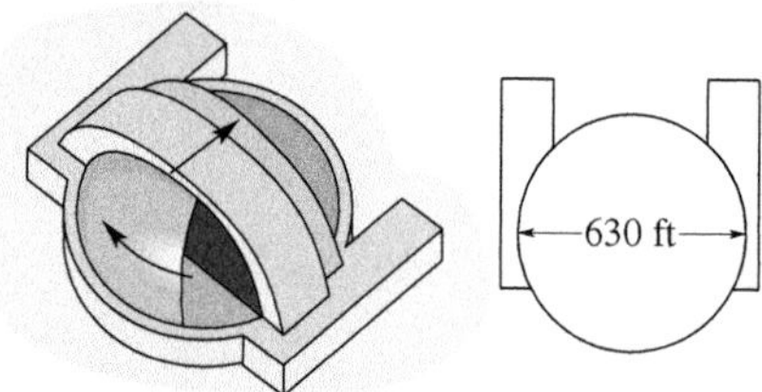


18. ***Area of a Shaded Figure*** What is the area of the shaded portion of the figure? Use 3.14 as an approximation for $\pi$.

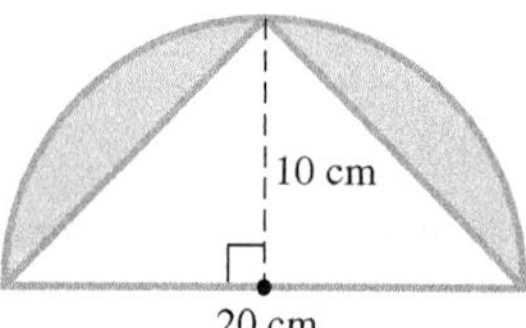

(a triangle within a semicircle)

19. Given: $\measuredangle CAB = \measuredangle DBA$; $DB = CA$
Prove: $\triangle ABD \cong \triangle BAC$

20. ***Height of a Pole*** If a 30-ft pole casts a shadow 45 ft long, how tall is a pole whose shadow is 30 ft long at the same time?

21. ***Diagonal of a Rectangle*** What is the measure of a diagonal of a rectangle that has width 20 m and length 21 m?

22. First reflect the given figure about line $n$, and then about line $m$.

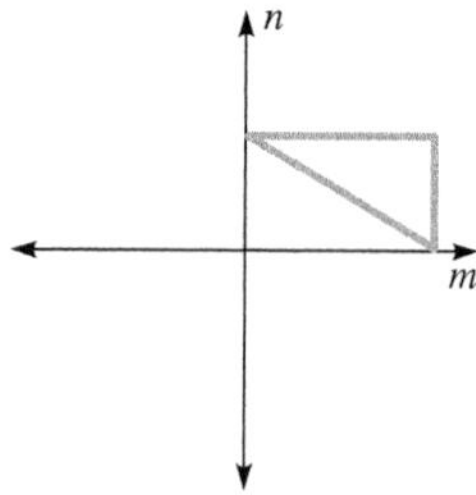


23. Find the point reflection image of the given figure with the given point as center.

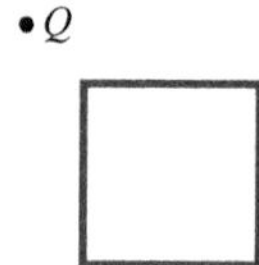


*Find* **(a)** *the volume and* **(b)** *the surface area of each of the following space figures. When necessary, use* 3.14 *as an approximation for* $\pi$.

24.

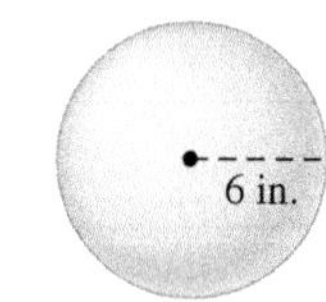

(a sphere)

25.

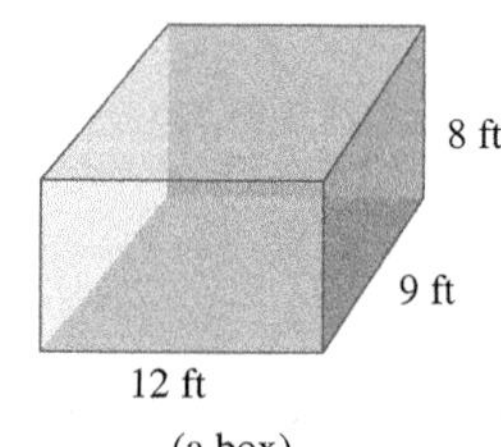

(a box)

26. 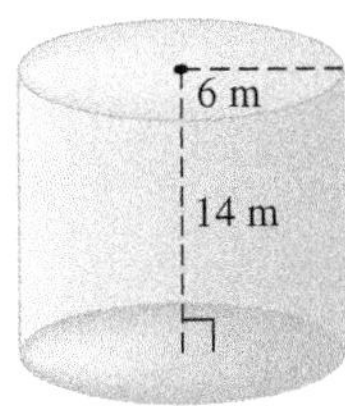


(a right circular cylinder)

27. List several main distinctions between Euclidean geometry and non-Euclidean geometry.

28. ***Topological Equivalence*** Are the following pairs of objects topologically equivalent?
(a) a page of a book and the cover of the same book
(b) a pair of glasses with the lenses removed, and the Mona Lisa

29. Decide whether it is possible to traverse the network shown. If it is possible, show how it can be done.
(a) (b)

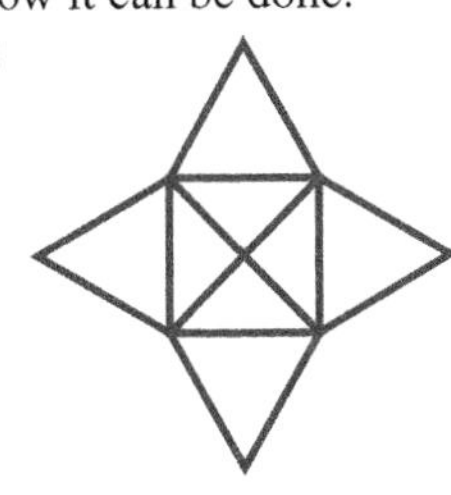

30. Use a calculator to determine the attractors for the sequence generated by the equation $y = 2.1x(1 - x)$, with initial value of $x = .6$.

# TRIGONOMETRY

The 1958 musical *Merry Andrew* starred Danny Kaye as Andrew Larabee, a teacher with a flair for using unconventional methods in his classes. He uses a musical number to teach the Pythagorean theorem, singing and dancing to "The Square of the Hypotenuse":

> *...Parallel lines don't connect, which is just about what you might expect. Though scientific laws may change and decimals can be moved, the following is constant, and has yet to be disproved:* ***The square of the hypotenuse of a right triangle is equal to the sum of the squares of the two adjacent sides.***

The Pythagorean theorem, introduced in the previous chapter, is used extensively in the study of *trigonometry*, the topic of this chapter. The foundations of trigonometry go back at least 3000 years. The ancient Egyptians, Babylonians, and Greeks developed trigonometry to find the lengths of the sides of triangles and the measures of their angles. In Egypt, trigonometry was used to reestablish land boundaries after the annual flood of the Nile River. In Babylonia it was used in astronomy. The word *trigonometry* comes from the Greek words for triangle (*trigon*) and measurement (*metry*). Today trigonometry is used in electronics, surveying, and other engineering areas, and is necessary for further courses in mathematics, such as calculus.

# 10.1 Angles and Their Measures

**Basic Terminology • Degree Measure • Angles in a Coordinate System**

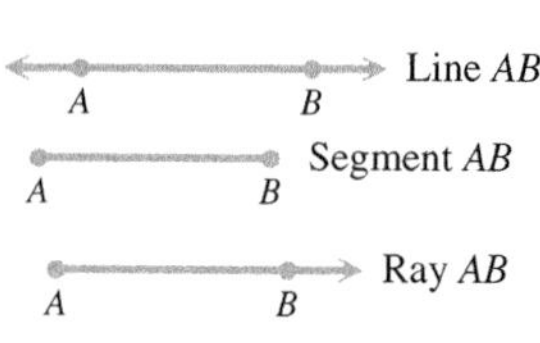


FIGURE 1

## Basic Terminology

A line may be drawn through the two distinct points $A$ and $B$. This line is called **line $AB$.** The portion of the line between $A$ and $B$, including points $A$ and $B$ themselves, is **segment $AB$.** The portion of the line $AB$ that starts at $A$ and continues through $B$, and on past $B$, is called **ray $AB$.** Point $A$ is the endpoint of the ray. See Figure 1.

In the study of trigonometry, an **angle** is formed by rotating a ray around its endpoint. The ray in its initial position is called the **initial side** of the angle, while the ray in its location after the rotation is the **terminal side** of the angle. The endpoint of the ray is the **vertex** of the angle. Figure 2 shows the initial and terminal sides of an angle with vertex $A$.

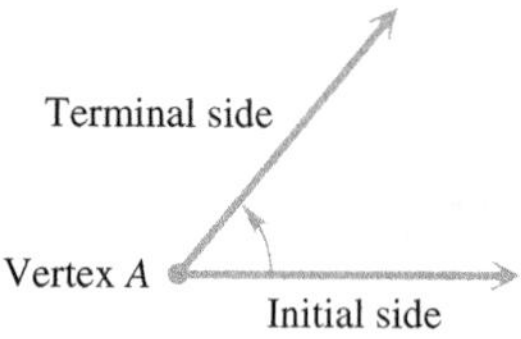


FIGURE 2

If the rotation of the terminal side is counterclockwise, the angle measure is **positive.** If the rotation is clockwise, the angle measure is **negative.** Figure 3 shows two angles, one positive and one negative.

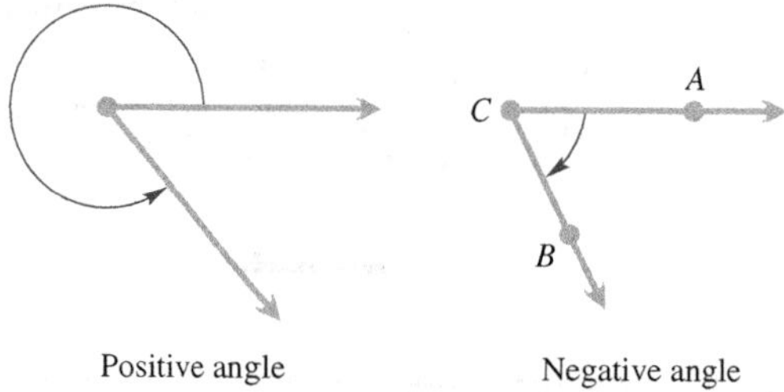


FIGURE 3

An angle can be named by using the name of its vertex. For example, the angle on the right in Figure 3 can be called angle $C$. Alternatively, an angle can be named using three letters, with the vertex letter in the middle. Thus, the angle on the right also could be named angle $ACB$ or angle $BCA$.

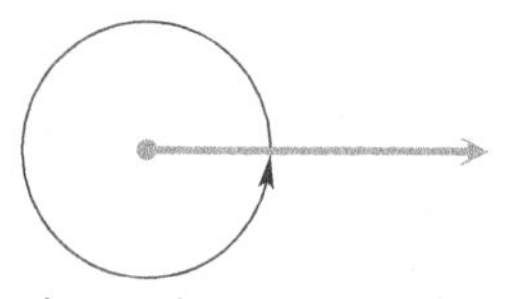

A complete rotation of a ray gives an angle whose measure is 360°.

FIGURE 4

## Degree Measure

There are two systems in common use for measuring the size of angles. The most common unit of measure is the **degree.** (The other common unit of measure is called the *radian.*) Degree measure was developed by the Babylonians 4000 years ago. To use degree measure we assign 360 degrees to a complete rotation of a ray. In Figure 4, notice that the terminal side of the angle corresponds to its initial side when it makes a complete rotation.

One degree, written $1°$, represents $\frac{1}{360}$ of a rotation. Therefore, $90°$ represents $\frac{90}{360} = \frac{1}{4}$ of a complete rotation, and $180°$ represents $\frac{180}{360} = \frac{1}{2}$ of a complete rotation. Angles of measure $1°$, $90°$, and $180°$ are shown in Figure 5.

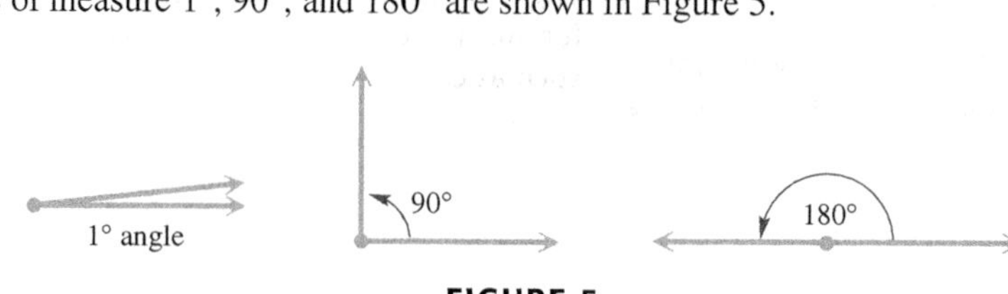


FIGURE 5

**"Trigonometry,** perhaps more than any other branch of mathematics, developed as the result of a continual and fertile interplay of supply and demand: the supply of applicable mathematical theories and techniques available at any given time and the demands of a single applied science, astronomy. So intimate was the relation that not until the thirteenth century was it useful to regard the two subjects as separate entities."(From "The History of Trigonometry" by Edward S. Kennedy, in *Historical Topics for the Mathematics Classroom,* the Thirty-first Yearbook of N.C.T.M., 1969.)

Special angles are named as shown in the following chart.

| Name | Angle Measure | Example(s) |
|---|---|---|
| **Acute angle** | Between 0° and 90° | 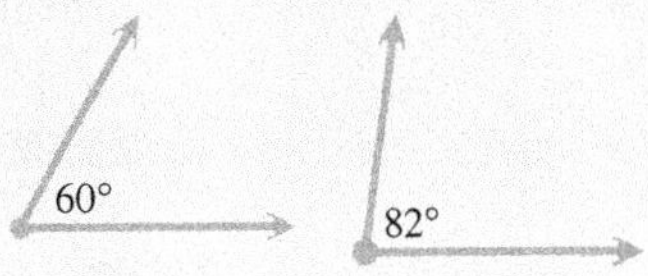 60°, 82° |
| **Right angle** | Exactly 90° | 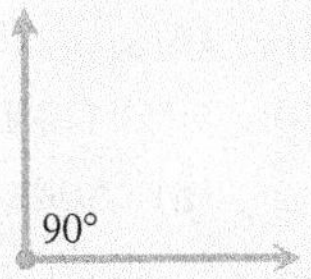 90° |
| **Obtuse angle** | Between 90° and 180° |  97°, 138° |
| **Straight angle** | Exactly 180° |  180° |

If the sum of the measures of two angles is 90°, the angles are called **complementary.** Two angles with measures whose sum is 180° are **supplementary.**

## EXAMPLE 1 Finding Complement and Supplement

Give the complement and the supplement of 50°.

**SOLUTION**

The complement of 50° is

$$90° - 50° = 40°,$$

while the supplement of 50° is

$$180° - 50° = 130°.$$

***Do not confuse an angle with its measure.*** The *angle itself* consists of the vertex together with the initial and terminal sides, whereas the *measure of the angle* is the size of the rotation angle from the initial to the terminal side (commonly expressed in degrees). If angle $A$ has a 35° rotation angle, we say that $m(\text{angle } A)$ is 35°, where $m(\text{angle } A)$ is read "the measure of angle $A$." It saves a lot of work, however, to abbreviate $m(\text{angle A}) = 35°$ as simply angle $A = 35°$.

Traditionally, portions of a degree have been measured with minutes and seconds. One **minute,** written $1'$, is $\frac{1}{60}$ of a degree.

$$1' = \frac{1}{60}^{\circ} \quad \text{or} \quad 60' = 1°$$

One **second,** $1''$, is $\frac{1}{60}$ of a minute.

$$1'' = \left(\frac{1}{60}\right)' = \left(\frac{1}{3600}\right)^\circ \quad \text{or} \quad 60'' = 1'$$

The measure 12° 42′ 38″ represents 12 degrees, 42 minutes, 38 seconds.

### EXAMPLE 2 Calculating with Degree Measure

Perform each calculation.

**(a)** 51° 29′ + 32° 46′ **(b)** 90° − 73° 12′

```
51°29'+32°46'▸DM
S
          84°15'0"
90°0'-73°12'▸DMS
          16°48'0"
```

The calculations explained in Example 2 can be done with a graphing calculator capable of working with degrees, minutes, and seconds.

**SOLUTION**

**(a)** Add the degrees and the minutes separately.

$$\begin{array}{r} 51^\circ\ 29' \\ +\ 32^\circ\ 46' \\ \hline 83^\circ\ 75' \end{array}$$

Since 75′ = 60′ + 15′ = 1° 15′, the sum is written

$$\begin{array}{r} 83^\circ \\ +\ 1^\circ\ 15' \\ \hline 84^\circ\ 15'. \end{array}$$

**(b)**

$$\begin{array}{r} 89^\circ\ 60' \\ -73^\circ\ 12' \\ \hline 16^\circ\ 48'. \end{array} \qquad \text{Write } 90^\circ \text{ as } 89^\circ\ 60'.$$

■

Angles can be measured in **decimal degrees.** For example, 12.4238° represents

$$12.4238^\circ = 12\frac{4238}{10{,}000}^\circ.$$

### EXAMPLE 3 Converting Between Decimal Degrees and Degrees, Minutes, Seconds

**(a)** Convert 74° 8′ 14″ to decimal degrees. Round to the nearest thousandth of a degree.
**(b)** Convert 34.817° to degrees, minutes and seconds. Round to the nearest second.

```
74°8'14"
        74.13722222
74°8'14"
             74.137
34.817▸DMS
         34°49'1.2"
```

The conversions in Example 3 can be done on some graphing calculators. The second displayed result was obtained by setting the calculator to show only three places after the decimal point.

**SOLUTION**

**(a)**
$$74^\circ 8'\ 14'' = 74^\circ + \left(\frac{8}{60}\right)^\circ + \left(\frac{14}{3600}\right)^\circ \qquad 1' = \left(\frac{1}{60}\right)^\circ \text{ and } 1'' = \left(\frac{1}{3600}\right)^\circ$$
$$\approx 74^\circ + .1333^\circ + .0039^\circ$$
$$= 74.137^\circ \qquad \text{Rounded to three decimal places}$$

**(b)**
$$34.817^\circ = 34^\circ + .817^\circ$$
$$= 34^\circ + (.817)(60') \qquad 1^\circ = 60'$$
$$= 34^\circ + 49.02'$$
$$= 34^\circ + 49' + .02'$$
$$= 34^\circ + 49' + (.02)(60'') \qquad 1' = 60''$$
$$= 34^\circ + 49' + 1.2''$$
$$\approx 34^\circ\ 49'\ 1''$$

**Angles in a Coordinate System** An angle $\theta$ (the Greek letter *theta*)* is in **standard position** if its vertex is at the origin of a rectangular coordinate system and its initial side lies along the positive $x$-axis. The two angles in Figure 6(a) and 6(b) are in standard position. An angle in standard position is said to lie in the quadrant in which its terminal side lies. For example, an acute angle is in quadrant I and an obtuse angle is in quadrant II. Figure 6(c) shows ranges of angle measures for each quadrant when $0° < \theta < 360°$. Angles in standard position having their terminal sides along the $x$-axis or $y$-axis, such as angles with measures 90°, 180°, 270°, and so on, are called **quadrantal angles.**

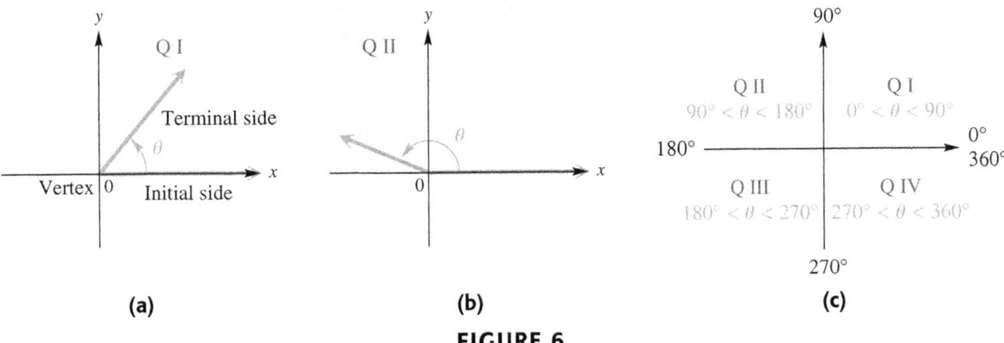

FIGURE 6

A complete rotation of a ray results in an angle of measure 360°. But there is no reason why the rotation need stop at 360°. By continuing the rotation, angles of measure larger than 360° can be produced. The angles in Figure 7(a) have measures 60° and 420°. These two angles have the same initial side and the same terminal side, but different amounts of rotation. Angles that have the same initial side and the same terminal side are called **coterminal angles.** As shown in Figure 7(b), angles with measures 110° and 830° are coterminal.

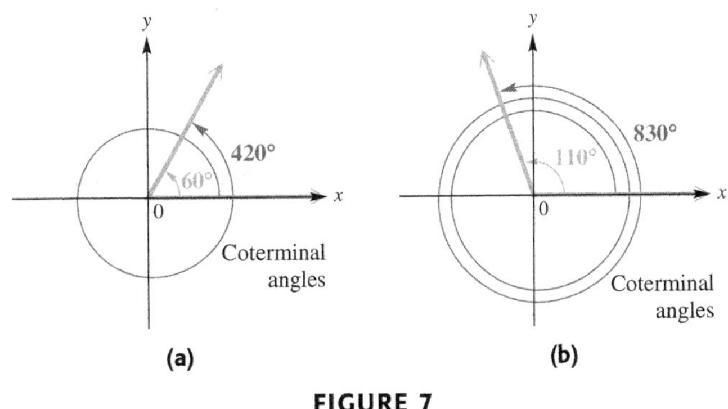

FIGURE 7

**EXAMPLE 4 Finding Measures of Coterminal Angles**

Find the angle of smallest possible positive measure coterminal with each angle.

**(a)** 908° **(b)** −75°

*The letters of the Greek alphabet are identified in a margin note on page 631.

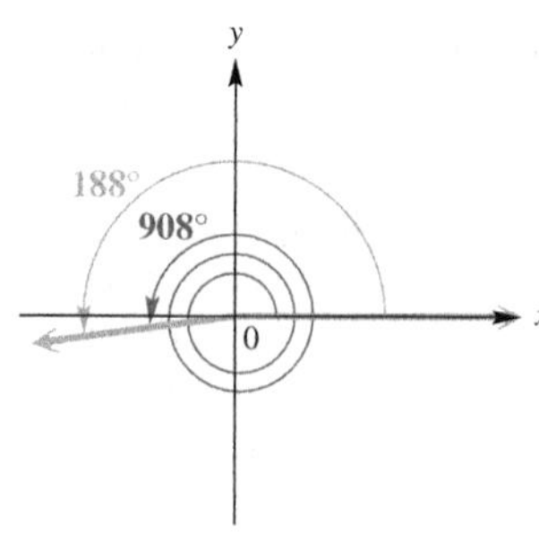

FIGURE 8

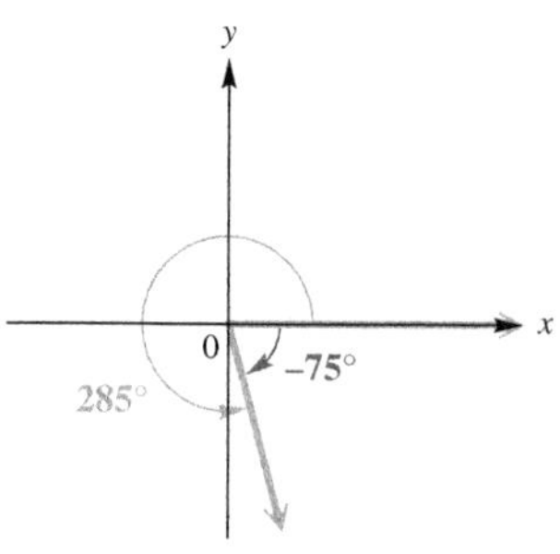

FIGURE 9

**SOLUTION**

**(a)** Add or subtract 360° from 908° as many times as needed to get an angle with measure greater than 0° but less than 360°. Because

$$908° - 2 \cdot 360° = 908° - 720° = 188°,$$

an angle of 188° is coterminal with an angle of 908°. See Figure 8.

**(b)** Use a rotation of $360° + (-75°) = 285°$. See Figure 9.

Sometimes it is necessary to find an expression that will generate all angles coterminal with a given angle. For example, suppose we wish to do this for a 60° angle. Because any angle coterminal with 60° can be obtained by adding an appropriate integer multiple of 360° to 60°, we can let $n$ represent any integer, and the expression

$$60° + n \cdot 360°$$

will represent all such coterminal angles. Table 1 shows a few possibilities.

**TABLE 1**

| Value of $n$ | Angle Coterminal with 60° |
|---|---|
| 2 | $60° + 2 \cdot 360° = 780°$ |
| 1 | $60° + 1 \cdot 360° = 420°$ |
| 0 | $60° + 0 \cdot 360° = 60°$ (the angle itself) |
| −1 | $60° + (-1) \cdot 360° = -300°$ |

## 10.1 Exercises

*Give* **(a)** *the complement and* **(b)** *the supplement of each angle.*

**1.** 30° **2.** 60° **3.** 45°

**4.** 55° **5.** 89° **6.** 2°

**7.** If an angle measures $x$ degrees, how can we represent its complement?

**8.** If an angle measures $x$ degrees, how can we represent its supplement?

*Perform each calculation.*

**9.** $62° 18' + 21° 41'$ **10.** $75° 15' + 83° 32'$ **11.** $71° 58' + 47° 29'$

**12.** $90° - 73° 48'$ **13.** $90° - 51° 28'$ **14.** $180° - 124° 51'$

**15.** $90° - 72° 58' 11''$ **16.** $90° - 36° 18' 47''$

*Convert each angle measure to decimal degrees. Use a calculator, and round to the nearest thousandth of a degree.*

**17.** $20° 54'$ **18.** $38° 42'$ **19.** $91° 35' 54''$

**20.** $34° 51' 35''$ **21.** $274° 18' 59''$ **22.** $165° 51' 9''$

*Convert each angle measure to degrees, minutes, and seconds. Use a calculator, and round to the nearest second.*

**23.** 31.4296° **24.** 59.0854° **25.** 89.9004°

**26.** 102.3771° **27.** 178.5994° **28.** 122.6853°

*Find the angle of smallest positive measure coterminal with each angle.*

**29.** $-40°$ **30.** $-98°$ **31.** $-125°$ **32.** $-203°$

**33.** $539°$ **34.** $699°$ **35.** $850°$ **36.** $1000°$

*Give an expression that generates all angles coterminal with the given angle. Let n represent any integer.*

**37.** $30°$ **38.** $45°$ **39.** $60°$ **40.** $90°$

*Sketch each angle in standard position. Draw an arrow representing the correct amount of rotation. Find the measure of two other angles, one positive and one negative, that are coterminal with the given angle. Give the quadrant of each angle.*

**41.** $75°$ **42.** $89°$ **43.** $174°$ **44.** $234°$

**45.** $300°$ **46.** $512°$ **47.** $-61°$ **48.** $-159°$

# 10.2 Trigonometric Functions of Angles

**Trigonometric Functions • Undefined Function Values**

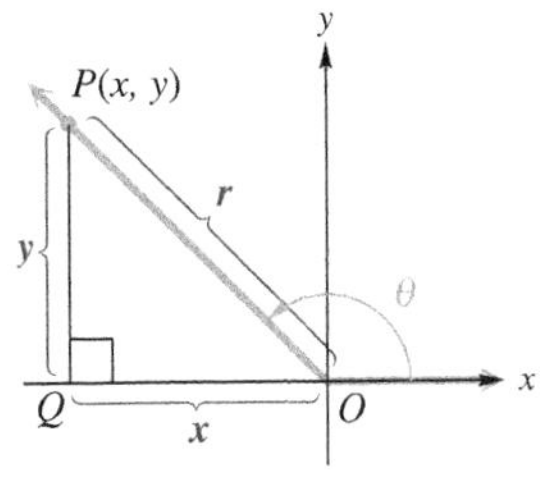


**FIGURE 10**

**Trigonometric Functions** The study of trigonometry covers the six trigonometric functions defined in this section. To define these six basic functions, start with an angle $\theta$ in standard position. Choose any point $P$ having coordinates $(x, y)$ on the terminal side of angle $\theta$. (The point $P$ must not be the vertex of the angle.) See Figure 10.

A perpendicular from $P$ to the $x$-axis at point $Q$ determines a triangle having vertices at $O$, $P$, and $Q$. The distance $r$ from $P(x, y)$ to the origin, $(0, 0)$, can be found from the distance formula.

$$r = \sqrt{(x - 0)^2 + (y - 0)^2}$$
$$r = \sqrt{x^2 + y^2}$$

Notice that $r > 0$, because distance is never negative.

The six trigonometric functions of angle $\theta$ are called **sine, cosine, tangent, cotangent, secant,** and **cosecant.** In the following definitions, we use the customary abbreviations for the names of these functions.

"The founder of trigonometry is **Hipparchus,** who lived in Rhodes and Alexandria and died about 125 B.C. We know rather little about him. Most of what we do know comes from Ptolemy, who credits Hipparchus with a number of ideas in trigonometry and astronomy. We owe to him many astronomical observations and discoveries, the most influential astronomical theory of ancient times, and works on geography." *(Source: Mathematical Thought From Ancient to Modern Times, Volume 1, by Morris Kline.)*

### Trigonometric Functions

Let $(x, y)$ be a point other than the origin on the terminal side of an angle $\theta$ in standard position. The distance from the point to the origin is $r = \sqrt{x^2 + y^2}$. The six trigonometric functions of $\theta$ are:

$$\sin\theta = \frac{y}{r} \qquad \cos\theta = \frac{x}{r} \qquad \tan\theta = \frac{y}{x} \; (x \neq 0)$$

$$\csc\theta = \frac{r}{y} \; (y \neq 0) \qquad \sec\theta = \frac{r}{x} \; (x \neq 0) \qquad \cot\theta = \frac{x}{y} \; (y \neq 0).$$

Although Figure 10 shows a second quadrant angle, these definitions apply to any angle $\theta$. Because of the restrictions on the denominators in the definitions of tangent, cotangent, secant, and cosecant, some angles will have undefined function values. This will be discussed in more detail later.

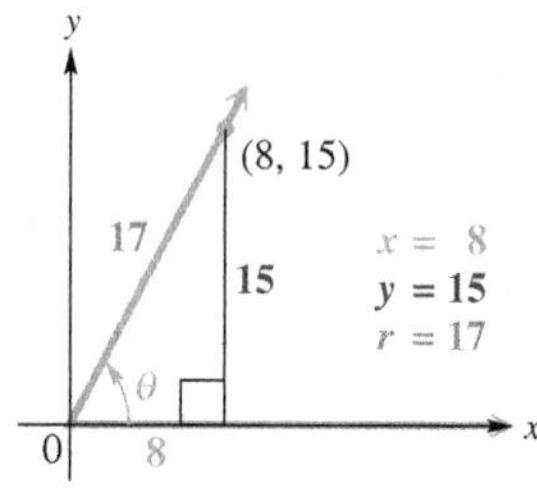


FIGURE 11

### EXAMPLE 1 Finding Function Values of an Angle

The terminal side of an angle $\theta$ in standard position goes through the point (8, 15). Find the values of the six trigonometric functions of angle $\theta$.

**SOLUTION**

Figure 11 shows angle $\theta$ and the triangle formed by dropping a perpendicular from the point (8, 15) to the $x$-axis. The point (8, 15) is 8 units to the right of the $y$-axis and 15 units above the $x$-axis, so that $x = 8$ and $y = 15$.

$$r = \sqrt{x^2 + y^2}$$
$$r = \sqrt{8^2 + 15^2} \qquad \text{Let } x = 8 \text{ and } y = 15.$$
$$r = \sqrt{64 + 225}$$
$$r = \sqrt{289}$$
$$r = 17$$

The values of the six trigonometric functions of angle $\theta$ can now be found with the definitions given above.

$$\sin\theta = \frac{y}{r} = \frac{15}{17} \qquad \cos\theta = \frac{x}{r} = \frac{8}{17} \qquad \tan\theta = \frac{y}{x} = \frac{15}{8}$$
$$\csc\theta = \frac{r}{y} = \frac{17}{15} \qquad \sec\theta = \frac{r}{x} = \frac{17}{8} \qquad \cot\theta = \frac{x}{y} = \frac{8}{15}$$

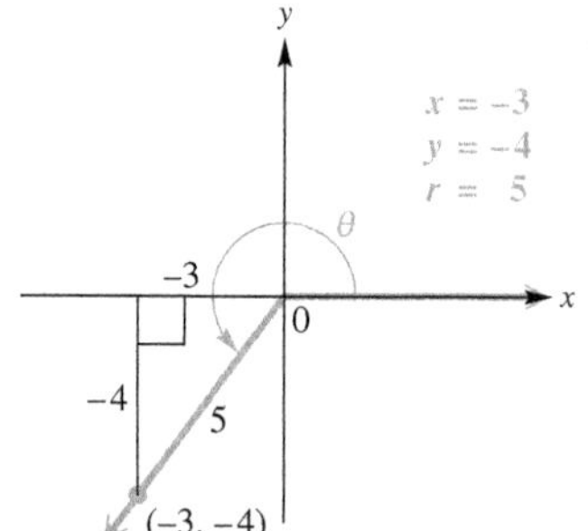


FIGURE 12

### EXAMPLE 2 Finding Function Values of an Angle

The terminal side of an angle $\theta$ in standard position goes through the point $(-3, -4)$. Find the values of the six trigonometric functions of $\theta$.

**SOLUTION**

As shown in Figure 12, $x = -3$ and $y = -4$. The value of $r$ is

$$r = \sqrt{(-3)^2 + (-4)^2}$$
$$r = \sqrt{25} \longleftarrow \text{(Remember that } r > 0.)$$
$$r = 5.$$

Then by the definitions of the trigonometric functions,

$$\sin\theta = \frac{-4}{5} = -\frac{4}{5} \qquad \cos\theta = \frac{-3}{5} = -\frac{3}{5} \qquad \tan\theta = \frac{-4}{-3} = \frac{4}{3}$$
$$\csc\theta = \frac{5}{-4} = -\frac{5}{4} \qquad \sec\theta = \frac{5}{-3} = -\frac{5}{3} \qquad \cot\theta = \frac{-3}{-4} = \frac{3}{4}.$$

The six trigonometric functions can be found from *any* point on the terminal side of the angle other than the origin. To see why any point may be used, refer to

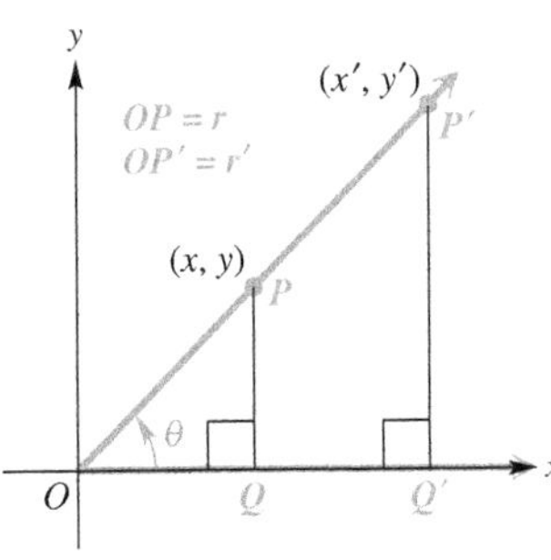


FIGURE 13

Figure 13, which shows an angle $\theta$ and two distinct points on its terminal side. Point $P$ has coordinates $(x, y)$ and point $P'$ (read "$P$-prime") has coordinates $(x', y')$. Let $r$ be the length of the hypotenuse of triangle $OPQ$, and let $r'$ be the length of the hypotenuse of triangle $OP'Q'$. Because corresponding sides of similar triangles are in proportion,

$$\frac{y}{r} = \frac{y'}{r'},$$

so that $\sin \theta = \frac{y}{r}$ is the same no matter which point is used to find it. Similar results hold for the other five functions.

**Undefined Function Values** If the terminal side of an angle in standard position lies along the $y$-axis, any point on this terminal side has $x$-coordinate 0. Similarly, an angle with terminal side on the $x$-axis has $y$-coordinate 0 for any point on the terminal side. Because the values of $x$ and $y$ appear in the denominators of some of the trigonometric functions, and because a fraction is undefined if its denominator is 0, some of the trigonometric function values of quadrantal angles (i.e., those with terminal side on an axis) will be undefined.

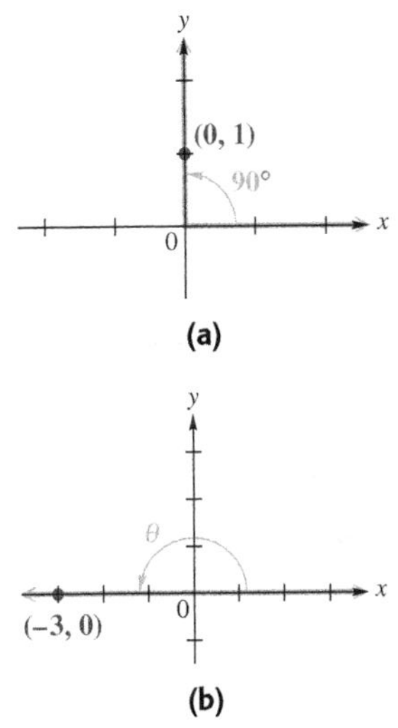


FIGURE 14

### EXAMPLE 3 Finding Function Values and Undefined Function Values

Find values of the trigonometric functions for each angle. Identify any that are undefined.

**(a)** an angle of 90°

**(b)** an angle in standard position with terminal side through $(-3, 0)$

**SOLUTION**

**(a)** First, select any point on the terminal side of a 90° angle. We select the point $(0, 1)$, as shown in Figure 14(a). Here $x = 0$ and $y = 1$. Verify that $r = 1$. Then, by the definitions of the trigonometric functions,

$$\sin 90° = \frac{1}{1} = 1 \qquad \cos 90° = \frac{0}{1} = 0 \qquad \tan 90° = \frac{1}{0} \text{ (undefined)}$$

$$\csc 90° = \frac{1}{1} = 1 \qquad \sec 90° = \frac{1}{0} \text{ (undefined)} \qquad \cot 90° = \frac{0}{1} = 0.$$

**(b)** Figure 14(b) shows the angle. Here, $x = -3$, $y = 0$, and $r = 3$, so the trigonometric functions have the following values.

$$\sin \theta = \frac{0}{3} = 0 \qquad \cos \theta = \frac{-3}{3} = -1 \qquad \tan \theta = \frac{0}{-3} = 0$$

$$\csc \theta = \frac{3}{0} \text{ (undefined)} \qquad \sec \theta = \frac{3}{-3} = -1 \qquad \cot \theta = \frac{-3}{0} \text{ (undefined)}$$

The conditions under which the trigonometric function values of quadrantal angles are undefined are summarized here.

**Undefined Function Values**

If the terminal side of a quadrantal angle lies along the $y$-axis, the tangent and secant functions are undefined. If it lies along the $x$-axis, the cotangent and cosecant functions are undefined.

Because the most commonly used quadrantal angles are 0°, 90°, 180°, 270° and 360°, the values of the functions of these angles are summarized in Table 2.

**TABLE 2** Quadrantal Angles

| $\theta$ | $\sin\theta$ | $\cos\theta$ | $\tan\theta$ | $\cot\theta$ | $\sec\theta$ | $\csc\theta$ |
|---|---|---|---|---|---|---|
| 0° | 0 | 1 | 0 | Undefined | 1 | Undefined |
| 90° | 1 | 0 | Undefined | 0 | Undefined | 1 |
| 180° | 0 | −1 | 0 | Undefined | −1 | Undefined |
| 270° | −1 | 0 | Undefined | 0 | Undefined | −1 |
| 360° | 0 | 1 | 0 | Undefined | 1 | Undefined |

## 10.2 Exercises

*In Exercises 1–4, sketch an angle $\theta$ in standard position such that $\theta$ has the smallest possible positive measure, and the given point is on the terminal side of $\theta$.*

**1.** $(-3, 4)$ **2.** $(-4, -3)$ **3.** $(5, -12)$ **4.** $(-12, -5)$

*Find the values of the trigonometric functions for the angles in standard position having the following points on their terminal sides. Identify any that are undefined. Rationalize denominators when applicable.*

**5.** $(-3, 4)$

**6.** $(-4, -3)$

**7.** $(0, 2)$

**8.** $(-4, 0)$

**9.** $(1, \sqrt{3})$

**10.** $(-2\sqrt{3}, -2)$

**11.** $(3, 5)$

**12.** $(-2, 7)$

**13.** $(-8, 0)$

**14.** $(0, 9)$

**15.** For any nonquadrantal angle $\theta$, $\sin\theta$ and $\csc\theta$ will have the same sign. Explain why this is so.

**16.** If $\cot\theta$ is undefined, what is the value of $\tan\theta$?

**17.** How is the value of $r$ interpreted geometrically in the definitions of the sine, cosine, secant, and cosecant functions?

**18.** If the terminal side of an angle $\theta$ is in quadrant III, what is the sign of each of the trigonometric function values of $\theta$?

*Suppose that the point (x, y) is in the indicated quadrant. Decide whether the given ratio is positive or negative. (Hint: It may be helpful to draw a sketch.)*

**19.** II, $\frac{y}{r}$ **20.** II, $\frac{x}{r}$ **21.** III, $\frac{y}{r}$ **22.** III, $\frac{x}{r}$

**23.** IV, $\frac{x}{r}$ **24.** IV, $\frac{y}{r}$ **25.** IV, $\frac{y}{x}$ **26.** IV, $\frac{x}{y}$

*Use the appropriate definition to determine each function value. If it is undefined, say so.*

**27.** $\cos 90°$ **28.** $\sin 90°$ **29.** $\tan 90°$ **30.** $\cot 90°$

**31.** $\sec 90°$ **32.** $\csc 90°$ **33.** $\sin 180°$ **34.** $\sin 270°$

**35.** $\tan 180°$ **36.** $\cot 270°$ **37.** $\sin(-270°)$ **38.** $\cos(-270°)$

**39.** $\tan 0°$ **40.** $\sec(-180°)$

# 10.3 Trigonometric Identities

**Reciprocal Identities • Signs of Function Values In Quadrants • Pythagorean Identities • Quotient Identities**

**The Greek Alphabet**

| | | |
|---|---|---|
| $A$ | $\alpha$ | alpha |
| $B$ | $\beta$ | beta |
| $\Gamma$ | $\gamma$ | gamma |
| $\Delta$ | $\delta$ | delta |
| $E$ | $\epsilon$ | epsilon |
| $Z$ | $\zeta$ | zeta |
| $H$ | $\eta$ | eta |
| $\Theta$ | $\theta$ | theta |
| $I$ | $\iota$ | iota |
| $K$ | $\kappa$ | kappa |
| $\Lambda$ | $\lambda$ | lambda |
| $M$ | $\mu$ | mu |
| $N$ | $\nu$ | nu |
| $\Xi$ | $\xi$ | xi |
| $O$ | $o$ | omicron |
| $\Pi$ | $\pi$ | pi |
| $P$ | $\rho$ | rho |
| $\Sigma$ | $\sigma$ | sigma |
| $T$ | $\tau$ | tau |
| $\Upsilon$ | $\upsilon$ | upsilon |
| $\Phi$ | $\phi$ | phi |
| $X$ | $\chi$ | chi |
| $\Psi$ | $\psi$ | psi |
| $\Omega$ | $\omega$ | omega |

## Reciprocal Identities

The definitions of the trigonometric functions on page 627 were written so that functions above and below one another are reciprocals of each other. Because $\sin\theta = \frac{y}{r}$ and $\csc\theta = \frac{r}{y}$,

$$\sin\theta = \frac{1}{\csc\theta} \quad \text{and} \quad \csc\theta = \frac{1}{\sin\theta}.$$

Also, $\cos\theta$ and $\sec\theta$ are reciprocals, as are $\tan\theta$ and $\cot\theta$. In summary, we have the **reciprocal identities** that hold for any angle $\theta$ that does not lead to a zero denominator.

**Reciprocal Identities**

$$\sin\theta = \frac{1}{\csc\theta} \qquad \cos\theta = \frac{1}{\sec\theta} \qquad \tan\theta = \frac{1}{\cot\theta}$$

$$\csc\theta = \frac{1}{\sin\theta} \qquad \sec\theta = \frac{1}{\cos\theta} \qquad \cot\theta = \frac{1}{\tan\theta}$$

**Identities** are equations that are true for all meaningful values of the variable. For example, both $(x + y)^2 = x^2 + 2xy + y^2$ and $2(x + 3) = 2x + 6$ are identities.

When studying identities, be aware that various forms exist. For example,

$$\sin\theta = \frac{1}{\csc\theta} \quad \text{can also be written} \quad \csc\theta = \frac{1}{\sin\theta} \quad \text{and} \quad (\sin\theta)(\csc\theta) = 1.$$

You should become familiar with all forms of these identities.

**EXAMPLE 1 Using the Reciprocal Identities**

Find each function value.

**(a)** $\cos\theta$, if $\sec\theta = \frac{5}{3}$ **(b)** $\sin\theta$, if $\csc\theta = -\frac{\sqrt{12}}{2}$

**SOLUTION**

**(a)** Because $\cos\theta$ is the reciprocal of $\sec\theta$,

$$\cos\theta = \frac{1}{\sec\theta} = \frac{1}{\frac{5}{3}} = 1 \div \frac{5}{3} = 1 \cdot \frac{3}{5} = \frac{3}{5}.$$

**(b)** $$\sin\theta = \frac{1}{-\sqrt{12}/2} = \frac{-2}{\sqrt{12}} = \frac{-2}{2\sqrt{3}} = \frac{-1}{\sqrt{3}} = \frac{-1}{\sqrt{3}} \cdot \frac{\sqrt{3}}{\sqrt{3}} = -\frac{\sqrt{3}}{3}$$

*sin θ is the reciprocal of csc θ.*

*Remember to rationalize the denominator.*

**Signs of Function Values in Quadrants** In the definitions of the trigonometric functions, $r$ is the distance from the origin to the point $(x, y)$. Distance is never negative, so $r > 0$. If we choose a point $(x, y)$ in quadrant I, then both $x$ and $y$ will be positive. Because $r > 0$, all six of the fractions used in the definitions of the trigonometric functions will be positive, so that the values of all six functions will be positive in quadrant I.

A point $(x, y)$ in quadrant II has $x < 0$ and $y > 0$. This makes the values of sine and cosecant positive for quadrant II angles, while the other four functions take on negative values. Similar results can be obtained for the other quadrants.

**Signs of Function Values**

| $\theta$ in Quadrant | $\sin\theta$ | $\cos\theta$ | $\tan\theta$ | $\cot\theta$ | $\sec\theta$ | $\csc\theta$ |
|---|---|---|---|---|---|---|
| I | + | + | + | + | + | + |
| II | + | − | − | − | − | + |
| III | − | − | + | + | − | − |
| IV | − | + | − | − | + | − |

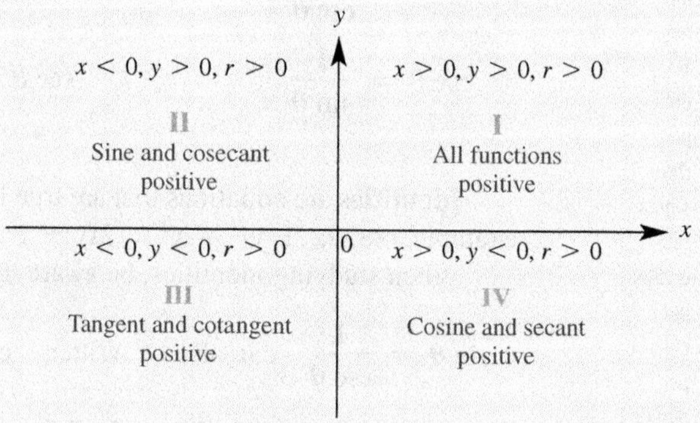

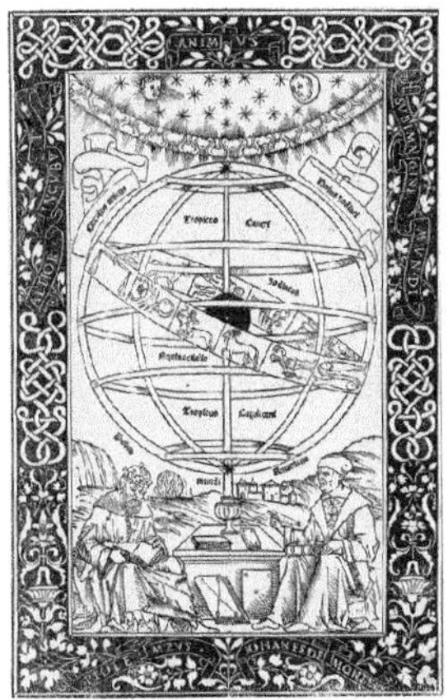

**Claudius Ptolemy** (c. 100–178) provided the most influential astronomical work of antiquity. Although Hipparchus is known in some circles as the founder of trigonometry, his works are lost; historians have used Ptolemy's work as their source of how the Greeks viewed trigonometry. His thirteen-book description of the Greek model of the universe, known as the *Mathematical Collection,* served as the basis for future studies both in the Islamic world and the West. Because of its importance, Islamic scientists referred to it as *al-magisti,* meaning "the greatest." Since that time, it has been called the *Almagest.* Seen here is a woodcut from one of its early printings. (*Source:* Katz, Victor J., *A History of Mathematics.*)

## EXAMPLE 2 Identifying the Quadrant of an Angle

Identify the quadrant (or quadrants) of any angle $\theta$ that satisfies $\sin\theta > 0$, $\tan\theta < 0$.

**SOLUTION**

Because $\sin\theta > 0$ in quadrants I and II, while $\tan\theta < 0$ in quadrants II and IV, both conditions are met only in quadrant II. ■

The six trigonometric functions are defined in terms of $x$, $y$, and $r$, where the Pythagorean theorem shows that $r^2 = x^2 + y^2$ and $r > 0$. With these relationships, knowing the value of only one function and the quadrant in which the angle lies makes it possible to find the values of all six of the trigonometric functions.

## EXAMPLE 3 Finding All Function Values Given One Value and the Quadrant

Suppose that angle $\alpha$ is in quadrant II and $\sin\alpha = \frac{2}{3}$. Find the values of the other five functions.

**SOLUTION**

We can choose any point on the terminal side of angle $\alpha$. For simplicity, because $\sin\alpha = \frac{y}{r}$, we choose the point with $r = 3$. Then $y = 2$, and

$$\frac{y}{r} = \frac{2}{3}.$$

To find $x$, use the result $x^2 + y^2 = r^2$.

$$x^2 + y^2 = r^2$$

$$x^2 + 2^2 = 3^2 \quad \text{Substitute.}$$

$$x^2 + 4 = 9$$

$$x^2 = 5 \quad \text{Subtract 4.}$$

$$x = \sqrt{5} \quad \text{or} \quad x = -\sqrt{5} \quad \text{Square root property}$$

Because $\alpha$ is in quadrant II, $x$ must be negative, as shown in Figure 15, so $x = -\sqrt{5}$. This puts the point $(-\sqrt{5}, 2)$ on the terminal side of $\alpha$.

Now that the values of $x$, $y$, and $r$ are known, the values of the remaining trigonometric functions can be found.

$$\cos\alpha = \frac{x}{r} = \frac{-\sqrt{5}}{3} = -\frac{\sqrt{5}}{3}$$

$$\sec\alpha = \frac{r}{x} = \frac{3}{-\sqrt{5}} = -\frac{3}{\sqrt{5}} \cdot \frac{\sqrt{5}}{\sqrt{5}} = -\frac{3\sqrt{5}}{5}$$

$$\tan\alpha = \frac{y}{x} = \frac{2}{-\sqrt{5}} = -\frac{2}{\sqrt{5}} \cdot \frac{\sqrt{5}}{\sqrt{5}} = -\frac{2\sqrt{5}}{5}$$

Remember to rationalize denominators.

$$\cot\alpha = \frac{x}{y} = \frac{-\sqrt{5}}{2} = -\frac{\sqrt{5}}{2} \qquad \csc\alpha = \frac{r}{y} = \frac{3}{2}$$

■

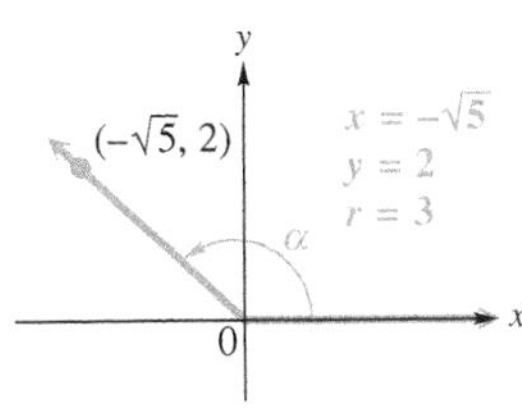


FIGURE 15

**Pythagorean Identities** We can derive three very useful new identities from the relationship $x^2 + y^2 = r^2$. Dividing both sides by $r^2$ gives

$$\frac{x^2}{r^2} + \frac{y^2}{r^2} = \frac{r^2}{r^2},$$

or

$$\left(\frac{x}{r}\right)^2 + \left(\frac{y}{r}\right)^2 = 1.$$

Because $\sin\theta = \frac{y}{r}$ and $\cos\theta = \frac{x}{r}$, this result becomes

$$(\cos\theta)^2 + (\sin\theta)^2 = 1,$$

or, as it is often written,

$$\mathbf{\sin^2\theta + \cos^2\theta = 1.}$$

Starting with $x^2 + y^2 = r^2$ and dividing through by $x^2$ gives

$$\frac{x^2}{x^2} + \frac{y^2}{x^2} = \frac{r^2}{x^2}$$

$$1 + \left(\frac{y}{x}\right)^2 = \left(\frac{r}{x}\right)^2$$

$$1 + (\tan\theta)^2 = (\sec\theta)^2$$

or

$$\mathbf{1 + \tan^2\theta = \sec^2\theta.}$$

On the other hand, dividing through by $y^2$ leads to

$$\mathbf{1 + \cot^2\theta = \csc^2\theta.}$$

These three identities are called the **Pythagorean identities** because the original equation that led to them, $x^2 + y^2 = r^2$, comes from the Pythagorean theorem.

| Pythagorean Identities | | |
|---|---|---|
| $\sin^2\theta + \cos^2\theta = 1$ | $1 + \tan^2\theta = \sec^2\theta$ | $1 + \cot^2\theta = \csc^2\theta$ |

As before, we have given only one form of each identity. However, algebraic transformations can be made to get equivalent identities. For example, by subtracting $\sin^2\theta$ from both sides of $\sin^2\theta + \cos^2\theta = 1$ we get the equivalent identity

$$\cos^2\theta = 1 - \sin^2\theta.$$

**Quotient Identities** Recall that $\sin\theta = \frac{y}{r}$ and $\cos\theta = \frac{x}{r}$. Consider the quotient of $\sin\theta$ and $\cos\theta$, where $\cos\theta \neq 0$.

$$\frac{\sin\theta}{\cos\theta} = \frac{\frac{y}{r}}{\frac{x}{r}} = \frac{y}{r} \div \frac{x}{r} = \frac{y}{r} \cdot \frac{r}{x} = \frac{y}{x} = \tan\theta$$

Similarly, it can be shown that $\frac{\cos\theta}{\sin\theta} = \cot\theta$, for $\sin\theta \neq 0$. Thus we have two more identities, called the **quotient identities.**

**Quotient Identities**

$$\frac{\sin\theta}{\cos\theta} = \tan\theta \qquad \frac{\cos\theta}{\sin\theta} = \cot\theta$$

**EXAMPLE 4 Finding Other Function Values Given One Value and the Quadrant**

Find $\sin\alpha$ and $\tan\alpha$ if $\cos\alpha = -\frac{\sqrt{3}}{4}$ and $\alpha$ is in quadrant II.

**SOLUTION**

Start with $\sin^2\alpha + \cos^2\alpha = 1$, and replace $\cos\alpha$ with $-\frac{\sqrt{3}}{4}$.

$$\sin^2\alpha + \left(-\frac{\sqrt{3}}{4}\right)^2 = 1 \qquad \text{Replace } \cos\alpha \text{ with } -\frac{\sqrt{3}}{4}.$$

$$\sin^2\alpha + \frac{3}{16} = 1$$

$$\sin^2\alpha = \frac{13}{16} \qquad \text{Subtract } \frac{3}{16}.$$

$$\sin\alpha = \pm\frac{\sqrt{13}}{4} \qquad \text{Take square roots.}$$

$$\sin\alpha = \frac{\sqrt{13}}{4} \qquad \alpha \text{ is in quadrant II, so } \sin\alpha > 0.$$

To find $\tan\alpha$, use the quotient identity $\tan\alpha = \frac{\sin\alpha}{\cos\alpha}$.

$$\tan\alpha = \frac{\sin\alpha}{\cos\alpha} = \frac{\frac{\sqrt{13}}{4}}{-\frac{\sqrt{3}}{4}} = \frac{\sqrt{13}}{4}\left(-\frac{4}{\sqrt{3}}\right) = -\frac{\sqrt{13}}{\sqrt{3}} = -\frac{\sqrt{13}}{\sqrt{3}} \cdot \frac{\sqrt{3}}{\sqrt{3}} = -\frac{\sqrt{39}}{3}$$

## 10.3 Exercises

*Use the appropriate reciprocal identity to find each function value. Rationalize denominators when applicable.*

**1.** $\tan\theta$, if $\cot\theta = -3$

**2.** $\cot\theta$, if $\tan\theta = 5$

**3.** $\sin\theta$, if $\csc\theta = 3$

**4.** $\cos\alpha$, if $\sec\alpha = -\frac{5}{2}$

**5.** $\cot\beta$, if $\tan\beta = -\frac{1}{5}$

**6.** $\sin\alpha$, if $\csc\alpha = \sqrt{15}$

**7.** $\csc\alpha$, if $\sin\alpha = \frac{\sqrt{2}}{4}$

**8.** $\sec\beta$, if $\cos\beta = -\frac{1}{\sqrt{7}}$

**9.** $\tan\theta$, if $\cot\theta = -\frac{\sqrt{5}}{3}$

**10.** $\cot\theta$, if $\tan\theta = \frac{\sqrt{11}}{5}$

**11.** $\sin\theta$, if $\csc\theta = 1.5$

**12.** $\cos\theta$, if $\sec\theta = 7.5$

*Identify the quadrant or quadrants for each angle satisfying the given conditions.*

**13.** $\sin \alpha > 0$, $\cos \alpha < 0$

**14.** $\cos \beta > 0$, $\tan \beta > 0$

**15.** $\tan \gamma > 0$, $\sin \gamma > 0$

**16.** $\sin \beta < 0$, $\cos \beta > 0$

**17.** $\tan \omega < 0$, $\cos \omega < 0$

**18.** $\csc \theta < 0$, $\cos \theta < 0$

**19.** $\cos \beta < 0$

**20.** $\tan \theta > 0$

*Give the signs of the six trigonometric functions for each angle.*

**21.** $74°$

**22.** $129°$

**23.** $183°$

**24.** $298°$

**25.** $302°$

**26.** $406°$

**27.** $412°$

**28.** $-82°$

**29.** $-14°$

**30.** $-121°$

*Use identities to find the indicated value.*

**31.** $\tan \alpha$, if $\sec \alpha = 3$, with $\alpha$ in quadrant IV

**32.** $\cos \theta$, if $\sin \theta = \frac{2}{3}$, with $\theta$ in quadrant II

**33.** $\sin \alpha$, if $\cos \alpha = -\frac{1}{4}$, with $\alpha$ in quadrant II

**34.** $\csc \beta$, if $\cot \beta = -\frac{1}{2}$, with $\beta$ in quadrant IV

**35.** $\tan \theta$, if $\cos \theta = \frac{1}{3}$, with $\theta$ in quadrant IV

**36.** $\sec \theta$, if $\tan \theta = \frac{\sqrt{7}}{3}$, with $\theta$ in quadrant III

**37.** $\cos \beta$, if $\csc \beta = -4$, with $\beta$ in quadrant III

**38.** $\sin \theta$, if $\sec \theta = 2$, with $\theta$ in quadrant IV

*Find all the trigonometric function values for each angle.*

**39.** $\tan \alpha = -\frac{15}{8}$, with $\alpha$ in quadrant II

**40.** $\cos \alpha = -\frac{3}{5}$, with $\alpha$ in quadrant III

**41.** $\cot \gamma = \frac{3}{4}$, with $\gamma$ in quadrant III

**42.** $\sin \beta = \frac{7}{25}$, with $\beta$ in quadrant II

**43.** $\tan \beta = \sqrt{3}$, with $\beta$ in quadrant III

**44.** $\csc \theta = 2$, with $\theta$ in quadrant II

**45.** $\sin \beta = \frac{\sqrt{5}}{7}$, with $\tan \beta > 0$

**46.** $\cot \alpha = \frac{\sqrt{3}}{8}$, with $\sin \alpha > 0$

**47.** Derive the identity $1 + \cot^2 \theta = \csc^2 \theta$ by dividing $x^2 + y^2 = r^2$ by $y^2$.

**48.** Using a method similar to the one given in this section showing that $\frac{\sin \theta}{\cos \theta} = \tan \theta$, show that

$$\frac{\cos \theta}{\sin \theta} = \cot \theta.$$

## 10.4 Right Triangles and Function Values

**Right Triangle Side Ratios • Cofunction Identities • Trigonometric Function Values of Special Angles • Reference Angles**

**Right Triangle Side Ratios** Figure 16 on the next page shows an acute angle $A$ in standard position. The definitions of the trigonometric function values of angle $A$ require $x$, $y$, and $r$. As drawn in Figure 16, $x$ and $y$ are the lengths of the two legs of the right triangle $ABC$, and $r$ is the length of the hypotenuse. The functions of trigonometry can be adapted to describe the ratios of these sides.

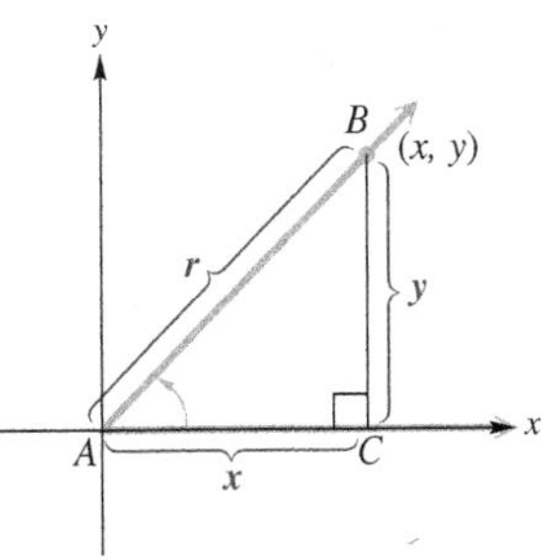


FIGURE 16

The side of length $y$ is called the **side opposite** angle $A$, and the side of length $x$ is called the **side adjacent** to angle $A$. The lengths of these sides can be used to replace $x$ and $y$ in the definitions of the trigonometric functions, with $r$ replaced by the length of the hypotenuse, to get the following right triangle-based definitions.

**Right Triangle-Based Definitions of Trigonometric Functions**

For any acute angle $A$ in standard position,

$$\sin A = \frac{y}{r} = \frac{\text{side opposite } A}{\text{hypotenuse}} \qquad \csc A = \frac{r}{y} = \frac{\text{hypotenuse}}{\text{side opposite } A}$$

$$\cos A = \frac{x}{r} = \frac{\text{side adjacent to } A}{\text{hypotenuse}} \qquad \sec A = \frac{r}{x} = \frac{\text{hypotenuse}}{\text{side adjacent to } A}$$

$$\tan A = \frac{y}{x} = \frac{\text{side opposite } A}{\text{side adjacent to } A} \qquad \cot A = \frac{x}{y} = \frac{\text{side adjacent to } A}{\text{side opposite } A}.$$

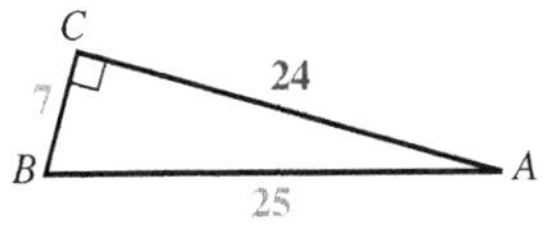

### EXAMPLE 1 Finding Trigonometric Function Values of an Acute Angle

Find the values of the trigonometric functions for angles $A$ and $B$ in the right triangle in Figure 17.

FIGURE 17

**SOLUTION**

The length of the side opposite angle $A$ is 7. The length of the side adjacent to angle $A$ is 24, and the length of the hypotenuse is 25. Using the relationships given above,

$$\sin A = \frac{\text{side opposite}}{\text{hypotenuse}} = \frac{7}{25} \qquad \csc A = \frac{\text{hypotenuse}}{\text{side opposite}} = \frac{25}{7}$$

$$\cos A = \frac{\text{side adjacent}}{\text{hypotenuse}} = \frac{24}{25} \qquad \sec A = \frac{\text{hypotenuse}}{\text{side adjacent}} = \frac{25}{24}$$

$$\tan A = \frac{\text{side opposite}}{\text{side adjacent}} = \frac{7}{24} \qquad \cot A = \frac{\text{side adjacent}}{\text{side opposite}} = \frac{24}{7}.$$

The length of the side opposite angle $B$ is 24, while the length of the side adjacent to $B$ is 7, making

$$\sin B = \frac{24}{25} \qquad \cos B = \frac{7}{25} \qquad \tan B = \frac{24}{7}$$

$$\csc B = \frac{25}{24} \qquad \sec B = \frac{25}{7} \qquad \cot B = \frac{7}{24}.$$

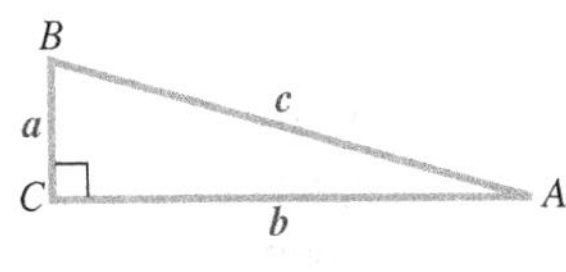


FIGURE 18

**Cofunction Identities** In Example 1, you may have noticed that $\sin A = \cos B$, $\cos A = \sin B$, and so on. Such relationships are always true for the two acute angles of a right triangle. Figure 18 shows a right triangle with acute angles $A$ and $B$ and a right angle at $C$. (Whenever we use $A$, $B$, and $C$ to name the angles in a right triangle, $C$ will be the right angle.) The length of the side opposite angle $A$ is $a$, and the length of the side opposite angle $B$ is $b$. The length of the hypotenuse is $c$.

By the definitions given above, $\sin A = \frac{a}{c}$. Because $\cos B$ is also equal to $\frac{a}{c}$,

$$\sin A = \frac{a}{c} = \cos B.$$

In a similar manner,

$$\tan A = \frac{a}{b} = \cot B \quad \text{and} \quad \sec A = \frac{c}{b} = \csc B.$$

The sum of the three angles in any triangle is 180°. Because angle $C$ equals 90°, angles $A$ and $B$ must have a sum of $180° - 90° = 90°$. As mentioned in Section 10.1, angles with a sum of 90° are called *complementary angles*. Because angles $A$ and $B$ are complementary and $\sin A = \cos B$, the functions sine and cosine are called **cofunctions.** Also, tangent and cotangent are cofunctions, as are secant and cosecant. And because the angles $A$ and $B$ are complementary, $A + B = 90°$, or

$$B = 90° - A,$$

giving

$$\sin A = \cos B = \cos(90° - A).$$

Similar results are true for the other trigonometric functions. We call these results the **cofunction identities.**

### Cofunction Identities

For any acute angle $A$,

$$\sin A = \cos(90° - A) \qquad \csc A = \sec(90° - A)$$
$$\cos A = \sin(90° - A) \qquad \sec A = \csc(90° - A)$$
$$\tan A = \cot(90° - A) \qquad \cot A = \tan(90° - A).$$

These identities can be extended to *any* angle $A$, and not just acute angles.

### EXAMPLE 2 Writing Functions in Terms of Cofunctions

Write each of the following in terms of cofunctions.

**(a)** cos 52° **(b)** tan 71° **(c)** sec 24°

**SOLUTION**

**(a)** Because $\cos A = \sin(90° - A)$,

$$\cos 52° = \sin(90° - 52°) = \sin 38°.$$

**(b)** $\tan 71° = \cot(90° - 71°) = \cot 19°$

**(c)** $\sec 24° = \csc 66°$

**Trigonometric Function Values of Special Angles** Certain special angles, such as 30°, 45°, and 60°, occur so often in applications of trigonometry that they deserve special study. We can find the exact trigonometric function values of these angles by using properties of geometry and the Pythagorean theorem.

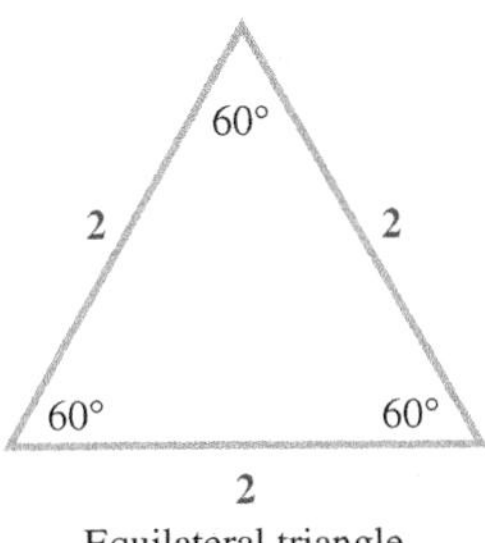

Equilateral triangle
(a)

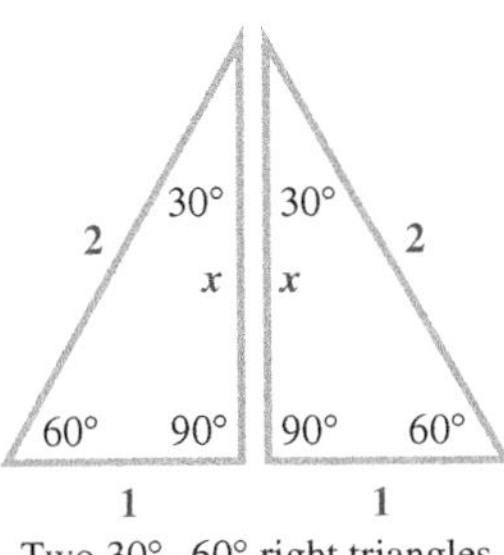

Two 30°–60° right triangles
(b)

**FIGURE 19**

To find the trigonometric function values for 30° and 60°, we start with an equilateral triangle, a triangle with all sides of equal length. Each angle of such a triangle has a measure of 60°. While the results we will obtain are independent of the length, for convenience, we choose the length of each side to be 2 units. See Figure 19(a).

Bisecting one angle of this equilateral triangle leads to two right triangles, each of which has angles of 30°, 60°, and 90°, as shown in Figure 19(b). Because the hypotenuse of one of these right triangles has a length of 2, the shortest side will have a length of 1. (Why?) If $x$ represents the length of the medium side, then,

$$
\begin{aligned}
2^2 &= 1^2 + x^2 && \text{Pythagorean theorem} \\
4 &= 1 + x^2 \\
3 &= x^2 && \text{Subtract 1.} \\
\sqrt{3} &= x. && \text{Square root property; } x > 0
\end{aligned}
$$

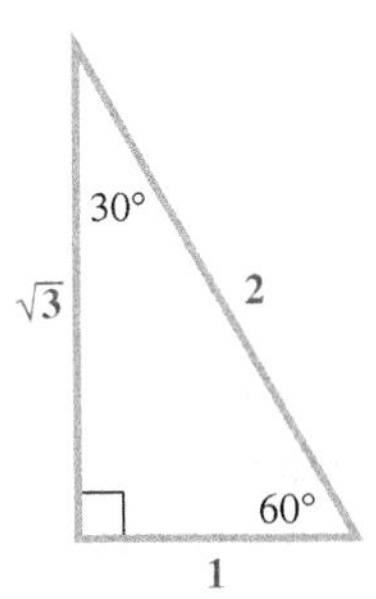


**FIGURE 20**

Figure 20 summarizes our results, showing a 30°–60° right triangle. As shown in the figure, the side opposite the 30° angle has length 1; that is, for the 30° angle,

$$\text{hypotenuse} = 2, \qquad \text{side opposite} = 1, \qquad \text{side adjacent} = \sqrt{3}.$$

Using the definitions of the trigonometric functions,

$$
\begin{aligned}
\sin 30^\circ &= \frac{\text{side opposite}}{\text{hypotenuse}} = \frac{1}{2} & \csc 30^\circ &= \frac{2}{1} = 2 \\
\cos 30^\circ &= \frac{\text{side adjacent}}{\text{hypotenuse}} = \frac{\sqrt{3}}{2} & \sec 30^\circ &= \frac{2}{\sqrt{3}} = \frac{2\sqrt{3}}{3} \\
\tan 30^\circ &= \frac{\text{side opposite}}{\text{side adjacent}} = \frac{1}{\sqrt{3}} = \frac{\sqrt{3}}{3} & \cot 30^\circ &= \frac{\sqrt{3}}{1} = \sqrt{3}.
\end{aligned}
$$

The denominator was rationalized for tan 30° and sec 30°.

In a similar manner,

$$
\sin 60^\circ = \frac{\sqrt{3}}{2} \qquad \cos 60^\circ = \frac{1}{2} \qquad \tan 60^\circ = \sqrt{3}
$$

$$
\csc 60^\circ = \frac{2\sqrt{3}}{3} \qquad \sec 60^\circ = 2 \qquad \cot 60^\circ = \frac{\sqrt{3}}{3}.
$$

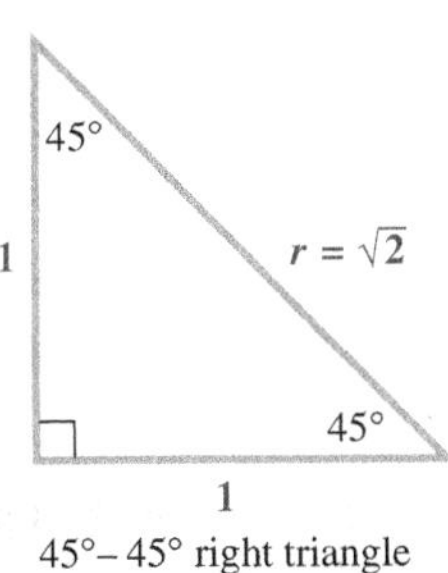

45°–45° right triangle

**FIGURE 21**

The values of the trigonometric functions for 45° can be found by starting with a 45°–45° right triangle, as shown in Figure 21. This triangle is isosceles, and, for convenience, we choose the lengths of the equal sides to be 1 unit. (As before, the results are independent of the length of the equal sides of the right triangle.) Because the shorter sides each have length 1, if $r$ represents the length of the hypotenuse, then

$$
\begin{aligned}
1^2 + 1^2 &= r^2 \\
2 &= r^2 \\
\sqrt{2} &= r.
\end{aligned}
$$

Using the measures indicated on the 45°–45° right triangle in Figure 21, we find

$$\sin 45^\circ = \frac{1}{\sqrt{2}} = \frac{\sqrt{2}}{2} \qquad \cos 45^\circ = \frac{1}{\sqrt{2}} = \frac{\sqrt{2}}{2} \qquad \tan 45^\circ = \frac{1}{1} = 1$$

$$\csc 45^\circ = \frac{\sqrt{2}}{1} = \sqrt{2} \qquad \sec 45^\circ = \frac{\sqrt{2}}{1} = \sqrt{2} \qquad \cot 45^\circ = \frac{1}{1} = 1.$$

***The importance of these exact trigonometric function values of 30°, 60°, and 45° angles cannot be overemphasized.*** They are summarized in Table 3. You should be able to reproduce the function values in the table if you remember the values of sin 30°, cos 30°, and sin 45°. Then complete the rest of the chart using the reciprocal, quotient, and cofunction identities. Another option is to visualize the appropriate triangles and use the ratios of the definitions.

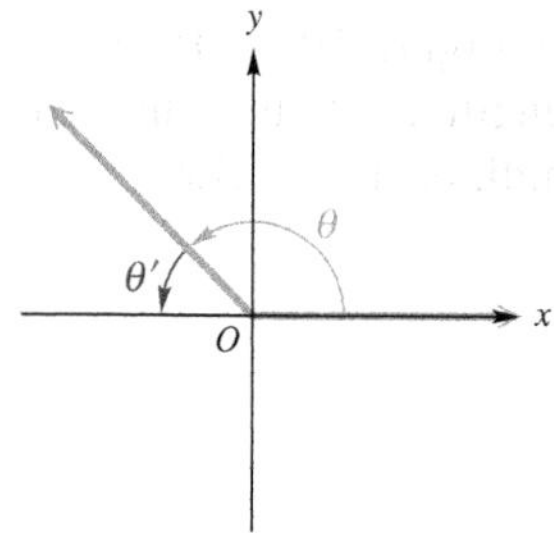

$\theta$ in quadrant II

**TABLE 3** **Function Values of Special Angles**

| $\theta$ | $\sin\theta$ | $\cos\theta$ | $\tan\theta$ | $\cot\theta$ | $\sec\theta$ | $\csc\theta$ |
|---|---|---|---|---|---|---|
| 30° | $\frac{1}{2}$ | $\frac{\sqrt{3}}{2}$ | $\frac{\sqrt{3}}{3}$ | $\sqrt{3}$ | $\frac{2\sqrt{3}}{3}$ | 2 |
| 45° | $\frac{\sqrt{2}}{2}$ | $\frac{\sqrt{2}}{2}$ | 1 | 1 | $\sqrt{2}$ | $\sqrt{2}$ |
| 60° | $\frac{\sqrt{3}}{2}$ | $\frac{1}{2}$ | $\sqrt{3}$ | $\frac{\sqrt{3}}{3}$ | 2 | $\frac{2\sqrt{3}}{3}$ |

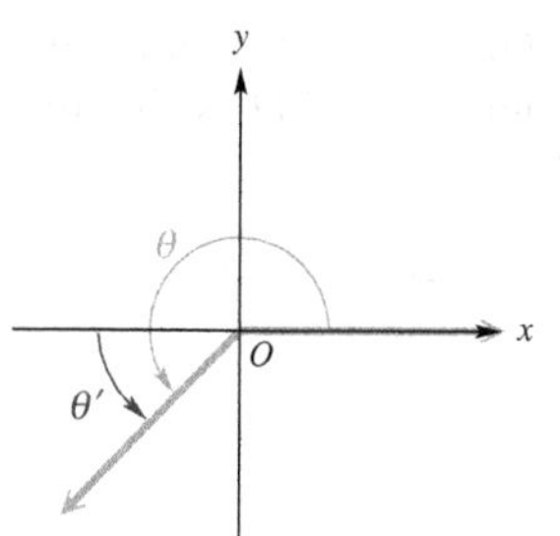

$\theta$ in quadrant III

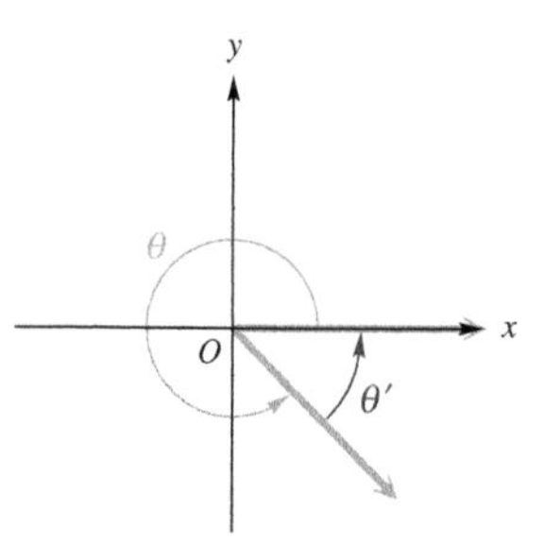

$\theta$ in quadrant IV

**FIGURE 22**

**Reference Angles** Now that we have discussed trigonometric function values for acute angles, we can use those results to find trigonometric function values for other types of angles. Associated with every nonquadrantal angle in standard position is a positive acute angle called its *reference angle*. A **reference angle** for an angle $\theta$, written $\theta'$, is the positive acute angle made by the terminal side of angle $\theta$ and the $x$-axis. Figure 22 shows several angles $\theta$ (each less than one complete counterclockwise revolution) in quadrants II, III, and IV, respectively, with the reference angle $\theta'$ also shown. In quadrant I, $\theta$ and $\theta'$ are the same. If an angle $\theta$ is negative or has measure greater than 360°, its reference angle is found by first finding its coterminal angle that is between 0° and 360°, and then using the diagram in Figure 22.

A common error is to find the reference angle by using the terminal side of $\theta$ and the $y$-axis. ***The reference angle is always found with reference to the x-axis.***

## EXAMPLE 3 Finding Reference Angles

Find the reference angles for each angle.

**(a)** 218° **(b)** 1387°

**SOLUTION**

**(a)** As shown in Figure 23 on the next page, the positive acute angle made by the terminal side of this angle and the $x$-axis is $218^\circ - 180^\circ = 38^\circ$. For $\theta = 218^\circ$, the reference angle is $\theta' = 38^\circ$.

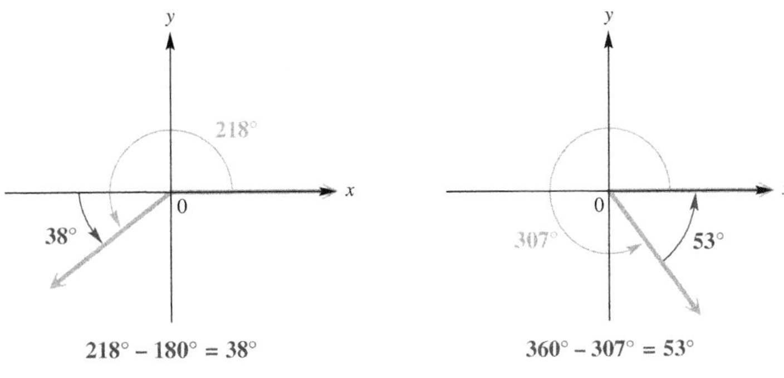


FIGURE 23

FIGURE 24

**(b)** First find a coterminal angle between 0° and 360°. Divide 1387° by 360° to get a quotient of about 3.9. Begin by subtracting 360° three times (because of the whole number 3 in 3.9):

$$1387° - 3 \cdot 360° = 307°.$$

The reference angle for 307° (and thus for 1387°) is $360° - 307° = 53°$. See Figure 24.

The preceding example suggests the following results for finding the reference angle $\theta'$ for any angle $\theta$ between 0° and 360°.

**Reference Angle $\theta'$ for $\theta$, where $0° < \theta < 360°$**

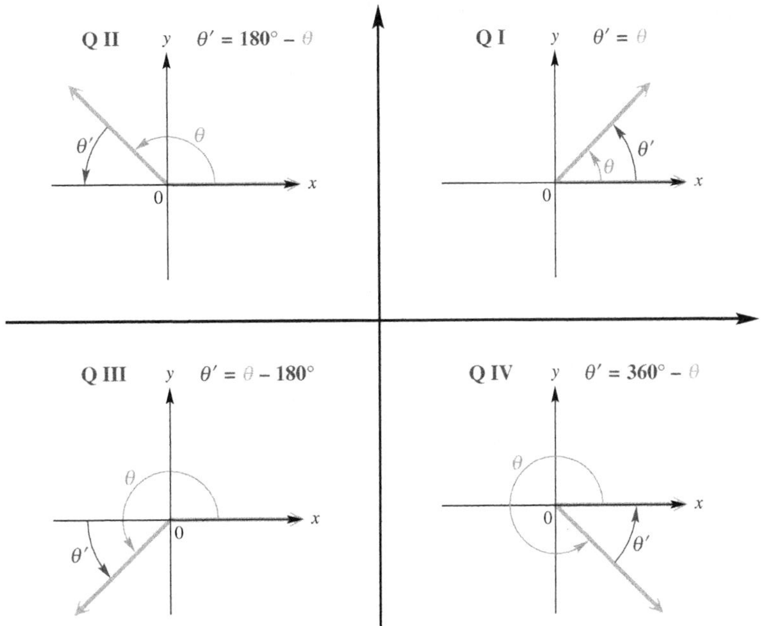


We can now find exact trigonometric function values of all angles with reference angles of 30°, 60°, or 45°. In Example 4 we show how to use these function values to find the trigonometric function values for 210°.

## EXAMPLE 4 Finding Trigonometric Function Values of a Quadrant III Angle

Find the exact values of the trigonometric functions for 210°.

**SOLUTION**

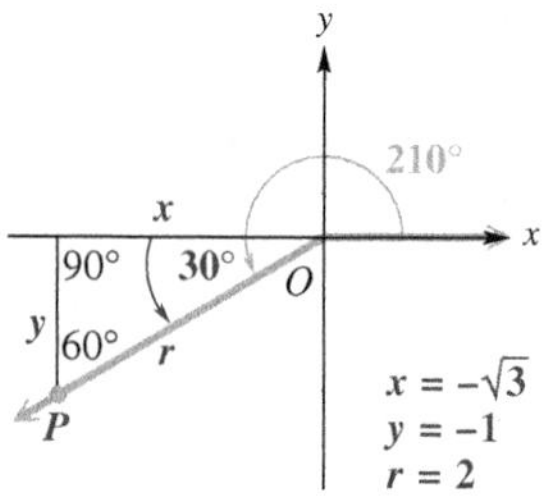

Even though a 210° angle is not an angle of a right triangle, the ideas mentioned earlier can still be used to find the trigonometric function values for this angle. To do so, we draw an angle of 210° in standard position, as shown in Figure 25. We choose point $P$ on the terminal side of the angle so that the distance from the origin $O$ to $P$ is 2. By the results from 30°–60° right triangles, the coordinates of point $P$ become $(-\sqrt{3}, -1)$, with $x = -\sqrt{3}$, $y = -1$, and $r = 2$. Then, by the definitions of the trigonometric functions,



**FIGURE 25**

$$\sin 210° = -\frac{1}{2} \qquad \cos 210° = -\frac{\sqrt{3}}{2} \qquad \tan 210° = \frac{\sqrt{3}}{3}$$

$$\csc 210° = -2 \qquad \sec 210° = -\frac{2\sqrt{3}}{3} \qquad \cot 210° = \sqrt{3}.$$

**Historian Reviel Netz** of Stanford University has been studying an ancient manuscript by the Greek mathematician Archimedes ("Unveiling the work of Archimedes," *Science News,* Vol. 157, p. 77, January 29, 2000). It is known as *Archimedes Palimpsest,* and dates from the 10th century A.D., surviving on a parchment that was later cut, scraped, and overwritten with a description of a church ritual. The use of ultraviolet photography and digital imaging makes it possible to read beneath the lines of the ritual and see Archimedes' text and diagrams. According to Netz, the diagrams suggest that Greek mathematicians emphasized qualitative relationships over quantitative accuracy.

Notice in Example 4 that the trigonometric function values of 210° correspond in absolute value to those of its reference angle 30°. The signs are different for the sine, cosine, secant, and cosecant functions, because 210° is a quadrant III angle. These results suggest a method for finding the trigonometric function values of a nonacute angle, using the reference angle. In Example 4, the reference angle for 210° is 30°, as shown in Figure 25. Simply by using the trigonometric function values of the reference angle, 30°, and choosing the correct signs for a quadrant III angle, we obtain the same results as found in Example 4.

The values of the trigonometric functions for any nonquadrantal angle $\theta$ can be determined by finding the function values for an angle between 0° and 90°. To do this, perform the following steps.

### Finding Trigonometric Function Values for Any Nonquadrantal Angle

***Step 1*** If $\theta > 360°$, or if $\theta < 0°$, find a coterminal angle by adding or subtracting 360° as many times as needed to obtain an angle greater than 0° but less than 360°.

***Step 2*** Find the reference angle $\theta'$.

***Step 3*** Find the necessary values of the trigonometric functions for the reference angle $\theta'$.

***Step 4*** Determine the correct signs for the values found in Step 3. (Use the table of signs in Section 10.3.) This result gives the values of the trigonometric functions for angle $\theta$.

## EXAMPLE 5 Finding Trigonometric Function Values Using Reference Angles

Use reference angles to find each exact value.

**(a)** $\cos(-240°)$ **(b)** $\tan 675°$

**SOLUTION**

**(a)** The reference angle for $-240°$ is $60°$, as shown in Figure 26. Because the cosine is negative in quadrant II,

$$\cos(-240°) = -\cos 60° = -\frac{1}{2}.$$

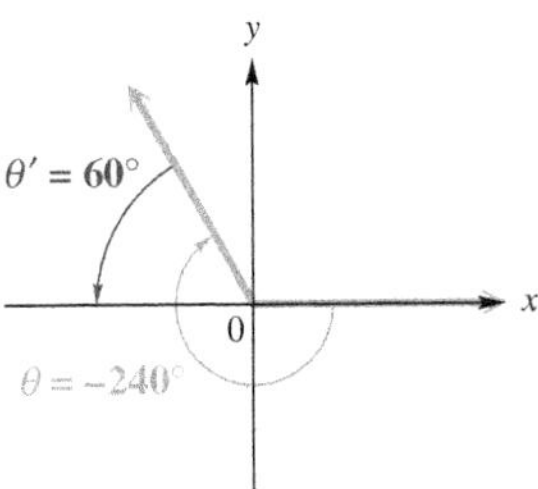


**FIGURE 26** **FIGURE 27**

**(b)** Begin by subtracting $360°$ to obtain a coterminal angle between $0°$ and $360°$.

$$675° - 360° = 315°$$

As shown in Figure 27, the reference angle is $360° - 315° = 45°$. An angle of $315°$ is in quadrant IV, so the tangent will be negative, and

$$\tan 675° = \tan 315° = -\tan 45° = -1.$$

The ideas discussed in this section can be used inversely to find the measures of certain angles, given a trigonometric function value and an interval in which an angle $\theta$ must lie. We are most often interested in the interval $0° \le \theta < 360°$.

## EXAMPLE 6 Finding Angle Measures Given an Interval and a Function Value

Find all values of $\theta$, if $0° \le \theta < 360°$ and $\cos \theta = -\frac{\sqrt{2}}{2}$.

**SOLUTION**

Because cosine here is negative, $\theta$ must lie in either quadrant II or III. The absolute value of $\cos \theta$ is $\frac{\sqrt{2}}{2}$, so the reference angle $\theta'$ must be $45°$. The two possible angles $\theta$ are sketched in Figure 28. The quadrant II angle $\theta$ must equal $180° - 45° = 135°$, and the quadrant III angle $\theta$ must equal $180° + 45° = 225°$.

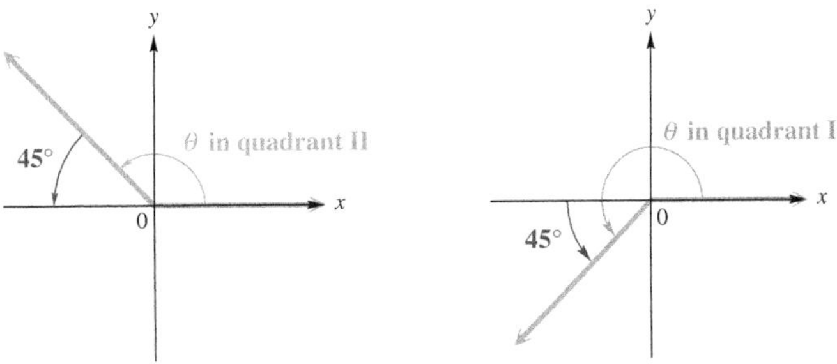


**FIGURE 28**

## 10.4 Exercises

*Find the values of the six trigonometric functions for angle A. (In Exercises 5 and 6, answers will be in terms of variables.) Leave answers as fractions.*

**1.**

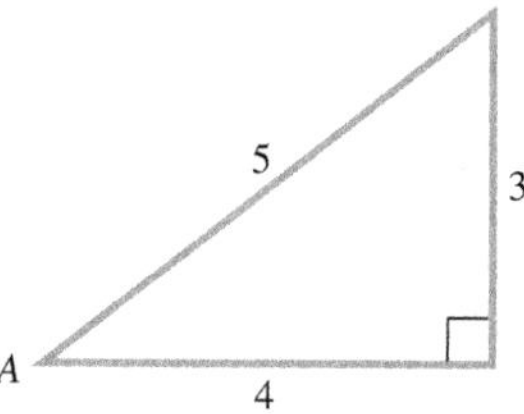


**2.**

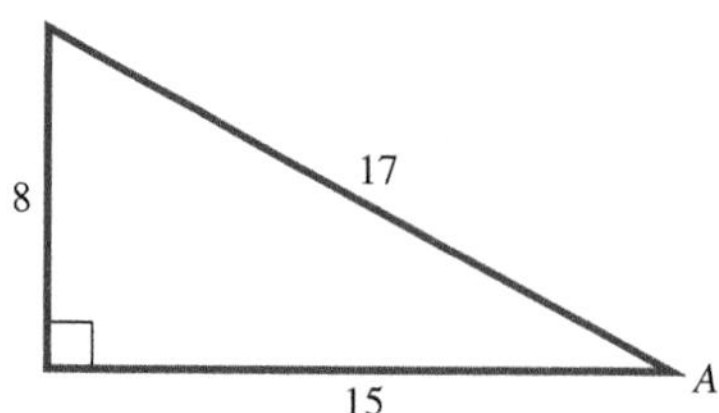


**3.**

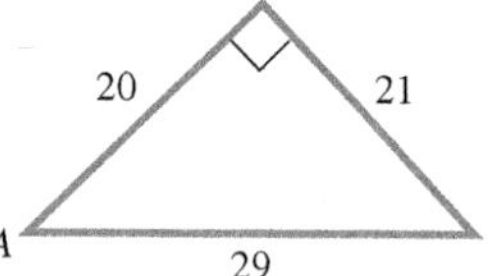


**4.**

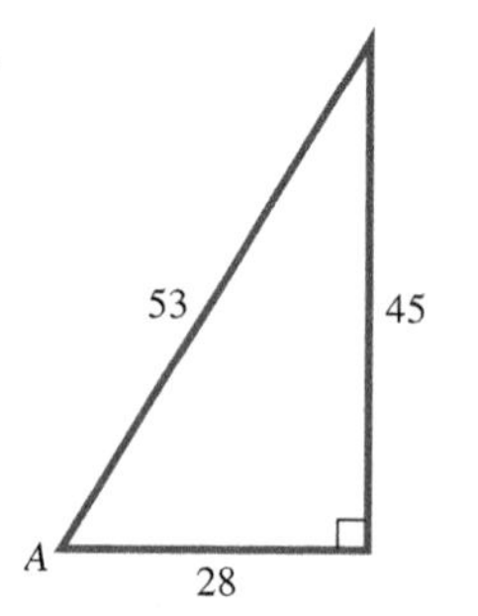


**5.**

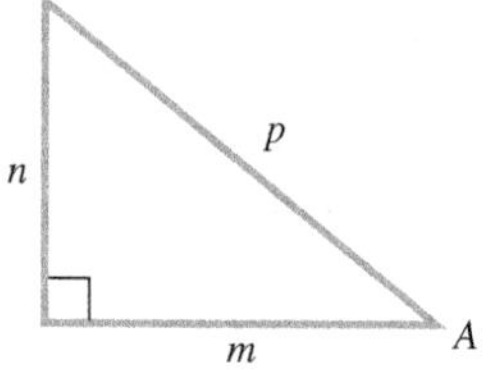


**6.**

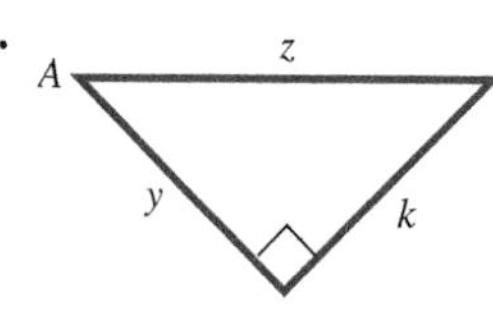


*Suppose ABC is a right triangle with sides of lengths a, b, and c, with right angle C (see Figure 18 on page 637). Find the unknown side length using the Pythagorean theorem, and then find the values of the six trigonometric functions for angle B. Rationalize denominators when applicable.*

**7.** $a = 5, b = 12$ **8.** $a = 3, b = 5$ **9.** $a = 6, c = 7$ **10.** $b = 7, c = 12$

*Write each of the following in terms of the cofunction.*

**11.** tan 50° **12.** cot 73° **13.** csc 47° **14.** sec 39°

**15.** tan 25.4° **16.** sin 38.7° **17.** cos 13° 30′ **18.** tan 26° 10′

*Give the* exact *trigonometric function value. Do not use a calculator.*

**19.** tan 30° **20.** cot 30° **21.** sin 30° **22.** cos 30°

**23.** csc 45° **24.** sec 45° **25.** cos 45° **26.** sin 45°

**27.** sin 60° **28.** cos 60° **29.** tan 60° **30.** cot 60°

*Find the reference angle for each angle.*

**31.** 98° **32.** 212° **33.** −135° **34.** −60° **35.** 750° **36.** 480°

*Find the* exact values *of the six trigonometric functions for each angle. Rationalize denominators when applicable.*

**37.** $120°$ **38.** $135°$ **39.** $150°$ **40.** $225°$ **41.** $240°$

**42.** $300°$ **43.** $315°$ **44.** $405°$ **45.** $420°$ **46.** $480°$

**47.** $495°$ **48.** $570°$ **49.** $750°$ **50.** $1305°$ **51.** $1500°$

**52.** $2670°$ **53.** $-390°$ **54.** $-510°$ **55.** $-1020°$ **56.** $-1290°$

*Complete the table with* exact *trigonometric function values using the methods of this section.*

| | $\theta$ | $\sin\theta$ | $\cos\theta$ | $\tan\theta$ | $\cot\theta$ | $\sec\theta$ | $\csc\theta$ |
|---|---|---|---|---|---|---|---|
| **57.** | **30°** | $\frac{1}{2}$ | $\frac{\sqrt{3}}{2}$ | | | $\frac{2\sqrt{3}}{3}$ | $2$ |
| **58.** | **45°** | | | $1$ | $1$ | | |
| **59.** | **60°** | | $\frac{1}{2}$ | $\sqrt{3}$ | | $2$ | |
| **60.** | **120°** | $\frac{\sqrt{3}}{2}$ | | $-\sqrt{3}$ | | | $\frac{2\sqrt{3}}{3}$ |
| **61.** | **135°** | $\frac{\sqrt{2}}{2}$ | $-\frac{\sqrt{2}}{2}$ | | | $-\sqrt{2}$ | $\sqrt{2}$ |
| **62.** | **150°** | $-$ | $-\frac{\sqrt{3}}{2}$ | $-\frac{\sqrt{3}}{3}$ | | | $2$ |
| **63.** | **210°** | $-\frac{1}{2}$ | | $\frac{\sqrt{3}}{3}$ | $\sqrt{3}$ | | $-2$ |
| **64.** | **240°** | $-\frac{\sqrt{3}}{2}$ | $-\frac{1}{2}$ | | | $-2$ | $-\frac{2\sqrt{3}}{3}$ |

*Find all values of $\theta$, if $0° \leq \theta < 360°$, and the given condition is true.*

**65.** $\sin\theta = -\frac{1}{2}$ **66.** $\cos\theta = -\frac{1}{2}$ **67.** $\tan\theta = 1$

**68.** $\cot\theta = \sqrt{3}$ **69.** $\sin\theta = \frac{\sqrt{3}}{2}$ **70.** $\cos\theta = \frac{\sqrt{3}}{2}$

**71.** $\sec\theta = -2$ **72.** $\csc\theta = -2$ **73.** $\sin\theta = -\frac{\sqrt{2}}{2}$

**74.** $\cos\theta = -\frac{\sqrt{2}}{2}$ **75.** $\tan\theta = -\sqrt{3}$ **76.** $\cot\theta = -1$

# 10.5 Applications of Right Triangles

**Calculator Approximations for Function Values • Finding Angles Using Inverse Functions • Significant Digits • Solving Triangles • Applications**

**Calculator Approximations for Function Values** With the technological advances of this era in mind, the examples and exercises that follow in this chapter assume that all students have access to scientific calculators. However, because calculators differ among makes and models, students should always consult their owner's manual for specific information if questions arise concerning their use.

Thus far in this book, we have studied only one type of measure for angles—degree measure; another type of measure, *radian measure*, is studied in more theoretical work. ***When evaluating trigonometric functions of angles given in degrees, it is a common error to use the incorrect mode; remember that the calculator must be set in the degree mode.***

```
sin(49°12')
      .7569950557
cos(97.977)
     -.1387755707
Ans-1
     -7.205879213
```

```
sin(130°48')
      .7569950557
```

The three screens above show the results for parts (a)—(e) in Example 1. Notice that the calculator permits entering the angle measure in degrees and minutes in parts (a) and (e). In the fifth line of the first screen, $\text{Ans}^{-1}$ tells the calculator to find the reciprocal of the answer given in the previous line.

### EXAMPLE 1 Finding Function Values with a Calculator

Use a calculator to approximate the value of each trigonometric function.

**(a)** $\sin 49° 12'$ **(b)** $\sec 97.977°$ **(c)** $\cot 51.4283°$
**(d)** $\sin(-246°)$ **(e)** $\sin 130° 48'$

**SOLUTION**

**(a)** Convert 49° 12′ to decimal degrees.

$$49° 12' = 49\frac{12}{60}° = 49.2°$$

$$\sin 49° 12' = \sin 49.2° \approx .75699506 \quad \text{To eight decimal places}$$

**(b)** Calculators do not have secant keys. However, $\sec\theta = \frac{1}{\cos\theta}$ for all angles $\theta$ where $\cos\theta \neq 0$. So find $\sec 97.977°$ by first finding $\cos 97.977°$ and then taking the reciprocal to get

$$\sec 97.977° \approx -7.20587921.$$

**(c)** Use the identity $\cot\theta = \frac{1}{\tan\theta}$.

$$\cot 51.4283° \approx .79748114$$

**(d)** $\sin(-246°) \approx .91354546$

**(e)** 130° 48′ is equal to 130.8°, so

$$\sin 130° 48' = \sin 130.8° \approx .75699506.$$

Notice that the values found in parts (a) and (e) of Example 1 are the same. The reason for this is that 49° 12′ is the reference angle for 130° 48′ and the sine function is positive for a quadrant II angle.

## Finding Angles Using Inverse Functions

So far in this section we have used a calculator to find trigonometric function values of angles. This process can be reversed using *inverse functions.* Inverse functions are denoted by using $-1$ as a superscript. For example, the inverse of $f$ is denoted $f^{-1}$ (read "$f$ inverse"). For now we restrict our attention to angles $\theta$ in the interval $0° \leq \theta \leq 90°$. The measure of an angle can be found from one of its trigonometric function values using inverse functions as shown in the next example.

### EXAMPLE 2 Using Inverse Functions to Find Angles

Use a calculator to find a value of $\theta$ such that $0° \leq \theta \leq 90°$, and $\theta$ satisfies each of the following. Leave answers in decimal degrees.

**(a)** $\sin\theta = .81815000$ **(b)** $\sec\theta = 1.0545829$

```
sin⁻¹(.81815000)
          54.90002816
1.0545829⁻¹
          .9482421913
cos⁻¹(Ans)
          18.51470432
```

This screen supports the results of Example 2.

**SOLUTION**

**(a)** We find $\theta$ using a key labeled [arc] or [INV] together with the [sin] key. Some calculators may require a key labeled [$\sin^{-1}$] instead. Check your owner's manual to see how your calculator handles this. Again, make sure the calculator is set for degree measure. You should get

$$\theta \approx 54.900028°.$$

**(b)** Use the identity $\cos \theta = \frac{1}{\sec \theta}$. Enter 1.0545829 and find the reciprocal. This gives $\cos \theta \approx .9482421913$. Now find $\theta$ as described in part (a) using inverse cosine. The result is

$$\theta \approx 18.514704°.$$

Compare Examples 1(b) and 2(b). Note that the reciprocal key is used *before* the inverse cosine key when finding the angle, but *after* the cosine key when finding the trigonometric function value.

## Significant Digits

Supppose we quickly measure a room as 15 feet by 18 feet. To calculate the length of a diagonal of the room, we can use the Pythagorean theorem.

$$d^2 = 15^2 + 18^2$$
$$d^2 = 549$$
$$d = \sqrt{549} \approx 23.430749$$

Should this answer be given as the length of the diagonal of the room? Of course not. The number 23.430749 contains 6 decimal places, while the original data of 15 feet and 18 feet are only accurate to the nearest foot. Because the results of a problem can be no more accurate than the least accurate number in any calculation, we really should say that the diagonal of the 15-by-18-foot room is 23 feet.

If a wall measured to the nearest foot is 18 feet long, this actually means that the wall has length between 17.5 feet and 18.5 feet. If the wall is measured more accurately as 18.3 feet long, then its length is really between 18.25 feet and 18.35 feet. A measurement of 18.00 feet would indicate that the length of the wall is between 17.995 feet and 18.005 feet. The measurement 18 feet is said to have two *significant digits* of accuracy; 18.0 has three significant digits, and 18.00 has four.

Consider the measurement 900 meters. We cannot tell whether this represents a measurement to the nearest meter, ten meters, or hundred meters. To avoid this problem, we write the number in scientific notation as $9.00 \times 10^2$ to the nearest meter, $9.0 \times 10^2$ to the nearest ten meters, or $9 \times 10^2$ to the nearest hundred meters. These three cases have three, two, and one significant digits, respectively.

A **significant digit** is a digit obtained by actual measurement. A number that represents the result of counting, or a number that results from theoretical work and is not the result of a measurement, is an **exact number.**

Most values of trigonometric functions are approximations, and virtually all measurements are approximations. To perform calculations on such approximate numbers, follow the rules given below. (The rules for rounding are found in Section 6.5.)

**Calculation with Significant Digits**

For *adding* and *subtracting,* round the answer so that the last digit you keep is in the rightmost column in which all the numbers have significant digits.

For *multiplying* or *dividing,* round the answer to the least number of significant digits found in any of the given numbers.

For *powers* and *roots,* round the answer so that it has the same number of significant digits as the numbers whose power or root you are finding.

When solving for angles, use Table 4 to determine the significant digits in angle measure.

**TABLE 4** Significant Digits for Angles

| Number of Significant Digits | Angle Measure to Nearest: |
|---|---|
| 2 | Degree |
| 3 | Ten minutes, or nearest tenth of a degree |
| 4 | Minute, or nearest hundredth of a degree |
| 5 | Tenth of a minute, or nearest thousandth of a degree |

For example, an angle measuring $52° 30'$ has three significant digits (assuming that $30'$ is measured to the nearest ten minutes).

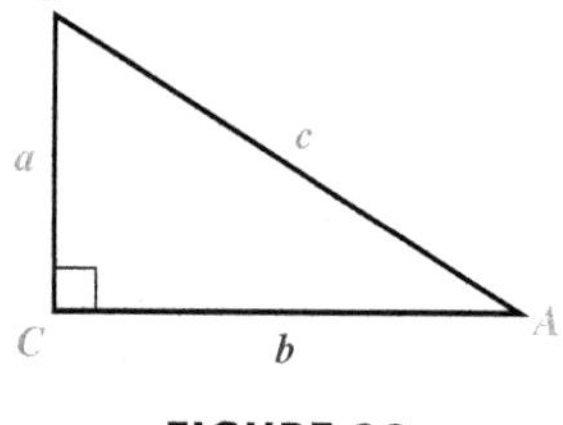


FIGURE 29

## Solving Triangles

To **solve a triangle** means to find the measures of all the angles and all the sides of the triangle. In using trigonometry to solve triangles, a labeled sketch is an important aid. It is conventional to use $a$ to represent the length of the side opposite angle $A$, $b$ for the length of the side opposite angle $B$, and so on. As mentioned earlier, in a right triangle the letter $c$ is reserved for the hypotenuse. Figure 29 shows the labeling of a typical right triangle.

In Examples 3–6, note that for convenience we use equality symbols (=), even though the side lengths and angle measures are often approximations.

FIGURE 30

### EXAMPLE 3 Solving a Right Triangle Given an Angle and a Side

Solve right triangle $ABC$, if $A = 34° 30'$ and $c = 12.7$ in. See Figure 30.

**SOLUTION**

To solve the triangle, find the measures of the remaining sides and angles. The value of $a$ can be found with a trigonometric function involving the known values of angle $A$ and side $c$. Because the sine of angle $A$ is given by the quotient of the side opposite $A$ and the hypotenuse, use $\sin A$.

$$\sin A = \frac{a}{c}$$

$$\sin 34° 30' = \frac{a}{12.7} \quad \text{Substitute known values.}$$

$$a = 12.7 \sin 34° 30' \quad \text{Multiply both sides by 12.7; rewrite.}$$
$$a = 12.7(.56640624) \quad \text{Use a calculator.}$$
$$a = 7.19 \text{ in.}$$

The value of $b$ could be found with the Pythagorean theorem. It is better, however, to use the information given in the problem rather than a result just calculated. If a mistake were to be made in finding $a$, then $b$ also would be incorrect. Also, rounding more than once may cause the result to be less accurate. Using $\cos A$ gives

$$\cos A = \frac{\text{side adjacent}}{\text{hypotenuse}} = \frac{b}{c}$$
$$\cos 34° 30' = \frac{b}{\mathbf{12.7}}$$
$$b = 12.7 \cos 34° 30'$$
$$b = 10.5 \text{ in.}$$

Once $b$ has been found, the Pythagorean theorem could be used as a check. All that remains to solve triangle $ABC$ is to find the measure of angle $B$.

$$A + B = 90°$$
$$B = 90° - A$$
$$B = 89° 60' - 34° 30'$$
$$B = 55° 30'$$

In Example 3 we could have started by finding the measure of angle $B$ and then used the trigonometric function values of $B$ to find the unknown sides. The process of solving a right triangle (like many problems in mathematics) can usually be done in several ways, each resulting in the correct answer. However, in order to retain as much accuracy as can be expected, always use the given information as much as possible, and avoid rounding off in intermediate steps.

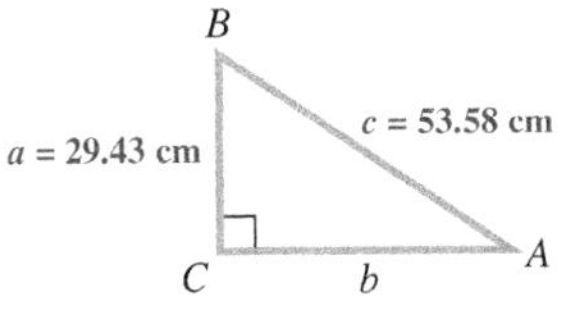

### EXAMPLE 4 Solving a Right Triangle Given Two Sides

Solve right triangle $ABC$ if $a = 29.43$ cm and $c = 53.58$ cm.



FIGURE 31

**SOLUTION**

Draw a sketch showing the given information, as in Figure 31. One way to begin is to find the sine of angle $A$, and then use inverse sine.

$$\sin A = \frac{\text{side opposite}}{\text{hypotenuse}} = \frac{29.43}{53.58}$$

Using [INV] [sin] or [sin⁻¹] on a calculator, we find that $A = 33.32°$. The measure of $B$ is $90° - 33.32° = 56.68°$.

We now find $b$ from the Pythagorean theorem, $a^2 + b^2 = c^2$, or $b^2 = c^2 - a^2$.

$$b^2 = 53.58^2 - 29.43^2 \quad c = 53.58 \text{ and } a = 29.43$$
$$b = 44.77 \text{ cm}$$

## Applications

**PROBLEM-SOLVING HINT** The process of solving right triangles is easily adapted to solving applied problems. ***A crucial step in such applications involves sketching the triangle and labeling the given parts correctly.*** Then we can use the methods described in the earlier examples to find the unknown value or values.

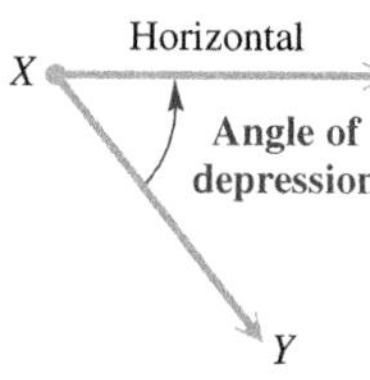


**FIGURE 32**

Many applications of right triangles involve the *angle of elevation* or the *angle of depression.* The **angle of elevation** from point $X$ to point $Y$ (above $X$) is the acute angle formed by ray $XY$ and a horizontal ray with endpoint at $X$. The angle of elevation is always measured from the horizontal. See the angle at the top of Figure 32. The **angle of depression** from point $X$ to point $Y$ (below $X$) is the acute angle formed by ray $XY$ and a horizontal ray with endpoint $X$, as shown at the bottom of Figure 32.

Errors are often made in interpreting the angle of depression. ***Remember that both the angle of elevation and the angle of depression are measured between the line of sight and the horizontal.***

### EXAMPLE 5 Finding a Length When the Angle of Elevation Is Known

Ana deArmas knows that when she stands 123 feet from the base of a flagpole, the angle of elevation to the top is $26° 40'$. If her eyes are 5.30 feet above the ground, find the height of the flagpole.

**SOLUTION**

The length of the side adjacent to Ana is known and the length of the side opposite her is to be found. (See Figure 33.) The ratio that involves these two values is the tangent.

Prior to the advent of the scientific calculator in the 1970s, trigonometry students were required to use **tables of trigonometric function values.** While most trigonometry texts included short versions of these tables, there were books like the one shown here that gave function values for angles, as well as information on their logarithms to make computations easier. (*Author's note:* Today's students don't know how fortunate they are not to have to use such tables.)

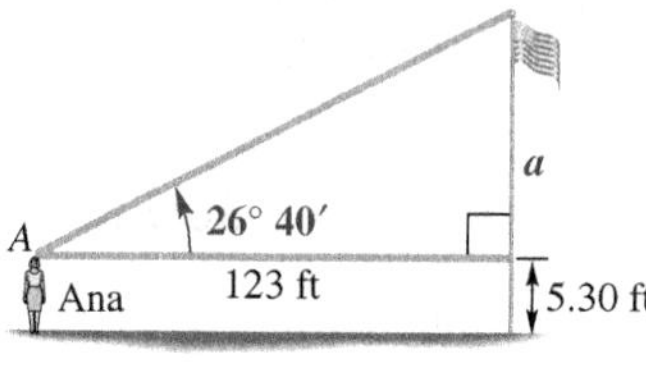


**FIGURE 33**

$$\tan A = \frac{\text{side opposite}}{\text{side adjacent}}$$

$$\tan 26° 40' = \frac{a}{123}$$

$$a = 123 \tan 26° 40'$$

$$a = 61.8 \text{ feet}$$

Because Ana's eyes are 5.30 feet above the ground, the height of the flagpole is

$$61.8 + 5.30 = 67.1 \text{ feet.}$$

### EXAMPLE 6 Finding the Angle of Elevation When Lengths Are Known

The length of the shadow of a building 34.09 meters tall is 37.62 meters. Find the angle of elevation of the sun.

**SOLUTION**

As shown in Figure 34, the angle of elevation of the sun is angle $B$. Because the side opposite $B$ and the side adjacent to $B$ are known, use the tangent ratio to find $B$.

$$\tan B = \frac{34.09}{37.62}$$

$$B = 42.18^\circ \quad \text{Use the inverse tangent function of a calculator.}$$

The angle of elevation of the sun is 42.18°.

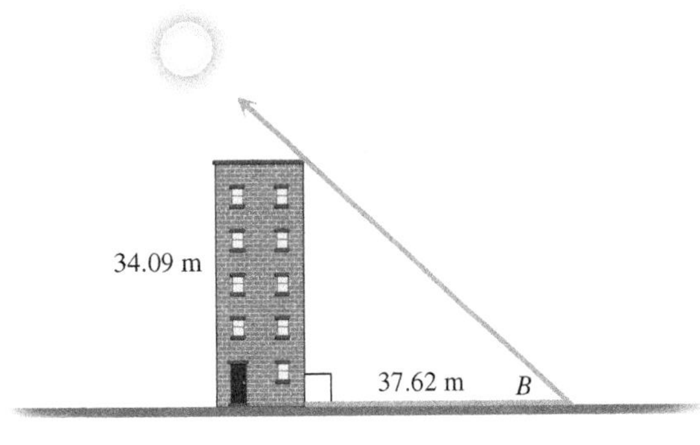


FIGURE 34

## 10.5 Exercises

*Use a calculator to find a decimal approximation for each value. Give as many digits as your calculator displays.*

**1.** $\tan 29^\circ\, 30'$

**2.** $\sin 38^\circ\, 42'$

**3.** $\cot 41^\circ\, 24'$

**4.** $\cos 27^\circ\, 10'$

**5.** $\sec 13^\circ\, 15'$

**6.** $\csc 44^\circ\, 30'$

**7.** $\sin 39^\circ\, 40'$

**8.** $\tan 17^\circ\, 12'$

**9.** $\csc 145^\circ\, 45'$

**10.** $\cot 183^\circ\, 48'$

**11.** $\cos 421^\circ\, 30'$

**12.** $\sec 312^\circ\, 12'$

**13.** $\tan(-80^\circ\, 6')$

**14.** $\sin(-317^\circ\, 36')$

**15.** $\cot(-512^\circ\, 20')$

**16.** $\cos(-15')$

*Find a value of $\theta$ such that $0^\circ \leq \theta \leq 90^\circ$, and $\theta$ satisfies the statement. Leave your answer in decimal degrees.*

**17.** $\sin \theta = .84802194$

**18.** $\tan \theta = 1.4739716$

**19.** $\sec \theta = 1.1606249$

**20.** $\cot \theta = 1.2575516$

**21.** $\sin \theta = .72144101$

**22.** $\sec \theta = 2.7496222$

**23.** $\tan \theta = 6.4358841$

**24.** $\sin \theta = .27843196$

*In the remaining exercises in this set, use a calculator as necessary.*

*Solve each right triangle.*

**25.**

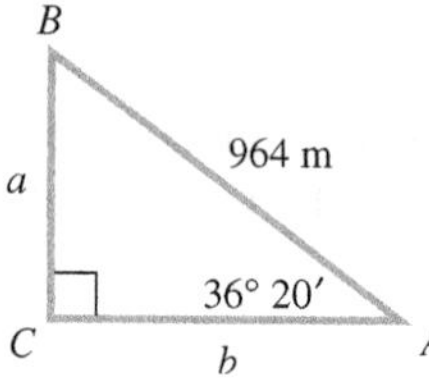


**26.**

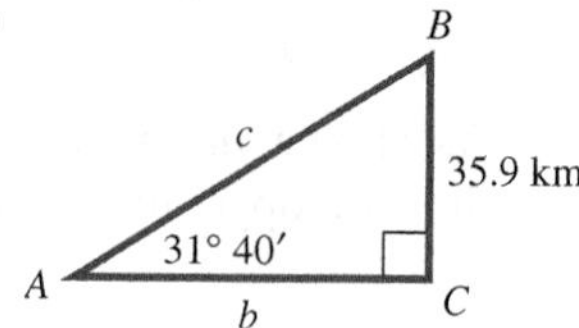


**27.**

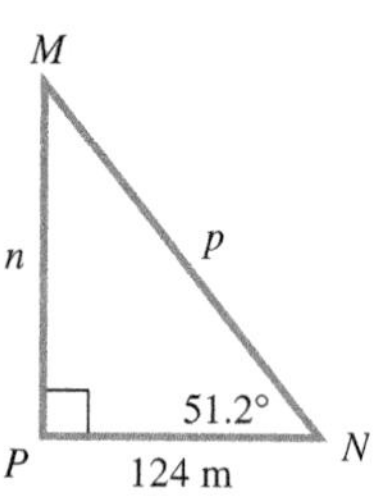


**28.**

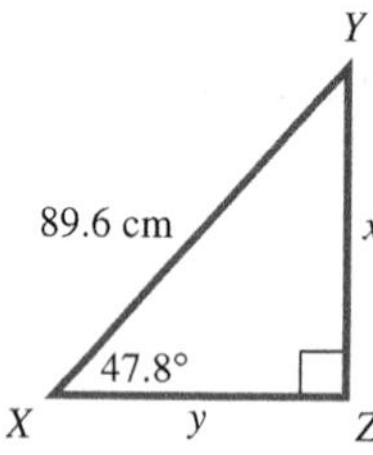


**29.**

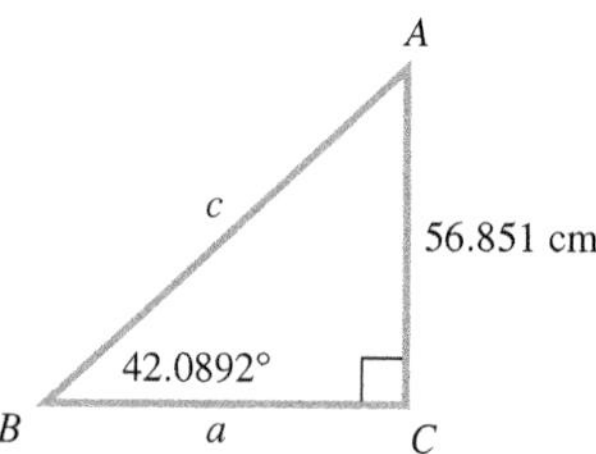


**30.**

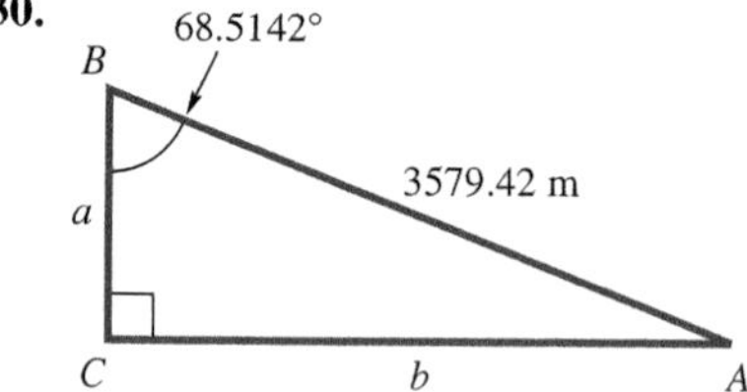


*Solve each right triangle. In each case, $C = 90°$. If the angle information is given in degrees and minutes, give the answers in the same way. If given in decimal degrees, do likewise in your answers. When two sides are given, give answers in degrees and minutes.*

**31.** $A = 28.00°$, $c = 17.4$ ft

**32.** $B = 46.00°$, $c = 29.7$ m

**33.** $B = 73.00°$, $b = 128$ in.

**34.** $A = 61° \, 00'$, $b = 39.2$ cm

**35.** $a = 76.4$ yd, $b = 39.3$ yd

**36.** $a = 958$ m, $b = 489$ m

**37.** $a = 18.9$ cm, $c = 46.3$ cm

**38.** $b = 219$ m, $c = 647$ m

**39.** $A = 53° \, 24'$, $c = 387.1$ ft

**40.** $A = 13° \, 47'$, $c = 1285$ m

**41.** $B = 39° \, 9'$, $c = .6231$ m

**42.** $B = 82° \, 51'$, $c = 4.825$ cm

*Solve each problem.*

43. ***Ladder Leaning Against a Wall*** A 13.5-meter fire-truck ladder is leaning against a wall. Find the distance the ladder goes up the wall if it makes an angle of 43° 50′ with the ground.

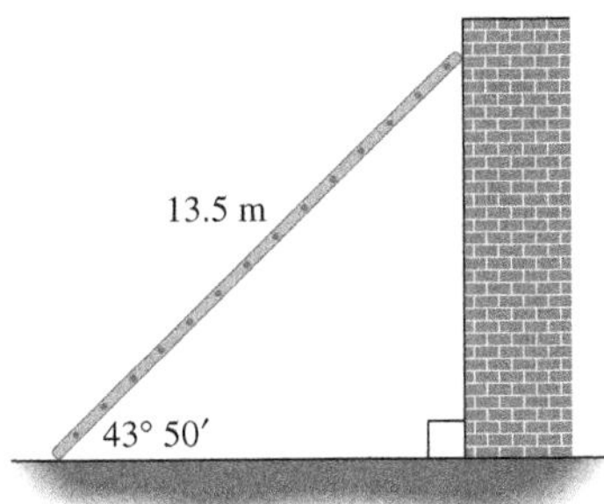


44. ***Antenna Mast Guy Wire*** A guy wire 77.4 meters long is attached to the top of an antenna mast that is 71.3 meters high. Find the angle that the wire makes with the ground.

45. ***Guy Wire to a Tower*** Find the length of a guy wire that makes an angle of 45° 30′ with the ground if the wire is attached to the top of a tower 63.0 meters high.

46. ***Distance Across a Lake*** To find the distance *RS* across a lake, a surveyor lays off $RT = 53.1$ meters, with angle $T = 32° 10′$ and angle $S = 57° 50′$. Find length *RS*.

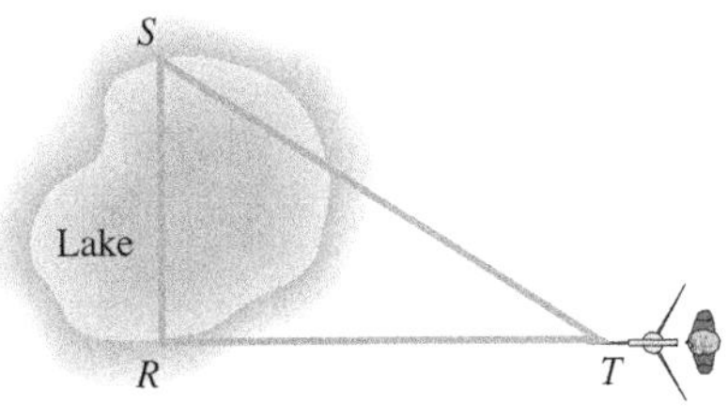


47. ***Side Lengths of a Triangle*** The length of the base of an isosceles triangle is 42.36 inches. Each base angle is 38.12°. Find the length of each of the two equal sides of the triangle. (*Hint:* Divide the triangle into two right triangles.)

48. ***Altitude of a Triangle*** Find the altitude of an isosceles triangle having a base of 184.2 cm if the angle opposite the base is 68° 44′.

49. ***Cloud Ceiling*** The U.S. Weather Bureau defines a *cloud ceiling* as the altitude of the lowest clouds that cover more than half the sky. To determine a cloud ceiling, a powerful searchlight projects a circle of light vertically on the bottom of the cloud. An observer sights the circle of light in the crosshairs of a tube called a *clinometer.* A pendant hanging vertically from the tube and resting on a protractor gives the angle of elevation. Find the cloud ceiling if the searchlight is located 1000 feet from the observer and the angle of elevation is 30.0° as measured with a clinometer at eye-height 6 feet. (Assume three significant digits.)

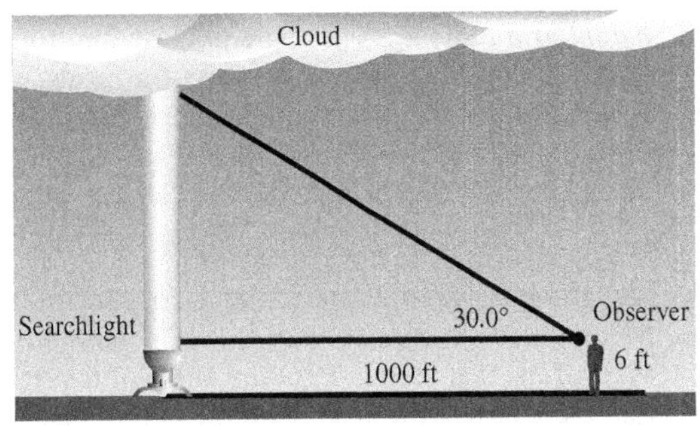


50. ***Length of a Shadow*** Suppose the angle of elevation of the sun is 23.4°. Find the length of the shadow cast by Cindy Newman, who is 5.75 feet tall.

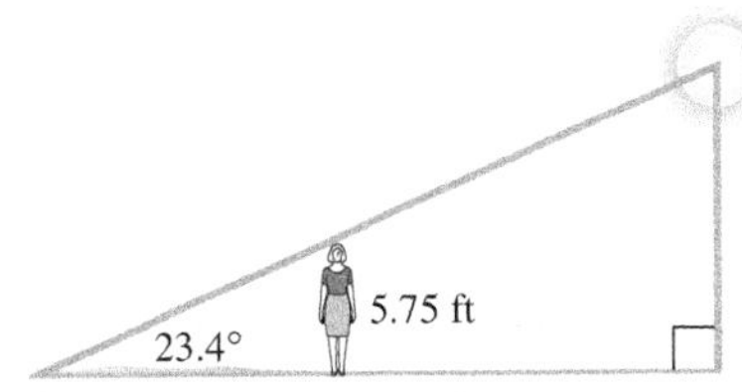


51. ***Height of a Tower*** The shadow of a vertical tower is 40.6 meters long when the angle of elevation of the sun is 34.6°. Find the height of the tower.

52. ***Angle of Elevation of the Sun*** Find the angle of elevation of the sun if a 48.6-foot flagpole casts a shadow 63.1 feet long.

53. ***Distance from the Ground to the Top of a Building*** The angle of depression from the top of a building to a point on the ground is 32° 30′. How far is the point on the ground from the top of the building if the building is 252 meters high?

54. ***Airplane Distance*** An airplane is flying 10,500 feet above the level ground. The angle of depression from the plane to the base of a tree is 13° 50′. How far horizontally must the plane fly to be directly over the tree?

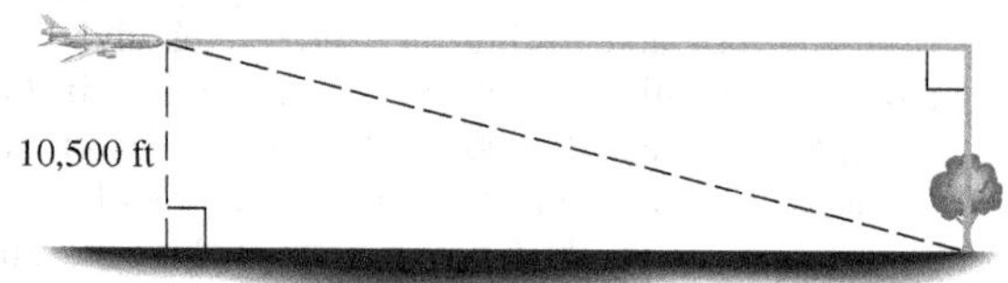


55. ***Height of a Building*** The angle of elevation from the top of a small building to the top of a nearby taller building is 46° 40′, while the angle of depression to the bottom is 14° 10′. If the smaller building is 28.0 meters high, find the height of the taller building.

56. ***Mounting a Video Camera*** A video camera is to be mounted on a bank wall so as to have a good view of the head teller. Find the angle of depression that the lens should make with the horizontal.

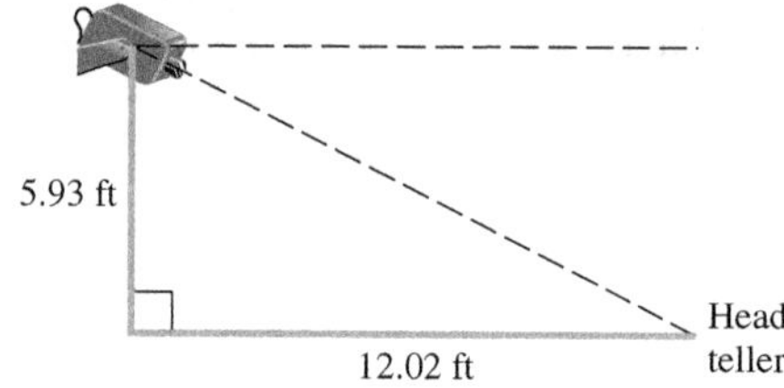


57. ***Error in Measurement*** A degree may seem like a very small unit, but an error of one degree in measuring an angle may be significant. For example, suppose a laser beam directed toward the visible center of the moon misses its assigned target by 30 seconds. How far is it (in miles) from its assigned target? Take the distance from the surface of Earth to that of the moon to be 234,000 miles. (*Source: A Sourcebook of Applications of School Mathematics* by Donald Bushaw et al. Copyright © 1980 by The Mathematical Association of America.)

58. ***Height of Mt. Everest*** The highest mountain peak in the world is Mt. Everest, located in the Himalayas. The height of this enormous mountain was determined in 1856 by surveyors using trigonometry long before it was first climbed in 1953. This difficult measurement had to be done from a great distance. At an altitude of 14,545 feet on a different mountain, the straight line distance to the peak of Mt. Everest is 27.0134 miles and its angle of elevation is $\theta = 5.82°$. (*Source:* Dunham, W., *The Mathematical Universe,* John Wiley & Sons, 1994.)

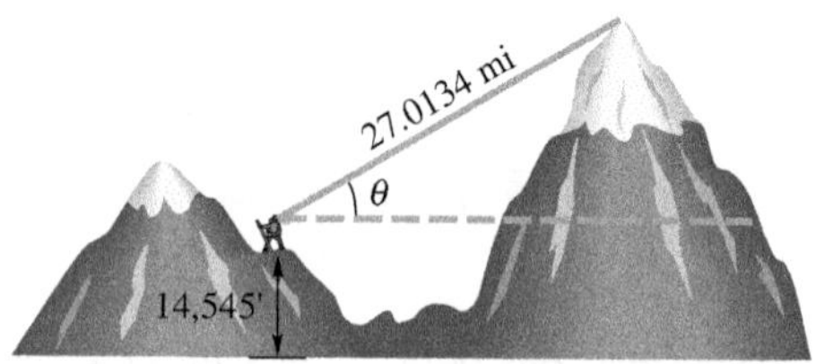


(a) Approximate the height (in feet) of Mt. Everest.

(b) In the actual measurement, Mt. Everest was over 100 miles away and the curvature of Earth had to be taken into account. Would the curvature of Earth make the peak appear taller or shorter than it actually is?

*Find the exact value of each labeled part in each figure.*

59.

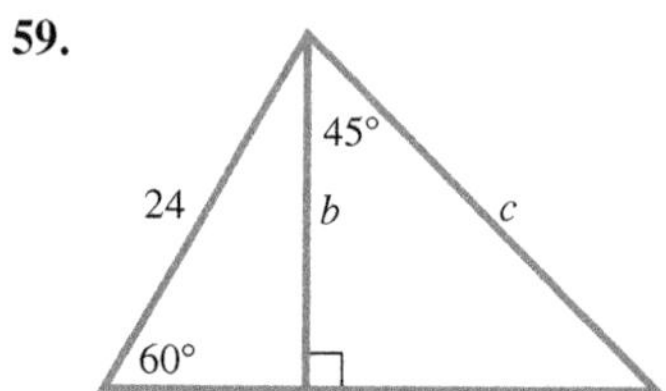


60.

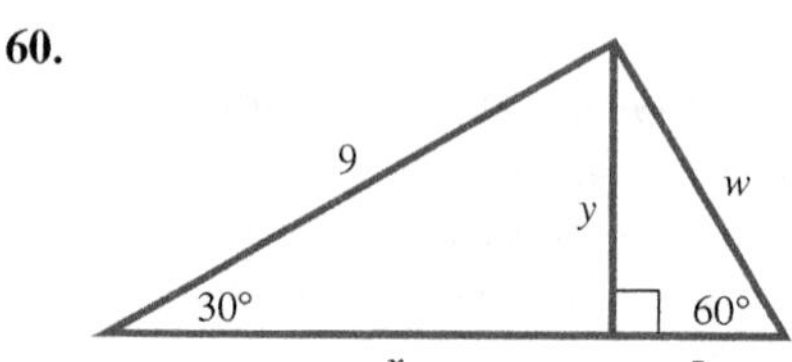

# 10.6 The Laws of Sines and Cosines; Area Formulas

**Oblique Triangles • Law of Sines • Law of Cosines • Area Formulas**

## Oblique Triangles

A triangle that is not a right triangle is called an **oblique triangle.** The measures of the three sides and the three angles of a triangle can be found if at least one side and any other two measures are known. There are four possible cases.

1. One side and two angles are known. (SAA)
2. Two sides and one angle not included between the two sides are known. (SSA; this case may lead to more than one triangle.)
3. Two sides and the angle included between the two sides are known. (SAS)
4. Three sides are known. (SSS)

If we know three angles of a triangle, we cannot find unique side lengths, because AAA assures us only of similarity, not congruence. For example, there are infinitely many triangles $ABC$ with $A = 35°$, $B = 65°$, and $C = 80°$.

To solve oblique triangles, we need to use the laws of sines and cosines.

## Law of Sines

To derive the law of sines, we start with an oblique triangle, such as the acute triangle in Figure 35(a) or the obtuse triangle in Figure 35(b). The following discussion applies to both triangles. First, construct the perpendicular from $B$ to side $AC$ or side $AC$ extended, meeting that side at point $D$. Let $h$ be the length of this perpendicular. Then $c$ is the hypotenuse of right triangle $ADB$, and $a$ is the hypotenuse of right triangle $BDC$. Therefore,

$$\text{in triangle } ADB, \quad \sin A = \frac{h}{c} \quad \text{or} \quad h = c \sin A,$$

$$\text{in triangle } BDC, \quad \sin C = \frac{h}{a} \quad \text{or} \quad h = a \sin C.$$

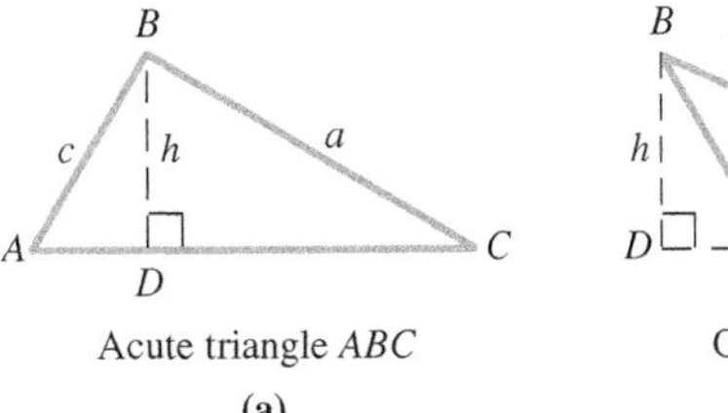

Acute triangle $ABC$

(a)

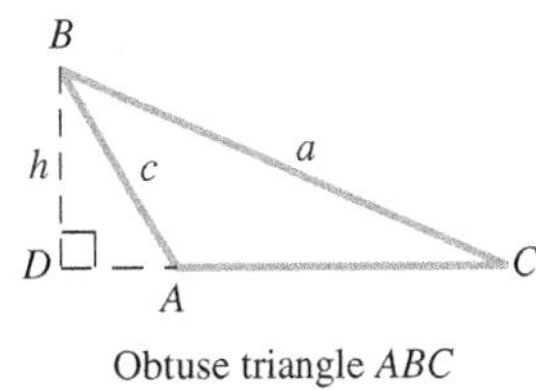

Obtuse triangle $ABC$

(b)

**FIGURE 35**

Because $h = c \sin A$ and $h = a \sin C$,

$$a \sin C = c \sin A$$

$$\frac{a}{\sin A} = \frac{c}{\sin C}. \quad \text{Divide both sides by } \sin A \sin C.$$

By constructing the perpendiculars from other vertices, it can also be shown that

$$\frac{a}{\sin A} = \frac{b}{\sin B} \quad \text{and} \quad \frac{b}{\sin B} = \frac{c}{\sin C}.$$

This discussion proves the following theorem.

### Law of Sines

In any triangle $ABC$ with sides $a$, $b$, and $c$,

$$\frac{a}{\sin A} = \frac{b}{\sin B}, \quad \frac{a}{\sin A} = \frac{c}{\sin C}, \quad \text{and} \quad \frac{b}{\sin B} = \frac{c}{\sin C}.$$

This can be written in compact form as

$$\frac{a}{\sin A} = \frac{b}{\sin B} = \frac{c}{\sin C}.$$

Sometimes an alternative form of the law of sines is more convenient to use.

$$\frac{\sin A}{a} = \frac{\sin B}{b} = \frac{\sin C}{c}$$

If two angles and the side opposite one of the angles are known, the law of sines can be used directly to solve for the side opposite the other known angle. The triangle can then be solved completely.

### EXAMPLE 1 Using the Law of Sines to Solve a Triangle (SAA)

Solve triangle $ABC$ if $A = 32.0°$, $B = 81.8°$, and $a = 42.9$ centimeters.

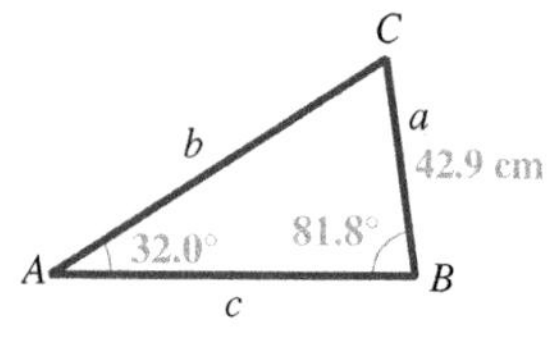


**FIGURE 36**

**SOLUTION**

Start by drawing a triangle, roughly to scale, and labeling the given parts as in Figure 36. Because the values of $A$, $B$, and $a$ are known, use the part of the law of sines that involves these variables.

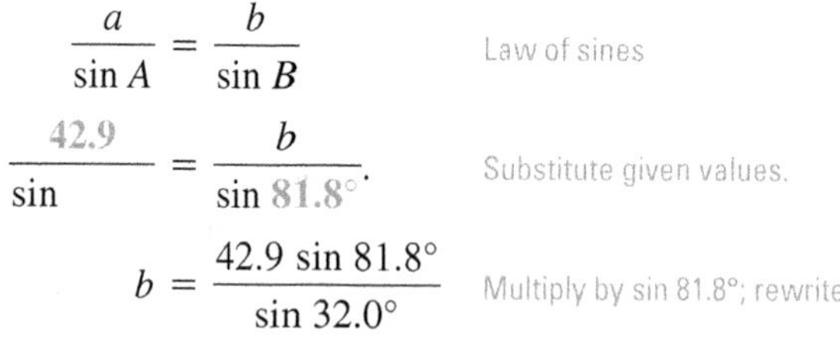

$$\frac{a}{\sin A} = \frac{b}{\sin B} \quad \text{Law of sines}$$

$$\frac{42.9}{\sin} = \frac{b}{\sin 81.8°} \quad \text{Substitute given values.}$$

$$b = \frac{42.9 \sin 81.8°}{\sin 32.0°} \quad \text{Multiply by sin 81.8°; rewrite.}$$

When using a calculator to find $b$, keep intermediate answers in the calculator until the final result is found. Then round to the proper number of significant digits. In this case, find sin 81.8°, and then multiply that number by 42.9. Keep the result in the calculator while you find sin 32.0°, and then divide. Because the given information is accurate to three significant digits, round the value of $b$ to get

$$b = \mathbf{80.1} \text{ centimeters.}$$

Find $C$ from the fact that the sum of the angles of any triangle is 180°.

$$A + B + C = 180°$$
$$C = 180° - A - B$$
$$C = 180° - 32.0° - 81.8°$$
$$C = 66.2°$$

Now use the law of sines again to find $c$. (Note that the Pythagorean theorem does not apply here, because triangle $ABC$ is oblique, and the Pythagorean theorem applies only to right triangles.)

$$\frac{a}{\sin A} = \frac{c}{\sin C}$$
$$\frac{42.9}{\sin 32.0°} = \frac{c}{\sin 66.2°}$$
$$c = \frac{42.9 \sin 66.2°}{\sin 32.0°}$$
$$c = \mathbf{74.1} \text{ centimeters}$$

**PROBLEM-SOLVING HINT** In applications of oblique triangles such as the one in Example 1, a correctly labeled sketch is essential in order to set up the correct equation.

## EXAMPLE 2 Using the Law of Sines in an Application (ASA)

Roosevelt Brown wishes to measure the distance across the Big Muddy River. See Figure 37. He finds that $C = 112.90°$, $A = 31.10°$, and $b = 347.6$ feet. Find the required distance.

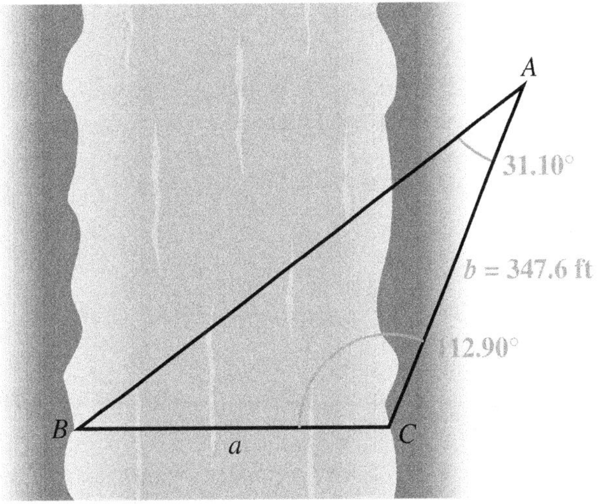


FIGURE 37

**SOLUTION**

To use the law of sines, one side and the angle opposite it must be known. Because the only side whose length is given is $b$, angle $B$ must be found before the law of sines can be used.

$$\begin{aligned} B &= 180° - A - C \\ &= 180° - 31.10° - 112.90° \\ &= 36.00° \end{aligned}$$

Now use the form of the law of sines involving $A$, $B$, and $b$ to find $a$, the distance across the river.

$$\frac{a}{\sin A} = \frac{b}{\sin B}$$

$$\frac{a}{\sin 31.10°} = \frac{347.6}{\sin 36.00°} \quad \text{Substitute.}$$

$$a = \frac{347.6 \sin 31.10°}{\sin 36.00°} \quad \text{Multiply by } \sin 31.10°.$$

$$a = \mathbf{305.5} \text{ feet} \quad \text{Use a calculator.}$$

**Law of Cosines** If we are given two sides and the included angle (SAS) or three sides of a triangle (SSS), a unique triangle is formed. In these cases, however, we cannot begin the solution of the triangle by using the law of sines because we are not given a side and the angle opposite it. Both cases require the use of the *law of cosines.*

Remember the following property of triangles when applying the law of cosines.

### Property of Triangle Side Lengths

In any triangle, the sum of the lengths of any two sides must be greater than the length of the remaining side.

For example, it would be impossible to construct a triangle with sides of lengths 3, 4, and 10. See Figure 38.

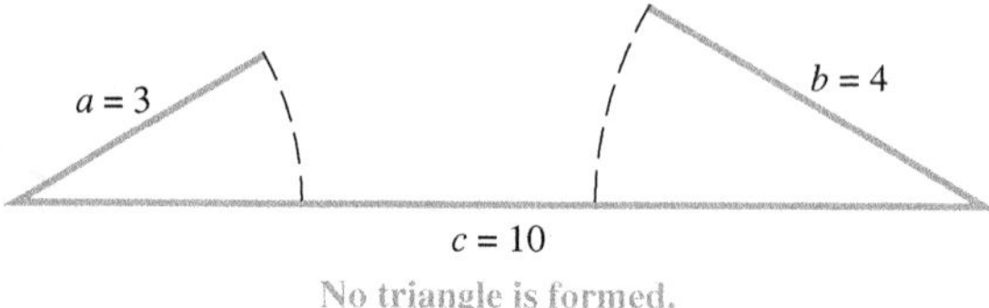


**FIGURE 38**

To derive the law of cosines, let $ABC$ be any oblique triangle. Choose a coordinate system so that vertex $B$ is at the origin and side $BC$ is along the positive $x$-axis. See Figure 39 on the next page.

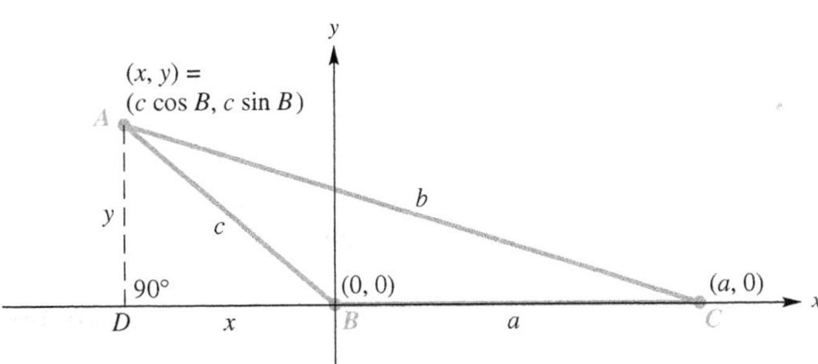


**FIGURE 39**

Let $(x, y)$ be the coordinates of vertex $A$ of the triangle. Verify that for angle $B$, whether obtuse or acute,

$$\sin B = \frac{y}{c} \quad \text{and} \quad \cos B = \frac{x}{c}.$$

(Here $x$ is negative if $B$ is obtuse.) From these results

$$y = c \sin B \quad \text{and} \quad x = c \cos B,$$

so that the coordinates of point $A$ become

$$(c \cos B, c \sin B).$$

Point $C$ has coordinates $(a, 0)$, and $AC$ has length $b$, so

$$\begin{aligned} b &= \sqrt{(c \cos B - a)^2 + (c \sin B - 0)^2} && \text{Distance formula} \\ b^2 &= (c \cos B - a)^2 + (c \sin B)^2 && \text{Square both sides.} \\ &= c^2 \cos^2 B - 2ac \cos B + a^2 + c^2 \sin^2 B \\ &= a^2 + c^2 (\cos^2 B + \sin^2 B) - 2ac \cos B \\ &= a^2 + c^2(1) - 2ac \cos B && \text{Pythagorean identity} \\ &= a^2 + c^2 - 2ac \cos B. \end{aligned}$$

This result is one form of the law of cosines. In the work above, we could just as easily have placed $A$ or $C$ at the origin. This would have given the same result, but with the variables rearranged. These various forms of the law of cosines are summarized in the following theorem.

### Law of Cosines

In any triangle $ABC$ with sides $a$, $b$, and $c$,

$$\begin{aligned} a^2 &= b^2 + c^2 - 2bc \cos A \\ b^2 &= a^2 + c^2 - 2ac \cos B \\ c^2 &= a^2 + b^2 - 2ab \cos C. \end{aligned}$$

The law of cosines says that the square of a side of a triangle is equal to the sum of the squares of the other two sides, minus twice the product of those two sides and the cosine of the angle included between them.

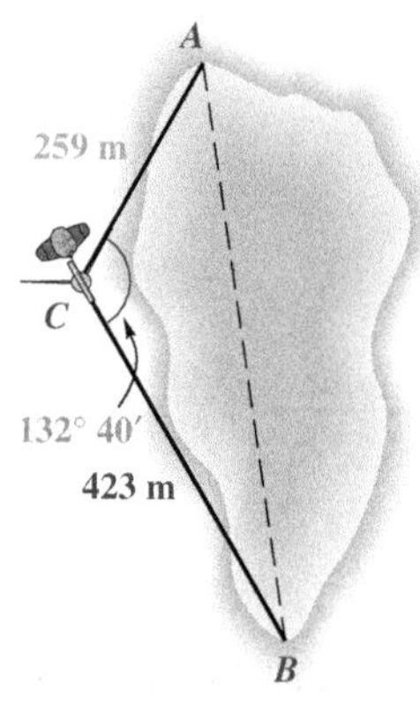


FIGURE 40

If we let $C = 90°$ in the third form of the law of cosines given above, we have $\cos C = \cos 90° = 0$, and the formula becomes

$$c^2 = a^2 + b^2,$$

the familiar equation of the Pythagorean theorem. Thus, the Pythagorean theorem is a special case of the law of cosines.

## EXAMPLE 3 Using the Law of Cosines in an Application (SAS)

A surveyor wishes to find the distance between two inaccessible points $A$ and $B$ on opposite sides of a lake. See Figure 40. While standing at point $C$, she finds that $AC = 259$ meters, $BC = 423$ meters, and angle $ACB$ measures $132° 40'$. Find the distance $AB$.

**SOLUTION**

The law of cosines can be used here, since we know the lengths of two sides of the triangle and the measure of the included angle.

$$AB^2 = 259^2 + 423^2 - 2(259)(423)\cos 132° 40'$$

$$AB^2 = 394{,}510.6 \quad \text{Use a calculator.}$$

$$AB \approx 628 \quad \text{Take the square root and round to 3 significant digits.}$$

The distance $AB$ is approximately 628 meters.

This photo shows the cover of a short text (only 60 pages) on **spherical trigonometry,** published in 1928. In the historical sketch provided at the end of the book, author Pauline Sperry states that Albattani, Geber of Seville, and Nassir Eddin continued the work of Ptolemy in the Arab world, while Johanne Müller (better known as **Regiomontanus**) did the same in Europe. Regiomontanus's work *De triangulis omnimodis* was "the first systematic treatment of trigonometry independent of astronomy in the western world and dominated the latter middle ages to a remarkable degree."

## EXAMPLE 4 Using the Law of Cosines to Solve a Triangle (SSS)

Solve triangle $ABC$ if $A = 42.3°$, $b = 12.9$ meters, and $c = 15.4$ meters. See Figure 41.

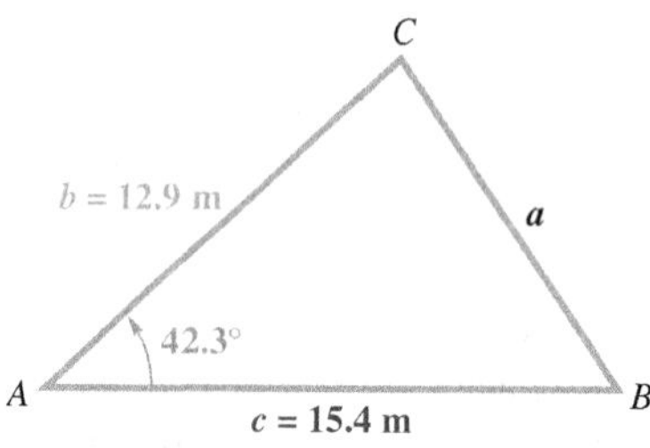


FIGURE 41

**SOLUTION**

$$a^2 = b^2 + c^2 - 2bc\cos A \quad \text{Law of cosines.}$$

$$a^2 = 12.9^2 + 15.4^2 - 2(12.9)(15.4)\cos 42.3° \quad \text{Substitute.}$$

$$a^2 = 109.7 \quad \text{Use a calculator.}$$

$$a = 10.5 \text{ meters} \quad \sqrt{109.7} \approx 10.47 \approx 10.5$$

We now must find the measures of angles $B$ and $C$. There are several approaches that can be used at this point. We shall use the law of sines to find one of these angles. Of the two remaining angles, $B$ must be the smaller, because it is opposite the shorter of the two sides $b$ and $c$. Therefore, it cannot be obtuse, and we will avoid any ambiguity when we find its sine.

When two sides and an angle opposite one of them are given as in Example 4, under certain conditions *two* triangles satisfying those conditions may exist. This is called the **ambiguous** case. See a standard trigonometry text for more information.

$$\frac{\sin 42.3^\circ}{10.47} = \frac{\sin B}{12.9}$$ Use 10.47, the approximation for *a* before rounding to 10.5.

$$\sin B = \frac{12.9 \sin 42.3^\circ}{10.47}$$ Multiply by 12.9; rewrite.

$$B = 56.0^\circ$$ Use the inverse sine function.

The easiest way to find $C$ is to subtract the measures of $A$ and $B$ from 180°.

$$C = 180^\circ - 42.3^\circ - 56.0^\circ$$
$$= 81.7^\circ$$

Had we chosen to use the law of sines to find $C$ rather than $B$ in Example 4, we would not have known whether $C$ equals 81.7° or its supplement, 98.3°.

### EXAMPLE 5 Using the Law of Cosines to Solve a Triangle (SSS)

Solve triangle $ABC$ if $a = 9.47$ feet, $b = 15.9$ feet, and $c = 21.1$ feet.

**SOLUTION**

We may use the law of cosines to solve for any angle of the triangle. We solve for $C$, the largest angle, using the law of cosines. We will be able to tell if $C$ is obtuse if $\cos C < 0$.

$$c^2 = a^2 + b^2 - 2ab \cos C$$ Law of cosines

$$\cos C = \frac{a^2 + b^2 - c^2}{2ab}$$ Solve for cos *C*.

$$\cos C = \frac{(9.47)^2 + (15.9)^2 - (21.1)^2}{2(9.47)(15.9)}$$ Substitute.

$$\cos C = -.34109402$$ Use a calculator.

$$C = 109.9^\circ$$ Use the inverse cosine function.

We can use either the law of sines or the law of cosines to find $B = 45.1^\circ$. (Verify this.) Because $A = 180^\circ - B - C$,

$$A = 25.0^\circ.$$

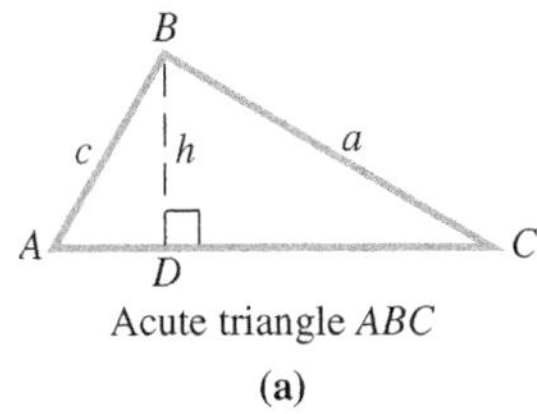

Acute triangle $ABC$

(a)

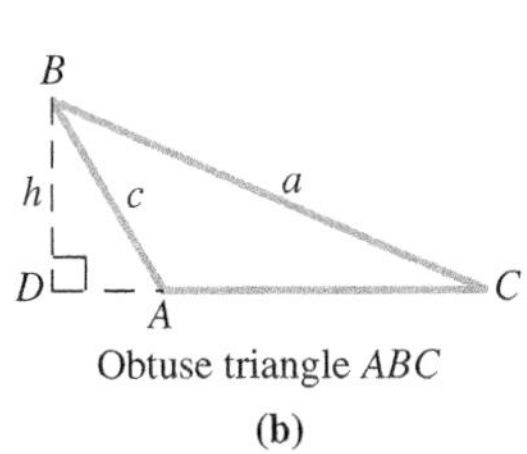

Obtuse triangle $ABC$

(b)

**FIGURE 42**

**Area Formulas** The method used to derive the law of sines can also be used to derive a useful formula to find the area of a triangle. A familiar formula for the area of a triangle is $\mathscr{A} = \frac{1}{2}bh$, where $\mathscr{A}$ represents the area, $b$ the base, and $h$ the height. This formula cannot always be used easily, because in practice $h$ is often unknown. To find an alternative formula, refer to acute triangle $ABC$ in Figure 42(a) or obtuse triangle $ABC$ in Figure 42(b).

A perpendicular has been drawn from $B$ to the base of the triangle (or the extension of the base). This perpendicular forms two right triangles. Using triangle $ABD$,

$$\sin A = \frac{h}{c},$$

or

$$h = c \sin A.$$

Substituting into the formula $\mathscr{A} = \frac{1}{2}bh$,

$$\mathscr{A} = \frac{1}{2}b(c \sin A)$$

or

$$\mathscr{A} = \frac{1}{2}bc \sin A.$$

Any other pair of sides and the angle between them could have been used, as stated in the next theorem.

### Area of a Triangle

In any triangle $ABC$, the area $\mathscr{A}$ is given by any of the following formulas:

$$\mathscr{A} = \frac{1}{2}bc \sin A, \quad \mathscr{A} = \frac{1}{2}ab \sin C, \quad \mathscr{A} = \frac{1}{2}ac \sin B.$$

That is, the area is given by half the product of the lengths of two sides and the sine of the angle included between them.

### EXAMPLE 6 Finding the Area of a Triangle Using $\mathscr{A} = \frac{1}{2}ab \sin C$

Find the area of triangle $ABC$ given $A = 24° 40'$, $b = 27.3$ centimeters, and $C = 52° 40'$.

**SOLUTION**

Before we can use the formula given above, we must use the law of sines to find either $a$ or $c$. Because the sum of the measures of the angles of any triangle is 180°,

$$B = 180° - 24° 40' - 52° 40' = 102° 40'.$$

Now use the form of the law of sines that relates $a$, $b$, $A$, and $B$ to find $a$.

$$\frac{a}{\sin A} = \frac{b}{\sin B}$$

$$\frac{a}{\sin 24° 40'} = \frac{27.3}{\sin 102° 40'}$$

Solve for $a$ to verify that $a = 11.7$ centimeters. Now find the area.

$$\mathscr{A} = \frac{1}{2}ab \sin C$$

$$= \frac{1}{2}(11.7)(27.3) \sin 52° 40'$$

$$= 127$$

The area of triangle $ABC$ is 127 square centimeters to three significant digits.

The law of cosines can be used to derive a formula for the area of a triangle when only the lengths of the three sides are known. This formula is known as Heron's formula, named after the Greek mathematician Heron of Alexandria.

**Heron of Alexandria** lived during approximately the same period as Ptolemy and Hipparchus. He wrote extensively on both mathematical and physical subjects. The most importmant of his mathematical works is *Metrica*, which was discovered in Constantinople in the late 19th century. The Arabian scholar al-Biruni claims that Archimedes actually discovered the triangle area formula which bears Heron's name. (*Source:* Eves, Howard, *An Introduction to the History of Mathematics*, 6th edition.)

### Heron's Area Formula

If a triangle has sides of lengths $a$, $b$, and $c$, and if the **semiperimeter** is

$$s = \frac{1}{2}(a + b + c),$$

then the area of the triangle is

$$\mathcal{A} = \sqrt{s(s - a)(s - b)(s - c)}.$$

### EXAMPLE 7 Finding the Area of a Triangle Using Heron's Formula

Determine the area of the triangle having sides of lengths $a = 29.7$ feet, $b = 42.3$ feet, and $c = 38.4$ feet.

**SOLUTION**

To use Heron's area formula, first find $s$.

$$s = \frac{1}{2}(a + b + c) \qquad \text{Semiperimeter formula}$$

$$s = \frac{1}{2}(29.7 + 42.3 + 38.4)$$

$$s = 55.2$$

The area is

$$\mathcal{A} = \sqrt{s(s - a)(s - b)(s - c)}$$

$$= \sqrt{55.2(55.2 - 29.7)(55.2 - 42.3)(55.2 - 38.4)} \qquad \text{Heron's area formula}$$

$$= \sqrt{55.2(25.5)(12.9)(16.8)}$$

$$\mathcal{A} = 552 \text{ square feet.} \qquad \text{Three significant digits}$$

## 10.6 EXERCISES

*Use the law of sines to solve each triangle.*

1. 

B
48°
18 m
37°
A
C

2. 

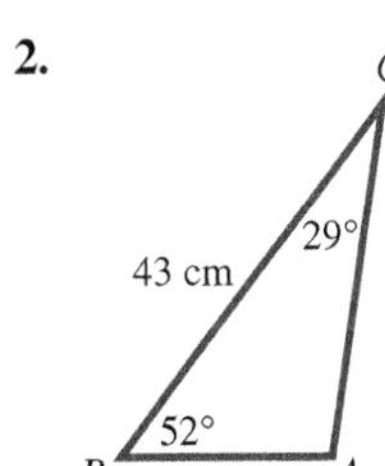

3.

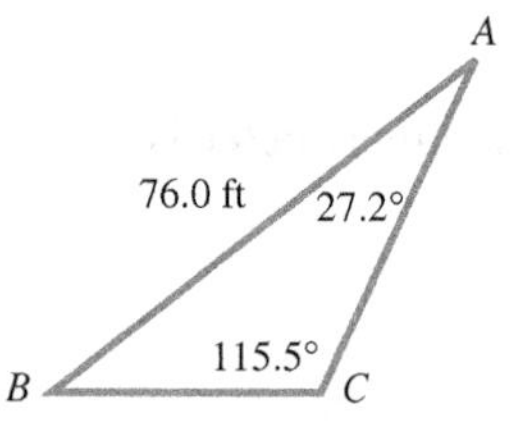


4.

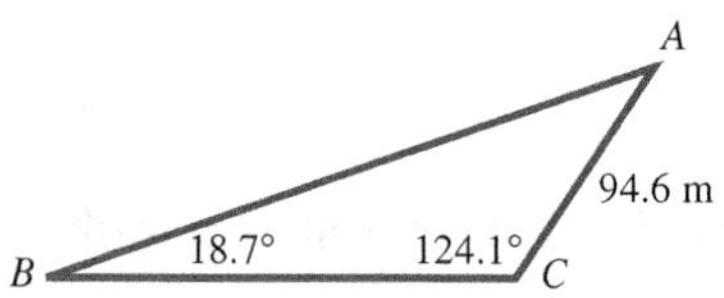


5. $A = 68.41°$, $B = 54.23°$, $a = 12.75$ ft

6. $C = 74.08°$, $B = 69.38°$, $c = 45.38$ m

7. $A = 87.2°$, $b = 75.9$ yd, $C = 74.3°$

8. $B = 38° 40'$, $a = 19.7$ cm, $C = 91° 40'$

9. $B = 20° 50'$, $C = 103° 10'$, $AC = 132$ ft

10. $A = 35.3°$, $B = 52.8°$, $AC = 675$ ft

11. $A = 39.70°$, $C = 30.35°$, $b = 39.74$ m

12. $C = 71.83°$, $B = 42.57°$, $a = 2.614$ cm

13. $B = 42.88°$, $C = 102.40°$, $b = 3974$ ft

14. $A = 18.75°$, $B = 51.53°$, $c = 2798$ yd

15. $A = 39° 54'$, $a = 268.7$ m, $B = 42° 32'$

16. $C = 79° 18'$, $c = 39.81$ mm, $A = 32° 57'$

*Use the law of sines to solve each problem.*

17. ***Distance Across a River*** To find the distance $AB$ across a river, a distance $BC = 354$ meters is laid off on one side of the river. It is found that $B = 112° 10'$ and $C = 15° 20'$. Find $AB$.

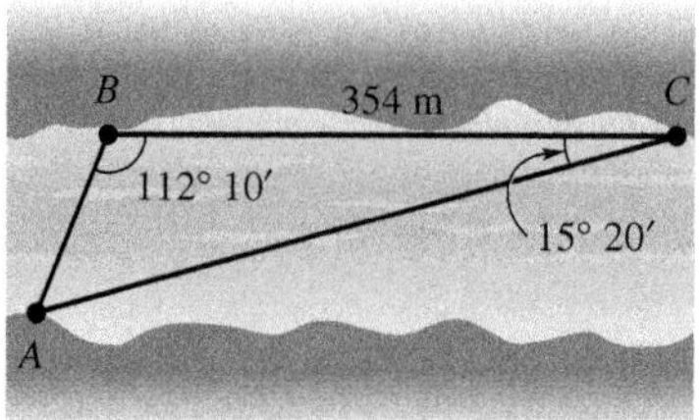


18. ***Distance Across a Canyon*** To determine the distance $RS$ across a deep canyon, Anne Tomlin lays off a distance $TR = 582$ yards. She then finds that $T = 32° 50'$ and $R = 102° 20'$. Find $RS$.

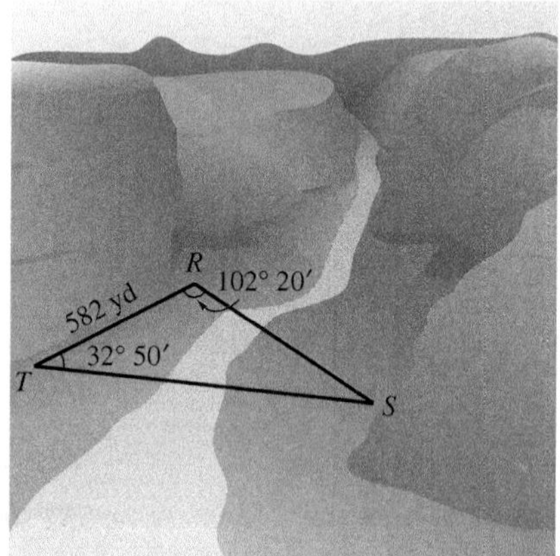


19. ***Measurement of a Folding Chair*** A folding chair is to have a seat 12.0 inches deep with angles as shown in the figure. How far down from the seat should the crossing legs be joined? (Find $x$ in the figure.)

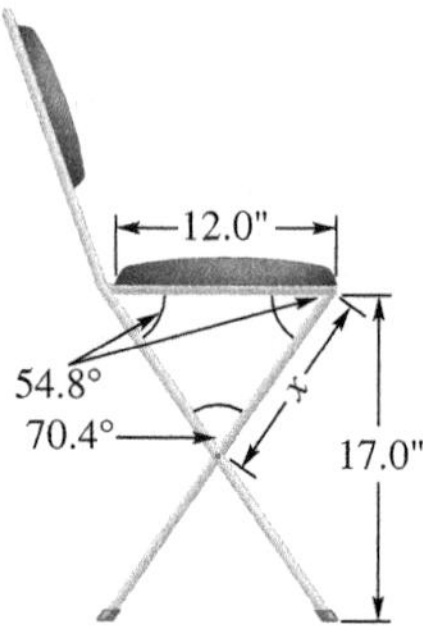

**20.** ***Angle Formed by Radii of Gears*** Three gears are arranged as shown in the figure. Find the measure of angle $\theta$.

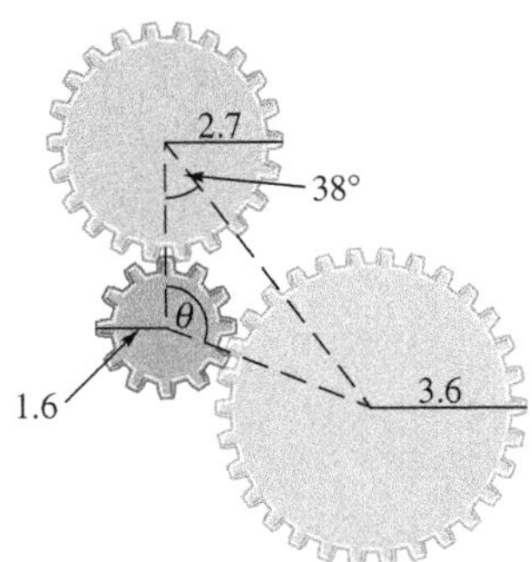


**21.** ***Distance Between Atoms*** Three atoms with atomic radii of 2.0, 3.0, and 4.5 are arranged as in the figure. Find the distance between the centers of atoms $A$ and $C$.

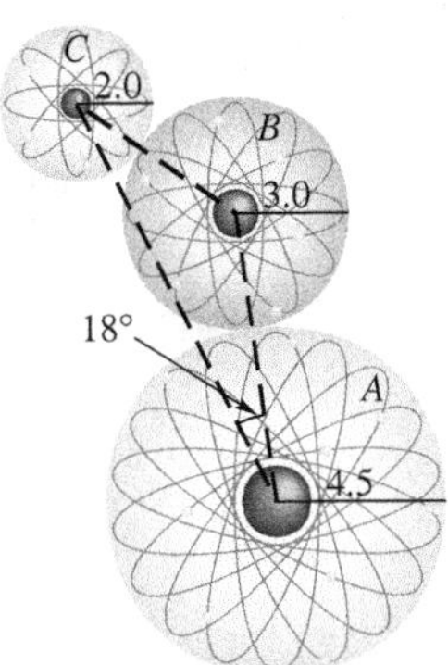


**22.** ***Height of a Balloon*** A balloonist is directly above a straight road 1.5 miles long that joins two villages. She finds that the town closer to her is at an angle of depression of 35°, and the farther town is at an angle of depression of 31°. How high above the ground is the balloon?

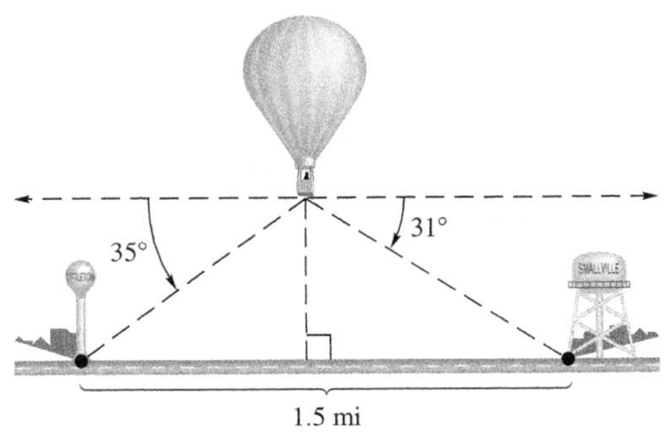


*Use the law of cosines to find the length of the remaining sides of each triangle. Do not use a calculator.*

**23.**

3
60°
8

**24.**

1
45°
$4\sqrt{2}$

*Use the law of cosines to find the value of $\theta$ in each triangle. Do not use a calculator.*

**25.**

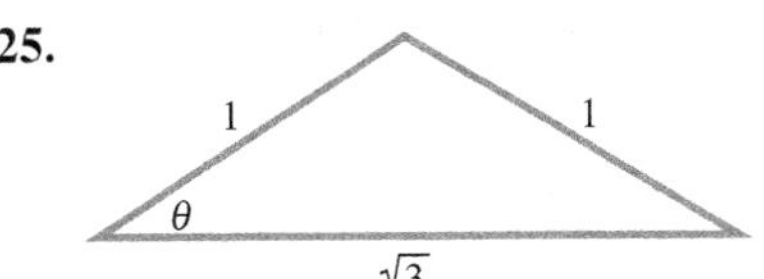


**26.**

3
7
θ
5

*Use the law of cosines to solve each triangle.*

**27.** $C = 28.3°, b = 5.71$ in., $a = 4.21$ in.

**28.** $A = 41.4°, b = 2.78$ yd, $c = 3.92$ yd

**29.** $C = 45.6°, b = 8.94$ m, $a = 7.23$ m

**30.** $A = 67.3°, b = 37.9$ km, $c = 40.8$ km

**31.** $A = 80° 40', b = 143$ cm, $c = 89.6$ cm

**32.** $C = 72° 40', a = 327$ ft, $b = 251$ ft

**33.** $B = 74.80°, a = 8.919$ in., $c = 6.427$ in.

**34.** $C = 59.70°, a = 3.725$ mi, $b = 4.698$ mi

**35.** $A = 112.8°, b = 6.28$ m, $c = 12.2$ m

**36.** $B = 168.2°, a = 15.1$ cm, $c = 19.2$ cm

**37.** $a = 3.0$ ft, $b = 5.0$ ft, $c = 6.0$ ft

**38.** $a = 4.0$ ft, $b = 5.0$ ft, $c = 8.0$ ft

**39.** $a = 9.3$ cm, $b = 5.7$ cm, $c = 8.2$ cm

**40.** $a = 28$ ft, $b = 47$ ft, $c = 58$ ft

**41.** $a = 42.9$ m, $b = 37.6$ m, $c = 62.7$ m

**42.** $a = 187$ yd, $b = 214$ yd, $c = 325$ yd

*Solve each problem, using the law of sines or the law of cosines as needed.*

**43.** ***Distance Across a Lake*** Points $A$ and $B$ are on opposite sides of Lake Yankee. From a third point, $C$, the angle between the lines of sight to $A$ and $B$ is 46.3°. If $AC$ is 350 meters long and $BC$ is 286 meters long, find the length $AB$.

**44.** ***Diagonals of a Parallelogram*** The sides of a parallelogram are 4.0 cm and 6.0 cm. One angle is 58° while another is 122°. Find the lengths of the diagonals of the parallelogram.

**45.** ***Playhouse Layout*** The layout for a child's playhouse in her backyard shows the dimensions given in the figure. Find the value of $x$.

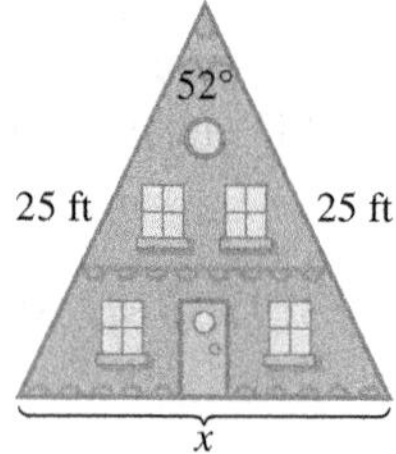


**46.** ***Distance Between Points on a Crane*** A crane with a counterweight is shown in the figure. Find the horizontal distance between points $A$ and $B$.

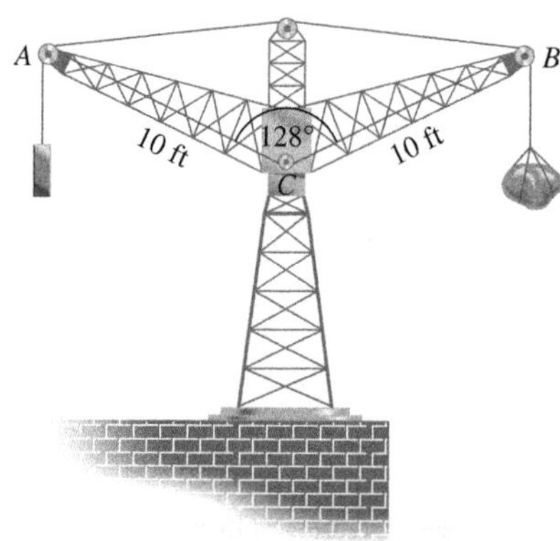


**47.** ***Angles Between a Beam and Cables*** A weight is supported by cables attached to both ends of a horizontal beam, as shown in the figure. What angles are formed between the beam and the cables?

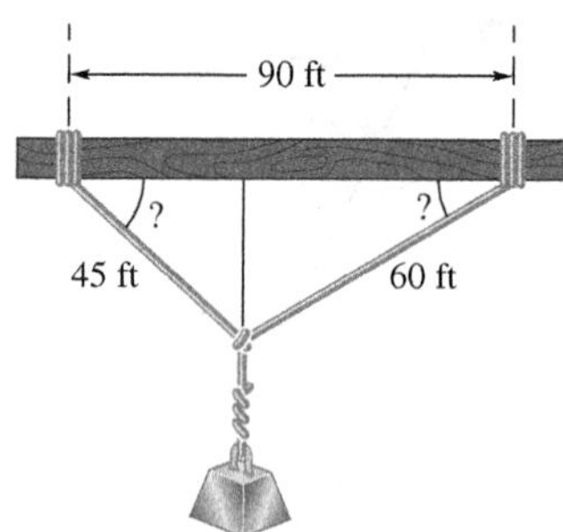


**48.** ***Measurement Using Triangulation*** Surveyors are often confronted with obstacles, such as trees, when measuring the boundary of a lot. One technique used to obtain an accurate measurement is the so-called *triangulation method.* In this technique, a triangle is

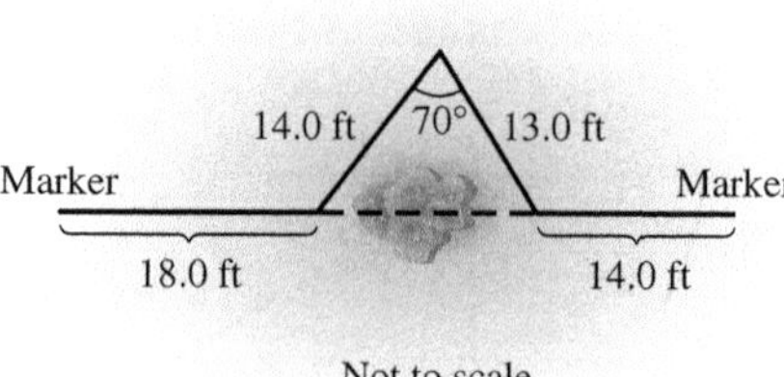

constructed around the obstacle and one angle and two sides of the triangle are measured. Use this technique to find the length of the property line (the straight line between the two markers) in the figure. (*Source:* Kavanagh, B. and S. Bird, *Surveying Principles and Applications,* Fifth Edition, Prentice Hall, 2000.)

*Find the exact area of each triangle using the formula $\mathcal{A} = \frac{1}{2}bh$, and then verify that the formula $\mathcal{A} = \frac{1}{2}ab \sin C$ gives the same result.*

**49.**

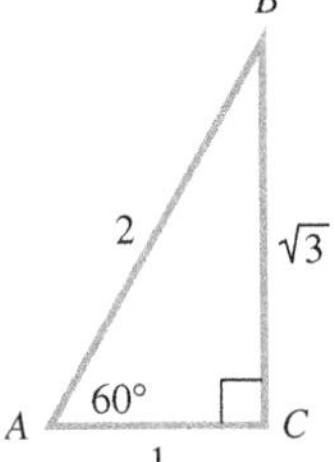


**50.**

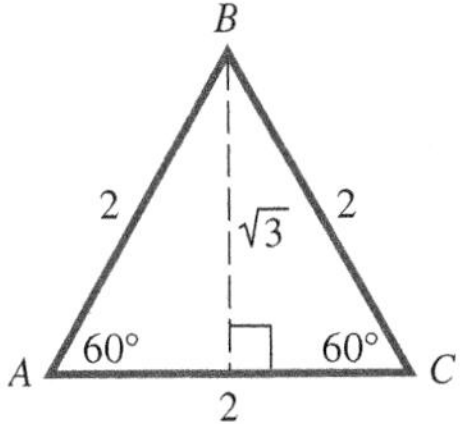


**51.**

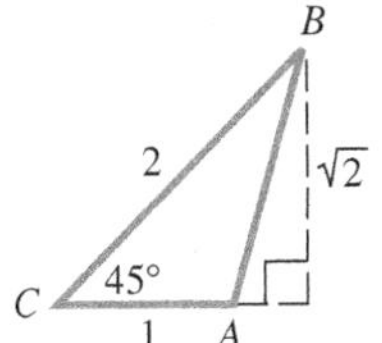


**52.**

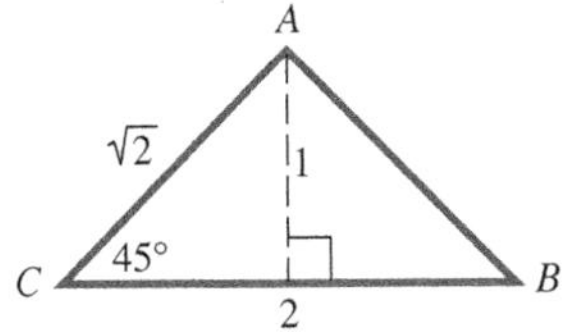


*Find the area of each triangle using the formula involving the sine function (page 662).*

**53.** $A = 42.5°$, $b = 13.6$ m, $c = 10.1$ m

**54.** $C = 72.2°$, $b = 43.8$ ft, $a = 35.1$ ft

**55.** $B = 124.5°$, $a = 30.4$ cm, $c = 28.4$ cm

**56.** $C = 142.7°$, $a = 21.9$ km, $b = 24.6$ km

**57.** $A = 56.80°$, $b = 32.67$ in., $c = 52.89$ in.

**58.** $A = 34.97°$, $b = 35.29$ m, $c = 28.67$ m

*Find the exact area of each triangle using the formula $\mathcal{A} = \frac{1}{2}bh$, and then verify that Heron's formula gives the same result.*

**59.**

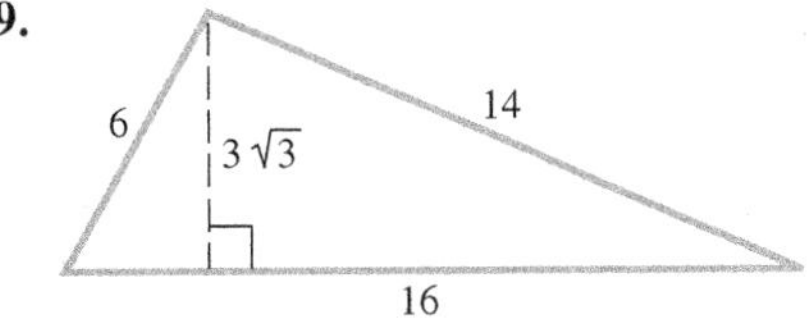


**60.**

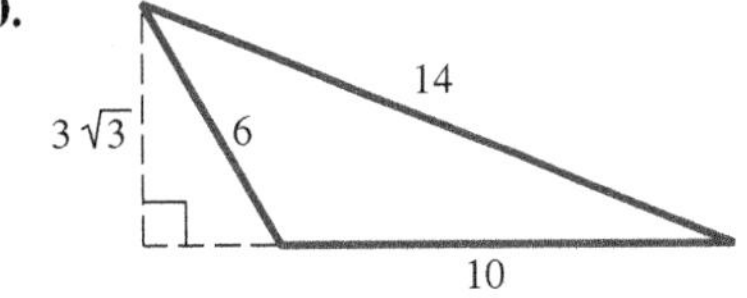


*Find the area of each triangle using Heron's formula.*

**61.** $a = 12$ m, $b = 16$ m, $c = 25$ m

**62.** $a = 22$ in., $b = 45$ in., $c = 31$ in.

**63.** $a = 154$ cm, $b = 179$ cm, $c = 183$ cm

**64.** $a = 25.4$ yd, $b = 38.2$ yd, $c = 19.8$ yd

**65.** $a = 76.3$ ft, $b = 109$ ft, $c = 98.8$ ft

**66.** $a = 15.89$ in., $b = 21.74$ in., $c = 10.92$ in.

*Solve each problem.*

**67.** ***Area of a Metal Plate*** A painter is going to apply a special coating to a triangular metal plate on a new building. Two sides measure 16.1 meters and 15.2 meters. She knows that the angle between these sides is 125°. What is the area of the surface she plans to cover with the coating?

**68.** ***Area of a Triangular Lot*** A real estate agent wants to find the area of a triangular lot. A surveyor takes measurements and finds the two sides are 52.1 meters and 21.3 meters, and the angle between them is 42.2°. What is the area of the triangular lot?

**69.** ***Required Amount of Paint*** A painter needs to cover a triangular region 75 meters by 68 meters by 85 meters. A can of paint covers 75 square meters of area. How many cans (to the next higher number of cans) will be needed?

**70.** ***Area of the Bermuda Triangle*** Find the area of the Bermuda Triangle if the sides of the triangle have approximate lengths 850 miles, 925 miles, and 1300 miles.

# COLLABORATIVE INVESTIGATION

## Making a *Point* About Trigonometric Function Values

An equation of the form $Ax + By = 0$ represents a line passing through the origin in the plane. By restricting $x$ to take on only nonpositive or only nonnegative values, we obtain a ray with endpoint at the origin. This ray can be considered the terminal side of an angle in standard position. For example, the figure shows an angle $\theta$ in standard position whose terminal side has the equation

$$2x - y = 0, x \geq 0.$$

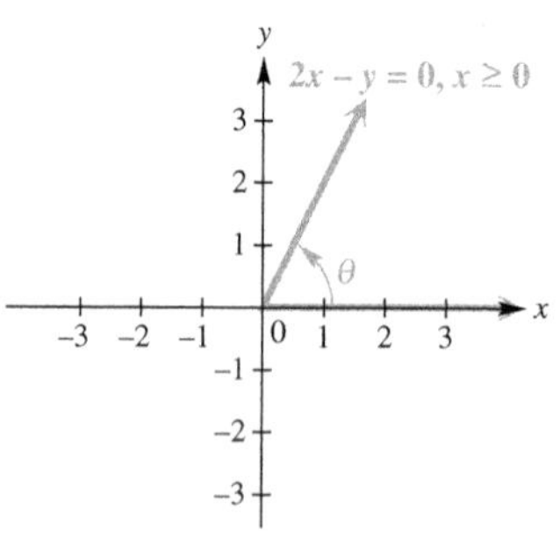


To find the trigonometric function values of $\theta$, we can use *any* point on its terminal side except the origin. Similarly, we can find the value of $\theta$ using any point and the appropriate inverse trigonometric function. This investigation supports these statements.

### Topics for Discussion

1. Divide the class into four groups: I, II, III, and IV. Each group will have a different value of $x$ assigned to it:
   Group I: $x = 2$ Group II: $x = 4$
   Group III: $x = 6$ Group IV: $x = 8$
2. Find the coordinates of the point on the terminal side of $\theta$ corresponding to your value of $x$.
3. Find the corresponding value of $r$ using the equation $r = \sqrt{x^2 + y^2}$.
4. Find the exact values of the trigonometric functions of $\theta$. Simplify any radical expressions completely.
5. With your calculator in degree mode, find each: **(a)** $\sin^{-1}(\frac{y}{r})$, **(b)** $\cos^{-1}(\frac{x}{r})$, and **(c)** $\tan^{-1}(\frac{y}{x})$.
6. Compare the results of Topic 4 among the different groups. Did the point chosen make any difference when finding the trigonometric function values?
7. Compare the results of Topic 5 among the different groups. Every value should be the same. What is this value? What does it represent?
8. Similar triangles have sides that are proportional, as discussed in Section 9.4. Discuss how this property justifies the results of Topic 4.

# CHAPTER 10 TEST

1. Convert 74° 17′ 54″ to decimal degrees.
2. Find the angle of smallest positive measure coterminal with −157°.
3. If $(2, -5)$ is on the terminal side of angle $\theta$ in standard position, find $\sin\theta$, $\cos\theta$, and $\tan\theta$.
4. If $\cos\theta < 0$ and $\cot\theta > 0$, in what quadrant does $\theta$ terminate?
5. If $\cos\theta = \frac{4}{5}$ and $\theta$ is in quadrant IV, find the values of the other trigonometric functions of $\theta$.
6. Give the six trigonometric function values of angle $A$ in the triangle at the top of the next page.

7. Give the *exact* value of each expression. If it is undefined, say so.
(a) $\cos 60°$ (b) $\tan 45°$
(c) $\tan(-270°)$ (d) $\sec 210°$
(e) $\csc(-180°)$ (f) $\sec 135°$

8. Use a calculator to approximate the following.
(a) $\sin 78° 21'$
(b) $\tan 11.7689°$
(c) $\sec 58.9041°$
(d) $\cot 13.5°$

9. Find a value of $\theta$ in the interval $0° \leq \theta \leq 90°$ in decimal degrees, if $\sin \theta = .27843196$.

10. Find two values of $\theta$ in the interval $0° \leq \theta < 360°$ that satisfy

$$\cos \theta = -\frac{\sqrt{2}}{2}.$$

11. Solve the triangle.

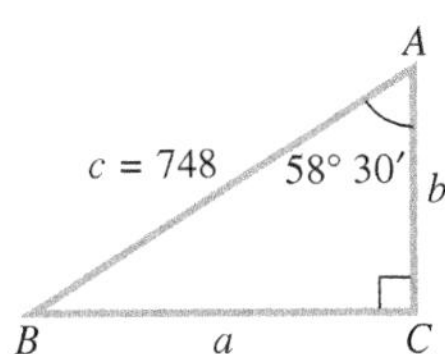


12. ***Height of a Flagpole*** To measure the height of a flagpole, Mike de la Hoz found that the angle of elevation from a point 24.7 feet from the base to the top is $32° 10'$. What is the height of the flagpole?

*Find the indicated part of each triangle.*

13. $A = 25.2°$, $a = 6.92$ yd, $b = 4.82$ yd; find $C$

14. $C = 118°$, $b = 130$ km, $a = 75$ km; find $c$

15. $a = 17.3$ ft, $b = 22.6$ ft, $c = 29.8$ ft; find $B$

16. Find the area of triangle $ABC$ in Exercise 14.

17. Find the area of a triangle having sides of lengths 22, 26, and 40.

*Solve each problem.*

18. ***Height of a Balloon*** The angles of elevation of a balloon from two points $A$ and $B$ on level ground are $24° 50'$ and $47° 20'$, respectively. As shown in the figure, points $A$, $B$, and $C$ are in the same vertical plane and $A$ and $B$ are 8.4 miles apart. Approximate the height of the balloon above the ground to the nearest tenth of a mile.

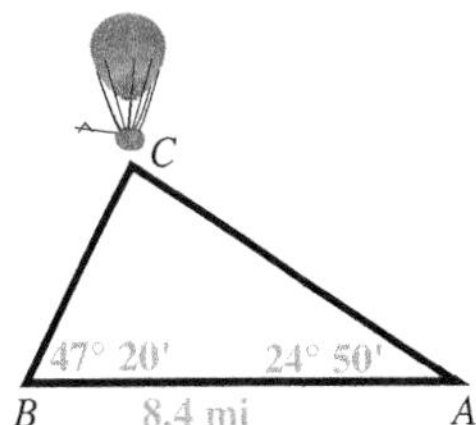


19. ***Length of a Tunnel*** To measure the distance through a mountain for a proposed tunnel, a point $C$ is chosen that can be reached from each end of the tunnel. If $AC = 3800$ meters, $BC = 2900$ meters, and angle $C = 110°$, find the length of the tunnel.

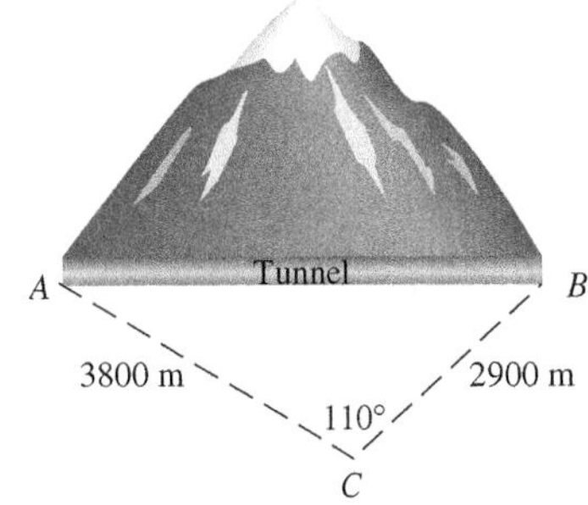


20. ***Distances on a Baseball Diamond*** A baseball diamond is a square 90.0 feet on a side, with home plate and the three bases as vertices. The pitcher's position is located 60.5 feet from home plate. Find the distance from the pitcher's position to each of the bases.

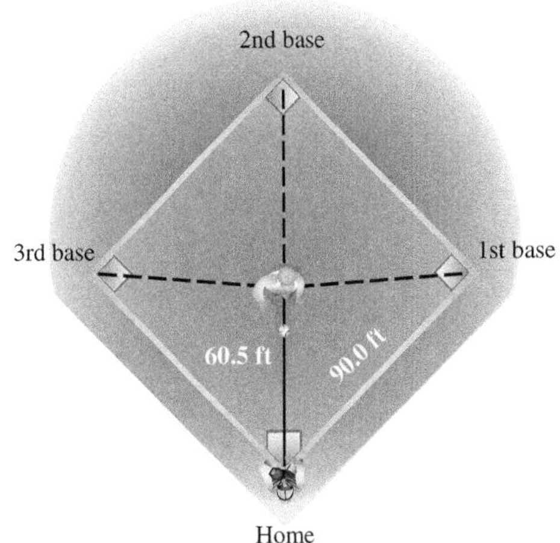

## 4.4 Exercises (Pages 199–203)

**1.** 5 **3.** 6 **5.** row 2: 0, 6, 10; row 3: 9, 0, 9; row 4: 0, 4, 0, 8, 0; row 5: 1, 9, 2, 7; row 6: 6, 0, 0; row 7: 4, 11, 6, 8, 3, 5; row 8: 8, 4, 0, 0; row 9: 6, 3, 9, 3, 9, 6, 3; row 10: 6, 4, 0, 10, 8, 6, 4; row 11: 10, 9, 8, 7, 6, 5, 4, 3, 2 **7.** yes **9.** row 1: 0; row 2: 0; row 3: 0, 1, 2 row 4: 0, 1, 2 **11.** yes **13.** yes (0 is its own inverse, 1 and 4 are inverses of each other, and 2 and 3 are inverses of each other.) **15.** yes **17.** yes (1 is the identity element.) **19.** 3 **21.** 4 **23.** Answers will vary. **25.** 0700 **27.** 0000 **29.** false **31.** true **33.** 3 **35.** 3 **37.** 1 **39.** 10 **41.** Answers will vary. **43.** 5 **45.** 4 **47.** row 1: 0; row 2: 2, 3, 4, 5, 6, 0, 1; row 3: 3, 4, 5, 6, 0, 1, 2; row 4: 4, 5, 6, 0, 1, 2, 3; row 5: 5, 6, 0, 1, 2, 3, 4; row 6: 6, 0, 1, 2, 3, 4, 5 **49.** row 2: 1 **51.** row 2: 1, 3, 7; row 3: 3, 0; row 4: 3, 2, 1; row 5: 6, 7, 4; row 7: 3, 1, 6, 4; row 8: 6, 5, 2 **53.** {3, 10, 17, 24, 31, 38, . . . } **55.** {1, 2, 3, 4, 5, 6, . . . } **57.** 100,000 **59.** **(a)** 365 **(b)** Friday **61.** 62 **63.** Chicago: July 23 and 29; New Orleans: July 5 and August 16; San Francisco: August 9 **65.** Sunday **67.** Wednesday **69.** June **71.** June **73.** yes **75.** 6 **77.** 2

## 4.5 Exercises (Pages 208–210)

**1.** all properties; 1 is the identity element; 1 is its own inverse, as is 2. **3.** closure, commutative, associative, and identity properties; 1 is the identity element; 2, 4, and 6 have no inverses. **5.** all properties except the inverse; 1 is the identity element; 5 has no inverse. **7.** all properties; *F* is the identity element; *A* and *B* are inverses; *F* is its own inverse. **9.** all properties; *t* is the identity element; *s* and *r* are inverses; *t* and *u* are their own inverses. **11.** *a* **13.** *a* **15.** row *b: d;* row *c: d, b;* row *d: b, c* **17.** associative, commutative, identity (*U*), closure **19.** Answers may vary. One possibility is shown.

| | *a* | *b* | *c* | *d* |
|---|---|---|---|---|
| ***a*** | *a* | *b* | *c* | *d* |
| ***b*** | *b* | *a* | *d* | *c* |
| ***c*** | *c* | *d* | *a* | *b* |
| ***d*** | *d* | *c* | *b* | *a* |

**21.** no **23.** **(a)** true **(b)** true **(c)** true **(d)** true

**25.** $a + b + c = 1$ or $a = 0$ **27.** **(a)** $a = 0$ **(b)** $a = 0$ **29.** Each side simplifies to *e*. **31.** Each side simplifies to *d*. **33.**

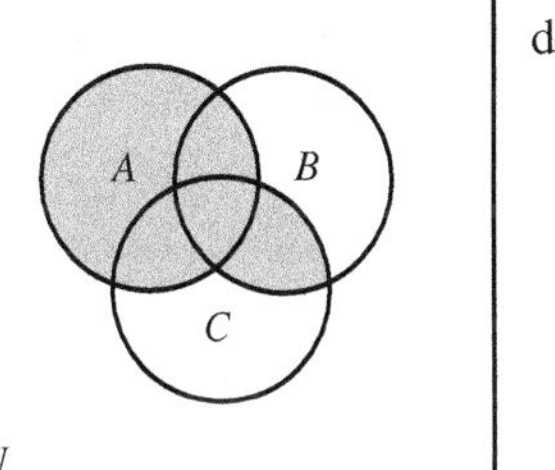


$A \cup (B \cap C) = (A \cup B) \cap (A \cup C)$

**35.** Both final columns read TTTTTFFF, when set up in the manner described in Chapter 3.

## 4.6 Exercises (Pages 216–218)

**1.** No operation is specified. **3.** yes **5.** no; closure, inverse **7.** yes **9.** no; inverse **11.** no; associative, identity, inverse **13.** no; inverse **15.** yes **17.** no; closure, identity, inverse **19.** Answers will vary. **21.** *S* **23.** *N* **25.** Each side is equal to *M*. **27.** Each side is equal to *Q*. **29.** *N* **31.** *R* **33.** *T* **35.** no **37.** yes **39.** Answers will vary. **41.** Answers will vary. **43.** row *B: D;* row *C: D, B;* row *D: C, B;* **45.** **(a)** yes **(b)** Answers will vary. **47.** **(a)** no **(b)** Answers will vary.

## Chapter 4 Test (Pages 219–220)

**1.** ancient Egyptian; 2426 **2.** 7561 **3.** $(6 \cdot 10^4) + (0 \cdot 10^3) + (9 \cdot 10^2) + (2 \cdot 10^1) + (3 \cdot 10^0)$ **4.** 1998 **5.** 22,184 **6.** 12,827 **7.** 89 **8.** 50 **9.** 57,007 **10.** $110001_{\text{two}}$ **11.** $43210_{\text{five}}$ **12.** $256_{\text{eight}}$ **13.** {2, 7, 12, 17, 22, 27, . . . } **14.** **(a)** 5 **(b)** 4 **(c)** 9 **(d)** 8 **15.** **(a)** 3 **(b)** 1 **16.** 48 **17.** There is less repetition of symbols. **18.** There are fewer symbols to learn. **19.** There are fewer digits in the numerals. **20.** 0 **21.** $\frac{1}{3}$ **22.** commutative **23.** row 3: 1, 7; row 5: 7, 3; row 7: 5, 1 **24.** **(a)** yes **(b)** 1 **25.** **(a)** yes **(b)** Answers will vary. **26.** **(a)** yes **(b)** Answers will vary. **27.** **(a)** no **(b)** Answers will vary. **28.** **(a)** yes **(b)** Answers will vary.

## CHAPTER 5 Number Theory

### 5.1 Exercises (Pages 230–233)

**1.** true **3.** false **5.** false **7.** true **9.** false **11.** false **13.** 1, 2, 3, 4, 6, 12 **15.** 1, 2, 4, 5, 10, 20 **17.** 1, 2, 3, 4, 5, 6, 8, 10, 12, 15, 20, 24, 30, 40, 60, 120 **19.** **(a)** no **(b)** yes **(c)** no **(d)** yes **(e)** no **(f)** no **(g)** yes **(h)** no **(i)** no **21.** **(a)** no **(b)** no **(c)** no **(d)** yes **(e)** no **(f)** no **(g)** no **(h)** no **(i)** no **23.** **(a)** no **(b)** yes **(c)** no **(d)** no **(e)** no **(f)** no **(g)** yes **(h)** no **(i)** no **25.** **(a)** Answers will vary. **(b)** 13 **(c)** square root; square root; square root **(d)** prime **27.** 2, 3; no **29.** It must be 0.
**31.**

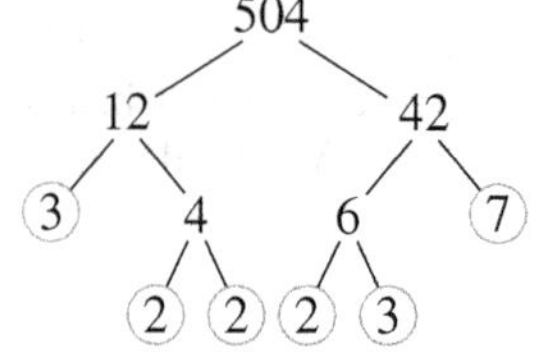


$504 = 3 \cdot 2^3 \cdot 3 \cdot 7$
$= 2^3 \cdot 3^2 \cdot 7$

**33.** $2^4 \cdot 3 \cdot 5$ **35.** $2^3 \cdot 3^2 \cdot 5$ **37.** $3 \cdot 13 \cdot 17$

**39.** yes **41.** no **43.** yes **45.** no **47.** The number must be divisible by both 3 and 5. That is, the sum of the digits must be divisible by 3, and the last digit must be 5 or 0. **49.** $75 = 3 \cdot 25$, $75 = 5 \cdot 15$ **51.** 0, 2, 4, 6, 8 **53.** 0, 4, 8 **55.** 0, 6 **57.** 6 **59.** 10 **61.** 27 **63.** leap year **65.** leap year **67.** Answers will vary. **69.** Answers will vary. **71.** $41^2 - 41 + 41 = 41^2$, and $41^2$ is not a prime. **72.** **(a)** 1763 **(b)** 1847 **73.** B **75.** **(a)** 65,537 **(b)** 251 **77.** Answers will vary. **79.** Answers will vary. **81.** composite: $30{,}031 = 59 \cdot 509$ **83.** 63 **85.** $2^p - 1$ **87.** 3 and 31

### 5.2 Exercises (Pages 238–240)

**1.** true **3.** true **5.** true **7.** false **9.** true **11.** The sum of the proper divisors is 496: $1 + 2 + 4 + 8 + 16 + 31 + 62 + 124 + 248 = 496$. **13.** 8191 is prime; 33,550,336 **15.** $1 + \frac{1}{2} + \frac{1}{3} + \frac{1}{6} = 2$ **17.** abundant **19.** deficient **21.** 12, 18, 20, 24 **23.** $1 + 3 + 5 + 7 + 9 + 15 + 21 + 27 + 35 + 45 + 63 + 105 + 135 + 189 + 315 = 975$, and $975 > 945$, so 945 is abundant. **25.** $1 + 2 + 4 + 8 + 16 + 32 + 37 + 74 + 148 + 296 + 592 = 1210$ and $1 + 2 + 5 + 10 + 11 + 22 + 55 + 110 + 121 + 242 + 605 = 1184$ **27.** $3 + 11$ **29.** $3 + 23$ **31.** Let $a = 5$ and $b = 3$; $11 = 5 + 2 \cdot 3$ **33.** 71 and 73 **35.** 137 and 139 **37.** **(a)** $5 = 9 - 4 = 3^2 - 2^2$ **(b)** $11 = 36 - 25 = 6^2 - 5^2$ **39.** $5^2 + 2 = 27 = 3^3$ **41.** Answers will vary. **43.** No; for the first six, the sequence is 6, 8, 6, 8, 6, 6. **45.** one; not happy **47.** both; happy **49.** Answers will vary. **51.** B **53.** 7; yes **55.** 15; no **57.** 27; no **59.** 24; 23; 25; yes; no **61.** Answers will vary. **63.** B

### 5.3 Exercises (Pages 247–249)

**1.** true **3.** true **5.** false **7.** true **9.** true **11.** 10 **13.** 120 **15.** 7 **17.** 12 **19.** 10 **21.** 6 **23.** 12 **25.** 12 **27.** 70 **29.** Answers will vary. **31.** 120 **33.** 672 **35.** 840 **37.** 96 **39.** 225 **41.** 2160 **43.** 180 **45.** 1260 **47.** 1680 **49.** **(a)** $p^b q^c r^c$ **(b)** $p^a q^a r^b$ **51.** 30 **53.** 15 **55.** 12 **57.** **(a)** 6 **(b)** 36 **59.** **(a)** 18 **(b)** 216 **61.** $p$ and $q$ are relatively prime. **63.** Answers will vary. **65.** 144th **67.** 48 **69.** \$600; 25 books

### Extension Exercises (Pages 256–257)

**1.** 3 **3.** 4 **5.** 5 **7.** 2 **9.** 2 **11.** 13 **13.** 12 **15.** 3 **17.** 55; 40 **19.** 65; 48 **21.** 5 **23.** 61 **25.** **(a)** 27 **(b)** 35 **27.** **(a)** 11 **(b)** 23 **29.** Answers will vary.

### 5.4 Exercises (Pages 262–265)

**1.** 2584 **3.** 46,368 **5.** $\frac{1+\sqrt{5}}{2}$ **7.** $1 + 1 + 2 + 3 + 5 + 8 = 21 - 1$; Each expression is equal to 20. **9.** $1 + 2 + 5 + 13 + 34 + 89 = 144$; Each expression is equal to 144. **11.** $13^2 - 5^2 = 144$; Each expression is equal to 144. **13.** $1 - 2 + 5 - 13 + 34 - 89 = -8^2$; Each expression is equal to $-64$. **15.** (There are other ways to do this.) **(a)** $37 = 34 + 3$ **(b)** $40 = 34 + 5 + 1$ **(c)** $52 = 34 + 13 + 5$ **17.** **(a)** The greatest common factor of 10 and 4 is 2, and the greatest common factor of $F_{10} = 55$ and $F_4 = 3$ is $F_2 = 1$. **(b)** The greatest common factor of 12 and 6 is 6, and the greatest common factor of $F_{12} = 144$ and $F_6 = 8$ is $F_6 = 8$. **(c)** The greatest common factor of 14 and 6 is 2, and the greatest common factor of $F_{14} = 377$ and $F_6 = 8$ is $F_2 = 1$. **19.** **(a)** $5 \cdot 34 - 13^2 = 1$ **(b)** $13^2 - 3 \cdot 55 = 4$ **(c)** $2 \cdot 89 - 13^2 = 9$ **(d)** The difference will be 25, because we are obtaining the squares of the terms of the Fibonacci sequence. $13^2 - 1 \cdot 144 = 25 = 5^2$. **21.** 199 **23.** Each sum is 2 less than a Lucas number. **25.** **(a)** $8 \cdot 18 = 144$; Each expression is equal to 144. **(b)** $8 + 21 = 29$; Each expression is equal to 29.

(c) $8 + 18 = 2 \cdot 13$; Each expression is equal to 26. **27.** 3, 4, 5 **29.** 16, 30, 34 **31.** The sums are 1, 1, 2, 3, 5, 8, 13. They are terms of the Fibonacci sequence. **33.** $\frac{1+\sqrt{5}}{2} \approx 1.618033989$ and $\frac{1-\sqrt{5}}{2} \approx -.618033989$. After the decimal point, the digits are the same. **35.** 377 **37.** 17,711

## Extension Exercises (Pages 267–269)

**1.**

| | | |
|---|---|---|
| 2 | 7 | 6 |
| 9 | 5 | 1 |
| 4 | 3 | 8 |

**3.**

| | | | | |
|---|---|---|---|---|
| 11 | 10 | 4 | 23 | 17 |
| 18 | 12 | 6 | 5 | 24 |
| 25 | 19 | 13 | 7 | 1 |
| 2 | 21 | 20 | 14 | 8 |
| 9 | 3 | 22 | 16 | 15 |

**5.**

| | | | | |
|---|---|---|---|---|
| 15 | 16 | 22 | 3 | 9 |
| 8 | 14 | 20 | 21 | 2 |
| 1 | 7 | 13 | 19 | 25 |
| 24 | 5 | 6 | 12 | 18 |
| 17 | 23 | 4 | 10 | 11 |

**7.**

| | | |
|---|---|---|
| 24 | 9 | 12 |
| 3 | 15 | 27 |
| 18 | 21 | 6 |

Magic sum is 45.

**9.**

| | | | | |
|---|---|---|---|---|
| $\frac{17}{2}$ | 12 | $\frac{1}{2}$ | 4 | $\frac{15}{2}$ |
| $\frac{23}{2}$ | $\frac{5}{2}$ | $\frac{7}{2}$ | 7 | 8 |
| 2 | 3 | $\frac{13}{2}$ | 10 | 11 |
| 5 | 6 | $\frac{19}{2}$ | $\frac{21}{2}$ | $\frac{3}{2}$ |
| $\frac{11}{2}$ | 9 | $\frac{25}{2}$ | 1 | $\frac{9}{2}$ |

Magic sum is $32\frac{1}{2}$.

**11.** 479 **13.** 467 **15.** 269 **17.** (a) 73 (b) 70 (c) 74 (d) 69 **19.** (a) 7 (b 22 (c) 5 (d) 4 (e) 15 (f) 19 (g) 6 (h) 23

**21.**

| | | | | | | |
|---|---|---|---|---|---|---|
| 30 | 39 | 48 | 1 | 10 | 19 | 28 |
| 38 | 47 | 7 | 9 | 18 | 27 | 29 |
| 46 | 6 | 8 | 17 | 26 | 35 | 37 |
| 5 | 14 | 16 | 25 | 34 | 36 | 45 |
| 13 | 15 | 24 | 33 | 42 | 44 | 4 |
| 21 | 23 | 32 | 41 | 43 | 3 | 12 |
| 22 | 31 | 40 | 49 | 2 | 11 | 20 |

**23.** Each sum is equal to 34. **25.** Each sum is equal to 68. **27.** Each sum is equal to 9248. **29.** Each sum is equal to 748. **31.**

| | | | |
|---|---|---|---|
| 16 | 2 | 3 | 13 |
| 5 | 11 | 10 | 8 |
| 9 | 7 | 6 | 12 |
| 4 | 14 | 15 | 1 |

The second and third columns are interchanged.

**33.**

| | | |
|---|---|---|
| 18 | 20 | 10 |
| 8 | 16 | 24 |
| 22 | 12 | 14 |

**35.**

| | | | | | | |
|---|---|---|---|---|---|---|
| 39 | 48 | 57 | 10 | 19 | 28 | 37 |
| 47 | 56 | 16 | 18 | 27 | 36 | 38 |
| 55 | 15 | 17 | 26 | 35 | 44 | 46 |
| 14 | 23 | 25 | 34 | 43 | 45 | 54 |
| 22 | 24 | 33 | 42 | 51 | 53 | 13 |
| 30 | 32 | 41 | 50 | 52 | 12 | 21 |
| 31 | 40 | 49 | 58 | 11 | 20 | 29 |

Magic sum is 238.

**37.** 260 **39.** $52 + 45 + 16 + 17 + 54 + 43 + 10 + 23 = 260$

**41.**

| | | | | |
|---|---|---|---|---|
| 5 | 13 | 21 | 9 | 17 |
| 6 | 19 | 2 | 15 | 23 |
| 12 | 25 | 8 | 16 | 4 |
| 18 | 1 | 14 | 22 | 10 |
| 24 | 7 | 20 | 3 | 11 |

## Chapter 5 Test (Pages 270–271)

**1.** false **2.** true **3.** true **4.** true **5.** true **6.** (a) yes (b) yes (c) no (d) yes (e) yes (f) no (g) yes (h) yes (i) no **7.** (a) composite (b) neither (c) prime **8.** $2^5 \cdot 3^2 \cdot 5$ **9.** Answers will vary. **10.** (a) deficient (b) perfect (c) abundant **11.** C **12.** 41 and 43 **13.** 90 **14.** 360

**15.** Monday **16.** 46,368 **17.** $89 - (8 + 13 + 21 + 34) = 13$; Each expression is equal to 13. **18.** B **19.** **(a)** 1, 5, 6, 11, 17, 28, 45, 73 **(b)** The process will yield 19 for any term chosen. **20.** A **21.** Answers will vary. **22.** Answers will vary.

## CHAPTER 6 The Real Numbers and Their Representations

### 6.1 Exercises (Pages 280–283)

**1.** 4 **3.** 0 **5.** $\sqrt{12}$ (There are others.) **7.** true **9.** true **11.** **(a)** 3, 7 **(b)** 0, 3, 7 **(c)** $-9, 0, 3, 7$ **(d)** $-9, -1\frac{1}{4}, -\frac{3}{5}, 0, 3, 5.9, 7$ **(e)** $-\sqrt{7}, \sqrt{5}$ **(f)** All are real numbers. **13.** Answers will vary. **15.** 1450 **17.** 5436 **19.** $-220°$ **21.** 20; 10°; $-9°$ **23.** **(a)** Pacific Ocean, Indian Ocean, Caribbean Sea, South China Sea, Gulf of California **(b)** Point Success, Ranier, Matlalcueyetl, Steele, McKinley **(c)** true **(d)** false

**25.** −6 −4 −2 0 2 4 **27.** $-3\frac{4}{5}$ $-1\frac{5}{8}$ $\frac{1}{4}$ $2\frac{1}{2}$ −4 −2 0 2 4 **29.** **(a)** A **(b)** A **(c)** B **(d)** B **31.** **(a)** 2 **(b)** 2

**33.** **(a)** $-6$ **(b)** 6 **35.** **(a)** $-3$ **(b)** 3 **37.** **(a)** 0 **(b)** 0 **39.** $a - b$ **41.** $-12$ **43.** $-8$ **45.** 3 **47.** $|-3|$ or 3 **49.** $-|-6|$ or $-6$ **51.** $|5 - 3|$ or 2 **53.** true **55.** true **57.** true **59.** false **61.** true **63.** false **65.** petroleum refineries, 2002 to 2003 **67.** construction machinery manufacturing, 2002 to 2003 **69.** computer/data processing services **Answers will vary in Exercises 71–75.** **71.** $\frac{1}{2}, \frac{5}{8}, 1\frac{3}{4}$ **73.** $-3\frac{1}{2}, -\frac{2}{3}, \frac{3}{7}$ **75.** $\sqrt{5}, \pi, -\sqrt{3}$

### 6.2 Exercises (Pages 292–296)

**1.** negative **3.** $-3$; 5 **5.** Answers will vary. **7.** $-20$ **9.** $-4$ **11.** $-11$ **13.** 9 **15.** 20 **17.** 4 **19.** 24 **21.** $-1296$ **23.** 6 **25.** $-6$ **27.** 0 **29.** $-6$ **31.** $-4$ **33.** 27 **35.** 39 **37.** $-2$ **39.** not a real number **41.** 13 **43.** A, B, C **45.** commutative property of addition **47.** associative property of addition **49.** inverse property of addition **51.** identity property of multiplication **53.** identity property of addition **55.** distributive property **57.** inverse property of addition **59.** closure property of multiplication **61.** **(c)** Yes; choose $a = b$. For example, $a = b = 2 : 2 - 2 = 2 - 2$. **63.** **(a)** messing up your room **(b)** spending money **(c)** decreasing the volume on your MP3 player **65.** identity **67.** No, it does not hold true. **69.** $-81$ **71.** 81 **73.** $-81$ **75.** $-81$ **77.** **(a)** $-3.6$ (billion dollars) **(b)** 7.8 (billion dollars) **(c)** 28.2 (billion dollars) **(d)** 32.4 (billion dollars) **79.** **(a)** 2000: \$129 billion; 2010: \$206 billion; 2020: \$74 billion; 2030: $-$\$501 billion **(b)** The cost of Social Security will exceed revenue in 2030 by \$501 billion. **81.** 16 **83.** \$1045.55 **85.** 14,776 feet **87.** 45°F **89.** 112°F **91.** $-41$°F **93.** 27 feet **95.** 469 B.C. **97.** \$2169

### 6.3 Exercises (Pages 306–310)

**1.** A, C, D **3.** C **5.** $\frac{1}{3}$ **7.** $-\frac{3}{7}$ **Answers will vary in Exercises 9 and 11.** **9.** $\frac{6}{16}, \frac{9}{24}, \frac{12}{32}$ **11.** $-\frac{10}{14}, -\frac{15}{21}, -\frac{20}{28}$ **13.** **(a)** $\frac{1}{3}$ **(b)** $\frac{1}{4}$ **(c)** $\frac{2}{5}$ **(d)** $\frac{1}{3}$ **15.** the dots in the intersection of the triangle and the rectangle as a part of the dots in the entire figure **17.** **(a)** O'Brien **(b)** Ha **(c)** Ha **(d)** Kelly **(e)** Taylor and Britz; $\frac{1}{2}$ **19.** $\frac{1}{2}$ **21.** $\frac{43}{48}$ **23.** $-\frac{5}{24}$ **25.** $\frac{23}{56}$ **27.** $\frac{27}{20}$ **29.** $\frac{5}{12}$ **31.** $\frac{1}{9}$ **33.** $\frac{3}{2}$ **35.** $\frac{3}{2}$ **37.** **(a)** $4\frac{1}{2}$ cups **(b)** $\frac{7}{8}$ cup **39.** $\frac{13}{3}$ **41.** $\frac{29}{10}$ **43.** $6\frac{3}{4}$ **45.** $6\frac{1}{8}$ **47.** $-17\frac{7}{8}$ **49.** $\frac{9}{16}$ inch **51.** 3 **53.** $\frac{3}{7}$ **55.** $-\frac{103}{89}$ **57.** $\frac{25}{9}$ **59.** $\frac{5}{8}$ **61.** $\frac{19}{30}$ **63.** $-\frac{3}{4}$ **65.** \$53,221 **67.** $\frac{14}{19}$ **69.** $\frac{13}{29}$ **71.** $\frac{5}{2}$ **73.** It gives the rational number halfway between the two integers (their average). **75.** .75 **77.** .1875 **79.** $.\overline{27}$ **81.** $.\overline{285714}$ **83.** $\frac{2}{5}$ **85.** $\frac{17}{20}$ **87.** $\frac{467}{500}$ **89.** repeating **91.** terminating **93.** terminating **95.** **(a)** $.\overline{3}$ or .333 . . . **(b)** $.\overline{6}$ or .666 . . . **(c)** $.\overline{9}$ or .999 . . . **(d)** $1 = .\overline{9}$ **97.** **(a)** $\frac{4}{5}$ **(b)** $\frac{4}{5}$ **99.** **(a)** $\frac{33}{50}$ **(b)** $\frac{33}{50}$

### 6.4 Exercises (Pages 318–321)

**1.** rational **3.** irrational **5.** rational **7.** rational **9.** irrational **11.** irrational **13.** rational **15.** **(a)** $.\overline{8}$ **(b)** irrational; rational **17.** 6.244997998 **19.** 3.885871846 **21.** 29.73213749 **23.** 1.060660172 **25.** $5\sqrt{2}$; 7.071067812 **27.** $5\sqrt{3}$; 8.660254038 **29.** $12\sqrt{2}$; 16.97056275 **31.** $\frac{5\sqrt{6}}{6}$; 2.041241452 **33.** $\frac{\sqrt{7}}{2}$; 1.322875656 **35.** $\frac{\sqrt{21}}{3}$; 1.527525232 **37.** $3\sqrt{17}$ **39.** $4\sqrt{7}$ **41.** $10\sqrt{2}$

**43.** $3\sqrt{3}$ **45.**

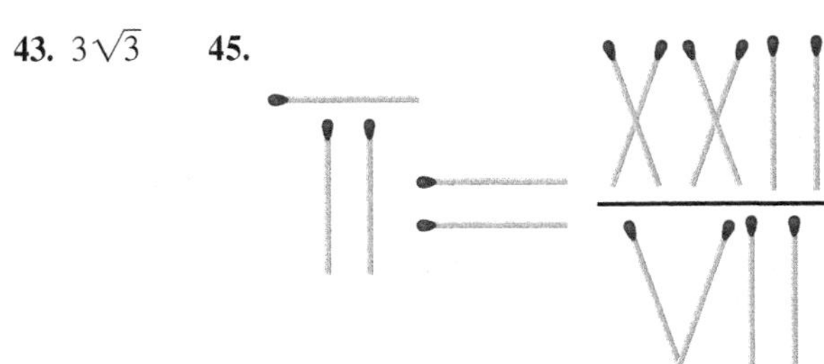

**47.** The result is 3.1415929, which agrees with the first seven digits in the decimal for $\pi$. **49.** 3 **51.** 4 **53.** 3.3 **55.** $\phi$ is positive, while its conjugate is negative. The units digit of $\phi$ is 1, and the units digit of its conjugate is 0. The decimal digits agree. **57.** It is just a coincidence that 1828 appears back-to-back early in the decimal. There is no repetition indefinitely, which would be indicative of a rational number. **59.** 2.5 seconds **61.** 15.3 miles **63.** 392,000 square miles **65.** The area and the perimeter are both numerically equal to 36. **67.** 5.4 feet **69.** (a) 70.5 mph (b) 59.8 mph (c) 53.9 mph **71.** 4 **73.** 7 **75.** 6 **77.** 1 **79.** 4 **81.** 8 **The number of decimal digits shown will vary among caculator models in Exercises 83–87.** **83.** 3.50339806 **85.** 5.828476683 **87.** 10.06565066

## 6.5 Exercises (Pages 331–335)

**1.** true **3.** false **5.** true **7.** true **9.** false **11.** 11.315 **13.** −4.215 **15.** .8224 **17.** 47.5 **19.** 31.6 **21.** Los Angeles; The population increased, as represented by 9.7%. **23.** three (and you would have .01¢ left over) **25.** $.06 or 6¢ **27.** 1000 **29.** (a) .031 (b) .035 **31.** 297 **33.** (a) 78.4 (b) 78.41 **35.** (a) .1 (b) .08 **37.** (a) 12.7 (b) 12.69 **39.** 42% **41.** 36.5% **43.** .8% **45.** 210% **47.** 20% **49.** 1% **51.** $37\frac{1}{2}\%$ **53.** 150% **55.** Answers will vary. **57.** (a) 5 (b) 24 (c) 8 (d) .5 or $\frac{1}{2}$ (e) 600 **59.** No, the price is $57.60. **61.** (a) .611 (b) .574 (c) .438 **63.** 124.8 **65.** 2.94 **67.** 150% **69.** 600 **71.** 1.4% **73.** A **75.** C **77.** about 67% **79.** (a) 14.7 − 40 · .13 (b) 9.5 (c) 8.075; walking (5 mph) **81.** 860% **83.** $4.50 **85.** $.75 **87.** $12.00 **89.** $36.00 **91.** Answers will vary.

## Extension Exercises (Page 338)

**1.** $12i$ **3.** $-15i$ **5.** $i\sqrt{3}$ **7.** $5i\sqrt{3}$ **9.** −5 **11.** −18 **13.** −40 **15.** $\sqrt{2}$ **17.** $3i$ **19.** 6 **21.** The product rule requires that $a$ and $b$ be nonnegative. **23.** 1 **25.** −1 **27.** $-i$ **29.** $i$

## Chapter 6 Test (Pages 340–342)

**1.** (a) 12 (b) 0, 12 (c) −4, 0, 12 (d) $-4, -\frac{3}{2}, -.5, 0, 4.1, 12$ (e) $-\sqrt{5}, \sqrt{3}$ (f) $-4, -\sqrt{5}, -\frac{3}{2}, -.5, 0, \sqrt{3}, 4.1, 12$ **2.** (a) C (b) B (c) D (d) A **3.** (a) false (b) true (c) true (d) false **4.** 4 **5.** 3 **6.** 10 **7.** (a) Hyundai; 50% (b) General Motors; −5% (c) false (d) true **8.** 5296 ft **9.** (a) $4900 (b) $5700 (c) $8800 (d) $10,300 **10.** (a) E (b) A (c) B (d) D (e) F (f) C **11.** (a) Whitney (b) Moura and Dawkins (c) Whitney (d) Pritchard and Miller; $\frac{2}{5}$ (e) McElwain ("J-Mac") **12.** $\frac{11}{16}$ **13.** $\frac{57}{160}$ **14.** $-\frac{2}{5}$ **15.** $\frac{3}{2}$ **16.** (a) .45 (b) $.41\overline{6}$ **17.** (a) $\frac{18}{25}$ (b) $\frac{58}{99}$ **18.** (a) irrational (b) rational (c) rational (d) rational (e) irrational (f) irrational **19.** (a) 12.247448714 (b) $5\sqrt{6}$ **20.** (a) 4.913538149 (b) $\frac{13\sqrt{7}}{7}$ **21.** (a) −45.254834 (b) $-32\sqrt{2}$ **22.** Answers will vary. **23.** (a) 13.81 (b) −.315 (c) 38.7 (d) −24.3 **24.** (a) 9.04 (b) 9.045 **25.** (a) 16.65 (b) 101.5 **26.** (a) $26\frac{2}{3}\%$ (b) $66\frac{2}{3}\%$ **27.** D **28.** 828; 504; 16%; 6% **29.** 17,415,000 **30.** − 13.8 (billion dollars)

# CHAPTER 7 The Basic Concepts of Algebra

## 7.1 Exercises (Pages 351–354)

**1.** A and C **3.** Both sides are evaluated as 30, so 6 is a solution. **5.** solution set **7.** B **9.** $\{-1\}$ **11.** $\{3\}$ **13.** $\{-7\}$ **15.** $\{0\}$ **17.** $\{-\frac{5}{3}\}$ **19.** $\{-\frac{1}{2}\}$ **21.** $\{2\}$ **23.** $\{-2\}$ **25.** $\{7\}$ **27.** $\{2\}$ **29.** $\{\frac{3}{2}\}$ **31.** $\{-5\}$ **33.** $\{3\}$ **35.** 2 (that is, $10^2$, or 100) **37.** $\{4\}$ **39.** $\{0\}$ **41.** $\{0\}$ **43.** $\{2000\}$ **45.** $\{25\}$ **47.** $\{40\}$ **49.** identity, contradiction **51.** contradiction; $\emptyset$ **53.** conditional; $\{-8\}$ **55.** conditional; $\{0\}$ **57.** identity; {all real numbers} **59.** D **61.** $t = \frac{d}{r}$ **63.** $b = \frac{A}{h}$ **65.** $a = P - b - c$ **67.** $b = \frac{2A}{h}$ **69.** $h = \frac{S - 2\pi r^2}{2\pi r}$ or $h = \frac{S}{2\pi r} - r$ **71.** $F = \frac{9}{5}C + 32$ **73.** $H = \frac{A - 2LW}{2W + 2L}$ **75.** (a) 16.8 million (b) 2009 **77.** (a) .0352 (b) approximately .015 or 1.5% (c) approximately 1 case **79.** (a) 800 cubic feet (b) 107,680 $\mu g$ (c) $F = 107{,}680x$ (d) approximately .25 day, or 6 hr

**7.2 Exercises (Pages 364–369)**

**1.** expression **3.** equation **5.** expression **7.** yes **9.** $x - 14$ **11.** $(x - 7)(x + 5)$ **13.** $\frac{15}{x}$ $(x \neq 0)$ **15.** Answers will vary. **17.** 3 **19.** 6 **21.** $-3$ **23.** Springsteen: \$115.9 million; Dion: \$80.5 million **25.** wins: 62; losses: 20 **27.** Democrats: 44; Republicans: 55 **29.** shortest piece: 15 inches; middle piece: 20 inches; longest piece: 24 inches **31.** gold: 35; silver: 39; bronze: 29 **33.** 35 milliliters **35.** \$350 **37.** \$14.15 **39.** 4 liters **41.** $18\frac{2}{11}$ liters **43.** 5 liters **45.** \$4000 at 3%; \$8000 at 4% **47.** \$10,000 at 4.5%; \$19,000 at 3% **49.** \$58,000 **51.** 17 pennies, 17 dimes, 10 quarters **53.** 305 students, 105 nonstudents **55.** 54 seats on Row 1; 51 seats on Row 2 **57.** 39-cent stamps: 28; 24-cent stamps: 17 **59.** 3.173 hours **61.** 1.715 hours **63.** 8.08 meters per second **65.** 8.40 meters per second **67.** 530 miles **69.** No, it is not correct. The distance is $45\left(\frac{1}{2}\right) = 22.5$ miles. **71.** $1\frac{3}{4}$ hours **73.** 10:00 A.M. **75.** 18 miles **77.** 8 hours

**7.3 Exercises (Pages 378–383)**

**1.** $\frac{5}{8}$ **3.** $\frac{1}{4}$ **5.** $\frac{2}{1}$ **7.** $\frac{3}{1}$ **9.** D **11.** Answers will vary. **13.** true **15.** false **17.** true **19.** $\{35\}$ **21.** $\{-1\}$ **23.** $\{-\frac{27}{4}\}$ **25.** \$30.00 **27.** \$8.75 **29.** \$67.50 **31.** \$38.85 **33.** 4 feet **35.** 2.7 inches **37.** 2.0 inches **39.** $2\frac{5}{8}$ cups **41.** \$363.84 **43.** 12,500 fish **45.** 10-lb size; \$.439 **47.** 32-oz size; \$.093 **49.** 128-oz size; \$.044 **51.** 36-oz size; \$.049 **53.** $x = 4$ **55.** $x = 1$; $y = 4$ **57.** **(a)**

x
Chair
18
Shadow
12
Pole
4
Shadow

**(b)** 54 feet **59.** \$144 **61.** \$165 **63.** 9 **65.** 125 **67.** $\frac{4}{9}$ **69.** \$40.32 **71.** 20 miles per hour **73.** about 302 pounds **75.** 100 pounds per square inch **77.** 20 pounds per square foot **79.** 144 feet **81.** 1.105 liters **83.** $\frac{8}{9}$ metric ton **85.** 6.2 pounds

**7.4 Exercises (Pages 391–394)**

**1.** D **3.** B **5.** F **7.** Use parentheses when the symbol is $<$ or $>$. Use brackets when the symbol is $\leq$ or $\geq$.

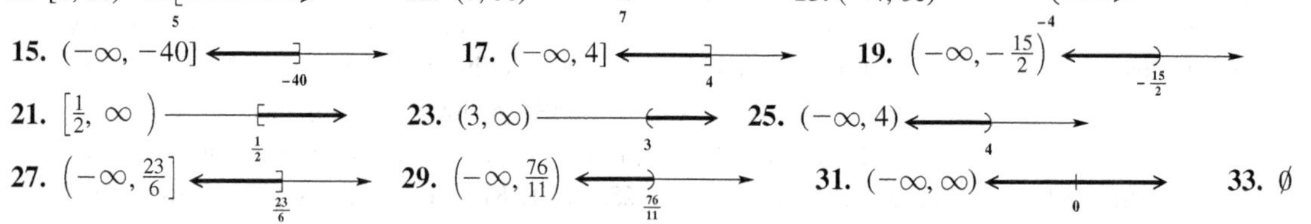

**9.** $[5, \infty)$ **11.** $(7, \infty)$ **13.** $(-4, \infty)$ **15.** $(-\infty, -40]$ **17.** $(-\infty, 4]$ **19.** $\left(-\infty, -\frac{15}{2}\right)$ **21.** $\left[\frac{1}{2}, \infty\right)$ **23.** $(3, \infty)$ **25.** $(-\infty, 4)$ **27.** $\left(-\infty, \frac{23}{6}\right]$ **29.** $\left(-\infty, \frac{76}{11}\right)$ **31.** $(-\infty, \infty)$ **33.** $\emptyset$ **35.** Answers will vary. **37.** $(1, 11)$ **39.** $[-14, 10]$ **41.** $[-5, 6]$ **43.** $\left[-\frac{14}{3}, 2\right]$ **45.** $\left[-\frac{1}{2}, \frac{35}{2}\right]$ **47.** $\left(-\frac{1}{3}, \frac{1}{9}\right]$ **49.** April, May, June, July **51.** January, February, March, August, September, October, November, December **53.** from about 2:30 P.M. to 6:00 P.M. **55.** about 84°F–91°F **57.** 2 miles **59.** at least 80 **61.** 50 miles **63.** **(a)** 140 to 184 pounds **(b)** Answers will vary. **65.** 26 DVDs

**7.5 Exercises (Pages 404–407)**

**1.** A **3.** A **5.** D **7.** 625 **9.** $-32$ **11.** $-8$ **13.** $-81$ **15.** $\frac{1}{49}$ **17.** $-\frac{1}{49}$ **19.** $-128$ **21.** $\frac{16}{5}$ **23.** 125 **25.** $\frac{25}{16}$ **27.** $\frac{9}{20}$ **29.** 1 **31.** 1 **33.** 0 **35.** reciprocal, additive inverse **37.** D **39.** $x^{16}$ **41.** 5 **43.** $\frac{1}{27}$ **45.** $\frac{1}{81}$ **47.** $\frac{1}{t^7}$ **49.** $9x^2$ **51.** $\frac{1}{a^5}$ **53.** $x^{11}$ **55.** $r^6$ **57.** $-\frac{56}{k^2}$ **59.** $\frac{1}{z^4}$ **61.** $-\frac{3}{r^7}$ **63.** $\frac{27}{a^{18}}$ **65.** $\frac{x^5}{y^2}$ **67.** D **69.** $2.3 \times 10^2$ **71.** $2 \times 10^{-2}$ **73.** 6500

**75.** .0152 **77.** $6 \times 10^5$ **79.** $2 \times 10^5$ **81.** $2 \times 10^5$ **83.** $1 \times 10^9$; $1 \times 10^{12}$; $2.128 \times 10^{12}$; $1.44419 \times 10^5$ **85.** $\$1.61964 \times 10^{10}$ **87.** $1 \times 10^{10}$ **89.** 2,000,000,000 **91.** $1392 **93.** approximately $9.474 \times 10^{-7}$ parsec **95.** 300 seconds **97.** approximately $5.87 \times 10^{12}$ miles **99.** 20,000 hours

### 7.6 Exercises (Pages 415–417)

**1.** $x^2 - x + 3$ **3.** $9y^2 - 4y + 4$ **5.** $6m^4 - 2m^3 - 7m^2 - 4m$ **7.** $-2x^2 - 13x + 11$ **9.** $x^2 - 5x - 24$ **11.** $28r^2 + r - 2$ **13.** $12x^5 + 8x^4 - 20x^3 + 4x^2$ **15.** $4m^2 - 9$ **17.** $16m^2 + 16mn + 4n^2$ **19.** $25r^2 + 30rt^2 + 9t^4$ **21.** $-2z^3 + 7z^2 - 11z + 4$ **23.** $m^2 + mn - 2n^2 - 2km + 5kn - 3k^2$ **25.** $a^2 - 2ab + b^2 + 4ac - 4bc + 4c^2$ **27.** A **29.** Answers will vary. **31.** $2m^2(4m^2 + 3m - 6)$ **33.** $4k^2m^3(1 + 2k^2 - 3m)$ **35.** $2(a + b)(1 + 2m)$ **37.** $(m - 1)(2m^2 - 7m + 7)$ **39.** $(2s + 3)(3t - 5)$ **41.** $(t^3 + s^2)(r - p)$ **43.** $(8a + 5b)(2a - 3b)$ **45.** $(5z - 2x)(4z - 9x)$ **47.** $(1 - a)(1 - b)$ **49.** $(x - 5)(x + 3)$ **51.** $(y + 7)(y - 5)$ **53.** $6(a - 10)(a + 2)$ **55.** $3m(m + 1)(m + 3)$ **57.** $(3k - 2p)(2k + 3p)$ **59.** $(5a + 3b)(a - 2b)$ **61.** $(7x + 2y)(3x - y)$ **63.** $2a^2(4a - b)(3a + 2b)$ **65.** Answers will vary. **67.** $(3m - 2)^2$ **69.** $2(4a - 3b)^2$ **71.** $(2xy + 7)^2$ **73.** $(x + 6)(x - 6)$ **75.** $(y + w)(y - w)$ **77.** $(3a + 4)(3a - 4)$ **79.** $(5s^2 + 3t)(5s^2 - 3t)$ **81.** $(p^2 + 25)(p + 5)(p - 5)$ **83.** $(2 - a)(4 + 2a + a^2)$ **85.** $(5x - 3)(25x^2 + 15x + 9)$ **87.** $(3y^3 + 5z^2)(9y^6 - 15y^3z^2 + 25z^4)$ **89.** $(x + y)(x - 5)$ **91.** $(m - 2n)(p^4 + q)$ **93.** $(2z + 7)^2$ **95.** $(10x + 7y)(100x^2 - 70xy + 49y^2)$ **97.** $(5m^2 - 6)(25m^4 + 30m^2 + 36)$ **99.** $(6m - 7n)(2m + 5n)$

### 7.7 Exercises (Pages 422–426)

**1.** 4, 5, −9 **3.** two **5.** $\{-3, 9\}$ **7.** $\left\{\frac{7}{2}, -\frac{1}{5}\right\}$ **9.** $\{-3, 4\}$ **11.** $\{-7, -2\}$ **13.** $\left\{-\frac{1}{2}, \frac{1}{6}\right\}$ **15.** $\{-2, 4\}$ **17.** $\{\pm 8\}$ **19.** $\{\pm 2\sqrt{6}\}$ **21.** $\emptyset$ **23.** $\{1, 7\}$ **25.** $\{4 \pm \sqrt{3}\}$ **27.** $\left\{\frac{5 \pm \sqrt{13}}{2}\right\}$ **29.** $\left\{\frac{2 \pm \sqrt{3}}{2}\right\}$ **31.** $\left\{\frac{1 \pm \sqrt{3}}{2}\right\}$ **33.** $\left\{\frac{1 \pm \sqrt{5}}{2}\right\}$ **35.** $\left\{\frac{-1 \pm \sqrt{2}}{2}\right\}$ **37.** $\left\{\frac{1 \pm \sqrt{29}}{2}\right\}$ **39.** $\emptyset$ **41.** Answers will vary. $\left\{\pm\frac{\sqrt{10}}{2}\right\}$ **43.** The presence of $2x^3$ makes it a *cubic* equation (degree 3). **45.** 0; (c) **47.** 121; (a) **49.** 360; (b) **51.** 5.2 seconds **53.** Find $s$ when $t = 0$. **55.** **(a)** 1 second and 8 seconds **(b)** 9 seconds after it is projected **57.** 2.3, 5.3, 5.8 **59.** 412.3 feet **61.** eastbound ship: 80 miles; southbound ship: 150 miles **63.** 5 centimeters, 12 centimeters, 13 centimeters **65.** length: 2 centimeters; width: 1.5 centimeters **67.** 1 foot **69.** length: 26 meters; width: 16 meters **71.** length: 20 inches; width: 12 inches **73.** $.80 **75.** 5.5 meters per second **77.** 5 or 14 **79.** $\{2\}$

### Chapter 7 Test (Pages 428–429)

**1.** $\{2\}$ **2.** $\{4\}$ **3.** identity; {all real numbers} **4.** $v = \frac{S + 16t^2}{t}$ **5.** Hawaii: 4021 square miles; Maui: 728 square miles; Kauai: 551 square miles **6.** 5 liters **7.** 2.2 hours **8.** 8 slices for $2.19 **9.** 2300 miles **10.** 200 amps **11.** $(-\infty, 4]$  **12.** $(-2, 6]$  **13.** C **14.** at least 82 **15.** $\frac{16}{9}$ **16.** −64 **17.** $\frac{64}{27}$ **18.** 0 **19.** $\frac{216}{p^4}$ **20.** $\frac{1}{m^{14}}$ **21.** **(a)** 693,000,000 **(b)** .000000125 **22.** $3 \times 10^{-4}$ **23.** about 15,300 seconds **24.** $4k^2 + 6k + 10$ **25.** $15x^2 - 14x - 8$ **26.** $16x^4 - 9$ **27.** $3x^3 + 20x^2 + 23x - 36$ **28.** One example is $t^5 + 2t^4 + 3t^3 - 4t^2 + 5t + 6$. **29.** $(2p - 3q)(p - q)$ **30.** $(10x + 7y)(10x - 7y)$ **31.** $(3y - 5x)(9y^2 + 15yx + 25x^2)$ **32.** $(4 - m)(x + y)$ **33.** $\left\{-\frac{3}{2}, \frac{1}{3}\right\}$ **34.** $\{\pm\sqrt{13}\}$ **35.** $\left\{\frac{1 \pm \sqrt{29}}{2}\right\}$ **36.** .87 second

## CHAPTER 8 Graphs, Functions, and Systems of Equations and Inequalities

### 8.1 Exercises (Pages 438–441)

**1.** **(a)** $x$ represents the year; $y$ represents the percent of women in mathematics or computer science professions. **(b)** 1990–2000 **(c)** 1990 **(d)** 1980 **3.** $x$ **5.** (0, 0) **7.** **(a)** I **(b)** III **(c)** II **(d)** IV **(e)** none

**9.** **(a)** I or III **(b)** II or IV **(c)** II or IV **(d)** I or III **11.–20.**

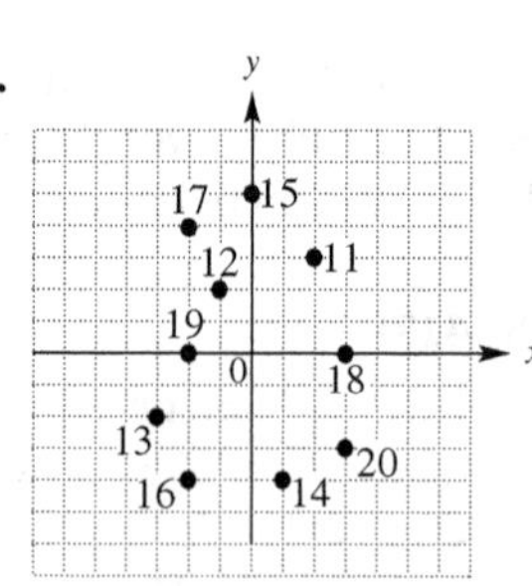


**21.** **(a)** $\sqrt{34}$ **(b)** $\left(\frac{1}{2}, \frac{5}{2}\right)$ **23.** **(a)** $\sqrt{61}$ **(b)** $\left(\frac{1}{2}, 1\right)$ **25.** **(a)** $\sqrt{146}$ **(b)** $\left(-\frac{1}{2}, \frac{3}{2}\right)$ **27.** B **29.** D
**31.** $x^2 + y^2 = 36$ **33.** $(x + 1)^2 + (y - 3)^2 = 16$ **35.** $x^2 + (y - 4)^2 = 3$ **37.** center: (0, 0); radius: $r$
**39.** $(-2, -3)$; 2 **41.** $(-5, 7)$; 9 **43.** (2, 4); 4 **45.**

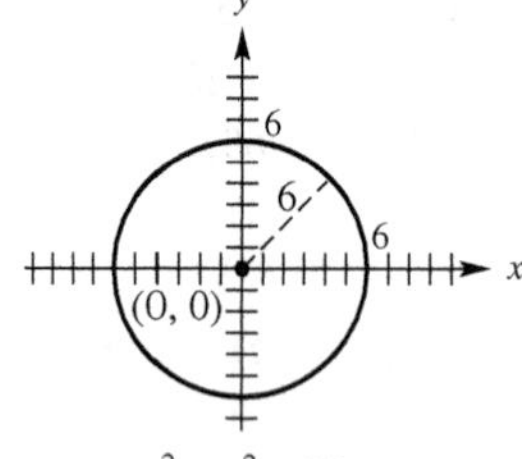


**47.**

$(x - 2)^2 + y^2 = 36$

**49.**

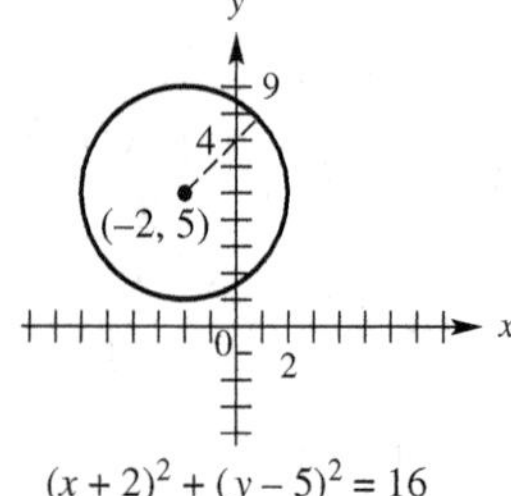


**51.**

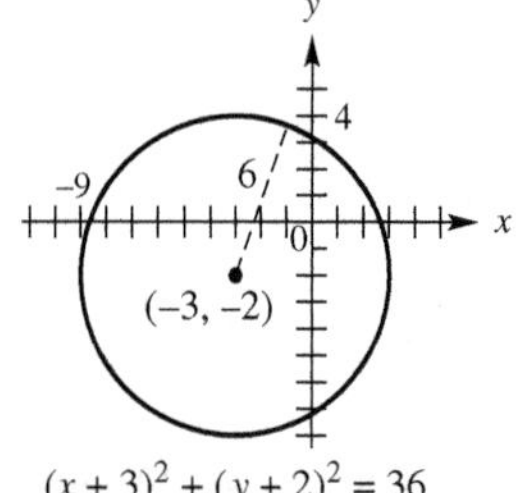


**53.** **(a)** $\sqrt{40} = 2\sqrt{10}$ **(b)** $(-1, 4)$

**55.** \$17,396 **57.** 1988: \$12,471; 1998: \$16,787 **59.** Answers will vary. **61.** Answers will vary.
**63.** The epicenter is $(-2, -2)$. **65.** Answers will vary. **67.** (9, 18)
**69.** Answers will vary.

## 8.2 Exercises (Pages 447–451)

**1.** $(0, 5), \left(\frac{5}{2}, 0\right), (1, 3), (2, 1)$ **3.** $(0, -4), (4, 0), (2, -2), (3, -1)$ **5.** $(0, 4), (5, 0), \left(3, \frac{8}{5}\right), \left(\frac{5}{2}, 2\right)$

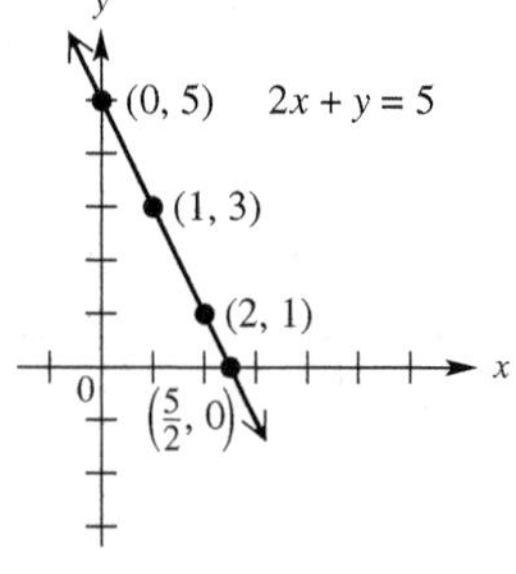


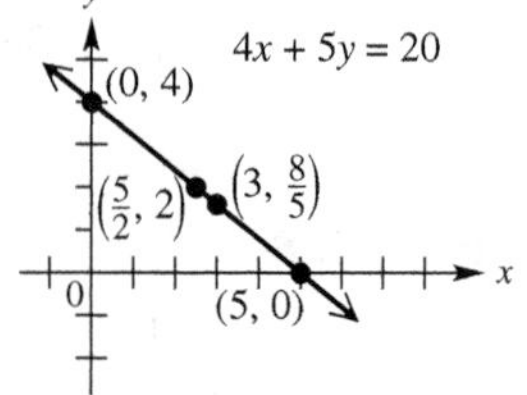

**7.** $(0, 4), \left(\frac{8}{3}, 0\right), (2, 1), (4, -2)$ **9.** Answers will vary. **11.** A **13.** $(4, 0)$; $(0, 6)$

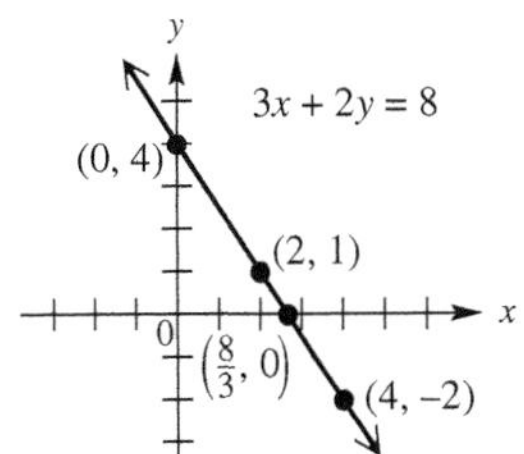


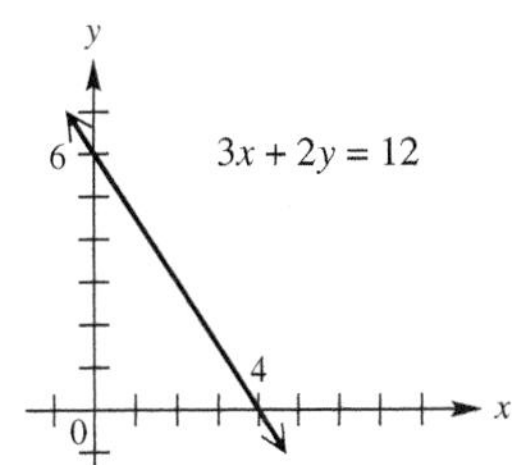


**15.** $(2, 0)$; $\left(0, \frac{5}{3}\right)$ **17.** $\left(\frac{5}{2}, 0\right)$; $(0, -5)$ **19.** $(2, 0)$; $\left(0, -\frac{2}{3}\right)$

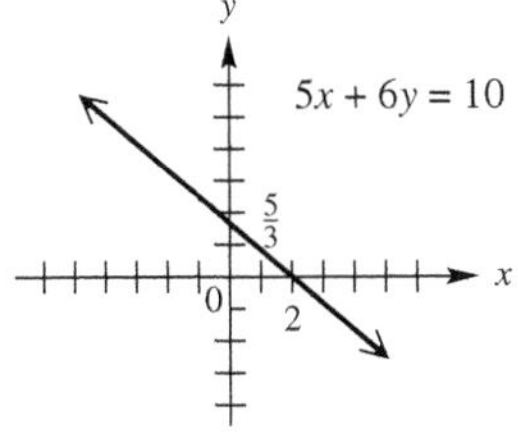


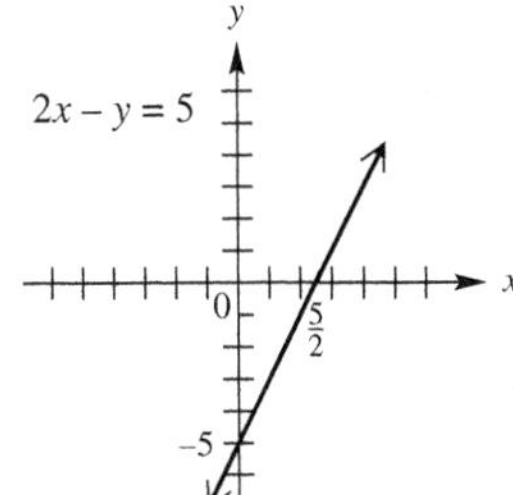


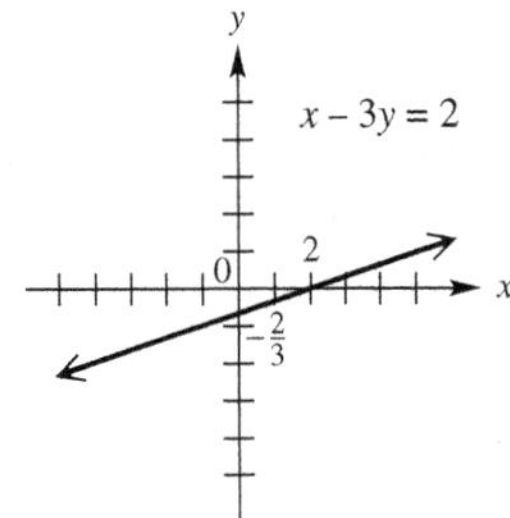


**21.** $(0, 0)$; $(0, 0)$ **23.** $(0, 0)$; $(0, 0)$ **25.** $(2, 0)$; none

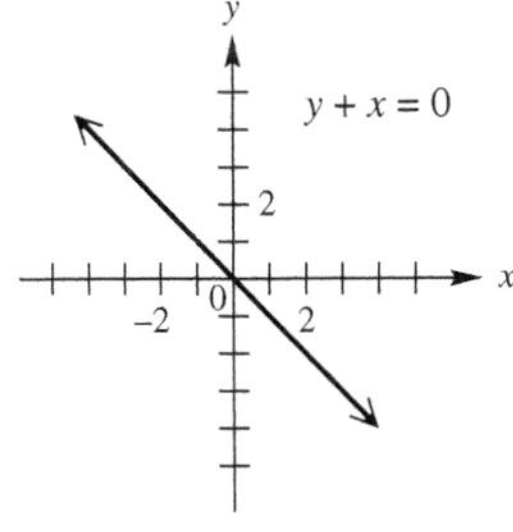


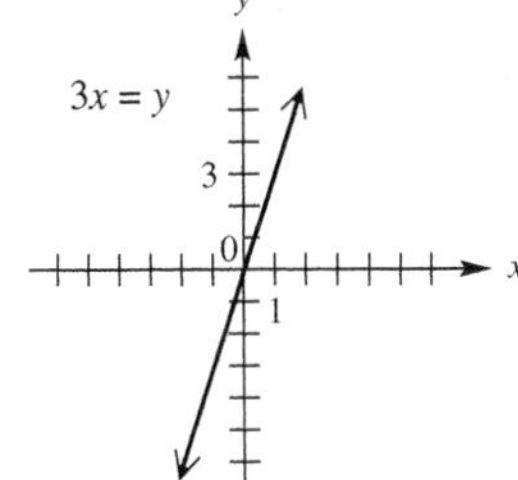


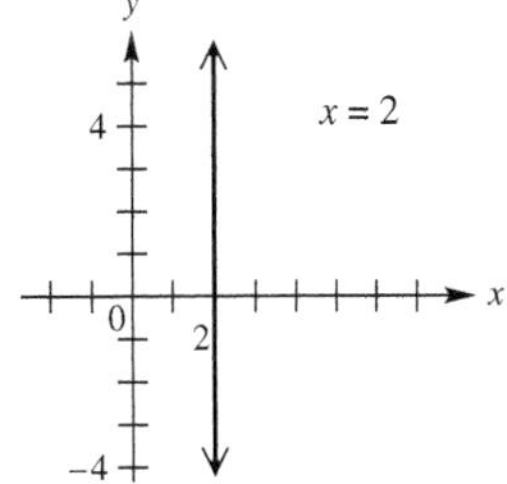


**27.** none; $(0, 4)$ **29.** C **31.** A **33.** D **35.** B **37.** $\frac{3}{10}$

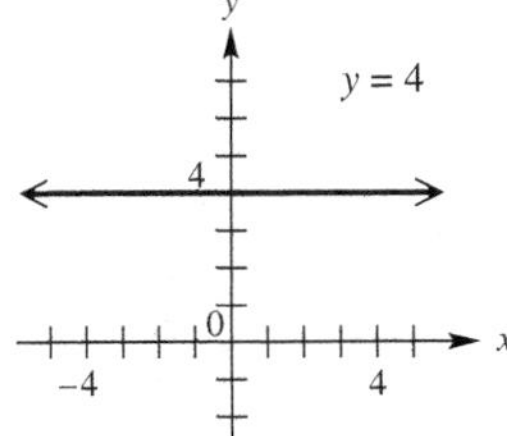


**39.** **(a)** $\frac{3}{2}$ **(b)** $-\frac{7}{4}$ **41.** 8 **43.** $-\frac{5}{6}$ **45.** 0 **47.** **(a)** slope = 232 (This represents enrollment in thousands.) **(b)** positive; increased **(c)** 232,000 students **(d)** $-1.66$ **(e)** negative; decreased **(f)** 1.66 students per computer

**49.**

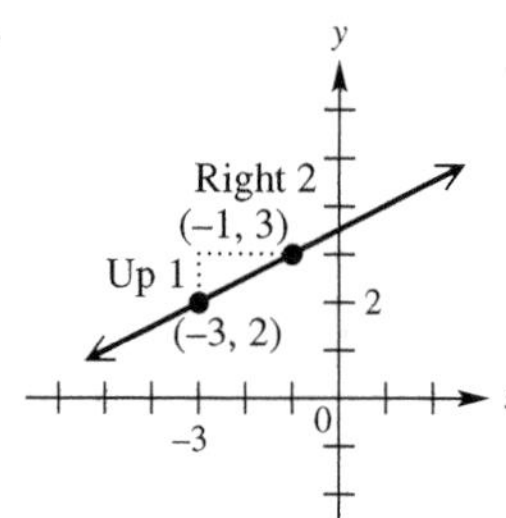


**51.**

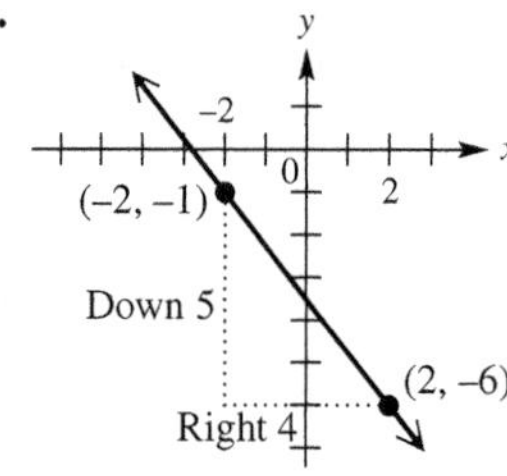


**53.**

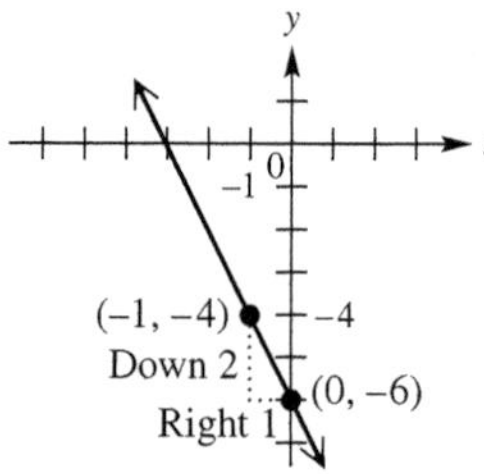


**55.**

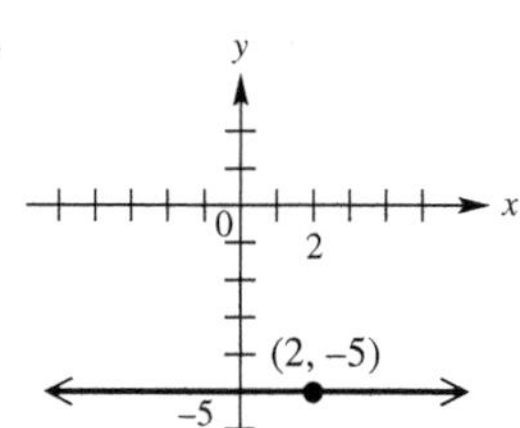


**57.** parallel **59.** perpendicular **61.** neither parallel nor perpendicular

**63.** $\frac{7}{10}$ **65.** **(a)** 3.8% per year **(b)** As the years increase, the number of electronic filings also increases. **67.** In each case, 1000 million per year; The average rate of change is the same. The data points lie on the same straight line. **69.** Answers will vary.

## 8.3 Exercises (Pages 456–460)

**1.** D **3.** B **5.** $y = 3x - 3$ **7.** $y = -x + 3$ **9.** A **11.** C **13.** H **15.** B **17.** $y = -\frac{3}{4}x + \frac{5}{2}$ **19.** $y = -2x + 18$ **21.** $y = \frac{1}{2}x + \frac{13}{2}$ **23.** $y = 4x - 12$ **25.** $y = 5$ **27.** $x = 9$ **29.** $x = .5$ **31.** $y = 8$ **33.** $y = 2x - 2$ **35.** $y = -\frac{1}{2}x + 4$ **37.** $y = \frac{2}{13}x + \frac{6}{13}$ **39.** $y = 5$ **41.** $x = 7$ **43.** $y = -3$ **45.** $y = 5x + 15$ **47.** $y = -\frac{2}{3}x + \frac{4}{5}$ **49.** $y = \frac{2}{5}x + 5$ **51.** Answers will vary. **53.** **(a)** $y = -x + 12$ **(b)** $-1$ **(c)** $(0, 12)$ **55.** **(a)** $y = -\frac{5}{2}x + 10$ **(b)** $-\frac{5}{2}$ **(c)** $(0, 10)$ **57.** **(a)** $y = \frac{2}{3}x - \frac{10}{3}$ **(b)** $\frac{2}{3}$ **(c)** $\left(0, -\frac{10}{3}\right)$ **59.** $y = 3x - 19$ **61.** $y = \frac{1}{2}x - 1$ **63.** $y = -\frac{1}{2}x + 9$ **65.** $y = 7$ **67.** **(a)** yes

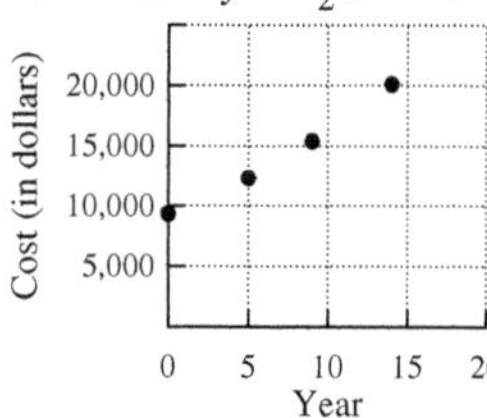


**(b)** $y = 763.6x + 9391$ **(c)** $23,136

**69.** **(a)** $y = -108.3x + 28,959$ **(b)** 27,335 **71.** **(a)** $y = 14.55x + 262.42$ **(b)** 2525 light-years **73.** **(a)** 32°; 212° **(b)** (0, 32); (100, 212) **(c)** $\frac{9}{5}$ **(d)** $F = \frac{9}{5}C + 32$ **(e)** $C = \frac{5}{9}(F - 32)$ **(f)** When Celsius temperature is 50°, Fahrenheit temperature is 122°.

## 8.4 Exercises (Pages 470–473)

**1.** Answers will vary. **3.** It is the independent variable. **5.** function; domain: {2, 3, 4, 5}; range: {5, 7, 9, 11} **7.** not a function; domain: $(0, \infty)$; range: $(-\infty, 0) \cup (0, \infty)$ **9.** function; domain: {Hispanic, Native American, Asian American, African American, White}; range in millions: {21.3, 1.6, 8.2, 24.6, 152.0} **11.** function; domain: $(-\infty, \infty)$; range: $(-\infty, 4]$ **13.** not a function; domain: $[-4, 4]$; range: $[-3, 3]$ **15.** function; domain: $(-\infty, \infty)$ **17.** not a function; domain: $[0, \infty)$ **19.** not a function; domain: $(-\infty, \infty)$ **21.** function; domain: $[0, \infty)$ **23.** function; domain: $(-\infty, 0) \cup (0, \infty)$ **25.** function; domain: $\left[-\frac{1}{2}, \infty\right)$ **27.** function; domain: $(-\infty, 9) \cup (9, \infty)$ **29.** **(a)** [0, 3000] **(b)** 25 hours; 25 hours **(c)** 2000 gallons **(d)** $g(0) = 0$; The pool is empty at time zero.

**31.** Here is one example: The cost of gasoline; number of gallons purchased; cost; number of gallons **33.** 5 **35.** 2
**37.** $-1$ **39.** $-13$

**41.**

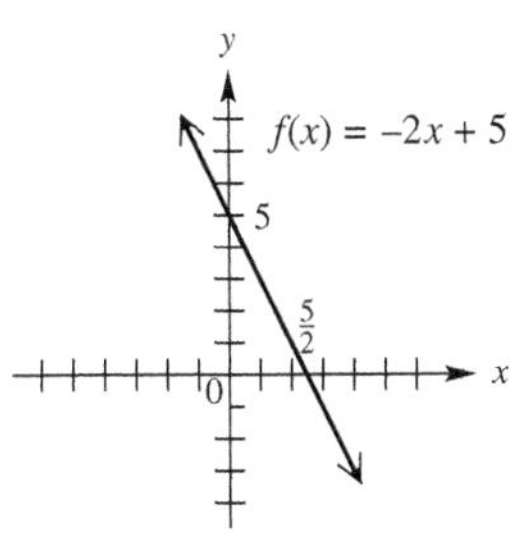


domain and range: $(-\infty, \infty)$

**43.**

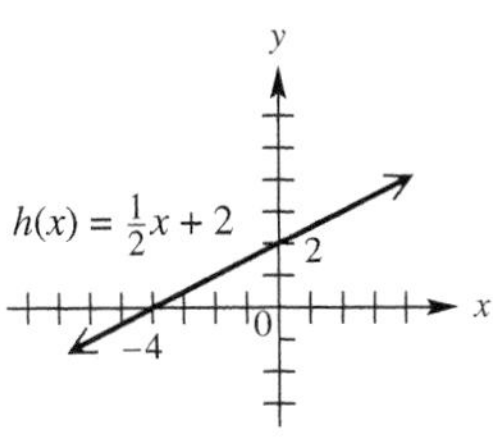


domain and range: $(-\infty, \infty)$

**45.**

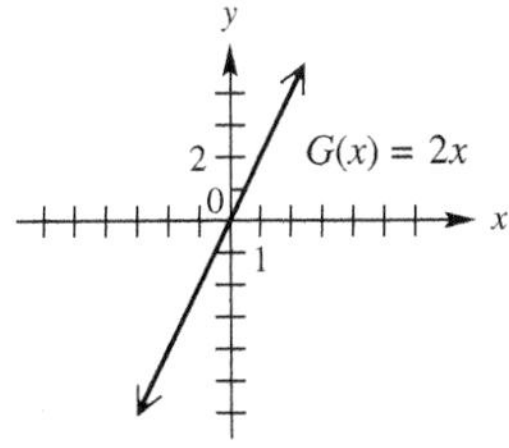


domain and range: $(-\infty, \infty)$

**47.**

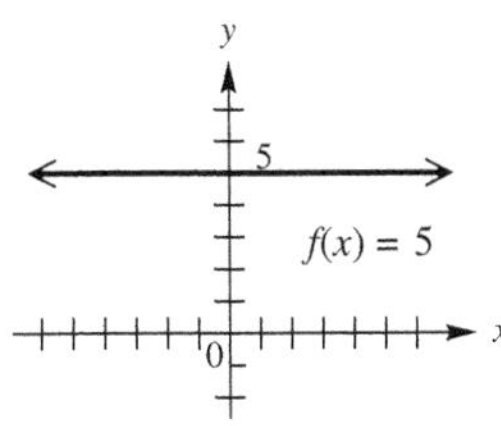


domain: $(-\infty, \infty)$; range: $\{5\}$

**49.** **(a)** $f(x) = 3 - 2x^2$ **(b)** $-15$ **51.** **(a)** $f(x) = \frac{8 - 4x}{-3}$ **(b)** $\frac{4}{3}$

**53.** line; $-2$; $-2x + 4$; $-2$; 3, $-2$ **55.** **(a)** \$0; \$1.50; \$3.00; \$4.50 **(b)** $1.50x$ **(c)**

**57.** **(a)** 194.53 centimeters **(b)** 177.29 centimeters **(c)** 177.41 centimeters **(d)** 163.65 centimeters **59.** **(a)** \$160 **(b)** 70 mph **(c)** 66 mph **(d)** for speeds more than 80 mph

**61.** **(a)** $C(x) = .02x + 200$
**(b)** $R(x) = .04x$
**(c)** 10,000
**(d)**

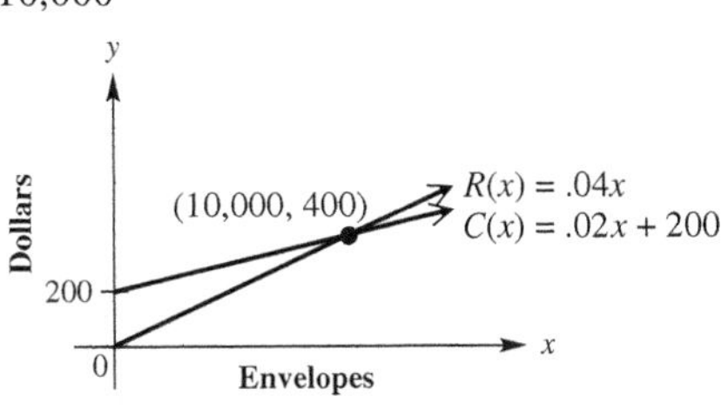


For $x < 10{,}000$, a loss
For $x > 10{,}000$, a profit

**63.** **(a)** $C(x) = 3.00x + 2300$
**(b)** $R(x) = 5.50x$
**(c)** 920
**(d)**

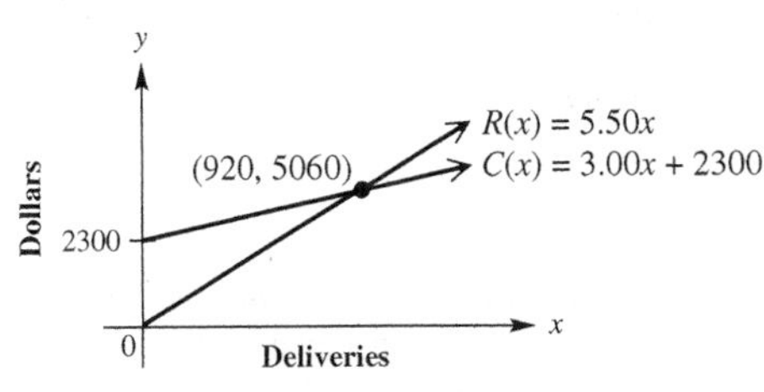


For $x < 920$, a loss
For $x > 920$, a profit

## 8.5 Exercises (Pages 481–484)

**1.** F **3.** C **5.** E **7.** Answers will vary **9.** (0, 0) **11.** (0, 4) **13.** (1, 0) **15.** $(-3, -4)$
**17.** Answers will vary **19.** downward; narrower **21.** upward; wider **23.** **(a)** I **(b)** IV **(c)** II **(d)** III

25.

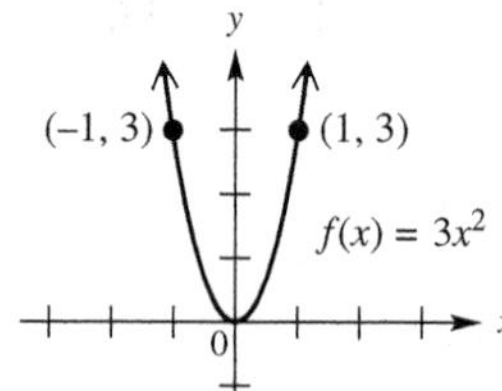


27.

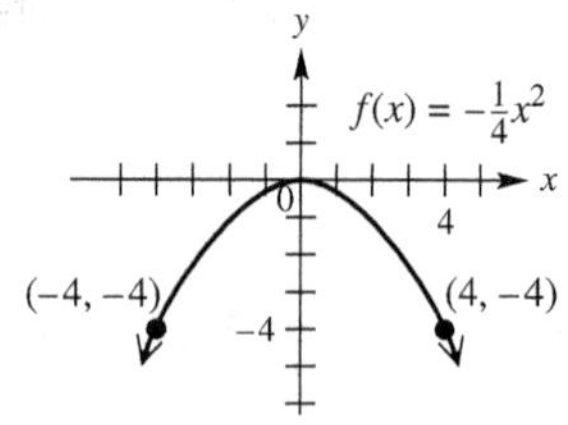


29.

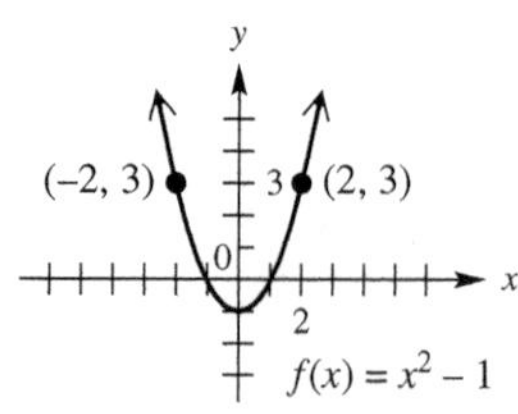


31.

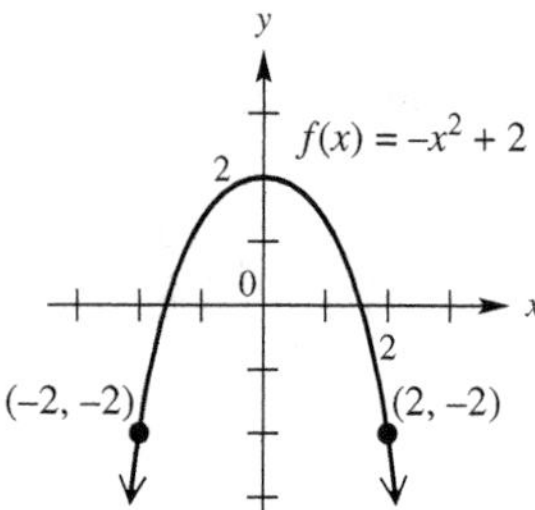


33.

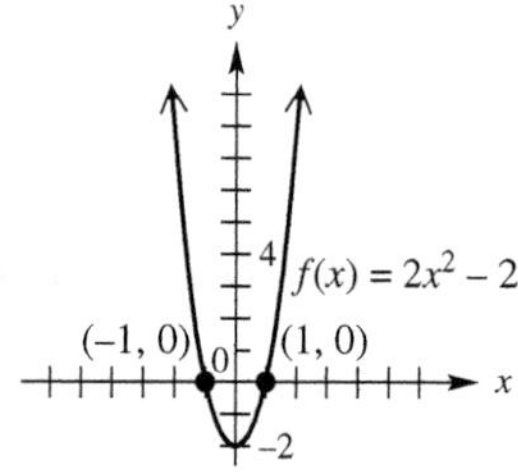


35.

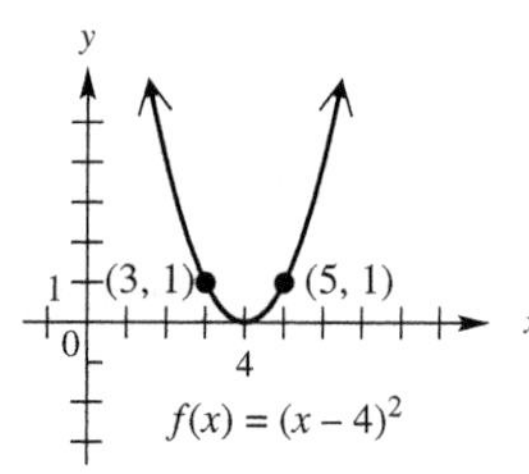


37.

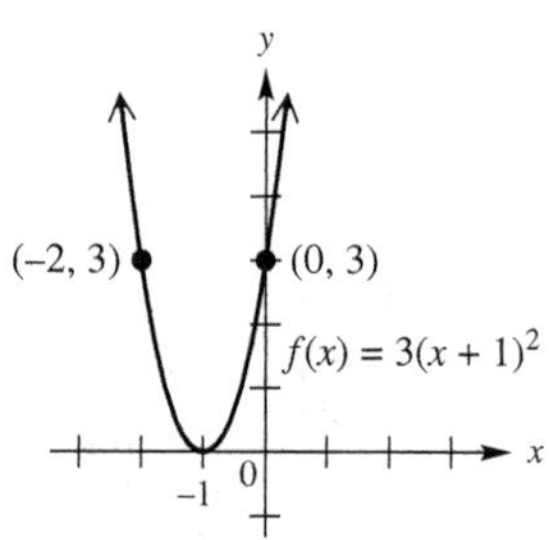


39.

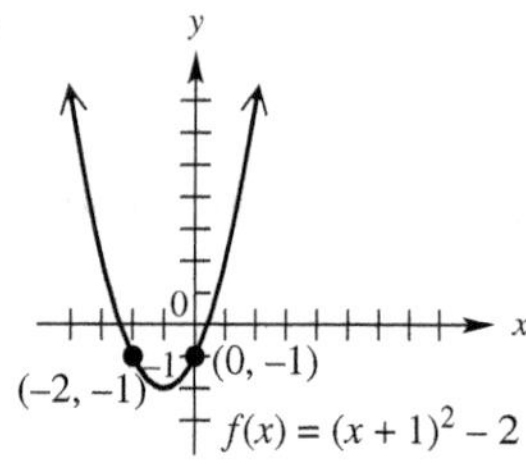


41.

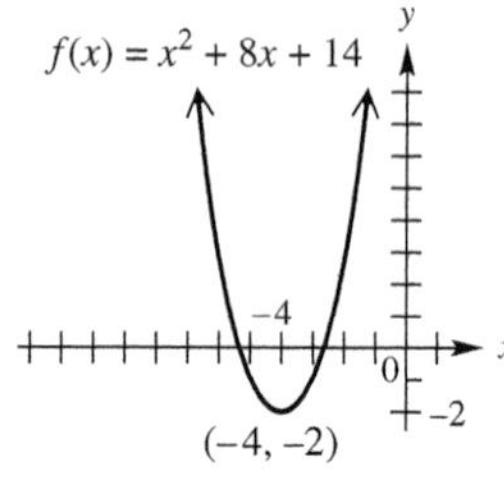


43.

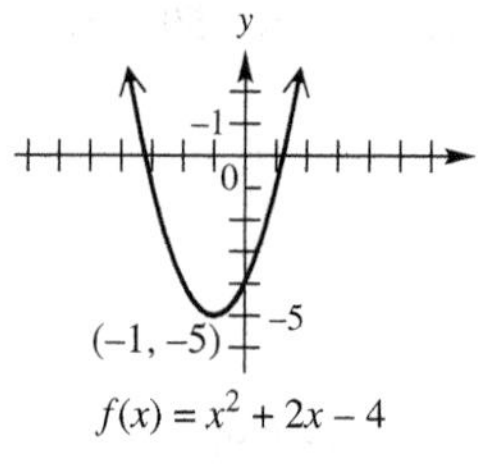


45.

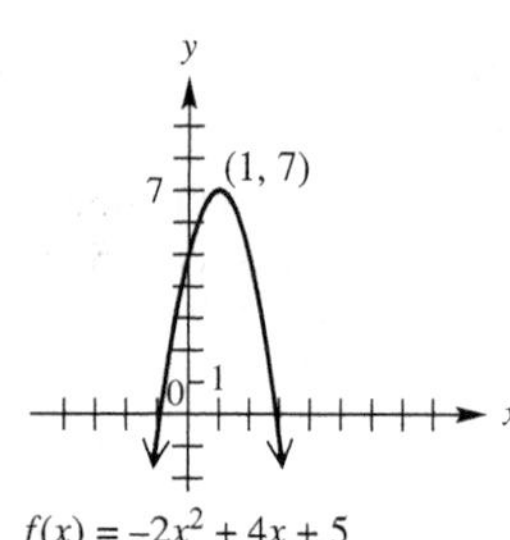


**47.** 25 meters **49.** 16 feet; 2 seconds

**51.** 4.1 seconds; 81.6 meters **53.** **(a)** 19.2 hours **(b)** 84.3 ppm **55.** $f(45) = 161.5$; This means that when the speed is 45 mph, the stopping distance is 161.5 feet.

**57.** **(a)** $R(x) = (100 - x)(200 + 4x) = 20{,}000 + 200x - 4x^2$ **(b)**

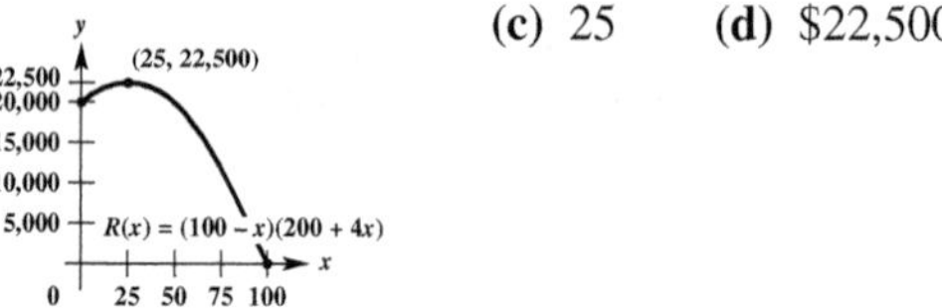


**(c)** 25 **(d)** $22,500

## 8.6 Exercises (Pages 492–494)

**1.** rises; falls **3.** does not **5.** rises; falls **7.** does not **9.** 2.56425419972 **11.** 1.25056505582 **13.** 7.41309466897 **15.** .0000210965628481

**17.**

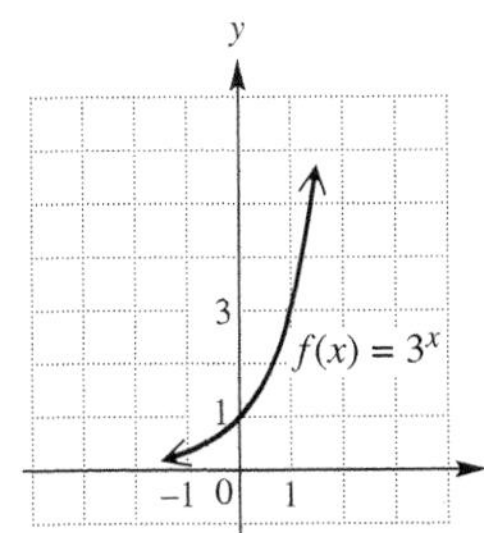


**19.**

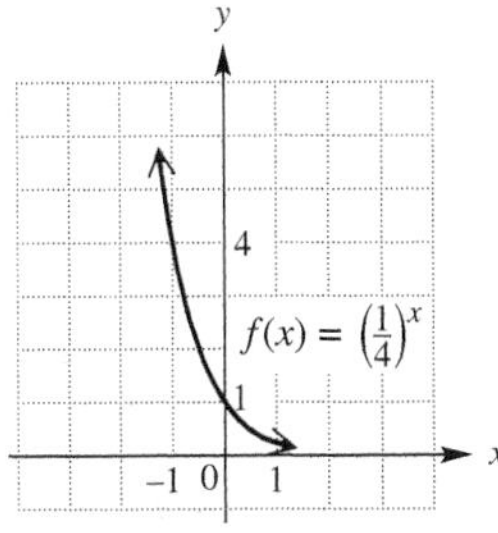


**21.** 20.0855369232 **23.** .018315638889 **25.** $2 = \log_4 16$ **27.** $-3 = \log_{2/3}\left(\frac{27}{8}\right)$ **29.** $2^5 = 32$ **31.** $3^1 = 3$ **33.** 1.38629436112 **35.** $-1.0498221245$ **37.** **(a)** .5°C **(b)** .35°C **39.** **(a)** 1.6°C **(b)** .5°C

**41.**

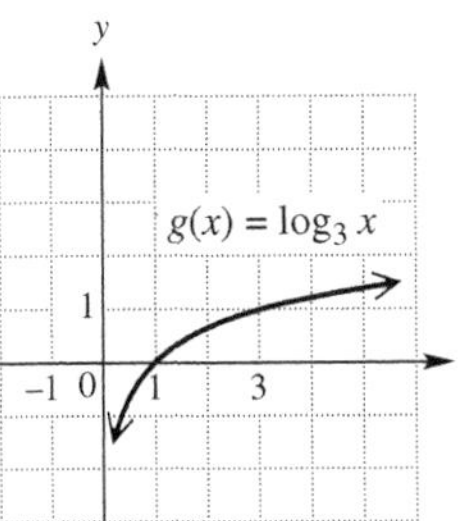


**43.**

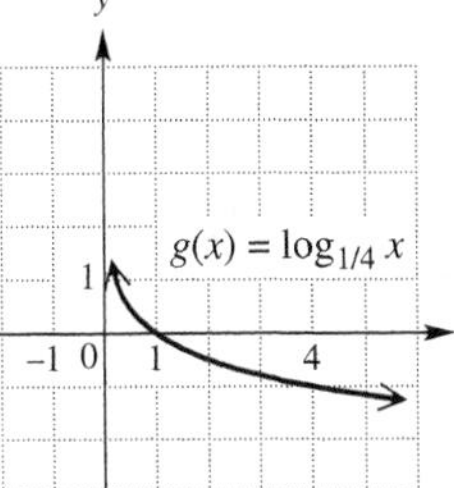


**45.** **(a)** \$22,510.18 **(b)** \$22,529.85

**47.** **(a)** \$33,504.35 **(b)** \$33,504.71 **49.** Plan A is better by \$102.65 **51.** **(a)** 828 millibars **(b)** 232 millibars **53.** **(a)** 146,250 **(b)** 198,403 **(c)** It will have increased by almost 36%. **55.** **(a)** 440 grams **(b)** 387 grams **(c)** 264 grams **(d)** 21.66 years **57.** 1611.97 years **59.** about 9000 years **61.** about 13,000 years **63.** almost 4 times as powerful

## 8.7 Exercises (Pages 508–514)

**1.** **(a)** 1991; about 350 million **(b)** (1987, 100 million) **(c)** 1988–1990 **(d)** CD production generally increased during these years; positive **(e)** The slope would be negative, because the line falls from left to right. **3.** yes **5.** no **7.** $\{(2, 2)\}$

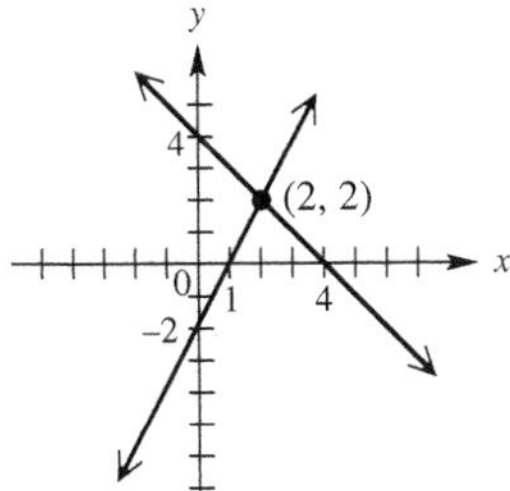


**9.** $\{(3, -1)\}$ **11.** $\{(2, -3)\}$ **13.** $\left\{\left(\frac{3}{2}, -\frac{3}{2}\right)\right\}$ **15.** $\left\{\left(\frac{6-2y}{7}, y\right)\right\}$

**17.** $\{(2, -4)\}$ **19.** $\emptyset$ **21.** $\{(1, 2)\}$ **23.** $\left\{\left(\frac{22}{9}, \frac{22}{3}\right)\right\}$ **25.** $\{(2, 3)\}$ **27.** $\{(5, 4)\}$ **29.** $\left\{\left(-5, -\frac{10}{3}\right)\right\}$ **31.** $\{(2, 6)\}$ **33.** Answers will vary. **35.** $\{(1, 4, -3)\}$ **37.** $\{(0, 2, -5)\}$ **39.** $\left\{\left(-\frac{7}{3}, \frac{22}{3}, 7\right)\right\}$ **41.** $\{(4, 5, 3)\}$ **43.** $\{(2, 2, 2)\}$ **45.** $\left\{\left(\frac{8}{3}, \frac{2}{3}, 3\right)\right\}$ **47.** wins: 100; losses: 62 **49.** length: 94 feet; width: 50 feet **51.** weekend days: 3; weekdays: 3 **53.** square: 12 centimeters; triangle: 8 centimeters **55.** cappuccino: \$1.95; house latte: \$2.35 **57.** NHL: \$247.32; NBA: \$267.37 **59.** Tokyo: \$430; New York: \$385 **61.** dark clay: \$5 per kilogram; light clay: \$4 per kilogram **63.** **(a)** 12 ounces **(b)** 30 ounces **(c)** 48 ounces **(d)** 60 ounces **65.** \$1.29$x$ **67.** 15% solution: $26\frac{2}{3}$ liters; 33% solution: $13\frac{1}{3}$ liters **69.** 3 liters **71.** 50% juice: 150 liters; 30% juice: 50 liters **73.** \$1.20 candy: 100 pounds; \$2.40 candy: 60 pounds **75.** at 4%: \$10,000; at 3%: \$5000 **77.** train: 60 kilometers per hour; plane: 160 kilometers per hour **79.** boat: 21 mph; current: 3 mph **81.** gold: 35; silver: 39; bronze: 29 **83.** shortest: 10 inches; middle: 20 inches; longest: 26 inches **85.** type A: 80; type B: 160; type C: 250 **87.** \$10 tickets: 350; \$18 tickets: 250; \$30 tickets: 50

**Extension Exercises (Page 518)**

**1.** $\{(2, 3)\}$ **3.** $\{(-3, 0)\}$ **5.** $\left\{\left(-\frac{7}{2}, -1\right)\right\}$ **7.** $\{(1, -4)\}$ **9.** $\{(-1, 23, 16)\}$ **11.** $\{(2, 1, -1)\}$ **13.** $\{(3, 2, -4)\}$ **15.** $\{(0, 1, 0)\}$ **17.** $\{(-1, 2, 0)\}$

**8.8 Exercises (Pages 524–526)**

**1.** C **3.** B **5.**

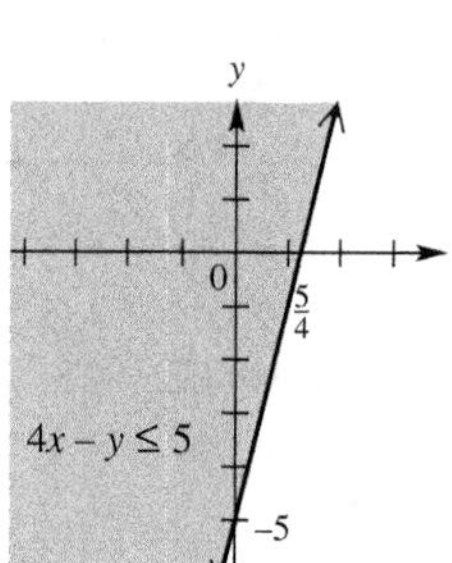


**7.**

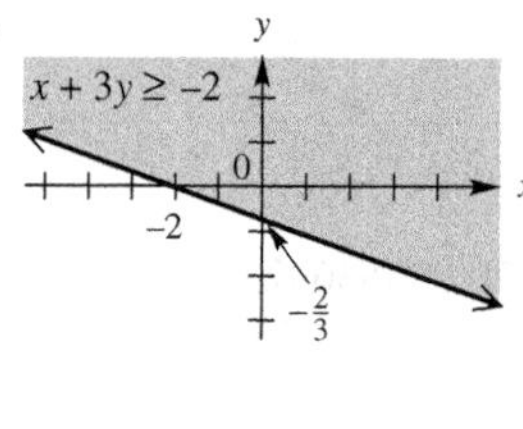


**9.**



**11.**

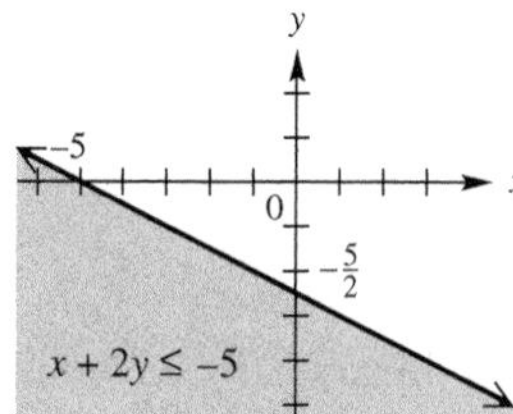


**13.**

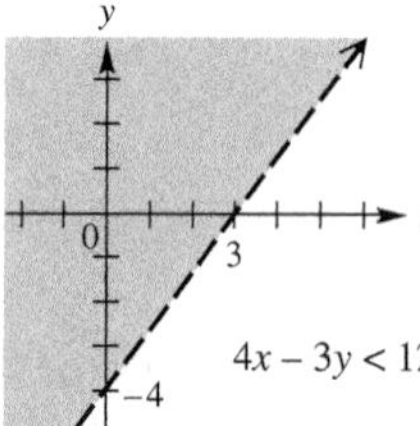


**15.**

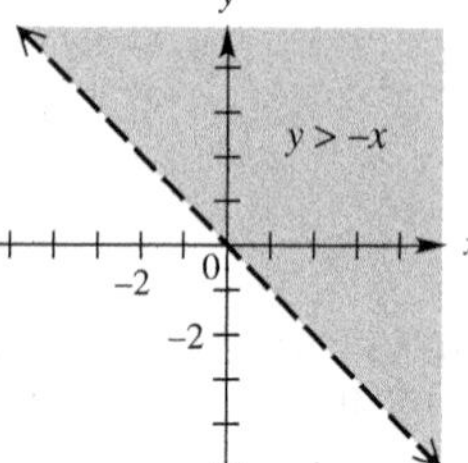


**17.**

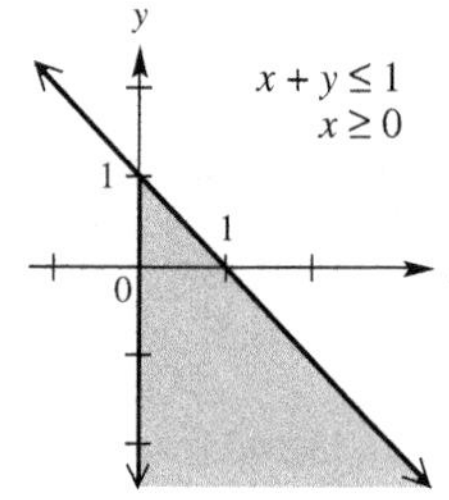


**19.**

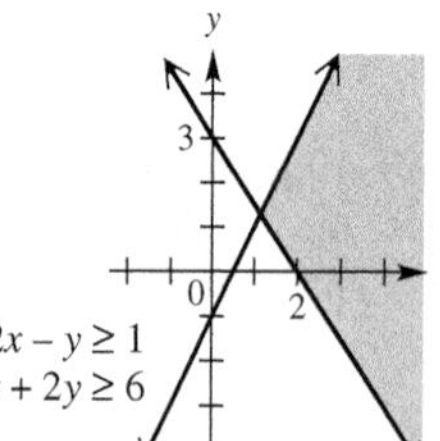


**21.**

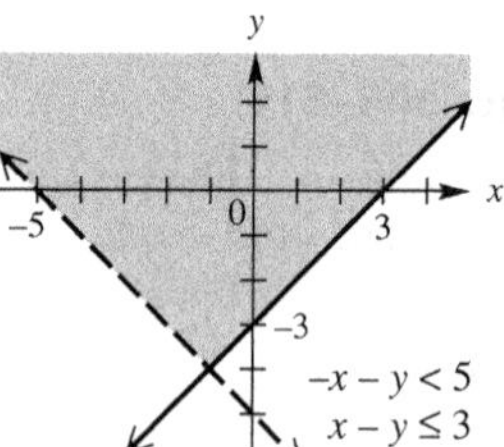


**23.** maximum of 65 at $(5, 10)$; minimum of 8 at $(1, 1)$ **25.** $\left(\frac{6}{5}, \frac{6}{5}\right); \frac{42}{5}$ **27.** $\left(\frac{17}{3}, 5\right); \frac{49}{3}$ **29.** Ship 20 to A and 80 to B, for a minimum cost of \$1040. **31.** Take 3 red pills and 2 blue pills, for a minimum cost of 70¢ per day. **33.** Produce 6.4 million gallons of gasoline and 3.2 million gallons of fuel oil, for a maximum revenue of \$16,960,000. **35.** Ship 4000 medical kits and 2000 containers of water.

**Chapter 8 Test (Pages 527–528)**

**1.** $\sqrt{41}$ **2.** $(x + 1)^2 + (y - 2)^2 = 9$

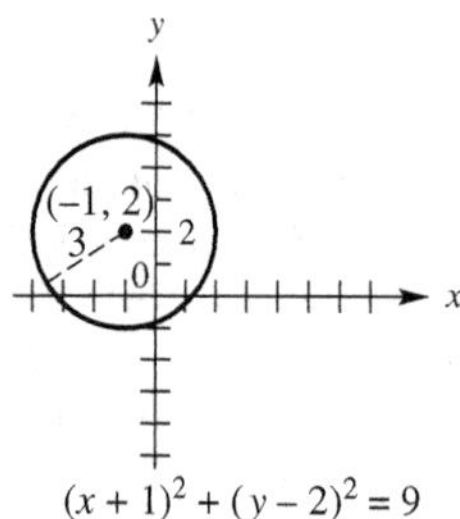


**3.** $x$-intercept: $\left(\frac{8}{3}, 0\right)$; $y$-intercept: $(0, -4)$

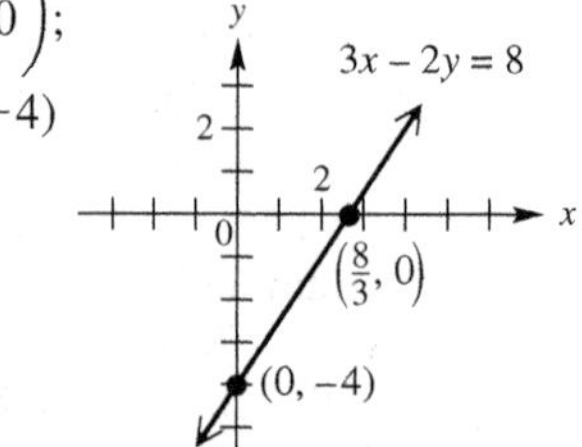


**4.** $\frac{2}{7}$ **5. (a)** $y = -\frac{2}{5}x + \frac{13}{5}$ **(b)** $y = -\frac{1}{2}x - \frac{3}{2}$ **(c)** $y = -\frac{1}{2}x + 2$ **6.** B **7. (a)** $y = 881x + 38{,}885$ **(b)** \$41,528; The model value is less than the actual income. **8.** $y = .05x + .50$; $(1, .55)$, $(5, .75)$, $(10, 1.00)$ **9.** $y = \frac{2}{3}x + 1$ **10. (a)** $(-\infty, \infty)$ **(b)** 22 **11.** $(-\infty, 3) \cup (3, \infty)$ **12.** 500 calculators; \$30,000

**13.** axis: $x = -3$; vertex: $(-3, 4)$; domain: $(-\infty, \infty)$; range: $(-\infty, 4]$

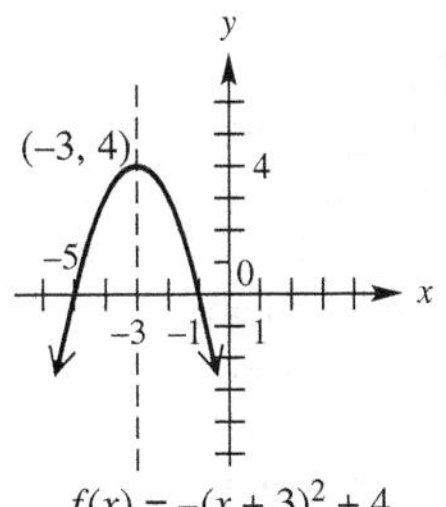


**14.** 80 feet by 160 feet

**15. (a)** 2116.31264888 **(b)** .157237166314 **(c)** 3.15955035878 **16.** A **17. (a)** \$13,521.90 **(b)** \$13,529.96 **18. (a)** 1.62 grams **(b)** 1.18 grams **(c)** .69 gram **(d)** 2.00 grams **19.** $\{(4, -2)\}$ **20.** $\{(2, 0, -1)\}$ **21.** $\{(1, 2z + 3, z)\}$ **22.** *Pretty Woman*: \$463.4 million; *Ocean's Eleven*: \$450.7 million **23.** \$40,000 at 10%; \$100,000 at 6%; \$140,000 at 5% **24.**

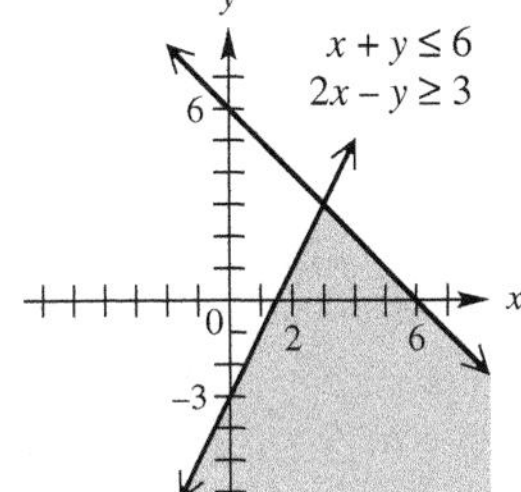


**25.** Manufacture 0 VIP rings and 24 SST rings, for a maximum profit of \$960.

## CHAPTER 9 GEOMETRY

### 9.1 Exercises (Pages 537–540)

**1.** 90 **3.** equal **5.** true **7.** false **9.** true **11.** true **13.** false
**15. (a)** $\overline{AB}$ **(b)** A———B **17. (a)** $\overleftrightarrow{CB}$ **(b)** ←A—B—C
**19. (a)** $\overrightarrow{BC}$ **(b)** B ○—C—D→ **21. (a)** $\overrightarrow{BA}$ **(b)** ←—A—B
**23. (a)** $\overline{CA}$ **(b)** A—B—C **25.** F **27.** D **29.** B **31.** E **There may be other correct forms of the answers in Exercises 33–39.** **33.** $\overline{MO}$ **35.** $\overline{MO}$ **37.** $\emptyset$ **39.** $\overrightarrow{OP}$ **41.** 62° **43.** 1° **45.** $(90 - x)°$ **47.** 48° **49.** 154° **51.** $(180 - y)°$ **53.** $\measuredangle CBD$ and $\measuredangle ABE$; $\measuredangle CBE$ and $\measuredangle DBA$ **55. (a)** 52° **(b)** 128° **57.** 107° and 73° **59.** 75° and 75° **61.** 139° and 139° **63.** 65° and 115° **65.** 35° and 55° **67.** 117° and 117° **69.** 141° and 141° **71.** 80° **73.** 52° **75.** Measures are given in numerical order, starting with angle 1: 55°, 65°, 60°, 65°, 60°, 120°, 60°, 60°, 55°, 55°. **77.** Answers will vary.

### 9.2 Exercises (Pages 545–548)

**1.** chord **3.** equilateral (or equiangular) **5.** false **7.** false **9.** true **11.** Answers will vary. **13.** both **15.** closed **17.** closed **19.** neither **21.** convex **23.** convex **25.** not convex **27.** right, scalene **29.** acute, equilateral **31.** right, scalene **33.** right, isosceles **35.** obtuse, scalene **37.** acute, isosceles **39.** Answers will vary. **41.** Answers will vary. **43.** $A = 50°$; $B = 70°$; $C = 60°$; **45.** $A = B = C = 60°$ **47.** $A = B = 52°$; $C = 76°$ **49.** 165° **51.** 170° **53. (a)** $O$ **(b)** $\overline{OA}$, $\overline{OC}$, $\overline{OB}$, $\overline{OD}$ **(c)** $\overline{AC}$, $\overline{BD}$ **(d)** $\overline{AC}$, $\overline{BD}$, $\overline{BC}$, $\overline{AB}$ **(e)** $\overleftrightarrow{BC}$, $\overleftrightarrow{AB}$ **(f)** $\overline{AE}$ **55. (e)** The sum of the measures of the angles of a triangle is 180° (because the pencil has gone through one-half of a complete rotation).

### Extension Exercises (Page 551)

**1.** With radius of the compasses greater than one-half the length $PQ$, place the point of the compasses at $P$ and swing arcs above and below line $r$. Then with the same radius and the point of the compasses at $Q$, swing two more arcs above and below line $r$. Locate the two points of intersections of the arcs above and below, and call them $A$ and $B$. With a straightedge, join $A$ and $B$. $AB$ is the perpendicular bisector of $PQ$. **3.** With the radius of the compasses

greater than the distance from $P$ to $r$, place the point of the compasses at $P$ and swing an arc intersecting line $r$ in two points. Call these points $A$ and $B$. Swing arcs of equal radius to the left of line $r$, with the point of the compasses at $A$ and at $B$, intersecting at points $Q$. With a straightedge, join $P$ and $Q$. $PQ$ is the perpendicular from $P$ to line $r$.
**5.** With any radius, place the point of the compasses at $P$ and swing arcs to the left and right, intersecting line $r$ in two points. Call these points $A$ and $B$. With an arc of sufficient length, place the point of the compasses first at $A$ and then at $B$, and swing arcs either both above or both below line $r$, intersecting at point $Q$. With a straightedge, join $P$ and $Q$. $PQ$ is perpendicular to line $r$ at $P$. **7.** With any radius, place the point of the compasses at $A$ and swing an arc intersecting the sides of angle $A$ at two points. Call the point of intersection on the horizontal side $B$ and call the other point of intersection $C$. Draw a horizontal working line, and locate any point $A'$ on this line. With the same radius used earlier, place the point of the compasses at $A'$ and swing an arc intersecting the working line at $B'$. Return to angle $A$, and set the radius of the compasses equal to $BC$. On the working line, place the point of the compasses at $B'$ and swing an arc intersecting the first arc at $C'$. Now draw line $A'C'$. Angle $A'$ is equal to angle $A$. **9.** Use Construction 3 to construct a perpendicular to a line at a point. Then use Construction 4 to bisect one of the right angles formed. This yields a 45° angle. **11.** Answers will vary.

## 9.3 Exercises (Pages 559–565)

**1.** 12 **3.** 6 **5.** circumference **7.** 12 $cm^2$ **9.** 5 $cm^2$ **11.** 8 $in.^2$ **13.** 4.5 $cm^2$ **15.** 418 $mm^2$ **17.** 8 $cm^2$ **19.** 3.14 $cm^2$ **21.** 1017.36 $m^2$ **23.** 4 m **25.** 300 ft, 400 ft, 500 ft **27.** 46 ft **29.** 23,800.10 $ft^2$ **31.** perimeter **33.** 12 in., $12\pi$ in., $36\pi$ $in.^2$ **35.** 5 ft, $10\pi$ ft, $25\pi$ $ft^2$ **37.** 6 cm, 12 cm, $36\pi$ $cm^2$ **39.** 10 in., 20 in., $20\pi$ in. **41.** 14.5 **43.** 7 **45.** 5.1 **47.** 5 **49.** 5 **51.** 1.5 **53.** **(a)** 20 $cm^2$ **(b)** 80 $cm^2$ **(c)** 180 $cm^2$ **(d)** 320 $cm^2$ **(e)** 4 **(f)** 3; 9 **(g)** 4; 16 **(h)** $n^2$ **55.** \$800 **57.** $n^2$ **59.** 80 **61.** 76.26 **63.** 132 $ft^2$ **65.** 5376 $cm^2$ **67.** 145.34 $m^2$ **69.** 14-in. pizza **71.** 14-in. pizza **73.** 26 in. **75.** 625 $ft^2$ **77.** 648 $in.^2$ **79.** $\frac{(4-\pi)r^2}{4}$

## 9.4 Exercises (Pages 572–578)

**1.**

| STATEMENTS | REASONS |
|---|---|
| 1. $AC = BD$ | 1. Given |
| 2. $AD = BC$ | 2. Given |
| 3. $AB = AB$ | 3. Reflexive property |
| 4. $\triangle ABD \cong \triangle BAC$ | 4. SSS congruence property |

**3.**

| STATEMENTS | REASONS |
|---|---|
| 1. $\overleftrightarrow{DB}$ is perpendicular to $\overleftrightarrow{AC}$. | 1. Given |
| 2. $AB = BC$ | 2. Given |
| 3. $\measuredangle ABD = \measuredangle CBD$ | 3. Both are right angles by definition of perpendicularity. |
| 4. $DB = DB$ | 4. Reflexive property |
| 5. $\triangle ABD \cong \triangle CBD$ | 5. SAS congruence property |

**5.**

| STATEMENTS | REASONS |
|---|---|
| 1. $\measuredangle BAC = \measuredangle DAC$ | 1. Given |
| 2. $\measuredangle BCA = \measuredangle DCA$ | 2. Given |
| 3. $AC = AC$ | 3. Reflexive property |
| 4. $\triangle ABD \cong \triangle ADC$ | 4. ASA congruence property |

**7.** 67°, 67° **9.** 6 in. **11.** Answers will vary. **13.** $\measuredangle A$ and $\measuredangle P$; $\measuredangle C$ and $\measuredangle R$; $\measuredangle B$ and $\measuredangle Q$; $\overleftrightarrow{AC}$ and $\overleftrightarrow{PR}$; $\overleftrightarrow{CB}$ and $\overleftrightarrow{RQ}$; $\overleftrightarrow{AB}$ and $\overleftrightarrow{PQ}$; **15.** $\measuredangle H$ and $\measuredangle F$; $\measuredangle K$ and $\measuredangle E$; $\measuredangle HGK$ and $\measuredangle FGE$; $\overleftrightarrow{HK}$ and $\overleftrightarrow{FE}$; $\overleftrightarrow{GK}$ and $\overleftrightarrow{GE}$; $\overleftrightarrow{HG}$ and $\overleftrightarrow{FG}$; **17.** $\measuredangle P = 78°$; $\measuredangle M = 46°$; $\measuredangle A = \measuredangle N = 56°$ **19.** $\measuredangle T = 74°$; $\measuredangle Y = 28°$; $\measuredangle Z = \measuredangle W = 78°$ **21.** $\measuredangle T = 20°$; $\measuredangle V = 64°$; $\measuredangle R = \measuredangle U = 96°$ **23.** $a = 20$; $b = 15$ **25.** $a = 6$; $b = \frac{15}{2}$ **27.** $x = 6$

**29.** $x = 110$ **31.** $c = 111\frac{1}{9}$ **33.** 30 m **35.** 500 m, 700 m **37.** 112.5 ft **39.** 8 ft, 11 in. **41.** $c = 17$ **43.** $a = 13$ **45.** $c = 50$ m **47.** $a = 20$ in. **49.** The sum of the squares of the two shorter sides of a right triangle is equal to the square of the longest side. **51.** (3, 4, 5) **53.** (7, 24, 25) **55.** (12, 16, 20) **57.** Answers will vary. **59.** (3, 4, 5) **61.** (7, 24, 25) **63.** Answers will vary. **65.** (4, 3, 5) **67.** (8, 15, 17) **69.** Answers will vary. **71.** 24 m **73.** 16 ft **75.** 4.55 ft **77.** 19 ft, 3 in. **79.** 28 ft, 10 in. **81. (a)** $\frac{1}{2}(a + b)(a + b)$ **(b)** $PWX$: $\frac{1}{2}ab$; $PZY$: $\frac{1}{2}ab$; $PXY$: $\frac{1}{2}c^2$ **(c)** $\frac{1}{2}(a + b)(a + b) = \frac{1}{2}ab + \frac{1}{2}ab + \frac{1}{2}c^2$. When simplified, this gives $a^2 + b^2 = c^2$. **83.** $24 + 4\sqrt{6}$ **85.** 10 **87.** $256 + 64\sqrt{3}$ **89.** 5 in. **91.** Answers will vary. **93.** Answers will vary.

## 9.5 Exercises (Pages 584–587)

**1.** true **3.** true **5.** false **7. (a)** $3\frac{3}{4}$ m$^3$ **(b)** $14\frac{3}{4}$ m$^2$ **9. (a)** 96 in.$^3$ **(b)** 130.4 in.$^2$ **11. (a)** 267,946.67 ft$^3$ **(b)** 20,096 ft$^2$ **13. (a)** 549.5 cm$^3$ **(b)** 376.8 cm$^2$ **15. (a)** 65.94 m$^3$ **(b)** 100.00 m$^2$ **17.** 168 in.$^3$ **19.** 1969.10 cm$^3$ **21.** 427.29 cm$^3$ **23.** 508.68 cm$^3$ **25.** 2,415,766.67 m$^3$ **27.** .52 m$^3$ **29.** 12 in., $288\pi$ in.$^3$, $144\pi$ in.$^2$ **31.** 5 ft, $\frac{500}{3}\pi$ ft$^3$, $100\pi$ ft$^2$ **33.** 2 cm, 4 cm, $16\pi$ cm$^2$ **35.** 1 m, 2 m, $\frac{4}{3}\pi$ m$^3$ **37.** volume **39.** $\sqrt[3]{2}\,x$ **41.** \$8100 **43.** \$37,500 **45.** 2.5 **47.** 6 **49.** 210 in.$^3$ **51.** $\frac{62{,}500}{3}\pi$ in.$^3$ **53.** 2 to 1 **55.** 288 **57.** 4, 4, 6, 2 **59.** 8, 6, 12, 2 **61.** 20, 12, 30, 2

## 9.6 Exercises (Pages 596–598)

The answers are given in blue for this section.

**1.**

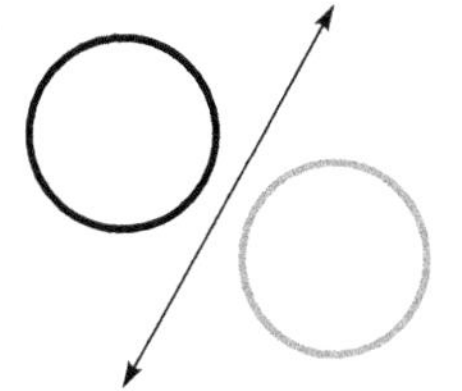

**3.**

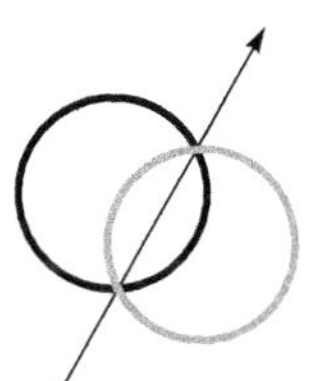

**5.**

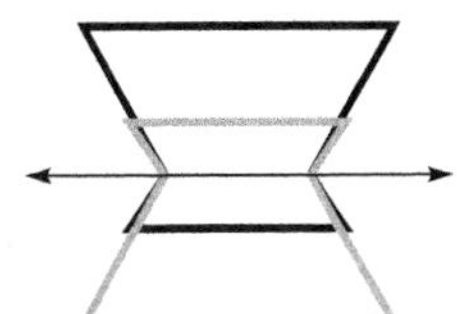

**7.** The figure is its own reflection image.

**9.**

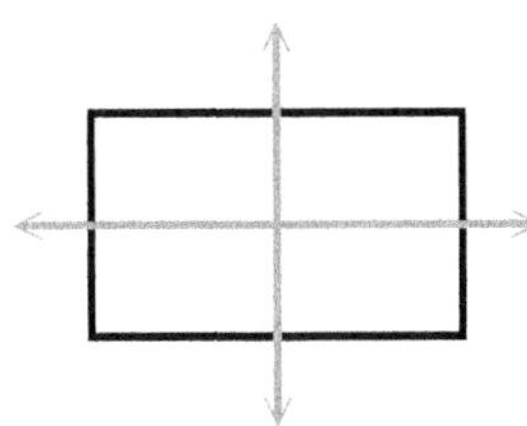

**11.**

**13.**

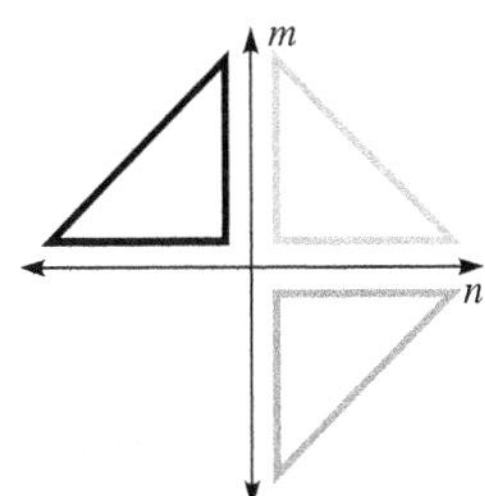


**15.**

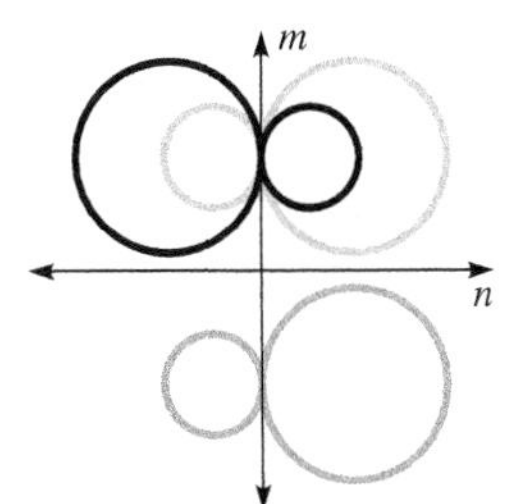


**17.**

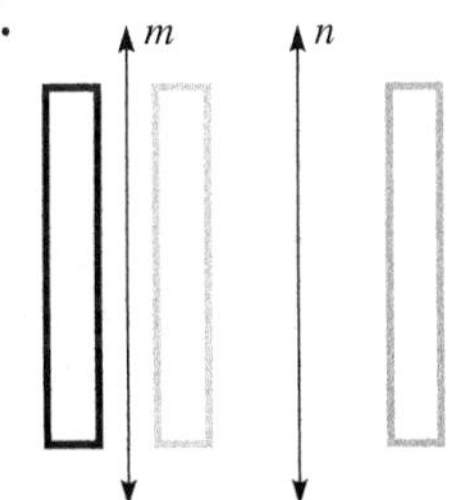


**19.**

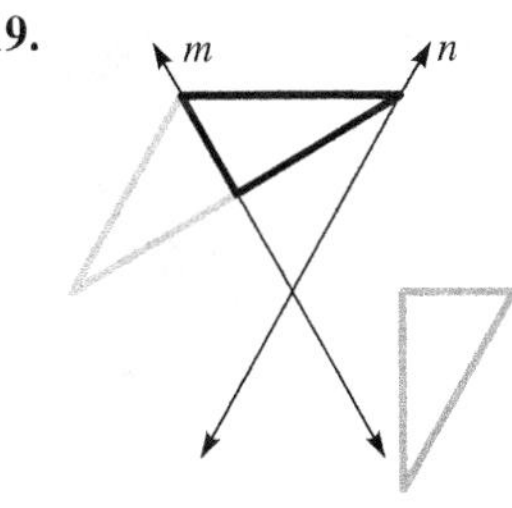

**21.**

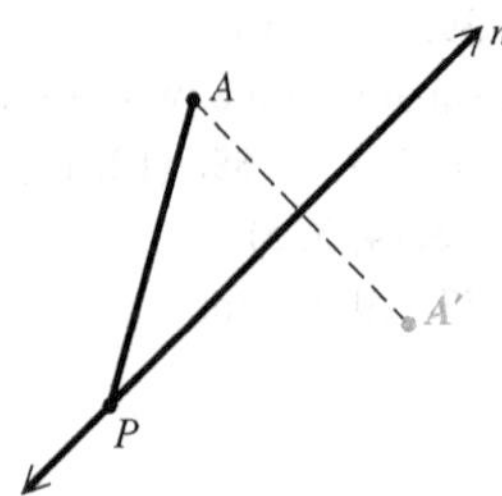


**23.**

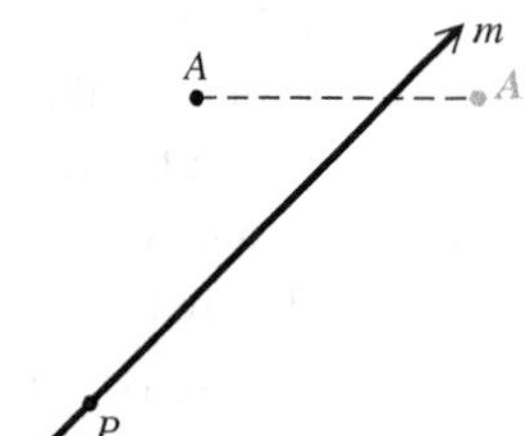


**25.**

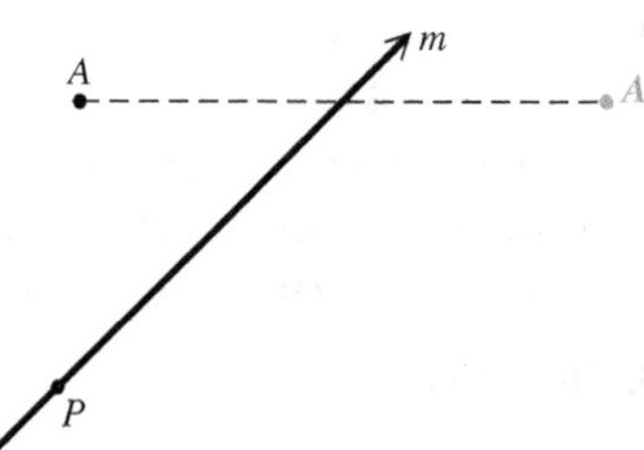


**27.**

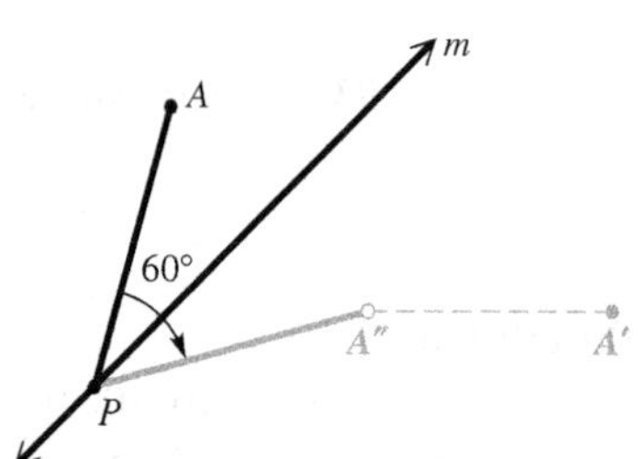


**29.**

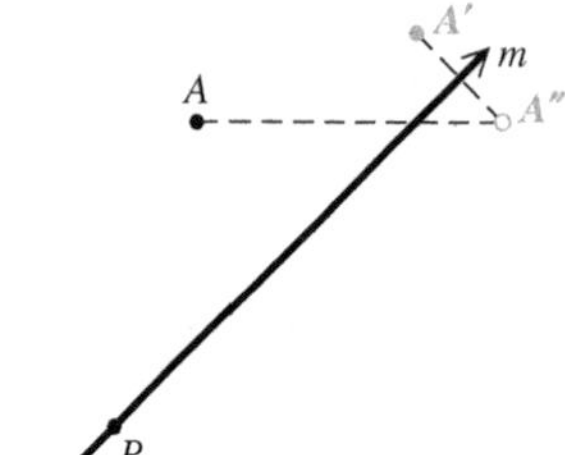


**31.**

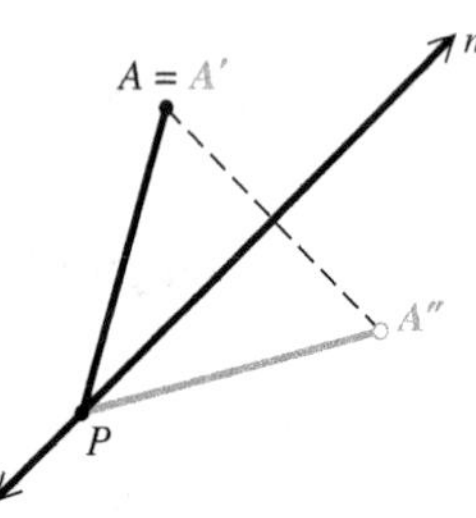


**33.** no **35.**

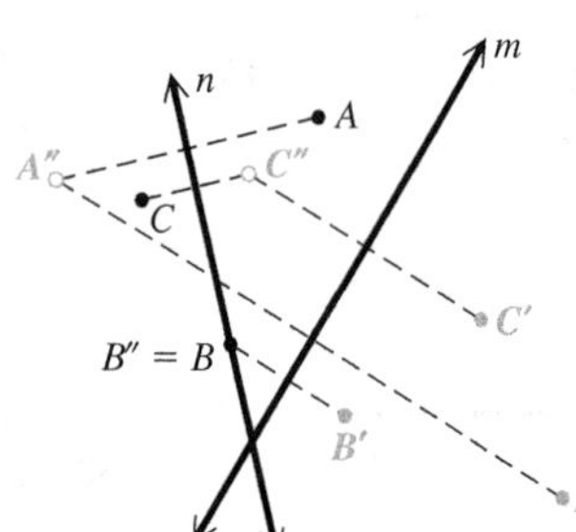


**37.**

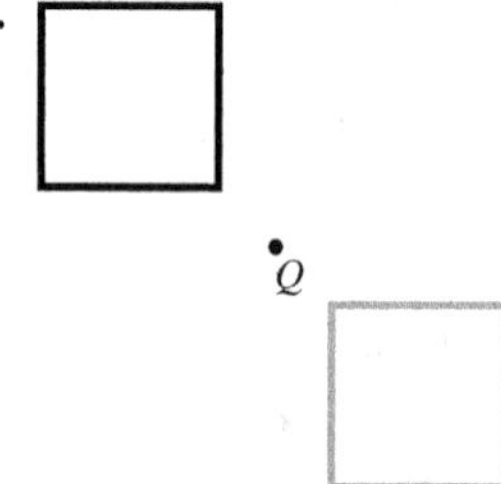


**39.**

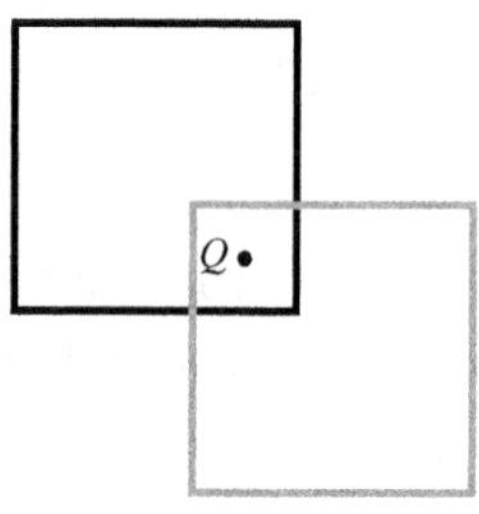


**41.**

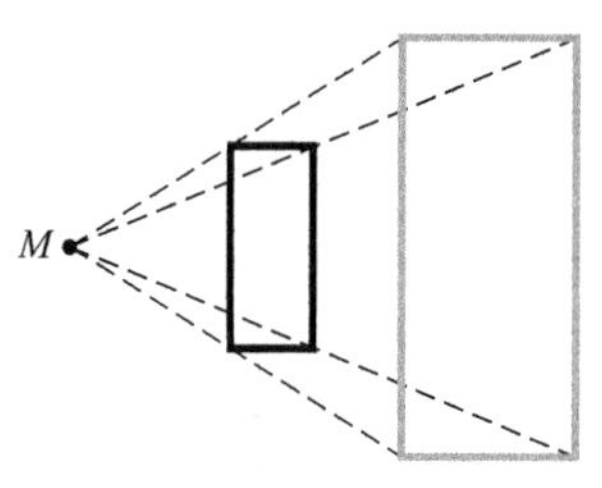


**43.**

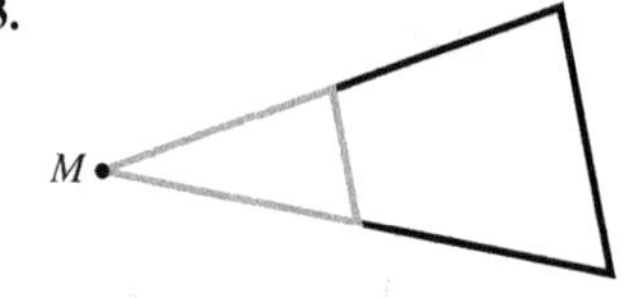


**45.**

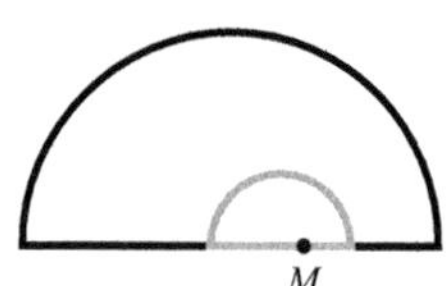


9.7 Exercises **(Pages 606–609)**

**1.** Euclidean **3.** Lobachevskian **5.** greater than **7.** Riemannian **9.** Euclidean

**11.** (a)–(g)

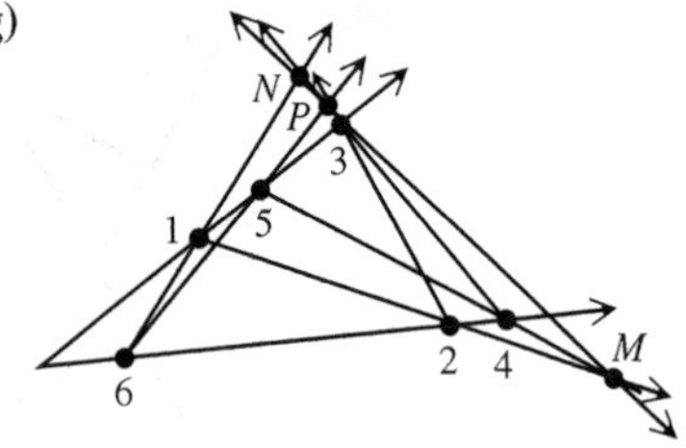


(h) Suppose that a hexagon is inscribed in an angle. Let each pair of opposite sides be extended so as to intersect. Then the three points of intersection thus obtained will lie in a straight line.

**13.** C **15.** A, E **17.** A, E **19.** none of them **21.** no **23.** yes **25.** 1 **27.** 3 **29.** 1 **31.** *A*, *C*, *D*, and *F* are even; *B* and *E* are odd. **33.** *A*, *B*, *C*, and *F* are odd; *D*, *E*, and *G* are even. **35.** *A*, *B*, *C*, and *D* are odd; *E* is even

**37.** traversable

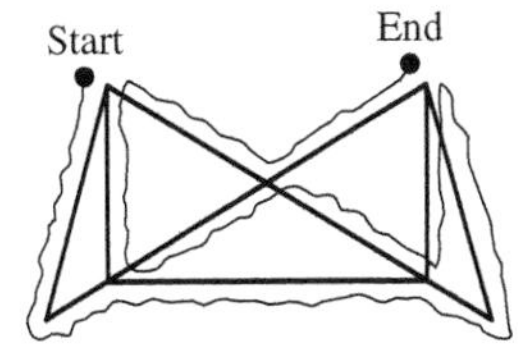


**39.** not traversable **41.** traversable

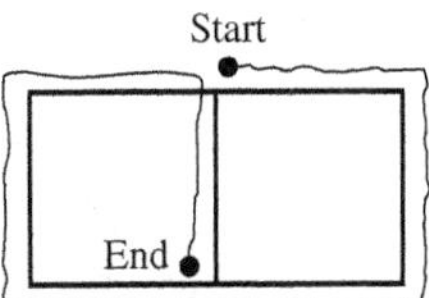


**43.** yes

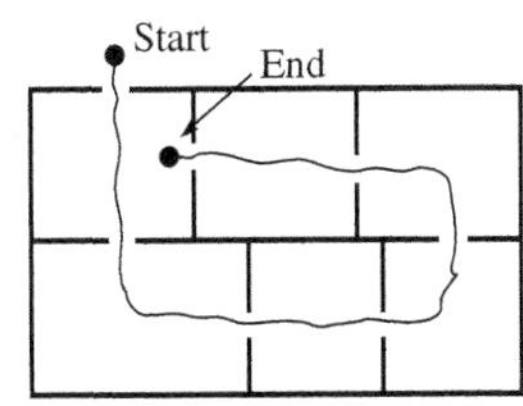


**45.** no

### 9.8 Exercises (Pages 613–615)

**1.** 4 **2.** 4 **3.** 2 **4.** $\frac{2}{1} = 2$ **5.** $\frac{4}{1} = 4$ **6.** $\frac{3}{1} = 3; \frac{9}{1} = 9$ **7.** $\frac{4}{1} = 4; \frac{16}{1} = 16$ **8.** 4, 9, 16, 25, 36, 100 **9.** Each ratio in the bottom row is the square of the scale factor in the top row. **10.** 4 **11.** 4, 9, 16, 25, 36, 100 **12.** Each ratio in the bottom row is again the square of the scale factor in the top row. **13.** Answers will vary. Some examples are: $3^d = 9$, thus $d = 2$; $5^d = 25$, thus $d = 2$; $4^d = 16$, thus $d = 2$. **14.** 8 **15.** $\frac{2}{1} = 2; \frac{8}{1} = 8$ **16.** 8, 27, 64, 125, 216, 1000 **17.** Each ratio in the bottom row is the cube of the scale factor in the top row. **18.** Since $2^3 = 8$, the value of $d$ in $2^d = 8$ must be 3 **19.** $\frac{3}{1} = 3.$ **20.** 4 **21.** 1.262 or $\frac{\ln 4}{\ln 3}$ **22.** $\frac{2}{1} = 2$ **23.** 3 **24.** It is between 1 and 2. **25.** 1.585 or $\frac{\ln 3}{\ln 2}$ **27.** .842, .452, .842, .452, . . . . The two attractors are .842 and .452.

### Chapter 9 Test (Pages 617–619)

**1.** **(a)** 52° **(b)** 142° **(c)** acute **2.** 40°, 140° **3.** 45°, 45° **4.** 30°, 60° **5.** 130°, 50° **6.** 117°, 117° **7.** Answers will vary. **8.** C **9.** both **10.** neither **11.** 30°, 45°, 105° **12.** 72 cm$^2$ **13.** 60 in.$^2$ **14.** 68 m$^2$ **15.** 180 m$^2$ **16.** 24 $\pi$ in. **17.** 1978 ft **18.** 57 cm$^2$

**19.**

| STATEMENTS | REASONS |
|---|---|
| **1.** $\angle CAB = \angle DBA$ | **1.** Given |
| **2.** $DB = CA$ | **2.** Given |
| **3.** $AB = AB$ | **3.** Reflexive property |
| **4.** $\triangle ABD \cong \triangle BAC$ | **4.** SAS congruence property |

**20.** 20 ft **21.** 29 m **22.**

**23.**

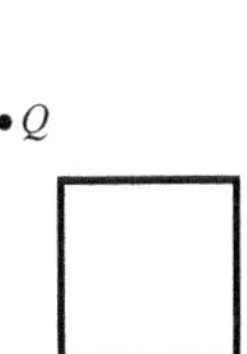


**24.** **(a)** 904.32 in.$^3$ **(b)** 452.16 in.$^2$ **25.** **(a)** 864 ft$^2$ **(b)** 552 ft$^2$ **26.** **(a)** 1582.56 m$^3$ **(b)** 753.60 m$^2$ **27.** Answers will vary. **28.** **(a)** yes **(b)** no

**29.** **(a)** yes

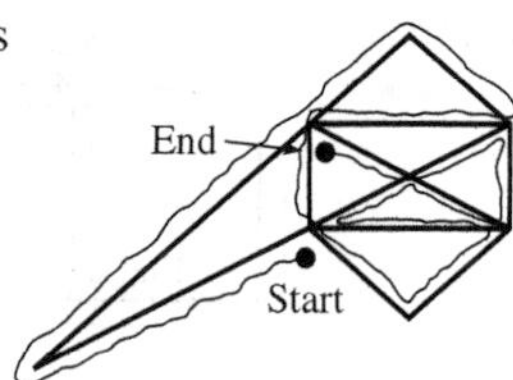


**(b)** no **30.** The only attractor is .5238095238.

## CHAPTER 10 Trigonometry

### 10.1 Exercises (Pages 626–627)

**1.** **(a)** 60° **(b)** 150° **3.** **(a)** 45° **(b)** 135° **5.** **(a)** 1° **(b)** 91° **7.** $(90 - x)$ degrees **9.** 83°59′ **11.** 119°27′ **13.** 38°32′ **15.** 17°1′49″ **17.** 20.900° **19.** 91.598° **21.** 274.316° **23.** 31°25′47″ **25.** 89°54′1″ **27.** 178°35′58″ **29.** 320° **31.** 235° **33.** 179° **35.** 130° **37.** $30° + n \cdot 360°$ **39.** $60° + n \cdot 360°$

**Angles other than those given are possible in Exercises 41–47.**

**41.**

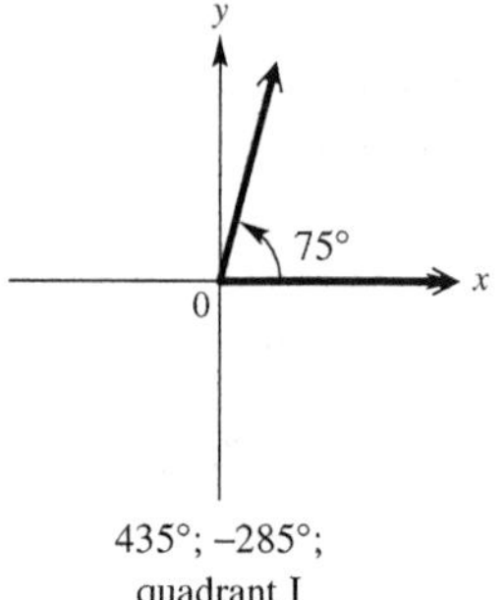


**43.**

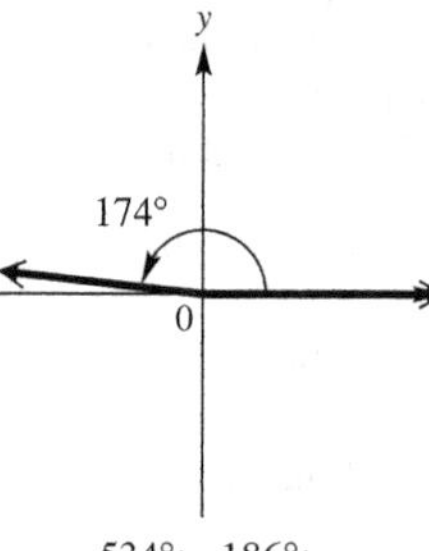


**45.**

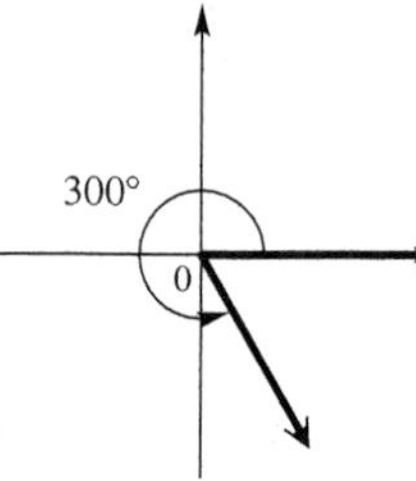


**47.**

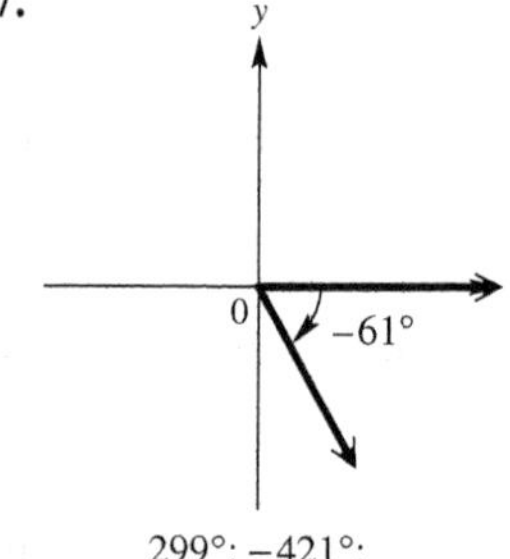


### 10.2 Exercises (Pages 630–631)

**1.**

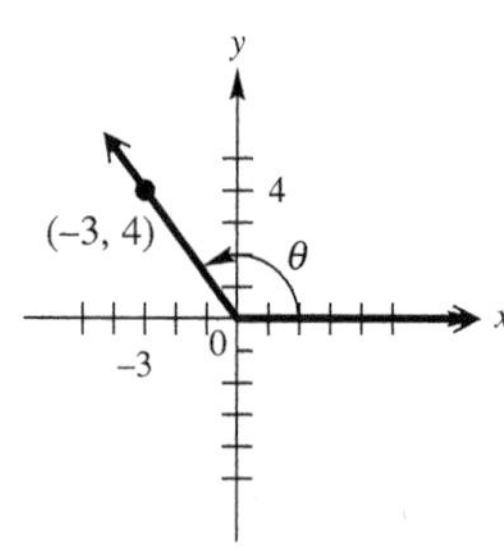


**3.**

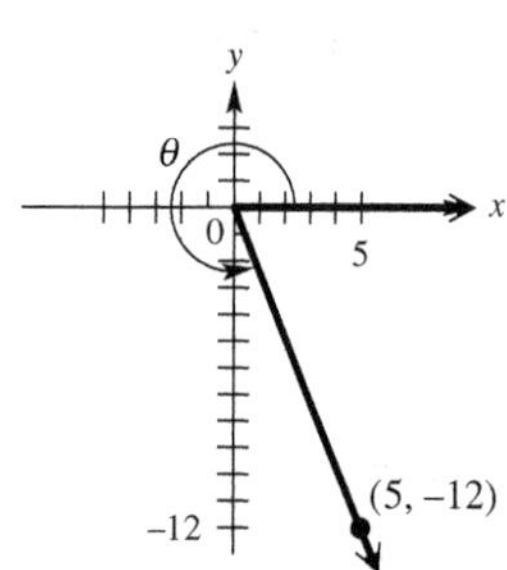


**5.** $\frac{4}{5}; -\frac{3}{5}; \frac{4}{3}; -\frac{3}{4}; -\frac{5}{3}; \frac{5}{4}$

**7.** 1; 0; undefined; 0; undefined; 1

**9.** $\frac{\sqrt{3}}{2}; \frac{1}{2}; \sqrt{3}; \frac{\sqrt{3}}{3}; 2; \frac{2\sqrt{3}}{3}$ **11.** $\frac{5\sqrt{34}}{34}; \frac{3\sqrt{34}}{34}; \frac{5}{3}; \frac{3}{5}; \frac{\sqrt{34}}{3}; \frac{\sqrt{34}}{5}$ **13.** 0; −1; 0; undefined; −1; undefined

**15.** Answers will vary. **17.** It is the distance from a point $(x, y)$ on the terminal side of the angle to the origin. **19.** positive **21.** negative **23.** positive **25.** negative **27.** 0 **29.** undefined **31.** undefined **33.** 0 **35.** 0 **37.** 1 **39.** 0

### 10.3 Exercises (Pages 635–636)

**1.** $-\frac{1}{3}$ **3.** $\frac{1}{3}$ **5.** −5 **7.** $2\sqrt{2}$ **9.** $-\frac{3\sqrt{5}}{5}$ **11.** $\frac{2}{3}$ **13.** II **15.** I **17.** II **19.** II or III

**21.** +; +; + **23.** −; −; + **25.** −; +; − **27.** +; +; + **29.** −; +; − **31.** $-2\sqrt{2}$ **33.** $\frac{\sqrt{15}}{4}$
**35.** $-2\sqrt{2}$ **37.** $\frac{\sqrt{15}}{4}$

**In Exercises 39–46, we give, in order, sine, cosine, tangent, cotangent, secant, and cosecant.**

**39.** $\frac{15}{17}; -\frac{8}{17}; -\frac{15}{8}; -\frac{8}{15}; -\frac{17}{8}; \frac{17}{15}$ **41.** $-\frac{4}{5}; -\frac{3}{5}; \frac{4}{3}; \frac{3}{4}; -\frac{5}{3}; -\frac{5}{4}$
**43.** $-\frac{\sqrt{3}}{2}; -\frac{1}{2}; \sqrt{3}; \frac{\sqrt{3}}{3}; -2; \frac{2\sqrt{3}}{3}$ **45.** $\frac{\sqrt{5}}{7}; \frac{2\sqrt{11}}{7}; \frac{\sqrt{55}}{22}; \frac{2\sqrt{55}}{5}; \frac{7\sqrt{11}}{22}; \frac{7\sqrt{5}}{5}$ **47.** Answers will vary.

## 10.4 Exercises (Pages 644–645)

**1.** $\frac{3}{5}; \frac{4}{5}; \frac{3}{4}; \frac{4}{3}; \frac{5}{4}; \frac{5}{3}$ **3.** $\frac{21}{29}; \frac{20}{29}; \frac{21}{20}; \frac{20}{21}; \frac{29}{20}; \frac{29}{21}$ **5.** $\frac{n}{p}; \frac{m}{p}; \frac{n}{m}; \frac{m}{n}; \frac{p}{m}; \frac{p}{n}$

**In Exercises 7 and 9, we give, in order, the unknown side, sine, cosine, tangent, cotangent, secant, and cosecant.**

**7.** $c = 13; \frac{12}{13}; \frac{5}{13}; \frac{12}{5}; \frac{5}{12}; \frac{13}{5}; \frac{13}{12}$ **9.** $b = \sqrt{13}; \frac{\sqrt{13}}{7}; \frac{6}{7}; \frac{\sqrt{13}}{6}; \frac{6\sqrt{13}}{13}; \frac{7}{6}; \frac{7\sqrt{13}}{13}$ **11.** cot 40°
**13.** sec 43° **15.** cot 64.6° **17.** sin 76°30′ **19.** $\frac{\sqrt{3}}{3}$ **21.** $\frac{1}{2}$ **23.** $\sqrt{2}$ **25.** $\frac{\sqrt{2}}{2}$ **27.** $\frac{\sqrt{3}}{2}$
**29.** $\sqrt{3}$ **31.** 82° **33.** 45° **35.** 30°

**In Exercises 37–55, we give, in order, sine, cosine, tangent, cotangent, secant, and cosecant.**

**37.** $\frac{\sqrt{3}}{2}; -\frac{1}{2}; -\sqrt{3}; -\frac{\sqrt{3}}{3}; -2; \frac{2\sqrt{3}}{3}$ **39.** $\frac{1}{2}; -\frac{\sqrt{3}}{2}; -\frac{\sqrt{3}}{3}; -\sqrt{3}; -\frac{2\sqrt{3}}{3}; 2$
**41.** $-\frac{\sqrt{3}}{2}; -\frac{1}{2}; \sqrt{3}; \frac{\sqrt{3}}{3}; -2; -\frac{2\sqrt{3}}{3}$ **43.** $-\frac{\sqrt{2}}{2}; \frac{\sqrt{2}}{2}; -1; -1; \sqrt{2}; -\sqrt{2}$ **45.** $\frac{\sqrt{3}}{2}; \frac{1}{2}; \sqrt{3}; \frac{\sqrt{3}}{3}; 2; \frac{2\sqrt{3}}{3}$
**47.** $\frac{\sqrt{2}}{2}; -\frac{\sqrt{2}}{2}; -1; -1; -\sqrt{2}; \sqrt{2}$ **49.** $\frac{1}{2}; \frac{\sqrt{3}}{2}; \frac{\sqrt{3}}{3}; \sqrt{3}; \frac{2\sqrt{3}}{3}; 2$ **51.** $\frac{\sqrt{3}}{2}; \frac{1}{2}; \sqrt{3}; \frac{\sqrt{3}}{3}; 2; \frac{2\sqrt{3}}{3}$
**53.** $-\frac{1}{2}; \frac{\sqrt{3}}{2}; -\frac{\sqrt{3}}{3}; -\sqrt{3}; \frac{2\sqrt{3}}{3}; -2$ **55.** $\frac{\sqrt{3}}{2}; \frac{1}{2}; \sqrt{3}; \frac{\sqrt{3}}{3}; 2; \frac{2\sqrt{3}}{3}$ **57.** $\frac{\sqrt{3}}{3}, \sqrt{3}$
**59.** $\frac{\sqrt{3}}{2}, \frac{\sqrt{3}}{3}, \frac{2\sqrt{3}}{3}$ **61.** −1, −1 **63.** $-\frac{\sqrt{3}}{2}, -\frac{2\sqrt{3}}{3}$ **65.** 210°, 330° **67.** 45°, 225° **69.** 60°, 120°
**71.** 120°, 240° **73.** 225°, 315° **75.** 120°, 300°

## 10.5 Exercises (Pages 651–654)

**1.** .5657728 **3.** 1.1342773 **5.** 1.0273488 **7.** .6383201 **9.** 1.7768146 **11.** .4771588
**13.** −5.7297416 **15.** 1.9074147 **17.** 57.997172° **19.** 30.502748° **21.** 46.173581°
**23.** 81.168073° **25.** $B = 53°40′; a = 571$ m; $b = 777$ m **27.** $M = 38.8°; n = 154$ m; $p = 198$ m
**29.** $A = 47.9108°; c = 84.816$ cm; $a = 62.942$ cm **31.** $B = 62.00°; a = 8.17$ ft; $b = 15.4$ ft
**33.** $A = 17.00°; a = 39.1$ in.; $c = 134$ in. **35.** $c = 85.9$ yd; $A = 62°50′; B = 27°10′$ **37.** $b = 42.3$ cm; $A = 24°10′; B = 65°50′$ **39.** $B = 36°36′; a = 310.8$ ft; $b = 230.8$ ft **41.** $A = 50°51′; a = .4832$ m; $b = .3934$ m **43.** 9.35 meters **45.** 88.3 meters **47.** 26.92 inches **49.** 583 feet **51.** 28.0 meters
**53.** 469 meters **55.** 146 meters **57.** 34.0 miles **59.** $a = 12, b = 12\sqrt{3}, d = 12\sqrt{3}, c = 12\sqrt{6}$

## 10.6 Exercises (Pages 663–668)

**1.** $C = 95°, b = 13$ m, $a = 11$ m **3.** $B = 37.3°, a = 38.5$ ft, $b = 51.0$ ft **5.** $C = 57.36°, b = 11.13$ ft, $c = 11.55$ ft **7.** $B = 18.5°, a = 239$ yd, $c = 230$ yd **9.** $A = 56°00′, AB = 361$ ft, $BC = 308$ ft
**11.** $B = 110.0°, a = 27.01$ m, $c = 21.36$ m **13.** $A = 34.72°, a = 3326$ ft, $c = 5704$ ft
**15.** $C = 97°34′, b = 283.2$ m, $c = 415.2$ m **17.** 118 meters **19.** 10.4 inches **21.** 12 **23.** 7 **25.** 30°

**27.** $c = 2.83$ in., $A = 44.9°$, $B = 106.8°$ **29.** $c = 6.46$ m, $A = 53.1°$, $B = 81.3°$ **31.** $a = 156$ cm, $B = 64°50'$, $C = 34°30'$ **33.** $b = 9.529$ in., $A = 64.59°$, $C = 40.61°$ **35.** $a = 15.7$ m, $B = 21.6°$, $C = 45.6°$ **37.** $A = 30°$, $B = 56°$, $C = 94°$ **39.** $A = 82°$, $B = 37°$, $C = 61°$ **41.** $A = 42.0°$, $B = 35.9°$, $C = 102.1°$ **43.** 257 meters **45.** 22 feet **47.** 36° with the 45-foot cable, 26° with the 60-foot cable **49.** $\frac{\sqrt{3}}{2}$ **51.** $\frac{\sqrt{2}}{2}$ **53.** 46.4 $m^2$ **55.** 356 $cm^2$ **57.** 722.9 in.$^2$ **59.** $24\sqrt{3}$ **61.** 78 $m^2$ **63.** 12,600 $cm^2$ **65.** 3650 $ft^2$ **67.** 100 $m^2$ **69.** 33 cans

## Chapter 10 Test (Pages 668–669)

**1.** 74.2983° **2.** 203° **3.** $\sin\theta = -\frac{5\sqrt{29}}{29}$; $\cos\theta = \frac{2\sqrt{29}}{29}$; $\tan\theta = -\frac{5}{2}$ **4.** III **5.** $\sin\theta = -\frac{3}{5}$; $\tan\theta = -\frac{3}{4}$; $\cot\theta = -\frac{4}{3}$; $\sec\theta = \frac{5}{4}$; $\csc\theta = -\frac{5}{3}$ **6.** $\sin A = \frac{12}{13}$; $\cos A = \frac{5}{13}$; $\tan A = \frac{12}{5}$; $\cot A = \frac{5}{12}$; $\sec A = \frac{13}{5}$; $\csc A = \frac{13}{12}$ **7. (a)** $\frac{1}{2}$ **(b)** 1 **(c)** undefined **(d)** $-\frac{2\sqrt{3}}{3}$ **(e)** undefined **(f)** $-\sqrt{2}$

**8. (a)** .97939940 **(b)** .20834446 **(c)** 1.9362132 **(d)** 4.16529977 **9.** 16.16664145° **10.** 135°, 225° **11.** $B = 31°30'$, $a = 638$, $b = 391$ **12.** 15.5 ft **13.** 137.5° **14.** 180 km **15.** 49.0° **16.** 4300 $km^2$ **17.** 264 square units **18.** 2.7 miles **19.** 5500 meters **20.** distance to both first and third bases: 63.7 feet; distance to second base: 66.8 feet

# CHAPTER 11 Counting Methods

## 11.1 Exercises (Pages 678–681)

**1.** *AB, AC, AD, AE, BA, BC, BD, BE, CA, CB, CD, CE, DA, DB, DC, DE, EA, EB, EC, ED*; 20 ways **3.** *AC, AE, BC, BE, CA, CB, CD, DC, DE, EA, EB, ED*; 12 ways **5.** *ACE, AEC, BCE, BEC, DCE, DEC*; 6 ways **7.** *ABC, ABD, ABE, ACD, ACE, ADE, BCD, BCE, BDE, CDE*; 10 ways **9.** 1 **11.** 3 **13.** 5 **15.** 5 **17.** 3 **19.** 1 **21.** 18 **23.** 15

**25.**

| | 1 | 2 | 3 | 4 | 5 | 6 |
|---|---|---|---|---|---|---|
| **1** | 11 | 12 | 13 | 14 | 15 | 16 |
| **2** | 21 | 22 | 23 | 24 | 25 | 26 |
| **3** | 31 | 32 | 33 | 34 | 35 | 36 |
| **4** | 41 | 42 | 43 | 44 | 45 | 46 |
| **5** | 51 | 52 | 53 | 54 | 55 | 56 |
| **6** | 61 | 62 | 63 | 64 | 65 | 66 |

**27.** 11, 22, 33, 44, 55, 66 **29.** 11, 13, 23, 31, 41, 43, 53, 61 **31.** 16, 25, 36, 64 **33.** 16, 32, 64

**35. (a)** tttt **(b)** hhhh, hhht, hhth, hhtt, hthh, htht, htth, thhh, thht, thth, tthh **(c)** httt, thtt, ttht, ttth, tttt **(d)** hhhh, hhht, hhth, hhtt, hthh, htht, htth, httt, thhh, thht, thth, thtt, tthh, ttht, ttth

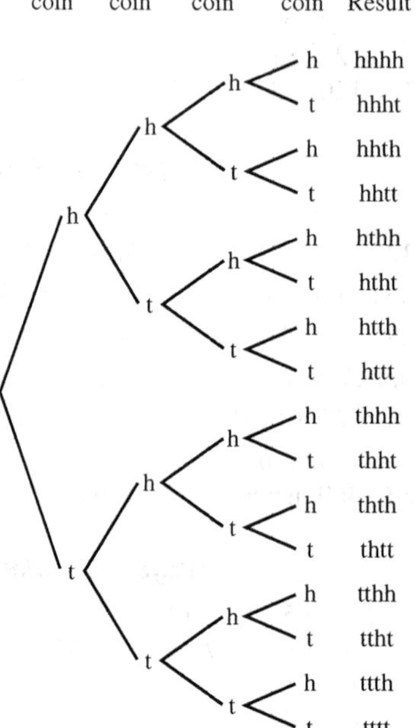

# CREDITS

**1** Cinergi Pictures/The Kobal Collection **4** ABC/Courtesy Everett Collection **6** Beth Anderson **6** Excerpted from *In Mathematical Circles, Volume 1* by Howard Eves. Published by the Mathematical Association of America. **7** Chris Pizzello/Reuters/Corbis **14** Digital Vision **20** Chuck Painter/Stanford News Service **20** Copyright 1945, © 1973 renewed by Princeton University Press; reprinted with permission of Princeton University Press. **22** CBS Broadcasting, Inc./Courtesy Everett Collection; Image used with permission. **22** Texas Instruments/NCTM. Images used with permission. **25** PhotoDisc **26** PhotoDisc **27** © 2004 by David Deutsch and Benjamin Goldman. All Rights Reserved. Reprinted with permission from *Mathematics Teacher*, Nov 2004. © 2004 by the National Council of Teachers of Mathematics. All Rights Reserved. **27–28** Reprinted with permission from *Mathematics Teacher*. © 2003–2005 by the National Council of Teachers of Mathematics. All Rights Reserved. **27** Warner Bros./The Kobal Collection **27** Corbis **29** PhotoDisc **30** Digital Vision **31** Beth Anderson **33** Beth Anderson **34** Beth Anderson **34** Corbis **34** William Perlman/Star Ledger/Corbis **39** Beth Anderson **39** Beth Anderson **40** Pier Paolo Cito/Pool/Reuters/Corbis **42–43** Reprinted with permission from *Mathematics Teacher*, Sept. 1991. © 1991 by the National Council of Teachers of Mathematics. All Rights Reserved. **48–49** Reprinted with permission from *Mathematics Teacher*. © 1994, 1997, 1998, 2000, 2002, 2004 by the National Council of Teachers of Mathematics. All Rights Reserved. **51** Sandollar/The Kobal Collection **52** Bavaria-Verlag **54** Beth Anderson **58** *Information Please* ® Database. © 2006 Pearson Education, Inc. All Rights Reserved. Data from NY Stock Exchange. **65** Beth Anderson **65** Beth Anderson **80** Reuters/Corbis **80** Reuters/Corbis **83** The Everett Collection **85** Neal Preston/CORBIS **86** Corbis **87** Silvio Fiore/Superstock **90** Image Source Getty **91** Digital Vision **92** PhotoDisc **95** PhotoDisc **96** PhotoDisc **97** Disney Enterprises, Inc. **98** Corbis/Bettmann **100** Erich Lessing/Art Resource, NY **102** Constantin Film/The Kobal Collection **103** Dream Works Photo/Entertainment Pictures/ZUMA/Corbis **104** Mathematical People, Copyright © 1985 by Berkhauser Boston. Reprinted by permission. **109** Library of Congress **111** Library of Congress **116** Digital Vision **117** PhotoFest **124** PhotoDisc **124** PhotoDisc **126** Digital Vision **126** Poirier/Roger Viollet/Getty Image (Getty Editorial) **128** Corbis/Bettmann **132** PhotoDisc **134** Corbis/Bettmann **134** John Hornsby **138** 2006 Penny Press, Inc. Used with permission **139–142, 155** "Copyright © 2004, Penny Press, Inc. England's Best Logic Problems, May 2004 used with permission of the publisher. All Rights Reserved." **140, 143–144, 155** Courtesy International Sudoku Authority **148** PhotoDisc **148** Python Pictures. Courtesy The Everett Collection **150** Courtesy Airmont Publishing Co., Inc. All Rights Reserved. **151** Reuters/Corbis **152** Jeff J Mitchell/Reuters/Corbis **154** Courtesy Airmont Publishing Co., Inc. All Rights Reserved. **159** Photofest NYC **160** PhotoDisc **160** Courtesy Prindle, Weber & Schmidt, Inc. **161** Bridgeman Art Library **161** The Metropolitan Museum, Egyptian Exhibition. Rogers Fund 1930 **165** American Museum of Natural History

**171** ©Trinity College. Reprinted by permission of the Master and Fellows of Trinity College Cambridge **172** Pearson Asset Library **173** Courtesy, IBM Corp. **181** Corbis/Bettmann **186** ® Kellogg Company **193** Tom Wurt/Stock Boston **212** Courtesy, Professor Noether **216** St. Andrew's University **221** Pearson Asset Library/Photofest **223** Warner Bros./Southside Amusement Co./The Kobal Collection **225** Hugh C. Williams, University of Manitoba **228** Roger Viollet/Liaison **236** Tri-Star/Phoenix Pictures/The Kobal Collection **236** Roger Viollet/Liaison **241** Giraudon/Art Resource NY **260** Getty **260** PhotoDisc **261** Scala/Art Resource NY **261** PhotoDisc **262** Disney Enterprises, Inc. **266** Francis G. Mayer/CORBIS **266** The Benjamin Franklin Collection/Sterling Memorial Library at Yale University **267** StadtmuseumAachen/ET Archive, London/SuperStock **268** Metropolitan Museum of Art, Harris Brisbane Dick Fund, 1943. **273** PhotoFest **280** PhotoDisc **291** © 2006 Pearson Education, Inc. All Rights Reserved. **295** © 2006 Pearson Education, Inc. All Rights Reserved. **300** Spanish Coins courtesy of Larry Stevens. Used with permission **301** Doug Plasencia/Courtesy of Bowers and Merena Galleries **307** Doug Plasencia/Courtesy of Bowers and Merena Galleries **308** © 2002 Pearson Education, Inc. All Rights Reserved. **309** PhotoDisc **309** PhotoDisc **316** Image courtesy of St. Martins Press. © 1976 St. Martin's Press. Used with permission. **316** The Everett Collection **317** Jacket cover copyright © 2002, from *The Golden Ratio: The Story of Phi, The World's Most Astonishing Number* by Mario Livio. Used by permission of Broadway Books, a division of Random House, Inc. **317** Cover copyright © 1994 from *e: The Story of a Number* by Eli Maor. Used by permission of Princeton University Press. **319** Courtesy of www.joyofpi.com. **320** PhotoDisc **325** Wolper/Warner Bros./The Kobal Collection **326** Paramount/The Kobal Collection **328** © 2006 Pearson Education, Inc. All Rights Reserved. **329** PhotoDisc **330** Photo provided by John C. D. Diamantopoulos, Ph. D. Mathematics and Computer Science Dept., Northeastern State University © 2006 John C. D. Diamantopoulos. All Rights Reserved. **334** © 2002 Pearson Education, Inc. All Rights Reserved. **334** PhotoDisc **335** Comstock **342** © 2006 Pearson Education, Inc. All Rights Reserved. **342** © 2006 Pearson Education, Inc. All Rights Reserved. **343** Columbia Pictures/courtesy The Everett Collection **345** Getty RF Blend Images **350** PhotoDisc **353** Comstock **353** Getty RF MedioImages **353–354** © 2004 Pearson Education, Inc. All Rights Reserved. **357** Corbis **358** The Everett Collection **359** © 2006 Pearson Education, Inc. All Rights Reserved. **360** 20th Century Fox Film Corp. Courtesy The Everett Collection **362** Getty Editorial **365** Albert Ferreira/Reuters/Corbis **365** Beth Anderson **366** MedioImages Getty **368** Warner Bros./Photofest **370** CBS-TV/The Kobal Collection **370** Beth Anderson **373** Corbis **377** PhotoDisc **379** Corbis **383** Bettmann/Corbis **386** © 2004 Pearson Education, Inc. All Rights Reserved. **387** © 2004 Pearson Education, Inc. All Rights Reserved. **390** Stockdisc Classic **393** Corbis **402** NBC/Photofest **404** PhotoDisc **406** PhotoDisc **407** NASA **419** WB Television/Photofest **431** Everett

Collection **435** © 2005 Pearson Education, Inc. All Rights Reserved. **435** Beth Anderson **437** National Information Service for Earthquake Engineering **450** AP/Wideworld Photos **450** © 2006 Pearson Education, Inc. All Rights Reserved. **456** © 2007 Pearson Education, Inc. All Rights Reserved. **456** PhotoDisc **459** © 2002 Pearson Education, Inc. All Rights Reserved **460** Data from Sahrov and Novikov, *Edwin Hubble: the Discoverer of the Big Bang Universe,* Cambridge University Press, 1993. Lial, et al., © 2006 Pearson Education, Inc. All Rights Reserved. **461** Digital Vision **462** Digital Vision **472** Corbis **477** NASA **483** Investment Management and Research, Inc. **487** The Everett Collection **490** Digital Vision **491** PhotoDisc **492** Reprinted by permission of the National Geographic Society **493** Beth Anderson **494** © 2002 Pearson Education, Inc. All Rights Reserved. **495** © 2002 Pearson Education, Inc. All Rights Reserved. **500** © 2005 Pearson Education, Inc. All Rights Reserved. **504** Getty Editorial **505** Nigel Cattlin/Photo Researchers, Inc. **507** PhotoDisc **508–509** © 2002 Pearson Education, Inc. All Rights Reserved. **511** AP/Wideworld Photos **513** PhotoDisc **514** Getty Editorial **514** Nigel Cattlin/Photo Researchers, Inc. **522** Stanford University News Service **528** The Kobal Collection **529** The Kobal Collection **531** PhotoDisc **544** Corbis/Bettmann **549** The Everett Collection **550** Reprinted with permission from *The Trisection Problem*, copyright © 1971 by the National Council of Teachers of Mathematics. All rights reserved. **551** Alinari/Art Resource, N.Y. **557** Corbis **559** PhotoDisc **566** George Arthur Plympton Coll, Columbia Univ **569** The Everett Collection **570** Photofest **571** Reprinted with permission from *The Pythagorean Theorem*, copyright © 1968 by the National Council of Teachers of Mathematics. All rights reserved. **571** John Hornsby **582** Photofest **583** Digital Vision **587** Custom Medical Stock Photo **587** Photo Researchers **589** courtesy of Gwen Hornsby **589** BrandX CD MagLands **589** The Image Bank Getty Images **591** PhotoDisc **592** The M.C. Escher Company - Holland **592** The M.C. Escher Company - Holland **594–596** The authors would like to thank The Math Forum at Drexel and Suzanne Alejandre for permission to reprint this article. **595–596** "Tessellations courtesy of Coolmath.com. All Rights Reserved." **599** Corbis-Hulton/UPI Bettmann **600** Reprise Records/Rhino Entertainment Company, a Warner Music Group Company **601** Corbis/Bettmann **604** Courtesy B. K. Tomlin **611** AP/Wideworld Photos **612** Courtesy of Philip Marcus **612** NASA **613–615** Pages 1–4 from National Council of Teachers of Mathematics Student Math Notes, November 1991. Reprinted by permission of the National Council of Teachers of Mathematics. **621** The Everett Collection **633** Smithsonian Institution **650** Courtesy of John Hornsby and John Wiley and Sons, Inc.. **657** PhotoDisc **671** Photofest **674** British Museum **680** Corbis **684** National Museum of American Art, Washington, DC/Art Resource, N.Y. **685** Corbis **695** Washington National Cathedral **699** Digital Vision **702** Stockbyte Platinum **704** Image Source **704** PhotoDisc **703** Corbis **705** PhotoDisc **723** The Everett Collection **724** Corbis **726** Lithograph by Rudolph Hoffman, 1859, after photoprint by Maull and Polyblanck/Library of Congress Prints and Photographs Division **734** Stockbyte Platinum/Getty **735** PhotoDisc **738** Stock Montage, Inc./Historical Pictures Archive **744** Beth Anderson **745** Bettmann/Corbis **749** PhotoDisc **750** Philippe Psaila/Liaison Agency **753** Courtesy of NASA **754** Jonathan Nourok/Photo Edit **756** Museum fur Volkerlunde un Schwerizerischches **760** PhotoDisc **761** PhotoDisc **765** PhotoDisc **766** From David C. Christensen, *Slot Machines: A Pictorial History.* Vestal Press, 1977. **768** Courtesy John Hornsby **771** PhotoDisc **772** Atlantide Phototravel/Corbis **775** David Loh/Reuters/Corbis **781** Dreamworks/Universal/The Kobal Collection/Reed, Eli **782** Courtesy Vern Heeren **787** PhotoDisc **790** From *The 2006 World Book Yearbook, Inc.* p. 169 **805** Doug Pensinger/Getty Images **812** Sovfoto **822** MedioImages/Getty **826** North Wind Picture Archives **830** Superstock **833** Corbis **833** StockDisc **834–840** From *How to Lie with Statistics* by Darrell Huff, illustrated by Irving Geis. Copyright © 1954 and renewed © 1982 by Darrell Huff and Irving Geis. Reprinted by Permission of W.W. Norton and Company, Inc. **844** Library of Congress **847** PhotoDisc **849** Sara Piaseczynski **852** Mike Cassese/Reuters/Corbis **853** The Everett Collection **856** Walt Disney/The Kobal Collection **857** Originally broadcast over the CBS News Radio Network as part of the Hourly News by Charles Osgood, March 2, 1977. © 1977 by CBS, Inc. All rights reserved. Reprinted by permission. **858** Oriental Institute Museum, University of Chicago **860** Warner Bros/The Kobal Collection **875** Wells Fargo Bank **878** Digital Vision **889** Cameramann International, Ltd. **891** © 2006 Hearst Communications, Inc. **896** www.business.to.business.resources.com **904** Jean Miele/Corbis **910** PhotoDisc **921** Edward Jones and Company, 2002. Used by permission.

# INDEX

**Bold number** = definition
*Italic number* = figure
*t* = *table*

## B



## C

## D

## H



## I

## J



## K



## L

## M

## Q



## R

# T

## U

# 2 SYSTEMS OF MEASUREMENT

*Metric conversion,* doctor . . . shortened the night shift by two hours!

## CHAPTER OBJECTIVES

- Perform calculations in the metric system of measure
- Convert units of measure within the metric, apothecaries', and household systems of measure
- Demonstrate proficiency with symbols in the metric, apothecaries', and household systems of measure
- Utilize the proportion method when changing units of measure from one system to another

## INTRODUCTION

The two basic systems of weight and measure in the United States are the metric system and the apothecaries' system. There is a definite trend toward adoption of the metric system exclusively, but since both systems are currently in use, nurses must be familiar with both and be able to use them interchangeably.

A third system of measure the nurse often needs is the household system of measure. This is the least accurate system of measure and is used only when it is not feasible to calculate and measure dosage by the metric or apothecaries' system. The household system of measure is generally used by nurses and patients in the home. Such familiar household measures as the teaspoon, tablespoon, ounce, drop, and glassful may be substituted for approximate equivalents of the two major systems of measure.

## THE METRIC SYSTEM

The metric system was devised by the French in 1791 in an effort to simplify measurement. The metric system is based on a uniform decimal system (a system of multiples or powers of 10).

The metric system utilizes three units of measure with which the nurse needs to be familiar:

| | | |
|---|---|---|
| Liter (l) | = | unit of volume |
| Gram (g) | = | unit of weight |
| Meter (m) | = | unit of length |

The abbreviations for each of the units is the first letter of each word, so for the gram the abbreviation is g. The abbreviations L., Gm., and M. for liters, grams, and meters, respectively, were formerly used in medical texts and may still be found in other sources.

To express multiples and parts of units, six basic prefixes are used:

| | | **Prefix** | **Symbol** |
|---|---|---|---|
| kilo | = | 1000 units | k |
| hecto | = | 100 units | h |
| deka | = | 10 units | da |
| deci | = | 0.1 unit | d |
| centi | = | 0.01 unit | c |
| milli | = | 0.001 unit | m |

Note that the abbreviation for each prefix is its first letter except for deka (da), where two letters are needed to distinguish between deka (da) and deci (d).

When a measurement is expressed in the metric system, a prefix and unit may be used. An example of a metric measurement is

47 milligrams

Two pieces of information are contained in the word milligram. First, the prefix, *milli-*, indicates the measure is in thousandths of a unit. Second, the unit indicates whether length, weight, or volume has been measured. In this case, the unit is gram, so the measurement is a weight measure. Thus, 47 milligrams means 47 thousandths of a gram, that is, 47 thousandths of a unit of weight. The abbreviation for 47 milligrams is

47 mg

When a prefix is written with the unit of measure, the abbreviation for the prefix is followed by the abbreviation for the unit.

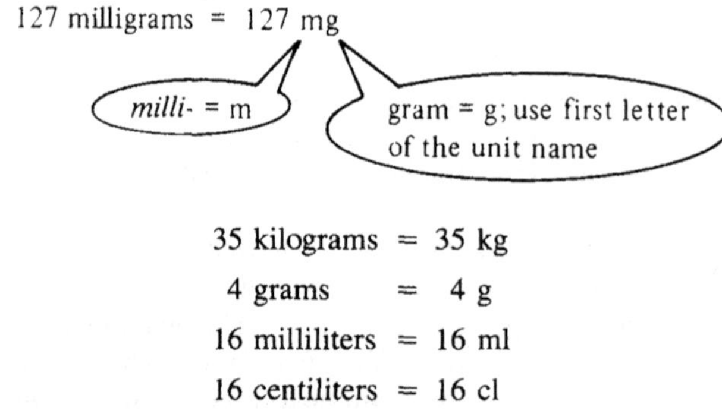

## EXAMPLE 2.1*

Along with the numerical data, provide the abbreviation if the name is given or the name if the abbreviation is given.

18 milliliters = 18 ml

4 cl = 4 centiliters

5 centigrams = 5 cc

7 meters = 1m

2 kilograms = 2Kg

3 dl = 3 decoliters

5 cm = 5 centimeters

The unit for weight, the *gram,* is equal to the weight of water contained in a 1 centimeter cube and at a temperature of 4°C. The water is at 4° because that is the temperature at which water is densest (and the most water can be contained in the cube).

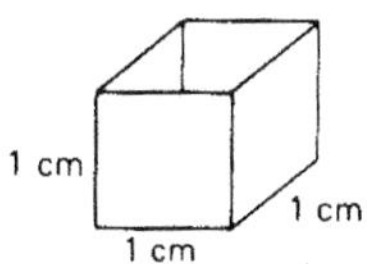


The unit for liquid measure, the *liter,* is the volume of fluid contained in a cube that is 10 centimeters on each edge. The volume of a cube 10 cm by 10 cm by 10 cm is 10 cm × 10 cm × 10 cm, or 1000 cubic centimeters ($cm^3$).

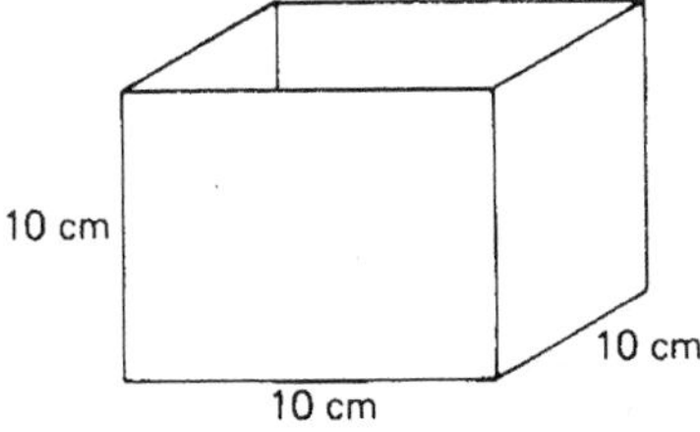


So $$1 \text{ liter} = 1000 \text{ cm}^3 = 1000 \text{ cc}$$

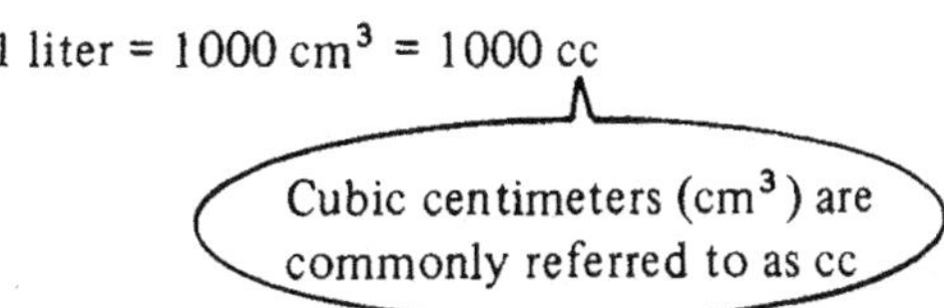


Thus, 1 liter is 1000 $cm^3$ (1000 cc). From previous discussions, 1 liter equals 1000 milliliters. Thus

$$1 \text{ liter} = 1000 \text{ cm}^3$$

$$1 \text{ liter} = 1000 \text{ ml}$$

$$1000 \text{ cm}^3 = 1000 \text{ ml}$$

$$1 \text{ cm}^3 = 1 \text{ ml}$$

Although 1 $cm^3$ is the same as 1 ml of fluid, 1 ml is the preferred abbreviation. The older form (1 cc) is still common, however.

*Answers to examples appear on pages 72-74.

The nurse usually works with grams or liters. The meter is seldom used. For the liter, the relationships between prefixes and units are

| | | | | | |
|---|---|---|---|---|---|
| 1000 liters | = | 1 kiloliter | 1 kl | = | 1000 liters |
| 100 liters | = | 1 hectoliter | 1 hl | = | 100 liters |
| 10 liters | = | 1 dekaliter | 1 dal | = | 10 liters |
| 1 liter | = | 1 liter | | | |
| 1 liter | = | 10 deciliters | 1 dl | = | 0.1 liter |
| 1 liter | = | 100 centiliters | 1 cl | = | 0.01 liter |
| 1 liter | = | 1000 milliliters | 1 ml | = | 0.001 liter |

Likewise, for the gram unit of weight

| | | | | | |
|---|---|---|---|---|---|
| 1 kg | = | 1000 g | 1 g | = | 0.001 kg |
| 1 hg | = | 100 g | 1 g | = | 0.01 hg |
| 1 dag | = | 10 g | 1 g | = | 0.1 dag |
| 1 g | = | 1 g | | | |
| 1 dg | = | 0.1 g | 1 g | = | 10 dg |
| 1 cg | = | 0.01 g | 1 g | = | 100 cg |
| 1 mg | = | 0.001 g | 1 g | = | 1000 mg |

## Converting Units Within the Metric System

For the nurse, the most frequent conversions involve liters and milliliters or grams and milligrams.

**TABLE 2.1**
**Metric table of weight, volume, and length**

| ***Metric weight (dry)*** | |
|---|---|
| 1 gram (g) = 1000 milligrams (mg) | 1 mg = 0.001 gm |
| 1000 grams (g) = 1 kilogram (kg) | 0.001 kg = 1 g |
| ***Metric volume (wet)*** | |
| 1 liter = 1000 milliliters (ml) | 1 ml = 0.001 liter |
| 1000 liters = 1 kiloliter (kl) | 0.001 kl = 1 liter |
| ***Metric length*** | |
| 1 meter (m) = 100 centimeters (cm) | 1 cm = 0.01 m |
| 1 meter (m) = 1000 millimeters (mm) | 1 mm = 0.001 m |
| 1 centimeter (cm) = 10 millimeters (mm) | 1 mm = 0.1 cm |
| 1000 meters (m) = 1 kilometer (km) | 1 m = 0.001 km |

Two methods for converting in the metric system are presented below, one using ratio and proportion and the second using rules. Although using the rules is simpler than using ratio and proportion when converting in this system, the proportion method will be essential later for solving drug problems successfully. Practicing the proportion method in these simple situations will make it easier in later chapters.

Convert 500 ml to liters. The problem stated mathematically is

$$500 \text{ ml} = \underline{\ .5\ } \text{ liters}$$

From the given problem, write a ratio

$$\frac{500 \text{ ml}}{x \text{ liters}}$$

Once the ratio is written, determine an equivalence between the units used in the ratio. Here 1000 ml is the same as 1 liter:

$$1000 \text{ ml} = 1 \text{ liter}$$

Use the values in the equivalence to write another ratio (make sure the units in the numerator and denominator are the same as in the first ratio):

$$\frac{1000 \text{ ml}}{1 \text{ liter}}$$

In both cases the ratio is milliliters to liters. Set the two ratios equal

$$\frac{500 \text{ ml}}{x \text{ liters}} = \frac{1000 \text{ ml}}{1 \text{ liter}}$$

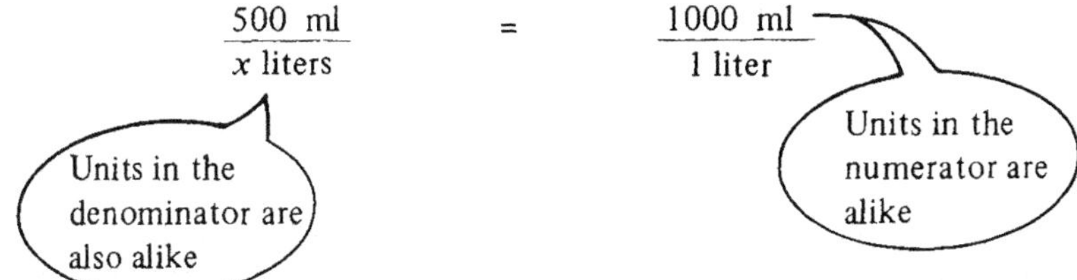


Use the numerical values and the method of cross-multiplying to solve for $x$:

$$\frac{500}{x} = \frac{1000}{1}$$

$$1000\,x = 1 \times 500$$

$$1000\,x = 500$$

$$x = \frac{500}{1000} = \frac{5}{10} = \frac{1}{2} = 0.5$$

$$x = 0.5 \text{ liter}$$

---

**EXAMPLE 2.2**

Solve the following:

$$450 \text{ ml} = \underline{\ x\ } \text{ liters}$$

1. Write a ratio from the given problem.

   450 mL / x L

2. Determine an equivalence between the given units.

   1000 mL / 1 L

3. Write a ratio using equivalence in step 2.

4. Set the two ratios equal. (Are like units in the numerators?)

   1000x=450

5. Use the numerical values in the proportion to solve for $x$. x=.45L

---

**EXAMPLE 2.3**

Solve

$$38 \text{ g} = \underline{\qquad\qquad} \text{ mg}$$

Use the above example as a guide if necessary.

---

---

**EXAMPLE 2.4**

Solve

$$54 \text{ cm} = \underline{\qquad\qquad} \text{ m}$$

Remember to set up a proportion.

---

## Rules

In each case that follows, a problem is solved using substitution and logic. Then, the rule is stated and is followed by guided application to a few problems.

Consider converting

$$3 \text{ liters} = \underline{\qquad\qquad} \text{ ml}$$

From the table, each liter equals 1000 ml. Note that 3 liters = 3 (1 liter). Substitute 1000 ml for 1 liter:

$$3 \text{ liters} = 3\,(1 \text{ liter}) = 3\,(1000 \text{ ml}) = 3000 \text{ ml}$$

Substituting
1 liter = 1000 ml

Recall from Chapter 1 that 3.0 = 3; thus

$$3 \text{ liters} = 3.0 \text{ liters}$$

and from the above work

$$3.0 \text{ liters} = 3000 \text{ ml}$$

**RULE 1:** *Liters to milliliters* To change liters to milliliters, multiply the number of liters by 1000 or move the decimal point three places to the right.

**RULE 2:** *Grams to milligrams* To change grams to milligrams, multiply the number of grams by 1000 or move the decimal point three places to the right.

**RULE 3:** *Meters to millimeters* To change meters to millimeters, multiply the number of meters by 1000 or move the decimal point three places to the right.

**EXAMPLE 2.5**

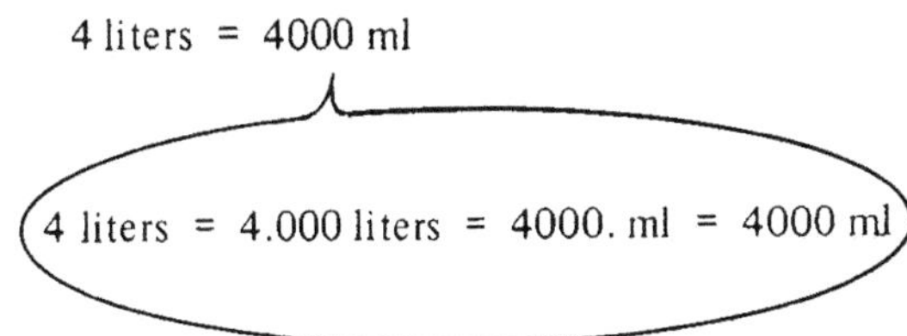


6 liters = 6000 ml
0.3 liter = 300 ml
7 g = 7000 mg
15 m = 15,000 mm

---

Now consider changing milliliters to liters. Change

600 ml = .6 liters

From Table 2.1, 1 ml = 0.001 liter. Note also

600 ml = 600 (1 ml)

Substituting gives

600 ml = 600 (1 ml) = 600 (0.001 liter) = 0.6 liter

1 ml = 0.001 liter

600 × 0.001 = 0.6

Thus

600 ml = 0.6 liter

**RULE 4:** *Milliliters to liters* To change milliliters to liters, multiply the number of milliliters by 0.001 or move the decimal point three places to the left.

**RULE 5:** *Milligrams to grams* To change milligrams to grams, multiply the number of milligrams by 0.001 or move the decimal point three places to the left.

**RULE 6:** *Millimeters to meters* To change millimeters to meters, multiply the number of millimeters by 0.001 or move the decimal point three places to the left.

---

**EXAMPLE 2.6**

Change the following as indicated.

480 ml = 0.480 liter

480 ml = 480.0 ml = 0.480 liter

750 ml = .75 liters
9800 mg = 9.8 g
42 mm = .042 m

---

**RULE 7:** *Kiloliters to liters* To change kiloliters to liters, multiply the number of kiloliters by 1000 or move the decimal point three places to the right.

**RULE 8:** *Kilograms to grams* To change the kilograms to grams, multiply the number of kilograms by 1000 or move the decimal point three places to the right.

**RULE 9:** *Kilometers to meters* To change kilometers to meters, multiply the number of kilometers by 1000 or move the decimal three places to the right.

---

**EXAMPLE 2.7**

Change the kilograms (kilometers) to grams (meters).

2.0 kg = 2000 g

2.0 kg = 2 (1 kg) = 2(1000 g) = 2000 g
Thus 2.0 kg = 2.0.0.0. g by rule 8

4 kg = 4000 g
4.23 kg = 4230 g
0.543 kg = 543 g
2.57 km = 2570 m

---

When changing grams to kilograms, as in the problem

349 g = .349 kg

recall that 1 g equals 0.001 kg. Also, 349 g = 349 (1 g); then

349 g = 349(1 g) = 349(0.001 kg) = 0.349 kg

1 g = 0.001 kg

349 X 0.001 = 0.349

**RULE 10:** *Liters to kiloliters* To change liters to kiloliters, multiply the number of liters by 0.001 or move the decimal point three places to the left.

**RULE 11:** *Grams to kilograms* To change grams to kilograms, multiply the number of grams by 0.001 or move the decimal point three places to the left.

**RULE 12:** *Meters to kilometers* To change meters to kilometers, multiply the number of meters by 0.001 or move the decimal three places to the left.

---

## EXAMPLE 2.8

Change the grams (liters or meters) to kilograms (kiloliters or kilometers).

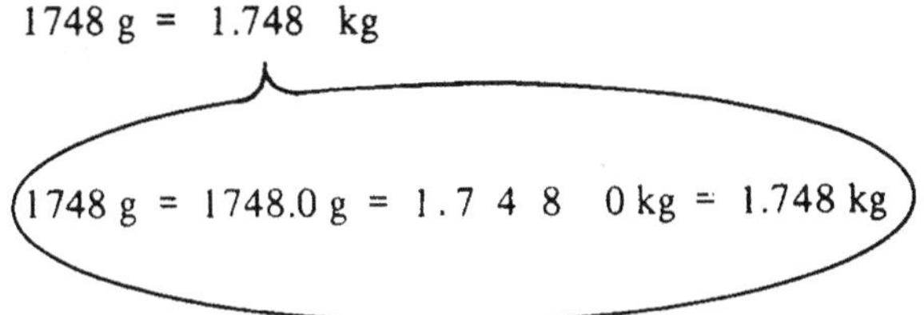


1545 g = __1.545__ kg
45 liters = __.045__ kl
137 m = __.137__ km

---

There are two additional rules necessary to complete metric system measures commonly used in everyday work. These involve the use of centimeters.

**RULE 13:** *Meters to centimeters* To change meters to centimeters, multiply the number of meters by 100 or move the decimal point two places to the right.

**RULE 14:** *Centimeters to meters* To change centimeters to meters, multiply the number of centimeters by 0.01 or move the decimal point two places to the left.

### Exercise 15

Complete the following using rules:

**1.** 1000 cc (mL) = __1__ liters  **2.** 500 liters = __500,000__ ml

**3.** 60 ml = __.06__ liters  **4.** 0.0080 liter = __8__ ml

**5.** 25 mm = __.025__ m  **6.** 1 g = __1000__ mg

**7.** 250 mg = __.25__ g  **8.** 6 g = __6000__ mg

**9.** 2000 g = 2 kg **10.** 3 km = 3000 m

**11.** 2185 cm = 21.85 m **12.** 8.45 kg = 8450 g

**13.** 30 liters = .03 kl **14.** 3 kl = 3000 liters

**15.** 40 g = .04 kg **16.** 60 mg = .06 g

**17.** 7 m = .007 km **18.** 250 cc = 250 ml

**19.** 600 kl = 600,000 liters **20.** 500 mg = .5 g

**21.** 1.4 m = 140 cm **22.** 1000 ml = 1 liters

**23.** 10 g = .01 kg **24.** 85 cm = .85 m

**25.** 8166 m = 8,166,000 mm **26.** 1.02 kg = 1020 g

## THE APOTHECARIES' SYSTEM

Although the metric system will inevitably replace the apothecaries' system, the apothecaries' system is still used today by physicians and nurses and will continue to be used for the next few decades. Therefore the nurse must understand both the apothecaries' and the metric systems.

In the apothecaries' system the basic unit for weight is the grain. When the system was established, the dry weight unit, the *grain,* was the weight of a grain of wheat. The abbreviation for grain is gr.

After the grain, the next larger unit of weight in the apothecaries' system is the scruple, but now it is seldom used as a unit. A *scruple* is 20 grains.

The dram is the next larger unit after the scruple. A *dram* is 60 grains. The symbol for the dram, ʒ, can be thought of as a z with a tail. After the dram, the ounce is the next larger unit in the apothecaries' system. An *ounce* equals 8 drams. The symbol for ounce is ℥. Thus

1 ℥ = 8 ʒ

**TABLE 2.2**
**Apothecaries' weights and measures**

| | | |
|---|---|---|
| ***Weight (dry)*** | | |
| 1 dram (ʒ) | = | 60 grains (gr) |
| 1 ounce (℥) | = | 8 drams (ʒ) |
| 1 pound (lb) | = | 12 ounces (℥) |
| ***Weight (liquid)*** | | |
| 1 fluidram (*f*ʒ) | = | 60 minims (♏) |
| 1 fluidounce (*f*℥) | = | 8 fluidrams (*f*ʒ) |
| 1 pint (pt) | = | 16 fluidounces (*f*℥) |
| 1 quart (qt) | = | 2 pints (pt) |
| 1 gallon (C) | = | 4 quarts (qt) |
| ***Derived measures*** | | |
| 1 ounce (℥) | = | 480 grains (gr) |
| 1 fluidounce (*f*℥) | = | 480 minims (♏) |
| 1 minim (♏) | = | 1 grain (gr) |

(This symbol, ℥, can be thought of as a "greater than" symbol, >, attached to the symbol for dram.) The larger unit is the pound (lb), which equals 12 ounces.

In the apothecaries' system both Roman numerals and Hindu-Arabic numerals are used in writing measurements. When the name is spelled out, Hindu-Arabic numerals are used to express the number value:

3 drams

When the symbol (abbreviation) for the unit is used, Roman numerals may be used to express the number value:

ʒiii

When Roman numerals are used, they always follow the unit symbol. As discussed in Chapter 1, lowercase letters (i, v, x) are used in writing numbers in the apothecaries' system.

Therefore,

1 ounce = 8 drams

can be written

℥i = ʒviii

Frequently large numbers (50 and over) are expressed using Hindu-Arabic numerals. Fractions are always written using Hindu-Arabic numerals, for example gr $\frac{1}{8}$, gr $\frac{1}{4}$, gr $\frac{1}{16}$. This means that decimals are expressed in fraction form. Decimals should not be used when expressing answers in this system. The fraction $\frac{1}{2}$ occurs so often that a special symbol is used. The Latin word for one-half is *semis,* abbreviated ss

$7\frac{1}{2}$ grains = gr viiss

---

**EXAMPLE 2.9**

What does each abbreviation mean?

1. gr vii = 7 grains
2. ʒ ix = 9 drams
3. ℥ v = 5 ounces
4. gr iss = 1 1/2 grains
5. gr $\frac{1}{4}$ = 1/4 grains

---

The *minim* (♏) is the unit of volume in the apothecaries' system. A minim was defined as the quantity of water weighing the same as one grain of wheat.

In the apothecaries' system the next largest unit of volume is the *fluidram* (*f*ʒ): 1 fluidram is 60 minims.

1 fluidram = 60 minims or *f*ʒi = 60♏

After the fluidram, the next largest unit is the *fluidounce* (*f*℥): 1 fluidounce (*f*℥) equals 8 fluidrams. Thus

*f*℥i = *f*ʒviii

A *pint* (pt) is 16 fluidounces. Pint is sometimes abbreviated using O, but since this is easily mistaken for zero, the abbreviation pt will be used instead. Two pints equal one *quart* (qt), and four quarts equal one *gallon* (C).

---

**EXAMPLE 2.10**

What does each abbreviation mean?

1. *f*ʒ viiss = 1 1/2 fluid drams
2. pt ss = 1/2 pint
3. *f*℥ iv = 4 fluid ounces
4. C iii = 3 gallons
5. ♏ v = 5 minims

---

Often it is necessary to change units within the apothecaries' system. Two methods for changing units follow. You should familiarize yourself with both.

Convert 1.5 fluidrams to minims. Mathematically the problem is

*f*ʒ iss = ♏ $\underline{x}$

From the given problem, write a ratio using the given information:

$$\frac{x \text{ minims}}{1.5 \text{ fluidrams}}$$

Once a ratio is written, determine an equivalence between the units used in the ratio (in this case minims and fluidrams).

1 fluidram = 60 minims
fʒi = ♏60

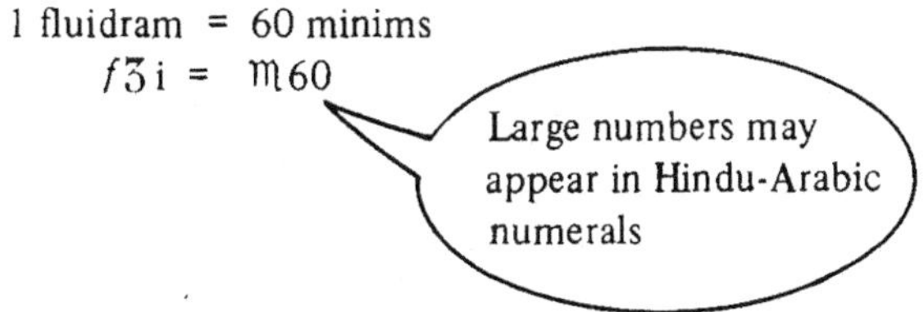


Form a ratio using the above equivalence; take care to form the second ratio with the same units in numerator and denominator as in the first ratio.

$$\frac{60 \text{ minims}}{1 \text{ fluidram}}$$

The proportion formed from the ratios is

$$\frac{x \text{ minims}}{1.5 \text{ fluidrams}} = \frac{60 \text{ minims}}{1 \text{ fluidram}}$$

In each case the relation is minims to fluidrams. Use the numerical values to solve for $x$:

$$\frac{x}{1.5} = \frac{60}{1}$$

$$1x = 1.5\,(60) \qquad \begin{array}{r} 1.5 \\ \times 60 \\ \hline 90.0 \end{array}$$

$$x = 90$$

Therefore 1.5 fluidrams equals 90 minims.

---

**EXAMPLE 2.11**

Convert 2 fluidrams to fluidounces.

fʒ ii = ______ f℥

1. From the given information, complete the ratio

$$\frac{\square \text{ f℥}}{\square \text{ fʒ}}$$

2. Determine an equivalence between fluidrams and fluidounces. *Hint:* Use Table 2.2

3. Write a second ratio from the information in step 2.

4. Set the two ratios equal.

5. Solve for $x$.

---

Sometimes the equivalence needed for converting units cannot be obtained directly from Table 2.2. Consider the problem

f℥ iiss = ______ ♏

The ratio formed from the given information is

$$\frac{x \quad \text{minims}}{2\frac{1}{2} \text{ fluidounces}}$$

Table 2.2 does not show an equivalence for minims and fluidounces, but

1 fluidounce = 8 fluidrams

and

1 fluidram = 60 minims

These two equivalences can be used to obtain a new equivalence.

1 fluidounce = 8 fluidrams = 8 (60 minims)

Each fluidram is 60 minims

So 1 fluidounce = 480 minims

Now a ratio can be formed from the equivalence:

$$\frac{480 \quad \text{minims}}{1 \quad \text{fluidounce}}$$

The proportion formed from the two ratios is

$$\frac{x \quad \text{minims}}{2\frac{1}{2} \text{ fluidounces}} = \frac{480 \quad \text{minims}}{1 \quad \text{fluidounce}}$$

Using the numerical data to solve for $x$ gives

$$\frac{x}{\frac{5}{2}} = \frac{480}{1}$$

$2\frac{1}{2} = \frac{5}{2}$

Cross-multiplying, we have

$$1x = \frac{5}{2}(480)$$

$$x = \frac{5 \times 480}{2} = 1200$$

$$= 1200 \text{ ♏}$$

$$\begin{array}{r} 480 \\ \times 5 \\ \hline 2400 \end{array}$$

$$\begin{array}{r} 1200 \\ 2\overline{)2400} \\ 2 \\ \hline 04 \\ 4 \end{array}$$

**EXAMPLE 2.12**

Solve the following

qt iii = ______ f℥

1. Write a ratio using the given information
2. Determine an equivalence between quarts and fluidounces. *Hint:* Use equivalence for pints and Table 2.2.
3. Write a second ratio using the equivalence from step 2.
4. Set the two ratios equal.
5. Solve for $x$.

---

**Exercise 16**

Use proportions to solve the following:

1. qt v = ______ pt
2. f℥ iiiss = ______ fʒ
3. C ii = ______ fluidounces
4. ♏ xlv = ______ fluidrams

Although the proportion method for changing units may be used to solve all changes or conversions of units, the changes needed are most often easiest to work using rules. The following rules are useful when changing units in the apothecaries' system of measure.

The rules involve the term *conversion constant*. A conversion constant is a number (obtained from Table 2.2) that aids in changing units of measure. From the table

1 dram = 60 grains

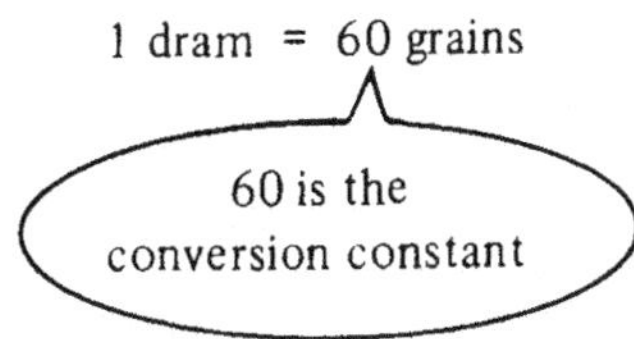


This equality between the units drams and grains involves a constant, 60. The number 60 is referred to as the conversion constant for drams and grains.

**RULE 1:** To change from a *larger* unit to a *smaller* unit, multiply the conversion constant by the number value of the larger unit.

**RULE 2:** To change from a *smaller* unit to a *larger* unit, divide the conversion constant into the number value of the smaller unit.

Consider the problem

ʒ iii = ______ gr

The dram unit is larger than the grain unit. Thus the change is from a larger unit to a smaller unit: use Rule 1. From Table 2.2 the conversion constant for drams and grains is 60. Using Rule 1, multiply 60 by the number value of the larger unit (3):

$$60 \times 3 = 180$$

180 grains is equal to 3 drams.

---

**EXAMPLE 2.13**

℥ iss = ________ ʒ

1. Rule ________ should be used.
2. What is the conversion constant?
3. How many ounces are given?
4. Find the number of drams.

---

---

**EXAMPLE 2.14**

gr cxx = ________ ʒ

1. Rule ________ should be used.
2. What is the conversion constant?
3. How many grains are given?
4. Find the number of drams.

---

**Exercise 17**

Solve using proportions:

1. gr lxx = ________ ʒ
2. ℥ xiv = ________ gr
3. 3 pt = ________ f℥
4. ʒ xlv = ________ gr

Solve using one of the rules:

5. 6 qt = ________ gallons
6. f℥ iiss = ________ ♏
7. ♏ viiss = ________ fʒ
8. f℥ xl = ________ pt
9. 600 gr = ________ ℥
10. ℥ iss = ________ ʒ
11. ʒ iii = ________ ℥
12. 7 pt = ________ fʒ

## THE HOUSEHOLD SYSTEM

The household system is the least accurate of the three systems of measure. However, these measures may be the only ones the patient is familiar with and may be safely used by the patient who is administering medications at home. The nurse should avoid these measures whenever possible because they are not as accurate as metric and apothecary measures.

**TABLE 2.3**

**Household measures**

| |
|---|
| 1 teaspoonful (t) = 60 drops (gtt) |
| 1 tablespoonful (T) = 3 teaspoonsful |
| 1 ounce (oz) = 2 tablespoonsful |
| 1 teacupful = 6 ounces |
| 1 glassful = 8 ounces |
| 1 ounce (oz) = 6 teaspoonsful |

The basic unit in the household system is the drop (gtt). The above table contains the equivalent measures in the household system. Many of the names are those commonly used in households today. The ounces referred to above are fluidounces, but the word fluid is generally omitted.

Two methods for changing unit measures are presented. It is suggested that you work with both and adopt the method that is easier for you to understand.

To change units of measure within the household system use ratio and proportions (discussed in Chapter 1). For example,

$$9 \text{ oz} = \underline{\hspace{2cm}} \text{ t}$$

First set up a ratio using the information given in the problem:

$$\frac{x \text{ t}}{9 \text{ oz}}$$

From Table 2.3 obtain the equivalence for ounces and teaspoonsful:

$$1 \text{ oz} = 6 \text{ t}$$

Set up a ratio using this equivalence, making sure that the units in the numerator and denominator are the same as in the first ratio:

$$\frac{6 \text{ t}}{1 \text{ oz}}$$

Set the two ratios equal and solve for the value of $x$:

$$\frac{x \text{ t}}{9 \text{ oz}} = \frac{6 \text{ t}}{1 \text{ oz}}$$

$$\frac{x}{9} = \frac{6}{1}$$

$$1x = 9\,(6)$$

$$x = 9\,(6) = 54$$

The answer is 54. There are 54 teaspoonsful in 9 ounces.

---

**EXAMPLE 2.15**

Changing ounces to drops.

$$3 \text{ oz} = \underline{\ x\ } \text{ gtt}$$

1. Set up the ratio from the given problem.

$$\frac{\boxed{10}\ \text{oz}}{\boxed{36}\ \text{gtt}}$$

2. From the table set up a ratio involving ounces and drops.
3. Set the two ratios equal.

4. Solve for the value of $x$.

1oz = 6t = 60gtt

6t × 60gtt = 360 gtt

If you encounter difficulty in step 4, review ratio and proportions in Chapter 1.

---

Change drops to ounces:

$$180 \text{ gtt} = \underline{\ 1/2\ } \text{ oz}$$

First, set up a ratio using information in the given problem:

$$\frac{180 \text{ gtt}}{x \text{ oz}}$$

From Table 2.3

$$1 \text{ oz} = 360 \text{ gtt}$$

$$\frac{360 \text{ gtt}}{1 \text{ oz}}$$

Set the two ratios equal:

$$\frac{180 \text{ gtt}}{x \text{ oz}} = \frac{360 \text{ gtt}}{1 \text{ oz}}$$

(Check to make sure like units appear in the two numerators and two denominators.)
Solve for $x$:

$$\frac{180}{x} = \frac{360}{1}$$

$$360x = 180(1)$$

$$x = \frac{180}{360} = 0.5$$

Thus

$$180 \text{ gtt} = 0.5 \text{ oz}$$

### Exercise 18

Use proportions to change units in the household system:

1. 4 T = __12__ t
2. 14 oz = __1.75__ glassfuls
3. 45 gtt = __.175__ oz
4. 3 t = __1__ T

Another method for changing (or converting) units is the rule method. The same rules used in changing units in the apothecaries' system are useful in the household system. The rules will be presented again but discussed only briefly since they were explained in detail in the previous section.

**RULE 1:** To change from a *larger* unit to a *smaller* unit, multiply the conversion constant by the number value of the larger unit.

**RULE 2:** To change from a *smaller* unit to a *larger* unit, divide the conversion constant into the number value of the smaller unit.

Change 3 t to drops:

3 t = __180__ gtt

To change a larger measure (teaspoons) to a smaller measure (drops), apply Rule 1. From Table 2.3

1 t = 60 gtt

Thus the conversion constant is 60. Applying Rule 1, multiply the conversion constant (60) by the number value of the larger unit (3):

$$60 \times 3 = 180$$

Therefore, 3 teaspoonsful equal 180 drops.

### Exercise 19

Solve by applying the correct rule:

1. 30 gtt = __1/2__ t
2. 8 oz = __1__ glassfuls
3. 2 oz = __12__ t
4. 180 gtt = __1/2__ oz
5. 2 T = __1__ oz
6. 1 T = __1/2__ oz
7. 40 gtt = __2/3__ t
8. 4 t = __240__ gtt
9. 4 oz = __1/2__ glassfuls
10. 16 oz = __2__ glassfuls
11. 2 T = __6__ t
12. 360 gtt = __6__ t
13. 9 t = __3__ T
14. 24 oz = __3__ glassfuls

## EQUIVALENTS

To change units between systems of measure, the proportions method works well. For changing units between the systems the proportion method is set up the same way as in past sections.

**TABLE 2.4**
**Approximate equivalents**

***Volume***

| Metric | | Apothecaries' | | Household[1] |
|---|---|---|---|---|
| 1 ml | = | 15 ♏ (or 16 ♏)[2] | = | 15 gtt |
| 4 ml | = | 1 ʒ (*f*ʒ) | = | 60 gtt (1 t) |
| 15 ml | = | 4 ʒ (*f*ʒ) | = | 1 T |
| 30 ml | = | 1 ℥ (*f*℥) | = | 2 T |
| 500 ml | = | 1 pt | | |
| 1000 ml | = | 1 qt | | |

***Weight***

| Metric | | Apothecaries' |
|---|---|---|
| 60 mg (0.06 g) | = | 1 gr |
| 1000 mg (1 g) | = | 15 gr |
| 4 g | = | 1 ʒ |
| 30 g | = | 1 ℥ |

[1]Household equivalents specified are those frequently used. Use the metric or apothecaries' system when measuring dosages because measurements are more accurate.
[2]1 ml = 15 minims will be used for computational purposes.

The equivalent for 1 milliliter is either 15 or 16 minims. Quite often the value chosen for use depends on whether the numbers involved in the computations are even or odd. This criterion is not theoretically or scientifically supported.

Because the equivalents are approximate, the answer can vary by as much as 10% and still be considered within safe limits. When the nurse rounds the computed answer to either minims or tenths of a milliliter, the resulting answer will be within the 10% allowable difference.

For the purpose of consistency throughout the remainder of this book, all computations will use 1 milliliter equivalent to 15 minims.

Change

40 ml to drams.

This means

40 ml = ___10___ ʒ

First, determine a ratio from the given information:

$$\frac{x\ ʒ}{40\ \text{ml}}$$

From Table 2.4 determine an equivalence using milliliters and drams:

4 ml = 1 ʒ

Use this equivalence to set up a second ratio (be sure the same units appear in the numerator and denominator of both ratios):

$$\frac{1\ ʒ}{4\ \text{ml}}$$

ʒ should be in the numerator and ml in the denominator because the first ratio is set up with these units

Once the two ratios are determined, set them equal:

$$\frac{x\ ʒ}{40\ \text{ml}} = \frac{1\ ʒ}{4\ \text{ml}}$$

Use the numerical values to solve for $x$:

$$\frac{x}{40} = \frac{1}{4}$$

$$4x = 40(1)$$

$$4x = 40$$

$$\frac{\cancel{4}x}{\cancel{4}} = \frac{40}{4}$$

$$x = \frac{40}{4} = 10$$

The correct answer is 10 drams; that is,

$$40\ \text{ml} = 10\ ʒ$$

---

**EXAMPLE 2.16**

2 ml = __30__ ♏

1. From the given problem complete the ratio: $\frac{\boxed{1}\ \text{ml}}{\boxed{15}\ ♏}$

2. Choose an equivalence for milliliters and minims from Table 2.4.

3. Write a ratio using the information in step 2.

4. Set the two ratios equal.

5. Solve for the unknown value.

---

**EXAMPLE 2.17**

$$\text{gr}\ \frac{1}{4} = \underline{\quad 15 \quad}\ \text{mg}$$

1. Use information in the problem and in Table 2.4 to determine a proportion (check before solving).

2. Solve for the unknown value. $\frac{\frac{1}{4}\ \text{gr}}{x\ \text{mg}} = \frac{1\text{g}}{60\ \text{mg}}$

---

**Exercise 20**

1. ʒ ii = ______ g
2. 3 T = ______ ml
3. Change gr $\frac{1}{8}$ to milligrams
4. How many drops in 3 ml?
5. 25 ♏ = ______ ml
6. Change 45 ml to ounces.

Although the proportion method for changing units applies uniformly to all changes between systems, applying rules is often a more expedient method for performing conversions. Rules for common conversions are presented below. But remember that if a required unit change does not directly fit a rule, the proportion method should be used.

**RULE 1:** *Grams to grains* To change grams to grains, multiply the number of grams by 15.

**RULE 2:** *Grains to grams* To change grains to grams, divide the number of grains by 15.

---

**EXAMPLE 2.18**

3 g = ______ gr

1. Changing ______ to ______, use Rule ______.
2. Number of grams = ______.
3. Solve for the unknown.

---

**EXAMPLE 2.19**

gr $\frac{1}{4}$ = ______ g

1. Changing ______ to ______, use Rule ______.
2. Number of grains = ______.
3. Find the number of grams.

---

**Exercise 21**

1. 0.2 g = ______ gr
2. gr $\frac{1}{15}$ = ______ g
3. 0.03 gr = ______ gr
4. gr xv = ______ g

**RULE 3:** *Grains to milligrams* To change grains to milligrams, multiply the number of grains by 60.

**RULE 4:** *Milligrams to grains* To change milligrams to grains, divide the number of milligrams by 60.

---

**EXAMPLE 2.20**

30 mg = ______ gr

1. Changing ______ to ______, use Rule ______.
2. Number of milligrams = ______.
3. Find the number of grains.

---

**EXAMPLE 2.21**

$\text{gr}\ \frac{1}{2}$ = ______ mg

1. Changing ______ to ______, use Rule ______.
2. Number of grains = ______.
3. Find the number of milligrams.

---

**Exercise 22**

1. $\text{gr}\ \frac{1}{4}$ = ______ mg
2. 0.25 mg = ______ gr
3. $\text{gr}\ \frac{1}{300}$ = ______ mg
4. 3 mg = ______ gr

**RULE 5:** *Ounces to grams* To change ounces to grams, multiply the number of ounces by 30.

**RULE 6:** *Grams to ounces* To change grams to ounces, divide the number of grams by 30.

---

**EXAMPLE 2.22**

60 g = ______ ℥

1. Changing ______ to ______, use Rule ______.
2. How many grams?
3. Find the number of ounces.

---

**EXAMPLE 2.23**

℥ iss = ______ g

1. Changing ______ to ______, use Rule ______.
2. How many ounces?
3. Find the number of grams.

---

**Exercise 23**

1. 30 g = ___1___ ℥
2. 150 g = ___5___ ℥
3. ℥ iii = ___90___ g (3)
4. ℥ ss = ___15___ g (1/2)

**RULE 7:** *Milliliters* to minims* To change milliliters to minims, multiply the number of milliliters by 15.

**RULE 8:** *Minims to milliliters** To change minims to milliliters, divide the number of minims by 15.

---

**EXAMPLE 2.24**

3 ml = ___45___ ♏

1. Changing ___milliliters___ to ___minims___, use Rule ___7___.
2. Number of milliliters = ___3___.
3. Find the number of minims. 3×15

---

---

**EXAMPLE 2.25**

♏ xviii = ___1.2___ ml

1. Changing ___minims___ to ___milliliters___, use Rule ___8___.
2. Number of minims = ___18___.
3. Find the number of milliliters. 18÷15

---

**Exercise 24**

1. $\frac{3}{4}$ ml = ___11.25___ ♏
2. ♏ xvi = ___1___ ml (16)
3. 0.9 ml = ___13.5___ ♏
4. ♏ xxx = ___2___ ml (30)

**RULE 9:** *Ounces to milliliters** To change ounces to milliliters, multiply the number of ounces by 30.

**RULE 10:** *Milliliters* to ounces* To change milliliters to ounces, divide the number of milliliters by 30.

---

**EXAMPLE 2.26**

75 ml = ___2.5___ ℥

1. Changing ___milliliters___ to ___ounces___, use Rule ___10___.
2. Number of milliliters = ___75___.
3. Find the number of ounces.

---

*Recall that 1 ml = 1 cc, that is, the word milliliter may be replaced by cubic centimeter (cc).

---

**EXAMPLE 2.27**

℥ ss = __15__ ml

1. Changing __ounces__ to __milliliters__ , use Rule __9__ .
2. Number of ounces = __1/2__ .
3. Find the number of milliliters. - 5x30

---

**Exercise 25**

1. ℥ c = __3,000__ ml
100

2. 25 ml = __.83__ ℥

3. ℥ i = __30__ ml

4. 150 ml = __5__ ℥

Occasionally weight measured in pounds needs to be changed to the equivalent value in kilograms and vice versa. This pound weight is in the Avoirdupois system. In this system, 2.2 pounds is equivalent to 1 kilogram.

**RULE 11:** *Kilograms to pounds* To change kilograms to pounds, multiply the number of kilograms by 2.2

**RULE 12:** *Pounds to kilograms* To change pounds to kilograms, divide the number of pounds by 2.2.

---

**EXAMPLE 2.28**

11 kg = __24.2__ lb

1. Changing __kilograms__ to __pounds__ , use Rule __11__ .
2. Number of kilograms = __11__ .
3. Find the number of pounds.

---

**EXAMPLE 2.29**

19.8 lb = __9__ kg

1. Changing __pounds__ to __kilograms__, use Rule __12__ .
2. Number of pounds = __19.8__ .
3. Find the number of kilograms.

---

**Exercise 26**

Solve the following. Express answers to the nearest tenth of a unit.

1. 3 kg = 6.6 lb
2. 20 lb = 9.1 kg
3. 14 kg = 30.8 lb
4. 53.4 lb = 24.3 kg
5. 24.3 kg = 53.5 lb
6. 37.5 lb = 17 kg

## TEMPERATURE EQUIVALENTS

Temperature is measured using two scales: Fahrenheit and Celsius. The relationship between the scales is:

| | Fahrenheit | Celsius |
|---|---|---|
| boiling | 212 | 100 |
| freezing | 32 | 0 |

The Celsius scale was an effort to obtain a scale where freezing was 0 and boiling was 100.

**RULE 13:** *Fahrenheit to Celsius* To change Fahrenheit to Celsius, subtract 32 from the number. Then divide the resulting difference by 1.8.

$$C = \frac{(F - 32)}{1.8}$$

**RULE 14:** *Celsius to Fahrenheit* To change Celsius to Fahrenheit, multiply the number by 1.8. Then add 32 to the resulting product.

$$F = 1.8\,(C) + 32$$

---

**EXAMPLE 2.30**

Solve the following.

78 F = 25.6 C

1. Changing fahrenheit to celsius, use Rule 13.
2. Number of degrees Fahrenheit = 78.
3. Find the number of degrees Celsius.

---

**EXAMPLE 2.31**

Solve the following.

17 C = 62.6 F

1. Changing celsius to fahrenheit, use Rule 14.
2. Number of degrees Celsius = 17.
3. Find the number of degrees Fahrenheit.

---

**Exercise 27**

Solve the following. Express answers to the nearest tenth of a degree.

1. 15 C = 59 F
2. 82.4 F = 28 C
3. 3 C = 37.4 F
4. 68 F = 20 C
5. 37 C = 98.6 F
6. 14 F = −10 C

**Exercise 28**

These problems review the conversions learned in this chapter. Solve using proportions:

1. gtt xv (15) = 15 ♏
2. 7 g = 105 gr
3. ℥ vii (7) = 14 T
4. 50 mg = .83 gr

Solve by applying the correct rule:

5. ℥ 1 = 1500 ml
6. ℥ xvi (16) = 480 g
7. ♏ 24 = 1.6 ml
8. gr xxx (30) = 2 g
9. gr $\frac{1}{6}$ = 10 mg
10. ♏ xx (20) = 1.33 ml
11. 50 ml = 1.67 ℥
12. ♏ xxx = 30 gtt
13. 4 mg = .115 gr
14. gr $\frac{3}{8}$ = 22.5 mg
15. 100 g = 3.33 ℥
16. 5 g = 75 gr
17. ℥ i = 30 g
18. 90 g = 3 ℥
19. 75 ml = 2.5 ℥
20. 4 g = 60 gr
21. 0.4 ml = 6 ♏
22. ℥ ii (2) = 60 ml
23. 45 mg .75 gr
24. 0.5 ml = 7.5 ♏
25. 50 F = 10 C
26. 7 C = 44.6 F
27. −2 C = 28.4 F
28. 102 F = 38.9 C
29. 98.6 F = 37 C
30. −11 C = 12.2 F

## ANSWERS TO EXAMPLES

### *Example 2.1*

18 ml
4 centiliters
5 cg
7 m
2 kg
3 deciliters
5 centimeters

### *Example 2.2*

1. $\frac{x \text{ liters}}{450 \text{ ml}}$
2. 1 liter = 1000 ml
3. $\frac{1 \text{ liter}}{1000 \text{ ml}}$
4. $\frac{x \text{ liters}}{450 \text{ ml}} = \frac{1 \text{ liter}}{1000 \text{ ml}}$
5. $\frac{x}{450} = \frac{1}{1000}$

   $1000x = 450$

   $x = \frac{450}{1000} = 0.45 \text{ liter}$

### *Example 2.3*

$\frac{x \text{ mg}}{38 \text{ g}}$

We know 1 g = 1000 mg

$\frac{1000 \text{ mg}}{1 \text{ g}}$

$\frac{x \text{ mg}}{38 \text{ g}} = \frac{1000 \text{ mg}}{1 \text{ g}}$

$\frac{x}{38} = \frac{1000}{1}$

$x = 38{,}000 \text{ mg}$

### *Example 2.4*

$\frac{54 \text{ cm}}{x \text{ m}}$

We know 1 m = 100 cm

$\frac{54}{x \text{ m}} = \frac{100 \text{ cm}}{1 \text{ m}}$

$\frac{54}{x} = \frac{100}{1}$

$100x = 54$

$x = \frac{54}{100}$

$x = 0.54 \text{ m}$

### *Example 2.5*

6000 ml
300 ml
7000 mg
15000 mm

### *Example 2.6*

0.750 liter
9.8 g
0.042 m

### *Example 2.7*

4000 g
4230 g
543 g
2570 m

### *Example 2.8*

1.545 kg
0.045 kl
0.137 km

### *Example 2.9*

2. 9 drams
3. 5 ounces
4. $1\frac{1}{2}$ grains
5. $\frac{1}{4}$ grain

***Example 2.10***

1. $7\frac{1}{2}$ fluidrams
2. $\frac{1}{2}$ pint
3. 4 fluidounces
4. 3 gallons
5. 5 minims

***Example 2.11***

1. $\frac{x\ f℥}{2\ fʒ}$
2. $1\ f℥ = 8\ fʒ$
3. $\frac{1\ f℥}{8\ fʒ}$
4. $\frac{x\ f℥}{2\ fʒ} = \frac{1\ f℥}{8\ fʒ}$
5. $\frac{x}{2} = \frac{1}{8}$

   $8x = 2$

   $x = \frac{2}{8} = \frac{1}{4}$

   $\frac{1}{4}\ f℥$

***Example 2.12***

1. $\frac{x\ f℥}{3\ \text{qt}}$
2. $1\ \text{qt} = 2\ \text{pt} = 2(16\ f℥) = 32\ f℥$
3. $\frac{32\ f℥}{1\ \text{qt}}$
4. $\frac{x\ f℥}{3\ \text{qt}} = \frac{32\ f℥}{1\ \text{qt}}$
5. $\frac{x}{3} = \frac{32}{1}$

   $x = 3(32) = 96$

   $96\ f℥$

***Example 2.13***

1. Rule 1
2. 8
3. $1\frac{1}{2}$
4. $1\frac{1}{2} \times 8 = 12$ drams

***Example 2.14***

1. Rule 2
2. 60
3. 120
4. $120 \div 60 = 2$ ʒ

***Example 2.15***

1. $\frac{3\ \text{oz}}{x\ \text{gtt}}$
2. $\frac{1\ \text{oz}}{360\ \text{gtt}}$
3. $\frac{3\ \text{oz}}{x\ \text{gtt}} = \frac{1\ \text{oz}}{360\ \text{gtt}}$
4. $\frac{3}{x} = \frac{1}{360}$

   $x = 3(360) = 1080$ gtt

***Example 2.16***

1. $\frac{2\ \text{ml}}{x\ ♏}$
2. $1\ \text{ml} = 15\ ♏$
3. $\frac{1\ \text{ml}}{15\ ♏}$
4. $\frac{2\ \text{ml}}{x\ ♏} = \frac{1\ \text{ml}}{15\ ♏}$
5. $\frac{2}{x} = \frac{1}{15}$

   $x = 2(15) = 30$

   30 ♏

***Example 2.17***

$$\frac{x\ \text{mg}}{\frac{1}{4}\ \text{gr}} = \frac{60\ \text{mg}}{1\ \text{gr}}$$

$$\frac{x}{\frac{1}{4}} = \frac{60}{1}$$

$$x = \frac{1}{4}(60)$$

$$x = 15\ \text{mg}$$

***Example 2.18***

1. grams to grains, Rule 1
2. 3
3. $3(15) = 45$ gr

***Example 2.19***

1. grains to grams, Rule 2
2. $\frac{1}{4}$
3. $\frac{1}{4} \div 15 = \frac{1}{4} \times \frac{1}{15} = \frac{1}{60}$

   $\frac{1}{60}$ g

***Example 2.20***

1. milligrams to grains, Rule 4
2. 30
3. $30 \div 60 = \frac{1}{2}$

   $\frac{1}{2}$ gr

***Example 2.21***

1. grains to milligrams, Rule 3
2. $\frac{1}{2}$
3. $\frac{1}{2}(60) = 30$

   30 mg

***Example 2.22***

1. grams to ounces, Rule 6
2. 60
3. $60 \div 30 = 2$

   2 ounces

***Example 2.23***

1. ounces to grams, Rule 5
2. $1\frac{1}{2}$
3. $\left(1\frac{1}{2}\right)(30) = (1.5)(30) = 45$

   45 g

***Example 2.24***

1. milliliters to minims, Rule 7
2. 73
3. $3(15) = 45$

   45 ♏

***Example 2.25***

1. minims to milliliters, Rule 8
2. 18
3. $18 \div 15 = \frac{18}{15} = \frac{6}{5}$

   $\frac{6}{5}$ ml = 1.2 ml

***Example 2.26***

1. milliliters to ounces, Rule 10
2. 75
3. $75 \div 30 = 2.5$

   2.5 ℥

***Example 2.27***

1. ounces to milliliters, Rule 9
2. $\frac{1}{2}$
3. $\frac{1}{2} \times 30 = 15$

   15 ml

***Example 2.28***

1. kilograms to pounds, Rule 11
2. 11
3. 11 (2.2) = 24.2 lbs

***Example 2.29***

1. pounds to kilograms, Rule 12
2. 19.8
3. $19.8 \div 2.2 = 9$ kg

***Example 2.30***

1. Fahrenheit to Celsius, Rule 13
2. 78
3. $\frac{(78 - 32)}{1.8} = \frac{46}{1.8} = 25.6$ C

***Example 2.31***

1. Celsius to Fahrenheit, Rule 14
2. 17
3. $1.8(17) + 3 = 62.6$ F

# UNIT II

Unit 2 consists of chapters dealing with medication computations associated with the different situations encountered by the nurse, such as pediatric medications, oral medications, intramuscular medications, or intravenous medications. The majority of the problems appearing in this unit were taken from actual physician orders while the remainder of the problems were chosen to provide additional practice with the applied mathematical techniques.

The mathematical problem originates with the drug order and the label on the vial. It is from these two sources that the nurse obtains the information used in the mathematical computations. Nurses usually refer to the drug order as the "desired" dosage and to the drug label information as the "on-hand" dosage.

To simulate the nurse's functioning as it relates to mathematical computations, the drug order and drug label have been used in the chapters in this unit. No two companies use exactly the same form for their labels, so a generic form is used in this book. The drug order, on the other hand, has been more of a problem to simulate. Some nursing practice environments still use a drug card and kardex, other situations use a unit-dose format, and computerized drug orders are used in some nursing practice situations. All of these are merely different formats used toward the same goal: communicating the physician's order for medication for a specific patient. Most nursing environments are currently implementing some form of computerized format for managing medication information. Therefore the authors have chosen to present drug orders using a drug order printout format.

Drug Order Printout

| **Name:** Lewis, George | **Room:** 204 |
|---|---|
| **Medication:** Kantrex 500 mg | |
| **Route:** I.M. | **Time:** bid |

There also seem to be some arbitrary "rules of thumb" regarding the appropriate equivalents for 1 milliliter. Sometimes the equivalent used is 1 ml = 15 minims, while at other times 1 ml = 16 minims. To accurately calculate and provide answers in this text, 1 ml = 15 minims is used in all exercises. It should be noted that within the 10% tolerance for allowable error, the computed answer should make negligible difference in the answers. When working problems, remember to use

1 ml = 15 minims

# 3 Oral Medications

## CHAPTER OBJECTIVES

- Use the basic operations of ratio and proportions to solve problems for the oral medications
- Demonstrate proficiency in correctly reading medication labels
- Exhibit proficiency in correctly reading medication orders
- Demonstrate proficiency in correctly interpreting medicine cup measurement scales
- Display proficiency in simulating desired volume of liquid medication on standard medicine cups

## INTRODUCTION

Oral administration is one of the most common methods of administering medicine in hospitals today. Therefore in many schools of nursing the student begins the administration of medicines with the oral route. Other methods for administering medications will be discussed in later chapters.

Often the medication you have on hand will be of a different dosage from the one ordered by the physician. When this occurs, the nurse performs some mathematical computations to determine what amount of the drug on hand is needed to give the patient the dosage ordered by the physician.

The following examples should help you develop a method for solving dosage problems encountered with oral medications.

## TABLETS

The physician has ordered propranolol hydrochloride 10 mg. The label indicates each tablet contains 20 mg.

The drug on hand is 20 mg per tablet; desired dosage is 10 mg. Set up a proportion and use the ideas discussed in Chapter 1 to compute the correct dosage.

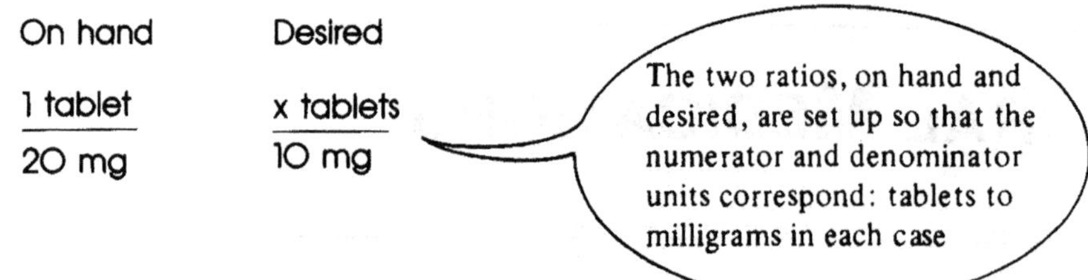


Now that two ratios are formed, set them equal and solve for the value of $x$.

| Step | | | If trouble going from step to step | | Go to page |
|---|---|---|---|---|---|
| 1 | $\frac{1}{20} = \frac{x}{10}$ | | | | |
| 2 | $20x = 10$ | now divide each side by 20 | 1 | 2 | 35 |
| 3 | $x = \frac{10}{20}$ | perform the division | 2 | 3 | 37 |
| 4 | $x = \frac{1}{2}$ tab | | 3 | 4 | 12 |

So $\frac{1}{2}$ tablet constitutes the correct dosage.
Read the following order:

**Name:** J. Doe **Room:** 18

**Medication:**

Codeine 30 mg every 4 hrs prn

**Route:** oral

Secure the codeine tablets for J. Doe. The label reads codeine sulfate 60 mg.

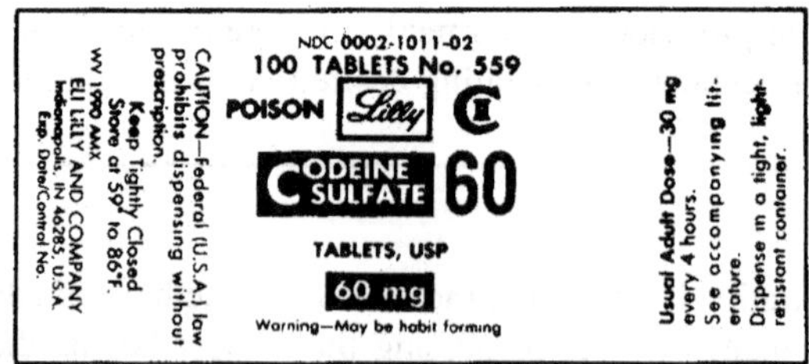


Since the dosage on the drug order (*desired* dosage) and the dosage on the drug label (*on-hand* dosage) are not the same, a computation is necessary.

The drug on hand is 60 mg per tablet. The desired dosage is 30 mg. Setting up a proportion, again use the ideas in Chapter 1.

| On hand | Desired |
|---|---|
| $\frac{1 \text{ tablet}}{60 \text{ mg}}$ | $\frac{x \text{ tablets}}{30 \text{ mg}}$ |

| Step | If trouble going from step to step | | Go to page |
|---|---|---|---|
| 1 $\frac{1}{60} = \frac{x}{30}$ | | | |
| 2 $60x = 30(1)$ | 1 | 2 | 35 |
| 3 $x = \frac{30}{60}$ | 2 | 3 | 37 |
| 4 $x = \frac{1}{2}$ tab | 3 | 4 | 12 |

If you had trouble obtaining $\frac{1}{2}$ tablet as the correct dosage, review the appropriate math review section.

For your benefit, the arithmetic computation involved in each step of the solution is outlined with reference to Chapter 1.

Work the following example.

---

**EXAMPLE 3.1***

Drug Order Printout

| **Name:** J. Doe | **Room:** 8 |
|---|---|
| **Medication:** aspirin gr xv | |
| **Route:** oral | **Time:** q 6 h prn |

Drug Label

N 0047-0606-32

6505-00-153-8750

**Aspirin Tablets, USP**

**Analgesic/Antipyretic**

For relief of minor aches and pains and reduction of fever.

**WARNING:** Children and teenagers should not use this medicine for chicken pox or flu symptoms before a doctor is consulted about Reye syndrome, a rare but serious illness.

**Ingredients:** Aspirin. Also contains corn starch; microcrystalline cellulose.

Quality Sealed for your protection*

1000 Tablets

5 grains (325 mg) each

WARNER CHILCOTT

$\frac{15\text{ gr}}{5\text{ gr}}$ x tab 3 tab

*Answers to examples appear on pages 96-98.

1. What is the drug dosage on hand? 15
2. What is the drug dosage desired? 5
3. Set up the proportion by filling the boxes with the missing information.

| On hand | Desired |
|---|---|
| [15] tablets / 5 gr | $x$ tablets / [15] gr |

4. Set up the proportion and solve for $x$.

5. How many tablets is the nurse to give? 3

---

## EXAMPLE 3.2

As the medicine nurse, you find the following drug order and drug label:

Drug Order Printout

| **Name:** J. Doe | **Room:** 8 |
|---|---|
| **Medication:** Phenobarbital 15 mg | |
| **Route:** oral | **Time:** 9:00 A.M. |

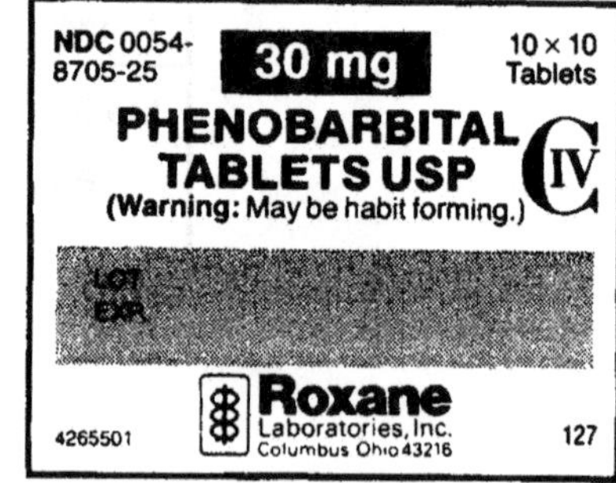


In the space below, determine the correct dosage to be administered. Work Example 3.2 here (when finished, check work in the answers section).

$\frac{30 \text{ mg}}{1 \text{ tab}} = \frac{15 \text{ mg}}{x \text{ tab}} \quad x = \frac{1}{2} \text{ tab}$

---

## EXAMPLE 3.3

The physician orders Lanoxin 0.5 mg. The drug label reads Lanoxin 0.25 mg. How many tablets should the patient receive?

$\frac{.5 \text{ mg}}{.25 \text{ mg}} \times 1 \text{ tab} = 2 \text{ tab}$

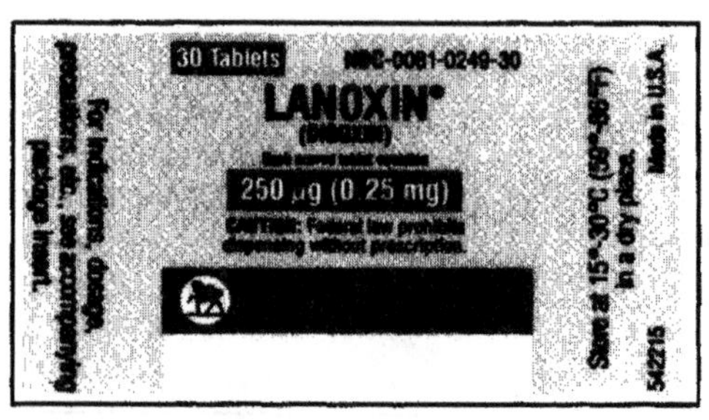

The physician orders Gantrisin gr xv. The label reads Gantrisin 250 mg.

Reading the drug order and drug label, your attention first focuses on the dose. The drug order is expressed in the apothecaries' system (gr xv), and the drug label is in the metric system (250 mg). First, determine an equivalency of units so that a proportion can be set up using like units for on hand and desired dosages.

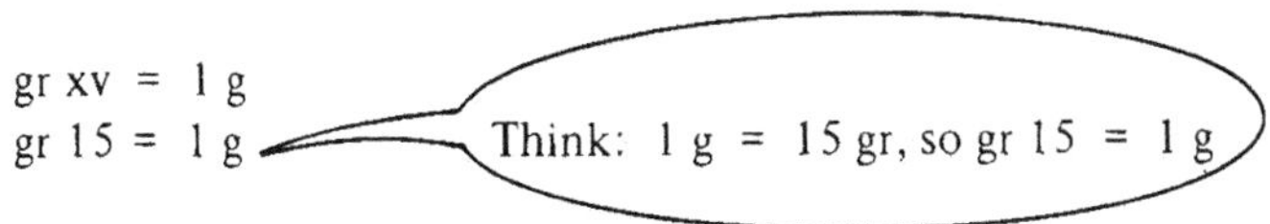


Set up the ratios:

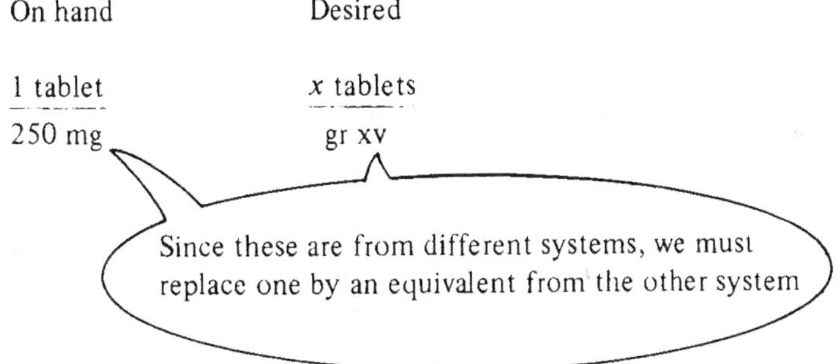


Replace gr xv by 1 g because 15 gr = 1 g.

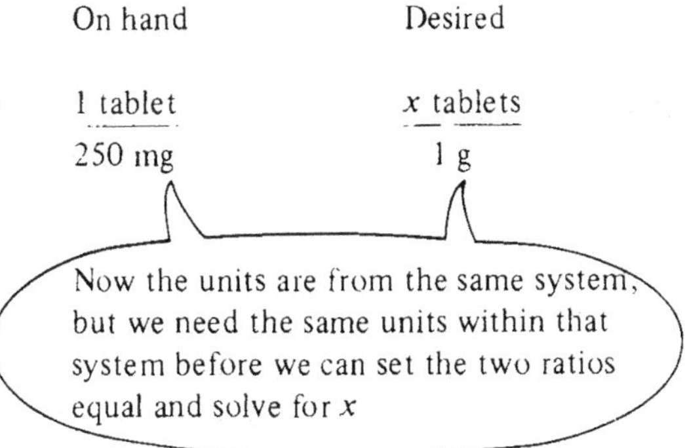


Recall that 1 g is 1000 mg (to change grams to milligrams, move the decimal three places to the right, so 1 g = 1000 mg). When 1 g is replaced by its equivalent, the proportion becomes

| On hand | Desired |
|---|---|
| $\frac{1 \text{ tablet}}{250 \text{ mg}}$ | $\frac{x \text{ tablets}}{1000 \text{ mg}}$ |

Since the units in the two ratios are identical, set the ratios equal and solve:

$$\frac{1}{250} = \frac{x}{1000}$$

$$250x = 1000$$

$$x = \frac{1000}{250} = 4$$

Four tablets, each containing 250 mg, will provide your patient with gr xv.

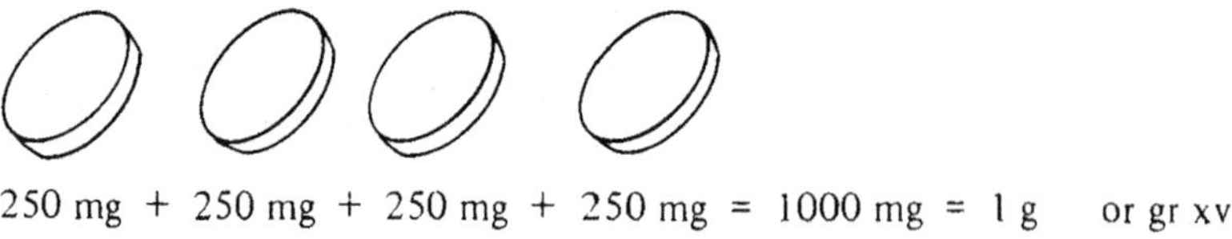

250 mg + 250 mg + 250 mg + 250 mg = 1000 mg = 1 g or gr xv

---

**EXAMPLE 3.4**

Read the following drug order and drug label:

| **Name:** J. Doe | **Room:** 13 |
|---|---|
| **Medication:** phenobarbital gr ss | |
| **Route:** oral | **Time:** 9/1/6 |

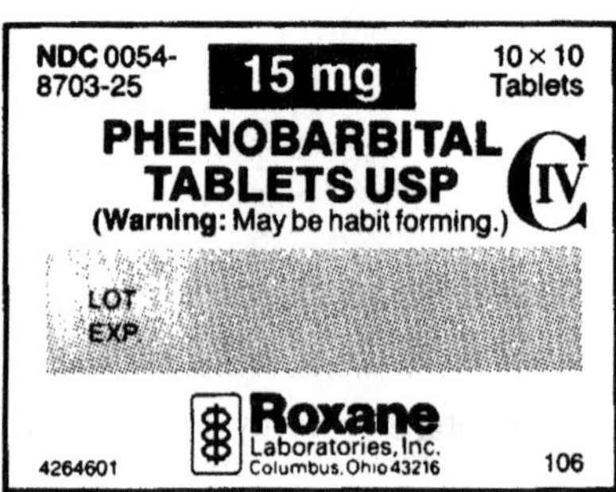


1. Use the information on the drug order and drug label to set up a proportion (but check your equation before solving).

2. Solve the equation to determine the dosage.

$\frac{1/2 \text{ gr}}{15 \text{ mg}} \times 1 \text{ tab}$

$\frac{30 \text{ mg}}{15 \text{ mg}} \times 1 \text{ tab} = \boxed{2 \text{ tab}}$

---

## LIQUIDS

The past few examples have dealt specifically with oral medications involving tablets. This section will focus on dosage for liquid medications. The physician orders Mellaril concentrate 60 mg. The nurse finds Mellaril concentrate 30 mg/ml in the drug cabinet. How much Mellaril should the nurse administer?

To compute the dosage, first check the drug available:

On hand

30 mg in 1 ml

The dosage requested by the physician should be considered next:

Desired

60 mg in ? ml

It is realized that 60 mg is requested, but the number of milliliters required to contain the 60 mg is not known. This has been represented above by a question mark. Liquid medication problems are similar to the tablet medications; indeed, the methods of solving the two types of problems are identical.

Set up the proportion as in the previous examples:

| On hand | Desired |
|---|---|
| $\dfrac{1\text{ ml}}{30\text{ mg}}$ | $\dfrac{x\text{ ml}}{60\text{ mg}}$ |

$$\frac{1}{30} = \frac{x}{60}$$

$$30x = 60\ (1)$$

$$x = \frac{60}{30} = 2\text{ ml}$$

The necessary dosage is 2 ml.

Is this answer reasonable? Yes, when you think that

| | | |
|---|---|---|
| | 1 ml contains 30 mg | and |
| add | 1 ml contains 30 mg | |
| yields | 2 ml contains 60 mg | |

So the procedure works for both tablets and liquid medications.

Work the following example.

---

**EXAMPLE 3.5**

The physician orders elixir of phenobarbital 4 mg. The bottle in the drug cabinet reads 4 mg/5 ml. How much elixir of phenobarbital must the nurse give to ensure correct dosage?

**1.** On hand Desired

$\dfrac{5\text{ ml}}{4\text{ mg}}$

Is milliliters the usual unit of measure? ________

2. Set up the proportion to solve the problem.

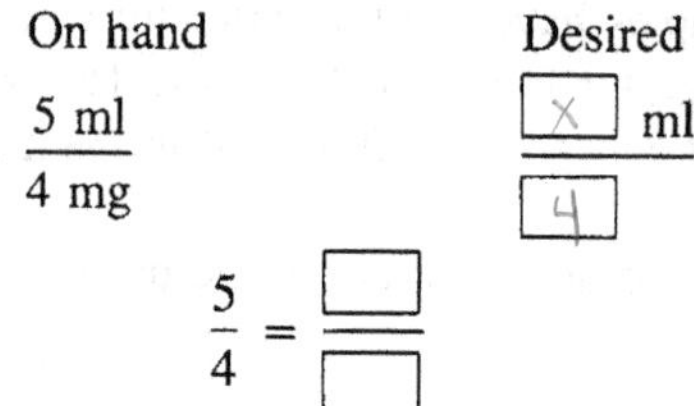

| On hand | Desired |
|---|---|
| $\frac{5\text{ ml}}{4\text{ mg}}$ | $\frac{\boxed{X}\text{ ml}}{\boxed{4}}$ |

$$\frac{5}{4} = \frac{\square}{\square}$$

3. Check the above equation before you solve.
4. Solve the equation.

$4x = 20$

$\boxed{x = 5}$

5. What is the correct dosage? ________

---

In the above example, did you realize that a mathematical computation was not necessary because both the on-hand and desired dosages were identical? When the desired and on-hand drugs are the same measure (4 mg), the number of units of volume (5 ml) on the drug label constitutes the correct dosage.

Read the following drug order and drug label:

Drug Order Printout

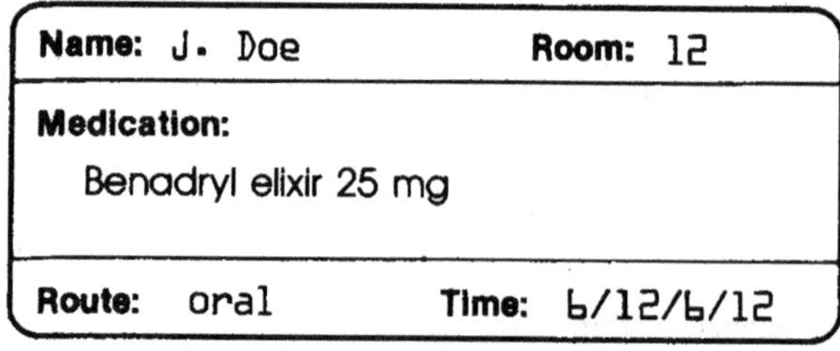

**Name:** J. Doe **Room:** 12

**Medication:**

Benadryl elixir 25 mg

**Route:** oral **Time:** 6/12/6/12

Drug Label

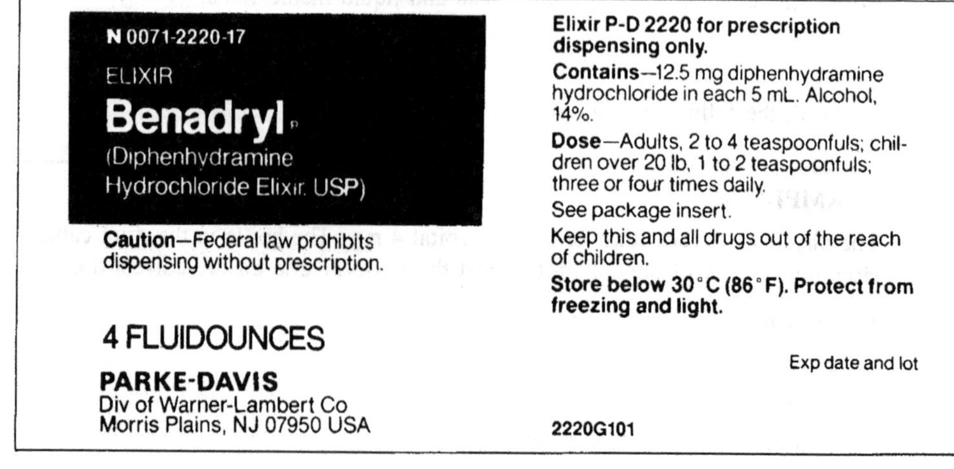

**N 0071-2220-17**

ELIXIR

**Benadryl**

(Diphenhydramine Hydrochloride Elixir, USP)

**Caution**—Federal law prohibits dispensing without prescription.

4 FLUIDOUNCES

**PARKE-DAVIS**
Div of Warner-Lambert Co
Morris Plains, NJ 07950 USA

**Elixir P-D 2220 for prescription dispensing only.**

**Contains**—12.5 mg diphenhydramine hydrochloride in each 5 mL. Alcohol, 14%.

**Dose**—Adults, 2 to 4 teaspoonfuls; children over 20 lb, 1 to 2 teaspoonfuls; three or four times daily.

See package insert.

Keep this and all drugs out of the reach of children.

**Store below 30°C (86°F). Protect from freezing and light.**

Exp date and lot

**2220G101**

Set up the proportion to determine the correct dosage:

| On hand | Desired |
|---|---|
| $\frac{12.5\text{ mg}}{5\text{ ml}}$ | $\frac{25\text{ mg}}{x\text{ ml}}$ |

| Step | | If trouble going from step to step | | Go to page |
|---|---|---|---|---|
| 1 | $\frac{12.5}{5} = \frac{25}{x}$ | | | |
| 2 | $12.5x = 125$ | 1 | 2 | 35 |
| 3 | $x = \frac{125}{12.5}$ | 2 | 3 | 37 |
| 4 | $x = 10$ | 3 | 4 | 12 |

The correct dosage is 10 ml.

---

## EXAMPLE 3.6

Drug Order Printout

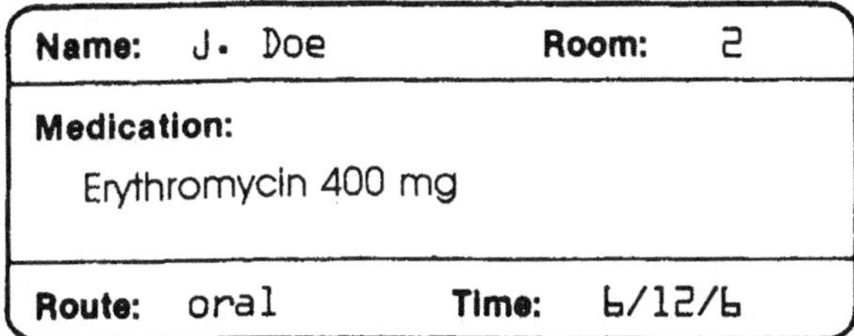

Name: J. Doe Room: 2

Medication:

Erythromycin 400 mg

Route: oral Time: 6/12/6

Drug Label

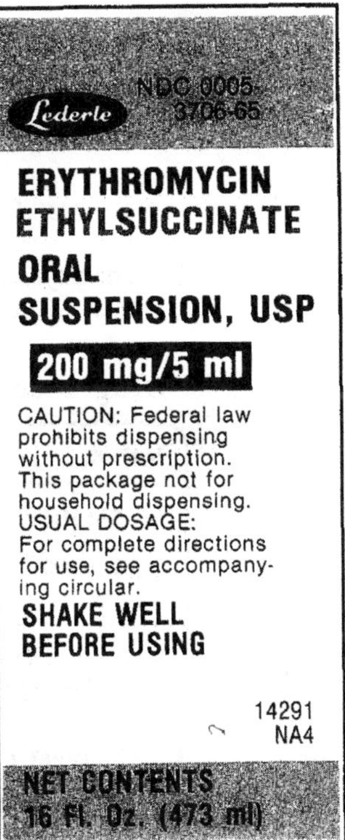


1. What is the dose of
   a. The drug on hand? 200/5ml
   b. The drug desired? 400 mg
2. Now set up a proportion to determine the correct dosage:

| On hand | Desired |
|---|---|
| $\frac{5\text{ ml}}{[200]\text{ mg}}$ | $\frac{[x]\text{ ml}}{400\text{ mg}}$ |

$$\frac{5}{\square} = \frac{\square}{400}$$

3. Solve for the unknown number of milliliters.

200x = 2000
x = 10

4. Mark the correct dosage on the medicine cup.

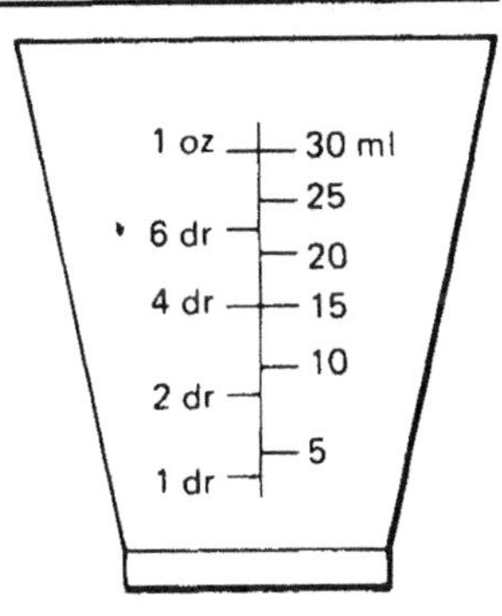

If you had difficulty in the above example, review the problem worked immediately preceding the example. If you still have difficulty, review the entire chapter before attempting the exercises.

### Exercise 29

**DIRECTIONS:** Some of the following problems will require you to extract information from drug orders and drug labels. For all problems compute the correct dosage. When a medicine cup is given, shade the medicine cup to indicate your answer.

1. The order is for Tylenol elixir 120 mg. The drug label reads Tylenol elixir 120 mg/5 ml. How many milliliters does the patient receive? ________

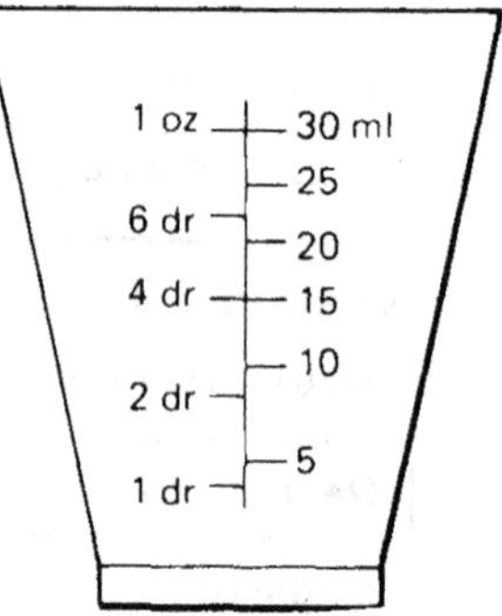


2. The physician orders ferrous sulfate 500 mg. The drug label reads ferrous sulfate 220 mg/5 ml. How many milliliters of ferrous sulfate does the patient receive? 11.4

Drug Order Printout

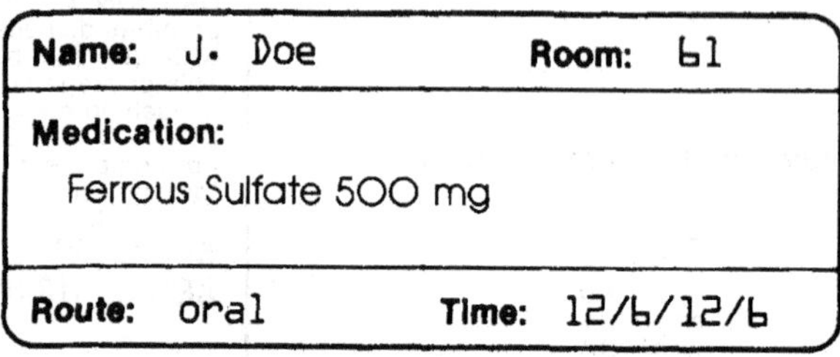

**Name:** J. Doe **Room:** 61

**Medication:**
Ferrous Sulfate 500 mg

**Route:** oral **Time:** 12/6/12/6

3. The order is for Pen-Vee K 250 mg. The drug label reads Pen-Vee K 125 mg/5 ml. How many milliliters does the patient receive?  10

**ART**

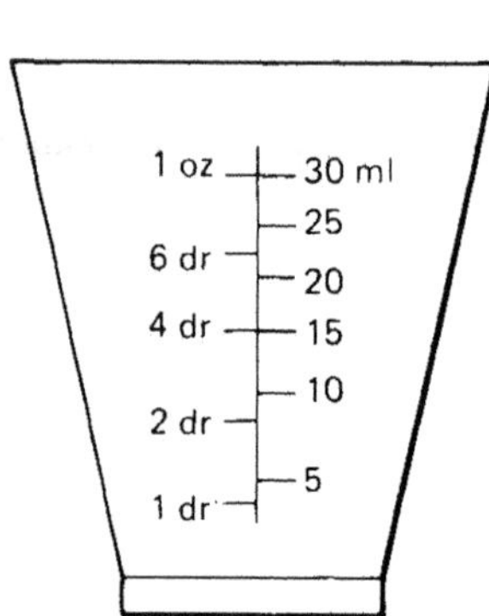

4.

| **Name:** J. Doe | **Room:** 30 |
|---|---|
| **Medication:** Synthroid 0.1 mg | |
| **Route:** oral | **Time:** stat |

Drug Label

BOOTS-FLINT

**SYNTHROID®**

**(Levothyroxine Sodium Tablets, USP)**

**100 mcg (0.1 mg)**

Dosage. Adults: Initial - 25 to 100 mcg (0.025 to 0.1 mg) daily. Usual maintenance dose - 100 to 200 mcg (0.1 to 0.2 mg) daily. Children: Initial - 25 mcg (0.025 mg) daily. Dosage adjusted by physician until desired response is obtained. See directions for higher maintenance dosage. SEE ACCOMPANYING DIRECTIONS.

Contains FD&C Yellow No. 5 (tartrazine) as a color additive.

Keep this and all medications out of the reach of children.

For hospital use only. Packaging is not child resistant.

**Caution: Federal (U.S.A.) law prohibits dispensing without prescription.**

Manufactured by Boots Puerto Rico Inc. Jayuya, Puerto Rico 00664 0795

For Boots-Flint, Inc. Lincolnshire, IL 60015 USA a subsidiary of The Boots Company (USA) Inc.

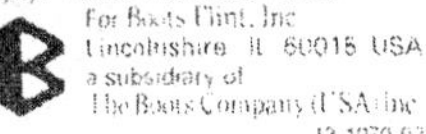

How many tablets of synthroid does the patient receive? 1

5. The order is for Nembutal elixir 60 mg. The drug label reads Nembutal elixir 20 mg/5 ml. How many milliliters of Nembutal elixir does the patient receive? 15

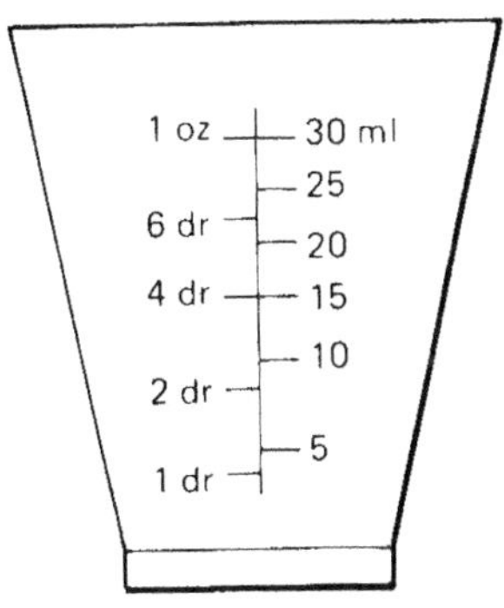

6. The order is for Feosol elixir 300 mg. The drug label reads Feosol elixir 220 mg/5 ml. How many milliliters does the patient receive? 6.8 ml

7. Drug Order Printout

**Name:** J. Doe **Room:** 91

**Medication:**

Aldomet 250 mg

**Route:** oral **Time:** 9/5

Drug Label

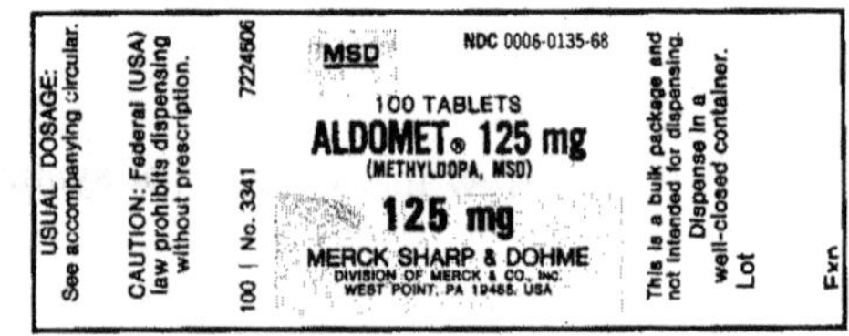


How many tablets of Aldomet does the patient receive? 2 tablets

8. The order is for chloral hydrate elixir 1 g. The drug label reads chloral hydrate elixir gr viiss/ 5 ml. How many milliliters does the patient receive? 10 ml

$\frac{1g}{7.5\ gr} \times 5ml \quad \frac{15gr}{7.5gr} \times 5ml = 10$

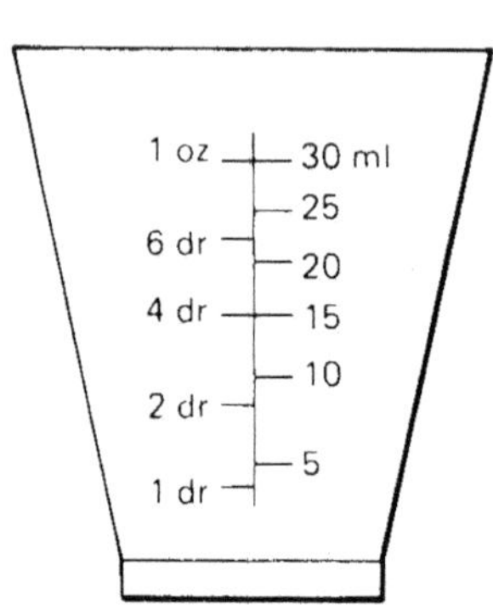

**9.** Drug Order Printout

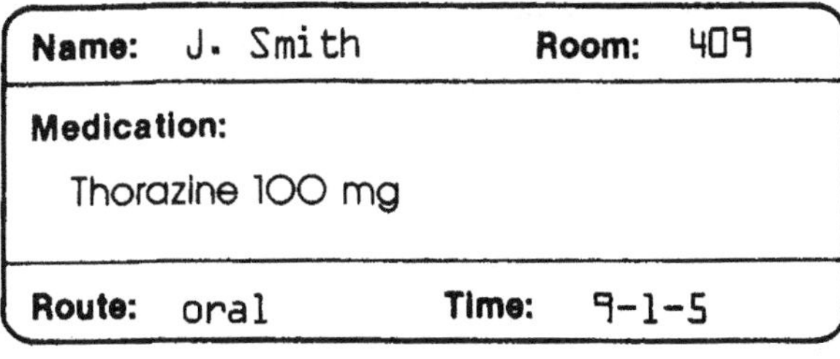

Name: J. Smith Room: 409

Medication:

Thorazine 100 mg

Route: oral Time: 9-1-5

Drug Label

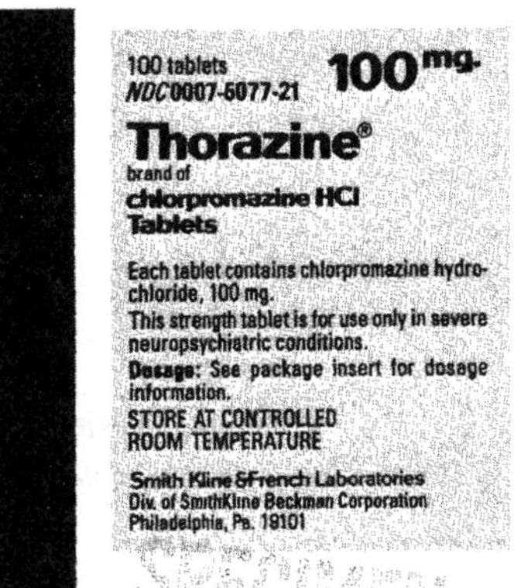


How many tablets should the patient receive?

1 tablet

**10.** The physician orders Keflex suspension 250 mg. The drug label reads Keflex 125 mg/5 ml. How many milliliters should the patient receive?

10 ml

**11.** The order is for 0.25 mg of Lanoxin elixir. The drug label reads Lanoxin elixir 0.05 mg/ml. How many milliliters should the patient receive?

5 ml

**12.** Drug Order Printout

| Name: M. Jones | Room: 101 |
|---|---|
| Medication: Thorazine 50 mg | |
| Route: oral | Time: tid |

Drug Label

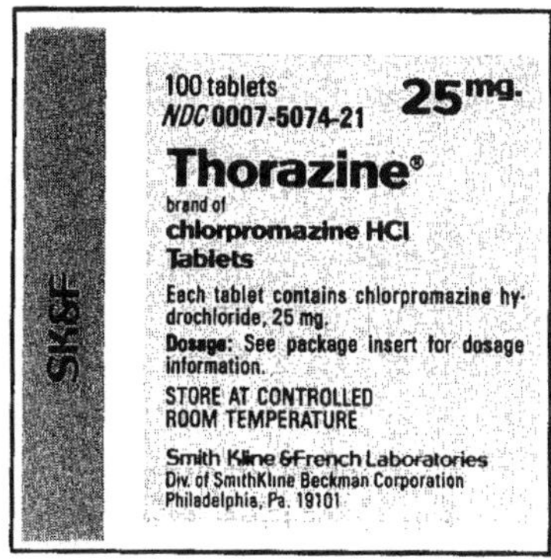


How many tablets should the patient receive?

2 tablets

**13.** The physician orders Thorazine concentrate 60 mg. The drug label reads Thorazine concentrate 100 mg/ml. How many milliliters should the patient receive?

.6 ml

**14.** The physician orders leuothyroxine 100 mcg. The drug label reads leuothyroxine 200 mcg. How many tablets should the patient receive?

½ tablets

**15.** How many tablets should the patient receive?

Drug Order Printout

| **Name:** P. Jones | **Room:** 102 |
|---|---|
| **Medication:** Aspirin gr x | |
| **Route:** oral | **Time:** tid |

2 tablets

Drug Label

**N 0047-0606-32**

6505-00-153-8750

# Aspirin Tablets, USP

**Analgesic/Antipyretic**

For relief of minor aches and pains and reduction of fever.

**WARNING:** Children and teenagers should not use this medicine for chicken pox or flu symptoms before a doctor is consulted about Reye syndrome, a rare but serious illness.

**Ingredients:** Aspirin. Also contains corn starch; microcrystalline cellulose.

**Quality Sealed for your protection**

1000 Tablets
5 grains (325 mg) each

WC WARNER CHILCOTT

16. The physician orders digitoxin 0.2 mg. How many tablets should the patient receive?

2 tablets

Drug Label

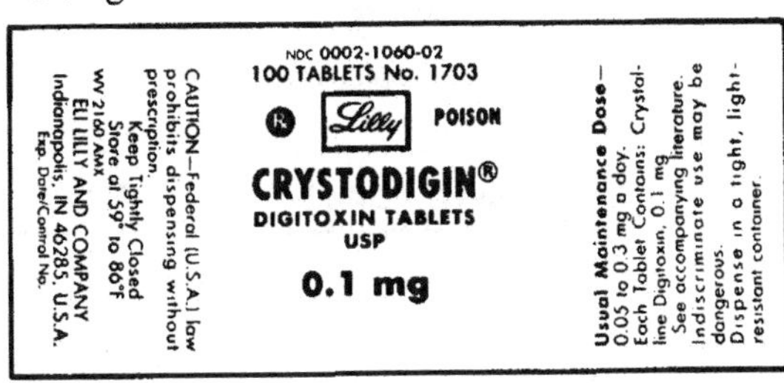


17. The order is for Ativan 2 mg. The drug label reads Ativan 1 mg. How many tablets should the patient receive?

2 tablets

18. The physician orders Hydrea 500 mg. How many tablets should the patient receive?

1 tablets

Drug Label

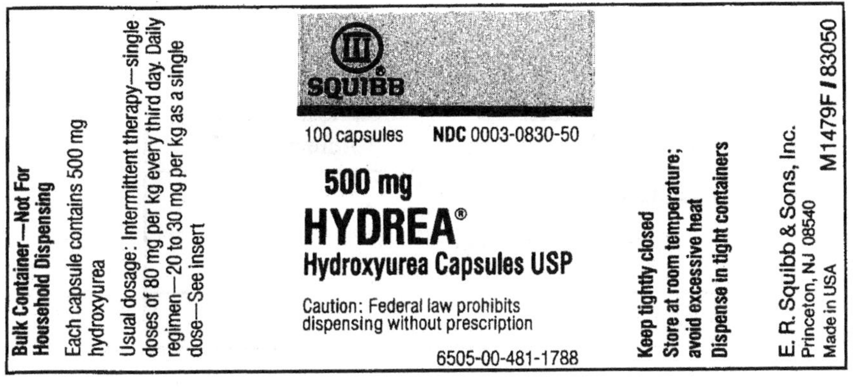

**19.** Drug Order Printout

| **Name:** M. Mere | **Room:** 601 |
|---|---|
| **Medication:** Synthroid 75 mcg | |
| **Route:** oral | **Time:** daily |

Drug Label

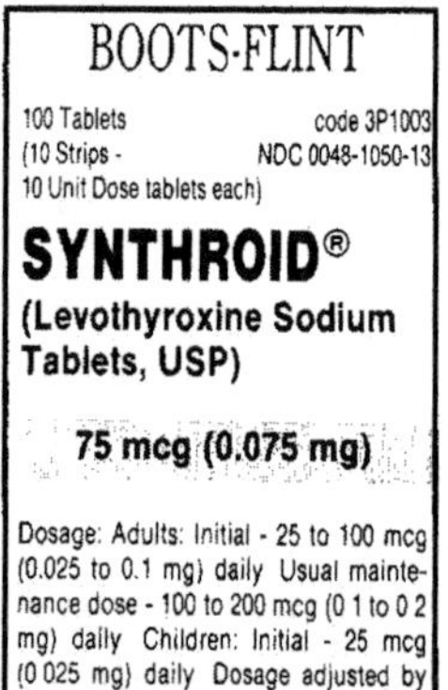


How many tablets should the patient receive?

1 tablet

**20.** The physician orders Gantrisin suspension 900 mg. The drug label reads Gantrisin suspension 1000 mg/10 ml. How many milliliters should the patient receive?

9 ml

**21.** Drug Order Printout

| **Name:** P. Potter | **Room:** 303 |
|---|---|
| **Medication:** Coumadin 10 mg | |
| **Route:** oral | **Time:** daily |

Drug Label

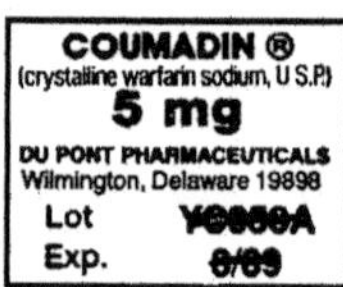


How many tablets should the patient receive?

2 tab

**22.** Drug Order Printout

| **Name:** J. Jones | **Room:** |
|---|---|
| **Medication:** Imuran 25 mg | |
| **Route:** oral | **Time:** |

Drug Label

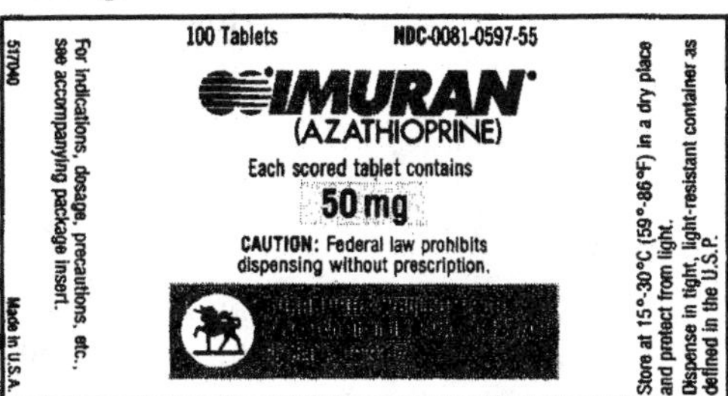


How many tablets should the patient receive?

**23.** The physician orders phenobarbital elixir 60 mg. The drug label reads phenobarbital elixir gr 1/4 per ml. How many milliliters should the patient receive?

4ml

**24.** The physician orders Ritalin 20 mg. The drug label reads Ritalin 10 mg. How many tablets should the patient receive?

2 tablets

**25.**

| **Name:** L. Smith | **Room:** 600 |
|---|---|
| **Medication:** Coumadin 2.5 mg | |
| **Route:** oral | **Time:** daily |

COUMADIN ®
(crystalline warfarin sodium, U.S.P.)
5 mg
DU PONT PHARMACEUTICALS
Wilmington, Delaware 19898
Lot
Exp.

How many tablets should the patient receive?

1/2 tablets

26. The physician orders Thorazine concentrate 60 mg. The drug label reads Thorazine concentrate 30 mg/ml. How many milliliters should the patient receive?

2 ml

**Exercise 30**

These will give you additional practice in oral medications.

1. The order is for phenobarbital gr iss. The drug label reads phenobarbital gr ss. How many tablets should the patient receive? ________

3 tablets

2. The order is for Synthroid 125 mcg. The drug label reads Synthroid 0.125 mg. How many tablets should the patient receive? ________

1 tab

3. The physician orders Prolixin 1 mg. The drug label reads Prolixin 2 mg. How many tablets does the patient receive? ________

1/2 tab

4. The physician orders Aldomet 500 mg. The drug label reads Aldomet 1 g. How many tablets should the patient receive?

1/2 tab

5. The order is for Persantine 25 mg. The drug label reads Persantine 50 mg. How many tablets does the patient receive? ________

1/2 tab

6. The physician orders furosemide oral solution 40 mg. The drug label reads furosemide 10 mg/ml. How many milliliters should the patient receive? ________

4ml

7. The order is for Lanoxin 0.5 mg. The drug label reads Lanoxin 0.25 mg. How many tablets should the patient receive? ______

2 tab

8. The order is for Elavil 25 mg. The drug label reads Elavil 10 mg. How many tablets should the patient receive? ______

2 1/2 tab

9. The physician orders aspirin gr x. The drug label reads aspirin 325 mg. How many tablets should the patient receive? ______

2 ml

10. The order is for chloral hydrate liquid gr viiss. The drug label reads chloral hydrate gr x per dram. How many milliliters should the patient receive? ______

3 ml

11. The order is for Mycostatin mouthwash 250,000 U. The drug label reads Mycostatin mouthwash 100,000 U ml. How many milliliters should the patient receive? ______

2 1/2 ml

12. The order is for Lanoxin elixir 0.125 mg. The drug label reads Lanoxin elixir 0.05 mg/ml. How many milliliters should the patient receive? ______

2 1/2 ml

## ANSWERS TO EXAMPLES

### *Example 3.1*

**1.** gr v per tablet

**2.** gr xv

**3.** On hand $\frac{1 \text{ tablet}}{5 \text{ gr}}$ Desired $\frac{x \text{ tablets}}{15 \text{ gr}}$

**4.** $\frac{1}{5} = \frac{x}{15}$

$5x = 15$

$x = \frac{15}{5}$

$x = 3$

**5.** Since our solution was $x = 3$, we give three tablets.

### *Example 3.2*

On hand Desired

**Step**

**1.** $\frac{1 \text{ tablet}}{30 \text{ mg}}$ $\frac{x \text{ tablets}}{15 \text{ mg}}$

**2.** $30x = 15$

**3.** $x = \frac{15}{30}$

$$\begin{array}{r} 0.5 \\ 30\overline{)15.0} \\ \underline{15\ 0} \end{array}$$

**4.** $x = 0.5$ or $\frac{1}{2}$ tablet

| If trouble going from step | to step | Go to page |
|---|---|---|
| 1 | 2 | 35 |
| 2 | 3 | 37 |
| 3 | 4 | 12 |

### *Example 3.3*

On hand Desired

$\frac{1 \text{ tablet}}{0.25 \text{ mg}}$ $\frac{x \text{ tablets}}{0.5 \text{ mg}}$

$\frac{1}{0.25} = \frac{x}{0.5}$

$0.25x = 0.5$

$x = \frac{0.5}{0.25} = 2$

Two tablets.

### *Example 3.4*

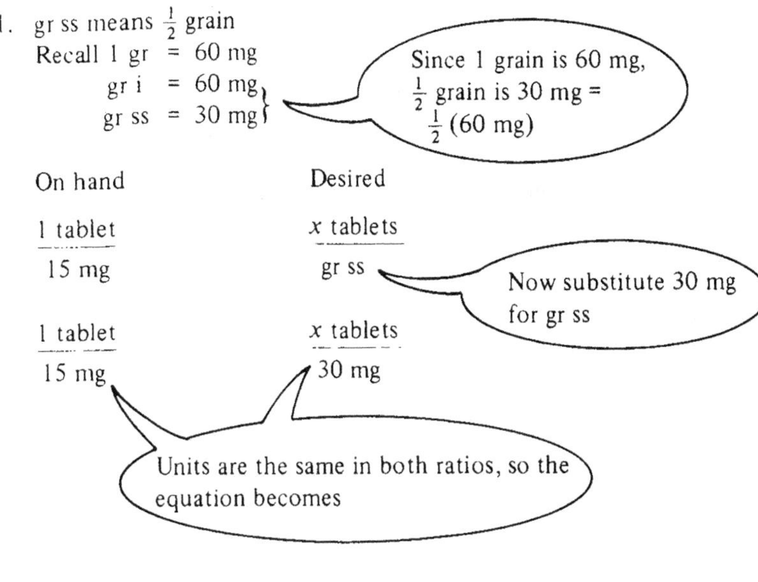


$$\frac{1}{15} = \frac{x}{30}$$

Did you get the correct equation?
If yes, return to the problem and continue as directed.
If no, review the previous exercise worked in the chapter, then rework the example again.

**2.** $\frac{1}{15} = \frac{x}{30}$

$$15x = 30$$

$$x = \frac{30}{15}$$

$$x = 2$$

Two tablets is the correct dosage.

### *Example 3.5*

On hand Desired

$\frac{5 \text{ ml}}{4 \text{ mg}}$

**1.** Since the medicine cup is graduated in 5 ml increments, it is *correct* to use milliliters as the unit of measure.

**2.** $\frac{5 \text{ ml}}{4 \text{ mg}}$ $\frac{x \text{ ml}}{4 \text{ mg}}$ (Given as the dosage desired)

**3.** The correct equation is

$$\frac{5}{4} = \frac{x}{4}$$

4. $4x = 20$

$x = \frac{20}{4}$

$x = 5$

5. 5 ml

***Example 3.6***

1. **a.** 200 mg/5 ml **b.** 400 mg

2. $\frac{5 \text{ ml}}{200 \text{ mg}} \quad \frac{x \text{ ml}}{400 \text{ mg}}$

$\frac{5}{200} = \frac{x}{400}$

3. $\frac{5}{200} = \frac{x}{400}$

$200x = 2000$

$x = \frac{2000}{200}$

$x = 10$

4. 10 ml

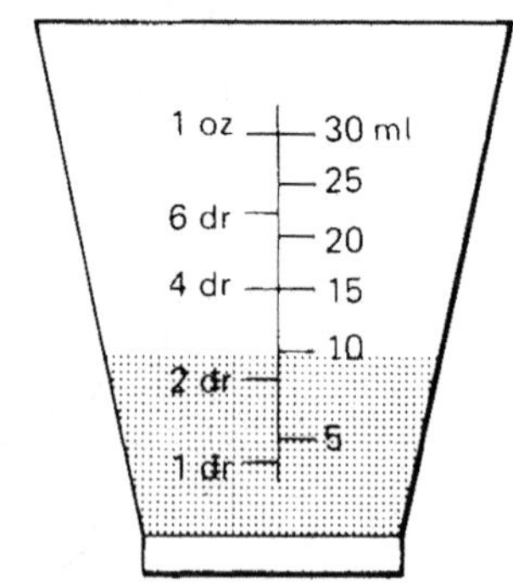

# 4 PARENTERAL MEDICATIONS

## CHAPTER OBJECTIVES

- Utilize the basic operations of ratio and proportions when solving medication problems for intramuscular and subcutaneous injections
- Demonstrate proficiency in correctly reading 2½ ml syringes
- Determine dosage for medications manufactured in units
- Exhibit proficiency in accurately reading U100 syringes

## INTRODUCTION

Chapter 3 dealt with oral medications. Another common method of administering medications is the parenteral route. You probably have not had many occasions to administer medications by the parenteral route before enrolling in nursing school. This method does require more specific nursing skill in that particular sites for injection must be carefully selected.

Parenteral medications are delivered by injection directly into subcutaneous tissue (subcutaneous injection), into selected muscles (intramuscular injection, abbreviated IM), or into veins (intravenous injection, abbreviated IV).

Intramuscular injection is probably the most common of the three, but nurses are assuming more and more responsibility for administering intravenous medications and solutions. Of the subcutaneous medications, insulin is probably the most common drug administered by nurses.

Because there are manufacturing differences in some drugs administered parenterally, each section begins with a short explanation of the characteristics of the drugs discussed in the section.

To correlate the arithmetical answer to the math problem with clinical applications, you will be asked to shade a syringe (such as the one pictured below) to indicate correct dosage. The amount of fluid drawn into the cylinder of the syringe is adjusted by manipulating the plunger. The plunger of the pictured syringe indicates eight-tenths of a milliliter of fluid is in the cylinder ready to be administered. For purposes of practice, the syringes used hereafter do not contain a plunger. This allows you to shade the syringe to the point where you would stop the plunger in drawing up the dosage. This simulates drawing up the medication to make the mathematical answer more meaningful.

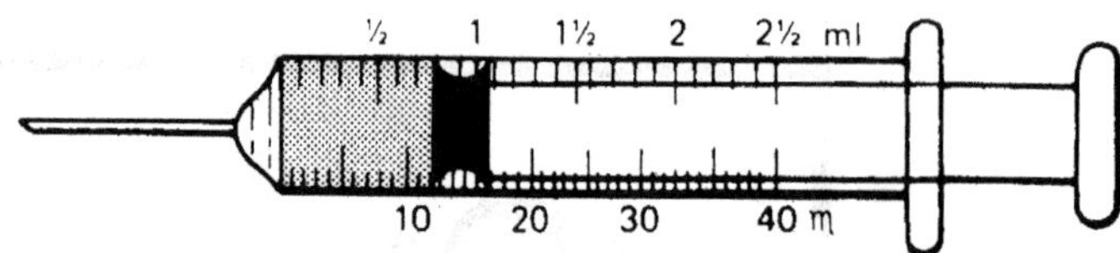


## INTRAMUSCULAR MEDICATIONS FROM PREPARED-STRENGTH LIQUIDS

This section concerns intramuscular medications contained in multiple-dose vials or single-dose ampules. An ampule contains only a single dose for one injection, such as morphine 10 mg. A multiple-dose vial may contain as many as 10 doses and will specify the amount of drug contained in each milliliter of solution, e.g., morphine 10 mg/ml.

The drug dosage of prepared liquids ordered by the physician may differ from the label on the ampule or vial. When this happens, the nurse must perform a mathematical computation to determine the amount of liquid volume for the correct drug dosage. The formula for computing these dosages is the same as that used in solving dosages for oral medications.

Read the following drug order:

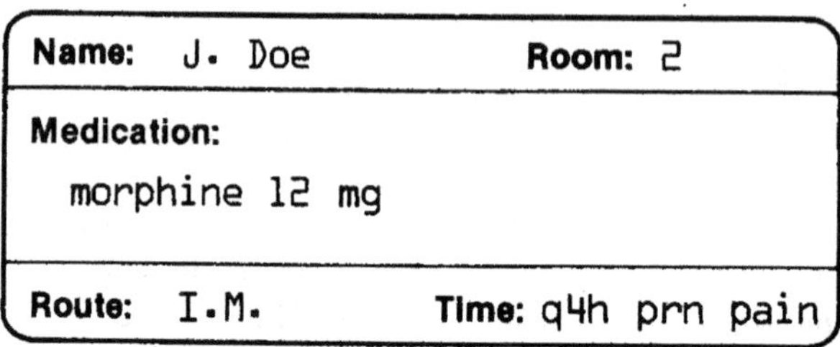

Name: J. Doe Room: 2

Medication:

morphine 12 mg

Route: I.M. Time: q4h prn pain

The label reads morphine 10 mg/ml. The on-hand drug is morphine, 10 milligrams per milliliter. The physician's order is for 12 mg of morphine. Set up the proportion to solve the drug problem:

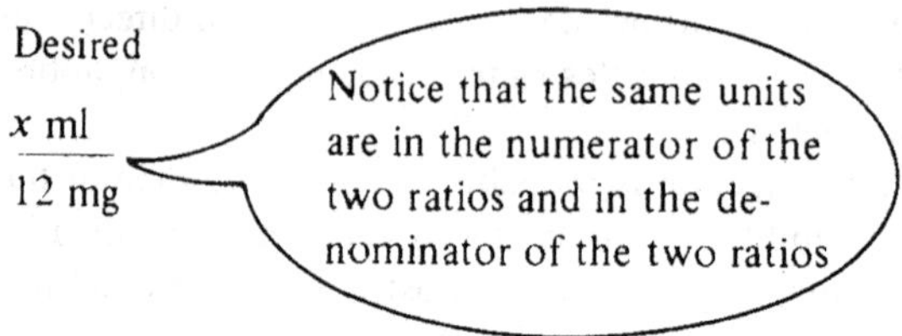

This yields the equation

$$\frac{1}{10} = \frac{x}{12}$$

$$10x = 12\ (1)$$

$$x = \frac{12}{10}$$

$$x = 1.2$$

The correct dosage is 1.2 ml.
To simulate drawing up the 1.2 ml of morphine, shade the syringe:

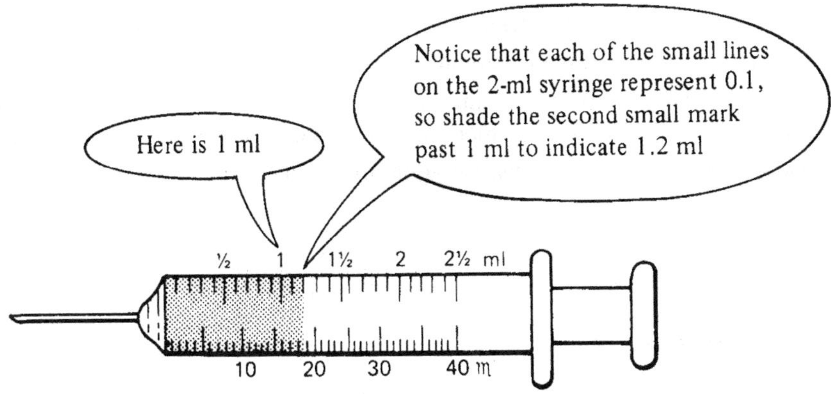


Solve the following example.

---

**EXAMPLE 4.1***

The order is for Librium 25 mg. The label reads 100 mg in two milliliters.

1. What is the dosage on hand?
2. What is the dosage desired?
3. Set up a proportion and determine the correct dosage.

4. Shade the syringe to indicate the proper dosage.

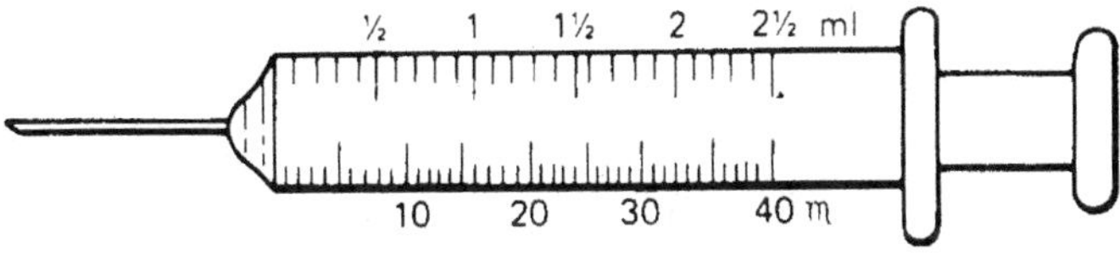


---

*Answers to examples appear on page 130.

---

**EXAMPLE 4.2**

The physician orders Nafcil 500 mg. The drug label reads Nafcil 1 g/2 ml. How many milliliters should the patient receive? ______

1. What is the dosage on hand?
2. What is the dosage desired?
3. Set up a proportion and determine the correct dosage.

---

Work the following problem before doing the exercises. The physician orders atropine 0.6 mg IM. The atropine vial reads atropine gr $\frac{1}{150}$ per ml. There are two avenues open at this point. Either the grains can be converted to milligrams or the milligrams can be converted to grains. As a general rule, using grains results in a more difficult math problem since the numbers involved are fractions, and so it is usually easier to convert grains to the other system of measure. Change gr $\frac{1}{150}$ to milligrams. From Table 2.4

$$\text{gr } \frac{1}{150} = 0.4 \text{ mg}$$

Set up the proportion as follows:

$$\begin{array}{cc} \text{On hand} & \text{Desired} \\ \dfrac{1 \text{ ml}}{\text{gr } \frac{1}{150}} & \dfrac{x \text{ ml}}{0.6 \text{ mg}} \end{array}$$

substituting

$$\frac{1 \text{ ml}}{0.4 \text{ mg}} \qquad \frac{x \text{ ml}}{0.6 \text{ mg}}$$

The resulting equation is

$$\frac{1}{0.4} = \frac{x}{0.6}$$

$$0.4x = 0.6\ (1)$$

$$0.4x = 0.6$$

$$x = \frac{0.6}{0.4}$$

Dividing yields

$$\begin{array}{r} 1.5 \\ 0.4 \overline{)\,0.6\,0\,0} \\ \underline{4\phantom{0\,0}} \\ 2\,0\phantom{0} \\ \underline{2\,0\phantom{0}} \\ 0\phantom{0} \end{array}$$

Add on zeros in case they are needed in the division

The value of $x$ is 1.5, so the correct dosage is 1.5 ml. Syringes are marked in milliliters as a general rule, but since milliliters and cubic centimeters are equivalent,

$$1.5 \text{ ml} = 1.5 \text{ cc}$$

Hence the correct dosage is 1.5 ml or 1.5 cc. Shading the 2 ml syringe to simulate drawing up 1.5 ml yields

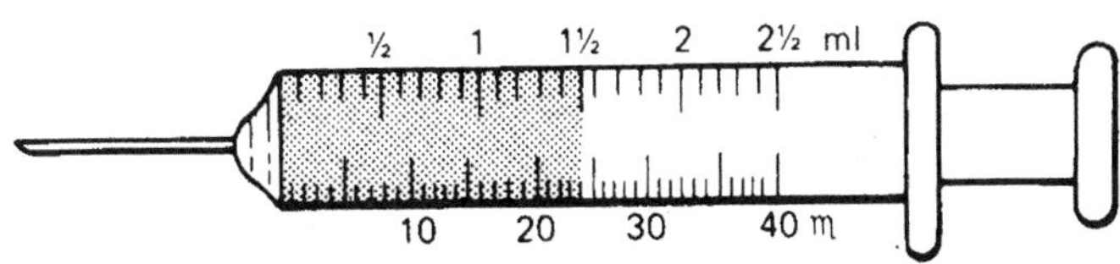


**Exercise 31**

**DIRECTIONS:** Some of the following problems will require you to extract information from drug orders and drug labels. For all problems compute the correct dosage. When a syringe is given, shade the syringe to indicate your answer.

1. The physician ordered gentamicin 60 mg IM. The drug label reads gentamicin 40 mg/ml. How many milliliters does the patient receive? 1.5

$\frac{60 \text{ mg}}{x \text{ ml}} = \frac{40 \text{ mg}}{1}$ $40x = 60$

$x = 1.5$

2. Drug Order Printout

| **Name:** J. Doe | **Room:** 20 |
|---|---|
| **Medication:** Kantrex 60 mg | |
| **Route:** I.M. | **Time:** 8/8 |

Drug Label

How many milliliters does the patient receive? 1.6

$\frac{60 \text{ mg}}{x \text{ ml}} = \frac{75 \text{ mg}}{2 \text{ ml}}$

$75x = 120$

$x = 1.6$

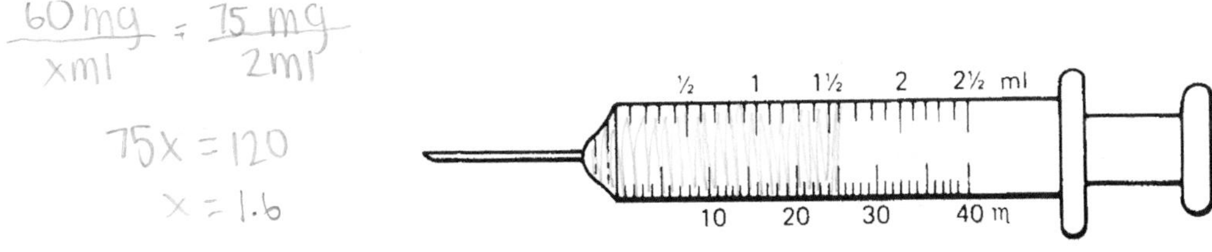

**3.** The physician ordered Demerol 15 mg IM. The drug label reads Demerol 50 mg/ml. How many milliliters does the patient receive? ________

15 mg / x ml = 50 mg / ml

50x = 15

x = .3

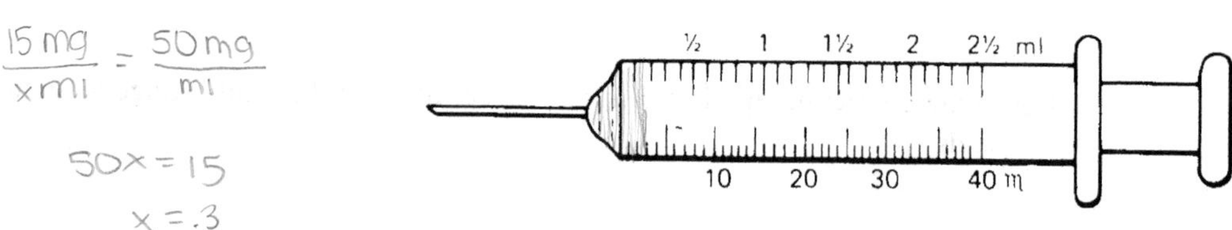


**4.** Drug Order Printout

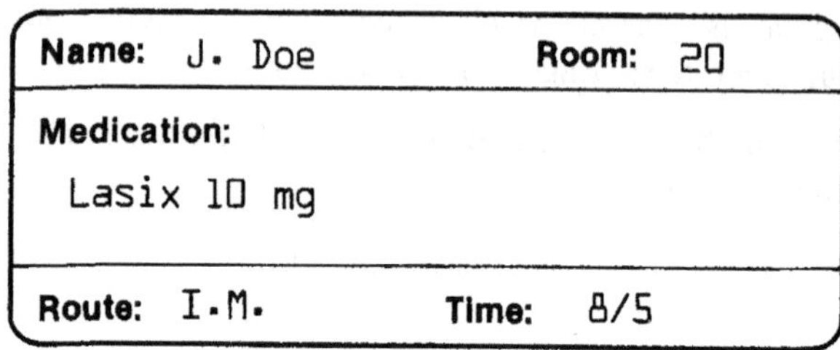

**Name:** J. Doe **Room:** 20

**Medication:**

Lasix 10 mg

**Route:** I.M. **Time:** 8/5

Drug Label

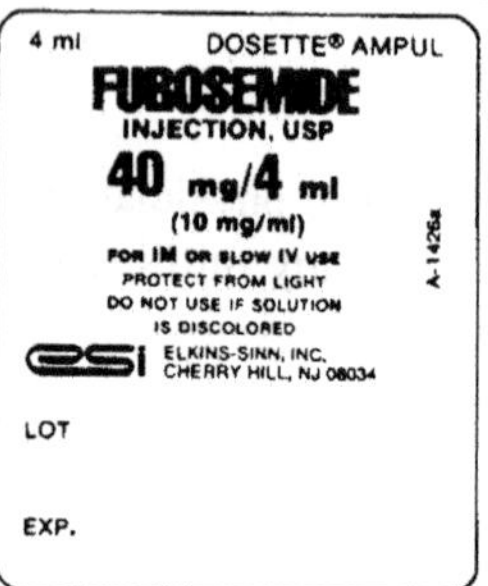


How many milliliters does the patient receive? __1__

10 mg / x ml = 40 mg / 4 ml

40x = 40

x = 1

**5.** The order is for morphine 8 mg IM. The drug label reads morphine 10 mg/ml. How many milliliters does the patient receive? __.8__

8 mg / x ml = 10 mg / ml

10x = 8

x = .8

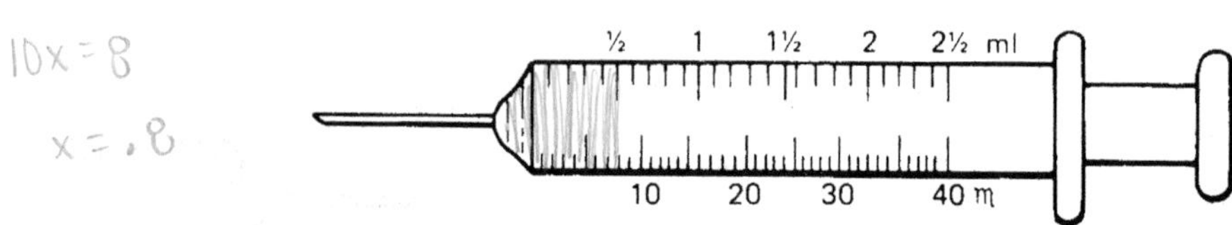

6. Drug Order Printout

| **Name:** J. Doe | **Room:** 24 |
|---|---|
| **Medication:** Digoxin 0.125 mg | |
| **Route:** I.M. | **Time:** 9:00 A.M. |

Drug Label

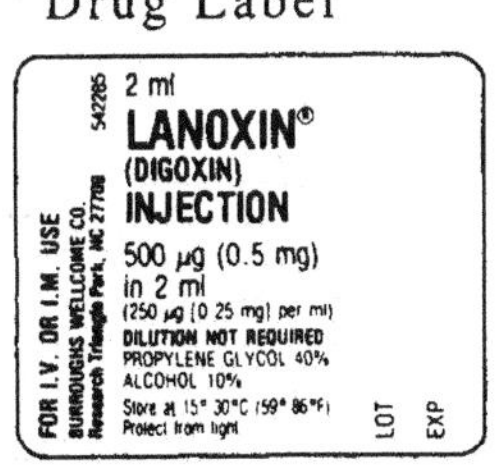


How many milliliters should the patient receive? .5

$\frac{0.125 \text{ mg}}{x \text{ ml}} = \frac{0.5 \text{ mg}}{2 \text{ ml}}$

$0.5x = .25$

$x = .5$

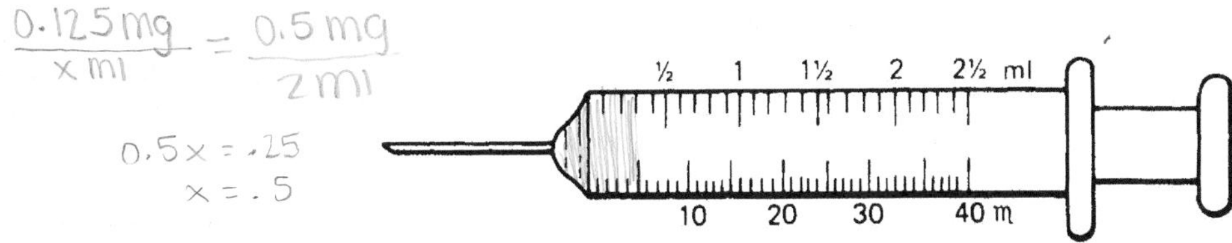


7. The order is for Dilaudid gr $\frac{1}{64}$. The drug label reads Dilaudid gr $\frac{1}{32}$ per milliliter. How many milliliters should the patient receive? .5

$\frac{\frac{1}{64} \text{ gr}}{x \text{ ml}} = \frac{\frac{1}{32} \text{ gr}}{\text{ml}}$

$\frac{1}{32}x = \frac{1}{64}$

$x = .5$

8. The order is for Prostaphlin 375 mg IM. How many milliliters does the patient receive? .75

$\frac{375 \text{ mg}}{x \text{ ml}} = \frac{250 \text{ mg}}{1.5 \text{ ml}}$

$x = 2.2$

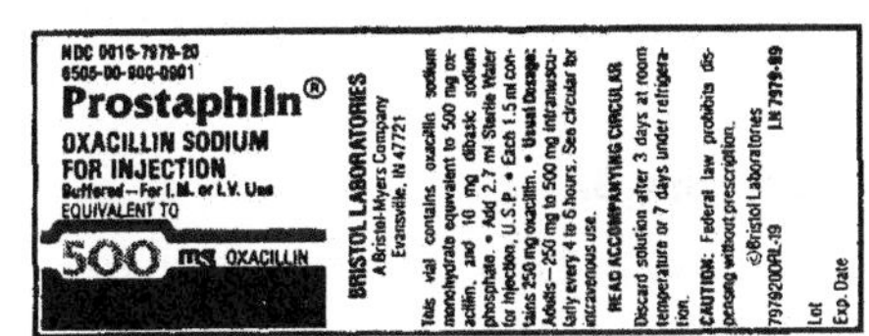


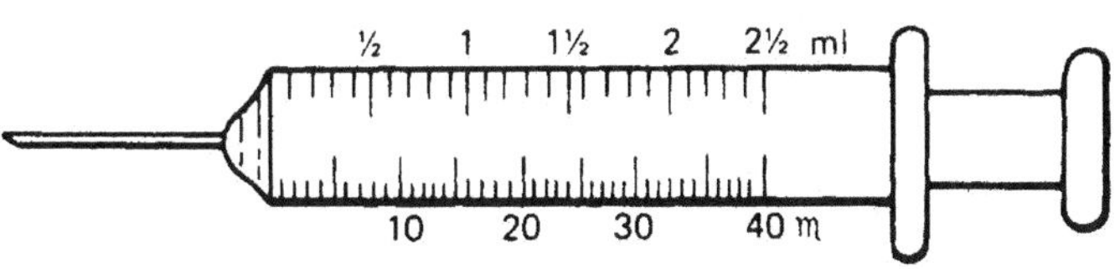

**9.** The order is for morphine gr $\frac{1}{6}$ IM. How many milliliters does the patient receive? __1____

$\frac{\frac{1}{6}\text{ gr}}{x\text{ ml}} = \frac{10\text{ mg}}{1\text{ ml}}$

$\frac{\frac{1}{6}\text{ gr}}{x\text{ mg}} = \frac{1\text{ gr}}{60\text{ mg}}$

$x = 10$

$\frac{10\text{ gr}}{x\text{ ml}} = \frac{10\text{ mg}}{1\text{ ml}}$

$x = 1$

Drug Label

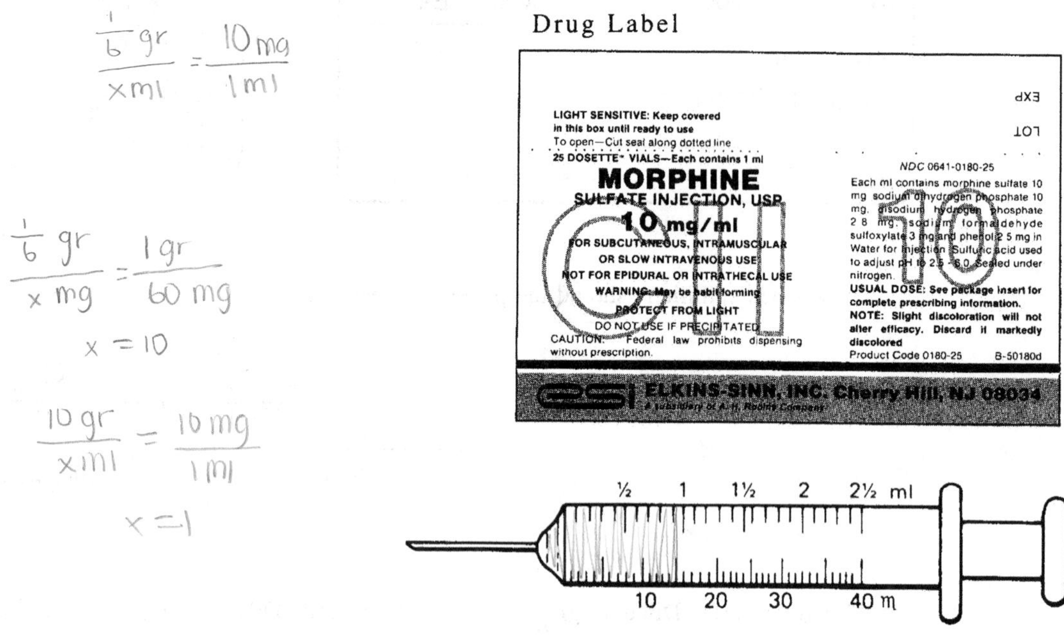


**10.** The order is for sodium luminal 60 mg. The label reads 130 mg/2 ml. How many milliliters does the patient receive? ________

$\frac{60\text{ mg}}{x\text{ ml}} = \frac{130\text{ mg}}{2\text{ ml}}$

$130x = 120$

$x = .92$

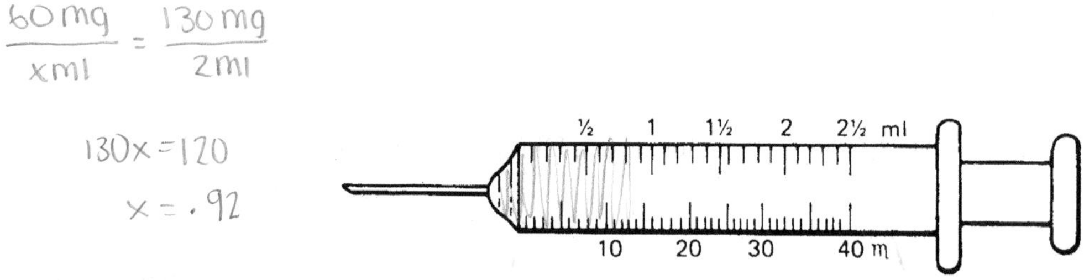


### Exercise 32

These problems will give you additional practice. (Be sure to round to tenths of a milliliter.)

1. The physician ordered Serpasil 2.5 mg IM. The drug label reads Serpasil 5 mg/ml. How many milliliters should the patient receive? __.5____

$\frac{2.5\text{ mg}}{x\text{ ml}} = \frac{5\text{ mg}}{\text{ml}}$

$5x = 2.5$

$x = .5$

2. The physician orders Benadryl 50 mg IM. The drug label reads Benadryl 25 mg/ml. How many milliliters does the patient receive? 2

$$\frac{50\text{ mg}}{x\text{ ml}} = \frac{25\text{ mg}}{\text{ml}}$$

$$x = 2$$

3. The order is for Thorazine 10 mg IM. The drug label reads Thorazine 25 mg/ml. How many milliliters should the patient receive? .4

$$\frac{10\text{ mg}}{x\text{ ml}} = \frac{25\text{ mg}}{\text{ml}}$$

$$25x = 10$$

$$x = .4$$

4. The physician orders Demerol 75 mg IM. The drug label reads Demerol 50 mg/ml. How many milliliters should the patient receive? 1.5

$$\frac{75\text{ mg}}{x\text{ ml}} = \frac{50\text{ mg}}{1\text{ ml}}$$

$$50x = 75$$

$$x = 1.5$$

5. The order is for morphine 3 mg. The drug label reads morphine gr $\frac{1}{10}$ per ml. How many milliliters should the patient receive? .5

$$\frac{3\text{ mg}}{\text{ml}} = \frac{\text{gr}\ \frac{1}{10}}{\text{ml}}$$

6. The physician orders digitoxin 0.3 mg. The drug label reads digitoxin 0.2 mg/ml. How many milliliters should the patient receive? 1.5

$$\frac{0.3\text{ mg}}{x\text{ ml}} = \frac{0.2\text{ mg}}{\text{ml}}$$

$$0.2x = 0.3$$

7. The order is for atropine gr $\frac{1}{100}$. The drug label reads atropine gr $\frac{1}{150}$ per ml. How many milliliters should the patient receive? 1.5

$$\frac{\text{gr}\ \frac{1}{100}}{\text{ml}} = \frac{\text{gr}\ \frac{1}{150}}{\text{ml}}$$

**8.** The order is for morphine gr $\frac{1}{12}$. The drug label reads morphine 10 mg/ml. How many milliliters should the patient receive? .5

$$\frac{gr\ \frac{1}{12}}{x\ ml} = \frac{10\ mg}{ml}$$

**9.** The physician orders gentamicin sulfate 10 mg. The drug label reads gentamicin 40 mg/ml. How many milliliters should the patient receive? ________

$$\frac{10\ mg}{x\ ml} = \frac{40\ mg}{ml}$$

$40x = 10 \quad x = .25$

**10.** The physician orders Demerol 75 mg. The drug label reads Demerol 100 mg in 1 milliliter. How many milliliters should the patient receive? ________

$$\frac{75\ mg}{x\ ml} = \frac{100\ mg}{ml}$$

$100x = 75 \quad x = .75$

**11.** The physician orders Decadron 16 mg. The drug label reads Decadron 24 mg/ml. How many milliliters should the patient receive?

$$\frac{16\ mg}{x\ ml} = \frac{24\ mg}{ml}$$

$24x = 16 \quad x = .67$

**12.** Drug Order Printout

Drug Label

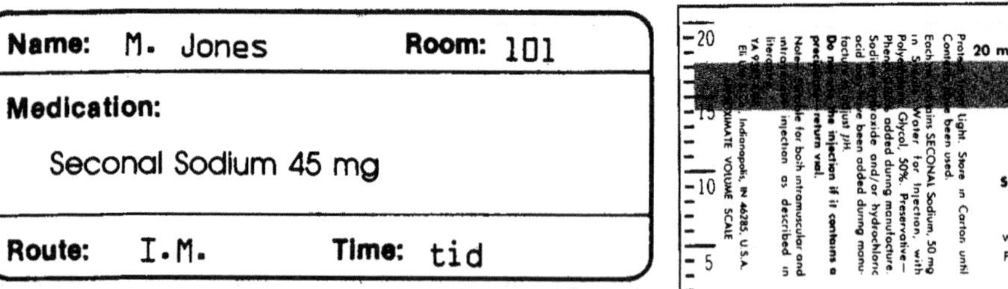

**Name:** M. Jones **Room:** 101

**Medication:**

Seconal Sodium 45 mg

**Route:** I.M. **Time:** tid



How many milliliters should the patient receive?

$$\frac{45\ mg}{x\ ml} = \frac{50\ mg}{ml}$$

$50mg = 45$

$x = .9$

13. The physician orders Decadron 5 mg. The drug label reads Decadron 4 mg/ml. How many milliliters should the patient receive?

$$\frac{5\text{ mg}}{x\text{ ml}} = \frac{4\text{ mg}}{\text{ml}}$$

$$4x = 5$$
$$x = 1.25$$

14. The physician orders Apresoline 15 mg. The drug label reads Apresoline 20 mg/ml. How many milliliters should the patient receive?

$$\frac{15\text{ mg}}{x\text{ ml}} = \frac{20\text{ mg}}{\text{ml}}$$

$$20x = 15$$
$$x = .75$$

15. The physician orders Nebcin 50 mg. The drug label reads Nebcin 40 mg/ml. How many milliliters should the patient receive?

$$\frac{50\text{ mg}}{x\text{ ml}} = \frac{40\text{ mg}}{\text{ml}}$$

$$40x = 50$$
$$x = 1.25$$

16. The physician orders Ancef 500 mg. The drug label reads Ancef 330 mg/ml. How many milliliters should the patient receive?

$$\frac{500\text{ mg}}{x\text{ ml}} = \frac{330\text{ mg}}{\text{ml}}$$

$$330x = 500$$
$$x = 1.52$$

17. The physician orders Demerol 10 mg. The drug label reads Demerol 50 mg/ml. How many milliliters should the patient receive?

$$\frac{10\text{ mg}}{x\text{ ml}} = \frac{50\text{ mg}}{\text{ml}}$$

$$50x = 10$$
$$x = .2$$

**18.** Drug Order Printout

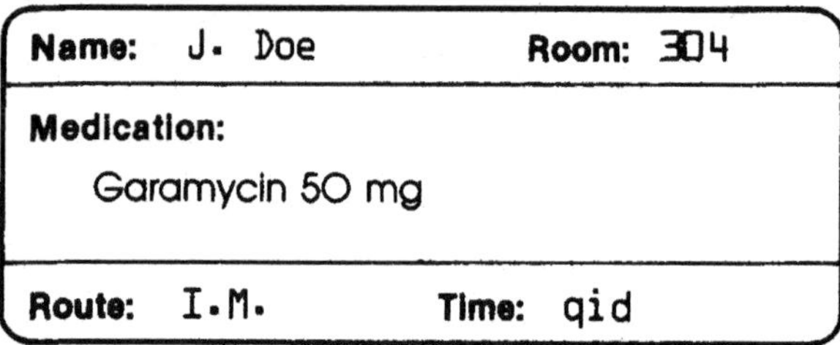

**Name:** J. Doe **Room:** 304

**Medication:**
Garamycin 50 mg

**Route:** I.M. **Time:** qid

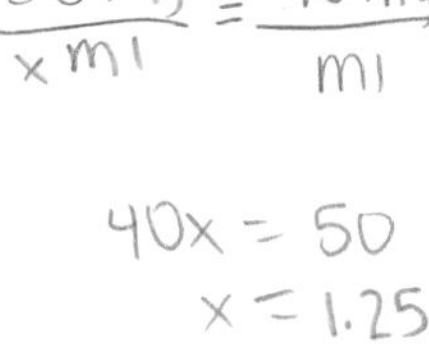

$$\frac{50\text{ mg}}{x\text{ ml}} = \frac{40\text{ mg}}{\text{ml}}$$

$40x = 50$

$x = 1.25$

Drug Label

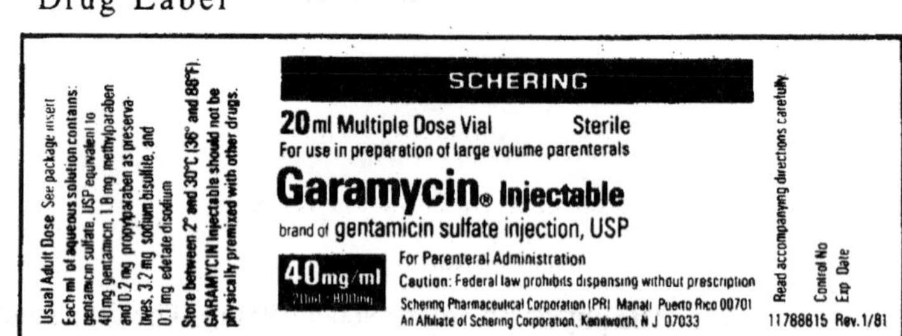


How many milliliters should the patient receive?

**19.** The physician orders Stadol 1 mg. The drug label reads Stadol 2 mg/ml. How many milliliters should the patient receive?

$$\frac{1\text{ mg}}{x\text{ ml}} = \frac{2\text{ mg}}{\text{ml}} \qquad 2x = 1$$

$x = .5$

**20.** The physician orders Haldol 2 mg. The drug label reads Haldol 5 mg/ml. How many milliliters does the patient receive?

$$\frac{2\text{ mg}}{x\text{ ml}} = \frac{5\text{ mg}}{\text{ml}}$$

$5x = 2$

$x = .4$

**21.** The physician orders morphine gr 1/6. How many milliliters should the patient receive?

$$\frac{gr \frac{1}{6}}{ml} = \frac{15\ mg}{ml}$$

$$x = .67$$

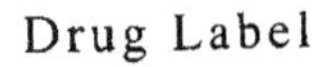
Drug Label

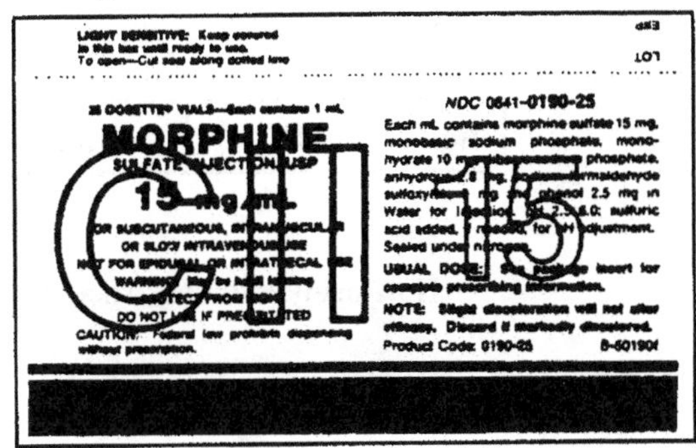


**22.** Drug Order Printout

| Name: V. Doe | Room: 202 |
|---|---|
| **Medication:** Digoxin 0.25 mg | |
| **Route:** I.M. | **Time:** daily |

Drug Label

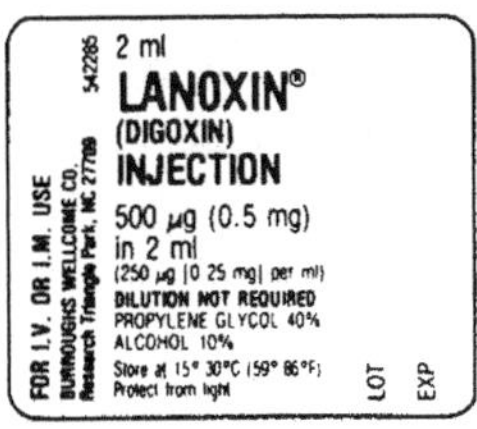


How many milliliters should the patient receive?

$$\frac{0.25\ mg}{x\ ml} = \frac{0.5\ mg}{2\ ml}$$

$$0.5x = .5$$

$$x = 1$$

**23.** The physician orders Aqua Mephyton 5 mg. The drug label reads Aqua Mephyton 10 mg/ml. How many milliliters should the patient receive?

$$\frac{5\ mg}{x\ ml} = \frac{10\ mg}{ml}$$

$$10x = 5$$

$$x = .5$$

**24.** Drug Order Printout

| **Name:** J. Smith | **Room:** 111 |
|---|---|
| **Medication:** Atropine 0.1 mg | |
| **Route:** I.M. | **Time:** on call |

Drug Label

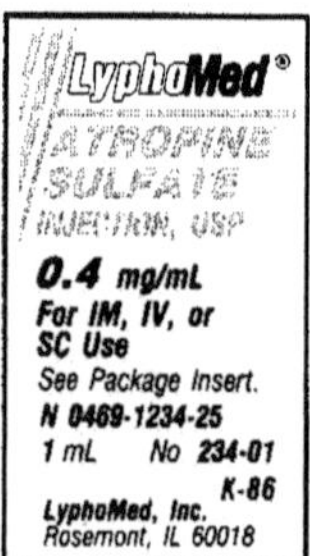


How many milliliters should the patient receive?

x=.25

**25.** The physician orders gentamicin 10 mg. The drug label reads gentamicin 40 mg/ml. How many milliliters should the patient receive?

x=.25

**26.** Drug Order Printout

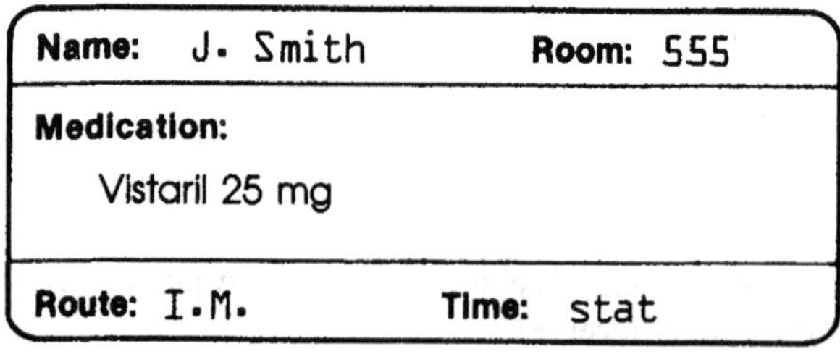

| **Name:** J. Smith | **Room:** 555 |
|---|---|
| **Medication:** Vistaril 25 mg | |
| **Route:** I.M. | **Time:** stat |

Drug Label

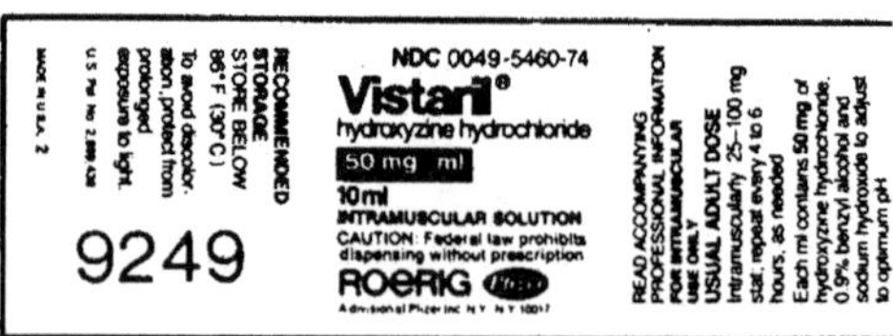


How many milliliters should the patient receive?

x= .5

**27.** The physician orders digoxin 0.125 mg. The drug label reads digoxin 0.5 mg/2 ml. How many milliliters should the patient receive?

x = .5

**28.** Drug Order Printout

| Name: J. Doe | Room: 304 |
|---|---|
| **Medication:** Meperidine 35 mg | |
| **Route:** I.M. | **Time:** bid |

How many milliliters should the patient receive?

x = .5

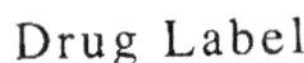


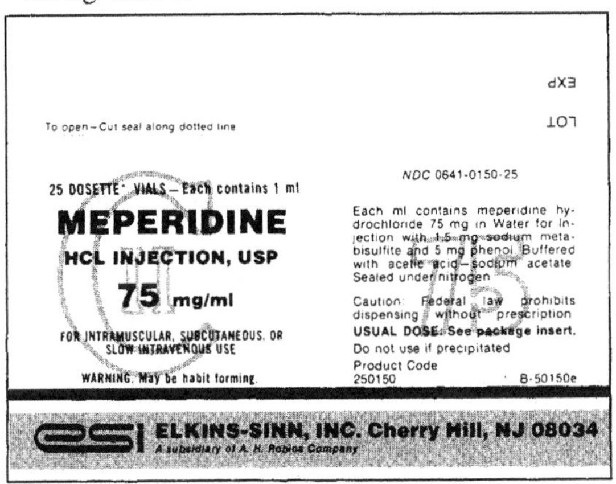


**29.** The physician orders atropine 0.15 mg. The drug label reads atropine 0.4 mg/ml. How many milliliters should the patient receive?

x = .4

**30.** The physician orders Dilaudid 1 mg. The drug label reads Dilaudid gr 1/32 per ml. How many milliliters should the patient receive?

x = .5

**31.** The physician orders Demerol 14 mg. The drug label reads Demerol 50 mg/ml. How many milliliters should the patient receive?

x = .3

**32.** The physician orders Compazine 10 mg. The drug label reads Compazine 5 mg/ml. How many milliliters should the patient receive?

x = 2

**33.** The physician orders atropine gr 1/300. The drug label reads atropine 0.2 mg/ml. How many milliliters should the patient receive?

x = 1

**34.** The physician orders Vistaril 25 mg. The drug label reads Vistaril 50 mg/ml. How many milliliters should the patient receive?

x = 0.5

**35.** The physician orders codeine gr 1/2. The drug label reads codeine 60 mg/ml. How many milliliters should the patient receive?

x = 0.5

## DETERMINING DOSAGE FOR DRUGS MANUFACTURED IN UNITS

Certain drugs are measured in USP units rather than in the apothecaries' or metric system. Vitamin preparations, hormones, and some antibiotics are a few examples.

One of the most common drugs measured in units is the hormone insulin. Insulin is manufactured in multiple-dose vials of U-100 strength. A U-100 vial contains 100 units of insulin per milliliter.

The insulin syringe is specifically designed for administering insulin and is calibrated in units. The insulin syringe is always a 1 ml syringe because the units (U100) are always contained in a 1 ml volume.

The physician ordering a drug manufactured in units will specify the number of units the patient should receive. It is the nurse's responsibility to determine the amount of liquid volume necessary to ensure the correct number of units for the patient.

The physician has ordered 12 U of NPH U-100 insulin to be administered each morning. Note the correct area for 12 U of U-100 insulin on the syringe below.

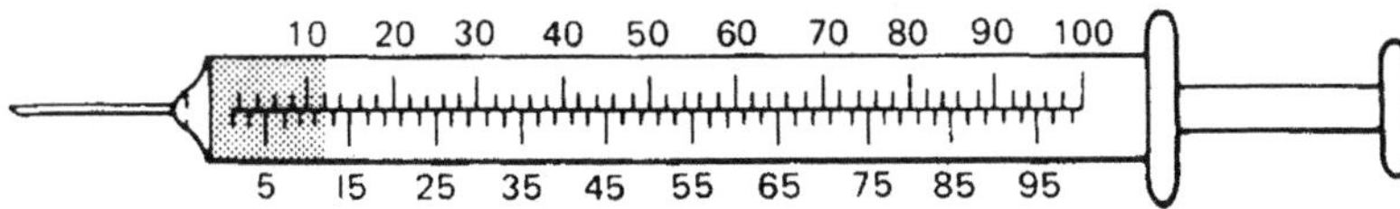


Another medication often ordered in units is heparin. The order is for 2500 U of heparin and the drug label reads heparin 5000 units per milliliter.

Drug Order Printout

| **Name:** J. Doe | **Room:** 18 |
|---|---|
| **Medication:** heparin 2500 U | |
| **Route:** sub q | **Time:** daily |

Determine the correct dosage of heparin for administration.

On hand Desired

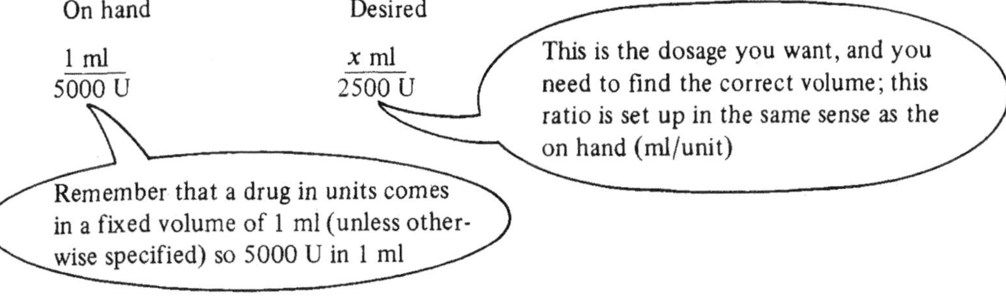

This results in the equation

$$\frac{1}{5000} = \frac{x}{2500}$$

$$5000x = 2500\,(1)$$

$$x = \frac{25\cancel{00}}{50\cancel{00}} = \frac{1}{2}$$

$$x = \frac{1}{2}$$

The correct dosage is $\frac{1}{2}$ ml. Shading the correct dosage on the syringe below, we have

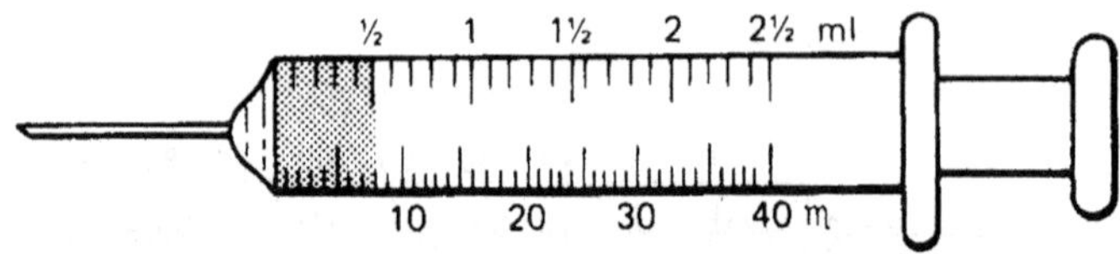


A drug commonly ordered in units is penicillin. The numbers associated with penicillin and other drugs ordered in units are usually quite large. Consider the following example using penicillin. The physician orders 150,000 U of penicillin IM. The label on the penicillin vial reads 3,000,000 U/10ml. Setting up the proportion

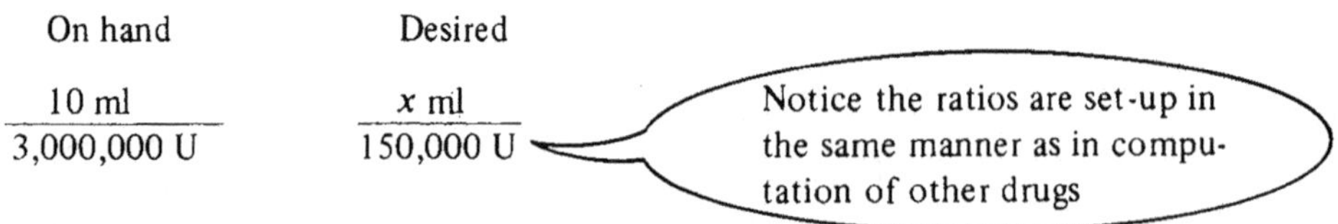


leads to the equation

$$\frac{10}{3{,}000{,}000} = \frac{x}{150{,}000}$$

$$3{,}000{,}000x = 150{,}000\,(10)$$

$$x = \frac{1{,}500{,}000}{3{,}000{,}000}$$

150,000 (10) = 1,500,000

$$x = \frac{1{,}5\cancel{00}{,}\cancel{000}}{3{,}0\cancel{00}{,}\cancel{000}}$$

canceling

$$x = \frac{15}{30} = \frac{1}{2}$$

The correct dosage is $\frac{1}{2}$ ml.

## Exercise 33

**DIRECTIONS:** Some of the following problems will require you to extract information from drug orders and drug labels. For all problems compute the correct dosage. When a syringe is given, shade the syringe to indicate your answer.

1. The order is for heparin 12,000 U subcutaneously. The drug label reads heparin 10,000 U/ml. How many milliliters does the patient receive? ________

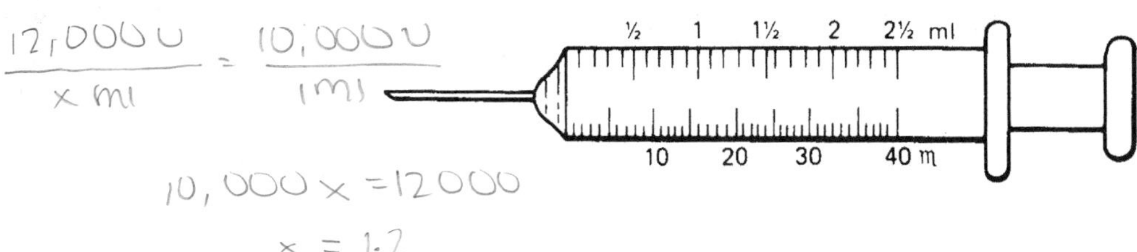


2. Drug Order Printout

| **Name:** J. Doe | **Room:** 80 |
|---|---|
| **Medication:** Procaine penicillin 600,000 U | |
| **Route:** I.M. | **Time:** 9-9 |

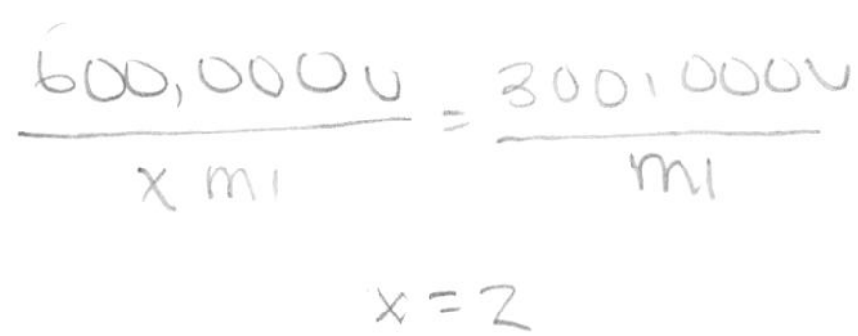

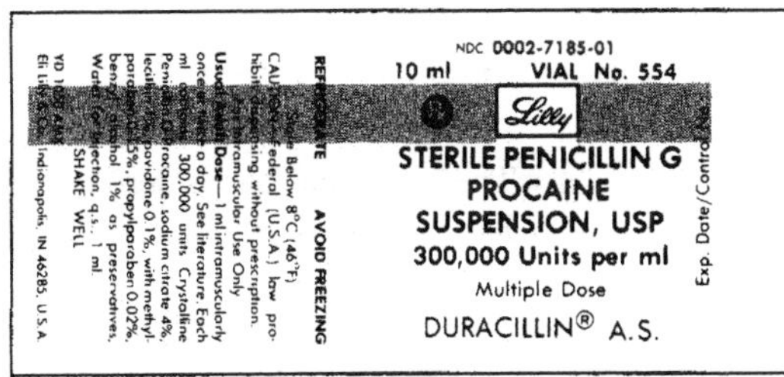


How many milliliters does the patient receive? ________

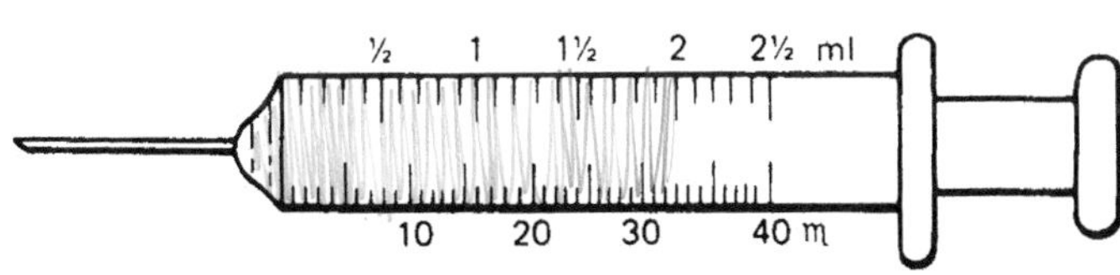

3. Drug Order Printout

| **Name:** J. Doe | **Room:** 16 |
|---|---|
| **Medication:** Lente insulin 35 U | |
| **Route:** sub-cutaneously | **Time:** 7:30 |

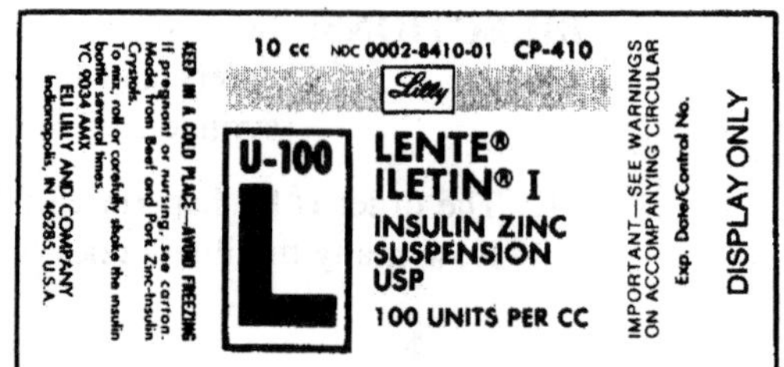


How many units of U-100 insulin does the patient receive? ________

35U / U-100 35

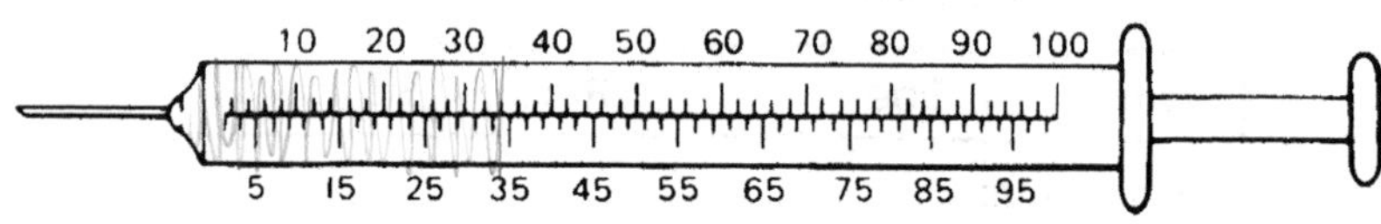


4. The physician has ordered penicillin G 600,000 U IM. The drug label reads 400,000 U/ml. How many milliliters does the patient receive? ________

600,000U / x ml = 400,000U / ml

x = 1.5

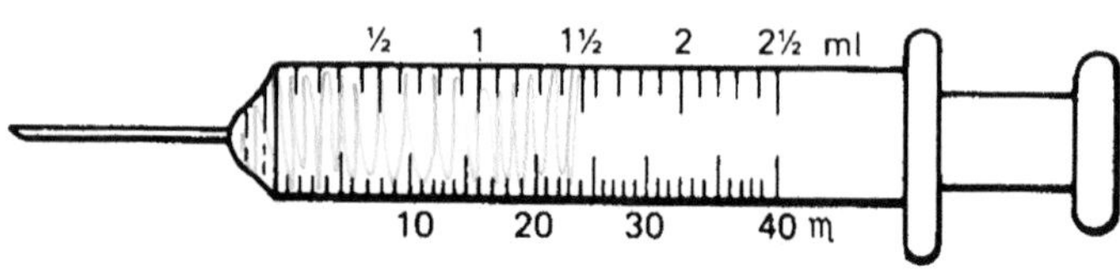

5. Drug Order Printout

| **Name:** J. Doe | **Room:** 80 |
|---|---|
| **Medication:** heparin 12,000 U | |
| **Route:** subcutaneous | **Time:** 8/4 |

Drug Label

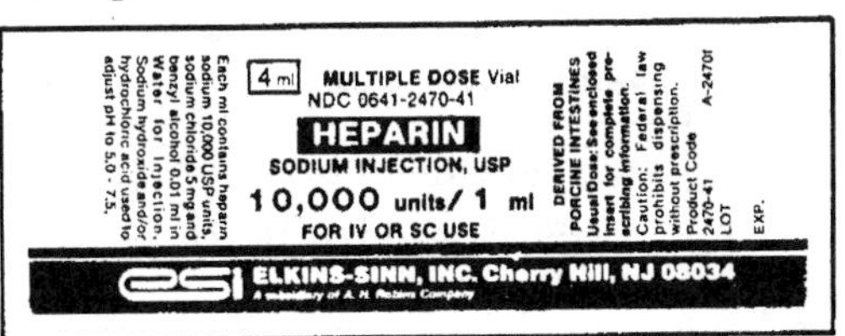


How many milliliters does the patient receive? ________

$\frac{12{,}000\text{U}}{x \text{ ml}} = \frac{10{,}000\text{U}}{1 \text{ ml}}$

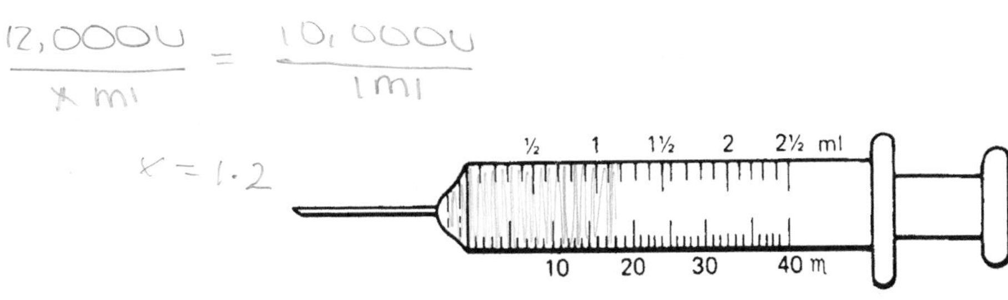


6. The physician orders heparin 15,000 U. The drug label reads heparin 20,000 U/ml. How many milliliters should the patient receive? ________

$\frac{15{,}000\text{U}}{x \text{ ml}} = \frac{20{,}000\text{U}}{\text{ml}}$

x = .75

7. The order is for procaine penicillin 400,000 U. The drug label reads procaine penicillin 300,000 U/ml. How many milliliters does the patient receive? ________

$\frac{400{,}000\text{U}}{x \text{ ml}} = \frac{300{,}000\text{U}}{\text{ml}}$

x = 1.3

**8.** Drug Order Printout

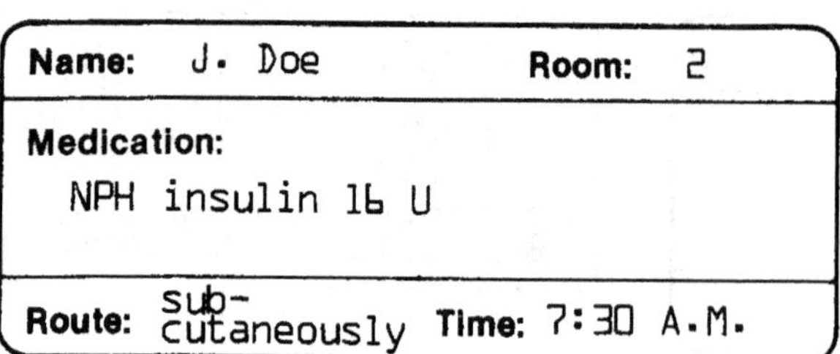

**Name:** J. Doe **Room:** 2

**Medication:**
NPH insulin 16 U

**Route:** sub-cutaneously **Time:** 7:30 A.M.

Drug Label

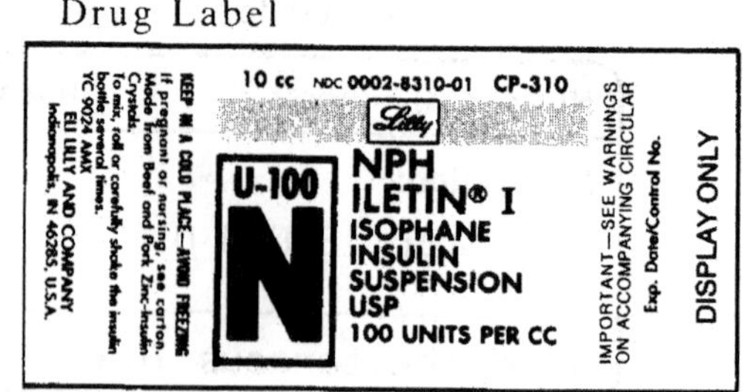


Indicate the correct dosage on the insulin syringe.

16 U / x ml = 100 U / ml

x = 16 U

10 20 30 40 50 60 70 80 90 100
5 15 25 35 45 55 65 75 85 95

**9.** The physician has ordered 19 U of NPH U-100 insulin. Mark the correct dosage.

19 U

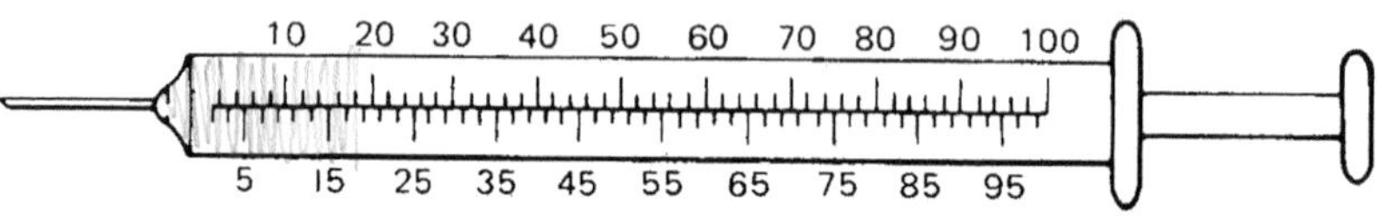


**10.** The physician has ordered heparin 4000 units. The drug label reads heparin 5000 units per milliliter. How many milliliters should the patient receive?

4000 U / x ml = 5000 / ml

x = 0.8

## DRUGS IN POWDERED FORM

Some drugs are unstable in liquid form. They are packaged in powdered form in sterile ampules or vials and must be dissolved in a diluent, usually sterile normal saline or sterile distilled water, before they can be administered. Directions for dissolving powdered drugs will usually be found on the vial or on accompanying literature. These directions will generally state the type and amount of diluent to be used and the amount of drug per milliliter of solution. If no directions are available, it is common practice to dissolve the drug in the amount of diluent that will yield 1 to 2 ml containing the desired dose. When a single-dose vial is used, one adds 1 to 2 ml of diluent and withdraws the contents. Multiple-dose vials usually have a 10 to 20 ml capacity (indicated on the label); therefore, when contents of a multiple-dose vial are dissolved, the vial must be labeled with the amount of diluent used and the amount of drug per milliliter of solution.

Consider the following problem:

| **Name:** J. Doe | **Room:** 3 |
|---|---|
| **Medication:** Keflin 500 mg | |
| **Route:** I.M. | **Time:** q 6 h |

Drug Label

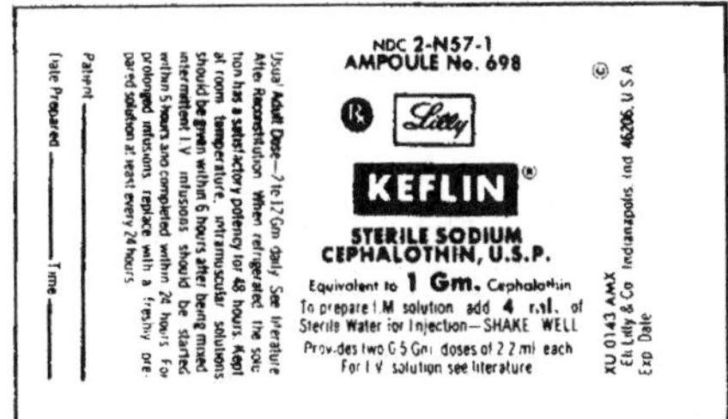


From the drug label, adding 4 ml of sterile water will yield enough solution for two doses. Each dose contains 0.5 g in 2.2 ml of solution.

The information on the drug label indicates

On hand

$$\frac{0.5\text{ g}}{2.2\text{ ml}}$$

From the drug order printout

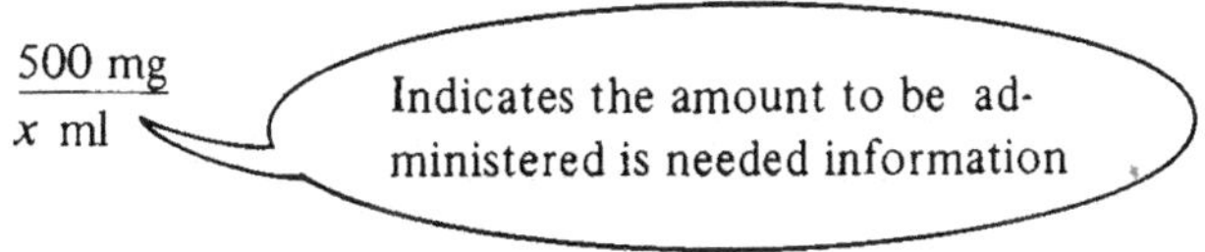


The ratio from the order is set up using similar units in numerator and denominator. Since the units in the two numerators are not exactly the same, one of the units must be converted to the unit used in the other ratio.

In this case, change 0.5 g to milligrams:

$$0.5\text{ g} = 500\text{ mg}$$

The ratios are

| Desired | On hand |
|---|---|
| $\dfrac{500 \text{ mg}}{x \text{ ml}}$ | $\dfrac{500 \text{ mg}}{2.2 \text{ ml}}$ |

(Replacing 0.5 g by 500 mg)

Set the two ratios equal to form the proportion.

$$\frac{500 \text{ mg}}{x \text{ ml}} = \frac{500 \text{ mg}}{2.2 \text{ ml}}$$

Use the numerical data to determine the value of $x$:

$$\frac{500}{x} = \frac{500}{2.2}$$

$$500x = 500\ (2.2)$$

$$x = \frac{500\ (2.2)}{500}$$

$$x = 2.2$$

The correct answer is 2.2 ml.

---

**EXAMPLE 4.3**

Determine the correct dosage from the following.

| **Name:** J. Doe | **Room:** 4 |
|---|---|
| **Medication:** Prostaphlin 500 mg | |
| **Route:** I.M. | **Time:** q 4 h |

Drug Label

1. How much sterile water must be added to the vial? ________
2. Once the solution is constituted, 1.5 ml contains ________ mg of sodium ampicillin.
3. Use the information in step 2 to set up the drug-on-hand ratio.

$$\frac{\square \text{ mg}}{\square \text{ ml}}$$

4. Write a similar ratio for the drug desired:

$$\frac{\square \text{ mg}}{\square \text{ ml}}$$

5. Write a proportion using steps 3 and 4.

6. Solve for the unknown.

The order is for crystalline penicillin 400,000 U every 4 hours. The drug label reads crystalline penicillin 1,000,000 U in powder form. How many milliliters are necessary to produce a solution with 400,000 U?

When working with drugs in powder form and an order for a drug in units, the nurse chooses the amount of solution to administer to the patient. Once the nurse chooses the amount to be administered, the problem is to determine the amount of diluent to add to the powder to assure the proper concentration of solution. The nurse normally chooses 1 to 2 ml to be administered to the patient.

In the above problem, plan to administer 1 ml to the patient. Then the desired dosage is

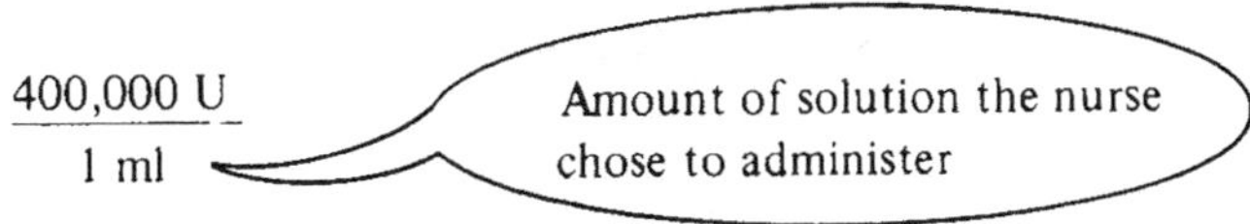


The on-hand information is

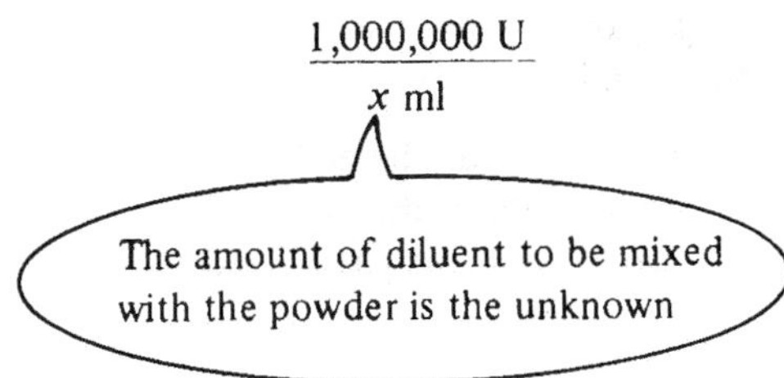


The number of milliliters to be mixed with the powder for a resulting solution containing 400,000 U/ml is the unknown. Set up the proportion

$$\begin{array}{ccc} \text{Desired} & & \text{On hand} \\ \dfrac{400{,}000 \text{ U}}{1 \text{ ml}} & = & \dfrac{1{,}000{,}000 \text{ U}}{x \text{ ml}} \end{array}$$

Solve for $x$:

$$\frac{400{,}000}{1} = \frac{1{,}000{,}000}{x}$$

$$400{,}000x = 1{,}000{,}000\ (1)$$

$$x = \frac{1{,}000{,}000}{400{,}000} = \frac{10}{4}$$

$$x = 2.5$$

Therefore 2.5 ml of diluent must be mixed with the powder.

**Exercise 34**

The following problems will give you practice with drugs in powdered form.

**DIRECTIONS:** Some of the following problems will require you to extract information from drug order printouts and drug labels. Compare the correct dosage for all problems. If a syringe is given, shade the syringe to indicate your answer.

1. The order is for Kefzol 500 mg IM bid. The drug label reads Kefzol equivalent to 1 g. Add 2.5 ml of sterile water for injection. Yields 3 ml reconstituted solution containing 330 mg/ml.

   How much sterile water should be added to the vial? 2.5 ml
   What is the dosage strength of the prepared solution? 330 mg/ml
   How many milliliters should the patient receive? 1.5 ml

   $$\frac{330 \text{ mg}}{1 \text{ ml}} = \frac{500 \text{ mg}}{x \text{ ml}}$$

   $$330x = 500$$
   $$x = 1.5$$

2. The order is for ampicillin 250 mg IM every 4 hours. The drug label reads sodium ampicillin equivalent to 1 g. Add 3.4 ml of sterile water for injection to yield 4 ml reconstituted solution containing 250 mg/ml.

   How much sterile water should be added to the vial? 3.4 ml
   What is the dosage strength of the prepared solution? 250 mg/ml
   How many milliliters should the patient receive? 1

   If the order reads ampicillin 150 mg every 4 hours, how many milliliters should the patient receive? .6

   $$\frac{250 \text{ mg}}{\text{ml}} = \frac{150 \text{ mg}}{x \text{ ml}}$$

   $$x = .6$$

3. Drug Order Printout

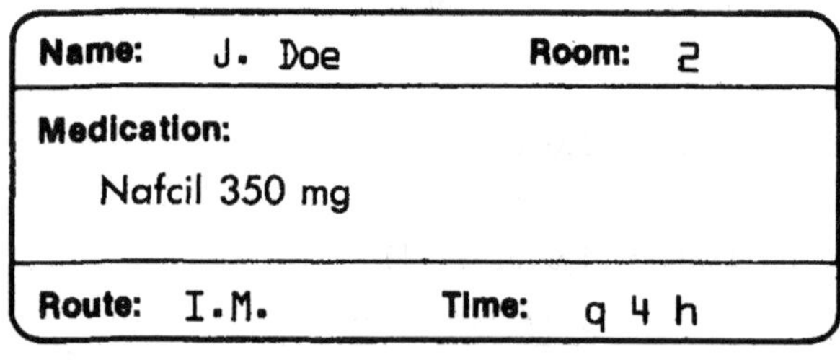

| Name: J. Doe | Room: 2 |
|---|---|
| **Medication:** Nafcil 350 mg | |
| **Route:** I.M. | **Time:** q 4 h |

Drug Label

   How much sterile water should be added to the vial? ________
   What is the dosage strength of the prepared solution? 250 mg/ml
   How many milliliters should the patient receive? 1.4 ml

**4.** Drug Order Printout

| **Name:** J. Doe | **Room:** 2 |
|---|---|
| **Medication:** Keflin 250 mg | |
| **Route:** I.M. | **Time:** q 4 h |

500 mg

$\frac{0.5 \text{ gm}}{2.2 \text{ ml}} = \frac{250 \text{ mg}}{x \text{ ml}}$

$x = 1.1$

Drug Label

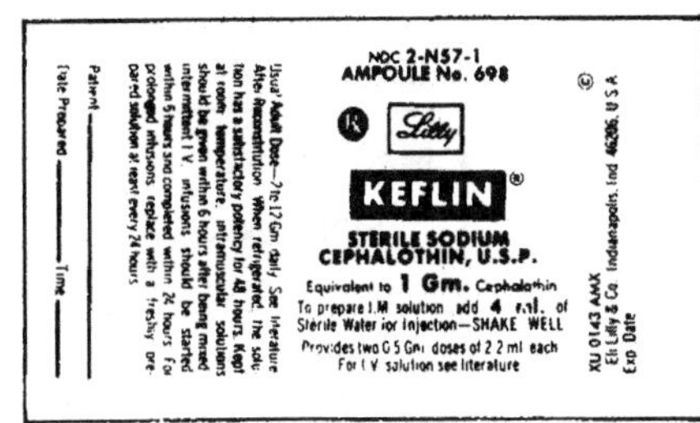


How much sterile water should be added to the vial? 4 ml

What is the dosage strength of the prepared solution? .5 g/2.2 ml

How many milliliters should the patient receive? 1.1 ml

**5.** The order is for streptomycin 500 mg every 6 hours. The drug label reads 5 g in 12.5 ml. How many milliliters should the patient receive? 1.25

$\frac{500 \text{ mg}}{x}$

**6.** The order is for Prostaphlin 500 mg every 8 hours. The drug label reads Prostaphlin 0.5 g. Add 2.7 ml of sterile water to yield 250 mg/1.5 ml.

How much sterile water should be added to the vial? 2.7 ml

What is the dosage strength of the prepared solution? 250 mg/1.5 ml

How many milliliters should the patient receive? 3

$\frac{250 \text{ mg}}{1.5 \text{ ml}} = \frac{500 \text{ mg}}{x \text{ ml}}$

$x = 3$

7. Drug Order Printout

| **Name:** J. Doe | **Room:** 2 |
|---|---|
| **Medication:** Streptomycin 500 mg | |
| **Route:** I.M. | **Time:** Every 4 h |

Drug Label

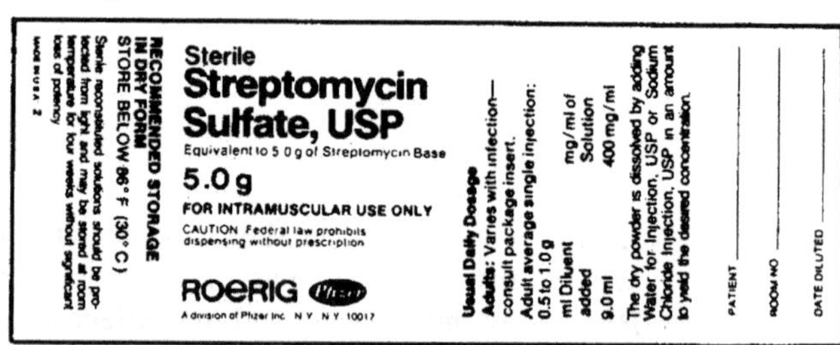


How much sterile water should be added to the vial? 9 ml
What is the dosage strength of the prepared solution? 400 mg/ml
How many milliliters should the patient receive? 1.3 ml

8. The order is for penicillin G 100,000 U IM every 6 hours. The drug label reads penicillin G 1,000,000 U. How many milliliters of sterile diluent are necessary to produce a solution with 100,000 U/ml?

100,000 U

x = 10

9. The order is for staphcillin 500 mg every 6 hours. The drug label reads staphcillin equivalent to 1.0 g. Add 1.8 ml of sterile water for injection to yield 500 mg/ml.

How much sterile water should be added to the vial? 1.8 ml
What is the dosage strength of the prepared solution? 500 mg/ml
How many milliliters should the patient receive? 1

$$\frac{500 \text{ mg}}{\text{ml}} = \frac{500 \text{ mg}}{x \text{ ml}}$$

**10.** Drug Order Printout

| **Name:** J. Doe | **Room:** 2 |
|---|---|
| **Medication:** Geopen 1 g | |
| **Route:** I.M. | **Time:** q 6 h |

Drug Label

How much sterile water should be added to the vial? 7 ml
What is the dosage strength of the prepared solution? 1g/2 ml
How many milliliters should the patient receive? 2 ml

**11.** The order is for streptomycin 500 mg IM every 6 hours. The drug label reads streptomycin equivalent to 5 g. How many milliliters of sterile diluent are necessary to produce a solution with 500 mg/ml?

**12.** The order is for Claforan 1 g IV every 8 hours. How many milliliters of sterile diluent are necessary to produce a solution with 1 g?

**PREPARATION OF CLAFORAN STERILE**

Claforan for IM or IV administration should be reconstituted as follows:

| Strength | Diluent (mL) | Withdrawable Volume (mL) | Approximate Concentration (mg/mL) |
|---|---|---|---|
| 1g vial (IM)* | 3 | 3 4 | 300 |
| 2g vial (IM)* | 5 | 6 0 | 330 |
| 1g vial (IV)* | 10 | 10 4 | 95 |
| 2g vial (IV)* | 10 | 11 0 | 180 |
| 1g infusion | 50-100 | 50-100 | 20-10 |
| 2g infusion | 50-100 | 50-100 | 40-20 |
| 10g bottle | 47 | 52 0 | 200 |
| 10g bottle | 97 | 102 0 | 100 |

*in conventional vials

Shake to dissolve; inspect for particulate matter and discoloration prior to use Solutions of Claforan range from very pale yellow to light amber, depending on concentration, diluent used, and length and condition of storage.

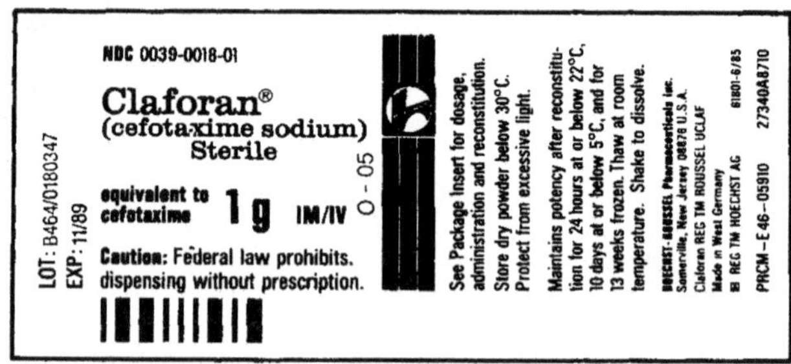


**13.** The order is for Chloromycetin 500 mg IM every 4 hours. How many milliliters of sterile diluent are necessary to produce a solution with 1 g?

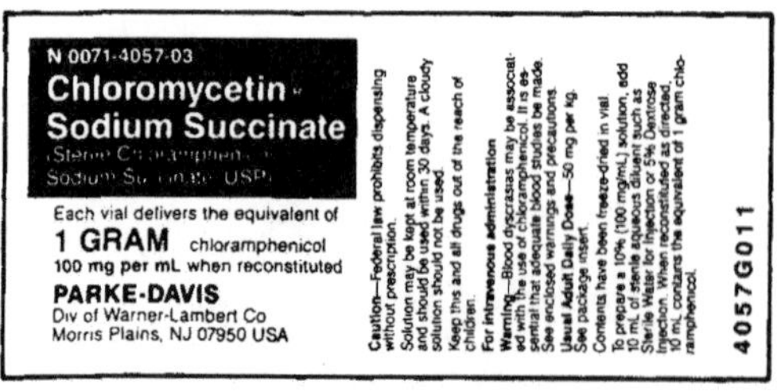

**14.** The order is for Keflin 250 mg. The drug label reads Keflin provides two 0.5 g doses of 2.2 ml each. How many milliliters does the patient receive?

**15.** The order is for Prostaphlin 150 mg. The drug label reads Prostaphlin equivalent to 1 g. Add 5.7 milliliters sterile water for injection. Each 1.5 ml contains 250 mg. How many milliliters does the patient receive?

## ANSWERS TO EXAMPLES

### *Example 4.1*

1. 100 mg/2 ml
2. 25 mg
3. On hand Desired

$\frac{2 \text{ ml}}{100 \text{ mg}}$ $\frac{x \text{ ml}}{25 \text{ mg}}$

$$\frac{2}{100} = \frac{x}{25}$$

$$100x = 2(25)$$

$$100x = 50$$

$$x = \frac{50}{100}$$

$$x = 0.5 \text{ or } \frac{1}{2}$$

correct dosage $\frac{1}{2}$ ml

4.

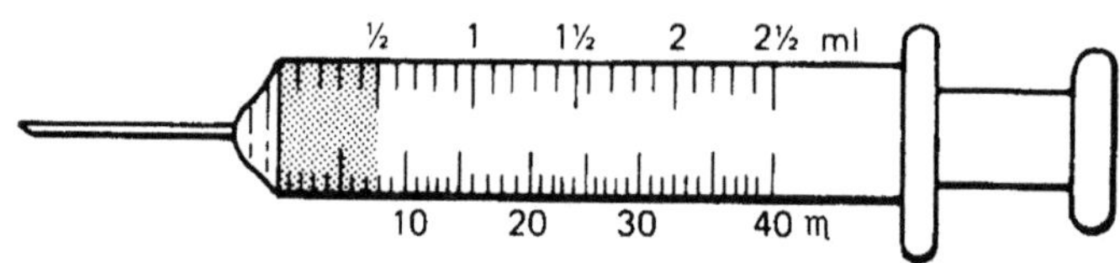


### *Example 4.2*

1. 1000 mg/2 ml
2. 500 mg
3. On hand Desired

$\frac{2 \text{ ml}}{1000 \text{ mg}}$ $\frac{x \text{ ml}}{500 \text{ mg}}$

$$\frac{2}{1000} = \frac{x}{500}$$

$$1000x = 1000$$

$$x = \frac{1000}{1000} = 1$$

1 ml is correct dosage

### *Example 4.3*

1. 2.7 ml

The directions on the drug label specify the exact amount of sterile water.

2. 1.5 ml contains 250 mg;

Drug label specifies the amount of solution yielded by adding sterile water.
250 ml is contained in each 1.5 ml

3. On hand

$\frac{250 \text{ mg}}{1.5 \text{ ml}}$

4. Desired

$\frac{500 \text{ mg}}{x \text{ ml}}$

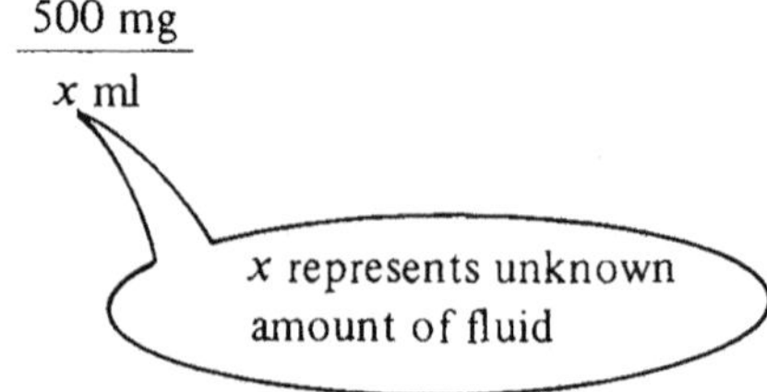


5. $\frac{500 \text{ mg}}{x \text{ ml}} = \frac{250 \text{ mg}}{1.5 \text{ ml}}$

6. $\frac{500}{x} = \frac{250}{1.5}$

$$250x = 750.0$$

$$x = \frac{750}{250} = 3$$

$$x = 3$$

3 ml is correct dosage.

# 5 INTRAVENOUS MEDICATIONS

## CHAPTER OBJECTIVES

- Demonstrate proficiency when calculating the intravenous infusion rates with varying drop factor sets
- Determine the correct length of time for intravenous infusions
- Calculate the correct flow rates for intravenous piggyback medications

## INTRODUCTION

This chapter focuses on the nurse's responsibility for adminstering intravenous fluids and medications. The two major areas of responsibility include the administration of intravenous fluids in large volumes (such as 1000 milliliters of dextrose in water) and the administration of intravenous piggybacks with small volumes of solution. These small volumes usually are 50 or 100 milliliters containing medications for intravenous infusion.

The nurse must be familiar with the drop factor of each intravenous set up. The drop factor refers to the size of each drop and the number of drops necessary to deliver one milliliter of solution. For example, some equipment yields 1 milliliter after 10 drops, while on other equipment 15 drops yields 1 milliliter; still other sets yield 1 milliliter after 60 drops. It is the nurse's responsibility to check drop factors on all equipment sets and correctly calculate infusion rates based on the drop factor.

To better understand the influence of the drop factor, look at the following situations. Consider an IV set up where the nurse adjusts the infusion rate to 20 drops per minute and runs the IV for 2 hours.

20 drops per minute yields
$20 \times 60$ drops in 60 minutes,
1200 drops in 1 hour, so
2400 drops in 2 hours.

Now consider the effect of the drop factor in three situations:

| Situation | Drop factor in gtt/ml | For 2400 drops in 2 hours the total volume infused |
|---|---|---|
| 1 | 10 gtt/ml | 2400/10 or 240 ml |
| 2 | 15 gtt/ml | 2400/15 or 160 ml |
| 3 | 60 gtt/ml | 2400/60 or 40 ml |

As one can see, the drop factor significantly influences the total volume infused over a fixed period of time at a fixed rate.

The drop factor of intravenous equipment is a fixed value (specific to that piece of equipment) and will appear on the instruction of the equipment. The nurse must calculate the infusion rate if the time and volume are given or must calculate the time of infusion if the rate and volume are given. Each of the following sections deals with these aspects of intravenous administration.

## DETERMINING INTRAVENOUS INFUSION RATES

This section focuses on the nurse's responsibility for administering intravenous fluids in large volumes. The intravenous route of administering fluids allows for the fastest absorption as the fluids are injected directly into the patient's circulatory system via selected veins. Intravenous fluids are often given to the patient to correct electrolyte imbalances or to treat various disorders or diseases.

The physician ordering intravenous fluids specifies the total volume, the type of solution, and the total infusion time. To deliver the requested volume in the time specified by the physician, it is the nurse's responsibility to calculate the proper rate of flow. All intravenous administration sets are calibrated in *drops per milliliter (gtt/ml)*. It is important that the nurse check the type of intravenous set used, as different manufacturers produce intravenous sets that yield a varying number of drops per milliliter.

The following formula will assist the nurse in determining the number of drops per minute to administer intravenous fluids correctly.

Number of drops per minute

$$\text{gtt/min} = \frac{\text{gtt/ml of given set}}{60} \times \text{total hourly volume}$$

Number of minutes in an hour

Use the formula to determine the correct drops per minute for the following problem. The physician has ordered 50 ml 5% dextrose in water with 50 mg ampicillin per hour. The set available yields 10 gtt/ml. The nurse must determine the number of drops per minute the intravenous should infuse. Referring to the formula and the physician's order, we have

gtt/ml of given set = 10

Total hourly volume = 50 ml

Substitute in the formula:

$$\text{gtt/min} = \frac{10}{60} \times 50 = \frac{500}{60} = 8.33$$

Regulate the infusion to 8 drops per minute.

## EXAMPLE 5.1*

The physician orders 100 ml 5% dextrose in water with 25 mg ampicillin per hour. Set yields 15 gtt/ml.

1. gtt per ml given set = 155 gtt/ml
2. Total hourly volume = 100 ml .
3. Substitute in the formula.

   gtt/min = $\frac{15 \text{ gtt}}{60}$ × 100 ml

4. Determine the drops per minute.

   25 gtt/min

---

Often the information is not in a form allowing direct substitution in the formula. Usually the rate is not given. In these cases you must calculate the rate at which the intravenous is to drip. Consider this problem. If 1000 ml of isotonic saline is to run over a period of 12 hours, how many drops are needed to regulate the flow (10 gtt/ml)?

Because the hourly rate is not given, you must determine the hourly rate before proceeding as in Example 4.6. Notice 1000 ml is to be given over 12 hours, so

$$\frac{1000 \text{ ml}}{12 \text{ h}}$$

will tell us the number of milliliters to be given each hour. Dividing 12 into 1000 yields

```
       83.33
12/ 1000.0
     96
      40
      36
       40
       36
        40
        36
         4
```

Thus 83.33 ml/hr. Substitute the values in the formula:

$$\text{gtt/min} = \frac{10}{60} \times 83.33$$

$$= \frac{1\not{0}}{6\not{0}} \times 83.33$$

$$= \frac{83.33}{6} = 13.89$$

The infusion should be regulated to 14 drops per minute.

---

*Answers to the examples appear on page 142.

---

**EXAMPLE 5.2**

The physician orders 1000 ml 5% dextrose in water to run for 8 hours (10 gtt/ml set).

1. What is the total hourly volume? 1000 ml / 8 hrs = 125 ml/hr
2. gtt/ml of the given set = 10 gtt/ml.
3. Substitute in the formula.

$$\text{gtt/min} = \frac{10 \text{ gtt/ml}}{60} \times 125$$

4. Determine the drops per minute.

20.83 → 21 gtt/min

---

$$\text{gtt/min} = \frac{\text{gtt/m given set}}{60} \cdot \text{hr} \cdot \text{vol}$$

**Exercise 35**

For practice with intravenous fluids, solve the following problems.

1. The physician has ordered 500 ml of 5% dextrose in water to run over a period of 12 hours. How many drops per minute should the IV infuse (10 gtt/ml set)?

$$\frac{10}{60}\left(\frac{500}{12}\right) = 7 \text{ gtt/min}$$

2. The physician has ordered 1000 ml of dextrose in water to run over a 12-hour period. How many drops per minute should the IV infuse (10 gtt/ml set)?

$$\frac{10}{60}\left(\frac{1000}{12}\right) = 14 \text{ gtt/min}$$

3. The physician orders 2000 ml 5% dextrose in water over a 24-hour period. How many drops per minute should the IV infuse (15 gtt/ml set)?

21

4. The order is for 1000 ml of 5% dextrose in water to run at 250 ml/hour. How many drops per minute should the IV infuse (20 gtt/ml set)?

   83

5. Administer 1000 ml isotonic saline in 4 hours. How many drops per minute should the IV infuse (10 gtt/ml set)?

   42

6. The physician orders 500 ml of 5% dextrose in water over an 8-hour period. How many drops per minute should the IV infuse (10 gtt/ml set)?

   10

7. The order is for 500 ml of 5% dextrose in water to be administered in 4 hours. How many drops per minute should the IV infuse (15 gtt/ml set)?

   31

8. The physician orders 3000 ml 5% dextrose in water to run over a 24-hour period. How many drops per minute should the IV infuse (10 gtt/ml set)?

   21

9. The physician orders 500 ml to run at 250 ml per hour. How many drops per minute should the IV infuse (10 gtt/ml set)?

   42

## LENGTH OF TIME FOR INTRAVENOUS INFUSIONS

Often a physician will order an intravenous infusion and specify the rate at which the IV is to be administered. To maintain an IV schedule for each individual patient, it is necessary that the nurse be able to calculate the number of hours the infusion should last.

The nurse should use the formula:

$$\text{number of gtt/min} = \frac{\text{number of ml ordered}}{\text{number of min the IV is to infuse}} \times \text{drop factor}$$

For example, the physician orders 1200 ml of normal saline to infuse at 50 gtt/min. The drop factor is 15 gtt/min. How many hours must the IV run?

Substituting:

$$50 = \frac{1200}{x}(15)$$

$$50x = 1200\,(15)$$

$$50x = 18000$$

$$x = \frac{18000}{50}$$

$$x = 360$$

This is the number of minutes, thus

$$\text{Hours} = \frac{x}{60} = \frac{360}{60} = 6$$

$$\text{Hours} = 6.$$

---

**EXAMPLE 5.3**

The physician orders 1000 ml of 5% dextrose in water to infuse at 40 gtt/min. How many hours must the IV infuse? (10 gtt/ml set)

1. What are the drops per minute requested? 40 gtt/min
2. What are the drops per milliliter of the given set? 10 gtt/ml
3. How many milliliters were ordered? 1000 ml
4. Substitute in the formula to determine the number of minutes for the IV to infuse.

   $40\text{ gtt/min} = \frac{1000\text{ ml}}{x} \times 10\text{ gtt/ml}$

5. What is the number of hours?

   250 min → 4 hrs 10 min

---

gtt/min = # ml / # min · drop #

**Exercise 36**

Calculate the time of infusion.

1. The physician orders 100 ml Ringers lactate to infuse at 20 gtt/min. How many hours must the IV infuse? (60 gtt/ml set)

$20 = \frac{100}{x} \cdot 60$

5hrs

2. The physician orders 1200 ml of normal saline to infuse at 50 gtt/min. How many hours must the IV infuse? (10 gtt/ml set)

4 hrs

3. The physician orders 1000 ml of 10% glucose to infuse at 35 gtt/min. How many hours must the IV infuse? (15 gtt/ml set)

$35 = \frac{1000 \text{ ml}}{x} \cdot 15$ $x = \frac{428.57}{60}$ 7 hrs 8 min

$.14(60) = 8$

4. The physician orders 900 ml of 5% dextrose in water to infuse at 40 gtt/min. How many hours must the IV infuse? (10 gtt/ml set)

3 hrs 45 min

5. The physician orders 1500 ml Ringers lactate to infuse at 45 gtt/min. How many hours must the IV infuse? (10 gtt/ml set)

333min 5 hrs 33 min

6. The physician orders 100 ml of 5% dextrose in water to infuse at 30 gtt/min. How many hours must the IV infuse? (60 gtt/ml set)

200 min 3 hrs 20 min

7. The physician orders 800 ml physiologic saline to infuse at 50 gtt/min. How many hours must the IV infuse? (10 gtt/ml set)

160 min 2hrs 40 min

8. The physician orders 500 ml of Ringers lactate to infuse at 40 gtt/min. How many hours must the IV infuse? (60 gtt/ml set)

12hrs 30 min

9. The physician orders 200 ml of 5% glucose to infuse at 50 gtt/min. How many hours must the IV infuse? (60 gtt/ml set)

4 hrs

## INTRAVENOUS PIGGYBACK MEDICATIONS

This section focuses on the nurse's responsibility for intravenous piggyback infusions. The piggyback intravenous medication is connected to a primary infusion set up and is ordered specifically for the purpose of delivering a variety of medications to a patient. The patient is usually already receiving intravenous fluids from a primary intravenous set up. The piggyback is attached via a needle to an adaptor on the existing primary tubing.

Intravenous piggyback (IVPB) medications are usually dissolved in 50 ml or 100 ml of dextrose in water or physiologic saline and are infused in 30 to 60 minutes. In many hospitals the pharmacy is responsible for preparing piggyback medications, and they are delivered to nursing units ready for administration. It is common practice for nurses to be responsible for administering numerous IVPB medications during a daily work experience.

Before administering IVPB medications, it is necessary to calculate the flow rate or drops per minute to deliver the 50 ml or 100 ml of solution in 30 to 60 minutes. To do this the nurse must first determine the drop factor of the equipment selected to infuse the IVPB. The drop factor (10 gtt/ml, 15 gtt/ml, or 60 gtt/ml) is usually indicated on the equipment selected to administer the infusion.

Nurses are always responsible for checking administration time for all intravenous medications in appropriate references. Intervals of 30 and 60 minutes have been arbitrarily chosen because these are commonly used infusion times for most IVPB medications.

The following formula will assist the nurse in determining the number of drops per minute to administer intravenous fluids piggyback.

**Numbers of drops per minute for piggybacks**

$$\text{number of gtt/min} = \frac{\text{number of ml ordered}}{\text{number of min the IV is to infuse}} \times \text{drop factor}$$

---

## EXAMPLE 5.4

Consider the following order:

Keflin 2 g IVPB q 6 hr
Infuse in 1 hour

The piggyback label reads:

Keflin 2 g in 100 ml 5% dextrose in water
(60 gtt/ml set)

1. gtt per ml of given set = 60 gtt/ml.
2. Total time in minutes = 60 min .
3. gtt per min = ________ .
4. Total milliliters ordered = 100 ml .
5. Substitute in the formula.

gtt/min = $\frac{100 \text{ ml}}{60 \text{ min}}$ = 60

6. Determine the drops per minute.

---

### Exercise 37

For practice with IV piggybacks, solve the following problems.

1. The physician has ordered Nebcin 60 mg IVPB. The IVPB label reads Nebcin 60 mg in 50 milliliters normal saline. The drop factor is 10 gtt/ml. Infuse in thirty minutes. How many drops per minute should the IVPB infuse?

2. The physician has ordered ampicillin 250 mg IVPB. The IVPB label reads ampicillin 250 mg in 100 milliliters 5% dextrose in water. The drop factor is 15 gtt/ml. Infuse in thirty minutes. How many drops per minute should the IVPB infuse?

3. The order is for Tagamet 300 mg IVPB. The IVPB label reads Tagamet 300 mg in 100 milliliters 5% dextrose in water. The drop factor is 60 gtt/ml. Infuse in one hour. How many drops per minute should the IVPB infuse?

4. The order is for gentamicin 50 mg IVPB. The IVPB label reads gentamicin 50 mg in 50 milliliters physiologic saline. The drop factor is 60 gtt/ml. Infuse in thirty minutes. How many drops per minute should the IVPB infuse?

5. The physician has ordered Ancef 1 g IVPB. The IVPB label reads Ancef 1 g in 50 milliliters physiologic saline. The drop factor is 10 gtt/ml. Infuse in thirty minutes. How many drops per minute should the IVPB infuse?

6. The physician has ordered Mefoxin 1 g IVPB. The IVPB label reads Mefoxin 1 g in 100 milliliters physiologic saline. The drop factor is 15 gtt/ml. Infuse in one hour. How many drops per minute should the IVPB infuse?

7. The order is for ampicillin 1 g IVPB. The IVPB label reads ampicillin 1 g in 100 milliliters of 5% dextrose in water. The drop factor is 60 gtt/ml. Infuse in one hour. How many drops per minute should the IVPB infuse?

**8.** The physician has ordered Cefabid 2 g IVPB. The IVPB label reads Cefabid 2 g in 100 milliliters physiologic saline. The drop factor is 10 gtt/ml. Infuse in thirty minutes. How many drops per minute should the IVPB infuse?

**9.** The order is for gentamicin 50 mg IVPB. The IVPB label reads gentamicin 50 mg in 100 milliliters 5% dextrose in water. The drop factor is 15 gtt/ml. Infuse in one hour. How many drops per minute should the IVPB infuse?

## ANSWERS TO EXAMPLES

### *Example 5.1*

1. 15
2. 100 ml
3. gtt/min $= \frac{15}{60} \times 100$
4. $\frac{15}{60} \times 100 = \frac{150\not{0}}{6\not{0}} = 25$

   25 gtt/min

### *Example 5.2*

1. 1000 ml to run for 8 hours. Divide 8 into 1000 to get the milliliters per hour:

$$\begin{array}{r} 125. \\ 8\overline{)1000.} \\ \underline{8} \\ 20 \\ \underline{16} \\ 40 \\ \underline{40} \\ 0 \end{array}$$

Result 125 ml/hour

2. gtt/ml = 10
3. gtt/min $= \frac{10}{60} \times 125$
4. $\frac{10}{60} \times 125 = \frac{1}{6} \times 125 = \frac{125}{6} = 20.83$

   Round off to 21

   Adjust infusion to 21 gtt/min

### *Example 5.3*

1. 40 gtt/min
2. 10 gtt/ml
3. 1000 ml
4. $40 = \frac{1000(10)}{x}$

   $40x = 1000(10)$

   $x = \frac{10000}{40}$

   $x = 250$ minutes
5. Hours $= \frac{250}{60} = 4$ hours 10 minutes

### *Example 5.4*

1. 60 gtt/ml
2. 60 minutes
3. $x$, the unknown
4. 100 ml
5. $x = \frac{100}{60}(60)$
6. $x = \frac{100}{60}(60)$

   $x = 100$ gtt/min

# 6 PEDIATRIC MEDICATIONS

But Timmy, this stuff will make you feel better!

### CHAPTER OBJECTIVES

- Calculate the correct pediatric dosage using weight in kilograms as well as various pediatric rules
- Determine the correct pediatric dosage when applying the surface-area formula

## INTRODUCTION

Many hospitals have special divisions for infants and children; sometimes infants and children are integrated with adult patients throughout the hospital. The child should not be considered a miniature adult but a unique individual who requires approaches and treatments different from those of adults.

This chapter focuses specifically on the calculation of dosage for infants and children. Infants and children always require smaller quantities of medications than adults; therefore it is important that nurses caring for children know the safe range of dosages. The physician will always prescribe medications, but nurses must be aware of usual dosage for frequently administered medications so that an overdose will not be given.

## RULES

### Young's Rule

Several rules have been formulated to serve as a guide for estimating the correct dosage for infants and children. One of these is Young's rule, designed for children from ages 1 or 2 years to 12 years.

*Young's rule* (1 or 2 years to 12 years of age):

$$\text{Child's dose} = \frac{\text{child age in years}}{\text{child age in years} + 12} \times \text{adult dose}$$

To determine how much aspirin a 3-year-old child should receive if the adult dose is 0.3 g, use Young's rule. The information needed is

$$\text{Child's age in years} = 3$$
$$\text{Child's age in years} + 12 = 15$$
$$\text{Adult dosage} = 0.3 \text{ g}$$

Substituting in the formula for Young's rule yields

$$\text{Child's dose} = \frac{3}{15} \times 0.3 \text{ g} = \frac{0.9}{15} \text{ g} = 0.06 \text{ g}$$

Performing the division gives the answer as 0.06 g.

Aspirin is usually measured in grains, so change the answer to grains:

$$0.06 \text{ g} = 1 \text{ gr}$$

Thus the child's dose is 0.06 g = gr i. The correct dosage is 1 grain.

---

**EXAMPLE 6.1***

How much Demerol should a 6-year-old child receive if the adult dose is 75 mg? Use young's rule.

1. Child's age in years = ________ .
2. Child's age in years + 12 = ________ .
3. Adult dose = ________ .
4. Substitute the values in Young's rule.

5. Solve for the child's dosage.

---

*Answers to examples appear on pages 155-156.

---

**EXAMPLE 6.2**

How much atropine sulfate should a 4-year-old child receive if the average adult dose is gr $\frac{1}{150}$? Use Young's rule.

1. Child's age in years = ________ .
2. Child's age in years + 12 = ________ .
3. Adult dose = ________ .
4. Substitute the values in Young's rule.

5. Solve for the child's dose.

---

## Fried's Rule

The second rule, Fried's rule, is designed for computing dosage for infants. Fried's rule is designed for infants from birth to 1 or 2 years of age.

*Fried's rule* (birth to 1 or 2 years of age):

$$\text{Infant's dose} = \frac{\text{age in months}}{150} \times \text{adult dose}$$

The physician orders codeine for a 10-month-old infant. If the adult dose is gr $\frac{1}{2}$, how much codeine should the infant receive? Since the infant is less than 2 years old, apply Fried's rule.

The child's age in months is 10.

The adult dose is gr $\frac{1}{2}$.

$$\text{Infant's dose} = \frac{10}{150} \times \frac{1}{2}$$

$$= \frac{\not{1}\not{0}}{15\not{0}} \times \frac{1}{2} = \frac{1}{15 \times 2} = \frac{1}{30}$$

Infant dose is gr $\frac{1}{30}$.

---

**EXAMPLE 6.3**

Find the dosage of Nembutal for a 6-month-old infant if the adult dose is 90 mg.

To apply Fried's rule determine:

1. Age of infant in months = ________ .
2. Adult dose = ________ .
3. Substitute the value in Fried's rule.

4. Solve for infant dosage.

---

---

**EXAMPLE 6.4**

If an adult receives 300 mg of Ilosone, what is the correct dosage for an 18-month-old infant?

1. Age of infant in months = ________ .
2. Adult dose = ________ .
3. Substitute values in Fried's rule.

4. Solve for infant dosage.

---

## Clark's Rule

The third rule, Clark's rule, uses the weight of the child and the weight of an average adult. Therefore it can be used to determine the dosage for infants and children, regardless of age. Clark's rule provides more accurate information than either Fried's or Young's rule.

*Clark's rule* (all ages):

$$\text{Child's dose} = \frac{\text{weight of child in pounds}}{150 \text{ lb}} \times \text{adult dose}$$

The 150 pounds in Clark's rule is the average weight of an adult.

How much phenobarbital should a 70-pound child receive if the adult dosage is 60 mg?

Child's weight = 70

Adult dosage = 60 mg

Substituting these values in Clark's rule gives

$$\text{Child's dose} = \frac{70}{150} \times 60 \text{ mg}$$

Solving for the child's dose, we have

$$\frac{70}{150} \times 60 = \frac{420}{15} = 28 \text{ mg}$$

Child's dose = 28 mg.

---

**EXAMPLE 6.5**

An adult receives aspirin gr *x*. How many grains of aspirin should be given to a child weighing 45 lbs?

1. Weight of child in pounds = ________ .
2. Adult dose = ________ .
3. Substitute the values in the formula for Clark's rule.

4. Solve for the child's dose.

---

**EXAMPLE 6.6**

An adult receives aspirin gr *x*. How many grains of aspirin should be given to a child weighing 60 lbs?

1. Weight of child in pounds = ________ .
2. Adult dose = ________ .

3. Solve for the child's dosage using Clark's rule.

---

## Surface-Area Rule

The fourth rule for determining children's drug dosage, the surface-area method, uses the surface area of the infant in computing the dosage. The surface area is measured in square meters ($m^2$), and a nomogram must be consulted to determine the body surface area. If the nomogram is available, this method provides the most accurate determination of the correct children's dosage.

*Surface-area rule*

$$\text{Child's dose} = \frac{\text{Surface area of child in square meters}}{1.7\ m^2} \times \text{adult dose}$$

The accepted average adult surface area is 1.7 $m^2$.

The physician orders Keflin for a child. The adult dosage for Keflin is 100 mg. What is the dosage for a child with a surface area of 1.2 $m^2$?

Using the surface-area formula

$$\text{Child's dose} = \frac{1.2\ m^2}{1.7\ m^2} \times 100\ \text{mg}$$

$$\text{Child's dose} = \frac{120}{1.7} = 70.6 = 71\ \text{mg}$$

The correct dosage for the child is 71 mg.

---

**EXAMPLE 6.7**

The adult dose for Demerol is 50 mg. A child with a surface area of 0.30 $m^2$ should receive how much Demerol?

1. Surface area of child in square meters = ________ .
2. Adult dose = ________ .
3. Substitute the values in the surface-area formula.

4. Solve for the child's dosage.

---

### Exercise 38

Find the correct child's dosage.

1. The adult dose of phenobarbital is 60 mg. How much should a 6-year-old receive?

2. The adult dose of morphine sulfate is 12 mg. How much should a 6-year-old receive?

3. The daily dose of Dilantin is 30 to 100 mg for an adult. Compute the dosage for a child weighing 35 lb using *(a)* the minimum adult dose and *(b)* the maximum adult dose.

4. The adult dose of aspirin is gr *x*. How many grains should be given to a child who weighs 20 lb?

5. The adult dose of codeine sulfate is 30 mg. What is the dose for a 20-month-old infant?

6. The adult dose of Demerol is 50 to 100 mg. Compute the dosage for a 6-month-old infant using *(a)* the minimum adult dose and *(b)* the maximum adult dose.

7. The adult dose for Garamycin is 80 mg. How much Garamycin would a child of 4 years receive?

**8.** The adult dose for Demerol is 75 mg. How much Demerol would a 3-year-old child receive?

**9.** The adult dose for streptomycin is 500 mg. How much streptomycin would a 3-year-old child receive?

**10.** The adult dose for tetracycline is 500 mg. How much tetracycline would a child of 7 years receive?

**11.** The adult dose for penicillin is 600,000 U. How much should a 3-year-old child receive?

**12.** The adult dose for Gantrisin is 1000 mg. What should be the dose for a 10-month-old infant?

**13.** The adult dose for Demerol is 50 mg. How much Demerol would a 9-month-old infant receive?

**14.** The adult dose for morphine is 12 mg. How much morphine should a 6-month-old infant receive?

**15.** The adult dose for ampicillin is 500 mg. How much ampicillin should a 12-month-old infant receive?

**16.** The adult dose of adrenalin is 1 mg. What is the dose of adrenalin for a child weighing 40 lb?

**17.** The adult dose of sodium luminal is 100 mg. What is the dose of sodium luminal for a child weighing 25 lb?

**18.** The adult dose of Keflin is 100 mg. What is the dose of Keflin for an infant weighing 10 lb?

**19.** The adult dose of Kefzol is 500 mg. What is the dose of Kefzol for an infant weighing 20 lb?

**20.** The adult dose of atropine is gr $\frac{1}{150}$. What is the dose for an infant with a body surface area of 0.44 $m^2$?

**21.** The adult dose of Keflin is 250 mg. What is the dose of Keflin for an infant with a body surface area of 0.45 $m^2$?

22. The adult dose of Demerol is 50 mg. What is the dose of Demerol for an infant with a body surface area of 0.22 $m^2$?

23. The adult dose of Garamycin is 60 mg. How much Garamycin should an infant with a body surface area of 0.40 $m^2$ receive?

## CALCULATING DOSAGE PER KILOGRAM OF BODY WEIGHT

Another very accurate method of calculating pediatric medications uses the child's weight in kilograms. A two-step process is used to calculate the child's dosage. First, calculate 24-hour dosage. Second, calculate the dosage for each administration using the 24-hour dosage information.

1. $\text{Child's 24-hour dosage} = \left(\begin{matrix}\text{medication dosage per} \\ \text{kilogram body weight}\end{matrix} \times \begin{matrix}\text{child's weight} \\ \text{in kilograms}\end{matrix}\right)$

2. $\text{Child's dosage} = \dfrac{(\text{child's 24-hour dosage}) \times (\text{hours between administration})}{24}$

Consider the problem:
The physician orders kanamycin sulfate IM q 12 hours.
The drug label reads: kanamycin sulfate 75 mg/2 ml.
Normal pediatric dosage is: 15 mg/kg/day.
How much kanamycin should a child weighing 10 kg be given?
From what is given, we know:
medication dosage per kilogram body weight = 15 mg/kg/day
child's weight in kilograms = 10 kg
hours between medication administrations = 12 hrs

1. Child's 24-hour dosage = 15 × 10 = 150 mg,
thus 150 mg of kanamycin in 24-hour period
2. $\text{Child's dosage} = \dfrac{150 \times 12}{24} = 75 \text{ mg}$

Thus the child is to receive 75 mg per dose.

---

**EXAMPLE 6.8**

The physician orders Pyopen IM q 6 hours. The drug label reads Pyopen 1 g/2.5 ml and the normal pediatric dosage is 100 mg/kg/day. How much Pyopen should a child weighing 20 kg be given?

1. What is the medication dosage per kilogram body weight?
2. What is the child's weight in kilograms?
3. How many hours between medication administrations?

4. Find the child's 24-hour dosage.

5. How many milligrams should the child receive each dose?

---

**Exercise 39**

Find the child's dosage.

1. Order: Kefzol IM q 12 hrs
   On hand: Kefzol 125 mg/ml
   Pediatric dosage: 25 mg/kg/day
   How much Kefzol should a child weighing 5 kg receive?

2. Order: Pyopen IM q 4 hrs
   On hand: Pyopen 1 g/2.5 ml
   Pediatric dosage: 100 mg/kg/day
   How much should a child weighing 25 kg receive?

3. Order: Ancef IM q 8 hrs
   On hand: Ancef 125 mg/ml
   Pediatric dosage: 50 mg/kg/day
   How much Ancef should a child weighing 9 kg receive?

4. Order: Velosef IM q 6 hrs
   On hand: Velosef 208 mg/ml
   Pediatric dosage: Velosef 50 mg/kg/day
   How much Velosef should a child weighing 15 kg receive?

5. Order: tetracycline hydrochloride bid
   On hand: tetracycline hydrochloride 360 mg/ml
   Pediatric dosage: 12 mg/kg/day
   How much tetracycline should a child weighing 30 kg be administered?

6. The order is for tetracycline q 6 hours. The tetracycline on hand is labeled 250 mg/5 ml. The pediatric dosage is 12 mg/kg/day. How much tetracycline should a child weighing 24 kg receive?

7. The order is for ampicillin every 4 hours. The ampicillin on hand is labeled 1 g/2.5 ml. The pediatric dosage is 100 mg/kg/day. How much should a child weighing 10 kg receive?

## ANSWERS TO EXAMPLES

### *Example 6.1*

1. 6
2. 18, adding 12 to child's age (6) = 18.
3. 75 mg
4. Child's dose $= \frac{6}{18} \times 75$
5. $$\begin{array}{r} 75 \\ \times 6 \\ \hline 450 \end{array} \qquad \begin{array}{r} 25 \\ 18\overline{)450} \\ \underline{36} \\ 90 \\ \underline{90} \\ 0 \end{array}$$

Short Method

$$\frac{\overset{1}{\cancel{6}}}{\underset{3}{\cancel{18}}} \times 75 = \frac{75}{3} = 25$$

Child's dose = 25 mg

### *Example 6.2*

1. 4
2. 16; 4 + 12 = 16
3. gr $\frac{1}{150}$
4. Child's dose $= \frac{4}{16} \times \frac{1}{150}$
5. $\frac{4}{16} \times \frac{1}{150} = \frac{\overset{1}{\cancel{4}}}{\underset{4}{\cancel{16}}} \times \frac{1}{150} = \frac{1}{600}$

   gr $\frac{1}{600}$

### *Example 6.3*

1. 6
2. 90 mg
3. Infant dosage $= \frac{6}{150} \times 90$
4. Infant dosage $= \frac{6}{150} \times 90 = \frac{54\cancel{0}}{15\cancel{0}} = 3.6$ mg

   4 mg is the correct dosage.

### *Example 6.4*

1. 18
2. 300 mg
3. Infant's dosage $= \frac{18}{150} \times 300$ mg
4. Infant's dosage $= \frac{18}{\underset{1}{\cancel{150}}} \times \overset{2}{\cancel{300}} = 18 \times 2 = 36$ mg

***Example 6.5***

**1.** 45

**2.** 10 gr

**3.** Child's dose $= \frac{45}{150} \times 10$ gr

**4.** Child's dose $= \frac{45}{\underset{15}{\cancel{150}}} \times \overset{1}{\cancel{10}} = \frac{45}{15} = 3$

3 gr is the child's dosage.

***Example 6.6***

**1.** 60

**2.** 10 gr

**3.** Child's dose $= \frac{60}{150} \times 10$

$= \frac{6\cancel{0}}{15\cancel{0}} \times 10$

$= \frac{60}{15} \times 4$

Child's dose $= 4$ gr

***Example 6.7***

**1.** 0.30

**2.** 50 mg

**3.** Child's dose $= \frac{0.30}{1.7} \times 50$

**4.** Child's dose $= \frac{0.30 \times 50}{1.7}$

$= \frac{15}{1.7} = 8.8$ mg

Child's dose $= 9$ mg

***Example 6.8***

**1.** 100 mg/kg/day

**2.** 20 kg

**3.** 6 hours

**4.** $100(20) = 2000$

**5.** $\frac{2000(6)}{24} = \frac{2000}{4} = 500$ mg

# 7 PREPARATION OF SOLUTIONS

## CHAPTER OBJECTIVES

- Calculate solutions prepared from powders, crystals, or tablets
- Demonstrate proficiency when computing solutions prepared from liquid solutes
- Exhibit proficiency calculating solutions prepared from solutes with concentrations other than 100 percent concentration

## INTRODUCTION

Most hospital pharmacies have stock supplies of the most common solutions, which are readily available upon request. However, in smaller hospitals or in rural areas it may become the nurse's responsibility to prepare solutions of varying strengths for patient treatments. Solutions are most often used as disinfectants, for soaks, irrigations, mouthwashes, and other topical applications.

Solutions are prepared from drugs obtained in three different forms. First, the drug may be a solid such as powders, tablets, or crystals. Powders, tablets, and crystals are usually pure drugs; that is, the contents are considered 100 percent drug. Second, the drug may be a liquid and pure drug (once again, 100 percent drug). Third, the drug may be in liquid form but have a concentration that is less than 100 percent pure. The drug label will indicate when a drug is of a concentration that is less than 100 percent by stating the concentration, such as

| 50% alcohol solution |
|---|

If the drug label does not indicate the concentration, it is assumed that the drug is 100 percent pure. A single mathematical formula is involved in calculations for preparing solutions. The formula is

$$\frac{\text{amount of solute needed for preparation}}{\text{amount of solution desired}} = \frac{\text{concentration of desired solution}}{\text{concentration of on-hand solute}}$$

The amount of solute needed for preparation is what the nurse must calculate to prepare a solution. The other three pieces of information should be obtained from the drug order and the drug label. From the drug order the nurse obtains an indication of the amount of solution desired and the percent concentration wanted in the solution. The nurse determines the percent concentration of the solute (drug) on hand using information on the drug label.

Although a single formula is involved in calculations for preparing solutions, this chapter is separated into three sections, reflecting the different forms in which the solutes (or drugs) are manufactured.

## SOLUTIONS PREPARED FROM POWDERS, CRYSTALS, AND TABLETS

The physician orders sterile warm 5% boric acid compresses for a patient. To prepare 1000 ml of boric acid solution, the nurse obtains the bottle of boric acid crystals. Use the formula

$$\frac{\text{amount of solute needed for preparation}}{\text{amount of solution desired}} = \frac{\text{concentration of desired solution}}{\text{concentration of on-hand solute}}$$

Amount of solution desired = 1000
Percentage concentration of desired solution = 5
Percentage concentration of on-hand solute = 100

Recall pure drugs are 100%

Amount of solute needed for preparation of solution = $x$ g

Crystals are measured in grams

Substituting in the formula gives

$$\frac{x}{1000} = \frac{5}{100}$$

Solving, we get

$$\frac{x}{1000} = \frac{5}{100}$$

$$100x = 5000$$

$$x = \frac{5000}{100} = 50$$

Therefore 50 g of boric acid crystals is added to 1000 ml of sterile water to prepare the solution.

When dealing with solutes in solid form, the nurse mixes the powder or crystals with about half the total volume of sterile water and stirs until the crystals dissolve or the mixture becomes saturated. The nurse then adds more sterile water and dilutes the mixture until the desired volume of solution is obtained. Because the volume of sterile water varies with the type of powder or crystals used, we will merely specify that the nurse is to dilute to the desired volume.

When using the formula with solutes in solid form, use the weight measure from the same system used to express the desired amount of solution. If milliliters are wanted, measure the solute in grams; if minims are wanted, measure the solute in grains.

---

**EXAMPLE 7.1***

Prepare 2 oz of 8% iodine solution (from iodine crystals).

1. Amount of solution desired = ________ .
2. Concentration of desired solution = ________ .
3. Concentration of on-hand solute = ________ .
4. Solve for the amount of solute needed to prepare the solution.

---

Frequently the solute is obtained in tablet form. The next example involves such a solute.

---

**EXAMPLE 7.2**

Prepare 30 ml of a 10% sodium bicarbonate solution.

1. Amount of solution desired = ________ .
2. Concentration of desired solution = ________ .
3. Concentration of on-hand solute = ________ .
4. Solve for the amount of solute needed to prepare the solution.

5. If each tablet contains 10 grains of sodium bicarbonate, how many tablets are used?

---

## SOLUTIONS PREPARED FROM PURE LIQUID SOLUTES

In working with pure liquid solutes, the amount of solute is determined using the same mathematical formula as in the previous section. The difference in working with liquid and solid solutes is the characteristics of the solutes. When sodium chloride solute (table salt) is added to sterile water and mixed, the salt dissolves, but more importantly the volume of water does not appreciably increase.

---

*Answers to examples appear on pages 166-167.

On the other hand, when a liquid solute such as 10 ml of fluid is added to 100 ml of water, the result is 110 ml of solution. Thus if it is determined (by using the formula) that 10 ml of solute is added, then the amount of solute is subtracted from the desired volume. The difference is the amount of sterile water to be used. When working with liquid measure, the nurse must subtract the amount of solute from the total desired volume. Consider an example:

Prepare 200 ml of a 10% glycerin solution.
Amount of solute needed for preparation $= x$
Amount of solution desired = 200 ml
Percentage concentration of desired solution = 10
Percentage concentration of on-hand solute = 100

Substituting in the formula gives

$$\frac{x}{200} = \frac{10}{100}$$

Solving for $x$, we have

$$\frac{x}{200} = \frac{10}{100}$$

$$100x = 2000$$

$$x = \frac{2000}{100}$$

$$x = 20 \text{ ml}$$

The amount of solute needed is 20 ml.
The desired volume in this problem is 200 ml.

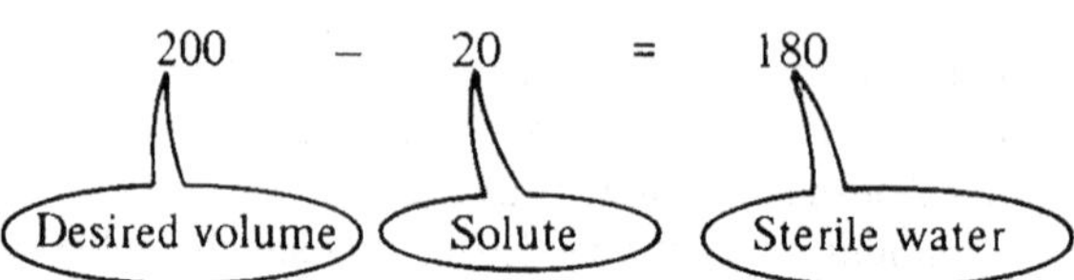


Thus the 20 ml of solute should be added to 180 ml of sterile water to yield 200 ml of solution.

---

**EXAMPLE 7.3**

Prepare 400 ml of a 1:50 silver nitrate solution.

1. Amount of solution desired = ________ .
2. Percentage concentration of desired solution = ________ .
3. Percentage concentration of on-hand solute = ________ .
4. Amount of solute needed for preparation = ________ .
5. Substitute the value in the formula.

6. Solve for the amount of solute.

7. How much sterile water should be added to the solute?

---

Often the desired concentration is expressed in ratio form, as in the last example. It is sometimes necessary to change units of measure in order to solve the problem, as the following example will illustrate.

---

### EXAMPLE 7.4

Prepare 1 qt of a 1:5 hydrogen peroxide solution.

1. Amount of solution desired = ________ . (Use metric units.)
2. Concentration of desired solution = ________ .
3. Concentration of on-hand solute = ________ .
4. Solve for the amount of solute = ________ .

5. How much sterile water should be added to the solute?

---

## SOLUTIONS PREPARED FROM LIQUID SOLUTES WITH CONCENTRATION OTHER THAN 100 PERCENT

Often the solute will be available in concentration other than 100 percent. Solutions are prepared from these solutes in exactly the same manner as in the previous section. In these cases the nurse must use the percentage concentration given on the solute label. Consider the following example: Prepare 1000 ml of a 25% alcohol solution from a 90% alcohol solution.

$$\text{Amount of solute needed for preparation} = x$$

In this case the solute comes from a solution that is on hand.

$$\text{Concentration of desired solution} = 25\%$$

The order is for a 25% alcohol solution.

$$\text{Concentration of on-hand solute} = 90\%$$

The alcohol on hand is in a solution with concentration equal to 90%.

$$\text{Amount of solution desired} = 1000 \text{ ml}$$

Substituting in the formula gives

$$\frac{x}{1000} = \frac{25}{90}$$

Solving for $x$, we have

$$\frac{x}{1000} = \frac{25}{90}$$

$$90x = 25{,}000$$

$$x = \frac{25{,}00\not{0}}{9\not{0}}$$

$$x = 277.77 = 278 \text{ ml}$$

Therefore 278 ml of the 90% alcohol solute should be used. In order to obtain 1000 ml of solution, since

$$1000 \text{ ml} - 278 \text{ ml} = 722 \text{ ml}$$

722 ml of sterile water should be added to the solute.

---

**EXAMPLE 7.5**

Prepare 1 liter of a 3% Lysol solution from a 10% Lysol solution.

1. Amount of solution desired = ________ .
2. Concentration of desired solution = ________ .
3. Concentration of on-hand solute = ________ .
4. Substitute the values in the formula.

5. Solve for the amount of solute.

6. How much sterile water should be mixed with the solute?

---

If the concentrations are stated in ratio form, the ratio must be converted to a percentage. The next example illustrates a situation where the concentration is stated in ratio form.

---

**EXAMPLE 7.6**

Prepare 300 ml of a 1:30 hydrogen peroxide solution from a 1:2 hydrogen peroxide solution.

1. Amount of solution desired = ________ .
2. Concentration of desired solution = ________ .
3. Concentration of on-hand solute = ________ .
4. Solve for the amount of solute.

5. How much sterile water should be mixed with the solute?

---

**Exercise 40**

These problems will give you experience in calculations necessary for the preparation of solutions.

1. Prepare 250 ml of 1% sodium chloride solution from a 10% sodium chloride solution.

2. Prepare 250 ml of 2% boric acid solution from boric acid crystals.

3. Prepare 2 liters of 20% sodium bicarbonate solution.

4. Prepare 100 ml of 2% boric acid solution from a 10% boric acid solution.

5. Prepare 500 ml of 10% glycerin solution from liquid glycerin.

6. Prepare 1000 ml of a 10% glucose solution.

7. Prepare 1000 ml of a 1:100 formaldehyde solution from a 50% solution of formaldehyde.

8. Prepare 250 ml of 1:20 glucose solution from crystalline glucose.

**9.** Prepare 1000 ml of physiologic salt solution (assume 0.9% concentration).

**10.** Prepare 1000 ml of 1:1000 potassium permanganate solution from 1:100 potassium permanganate solution.

**11.** Prepare 1000 ml of 1:1000 epinephrine solution from solid epinephrine.

**12.** Prepare 1 liter of a 2.5% boric acid solution from boric acid crystals.

**13.** Prepare 500 ml of a 25% cresol solution from a 1:2 solution.

**14.** Prepare 1000 ml of a 2% vinegar solution.

**15.** Prepare 2000 ml of a 1:1000 solution of Zephiran.

## ANSWERS TO EXAMPLES

### *Example 7.1*

1. 2 oz; change to metric unit of 60 ml
2. 8
3. 100; answer 100% since concentration is not specified.
4. $x$ = grams of crystals

$$\frac{x}{60} = \frac{8}{100}$$

$$100x = 480$$

$$x = \frac{480}{100} = 4.8$$

4.8 g of iodine crystals

### *Example 7.2*

1. 30 ml   2. 10   3. 100

4. $$\frac{x}{30} = \frac{10}{100}$$

$$100x = 300$$

$$x = \frac{300}{100} = 3$$

3 g of solute used

5. To find how many 10 gr tablets, convert 3 g to grains (1 g = 15 gr)
3 g = 45 gr

Each tablet contains 10 gr; thus the nurse uses 4.5 tablets.

### *Example 7.3*

1. 400 ml
2. 2%; use the ratio 1:50 and divide 50 into 1 yielding 0.02. Recall that to change a decimal to a percent, move the decimal two places to the right. Thus 2% is the answer.
3. 100%, assumed
4. $x$; this is unknown and is in milliliters

5. $$\frac{x}{400} = \frac{2}{100}$$

6. $$\frac{x}{400} = \frac{2}{100}$$

$$100x = 800$$

$$x = \frac{800}{100} = 8 \text{ ml}$$

8 ml of solute used.

7. 392 ml, obtained from

$$\begin{array}{r} 400 \text{ ml} \\ -8 \text{ ml} \\ \hline 392 \text{ ml} \end{array}$$

***Example 7.4***

1. 1000 ml (1 qt = 1000 ml)
2. 20%. A 1:5 concentration is 20%

$$\begin{array}{r} 0.20 \\ 5\overline{)1.00} \\ \underline{1.00} \end{array}$$

move the decimal two places to the right for percent

3. 100%
4. $\frac{x}{1000} = \frac{20}{100}$

$100x = 20{,}000$

$x = \frac{20{,}000}{100}$

$x = 200$ ml

200 ml of solute used.

5. 800 ml – obtained from

$$\begin{array}{rl} 1000 \text{ ml} & \text{desired} \\ -\underline{200 \text{ ml}} & \text{solute} \\ 800 \text{ ml} & \text{sterile water} \end{array}$$

***Example 7.5***

1. 1 liter or 1000 ml
2. 3
3. 10
4. $\frac{x}{1000} = \frac{3}{10}$
5. $\frac{x}{1000} = \frac{3}{10}$

$10x = 3000$

$x = \frac{3000}{10}$

300 ml of solute

6. 700 ml – obtained from

$$\begin{array}{r} 1000 \text{ ml} \\ -\underline{300 \text{ ml}} \\ 700 \text{ ml} \end{array}$$

***Example 7.6***

1. 300 ml
2. 3.33%; 1:30 is 3.33%
3. 50%; 1:2 is 50%
4. $\frac{x}{300} = \frac{3.33}{50}$

$50x = 999$

$x = \frac{999}{50} = 19.98$

$x = 20$ ml, 19.98 is rounded to 20

5. 280 ml, obtained from 300 ml – 20 ml = 280 ml

### Exercise 15

1. 1 liter
2. 500,000 ml
3. 0.06 liter
4. 8.0 ml
5. 0.025 m
6. 1000 mg
7. 0.25 g
8. 6000 mg
9. 2 kg
10. 3000 m
11. 21.85 m
12. 8450 g
13. 0.03 kl
14. 3000 liters
15. 0.04 kg
16. 0.06 g
17. 0.007 km
18. 250 ml
19. 600,000 liters
20. 0.5 g
21. 140 cm
22. 1 liter
23. 0.01 kg
24. 0.85 m
25. 8,166,000 mm
26. 1020 g

### Exercise 16

1. 10 pt
2. 28 fluidrams
3. 256 fluidounces
4. $\frac{3}{4}$ or 0.75 fluidrams

### Exercise 17

1. $1\frac{1}{6}$ drams
2. 6720 gr
3. 48 f℥
4. 2700 gr
5. 1.5 gallons
6. 1200 ♏
7. $\frac{1}{8}$ or 0.125 fʒ
8. 2.5 pt
9. 1.25 ℥
10. 12 ʒ
11. 0.375 ℥
12. 896 fʒ

### Exercise 18

1. 12 t
2. 1.75 glassfuls
3. 1/8 or 0.125 oz
4. 1 T

### Exercise 19

1. $\frac{1}{2}$ t
2. 1 glassful
3. 12 t
4. $\frac{1}{2}$ oz
5. 1 oz
6. $\frac{1}{2}$ oz
7. $\frac{2}{3}$ t
8. 240 gtt
9. $\frac{1}{2}$ glassful
10. 2 glassfuls
11. 6 t
12. 6 t
13. 3 T
14. 3 glassfuls
15. 15 gtt

### Exercise 20

1. 8 g
2. 45 ml
3. 7.5 mg
4. 45 gtt
5. 1.66 ml
6. 1.5 oz

### Exercise 21

1. 3 gr
2. 0.004 g
3. $\frac{1}{2}$ gr
4. 1 g

### Exercise 22

1. 15 mg
2. $\frac{1}{240}$ gr
3. 0.2 mg
4. $\frac{1}{20}$ gr

### Exercise 23

1. 1 ℥
2. 5 ℥
3. 90 g
4. 15 g

### Exercise 24

1. 11.25 ♏
2. 1 ml
3. 13.5 ♏
4. 2 ml

### Exercise 25

1. 3000 ml
2. $\frac{5}{6}$ ℥
3. 30 ml
4. 5 ℥

### Exercise 26

1. 6.6 lb
2. 9.1 kg
3. 30.8 lb
4. 24.3 kg
5. 53.5 lb
6. 17 kg

### Exercise 27

1. 59 F
2. 28 C
3. 37.4 F
4. 20 C
5. 98.6 F
6. −10 C

### Exercise 28

1. 15 ♏
2. 105 gr
3. 14 T
4. $\frac{5}{6}$ gr
5. 1500 ml
6. 480 g
7. 1.6 ml
8. 2 g
9. 10 mg
10. 1.33 or $1\frac{1}{3}$ ml
11. $1\frac{2}{3}$ ʒ
12. 30 gtt
13. $\frac{1}{15}$ gr
14. 22.5 mg
15. $3\frac{1}{3}$ ℥
16. 75 gr
17. 30 g
18. 3 ℥
19. 2.5 ℥
20. 60 gr
21. 6 ♏
22. 60 ml
23. $\frac{3}{4}$ gr
24. 7.5 ♏
25. 10 C
26. 44.6 F
27. 28.4 F
28. 38.9 C
29. 37 C
30. 12.2 F

### *Exercise 29*

1. 5 ml

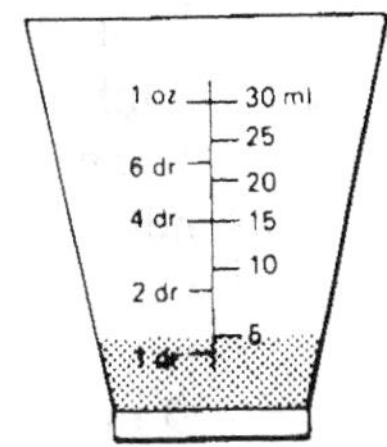


2. 11.4 ml
3. 10 ml

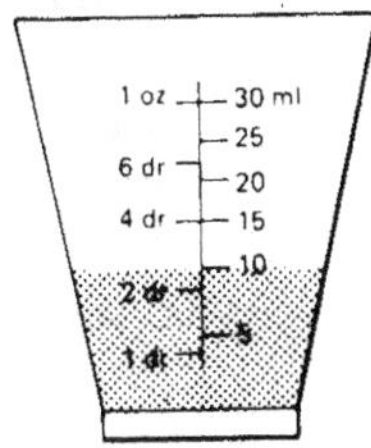


4. One tablet
5. 15 ml

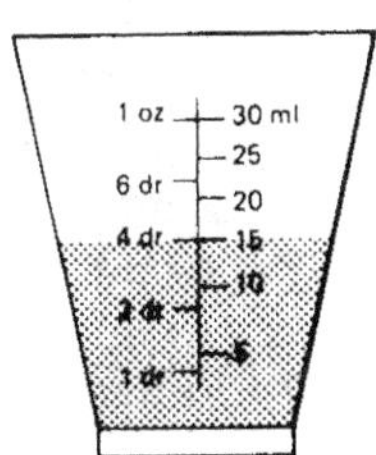


6. 6.8 ml
7. 2 tablets
8. 10 ml

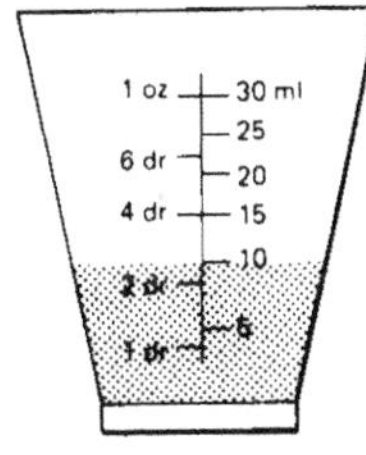


9. 1 tablet
10. 10 ml
11. 5.0 ml
12. 2 tablets
13. 0.6 ml
14. $\frac{1}{2}$ tablet
15. 2 tablets
16. 2 tablets
17. 2 tablets
18. 1 capsule
19. 1 tablet
20. 9 ml
21. 2 tablets
22. $\frac{1}{2}$ tablet
23. 4 ml
24. 2 tablets
25. $\frac{1}{2}$ tablet
26. 2 ml

### *Exercise 30*

1. 3 tablets
2. 1 tablet
3. $\frac{1}{2}$ tablet
4. $\frac{1}{2}$ tablet
5. $\frac{1}{2}$ tablet
6. 4 ml
7. 2 tablets
8. $2\frac{1}{2}$ tablets
9. 2 tablets
10. 3 ml
11. 2.5 ml
12. 2.5 ml

### *Exercise 31*

1. 1.5 ml
2. 1.6 ml

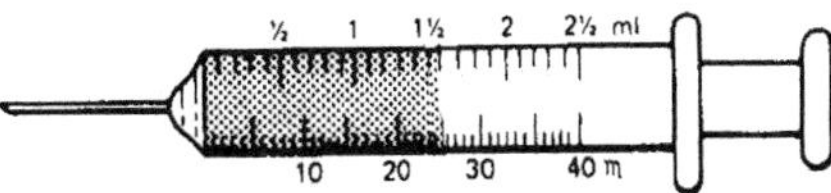


3. 0.3 ml

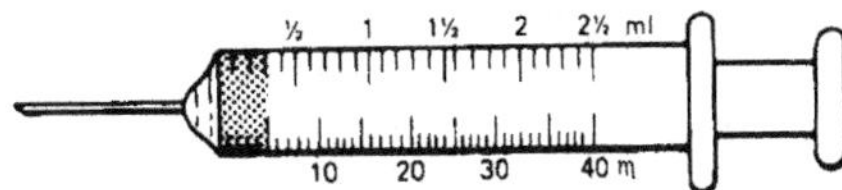


4. 1 ml
5. 0.8 ml or 12 ♏

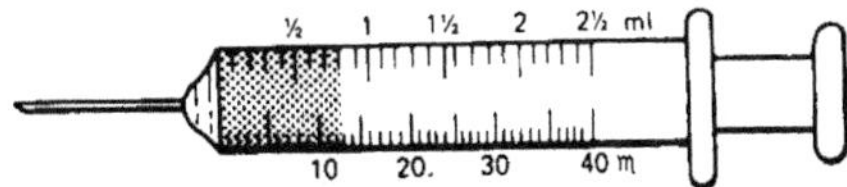


6. $\frac{1}{2}$ ml

7. $\frac{1}{2}$ ml
8. 2.2 ml

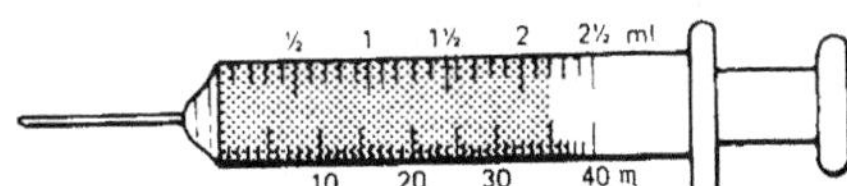


9. 1 ml

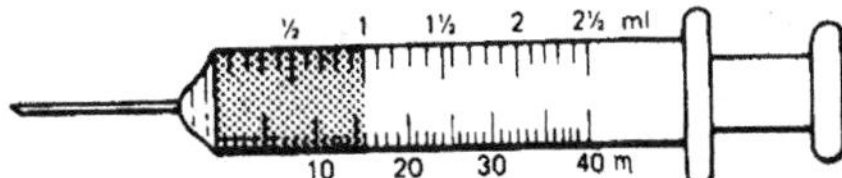


10. 0.9 ml or 14 ♏

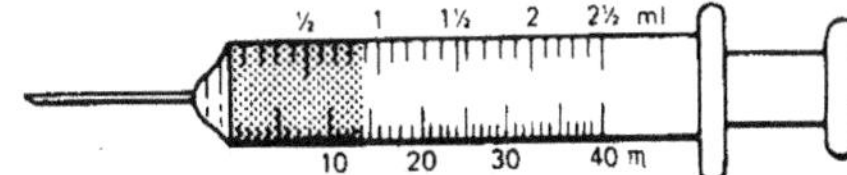

***Exercise 32***

1. $\frac{1}{2}$ ml
2. 2 ml
3. 0.4 ml or 6 ♏
4. 1.5 ml
5. $\frac{1}{2}$ ml
6. 1.5 ml
7. 1.5 ml
8. $\frac{1}{2}$ ml
9. 0.25 ml or 4 ♏
10. 0.8 ml (0.75)
11. 0.7 ml (0.67)
12. 0.9 ml
13. 1.2 ml (1.25)
14. 0.8 ml (0.75)
15. 1.2 ml (1.25)
16. 1.5 ml (1.52)
17. 0.2 ml
18. 1.2 ml (1.25)
19. 0.5 ml
20. 0.4 ml
21. 0.7 ml (0.67)
22. 1 ml
23. 0.5 ml
24. 0.2 ml (0.25)
25. 0.2 ml (0.25)
26. 0.5 ml
27. 0.5 ml
28. 0.5 ml (0.47)
29. 0.4 ml (0.375)
30. 0.5 ml (0.53)
31. 0.3 ml (0.28)
32. 2 ml
33. 1 ml
34. 0.5 ml
35. 0.5 ml

***Exercise 33***

1. 1.2 ml

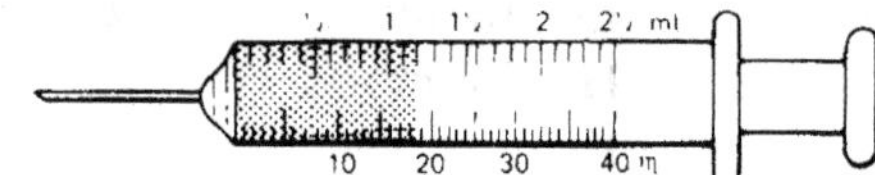


2. 2 ml

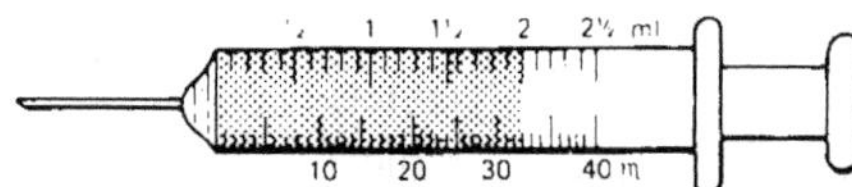


3. 35 U

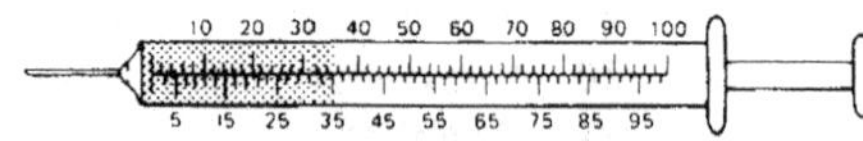


4. 1.5 ml

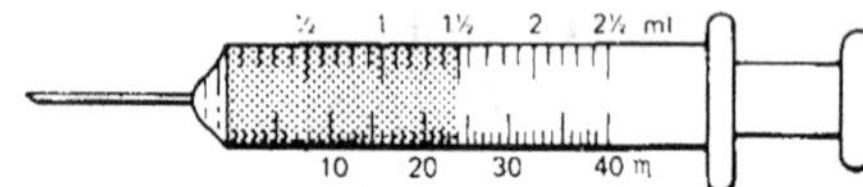


5. 1.2 ml

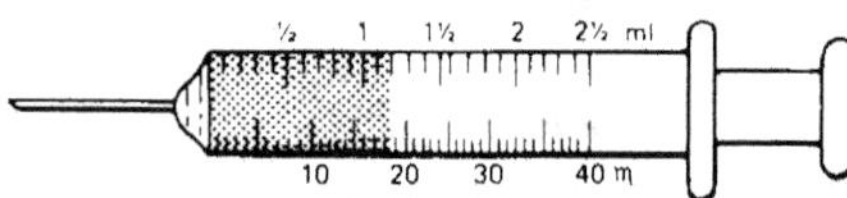


6. 0.8 ml (0.75)
7. 1.3 ml
8. 16 U

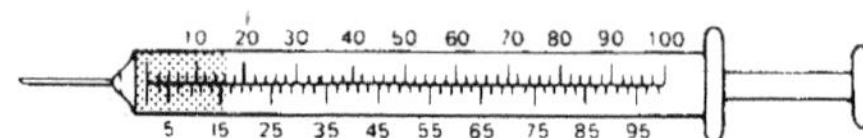


9. 19 U

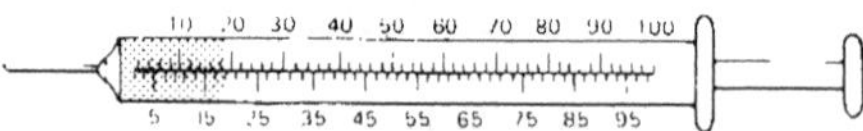

10. 0.8 ml

***Exercise 34***

1. 2.5 ml
   330 mg/ml
   1.5 ml
2. 3.4 ml
   250 mg/ml
   1 ml
   0.6 ml
3. 6.6 ml
   250 mg/ml
   1.4 ml
4. 4 ml
   0.5 g/2.2 ml
   1.1 ml
5. 1.25 ml
6. 2.7 ml
   250 mg/1.5 ml
   3 ml
7. 9.0 ml
   400 mg/ml
   1.25 ml
8. 10 ml
9. 1.8 ml
   500 mg/ml
   1 ml
10. 7.0 ml
    1 g/2.0 ml
    2 ml
11. 10 ml
12. 10 ml
13. 10 ml
14. 1.1 ml
15. 0.9 ml

*Exercise 35*

1. 7 gtt/min
2. 14 gtt/min
3. 21 gtt/min
4. 83 gtt/min
5. 42 gtt/min
6. 10 gtt/min
7. 31 gtt/min
8. 21 gtt/min
9. 42 gtt/min

*Exercise 36*

1. 5 hours
2. 4 hours
3. 7 hours 8 minutes
4. 3 hours 45 minutes
5. 5 hours 33 minutes
6. 3 hours 20 minutes
7. 2 hours 40 minutes
8. 12 hours 30 minutes
9. 4 hours

*Exercise 37*

1. 17 gtt/min
2. 50 gtt/min
3. 100 gtt/min
4. 100 gtt/min
5. 17 gtt/min
6. 25 gtt/min
7. 100 gtt/min
8. 33 gtt/min
9. 25 gtt/min

*Exercise 38*

1. 20 mg
2. 4 mg
3. (a) 7 mg
   (b) 23 mg
4. 1.3 gr
5. 4 mg
6. (a) 2 mg
   (b) 4 mg
7. 20 mg
8. 15 mg
9. 100 mg
10. 184 mg
11. 120,000 U
12. 67 mg
13. 3 mg
14. 0.5 mg
15. 40 mg
16. 0.27 mg
17. 16.7 mg
18. 6.67 mg
19. 66.7 mg
20. 0.1 mg
21. 66 mg
22. 6.5 mg
23. 14 mg

*Exercise 39*

1. 62.5 mg per dose
   (125 mg per day)
2. 416.7 mg per dose
   (2500 mg per day)
3. 150 mg per dose
   (450 mg per day)
4. 187.5 mg per dose
   (750 mg per day)
5. 180 mg per dose
   (360 mg per day)
6. 72 mg per dose
   (288 mg per day)
7. 166.7 mg per dose
   (1000 mg per day)

*Exercise 40*

1. 25 ml solute
   225 ml sterile water
2. 5 g solute
   250 ml solution
3. 400 g solute
   1600 ml sterile water
4. 20 ml solute
   80 ml sterile water
5. 50 ml solute
   450 ml sterile water
6. 100 g solute
   dilute to 1000 ml mark
7. 20 ml solute
   980 ml sterile water
8. 12.5 g solute
   dilute to 250 ml mark
9. 9 g solute
   dilute to 1000 ml mark
10. 100 ml solute
    900 ml sterile water
11. 1 g solute
    dilute to 1000 ml mark
12. 25 g solute
    dilute to 1000 ml mark
13. 250 ml solute
    250 ml sterile water
14. 20 ml solute
    980 ml sterile water
15. 2 ml solute
    1998 ml sterile water

# INDEX